**The Editor.**

Paul Henry Mussen is Associate Professor of Psychology at the University of California, Berkeley.

**Contributors.**

A. Anastasi, *Fordham University*

A. L. Baldwin, *Cornell University*

J. Berko & R. Brown, *M.I.T.*

S. W. Bijou & D. M. Baer, *University of Washington*

U. Bronfenbrenner & H. Ricciuti, *Cornell University*

E. J. Gibson & V. Olum, *Cornell University*

W. E. Henry, *University of Chicago*

L. W. Hoffman & R. Lippitt, *University of Michigan*

B. Inhelder & B. Matalon, *University of Geneva*

O. C. Irwin, *Institute of Logopedics, Wichita, Kansas*

W. Kessen, *Yale University*

W. Lambert, *Cornell University*

I. G. Macy & H. Kelly, *Merrill-Palmer Institute*

H. V. Meredith, *State University of Iowa*

D. R. Miller, *University of Michigan*

A. H. Reisen, *University of Chicago*

C. C. Spiker, *State University of Iowa*

G. G. Thompson, *Ohio State University*

J. W. M. Whiting & B. B. Whiting, *Harvard University*

H. F. Wright, *University of Kansas*

L. Yarrow, *Family & Child Services, Washington, D. C.*

M. R. Yarrow, *National Institute of Mental Health*

*Handbook of*
*Research Methods in*
# CHILD DEVELOPMENT

*Edited by*
PAUL H. MUSSEN
*University of California*

## Contributors

ALFRED L. BALDWIN, *Cornell University*

WILLIAM KESSEN, *Yale University*

HERBERT F. WRIGHT, *University of Kansas*

SIDNEY W. BIJOU *and* DONALD M. BAER, *University of Washington*

HOWARD V. MEREDITH, *State University of Iowa*

ICIE G. MACY *and* HARRIET J. KELLY, *Merrill-Palmer Institute*

AUSTIN H. REISEN, *University of Chicago*

ELEANOR J. GIBSON *and* VIVIAN OLUM, *Cornell University*

CHARLES C. SPIKER, *State University of Iowa*

BÄRBEL INHELDER *and* BENJAMIN MATALON, *University of Geneva*

ANNE ANASTASI, *Graduate School, Fordham University*

ORVIS C. IRWIN, *Institute of Logopedics, Wichita, Kansas*

JEAN BERKO *and* ROGER BROWN, *Massachusetts Institute of Technology*

LEON J. YARROW, *Family and Child Services, Washington, D. C.*

WILLIAM E. HENRY, *University of Chicago*

MARIAN RADKE YARROW, *National Institute of Mental Health*

DANIEL R. MILLER, *University of Michigan*

URIE BRONFENBRENNER *and* HENRY N. RICCIUTI, *Cornell University*

GEORGE G. THOMPSON, *The Ohio State University*

WILLIAM W. LAMBERT, *Cornell University*

JOHN W. M. WHITING *and* BEATRICE B. WHITING, *Harvard University*

LOIS WLADIS HOFFMAN *and* RONALD LIPPITT, *University of Michigan*

NEW YORK · LONDON, JOHN WILEY & SONS, INC.

*Handbook of*
*Research Methods in*
# CHILD DEVELOPMENT

# *Preface*

The subject matter, facts, principles, and theories of child development are inherently interesting to many people and strongly influence the work of many specialists, both researchers and practitioners, in the biological and behavioral sciences. In spite of this, research in this field since the mid-twenties has not generally improved in quality or increased in quantity as much as research in many other scientific disciplines. Recognizing this state of affairs, members of the Committee on Child Development of the National Academy of Sciences—National Research Council (Alfred Baldwin, Chairman, Roger Barker, Boyd McCandless, and George G. Thompson) proposed publishing this handbook which, the Committee hoped, might help to accelerate the rate and raise the caliber of empirical investigations of growth and development. The National Academy of Sciences—National Research Council agreed to sponsor it.

The specific purpose of the handbook is to make available in a single source concrete descriptions and evaluations of the most widely used research techniques in many aspects of the study of child growth and behavior. In addition, it purports to communicate,

wherever possible, some of the methodological sophistication and "wisdom" that investigators gradually acquire but rarely make explicit in their publications. For example, problems of ethics, feasibility, and public relations may affect the selection of subject populations, the development of instruments, and the manipulation of environmental variables. Experienced investigators may be able to offer good advice on these issues, which often make research programs involving children extremely complicated.

The exclusive emphasis of the handbook is research methods; substantive content is included only for illustrative purposes. In a sense, the volume is addressed directly to present and potential investigators who can use it as a basic reference and a guide to research matters outside their own research specialties. It should also be valuable to advanced scholars and graduate students interested in a balanced picture of the techniques applied in child study.

Although the objective was a comprehensive presentation of methods, it is obviously impossible to encompass all techniques and all areas of research. Therefore, early in the planning of the book the Committee and the Editor met to formulate principles for selection and organization of topics. It was decided to include only methods that have actually been used with children and have not been thoroughly described in other volumes, as intelligence tests, for example, have been. Discussions would be limited to the research—as opposed to diagnostic or therapeutic—uses of these methods. Furthermore, primary emphasis should be given to methods that require special modifications when used with children; thus statistical procedures would be omitted. These principles guided the writing and editing of this work.

The Committee and the Editor devised a necessarily arbitrary organizational plan and table of contents. To assure comprehensive coverage, several chapters had to be devoted to problems of general design and broad research orientations (e.g., experimental and naturalistic approaches); others dealt with specific techniques appropriate to a wide range of research activities (e.g., interview, projective techniques); still others focused on the most fruitful methods for studying particular content areas (e.g., physical growth, personality).

Although such an arrangement inevitably leads to some degree of overlap among chapters, it is often desirable. There are numerous techniques, useful over a broad range of investigatory problems, that can be appreciated most fully if they are considered from several points of view. For example, descriptions of specialized uses of projective and interview techniques are presented in the chapters on the assessment of personality characteristics and on attitudes, even though comprehensive discussions of these techniques appear in other chapters.

A volume of this sort has several obvious limitations. For one thing, research skills cannot be learned from books; they can be developed only through practice. At most, a handbook of this kind can aid the investigator only by informing him of available techniques, their advantages and limitations, and the rules to be followed in applying them. Second, the book necessarily reflects the present status of research methods in the field. With progress in this field, as in any other, available methods will be improved and new and better methods will be invented. As this occurs, this volume will become outdated and less useful. Thus, in a sense, the venture contains the germ of its own destruction: its goal is to stimulate advances that may make it obsolete.

The actual organization and development of this book required the cooperation, advice, and hard work of many. In the early stages of planning, letters explaining the project and tentative outlines were sent to a number of distinguished scholars who were asked to comment and criticize. Their enthusiastic and gratifying responses brought many suggestions for revision and expansion. After incorporating most of these suggestions into a revised outline, the Committee and the Editor invited a number of outstanding specialists to prepare the chapters of the volume. We were fortunate, indeed, to have so many experts accept invitations to undertake extremely arduous scholarly and writing responsibilities. The Committee and the Editor are deeply grateful to these contributors for their indispensable efforts throughout the project.

The assistance of many others must also be acknowledged. In a real sense members of the Committee on Child Development of the National Academy of Sciences—National Research Council (Alfred Baldwin, Boyd McCandless, Glen Finch, Irving Hallowell, and Richard Solomon) were collaborating editors. They gave their time and energy generously, working with me on the formulation of the original outlines, the selection of the contributing authors, and the critical evaluation of the "working" outlines submitted by the authors before they began writing their chapters. I also sought the advice of colleagues at the University of California and at other institutions, who read one or more of the working outlines or chapters and made valuable suggestions for changes, deletions, or additions. For this kind of assistance, I am indebted to Nancy Bayley, Merl E. Bonney, Orville Brim, Alfred Castaneda, Kenneth B. Clark, Susan Ervin, Mary Ford, Stanley Garn, Dale Harris, Edna Heidbreder, Alan Holmberg, Harry Levin, Eleanor E. Maccoby, John McKee, Norman Munn, Ethel Mussen, Norman Polansky, Philburn Ratoosh, Milton Rokeach, Earl Schaefer, Pauline Sears, Robert Sears, Melford Spiro, Celia B. Stendler, Mildred Templin, Leona Tyler, Sam Witryol, and John Zubek. Patricia Jones and Ethel Mussen prepared the index.

PAUL H. MUSSEN
*Berkeley, California*     EDITOR
*July 1960*

# Contents

ix

part I

# General Research Methodology in Child Development

# chapter 1

# The Study of Child Behavior and Development

Alfred L. Baldwin
*Cornell University*

It is proverbial that any actor foolish enough to appear on the same stage with a child should resign himself to having the scene stolen away from him. Children are one of the most interesting phenomena in the world; they are newsworthy, they are good copy for advertisements, their cute sayings appear in hundreds of magazines and newspapers every day.

## VALUES OF CHILD STUDY

Although the inherent fascination children have for adults has not been an unmixed blessing for the progress of the science of child psychology, it is novel and pleasant to find business and pleasure so conveniently combined as they are in the study of child development. For the study of children is an important business. On the one hand, a better knowledge of children and their development contributes in a very practical way to human betterment. On the other hand, a better understanding of children has many implications for a theory of human behavior.

Undoubtedly the greatest potential contribution of the study of children to human welfare stems from the special importance of childhood to the achievement of mental health. The generally deleterious effects of institutionalization, broken homes, parental rejection, or inadequate parental supervision during childhood can hardly be denied. But the identification of the "toxic agents" in these experiences has hardly begun, and our knowledge of the psychological mechanisms that mediate their influence is even scantier. Because of the absence of sound knowledge of these mechanisms we cannot justify or perhaps even have faith in the efficacy of current procedures for counteracting and nullifying these detrimental effects. Although the potential benefits are tremendous, we must admit that the contributions of child study to the improvement of mental health are still largely potential. These promises can be realized only by laborious and painstaking research.

If mental health is the most important beneficiary of child-development research, education runs a close second. The current state of education, with its strongly antagonistic positions vying for acceptance, its rapid shifts from one procedure to another, its vulnerability to sloganized programs initiated by uninformed pressure groups, and its genuine failure to advance more rapidly, clearly points to a basic lack of solid empirical data on fundamental processes. A great quantity of research in problems of learning, language development, and thinking, among others, must be carried out, confirmed, and then applied to the practical problems of education.

Numerous other practical questions also demand research in child development. Social and political attitudes are developed and strengthened during childhood. Family stability in future generations partly depends upon the interpersonal patterns of adjustment and adaptation being developed in today's children. Precision of motor behavior as well as accurate thinking are required in a technological age. There is no end to the potential contributions of research in child development to human welfare.

How can the possible benefits be realized? One research strategy, of course, is the direct frontal attack. There have been many attempts to change attitudes, to improve teaching techniques, or to build up resistance to the deleterious effects of anxiety. There should be many others. This book contains advice and suggestions for meeting the many intricate problems faced by such research efforts.

If the examples of our sister sciences are valid for behavioral science, the most important contributions to practical problems will not come from an immediate frontal attack but instead from the development of a sound theory of behavior. Progress toward this difficult goal does not turn upon the contributions of any single field. It requires the maintenance of a broad research front involving studies of humans and animals, adults and children, normals and abnormals. It is well to recognize, however, some of the special contributions that the study of children may make to the development and testing of theoretical hypotheses.

First, children pose a theoretical problem. A behavior theory must encompass the behavior of children as well as adults, and its parameters must describe the differences between individuals of different ages.

Second, children are strategically valuable subjects for those whose aim is to add to general psychological theory. Especially for those whose concern lies in the elucidation of symbolic processes, children might be expected to provide unusually valuable experimental material. The relatively great impulsivity of children might make them useful subjects for the investigation of affective responses and the structure of defense mechanisms. By being relatively complicated, yet relatively inexperienced, children offer many attractive research possibilities to psychologists interested in learning problems.

Third, child development is the ultimate problem of developmental psychology. Other species develop, of course, but most people's interest in animal development lies in the potential contribution of this kind of study to the understanding of child development.

There is no need to expound further on the potential values of child study for both practical and theoretical purposes. It is more important to assess the current state of the field, and this appraisal will be more intelligible if we look first at the historical development of child psychology. A review of the succession of problems that have captured the attention of developmental psychologists will show how the purpose of this book is conceived.

## HISTORICAL SURVEY
## OF CHILD PSYCHOLOGY

At one time child development was considered of such central importance that nearly every major theorist wrote on the subject. G. S. Hall, J. M. Baldwin, William McDougall, E. Claparede, Wilhelm Stern, Kurt Koffka, and J. B. Watson all made major attempts to encompass the facts of child behavior and development into their general theories. Unfortunately, however, there was no great abundance of empirical data to be embraced by the theories. The empirical studies of the early period were largely descriptive accounts of the development of individual children, although Hall made an interesting survey of the "content of children's minds" (Hall, 1891).

Certainly a major shift of interest and an advance in the quality of empirical data began with the work of Binet (1903). The mental-testing movement for a time comprised almost the entire field of developmental psychology, and mental testing is still a major practical service of child psychologists. Although psychometrics began with the study of intelligence in children, it rapidly expanded both in its coverage of other areas of personality and ability and in its attention to other age levels.

Mental tests of all kinds were of immense practical value. They also provided important data on children's behavior, although the search for diagnostic items seriously restricted its coverage. As test items, the ball and field test, absurdities, analogies, similarities, and differences are all valuable, but the data are too spotty to be as useful as they might be for those interested in the development of thinking. The use of the slope of the "per cent passing" curve as the major criterion for item selection in intelligence tests means that data are collected primarily at the age levels at which abilities change rapidly rather than in periods in which growth is more gradual.

Although they do not describe all aspects of development—or any single one for that matter—mental tests do provide scores that are designed to show a continual gradual growth with age. This feature of the scores stimulated a somewhat unwarranted optimism that they described the psychological growth of the child in the same way that height and weight described his physical growth. It was not so apparent then as it is now that these curves are far from raw, theoretically neutral data and are dependent upon particular statistical manipulation. They are composite scores, very well suited for predicting such composite criteria as school achievement but not so useful for building developmental theory.

For various reasons, perhaps including these, the decade 1920–1930 marked the initiation of a number of "Growth Studies" at Harvard, the Brush Foundation, the University of California, the Child Research Council at Denver, Fels Institute, Merrill-Palmer, and other places. These long-range, longitudinal research programs were not all alike by any means, but, as originally conceived, they proposed to chart the physical, physiological, and psychological growth of individual children over a period of years. For ten to fifteen years these programs and the scientists involved in them dominated the field of child development. The Committee on Child Development of the National Academy of Sciences—National Research Council, the group that is sponsoring this book began in 1920. One of its actions was the formation of the Society for Research in Child Development.

This period of the 1920's was also marked by a certain fragmentation in the field. Psychometrics went its own way. Statistical sophistication became increasingly important in psychometric research, and psychometrics kept its close tie to applied problems.

Child development, as represented in the longitudinal studies, became more closely linked to biological science than it had been formerly. Mental and psychological development viewed as one aspect of biological growth led research in child development in a somewhat different direction from the main stream of psychological research. This same organismic viewpoint did not encourage the belief that the fate of developmental psychology was closely tied to the growth of a general theory of behavior. At the same time, the main stream of psychological research was gradually turning toward the study of learning as the core problem, this emphasis becoming more prominent after 1930. Child development and behavior theory became separated from each other, and the field of developmental psychology was no longer a part of the main stream of psychological research.

This does not mean that there were not conspicuous theoretical issues that marked the whole field of developmental psychology in the 1920's and early 1930's. The controversy between heredity and environment, maturation and learning, raged throughout the period— although the hereditary position was considerably more popular. The controversy appeared in the many studies of constancy of the IQ and its modifiability by various sorts of environmental treatments and special educational procedures (e.g., Terman, 1928; Goodenough, 1928). It appeared in the studies of the development of instinctive responses, such as pecking in chicks (Bird, 1933), and in the studies showing how pecking can be modified by conditions in the egg (Kuo, 1932). It appeared in the flurry of studies on the susceptibility of stair climbing, cutting with scissors, buttoning buttons, etc., to special training (Gesell and Thompson, 1929; Hilgard, 1933). Many of these studies were excellent, and we now need more of them, but they were tied to a theoretical controversy, and as the heat died away the studies disappeared with it. Another hot issue was whether development proceeded from the general to the specific or the specific to the general (Carmichael, 1934; Kuo, 1939).

If mental tests marked one turning point in child development, the growth of interest in the effects of childhood experience upon adult personality marked a second. Somewhere between 1935 and 1945 the entire atmosphere of child-development research shifted. Without ever repudiating openly the implied predictability of psychological development that was implicit in the original conception of the growth studies, the field turned to studies of the effects of weaning, toilet training, birth injuries, broken homes, institutionalization, maternal absence, and maternal rejection upon the psychological development of the child. Without question, this turn of affairs stems from the influence of Freud. It is no accident that the early research was designed to test specific Freudian hypotheses—generally so oversimplified that no Freudian would accept them as valid tests. Gradually the interest spread from specific factors, such as weaning and toilet training, to more general characteristics of childhood experience. Also, the research became less tied to any specific theoretical hypothesis and became a more general study of the influence of childhood experience upon personality and its growth. This period marks the convergence of learning theory and research in child development by way of the translation of Freudian concepts into the terminology of general behavior theory by such theorists as Dollard and Miller (1950), Whiting and Child (1953), and Mowrer (1950).

This history is oversimplified and points out only the most general trends. It neglects entirely, for example, the research stemming from the work of Piaget on thought, morals, etc. (Piaget, 1926, 1932, 1950). It also fails to indicate the interrelations between cultural anthropology and child development that have played an important part in the history of research in family relations and family sociology paralleling child-development research. The interrelations between these two fields have not been outlined.

The fact that child-development research has only recently begun to be reintegrated into the general field of psychology has implications for research in both areas. Developmental psychologists have devised techniques and problems that are not common knowledge in the field of general psychology, and they have acquired a wisdom that will be useful to those who plan to conduct research with children. Conversely, there are techniques, experiments, and problems in the general psychological literature that may not be familiar to those research workers who have kept close to the main stream of child-development research.

It seems appropriate, therefore, to try to collect in one volume an account of the research methods that have been used in the study of children. Some are methods that were developed for use with adults and require some modification before they can be made suitable for children. Others are buried in the literature and deserve to be brought to light. Partly, then, this book is a collection of specific methods. It also has another function: to describe some of the general problems involved in working with children. There are practical and ethical problems involved in obtaining subjects. There are methodological problems in which interview methods, questionnaires, attitudes scales, are employed and observational procedures, involving children, that are not required or are less important in the study of adults.

We have attempted, therefore, to limit the contents of this book in two ways. First, it reports methods that have been used; only in a few cases have we tried to include interesting possibilities of extending present methods of research among adults or animals to the study of children. Second, it is limited, more or less, to methods that require some modification when they are used with children. There is almost nothing on statistical prodecures, for example, since there are no special children's statistics.

In organization, the book moves from the general to the specific. The remainder of this chapter is concerned with the most general problems of research in child development, scientific method and strategy, the classification of the problems of the field, the ethical problems involved in studying children, and, finally, the practical problems of procurement of subjects. The next few chapters deal with general methods that are suitable for many different problems, such as experimentation and observation. Then we move into specific areas of research and discuss specific methods for investigating particular problems. Each of the chapters has been written by an active investigator who has consented to survey the field and to describe the particular procedures that have been found suitable for the study of children.

### The Logic of Science and Scientific Strategy

Behavioral scientists are rather self-conscious these days about the nature of scientific theory, and it is only proper that they should be. It is easy to confuse definitions with assumptions and terminology with findings in the difficult area of psychological research. At the same time, however, there is some danger that a preoccupation with the canons of theory construction may hamper research rather than aid it and may interfere with theory building rather than improve it.

Consequently, the present discussion is divided into two portions. The first is concerned with the nature of scientific theory and the criteria a conceptual scheme must meet before it can be called a genuinely scientific theory. These criteria are somewhat like ideals in that they mark the end of the road for theory building. We strive to produce a theory that satisfies our ideals, but if we ever achieved it our job would be finished. All good theories in this sense are dead theories.

Therefore, the second portion of the discussion is concerned with theory building, and it deals especially with the early stages of a science when non-sense questions and tacit assumptions lurk behind every hypothesis. A science in the making is an untidy affair, and wise answers to everyday problems are not obtained by knowing clearly what a mature science looks like. It is easier to know what we are striving for than how to attain it.

### NATURE OF SCIENTIFIC THEORY

Turning then to the criteria of a scientific theory, we find a consensus on most of the elementary issues despite serious controversy on the basic principles and a lamentable lack of agreement on terminology. The present discussion is couched largely in the language of Braithwaite (1955).

A scientific theory is a deductive system. It contains a set of hypotheses, some of which may be logically deduced from the others in the set. These hypotheses can be arranged in a sort of hierarchical order.

1. There will be a set of highest-level hypotheses, generally called assumptions and definitions, from which all the rest of the set can be deduced. Which ones are called assumptions and which ones are deduced from them is sometimes an arbitrary matter; there may be more than one way that the same set of hypotheses can be arranged into a deductive system.

2. There will be middle-level hypotheses that are deducible from the fundamental assumptions and are also the premises from which lower-level hypotheses are deduced—similar to the early theorem in a geometry course.

3. There will be lowest-level hypotheses that are deducible from the rest of the system but are not premises for further deductions. These are empirically testable hypotheses or predictions if the system as a whole is testable.

We can illustrate these properties of a deductive system with the following set of hypotheses. It is a sort of caricature of the theory of rational man.

1. Any person who chooses between several actions will choose the act whose consequences have the highest value for him.

2. A financial gain has a higher value than a financial loss.

3. Any person will choose a financial gain over a financial loss.

4. If I give John Jones a choice between gaining a one dollar bill and losing one dollar in my laboratory on Friday, April 10, at 2:00 P.M., he will choose to gain the dollar.

In this system hypotheses 1 and 2 are "highest-level" hypotheses i.e., assumptions. Hypothesis 3 is a middle-level hypothesis. It is deduced from 1 and 2 and is in turn the premise for the deduction of hypothesis 4. Hypothesis 4 is an empirically testable hypothesis deduced from 3. It is a specific description of one example of the class of events described by hypothesis 3. Actually, to make the deduction completely rigorous, we would have to specify that John Jones is a person, that gaining the dollar bill is a financial gain, etc. But is it characteristic of testable hypotheses that they are couched in a terminology that permits the events described in them to be easily recognized. This problem is discussed later, along with other problems of operational definitions. Suffice it to say here that for the theoretical system to be testable it must contain these lowest-level empirical hypotheses that predict specific empirical events.

Let us consider now the problem of confirmation and disconfirmation of the system. Any particular empirical hypothesis is necessarily derived from some of the highest-level hypotheses of the system, but it need not depend on all of them. If the empirical hypothesis is confirmed, the higher-level hypotheses from which it is derived are supported but not proved. On the other hand, the failure of the empirical hypothesis is proof that one or more of the hypotheses at the highest level from which it was derived are wrong. Usually, however, it is impossible to assign the error precisely to one specific highest-level hypothesis. There is an error "somewhere," but it is not clear where, and any one of several changes may remedy the problem.

How precisely the faulty hypothesis may be located depends upon how many are involved in the derivation. A disconfirmation of a lowest-level hypothesis almost always disproves the hypothesis at the next level up because the lowest-level hypothesis is almost always merely a specific case of a general statement and is derived totally from one second-level hypothesis. Where the error lies above that point is generally problematical.

Turning again to the consequences of a confirmation, we notice that a confirmation lends support to the higher-level hypotheses from which it is derived, and it also provides indirect confirmation to other collateral hypotheses that represent derivations from the same set of highest-level hypotheses. In other words, any support for a general hypothesis lends support to *all* its implications, not merely to those in the direct line of derivation.

Suppose, for example, we inserted a pair of hypotheses 1a and 1b just after hypothesis 1 in the example. Hypothesis 1a restates hypothesis 1 for men, i.e., "any *man* who chooses between . . ." and hypothesis 1b states the same hypothesis for women. Now, the empirical hypothesis 4 is deduced by 1a, not 1b, since John Jones is a man. Thus, if the empirical hypothesis is confirmed, it supports hypothesis 1a and, through it, hypothesis 1. Now, if hypothesis 1 is true, hypothesis 1b is necessarily true; therefore, whatever support hypothesis 1 receives from the test is also support for hypothesis 1b, even though hypothesis 1b is not in the direct line of deduction.

Intuitively, it seems that the test provides less support for 1 and 1b than for 1a because the hypothesis might hold for men and not for women. There have been some attempts to formulate these intuitive notions into a system that would quantify the support a particular finding provided for the various higher-level hypotheses that were involved in the deductive system, but the problem is extremely difficult, and the attempts have not been very successful so far.

This view of scientific theories as deductive systems is straightforward enough in its general features, but the exposition hides the multitude of difficulties that arise from the fact that a scientific theory is a language as well as a deductive system. For example, in the little theory described earlier the term "value" is used in hypothesis 1. Depending upon the way that term is defined, the entire impact of the theory is changed. In the example it was defined in part by hypothesis 2. Financial gain is said by definition to have a higher value than financial loss. If hypothesis 2 is taken as a definition of value, then a failure of the prediction on John Jones would invalidate hypothesis 1 because a definition cannot be invalid.

On the other hand, we could define value in terms of preference. "The value of A is higher than the value of B if a person chooses A rather than B." Now, hypothesis 1 is essentially a definition, and hypothesis 2 becomes a testable hypothesis of the values of financial gains and losses. A failure of the prediction on John Jones would in this case invalidate hypothesis 2 rather than hypothesis 1.

We can see from this discussion how complicated and at times arbitrary is the problem of distinguishing definitions from assumptions. Basically the problem is that of deciding which hypotheses are "contingent" and which are "noncontingent." A contingent hypothesis is one that makes some testable deduction that may be right or wrong. It can in theory be disproved. A noncontingent hypothesis is really a statement about the language in the theoretical system or about the rules of deduction and not about the subject matter. Noncontingent hypotheses cannot be tested or proved wrong. The scientist may decide, however, that a definition is not useful and redefine his conceptual terms in an attempt to improve a theory.

Noncontingent hypotheses form a part of every theory because they permit the contingent hypotheses to be tested. The terms in the statement "all men are mortal" must be defined so that the scientist can recognize a "man" when he sees one and determine whether or not something is "mortal." In other words, the terms in a directly testable hypothesis must be operationally or empirically defined—otherwise the hypothesis is not testable.

Thus definitions are essential for testing a theory, but they may also reduce apparently testable hypotheses to logical tautologies. It is all too easy in an experiment to define the terms in a hypothesis so that the definitions and the derivations from the hypothesis coincide completely. In this case the hypothesis is completely deducible from the definition and is, therefore, not testable, since it cannot be disconfirmed. For example, the hypothesis that aggressive children will seize opportunities to hurt children who cannot retaliate may be derived from some high-level hypotheses about aggression, but if the definition of aggressive is "a tendency to injure others when there are no negative consequences" then the hypothesis becomes directly derivable from the definition. Consequently, it cannot be disconfirmed, and it lends no support to the higher-level hypothesis from which it was presumably derived.

In summary, then, hypotheses may be untestable for a variety of reasons. They may not lead to empirical hypotheses either because empirical definitions of the terms are lacking or because no lower-level hypotheses can be derived from them. On the other hand, the terms may be so defined that the empirical hypothesis is derivable from the definition rather than from the hypothesis to be tested.

Let us turn now to the discussion of operational or empirical definitions. The necessity for operational definitions of the terms in a scientific theory has been strongly emphasized in methodological discussions of psychological research during the last twenty years. The emphasis has been valuable and has certainly improved the quality of psychological research. But the demand for operational definitions has sometimes been interpreted so rigidly and dogmatically that fruitful research activity has been curtailed.

There is no question but that a good scientific theory must be testable, i.e., its lowest-level hypotheses must be empirical hypotheses that can be checked against the facts and confirmed or not. These tests cannot be made unless the terms in the lower-level hypotheses have some sort of operational definition, but it is important not to put unnecessarily strict requirements upon the operationalization of a theory.

We propose, therefore, to state the requirements for operationalization in a somewhat weaker form than that in which they are usually put. Without losing the essential value of operational definitions, we can make the following four statements in regard to those situations in which unique operational definitions of every term are *not* necessary.

1. The same term may have different operational definitions in different hypotheses.

2. There is no necessity for a term to have an operational definition that is applicable in situations in which there are no hypotheses to test.

3. The lack of explicit operational definitions of some of the terms in the higher-level hypotheses does not imply that the lower-level hypotheses are untestable.

4. It is not necessary for every individual term to have an individual operational definition. Sets of terms may correspond to sets of empirical events without each term corresponding to an individual event. The third and fourth statements may be equivalent ways of saying the same thing.

**Equivalence of Different Definitions.** It is obvious in other sciences that the same term is not always operationally defined in the same way. The measurement of the temperature of the sun is made in a completely different way from the measurement of the temperature of a room. This does not mean that the selection of the measurement device is arbitrary or that the two measures of temperature are not equivalent. In physics, a complicated scientific system containing many terms, it often turns out that the same term *temperature* turns up all alone on one side of a formula, with some set of terms on the other side that does not include temperature. It may be related to the length of a solid bar in one formula, the color of molten metal in another, and the pressure of a gas in a third. Every such formula is a potential definition of the term *temperature*. As long as all of these different formulas are members of the same set of hypotheses forming a deductive system, then the different measures of temperature will be equivalent. There may be some situations in which one measurement is technically or theoretically inapplicable. The equivalence lies in the coherent structure of the whole system, not in the detailed matching of one instrument against the other.

In behavioral science the same term frequently appears in different contexts, but seldom do the different usages fit into a coherent logical system. Aggression may be measured by fights per hour in nursery school, by aggressive stories on the Thematic Apperception Test (TAT) or by violations of the rules of a game. There is no doubt that aggression has different operational definitions in different situations, but the trouble lies in the fact that these three definitions are not all parts of a coherent connected set of hypotheses. There is no assurance that the three measures are equivalent or compatible.

It is common practice to correlate two measures to test for equivalence, and a high correlation is surely comforting. On the other hand, two operational definitions may be equivalent yet uncorrelatable. The length of the solid bar and the color of the molten metal are uncorrelatable yet compatible definitions of temperature.

*Inapplicability of Definitions.* The statement that there is no need for operational definitions when there are no hypotheses to test seems obvious. If a theory makes no predictions about children, its terms need not be defined for children. This fact has not always been fully recognized, however. In some writings about operational definitions of motives, for example (Estes et al., 1954), it has been tacitly assumed that a proper operational definition of a motive is one that permits us to watch an animal or a person in a free situation and to infer his motives from the observation of his ongoing behavior. This is equivalent to asking for an operational definition of gravity or friction that could be applied by an observer of an avalanche. Although a generally applicable operational definition of a motive would be a real achievement, it is not a necessity for scientific progress. We can be well satisfied at first if a theory can make testable predictions even in very special purified situations —analogous to the fall of a body in a vacuum—and leave for later the more complicated problem of measuring gravity from the path of a projectile in the air.

Fortunately, psychologists most often set these strict requirements when they are talking about methodology not when they are doing research. Hull, for example, defined habit strength in terms of the number of reinforcements of the response (Hull, 1943). This is a clear operational definition, but it is possible to use it only if the history of the organism is known. Given a strange animal, this definition does not provide any way of diagnosing the habits it has and how strong they are. Although this might be considered a sign of the theory's incompleteness, the theory cannot be criticized on methodological grounds for failing to provide an adequate operational definition.

*Necessity of Operational Definitions.* We have seen, thus far, that the same operational definition cannot be employed in every situation in which a theory is relevant and that there may be others in which a theory provides no operational definition. Let us turn now to a more debatable point, that some of the terms in a theory may not have operational definitions at all. Such terms, if they exist, cannot occur in the two lowest levels of the system of hypotheses because these are the levels at which hypotheses must be directly testable. At the higher levels such terms may exist. Braithwaite (1955) gives a very simple example. Suppose A, B, and C are three observable characteristics. In the theoretical system the following three hypotheses might occur:

Everything that is A is also L and M.
Everything that is B is also M and N.
Everything that is C is also N and L.

This system has a number of testable

consequences, e.g., everything that is A and B is also C. However, the important feature of this discussion is that these testable hypotheses stem from the three listed above without requiring any operational definition of L, M, and N.

The reader may feel that to invent three undefined terms to account for three observable terms is no great achievement. It is hardly parsimonious in the present case. If the model is extended, however, the number of factors will be considerably less than the number of observables. Thus six observables will correspond to four factors, fifteen observables to five factors, etc. The resemblance to factor analysis is more than superficial.

In a brilliant discussion Braithwaite shows that there is no way to "solve" the three formulas for L, M, and N in terms of A, B, and C without making some added assumptions. If, for example, we assume that A is *equivalent* to L and M, rather than merely *implying* L and M, and make similar assumptions for the other formulas, then we can come to definitions of L, M, and N. But, as Braithwaite then shows, these assumptions so rigidify the theoretical system that it cannot easily be expanded to four factors to accommodate additional observations.

Regardless of whether we agree that there are actual disadvantages in demanding operational definitions of all the higher-level terms in a theory, this illustration does demonstrate that the lack of such definitions does not prevent the system from having testable hypotheses.

A similar sort of example could be used to illustrate the fact that in some situations a whole set of theoretical terms is operationally defined by a whole set of performance variables. In factor analysis, for example, in the absence of pure tests factor scores are determined by weighting a battery of test scores in a particular way. The same set of test scores is weighted differently to measure a different factor. Thus no single test score is related in a one-to-one fashion to a factor, but the whole battery serves to define a set of factor scores.

We see that even in a well-developed theoretical system operational definitions are not simple universal behavioral indicators of every theoretical term. The absolutely essential feature of a theory is its testability, and the demand for operational definitions has been intended to achieve that objective. We do well, however, to focus our attention on the adequate testability of the theory rather than an insistence upon operational definitions for every individual term.

## SCIENTIFIC STRATEGY

The discussion thus far has been limited to those characteristics of a theory that make it adequate or inadequate to explain a body of data. As scientists, we should have such a theory as our objective, but in a real sense these criteria have to do with theory testing rather than theory building. It is not obvious that the greatest contributions to a science come from theories that meet these criteria of logical deducibility of subordinate from superordinate hypotheses or of maximum testability. In fact, there have been extremely stimulating conceptual systems whose fertility as sources of research activities cannot be doubted, despite the fact that they were poor theories from the point of view of logic and testability. Freud's and Lewin's writings come to mind immediately. On the other hand, Hull's theory has also been very fruitful as a stimulus to research, and it was deliberately constructed to be a model of logic and testability.

Just what makes one point of view fruitful and another sterile is not likely to be describable in a few simple principles. It is almost certainly not a function of the theory alone; the man behind the theory can be the source of its popularity or its lack of acceptance. The state of the field is also important; there are numerous cases in the history of science in which precocious theoretical suggestions were ignored until the field caught up. The present discussion, therefore, will not attempt a set of criteria for "good" errors or fruitful speculation in scientific thinking. On the other hand, it does seem worthwhile to consider the variety of contributions to the psychological literature that are called theoretical discussions and make some distinctions among them.

*Empirical Speculation.* One type of discussion is called theoretical because it does not deal with established data, but in fact it is not properly theoretical at all. It is empirical speculation without empirical evidence. Freud's hypotheses that in the early history of society people were organized into "primal hordes" is an example. Arguments about the extent to which young infants perceive the mother's anxiety and/or dislikes are essentially empirical arguments.

Such hypotheses are frequently not integrated into any system; they are merely stated. Sometimes they are stated as facts, sometimes as empirical hypotheses; but, in either case, the controversies they arouse usually concern the truth of the statement. In many cases the statements are testable enough in principle but are untestable in actuality because of technical difficulties. There is nothing essentially unobservable about a primal horde; we are hampered by technical difficulties, i.e., no time machine to take us back into the past.

Such empirical hypotheses are frequently fruitful because they stimulate research to confirm or disconfirm them. When they are firmly deduced from theoretical systems, they can be exceedingly fruitful as predictions whose confirmation will lend strong support to the theory. Even when they are not genuinely based upon a theoretical system, they may still lead to important investigations.

There are two ways, however, that they may actually interfere with the progress of a science. First, they may lead to a merely verbal controversy that seems to assume that logic can decide the issue without any apparent realization that the question is an empirical one. Second, the empirical hypothesis, if it is confirmed, may be interpreted as supporting other statements made by the same person even though they are not logically related to the confirmed hypothesis. One of the consequences of the current insistence upon testing hypotheses is that the investigator may pull his hypotheses out of thin air or out of his intuitive wisdom. The confirmation of such hypotheses may establish the fact in question, but beyond that it constitutes evidence for the investigator's perspicacity or luck rather than evidence of his other theoretical statements.

*Terminology and Definitions.* A second type of theoretical contribution might be described as the proposal of a terminology or a definition. Lists of needs, classifications of types of social groups, definitional distinctions between *guilt* and *shame* or between *hope for success* and *fear of failure* are examples of such contributions. Definitions and terminology are important parts of a theoretical system, and many of the major scientific advances can be traced to a novel definition of the problem or a happy classification of the phenomena to be explained. Frequently such attempts stem from the effort to refine our ordinary language descriptions to avoid confusions that have plagued previous attempts to structure the field.

The fruitfulness of a definition is judged ultimately on the success of the theory that utilizes it. Definitions are untestable in isolation but they contain the implicit assumption that those events included in a single definitional category belong together. By being defined in the same term, they lose some individuality and must behave alike in many situations in which the term is involved in an empirical prediction. A defect in a theory may certainly be the result of poor definition, but still a definition is untestable except in connection with a theory. A proposed definition unaccompanied by a theory that permits the whole structure to be tested may, therefore, appear to some people merely as the spinning of verbal webs. Arguments about definitions can be fruitless, and one mark of an advanced science is less controversy over definitions. There certainly seems to be little value in trying to determine whether or not one person's definition contains the "real" meaning of a term; for example, whether or not "motives are *really* just behavior sequences." On the other hand, there may be a strong tendency in modern psychology to dismiss such discussions by saying that "it is just a matter of definition," as if such matters were unimportant.

*Proto-Theories.* A third type of theoretical contribution is the proposal of a genuine but incompletely specified theory, containing contingent statements as higher-level hypotheses and leading to predictions of one sort or another. These have been called "proto-theories."

Most psychological theories, especially those of the cognitive variety, such as Lewin's and Tolman's, and psychoanalytic theories are proto-theories in this sense. The more rigorous behavior theories, such as Hull's, are usually well specified in regard to the particular data of animal behavior they were designed to explain, but when they are applied to complex problems of human behavior or child development, as in Dollard and Miller (1950) or Sears, Maccoby, and Levin (1957), they must still be considered largely proto-theory.

When proto-theories of human behavior are carefully examined, their defects as scientific systems are frequently of two sorts. First, they are not sufficiently testable—the terms have inadequate operational definitions. Second, the so-called derivations from the theory are not strictly logical; they skip steps, they depend on tacit assumptions, and they substitute intuitive reasonableness for rigorous logical deduction.

To illustrate the first type of difficulty, the cognitive theories of Lewin and Tolman have been quite justly described as postperceptual and prebehavioral. The actual stimulus conditions that result in a given valence, or cognitive structure, are not specified. Similarly, the conditions under which a force leads to locomotion are left unclear. All these are defects in operational definitions. Similar problems arise in Sears' definition of aggression as behavior intended to injure.

The trouble can often be traced to the fact that our "naïve" theory of human behavior interferes with our "scientific" theory. In everyday life psychologists, like other people, operate on the assumption that others have an awareness of their surroundings, including such future events as the consequences of an act. They assume people are purposive, intentional, and rational, i.e., they choose what they do in terms of its consequences and behave as they do in order to attain good consequences and avoid bad. These assumptions of naïve theory have been described in more detail by Heider (1958).

In everyday life we recognize other people's intentions, we judge pretty well what they are aware of. We judge, for example, whether we have been intentionally ignored or actually not seen. Although these judgments are apparently reasonably accurate—at least

we get by in everyday life—we have very little clear knowledge of the cues. Psychologists, therefore, who try to build this naïve theory into a scientific one have great trouble in providing clear operational definitions. We are so sure that goal-directed behavior exists that the extreme difficulty of defining it in operational terms is never quite recognized.

Despite the lack of operational definitions, hypotheses couched in ordinary language may lead to research. The investigator who is willing to step outside his behavioristic role can understand everyday language as well as anyone else. If he is sympathetic with cognitive theories of behavior, he devises experiments based on what the theory means as well as what it says. The danger is that he will not recognize the absence of the genuine operational definition.

The second common defect in prototheories of human behavior is the lack of strictly logical derivations of conclusions from premises. "His mother constantly compared him unfavorably with his brother; therefore he developed a strong resentment of the brother" illustrates this point. The statement is an unsatisfactory derivation. It follows common sense but does not fill in the logical gaps that are necessary to make it a true derivation. Similarly, to say that a person moves toward a goal object because he sees where it is may be excellent sense, but it is not a logical derivation unless many of the tacit assumptions are made explicit.

The intuitive reasonableness of a consequence following an antecedent is affected by experience. In psychoanalytic circles such statements as "his conformity was so rigid that it must conceal a real impulse to rebel" have become customary and now appear intuitively sensible. Yet such a phrase conceals much ambiguity. The definition of "rigid" is not clear; other criteria than rigidity are necessary before a behavior can be realistically attributed to reaction formation. The terms "conceal" and "real impulse" carry many connotations that are difficult to specify and may even distort the intended meaning of the phrase.

From the point of view of scientific strategy, what is the value of proto-theories with their poor operational definitions and their loose and shaky derivations? One opinion is that such theories are actual blocks to progress. The only way that we can progress is to state predictions in such a form that everybody knows just what they mean and everybody will agree when they are confirmed or invalidated. Then we can change the theory in the light of the revealed weaknesses and move on to another attempt. From this point of view, pseudo-deductions such as the ones illustrated merely hide problems, and any satisfactions obtained from their confirmation are illusory.

A second point of view is that such theoretical statements, inadequate though they may be, are steps toward an eventual adequate theory. Those who hold this position frequently maintain that the insistence upon highly objective testable predictions and rigorously logical derivations tends to focus the scientist's attention upon relatively insignificant problems and results in very narrow theories. They argue that if we must wait for a completely adequate theory of perception and motor behavior before we begin to investigate attitudes, motives, feelings, and coflicts we will never get to the important problems. Such people view scientific progress as the gradual refinement and differentiation of a broad theoretical position whose scope is adequate to include all varieties of behavior. Their opponents argue for establishing miniature theories of limited scope and then for gradually increasing the scope.

A second issue also separates these two camps. How close will our eventual behavior theory be to "naïve" theory (see p. 17.) If the tacit theories of the man on the street are distillations of generations of human interaction, then common sense is a good base for theory building. Psychology should first try to catch up with common sense by making naïve theories explicit before it tries to forge ahead into new territory. If, on the other hand, common-sense psychology is merely a projective system as far from the truth as primitive theories of disease and astronomy, then we must cut loose immediately and try to build theories from the ground up.

This controversy is especially relevant for the study of children because the man in the street makes little distinction between adults and children. Mothers frequently say that the 3- or 4-month-old child begins to act human. By this she probably means that she now attributes consciousness, intentions, and goal-directed behavior to him. The child is seen as an inadequate, poorly controlled, irresponsible adult for several more years but not as qualitatively different. This view is probably what is meant by the "miniature-adult" theory of children that begins so many authors' surveys of theories of child behavior. The validity of the naïve theory of children is then considerably more questionable than the naïve theory of adult behavior.

Still a third point of view on scientific strategy would argue that science, at least in its early stages, should not try theory building at all but should concentrate upon establishing a solid body of theoretically neutral factual data. Gradually we can organize these data in terms of lower-level hypotheses and build from the data up to an eventual theoretical system. Extremists maintain that the facts will eventually build the theory for us. If an anatomist wants to know about the course of the carotid artery, he dissects and finds out where it goes without waiting until he has a theory that predicts where it goes. He does not even need a hypothesis to test. Many examples of theoretically blind yet useful data collection can be found in anatomy, taxonomy, geology, and other sciences.

Those who maintain the importance of theory as a guide to scientific development argue that in behavioral science no data is theoretically neutral and that an antitheoretical position merely allows a number of tacit theoretical assumptions to have full sway under the guise of theoretical neutrality. They can point to the implicit theory in any attempt to categorize behavior. Does the boy move his arm or slam the door? The first phrase is not more theoretically neutral than the other; it merely denies goal-directed behavior tacitly rather than explicitly.

We have described three scientific strategies and tried to present the arguments for and against each. The first strategy is to make every theory formally sound with clear operational definitions and rigorous derivations. The second is to begin with global theories, necessarily vague, and refine them by research. The third strategy argues for fact finding rather than theory building at all.

Perhaps it is important to recognize that all of these positions are proposing empirical hypotheses about the development of a science without any real evidence. Theory building is a variety of human behavior and is within the realm of behavioral science. But it is a realm in which we have very little data. Although it seems quite likely that each of the three approaches is a sound strategy under some conditions and that behavioral science will profit from the existence of all these points of view, we really have little evidence to support any position. The soundest statement is the negative one that until better evidence emerges it would seem rash to maintain dogmatically the worthlessness of any of these strategies of scientific advance.

## Specifications for a Theory

The purpose of this section is to provide a table of contents of a sort for a theory of child behavior and development. It is in no way a statement of the content of a theory but rather of the specifications for a theory. It is an outline of the problem areas that an adequate theoretical system must some time fill in with actual theoretical hypotheses. The discussion is intended to be theoretically neutral, but like all such attempts it probably contains implicit theoretical assumptions. Let us hope they are not too numerous or too restricting.

## SPECIFICATION FOR A THEORY OF BEHAVIOR

Since psychology is concerned with the behavior of organisms, it seems only reasonable to make a basic division between the organism and the situation it is in. The organism, or, in our case, the person, has a number of properties or characteristics. Because of these characteristics he behaves the way he does in the situation. On the other hand, it is equally valid to say that he behaves the way he does because of the characteristics of the situation. The same organism behaves differently in different situations; different organisms behave differently in the same situation. The behavior is, therefore, a function both of the characteristics of the person and the characteristics of the situation. This division is not an a priori requirement, but it seems inherent in the definition of psychology, with its tacit assumption that the behavior of organisms represents a set of events belonging to a single discipline.

If we adopt this basic division, then three research areas suggest themselves immediately: (1) functional relation of situation and behavior, (2) assessment of personal parameters, (3) assessment of situational parameters. The first is the elucidation of the functional relation just described. What behavior is elicited when a person with certain characteristics (which might well be called personality characteristics) is put in a situation with certain properties? This is certainly a central task for the science. It involves the proper classification and definition of personality characteristics, and it involves just as much the classification and definition of those situational properties that describe the impact or the stimulus properties of the situation. Both of these definitional tasks are on the side of the independent variables; there is a similar task of classification and definition of the dependent variables, the behavior of the person. What acts should be classed together by definitions of behavioral variables so that they are lawfully related to personality and situation?

If the experience of other sciences and the history of our own is any guide, the theoretical hypotheses or "laws" that emerge from such investigation will be laws of "pure cases" in which other factors than those involved in the hypothesis are absent. Newton's assumption that in the absence of other influences a body will remain in uniform motion is an example of a pure case. If these are the sorts of laws that do emerge, they will be approximately verified in artificially purified situations in which the influence of other factors is minimized.

The second and third areas of research reflect the two assessment problems that must be solved before such laws can be made useful. We must learn how to assess the personality of complex individuals in order to describe people in terms of the appropriate variables. We must also learn how to assess the complicated situations of real life so that we may know what relevant stimulus properties are present in such complex situations as two-person games, small groups, nursery schools, and family situations. This is one task of ecological description.

Although there is a certain logic in considering the general laws first and then dealing with the problems of assessment, all areas seem to move hand in hand in the progress of a science. In trying to solve practical problems of assessment and prediction promising variables whose careful theoretical definition may require carefully controlled situations are unearthed. Similarly, tasks of job analysis or comparisons of different environments lead to situational characteristics whose role in a conceptual system is later clarified. Everyday language may be a rich storehouse of possible theoretical terms that have arisen in the course of human interaction.

What is the role of child psychology in this scientific undertaking? For this aspect of behavioral science, child psychology belongs to the fields of comparative psychology and individual differences. Since behavioral scientists are very much restricted in their ability to modify the properties of organisms experimentally, we must take every possible advantage of the naturally occurring differences among organisms to elucidate the characteristics that are theoretically useful. Species differences, age differences, and pathological changes in organisms are especially important to investigate because they are so large and obvious. One of the unique contributions that child psychology can

make to behavioral science is the careful comparative study of children of different ages to determine the most valuable categorization of those characteristics that are a function of age.

## SPECIFICATION FOR A THEORY OF CHANGE

The discussion thus far has proceeded as if organisms never changed. We have been concerned with the contemporaneous factors in behavior, to use a Lewinian phrase, or, in the words of Hull, with performance variables. Of course, organisms do change, and their changes pose another set of theoretical problems.

To some extent, the distinction between behavior and personality change is arbitrary. Any behavioral sequence might be viewed as a short-term change in the individual's properties. Furthermore, the many varieties of change that take place, changes of set, mood changes, learning processes, reversible pathological changes, and irreversible changes occurring as part of growth and development, certainly must be distinguished one from the other. On the other hand, the attempt to describe personality characteristics implies that these properties are not entirely evanescent. Otherwise it would be impossible to predict from the measurement situation to the criterion situation. Even though any behavioral sequence does produce temporary changes in the individual's characteristics—such as involvement in the activity—these changes are in most cases reversible so that the individual's characteristics after a behavioral act are essentially what they were before it. These considerations make it convenient to distinguish between the contemporaneous causes of behavior and the temporal changes in the individual's properties caused by factors operating over a period of time.

The factors related to change may be conveniently classified into those descriptive of the individual before the change took place and the environmental impacts occurring between that time and the time the change occurred. If there are developmental changes that are internally controlled and uninfluenced by intervening environmental events, they represent a limiting case.

Just as in the study of behavior, the research task consists of properly defining the characteristics of the person and the characteristics of the intervening events so that they may be related by a system of theoretical hypotheses. Since the characteristics of the person enter into both a theory of behavior and a theory of change, it would be very convenient for the investigator if the same set of personality variables appeared in the two theories, but such a convenient simplification may not be valid. There is no a priori reason that the categories of personal traits that cohere meaningfully in the analysis of the contemporaneous situation must be the same categories that are homogeneous with respect to the process of change.

For example, one possible consequence of being deprived of social relations for a period of time may be to lose the desire for human companionship. One sort of personality characteristic might be this tendency to adapt readily to social isolation. Whether this personality variable would be detectable by any purely behavioral measure restricted to a study of the contemporary situation is a debatable but empirical question. It might be as difficult to measure as the trait of "early menarche" in the 4-year-old.

On the side of the environment, it seems almost certain that the description of the stimulus properties of the situation will not be an adequate description of the total impact of an environment in changing the person. In terms of present notions, the latter includes all of the reinforcements that an environment provides as well as the stimuli that elicit responses. Also, the environment includes more than a single situation. It might well be thought of as containing distributions, sequences, and sets of situations. Its description might be couched, therefore, in such terms as the probability of various situations within the environmental setting and the contingent probability of sequences of situations following upon various actions of the organism. The uncertainty about the basic description of a psychological environment shows how little attention this fundamental problem has received in behavioral science.

The role of child and developmental psychology in achieving a theory of change is quite obvious. The central problem of developmental psychology is to explain those changes that occur as the child grows up to become mature and socialized.

## Special Research Problems

This grand overview of the fields of behavioral science and the role of child psychology is exhilarating in its breadth, but it contains more than a little Utopian thinking. It is well, therefore, to come back down out of the clouds to some of the more mundane problems of research in child development. This whole volume is founded upon the supposition that research in child development offers some special problems, some unique challenges, and some unusual opportunities. What are these problems?

## PROBLEMS ARISING FROM CHILDREN'S CHARACTERISTICS

One set of special problems arises from the fact that the subjects of child-development research are children. Quite aside from the fact that the job of child psychology is to understand children, we must understand them somewhat even to conduct research with them. In terms of traditional research operations, children are somewhere between animals and adults. In research on adults we are accustomed to structuring the situation with language, to instructing the subjects with language, and, in many experiments, to collecting verbal responses that are treated as communications by the subject about some subject matter. Research with animals is conducted on quite a different basis. The situation is structured by such things as walls, electric grills, and stimulus patterns, and the behavior of the animals is taken as a reaction, not a communication. Children fall in between. For very young children, the techniques used with animals are necessary, but as the child grows older we can begin to utilize language as a research tool. The trouble is that children do not understand instructions very well, and verbal structuring of the situation does not always produce the same results that it does with adults. We cannot count upon the effectiveness of these verbal procedures with children. We can, of course, treat children as if they were animals and study them nonverbally, but that is to sacrifice the very thing about children that makes them especially valuable as research subjects. This very lack of docility of children to verbal procedures is a major field for investigation; we ought to study it, not circumvent it.

How do these characteristics of children affect research? One of the problems is to establish a prescribed psychological situation for the child. Suppose, for example, that we want to offer the child a choice between two alternatives to determine preference. For an adult, we can be reasonably sure that when we give him a choice he is actually choosing. A child may pick the first alternative he sees without ever looking at the other one. He may vacillate so much from one alternative to the other that we suspect his final behavior is more accidental than deliberate, or he may break down emotionally because he cannot have both alternatives.

In many experimental conflict situations, for example, we want to be sure the subject knows what he can do, what the consequences are of each possible course of action, and what courses of action are not permitted in the experiment. With adults these objectives can usually be achieved by making the apparatus clear and the instructions specific, but children may pay no attention to the directions or may be attracted to one feature of the apparatus at the expense of another. They may insist on the experimenter's help when the adult would conform to the proper mores of the experiment. These behaviors might be made the subject of investigation, but when we want to study some other aspect of child behavior we do not want to be sidetracked into an investigation of all these difficulties. Consequently, the experimenter must use considerable skill to be sure that the psychological impact of the situation is what the experimenter intends. In later chapters specific methods are discussed.

If one of the problems of working with children is on the stimulus side, there are equivalent problems in interpreting the meaning of the child's response. In most research with adults we operate on the assumption that the behavior is either a communication to the experimenter or that it is a response to the situation. In the latter case, its communicative aspects are interferences. When we want to determine the subject's response to some harmful stimulus imposed upon him by another person, we recognize that one factor that may inhibit his hostile behavior is his unwillingness to appear to be hostile in the eyes of the experimenter. Here the communicative significance of the behavior interferes with the measurement of the subject's reaction to instigation.

With adults, we count upon our good intuitive knowledge of other adults to keep us out of trouble. It is part of the art of experimentation to design situations that do not inhibit the behavior we wish to study. In the case of children our intuitions are more likely to play us false. Sometimes it seems as if the child's response is uninfluenced by any recognition of its meaning to the experimenter, and in fact one attraction about working with children is their relative freedom from convention. But again the child cannot be counted on to be consistent in such matters—adults are not either, but relatively more so. So, in interpreting the child's response, whether it is a reaction or whether it is a story or self-report that is to be treated as a communication, there are special skills that experienced investigators have acquired. These questions are discussed in much more detail in the chapters that follow.

Another illustration points to a slightly different problem. When a child is asked to repeat digits, he may suddenly start to count in the middle of the repetition, "4, 1, 3, 7, 8, 9, 10." If an adult fails on repeating digits, we can reasonably assume that he forgot and attribute the error to memory. The same thing may be true of the child, but another possibility is that he lost his task orientation and wandered off into a habitual response. As far as being a failure on the intelligence test is concerned, there is no serious problem; but in interpreting the failure the particular characteristics of children need to be kept in mind.

This difference between children and adults is, of course, only an extreme example of the difference between children of different ages. Such differences

make it quite difficult to plot development from one age level to another
because we do not know the fundamental dimensions of behavior in terms
of which children of different ages can
be compared. The difficulties in describing the growth of intelligence illustrate the point. When individual
growth curves on mental age are
plotted, it is quite common to find considerable variability from one time to
another. These are frequently attributed
to the effects of environment, but such
an interpretation is not the only possibility. Bayley (1933), for example,
suggests that such variation may well be
due to the fact that intelligence tests
measure different abilities at different
age levels. In view of the way intelligence test items are selected, this interpretation seems reasonable.

If Bayley's interpretation is true, it
means that intelligence is not a comparable measure at all age levels. What
then is a dimension on which child development can be plotted with the assurance that the same thing is being
measured at each age level? A complete
answer to this question would require
a really adequate theory of development, but until we do answer it we can
expect difficulty in knowing whether or
not the variables we choose for the
comparison of age levels are the proper
ones. Until a more adequate theory is
available, we shall probably do well to
study direct behavioral indices, which
are as close to the raw data as possible.
Height is such a physical measurement.
A change in height does not always
mean the same thing; it may mean
growth in the length of the legs in some

cases and change in sitting height in
others. Even so, it has real advantages
over such a highly derived index as
mental age.

## PROBLEMS ARISING
## FROM THE STUDY OF CHANGE

These general research problems
plague and challenge research workers
in the interpretation of the behavior
of a child of any particular age. There
are other problems that are inherent in
the study of changes, especially long-
term developmental changes.

The most serious technical problem
is the real inability to control the environment of a child over any reasonably long period. In longitudinal
studies we must be content with very
inadequate controls over the events in
the child's life.

Longitudinal studies, as they were
originally conceived, seemed to have
gambled on the existence of clear developmental trends that would shine
through the welter of influences of uncontrolled events. In physical growth
the gamble paid off quite well. Many
measures of physical growth are relatively uninfluenced by the disturbances found in the normal life of the
child. Even though illnesses slow down
the growth of long bones and delay the
appearance of ossification centers, the
disturbance is relatively minor. The
general shape of the growth curve is
quite apparent, and the extrinsic disturbances do not affect the individual's
growth pattern enough to destroy the
predictability of early or late maturation, adolescent growth rate, adult

height, etc. The organism's own growth pattern can be identified despite lack of control over many environmental factors.

On the face of it, major psychological changes, which are part of growth, appear equally prominent and obvious. The increase in ability, self-control, and perceptual sensitivity seems almost as obvious and as universal as the increase in height and weight. But diligent and competent attempts to identify meaningful individual patterns in psychological development analogous to the various physical growth patterns have not yet been very successful.

When the interest of child-development research shifted from the study of the maturational process to the study of the effect of early childhood experiences, the famous longitudinal studies were caught in mid-stream. They were committed to a research design that involved the careful periodic description of a relatively unselected group of children from birth onward. The design was a reasonable one for the purposes that guided its inception, but for the investigation of the effects of early childhood experiences it was not so well selected. Yet in a way the longitudinal method as a whole has been evaluated on the basis of these studies, which were originally designed for another purpose.

What are the problems of a longitudinal investigation of the effects of early childhood experiences? The first is the determination of the early childhood experiences and effects to study. This is no light task because the introduction of any variable into a longitudinal program that will last for several years is expensive in time, money, and

personnel. The same care and pretesting should go into the selection of the proper variables that go into the selection of measuring instruments for an artificial satellite.

The problem is especially serious on the side of the independent variable because this determines the selection of cases. To expect that enough of the right kind of cases will turn up in an unselected longitudinal sample is foolhardy indeed. Yet to set up a new longitudinal sample for every new experimental and control variable is out of the question. So a major problem is to pick out likely variables whose effects will be so strong that they will show up even when the error term contains all of the variations introduced by uncontrolled events in the child's life.

A second problem is the selection of control variables. These controls are maintained in the usual research design because they probably influence the dependent variable. If they can be kept constant, the residual error variation is reduced. In a longitudinal study the control may also be used to select cases whose lives are less likely to be subjected to violent upheavals because those upheavals increase the error variance. Therefore, geographical stability is highly desirable—for practical as well as theoretical reasons. Perhaps the limitation of the study to cooperative middle-class families is to be desired rather than deplored because of the relative placidity and stability of middle-class family life. To be sure, generality is sacrificed, but there are strong arguments for maximizing the chances of finding something before worrying about the generality of what is found.

A third problem is the selection of the dependent variables and measuring instruments. There is an almost irresistible urge in a longitudinal study to cover all aspects of personality, since the cost of just one more test or one more observation seems so small by comparison with what is already invested in the program. In a sense, the argument is justified; it probably is better to err on the side of too much rather than too little coverage. But the additional dependent variable is sometimes just a shot in the dark and has no theoretical reason for being influenced by the variables under investigation. In that case it would be well to consider its cost, not in relation to the tremendous investment of the total program, but in terms of what the same time and money could accomplish in a completely separate small study to determine what the variable *is* related to.

It should be apparent that a longitudinal study of the effects of one, two, or three variables of childhood experience upon later personality is a big investment for relatively small return— quantitatively speaking. It behooves us, therefore, to precede such an undertaking with careful pretesting, study of cross-sectional differences, and cruder retrospective studies to establish the likelihood of major effects. A longitudinal study is the last, not the first, step in a research program. It is an absolutely essential research method if we are to get firm knowledge of psychological change, but paradoxically it is to be avoided whenever possible.

There is another type of longitudinal study, the analysis of the individual cases based upon records as complete as possible. This type of research is often defended as an exploratory study to suggest hypotheses. Although it has been useful at times for that purpose, it seems a very laborious and inefficient procedure for generating hypotheses.

In the author's opinion the elaborate longitudinal case study belongs at exactly the opposite end of the continuum. Human behavior is so complex that theories must eventually outgrow the restrictions of the three- or four-variable research design. Once behavior theories become genuinely multivariate, it is impossible to find any sample of cases that is alike on enough variables to belong in the same cell. Then we must move to the case study. We shall appraise individual cases on the ten or twenty variables contained in the theory and let the theory make testable individual predictions about each case. The predictions will be different for every case, but the accuracy of the predictions on a sequence of cases will permit the theory to be tested just as rigorously as the more orthodox design.

Whether there are theories ready for this type of test is an open question. John Benjamin (1949) who has written an excellent analysis of this problem, thinks that psychoanalytic theory can make some predictions on this basis. He believes, for example, that the theory can predict that certain children cannot under *any* circumstances develop a particular mental disease. If they become mentally ill, the illness will take some other form. This type of prediction, if it can be successfully upheld, neatly circumvents all the problems of uncontrolled environmental events that occur between the prediction and its test.

In this section we have discussed the field of child-development research, have tried to identify the problems it must solve, and have pointed to some of the difficulties that must be overcome. The problems of investigating personality changes over long periods have come in for extensive discussion because they are so particularly central for the field of child development. Later chapters in this volume treat of many of these problems in much more detail.

## Ethical Problems of Research

We saw how some of the research problems relating to children stem from their being half human, half animal. In an interesting way, this same marginal position is at the root of the special ethical problems of research on children. They are both precious and vulnerable. Unlike animals, they cannot be sacrificed for research. They must be treated with all the safeguards that our civilization demands for the study of human beings.

At the same time, they are vulnerable. There is a widespread assumption that children are less resistant and resilient than adults; that is, that stress, frustration, emotional experiences, and pressures that would cause only temporary discomfort in adults may produce long-range consequences in children. Actually, the evidence for this belief is almost nonexistent, but neither is there clear contradictory evidence. Since nobody wants to take any chances, behavioral research among children is restricted by narrower limits than comparable research among adults.

Not only are children perhaps more vulnerable, but they are also not free agents, able to make their own decisions and to take the consequences of them. They are below the age of consent, so to speak, and the investigator who undertakes the research must obtain consent from the people responsible for the child and must act *in loco parentis* while the child is in his care.

It is necessary on some occasions that the adult subject be unaware of the purpose or the procedure of an experiment. This circumstance is sometimes used as an excuse to put adult subjects into experiments that they would never enter voluntarily, even when the knowledge would not affect their behavior in the experiment as much as it would lead them to refuse to participate. The general practice of deceiving the subjects of psychological experiments is roundly condemned by a large section of the psychological profession, perhaps the majority. They argue that in most cases the experiment can be done equally well without deception, that if necessary the subject can be told frankly that it is necessary for him to be ignorant of the purpose of the experiment and that the few experiments in which deception is absolutely required are better left undone. These psychologists point to the growing public image of the psychologist as underhanded. The widespread use of deception in experiments and in disguised forms of testing, such as projective methods, does justify this mistrust. Such procedures are used to make the subjects reveal information without the subject's knowledge or consent. These suspicions of the intent of psychologists can have serious consequences, indeed. One of the ironic features of the situation is that in most cases the deception is unnecessary; consent could be readily obtained by a frank discussion of the psychologist's interests.

When we study children instead of adults, the issue is put more squarely. Clearly there is no reason to deceive the child's parent or teacher about the purpose of the experiment, except the fear that that person would be unwilling to allow the child to participate or that he would by coaching or instruction try to ensure that the child's behavior would not reflect unfavorably on him or his parents. The ways in which the parent or teacher might interfere with the experiment may seem unfortunate to the psychologist, but in a real sense they are the prerogatives of the person in whose care the child is placed. If he is not convinced that the psychologist will do the child no harm or fears the implications the experimenter might draw from the child's behavior, the psychologist has either done a poor job of explaining what he is going to do or has persuaded the parent against his will to let the child participate. Although the experimenter may be convinced that the parent's anxieties are groundless and that his fears are defensive, it is still the prerogative of the parent to have them and to behave accordingly. The psychologist who takes it upon himself to decide when another free agent's fears are groundless without having been delegated that power is treading upon

dangerous ground. All the arguments against deceiving adult subjects hold even more strongly when we consider the problem of deceiving not the child subject but his caretaker.

The experimenter is well advised, therefore, to explain quite frankly to the person responsible for the child what he is interested in studying and how he intends to proceed and to answer openly any questions about the effects of the experiment on the child. If he feels sure that he cannot explain everything to the parent, then he should say that he cannot and ask the parent to trust him. In the vast majority of cases he can obtain consent; the experimenter's fear of being refused permission are almost as groundless as the groundless anxieties he attributes to the subject. There will be refusals, but we have to accept them. Their frequency will be increased only if we adopt the short-sighted strategy of obtaining consent by deception.

Once the caretaker's consent has been obtained, then the experimenter faces a similar set of problems as far as the child is concerned. Here there may be real necessity to conceal some of the purposes of the experiment from the child, and in the case of younger children it may be quite impossible to make the child understand the purpose of the experimenter. The quite sensible general practice is to treat the child more and more like an adult subject the older he is. With preschool children, the request to "play some games with the experimenter" or the explanation that "we want to see how children like you play with these games" is probably about as good as can be done.

After the experiment is over, particularly if some deception of the child is necessary, the research worker can well take the time to give an explanation that is geared to the level of the child. School-age children can understand the purposes of research and the need for experimental and control groups. Such an explanation has many good effects. It makes the child feel that he is a participant in scientific research—science is a highly esteemed activity to which most people are delighted to contribute. It makes the children feel that the experimenter is an honest person whose intentions in his experiment were not malevolent. It allays some anxiety and provides an opportunity for the experimenter and the caretaker to recognize individual children who should be given some special explanation and reassurance. Finally, it is an excellent concrete teaching device for the discussion of the scientific method and allows the experimenter to communicate some of the basic scientific values that we feel are important.

## Procurement of Subjects

Ethical problems merge imperceptibly into the practical problems of procuring and working with child subjects. Many of the arguments for frankness and honesty are as strongly supported by the need for maintaining continuing access to schools, homes, and institutions as by strictly ethical arguments. There are, however, some practical issues in the procurement of subjects in which ethical issues are not central.

## THE APPROACH
## TO INDIVIDUAL HOMES

The ultimate source of child subjects is, of course, the home. Although it is often more convenient to try to obtain subjects at school, it is often necessary to approach the home directly. Naturally, the contact to be made is with one or both parents of the child. Parents are responsible for their children, and legally they are the only ones who can agree to the use of the child as a subject. With young children, it is natural to obtain consent from the parent, but with school-age children and adolescents it is often practical to ask for volunteers. This means that the child is acting independently—something he has no right to do. In every case it is important to approach the people in charge. Within the school, of course, volunteer subjects are in the care of the school authorities, who have the right to consent to their being subjects during school time. If, however, the child is to be tested outside the school, when the school is not responsible for him, then the parent is the responsible agent, and the parent's cooperation should be sought before the child is actually tested.

Frankness in approaching the parent is not only the most honest but also the soundest policy. Investigators who work with children a great deal are almost universal in expressing amazement at the cooperativeness of parents, particularly at the middle and upper socioeconomic levels. Most people feel pleased to participate in scientific research and will often go to great lengths to be helpful.

There are various things the investigator may be able to do to make the parent continue to feel cooperative after the experiment is over. Conservation practices are just as important in the maintenance of research subjects as in the treatment of other natural resources. One good rule is not to push the subject to the limit of his cooperativeness. By providing, when needed, such things as transportation, baby sitters, and comfortable waiting space and by a generally friendly sociability, the experimenter can leave the parent with the feeling that psychologists are human beings and not bad ones at that. The offer to report back on the results of the research, either to the parents individually or in a group or by way of local mothers' clubs or PTA meetings, is highly desirable. If the experiment has been described frankly, the parents will usually be interested in the findings. Naturally, they are most interested in what the experiment can tell them about their own child, but in many experiments individual scores are highly unreliable. It is important in these cases to make some point of the fact to avoid the overinterpretation of individual scores. Often the discussion of individual scores can be avoided.

We have, however, passed over the most difficult problem—how to gain access to the home to begin with. There are relatively easy ways to approach parents through groups like the PTA, but if the sampling problem is an important one we must recognize that these groups are highly selected. One general procedure, commonly used, is to begin by writing a letter to each parent, introducing the project and naming by name the individual who will later telephone for an appointment. This letter on official stationery establishes the bona fide character of the research; it offers the parents the opportunity to call the writer of the letter for reassurance that the research project has the endorsement of the institution under whose auspices the experiment is being conducted. In university towns, particularly, there are some unauthorized research activities carried on independently by students. These unsupervised studies are sometimes not so carefully thought through as they should be, and they may involve such ticklish public relations issues as sex practices or racial attitudes. Most such studies can be done, but there is real value in thinking them through carefully and preparing ahead of time for possible difficulties. The general plan of beginning with a letter from the institution endorsing the project and introducing the investigator is one way to avoid unnecessary trouble. The experimenter can then make the telephone call within a few days; he can answer further questions and, depending upon the circumstances, follow up with a personal visit to explain the project more fully.

Another procedure may begin with an actual visit to the home. If the sampling is geographical, the investigator may not know the names of the people he wishes to study and cannot write them a letter. He then introduces the project at the door, offering the alternative of doing the interview or experiment then and there or making an appointment to come back at some other time. The details, of course, depend upon who must be seen, where the experiment must be carried out, etc. This procedure probably makes it harder for the prospective subjects to say "no," but it also makes research compete with door-to-door salesmen and may be viewed by the subjects as a high-pressure technique. When the investigation involves an interview or some easily portable experiment, so that the experimenter can reasonably offer the opportunity to carry it out immediately, this direct procedure may well save time and energy. In fact, it saves so much time and has been so successful that door-to-door salesmen sometimes gain access to the home by posing as interviewers for a survey.

## WORKING WITH SCHOOLS AND INSTITUTIONS

The procurement of subjects in large groups in a school or other institution is a different problem entirely. There are several very important things to keep in mind in connection with this problem. The first one is that there are fewer schools than homes, so that a bad experience in a school system can shut off a large group of subjects for a long time. In view of the amount of child-development and educational research that must be done in the next twenty years, conservation practices are most important indeed.

A second principle stems from the fact that the basic responsibility for the children in an institution lies with the senior administrator, the school superintendent, the principal, or the director. The place to begin is at the top because that is where the responsibility lies. In a city school system the superintendent is nearly always the first person to interview; in rural districts the principal may be autonomous and be able to make the decision himself. The principle of starting at the top applies on down the line. Within a school, see the principal first, hopeful that the superintendent has already passed down his endorsement. In most schools every visitor should check in at the office on every visit. The research worker may be a good friend of a teacher who is more than glad to cooperate in a small study, but the teacher does not have the right to consent to a research study or even to give an outsider access to her records.

The injunction to start at the top does not mean that the project should be kept a secret from everybody who would be most actively involved. Preliminary discussions to design the study so that it will be feasible to do it in a school situation might involve a teacher, on her own time, the school psychologist, or somebody else. When, however, the investigator actually wants to obtain consent to do the study, the top man is the one to see.

A third principle of working with school systems is to recognize that the schools have other jobs to do besides releasing children for research projects. Very few, if any, school administrators are against research activities. Their questions about a research project are likely to be the following: (1) Will it hurt the children? (2) Will it interfere too much with school activities? (3) Will it make parents or school-board members protest?

The experimenter should prepare his

request with these three questions in mind. To answer the first, he should describe exactly what he proposes to do with each child subject. In case there are debatable points, he may wish to justify an unpleasant treatment of the child as temporary, as no worse than the child experiences every day in school or on the playground, and as an absolutely necessary feature of the experiment that could not be avoided without losing the whole value of the project. He may also describe how he proposes to justify the treatment to the children afterward. Beyond that, he must let the superintendent or principal decide.

In anticipation of the second question, the experimenter will do well to know exactly how many children he needs, in what age groups, how many sessions with each, how long each session will be, and how many children will be needed in the experiment at one time. These are the facts the administrator needs. In designing the study, it may be possible to make it more acceptable. In general, schools would rather turn over a whole class to an experimenter for an hour than to have the experimenter remove every child individually for fifteen minutes. This is partly a function of what the rest of the class will be doing while each child is out and is not a hard and fast rule.

The problem of interference of research with other school activities is especially serious in the vicinity of a university because so many of the research plans of students involve the cooperation of the school system. Any school system must draw a line somewhere on the number of different research programs it can accommodate. There are real advantages, therefore, in trying to find a school system that is not used by many other research workers. Although superintendents, principals, and school boards in such towns may be less accustomed to the idea of cooperating with research programs and may require more explanation, they frequently welcome the opportunity to cooperate.

The last problem of the school administrator, protests from the public, is much more difficult to anticipate. There is a large amount of unpredictability in public reaction. Probably there are relatively few research projects, if they were explained fully to the public, that would not be generally acceptable, but very few of them would be completely immune to criticism. Somebody would almost surely think they were a waste of time at best and a positive evil at worst. These are the people who will refuse to cooperate as individuals in a research program, but they can create real difficulty in a school system if they actively protest. It takes only a few protests to discourage school administrators from cooperating.

There seem to be a few subjects that are particularly dangerous. One, of course, is sex. Questionnaires on sexual attitudes and sexual activities are more likely than most to antagonize some people in the community. Discretion is probably the better part of wisdom, and the experimenter should not try to obtain such information through the public schools.

A second ticklish issue is the invasion of the privacy of the home through questionnaires administered to children.

Parents who would not object to answering questions about their own child-rearing practices may well object to having these practices reported by the child. It appears somewhat like the child's being asked to spy on his parents.

Any local issue on which there are strong feelings may be a very ticklish one for the research worker, particularly if his manner of investigation leads to the perception that his sympathies are on one side rather than another.

The sensitivity of public administrators to public relations may appear to the investigator as a sort of cowardice. Perhaps it is in a way, but the research worker must remember that his project is much more important to him than to anybody else. There is little benefit to the school system from most individual research projects except the sense of virtue in having cooperated and the cumulative benefits of the entire field of research activities. These are important, and most administrators recognize it, but there is not a lot to make them feel a risky individual study is worthwhile. Finally, most administrators realize that social-science research is still on precarious ground as far as public acceptance is concerned. Probably, if the question of allowing 2 or 3 per cent of the child's time in school to be spent in serving as a research subject were brought to a vote, it would be rejected by the public as less important than the same time spent in academic work. From the point of view of practical politics, therefore, it is wise to be very cautious about public reaction.

There are no hard and fast rules relating to any aspect of human relations. These suggestions may be helpful, but the most important principle is to exercise the same tact and consideration with research subjects that is appropriate in dealing with colleagues, classmates, or professors.

## *Summary*

This chapter has the double purpose of serving as a preface to a volume and as a general introduction to research in child development.

This book has been compiled in the belief that child-development research has much to gain from and to contribute to other branches of behavioral science. It has been written in the hope of stimulating and improving the quality of research with children. To this end, it is intended to be a handbook of research methods for special use in the study of children and to contain some of the practical wisdom of experienced investigators.

As an introduction, this chapter has been concerned with the most general issues in research in child development, running the gamut from the philosophy of science to the procurement of subjects. The topics that have been discussed are (1) the logic of science and scientific strategy, (2) specifications for theories of child behavior and development, (3) the special problems met in research in these fields, (4) ethical problems of working with children and (5) problems of procuring subjects.

## REFERENCES

Bayley, Nancy. 1933. Mental growth during the first three years. A developmental study of 61 children by repeated tests. *Genet. Psychol. Monogr.*, **14**, 1–92.

Benjamin, J. D. 1949. Methodological considerations in the validation and elaboration of psychoanalytic personality theory. *Amer. J. Orthopsychiat.*, **19**, 342–350.

Binet, A. 1903. *L'Étude expérimentale de l'intelligence.* Paris: Ancienne Librairie Schleicher, 1903.

Bird, C. 1933. Maturation and practice: their effects upon the feeding reactions of chicks. *J. comp. Psychol.*, **16**, 343–366.

Braithwaite, R. B. 1955. *Scientific explanation: A study of the function of theory, probability and law in science.* Cambridge: Cambridge Univer. Press.

Carmichael, L. 1934. An experimental study in the prenatal guinea-pig of the origin and development of reflexes and patterns of behavior in relation to the stimulation of specific receptor areas during the period of active fetal life. *Genet. Psychol. Monogr.*, **16**, 337–491.

Dollard, J. E., and N. E. Miller. 1950. *Personality and psychotherapy: An analysis in terms of learning, thinking and culture.* New York: McGraw-Hill.

Estes, W. K., et al. 1954. *Modern learning theories.* New York: Appleton-Century.

Gesell, A., and H. Thompson. 1929. Learning and growth in identical twins: An experimental study by the method of co-twin control. *Genet. Psychol. Monogr.*, **6**, 1–123.

Goodenough, Florence L. 1928. A preliminary report on the effect of nursery school training upon the intelligence test scores of young children. *Yearb. nat. Soc. Stud. Educ.*, **27**, Part I, 361–369.

Hall, G. S. 1891. The contents of children's minds on entering school. *Pedag. Sem.*, **1**, 139–173.

Heider, F. 1958. *Psychology of interpersonal relations.* New York: Wiley.

Hilgard, J. R. 1933. The effect of early and delayed practice on memory and motor performances studied by the method of co-twin control. *Genet. Psychol. Monogr.*, **14**, 493–567.

Hull, C. L. 1943. *Principles of behavior.* New York: Appleton-Century, 1943.

Kuo, Z. Y. 1932. Ontogeny of embryonic behavior in Aves: II. The mechanical factors in the various stages leading to hatching. *J. exp. Zool.*, **62**, 453–487.

———. 1939. Total pattern or local reflexes. *Psychol. Rev.*, **46**, 93–122.

Mowrer, O. H. 1950. *Learning theory and personality dynamics.* New York: Ronald.

Piaget, J. 1926. *The language and thought of the child.* New York: Harcourt, Brace.

———. 1932. *The moral judgement of the child.* New York: Harcourt, Brace.

———. 1950. *The psychology of intelligence.* Trans. by M. Pearcy and D. E. Berlyne. New York: Harcourt, Brace.

Sears, R. R., Eleanor E. Maccoby, and H. Levin. 1957. *Patterns of child rearing.* Evanston, Ill.: Row, Peterson.

Terman, L. M. 1928. Nature and nurture: Part I. Their influence upon intelligence. *Yearb. nat. Soc. Stud. Educ.*, **27**, Part I.

Whiting, J. W. M., and I. L. Child. 1953. *Child training and personality.* New Haven: Yale Univer. Press.

chapter 2

# Research Design in the Study of Developmental Problems

William Kessen
*Yale University*

The study of child development derives from the primitive observation that human beings change as they grow older. Whether the psychologist turns his attention to physical growth, or to language, or to motility, or to personality, he can readily confirm the common-sense principle that assigns to *age* an important place in the description of human behavior. From the days of the early baby biographers, students of child development have attempted to make systematic and reliable statements about this fundamental relationship. Classically, these statements have contained two kinds of terms or variables:

The author is grateful to David E. Hunt and George Mandler, who read parts of this chapter and made important contributions to it. Many of the points raised here developed from conversations with the late Katherine M. Wolf, and her contribution is incalculable.

on one side, a description of behavior (e.g., test performance, skill, use of words) or of state (e.g., height, endocrine level, organ size); on the other side, some index of chronological age or developmental status (e.g., degree of ossification, mental age, sexual maturity). Much of the work of developmental psychologists can be cast in the summary form $R = f(A)$, if it is recognized that $R$ (response) may be as various as color naming and length of tibia and that $A$ (age) represents not only time since birth but includes as well such variants as physiological age and mental age. With these reservations entered, the following formulation may be proposed: *a characteristic is said to be developmental if it can be related to age in an orderly or lawful way.* This chapter has as its central theme a discussion of research designs and procedures which permit the effective investigations of developmental phenomena.

## The Analysis of Developmental Change

It should be noted at the outset that although the foregoing specification of "developmental" may represent fairly the common usage of the term the establishment of a lawful relationship between behavior and age is by no means the only, or even the most important, task of the child psychologist. The formulation is inadequate as a general statement of the procedures of child study in at least three ways. In the first place, there are important aspects of child behavior that show an orderly relationship to age, yet they demand an analysis in terms of other variables. For example, the size of a child's vocabulary can be set in a relatively simple relationship with chronological age, but most psychologists would insist that this development is dependent at least in part on the child's history, or more generally, on variables other than time since birth.

A second and closely related reservation which must be stated in considering the $R = f(A)$ formula has to do with failure of control. One of the chief goals of systematic study is the segregation of *determinants* of events, that is, of those antecedent conditions or events which can be manipulated to produce a change in the phenomena under study. No matter how neat the function relating behavior to age may be, there is almost always some dissatisfaction for the researcher unless he can go beyond the functional statement to say something about causes of or explanations for the effect. Even without an extended treatment of scientific explanation, the issue raised here can be understood by reflecting on the inadequacy of a statement such as the following:

"Four-year-old children weigh 45 pounds *because* they are four years old."

Child psychologists, whatever their theoretical color, have with scarcely an exception postulated the action of some "more fundamental" or "less superficial" variable than age to account for developmental change. In general, the explanatory notions advanced have emphasized either physiological and morphological control (e.g., maturation, neural development) or environmental control (e.g., learning, trauma), but advocates of both positions seem equally uneasy about the use of age as an *explanation* of behavioral change. This is not mere prejudice; one of the goals of scientific explanation is to provide directions for the control of phenomena. The simple age-functions do not tell us how to change behavior and are therefore frequently given a restatement in terms of manipulable antecedents.

A third limitation of $R = f(A)$ statements is their failure to take into account individual variation. Because age is a parameter for the entire population under study, the age-functional generalizations do not provide an expression of the fact that children not only change with age but also show differences one from another at the same age. Child psychologists seem, from the evidence of their research reports, to be increasingly concerned with the general question of why one group of children is different from another group of the same age rather than with the simple statement of age-to-age variation. For this purpose of describing variation, the age-functional statements are quite limited in usefulness.

Although these reservations must be taken into account in a treatment of age-functional generalizations, the $R = f(A)$ formula will continue to express a good part of what is known about children. In a large number of cases, the general statement must suffice because we are ignorant of "true" or controlling antecedents. In plotting problem-solving ability against chronological age, the researcher may be convinced that he is studying some complex resultant of neuronal maturation, history of reinforcement, and so on, but until he has more precise information about how such variables affect child behavior he must be content with the less detailed expression of variation with age.

There are other aspects of child behavior in which the psychologist may be strongly persuaded that an environmental variation is relevant to a change in behavior but in which appropriate tests are impossible on ethical grounds. Thus the occurrence of smiling in the infant, although apparently universal, may be linked to the regularity of social contact in the first weeks. Clearly, the soundest test of this possibility is the complete isolation of a group of babies and the comparison of their smiling behavior with that of normally reared infants. This procedure is manifestly out of the question, so that the researcher is once more thrown back on an age-functional expression for the occurrence and development of smiling. There are many developmental phenomena of this order that will remain resistant to further analysis because of the dangers of irreversible damage involved in manipulative study.

Finally, the age-functional type of statement may remain part of the corpus of child psychology simply because, as a matter of empirical fact, some changes in behavior can be described most fruitfully as functions of age. Much of the research on physical growth, for example, and the bulk of our knowledge about developmental changes in intelligence-test performance have their basic statement in age-functional relationships. It is never possible to be certain that no change will take place in our treatment of these phenomena, but room should be left for the possibility that $R = f(A)$ statements will remain as unreduced principles in a future child psychology.

These arguments suggest that the study of development is a two-part enterprise—the search for regular relationships between behavior and age and the analysis of such relationships to provide precise and effective ways of predicting child behavior. These goals of the developmental psychologist are by no means independent; the regularities we observe as children grow will influence the kind of systematic statement we make, and the preconceptions or theories that we bring to our research will influence the selection of our observations. Theories of child development are, in a sense, systems of proposals about the processes that lie behind changes in behavior with age, but we are so far from an acceptable general theory of development that we must continue for some time the slow accumulation of evidence that is expressed in age-functional generalizations.

In any case, whether the psychologist's primary interest is in general developmental formulas or in a more complex analysis of the changes in children's behavior, the research design chosen will depend in large measure on the kinds of statements he wants to make. An investigator concerned with a description of the development of form-perception will choose a design different from that used to study variation of behavior as a function of early feeding patterns; a researcher interested in the details of learning will set up his study in a way quite different from that of the researcher interested in personality variation; and so on. There is no "standard" design for the study of child development; rather it is necessary to know the goal of the research before a sensible decision can be made about the appropriate research design.

In the pages to follow a number of prototypical statements about the behavior of children are put under examination. The choice of research design in the study of development is discussed in the light of what these statements demand. This is followed by a discussion of some of the ways in which preconception or theory determines the course of developmental research. Finally, a treatment of practical problems in the study of development brings us back to current issues in the investigation of children's behavior.

### Statements About Developmental Change

RESPONSE VARIATION
AS A SIMPLE FUNCTION
OF AGE: $R = f(A)$

The most general statement of developmental change sets in relationship some behavior of the child and some index of his age or level of maturity. From the observations of Tiedemann down to the present, statements of this sort have made up a great part of our knowledge of child development.

The classical work of Scammon (1930) on physical growth and of Gesell (1945) on changes in motor behavior may stand as exemplary illustrations of the basic age-functional generalization. Although research in support of such general formulations is apparently becoming less popular, child psychologists continue to talk about "Twos" and "Tens," expressing in this way the regularities observed in children's behavior as they grow older.

*Choice of Research Design.* In studying generalizations of the $R = f(A)$ order, the chief task of the researcher is to reduce the variation in behavior contributed by factors other than age. This is obviously an impossible assignment if our goal is "pure age" generalizations; older children are always children of more extensive and complex history, bigger, more intelligent, better educated, and so on. To put the point in the language of method, there is no control group for studies of the basic developmental generalization, no group in which age and associated variables do *not* change. However, once this irremedial difficulty is stipulated, there remains wide variation in the degree of possible contamination from variables other than age. Most researchers would be unhappy with a study of preference for play materials, say, in which the 1-year-old group were girls and the 2-year-old group, boys, or a study of adolescent disturbance in which different age groups were drawn from widely different socioeconomic levels. The problem can be stated in a general form: to what degree do groups differing in age differ on other dimensions as well?

There are two ways of reducing unwanted variation among groups—choice of sampling procedures and the method of data collection.

*Sampling.* The issues raised in a

treatment of sampling procedures are important to all psychological research, but, for reasons which will become clear shortly, the student of children seems peculiarly likely to stub his toe on this problem. The statisticians' rule is deceptively simple; for justified generalization of findings to a specified population, each member of the population should have an equal chance of being included in the research sample. The implication of this mandate is that the researcher, having decided to study a certain population (e.g., American children), should arrange his enlistment procedures to sample at random from this group. For better or worse, this instruction cannot be obeyed in present-day studies of development; the cost in time and money of random sampling is prohibitive. Nor can the child psychologist usually take the way out available to the pollster, that is, by the use of a stratified sample from the population under study. Aside from practical problems almost as great as those of random sampling, the kind of information that would indicate the variables to be used for appropriate stratification is frequently not available. The result of these constraints is the almost universal use of "unsampled" subjects in developmental research; the researcher uses the children who are available when he needs them, often without convincing evidence of their representativeness in relation to some larger population. This necessary compromise with ideal standards sets two demands on child development research: first, that replication with more than one sample take place in order to provide *empirical* support for the gen-

eralization of findings from unsampled groups and, second, that we seek out information that will tell us what variables can be disregarded in the selection of subjects and what variables must be controlled by more sophisticated sampling techniques. It may be a long time before the child psychologist can have, in his selection of subjects, the confidence that the chemist has in sampling distilled water in New York and distilled water in Ann Arbor, but the results of developmental study will carry greater conviction as we are better able to state dimensions of variation in the populations studied. It should be noted that the animal psychologist also normally uses "unsampled" groups in much of his research; the advantages he can claim over the student of children are better knowledge and control of individual history and perhaps better information of what variables require special treatment.

In short, the child psychologist cannot ordinarily reduce complicating variation between groups by means of sophisticated sampling procedures; he must depend on replication and on his knowledge of the variables that tend to vary with age in order to gain confidence in his age-functional generalizations.

*Methods of Data Collection.* A second approach to the problem of reducing variation in behavior from sources other than age lies in the choice of a technique for data collection. Stripped of subtleties that will require attention later, a distinction can be made between two methods of gathering observations on the development of children. In one of these the researcher makes repeated observations on the same group of subjects—the longitudinal technique; in the other he makes a limited number of observations on different groups of subjects—the cross-sectional technique. In many problems in the study of development either of the two methods may be used. For example, the growth of vocabulary may be observed by following 20 children from preverbal age to adolescence, with annual examination of their language skills, or, alternatively, groups of 20 children of different ages may be studied at more or less the same time, with no overlap in the membership of groups.[1] If we take this example as prototypical, several points of comparison are apparent at once. The repeated-measurements or longitudinal program will extend over a longer period of time than the cross-sectional (in the hypothetical case of vocabulary development, a dozen years as compared with as many weeks), even though the amount of time spent gathering data is precisely the same in both cases. It is largely for this reason that the longitudinal technique often appears to be inefficient or cumbersome, and there is no doubt that the literature contains relatively few reports of repeated measurements over long periods of time.[2]

[1] Bell (1953, 1954) has suggested a compromise between cross-sectional and longitudinal study based on the assumption of equivalence in the behavior of different children. This promising proposal may serve to reduce some of the difficulties in developmental research that are discussed later.

[2] Stone and Onqué (1959) present a bibliography of longitudinal studies, from Pestalozzi to 1954. More recent longitudinal research has been noted in several volumes of the *Annual Review of Psychology*.

Nonetheless, there are advantages to be claimed for the longitudinal method that warrant closer examination of its properties.

The longitudinal study in child-development research is a variation of the "matched group" research design used in many studies of behavior, and it is this characteristic that supplies whatever formal advantage it has over cross-sectional studies of $R = f(A)$ generalizations. Instead of comparing independently derived groups of scores and being limited thereby to statements of the differences between group means, the researcher is able to put his repeated measures in parallel, comparing each observation of a subject's behavior with some earlier or later observation. An examination of the fictitious data in Table 2-1 will illustrate this difference between the methods and one of its implications. If there are small but reliable changes in the behavior of subjects over age (Table 2-1 $A$), then longitudinal study provides, because of the matching characteristic, more sensitive estimates of such changes. When the differences between groups are large (Table 2-1 $B$), the advantage of the longitudinal technique is less impressive. Making the point more generally, we may say that the longitudinal design is to be favored in the study of those age-functional relationships in which relatively small but individually stable changes over age are expected.

Following the general prescription to reduce variation from factors other than age, we can segregate another class of age-functional generalizations that profit from longitudinal study, namely, those in which age differences are cor-

**TABLE 2-1. FICTITIOUS DATA WHICH ILLUSTRATE THE "MATCHED GROUP" CHARACTERISTIC OF LONGITUDINAL RESEARCH DESIGN**

| *A* | | | *B* | |
|---|---|---|---|---|
| Scores at Age *a* | Scores at Age *a* + *t* | | Scores at Age *a* | Scores at Age *a* + *t* |
| 4 | 5 | | 4 | 13 |
| 5 | 6 | | 5 | 14 |
| 6 | 7 | | 6 | 15 |
| 7 | 8 | | 7 | 16 |
| 8 | 9 | | 8 | 17 |
| 9 | 10 | | 9 | 18 |
| 10 | 11 | | 10 | 19 |
| 11 | 12 | | 11 | 20 |
| 12 | 13 | | 12 | 21 |
| Mean score    8 | 9 | Mean score    8 | 17 |

related with cultural shifts. For example, a cross-sectional study of night fears or response to sudden awakening among London children might well show striking changes at ages 15 to 18, not necessarily because of some characteristic of late adolescence, but because these children had been through the Battle of Britain at susceptible ages. Students of child-rearing practices in primitive groups (Whiting and Child, 1953) may defend convincingly the presence of a stable cultural frame which permits cross-sectional assessment, but the speed and variety of change in the technology of modern communities make it increasingly difficult for the child psychologist to assume with confidence that his 8-year-olds had much the same kind of early experience that his 3-year-olds had.[1] It

[1] There are, of course, cases in which variation assignable to cultural shifts need not be assessed or reduced; the educational psychologist planning a curriculum for third and fourth graders is interested in how well they can read, not in whether differences between the two groups are "age-determined" or "culture-determined."

should be clear, however, that the application of longitudinal methods will not by itself solve the problem of analyzing variation ascribable to cultural change. In fact, if a repeated-measurements study extends over a long period of time, conclusions drawn from it may be of limited generalizability to later and changed cultural settings. However, the longitudinal researcher is in a better position to assess the impact of shifts in milieu than is the investigator who studies at one time the behavior of age-differing groups of children.

In summary, statements of the general form $R = f(A)$ require for their appropriate investigation the selection of age-differing groups which vary as little as possible on dimensions other than age. Homogeneity of groups can usually be increased by the use of repeated measurements on the same children, but the decision for longitudinal or cross-sectional methods must be made on the further criteria of research economy and the necessity of evaluating cultural trends. Beyond this, the recognition by psychologists that much of the child behavior that interests them varies over age in different ways for different subpopulations of children has resulted in a striking reduction in research emphasis on generalizations of the bald $R = f(A)$ sort.

## RESPONSE VARIATION WITH AGE IN LIMITED POPULATIONS: $R = f(A, P)$

The simple age-function relationships discussed in the preceding section are usually extended or supplemented by statements of developmental variation in subgroups defined by some special characteristic. The most usual criterion for separation into different groups is sex, and the literature is replete with descriptions of developmental phenomena plotted separately for boys and girls (Terman and Tyler, 1954). Analogous subgroups may be established on other criteria, e.g., hypothesized genetic variation, intelligence differences, birth order, etc., to establish generalizations of the order $R = f(A, P)$. Goodenough's (1931) investigation of sex differences in the occurrence of anger outbursts and Shuttleworth's (1939) description of mental age changes in early- and late-maturing boys may serve as typical representatives of studies leading to $R = f(A, P)$ statements.

***Choice of Research Design.*** The considerations relevant in the selection of design for the investigation of simple age-functional relationships are relevant to the study of development in subpopulations. The basic problem of extraneous variation is compounded, of course, because the researcher must aim at reducing not only the variation in

age-differing groups but must also try to guard against additional sources of variation on the dimension that defines special groups. On occasion, this latter issue may be given negligible attention. For example, a study of physical growth in first- and second-born children will be relatively free of systematic variation from sources other than age and birth order. It is extremely difficult, however, to extend this list of "safe" splits in population very far; even in the classical study of sex differences the differential *history* of boys and girls exerts an incalculable effect on the course of development. When one shifts to a study of racial differences or differences in social class, the number of confounding variables becomes enormous.[1] In a sense, $R = f(A, P)$ generalizations are shorthand for the more accurate expression $R = f(A, P_1 \cdots P_n)$, in which variables correlated with the variable under consideration are recognized as relevant to the conclusions drawn from an investigation of subpopulations of children. It is convenient to express obtained differences in the behavior, say, of boys and girls as a simple function of age and sex; it is obviously far different to conclude that the groups do not differ on other dimensions as well.

Once the complexity of $R = f(A, P)$ generalizations is recognized, the psychologist can proceed in his study, tak-

[1] Once more, it should be noted that for some usually practical purposes contamination from correlated variables does not have to be reduced. An educator in New York may be concerned simply with how well 8-year-old Puerto Ricans understand English, not in the sources of their difference from native-born children.

ing the precautions or the risks discussed earlier in regard to sampling and the choice between longitudinal and cross-sectional data-collection techniques. There are, however, two special and important instances of the $R = f(A, P)$ sort that almost invariably demand longitudinal study—the case of the "lost sign" and the case of differential rates of change.

To illustrate the group of problems included in the category of "lost signs," compare the study of sex differences with the study of early differences in general activity. When sex is the subpopulation under study, the researcher has no difficulty in deciding the assignment of his subjects; at birth, at age 6, or at age 16, boys are discriminably separable from girls. In the study of general activity, however, the researcher is unable to tell whether his 16-year-old subjects belong in the "high early activity" group or the "low early activity" group. Segregation on dimensions of this variety involve a "lost sign" in that the investigator cannot determine, at some later age, the characteristics of his population at an earlier age. In order to assess the differential development of children who vary in early general activity, it is necessary to set up the subpopulations at an early age and to make repeated measurements on the same subjects over the course of time. Quite a few characteristics of children that interest the student of child development fall into this category, e.g., the relation to later behavior of early intellectual differences, of autoerotic activity in infancy, of degree of disturbance at puberty, or of response to the first months of school.

The study of populations assigned on these dimensions ordinarily requires longitudinal study. Suppose, for example, that a researcher is interested in the relationship between intensity of stranger anxiety and dependence on the mother in the first days of nursery school. To get his groups for study, he must observe children during the second half of the first year, make his evaluations of degree of stranger anxiety, then wait for the children to age. Only when they have entered nursery school and their dependency can be assessed will the research be completed.

There is an alternative to the longitudinal study of behavior related to "lost signs" that depends on the *report* of behavior rather than on its observation. In the example of stranger anxiety the researcher may observe his subjects in nursery school to determine dependency score and interview the children's mothers to establish the level of stranger anxiety observed in the past. In a study based completely on report the researcher may assess both dependency and anxiety by examination of retrospective maternal report. There is no doubt that the use of maternal recollection introduces enormous savings of time and effort in the study of child development. One does not have to wait for children to grow, and one can get information rather quickly on many aspects of the child's behavior, information that would be laboriously obtained if one drew it from observation of the children themselves.

These remarkable gains from the analysis of report rather than the analysis of observations of behavior have brought the maternal interview to the forefront of substitutes for longitudinal study. However, several questions must be addressed to the researcher using this technique. The first concerns the accuracy of maternal report about contemporaneous events; how well is the mother able to describe or categorize her child's behavior at any moment? Will she, for example, make evaluations of dependency in nursery school that bear a systematic relationship to teacher's report or to the summary of the psychologist's observations of the child? Fortunately, this is a testable question in many cases, so that the investigator concerned with the validity of maternal accounts of child behavior can compare what he sees with what the mother says about her child. It is less fortunate for our assurance on this issue that checks of validity are infrequently carried out, although Gordon (1957) and Smith (1958), among others, have provided some evidence on the accuracy of maternal report. Usually, the mother's report is accepted as valid without external support, or else its validity is assumed from its stability, i.e., from the mother's tendency to be consistent in her account. It should be noted, however, that the child psychologist frequently has no choice in this regard; there are responses of the child that the mother alone (or some other adult member of the family) is competent to report on. Unless the observer can maintain a twenty-four hour vigil, he must rely on the mother to tell him about the child's response to normal routines in feeding and sleep, about the child's reaction to special events such as the visit of relatives or the introduction of a pet, and about many aspects of the child's life that are considered relevant to his development.

A satisfactory solution to the problem of validity of contemporaneous report is difficult to achieve, but two safeguards seem reasonable; first, to check maternal report against the report of other family members or, better, against observation of the child whenever this is possible and, second, to attempt an evaluation of the likelihood of error in maternal report. This precaution would probably demand attention both to individual differences in tendency to distort and to variations in distorting as a function of the particular behavior under study. It is to be expected that some mothers will distort more than others and that some responses of the child will be more liable to distorted report than others. Research related to the validity of maternal accounts is fundamental to the study of children because even the most industrious investigator will not be able to make the variety and number of observations that a mother can.

The validity of report about contemporaneous events is a problem of equal standing for both longitudinal and cross-sectional methods of data collection, but the second general question about information obtained from parents—the validity of retrospective report—is peculiar to single-measurement studies. Suppose, for example, that the researcher studying stranger anxiety and dependency in nursery school is satisfied that his dependency measure is sound, either because he has made careful observations himself or because he has evidence of the accuracy of maternal reports of contemporaneous events. What confidence can he place in their retrospective evaluation of their children's stranger anxiety? Once again, the problem is a complex one, with several considerations relevant to the researcher's decision. There is, of course, the fact that retrospective report is based on events at a greater distance in time than events reported contemporaneously, and some decrease in accuracy as a function of time may be expected. But beyond this obvious source of error there are several further infusions of potential error in mothers' retrospective accounts of child behavior. For one, child psychologists frequently depend on maternal recall for information about behavior in the child that is likely to be far from neutral in its impact on the mother. We may ask about thumb sucking, or responses to weaning, or reactions to the birth of a sibling —questions that are probably different in their effect from questions about physical growth, or age of walking, or responses to the family cat. If the mother had been in conflict about her own behavior at crucial points in the child's life and if she has some "theory" about what the "right" answer should be, it is to be expected that her recall will be influenced by factors other than the behavior of her child. It is undoubtedly risky for the child psychologist to depend on the mother of a 6-year-old to tell him what the child's behavior was when toilet training was begun at 9 months; we are ignorant of the relation between her statement and the statement that would have been made by an observer (even the mother) of the child at 9 months.

Beyond the distortions to be expected in the report of so-called crucial events, there is a less obvious source of error in retrospective accounts—the error of the limited sample. Unless the reporting mother has had some professional contact with children, her knowledge about "normal" or "average" behavior is likely to be slim indeed. In response to questions about the child's response to toilet training or about the intensity and duration of his early crying, the untrained mother has no normative context from which to draw her answer. The same duration and intensity of crying may be for one mother "a lot" and for another "a little," not because of profound personality variation but because of ignorance about how much children cry. Of course, sophisticated researchers take pains to set up interviews that reduce gross errors of this sort, but there will be some influence on maternal report derived from naïveté, at least so long as child psychologists depend on data that resist simple numerical statement.

For these several reasons, the child psychologist interested in the sequelae of "lost signs" will do well to examine the assumptions he must make in using retrospective maternal accounts to place his subjects in subpopulations for study. There is some danger that he may not be studying the development of children but rather the relationships that exist between different responses of mothers. As was noted earlier, most of the problems raised here are susceptible to empirical study, and much suggestive research on children can be more adequately evaluated when we have evidence on the accuracy of maternal report, contemporaneous and retrospective. In the meantime, the investigator of this special group of $R = f(A, P)$ generalizations should consider the utility of longitudinal study in reducing error.

The repeated-measurement technique is also the method of choice in studies that deal with rates of change of behavior or state. For example, in the study of the spurt in height near menarche, a cross-sectional investigation will show a smooth and gradual change in increments of height over age. If, however, longitudinal data are available, it can be demonstrated that this representation poorly expresses the dramatic shifts seen in individual curves (Tanner, 1955). By replotting the data around age of menarche instead of along a simple chronological baseline, a fairer picture is provided of adolescent growth. It should be noted, of course, that if the researcher is interested *only* in the mean increment in height at each age cross-sectional study will do the job as well as longitudinal. If a representation that reflects the pattern of individual growth of behavior is desired *and* there is reason to suspect variation among subjects in the timing of change, then the longitudinal method is to be preferred over the cross-sectional.

A related design, in which there is no substitute for longitudinal study, is that in which the subpopulations are established by examination of rate of change. If one wants to know about personality changes in fast-maturing boys as compared with slow-maturing boys (Jones and Bayley, 1950), it is necessary to determine with repeated measurement the appropriate assignment to groups. Similarly, there are suggestions in the literature that rate of intellectual development may show wide individual variation that warrants further study of associated behavior (Bayley, 1955). It is clear that repeated measures are necessary to assess rate of change, and studies of this order will always require longitudinal investigation.

In summary, statements of the $R = f(A, P)$ kind are somewhat more complicated extensions of the simple age-functional relationship. They can be established by cross-sectional study when it is possible to segregate subpopulations on the variable under study ($P$) across the age range being investigated. For two special classes of $R = f(A, P)$ generalizations—the study of the sequelae of lost signs and the analysis of sequence or rate of change of behavior and state—the longitudinal method is usually preferable to the cross-sectional.

## RESPONSE VARIATION WITH AGE, INTERACTING WITH ENVIRONMENTAL CHANGE: $R = f(A, S)$

Control of behavior becomes possible and prediction of behavior often becomes more precise when the psychologist is able to relate behavioral change to some discriminable aspect of the environment. As the broad outlines of development are sketched, there is an increasing interest in the isolation of manipulable antecedents in the behavior of children. The results of studies with such aims can usually be stated in the form $R = f(A, S)$.

In general, our knowledge of the interactive effect of age and environment derives from two kinds of research setting, one involving experimental manipulation and the other involving variation in conditions. The first of these settings is given detailed treatment in Chapter 4, and only a cursory summary is given here of its place in the study of development. As in all experimental study, the chief advantage of this technique for the study of children is the possibility of random assignment to groups treated differently; there is no need to worry about correlated differences when assignment to subgroups is made purely by chance. It deserves iteration that an experiment is not defined by manipulation but rather by manipulation applied to one of a randomly selected set of subject groups. Thus a study of learning in high- and low-dependency children does not meet this basic criterion; this is rather a study of interaction among environmental change, dependency, *and* whatever variables correlate with the dependency segregation. Stated in the notation adopted here, such a study is of the $R = f(A, P, S)$ variety and not a "pure" experiment. If studies like this are excluded from consideration as examples of $R = f(A, S)$ generalizations, the number of developmental researches that fit this category is seen to be quite small. The bulk is concerned with learning over relatively short periods of time (McGinnis, 1929; Bijou, 1957) and are, like all learning studies, longitudinal (i.e., repeated-measurement) rather than cross-sectional. An exception to this general statement are investigations of training effects in twins (McGraw, 1935; Gesell and Thompson, 1929). Psychologists are usually blocked in

their study of development by experimental techniques because they lack the power to effect important manipulations or because of ethical proscriptions. It is at this point that animal research on developmental problems can provide us with useful data, and important information is beginning to enter the literature from comparative developmental studies using experimental methods (Beach and Jaynes, 1954).

A caution should be sounded in the experimental study of children. It is almost always necessary to have a control group that does not receive experimental treatment. The need for an "aging" control is clear enough in the study of practice effects on "maturing" behavior; it is not perhaps so obvious in the case of short-term longitudinal studies such as those of learning. However, until we are in possession of better information about the changes that take place in a child's behavior over varying periods of time in the absence of special "training" or learning, it will be wise to run a "maturational" control group in experimental studies that extend beyond quite brief durations. Once more, there is no cookbook answer for how brief is "brief"; for the study of postadolescent learning, important "maturational" changes would be unlikely over months, whereas, for the study of newborn learning, a control group would be necessary for an investigation that ran only for several hours. In the absence of reliable information on the safe duration of a study, the researcher probably should err on the side of caution and arrange for a developmental control whenever he suspects that there may be "aging" effects.

The second research setting for establishing $R = f(A, S)$ statements belongs in a class quite different from that containing the experiment. Although they aim at describing variations in behavior as a function of environmental change, the studies of *variation in conditions* are almost always perfectly analogous with $R = f(A, P)$ studies and share the design problems of this group. Research on the effects of institutionalization, on the impact of the pathological mother, or on variation in child-rearing practice are usually summarized in the $R = f(A, S)$ paradigm, but the critical absence of the possibility of random assignment to subgroups makes these so-called "natural experiments" incomparable with the experiments already discussed. Take the case of infantile institutionalization as an example. Even if a "control" group of noninstitutionalized children is set up for comparison, there is usually no guarantee that the two groups will be drawn from the same basic population, nor is there usually any precise description of the dimensions other than residence in an institution along which they may vary from one another. This consideration represents one of the fundamental difficulties in studying variation in conditions—the establishment of relevant comparison groups. Whether our interest is in enriched versus deprived environments, in social-class differences in child-rearing procedures, or in the effects of early exposure to sex differences, we face the task of ascertaining the further differences that may exist among the groups under study.

Nevertheless, if we recognize that investigations of variation in conditions cannot be considered as experiments but rather must be understood as close cousins of $R = f(A, P)$ studies, it is possible to state several safeguards against serious error. It should be noted in passing that many studies of variation in conditions permit less ambiguous assignment to groups than is possible in $R = f(A, P)$ research. There are public records of institutionalization, there are external criteria for the assignment into social class, there are pathological mothers who often remain pathological across the child's development, and so on. But, once more, many of the most interesting conditions determining development are in the nature of "lost signs," e.g., handling of toilet training or feeding, parental tolerance for aggression, and early sibling interactions. For such cases, dependence must often be laid on parental retrospective report, with all the doubts that have been already noted. Moreover, in the special instance of child-rearing practices there is evidence that parental responses tend to go together in clusters (Sears, et al., 1957), making it difficult to assess determination, even if one is satisfied with the validity of retrospective report.

For these several reasons, chiefly the difficulty of establishing initial comparability and the problem of interpreting complex interactions of variables, there is sound reason for choosing a repeated-measurements design in the investigation of variation in conditions. Such longitudinal study offers no guarantee that all research problems will be solved, but the thoughtful researcher will be made more tellingly aware of other variations that follow along with the one he is studying. To return to the case of institutionalization, it is possible to perform a single-measurement study, observing at age 15 children known to have been institutionalized in infancy. There may be, however, a grave temptation to make too much of the research outcome, a temptation that would be sharply reduced had these same children been seen as they entered the institution and as they developed (usually in settings far different from the "normal") after they left institutional care. Longitudinal study is laborious and time consuming, but it exerts a calming influence on the tendency to make simple what is very complicated in child development. Just as it was necessary to expand the statement of $R = f(A, P)$ generalizations, so is it proper to think of statements drawn from "natural experiments" as $R = f(A, S_1 \cdots S_n)$, in which the environmental change on which the researcher is focused represents only one of an indeterminantly large number of variations in the environment of the child. We shall be more certain of our conclusions about environmental control of development to the degree that evaluation of these supposedly ancillary variations is possible.

In summary, the most powerful statements for the control of behavior that can be made about developmental change are those that take into account environmental variation. In experimental settings permitting random assignment to groups rigorous analysis is possible. In the commoner study of variation in conditions problems of comparability of groups and of complex interactions arise in which an ex-

amination much like that discussed in relation to $R = f(A, P)$ studies is required. Oftentimes, if only as a safeguard against oversimplification, the longitudinal method is to be preferred to a single-measurement design with recourse to public record or retrospective report.

## Theoretical Principles in the Study of Developmental Change

The analysis of developmental change presented in the foregoing pages has bypassed a group of fundamental problems in the study of children. Although there is a gain in convenience when we talk about types of developmental generalizations, such a classificatory scheme tends to hide the impact of preconception, or, more elegantly, of theory in the selection of research design and procedures. No psychologist starts his investigation of child behavior without an intricate set of assumptions, guesses, and prejudices about techniques and about what is important in child behavior. There are, for example, several kinds of "longitudinal" studies—what determines the selection of one rather than another? There is an infinite variety of behavior that could be fitted to the developmental formula —what are the grounds for selecting among them? There are many different ways of organizing developmental findings—how do these variations influence the design of research? Perhaps because child behavior can be so readily described in "natural" terms and because its study has long been dominated by a purely empirical orientation, insufficient attention has been given to the operation in developmental research of theoretical principles. No brief survey can encompass the complexities of theorizing, explicit and hidden, that limit the study of children, but an attempt can be made to review some of the factors in the design of research that lie behind the statement of empirical generalizations.

## GOALS OF THE RESEARCH

*Exploration.* The simplest definition of a research program in child psychology derives from an interest in "seeing what happens" to some aspect of behavior over age. Such an interest may arise from casual observation, from a hunch about the way children develop, or from an articulated theory, but the aim of the researcher is not a systematic and detailed statement of a functional relationship; he is concerned rather with a preliminary survey, or exploration, of some response system. The establishment of a natural history of child behavior on the basis of such exploration has much to recommend it; the changes we see as children grow are so various and complicated that a primitive taxonomy of behavior provides initial categories that we may use in building more refined treatments. Over the years, a substantial part of developmental research had been of this kind, dominated by studies of physical growth and of test performance.

The use of exploratory survey is not limited to any particular aspect of child behavior; whether one is interested in newborn behavior, in the effect of nursery school, in the psychological changes that occur in adolescence, or in social-class variation in rearing patterns, it is usually appropriate to seek out the edges of the problem by an exploratory survey.

For most of the studies that are designed to provide general guidelines for later intensive study, the cross-sectional method is almost ideally suited. For a relatively small expenditure of time and effort, the general character of a developmental pattern can be discerned. For example, if a psychologist is interested in the behavior of children when their mothers become pregnant again, he can reasonably set up an interview schedule or an observational procedure to study their behavior. His comparison group could be obtained from children whose mothers are not pregnant, perhaps with the precaution of matching this exploratory "control" group with the first on age and sex, but, by and large, the exploratory researcher organizes his study to show up relatively gross effects, leaving a more subtle analysis for later on. Similarly, the psychologist who is interested in children's handling of number concepts might profitably survey this area by observing at more or less the same time groups of children in different school grades. He probably would not gain from such an exploration a precise statement of stages of change or of details of development, but he would have put some helpful limitation on his next try, and he would have learned a great deal about techniques of study, changes in aspects of the child's behavior other than the use of numbers, and so on.

In general, for the purpose of staking out an area of child behavior for study, the cross-sectional method usually has an advantage over the repeated-measurements method in permitting the rapid collection of data. This advantage is, of course, much greater when the behavior under study changes across a wide span of time, e.g., development of fears, changes in attitude toward parental authority, and dependence on peers. Longitudinal study is normally too expensive and too hazardous to be optimally effective in the rough exploratory assessment under discussion here. For some problems noted earlier, there is no alternative to repeated-measures investigation, but it is generally the case that such problems have less ambiguous definition, i.e., they are not simply exploratory. It is unfortunate that the notion of longitudinal study has become for many psychologists too closely identified with ill-defined attempts to collect as many data over as long a developmental period as possible. The repeated-measurements method by no means demands such omnivorous planning and is probably badly suited for it. Moreover, as we shall see later, there is too much that can be observed and described in human behavior to set out on a study of developmental phenomena without *some* definition of intent. When this definition is limited by a general interest in some developmental behavior but without explicit hypotheses concerning subpopulation variation or the details of change (e.g., most "exploratory" studies of the simple $R = f(A)$ sort), then the researcher should look to cross-sectional study to provide the rough outlines of

a phenomenon. When the information obtained in this way is analyzed and used as a source of more specific hypotheses, the researcher may proceed to a longitudinal analysis with more confidence and with a markedly increased chance of finding significant relationships.

***Variation Study.*** Once the over-all picture of a developmental sequence has been drawn by cross-sectional survey, the psychologist's interest often turns to a closer analysis of variation in the behavior. He sets up subpopulations for the study of *differences* within his age groups, the research becomes more focused, and, although the researcher cannot anticipate his findings in detail, he knows at least the kinds of observations he should make. Two kinds of specification are usually involved here—the more precise definition of the observations of child behavior to be made and the selection of subpopulations on $P$ or $S$ dimensions. Thus in the case of the child's responses to maternal pregnancy the researcher may decide from his earlier survey that a sensitive index of change in response is the child's concern with his own bodily functions; analogously, the researcher may have a suspicion that sex and age will influence the character of the child's behavior markedly. As a result of these refinements of his original interest, he may fruitfully set up a study that is limited to observation of a particular set of responses in groups of subjects selected on explicit criteria.

When the child psychologist has put some limitation on his goals, he faces once more the choice between longitudinal and cross-sectional study. It will be clear from what has already been noted that no simple rule of thumb can dictate a universally satisfactory answer. However, it can be maintained that variation study represents the most effective present-day use of longitudinal study. In research on physical growth (Tanner, 1955), on test performance (Hofstaetter, 1954), and on the stability of behavior (Morris et al., 1954) the problems of repeated-measurements study are reduced by the existence of a primitive but important theoretical stance—the concentration on a limited set of observations and on limited subpopulations of subjects. With research goals specified in this way, the advantages that come from studying "matched" subjects can be claimed. These advantages, it must be remembered, are often quite striking. If it turns out, for example, that dependent children become more dependent during mother's pregnancy and that independent children become more independent, then cross-sectional study can tell you only that the variance of dependency behavior changes, never that there is a systematic direction in the change. Similarly, and doubtlessly of even greater importance, having the same children under observation over a period of time increases the likelihood that the researcher will notice relationships that would escape him in cross-sectional study. To return to the "effects-of-pregnancy" study for another illustration, most children may show no systematic response to maternal pregnancy but a small subgroup may show marked behavior change. Ordinary statistical analysis may not demonstrate a difference when the full groups are compared, but the longitudinal researcher has a chance to look back to his earlier observations to determine whether there is anything systematically different about the earlier behavior of overresponders.

This susceptibility to after-the-fact analysis is one of the chief merits of repeated-measurements study. In an investigation of psychological changes during adolescence one may find, during the third year of study, that several of the children show autistic symptoms. This behavior in a sense defines a new group for study, and the researcher with observations on the same children over the two preceding years may explore his material to determine what earlier data might be related to the development of autistic behavior. It should be stated at once that this gain for longitudinal study carries with it a serious danger. If there is a sizable quantity of information relating to a group of children studied over a period of time and if the investigator examines it in a *post hoc* search for regularities, he may very well find them and they may very well be fortuitous. The hypothetical researcher's autistic adolescents may have been unique in that they were early-maturers, lost a parent before age 15, and had only one sibling, a pattern that a skillful psychologist could work up into a plausible "explanation" for later autism. Here we run against a perennial problem in psychology at large and child psychology in particular. Our theoretical principles are often flexible enough to encompass rather diverse findings, and in all innocence we may be led to explanations that are no more than personally satisfying. The major safeguard to be built against this danger of "discovering" merely accidental relationships in *post hoc* longitudinal analysis is *replication* or *cross-validation*. The researcher who notices discriminating characteristics of his autistic adolescents cannot stop there; he must proceed to check this profile of characteristics in a new group to determine how stable the relationship is.

The replication safeguard against error in *post hoc* analysis is an elemental principle of competent research, and the failure of child psychologists always to respect it may be understood by consideration of two points. First, the investigator who has invested a great deal of time and effort in the collection of his longitudinal data will be humanly reluctant to begin again before he has stated publicly the results of his work. Most researchers are careful to note the absence of replication and the danger of inappropriate generalization, but the promised validation often does not take place. The second deterrent to carefully designed replication of findings from longitudinal (or, occasionally, cross-sectional) analysis is subtler and more persuasive. Having "found" a relationship, it is altogether too easy for the researcher to construct a convincing explanation, and his achievement of this step will tend to make doubts and potential criticisms less obvious to him. Moreover, in writing up his results, his commitment to a particular understanding of his data may frequently lead to a further constriction in the range of alternative explanations. Nothing in this critique should suggest that psychologists set out to present and defend dubious relationships, but we should recognize with great clarity the pitfalls that grow from the human desire to impose order on a set of data. The sole guarantee against error of this variety is the establishment of a new test or the examination of unanalyzed data to determine stability of a relationship.

With these cautions in view, the place of longitudinal study of variation can be better assessed. It provides more precise assessment of change, it supplies the researcher with suggestions for further study, and it permits *post hoc* developmental analysis of phenomena that appear in the course of study. These are striking advantages over single-measurement techniques, and the longitudinal method will be the method of power in studying variation to the degree that precautions are taken against improper generalization.

***Testing of Explicit and Detailed Hypotheses.*** Realistic examples are hard to come by in our present stage of knowledge of children, but it is hoped that one day child-development research can set about the testing of quite precise hypotheses. When clear-cut predictions can be stated, much of the objection to the cumbersomeness and inefficiency of longitudinal study will be answered. For example, if the psychologist can state an explicit and detailed hypothesis about the relationship between behavior at weaning and separation problems in school, he will be able to make two sets of observations widely separated in time, without the need to record everything he can about the behavior of his subjects and their families in the interval between observations. The analogue of this procedure is the study of learning in animals and adults. A very limited number of observations of behavior are made, and it is clear in advance what will constitute a confirmation of the hypothesis. We still will not usually have the central advantage of random assignment available to learning studies, and most developmental research will spread out over much longer periods of time than are typical in animal work, but the advance over our present circumstances is clear. The powerful use of longitudinal methods in the testing of explicit hypotheses demands not only the continued careful collection of data but also the building of appropriate and meaningful theories of child development.

## SELECTION OF RELEVANT OBSERVATIONS

At no point in the design of child-development research does the role of guiding principles bulk larger than in the selection of *what* behavior to observe. Decisions in this regard are by no means routine or obvious; it is necessary only to reflect on the infinite variety of observations that could be made to recognize the operation of selective rules. The behavior of human beings can be classified in many different ways, with the psychologist isolating one aspect or another of responding, and it is plausible to believe that many of these behavior categories will show change over age. Some hint can be had of the range of potential observations by examining the brief history of child psychology. Compare Stern's (1924) treatment of infancy with Freud's (1905),

Koffka's (1925) observations of development with Gesell's (1941), or a "classical" text such as Karl Bühler's (1930) with a recent text such as Hurlock's (1956) or Mussen and Conger's (1956) and the message of variety will become almost unbearably clear. If child psychology is in a natural-history phase of its growth, one may suspect that our behavioral botanists are looking at quite different species, and it will not be surprising if they come up with quite different conclusions about the flora. This is to recommend neither a shift in research on children toward "rawer data" nor a limitation of research to that derived from available theoretical positions. The first is regressive—it is impossible to observe *all* behavior—and the second is at best premature; but there may be merit in attempting to sketch out some of the principles that determine the selection of particular observations.

***Selection Based on Natural Occurrence.*** In some ways, the problems of a science are not selected—they are inherited. Particularly in the early decades of systematic study the major determinant of what constitutes important or relevant observation is Everyman's opinion. Landowners set the first problems for geometers, gamblers set the first problems for statisticians, and parents set the first problems for child psychologists. Will Johnny be ready for second grade in September? Why is he so hard to train? Why is he so much like his father? Do all boys like to wrestle? Why can't he read? Over the years, there is a tendency for the scientific discipline to draw back from such practical problems to an increasing interest in the general statement of issues and the precise formulation of research problems, but child psychology is still relatively close to a "natural" or common-sense definition of its aims. Parents *and* child psychologists remain interested in discipline, language development, school success, psychopathology, and a host of other problem areas that are practical in their definition. Orientation toward issues of this order seems to produce a particular brand of research, which has as its chief functions classification and diagnosis. In order to assess prospects for school success more adequately, it is necessary to develop standard assessment techniques; an understanding of psychopathology requires a system of categories and reliable routines for assignment into these categories; and so on.

The psychologist is called on to refine and extend categories or clusters of behavior that already have a primitive statement in the psychology of the layman. It is interesting to note, too, that our first ways of conceptualizing research problems derive in large measure from common sense or what has been called "protopsychology" (Mandler and Kessen, 1959). For example, early studies of language development took as their categories of description the grammarian's classification into nouns, verbs, and so on, a procedure that inadequately reflects fundamental changes in verbal behavior (Brown, 1958; Skinner, 1957). Similarly, classical studies of infantile emotion borrowed from common speech the distinctions of "rage" and "fear" that were held to be somehow fundamental.

There are several consequences of this early dependence of systematic child psychology on the child psychology of the street and the home. First, there are so many immediately important problems delivered by a practical view of child behavior that our energies could be consumed for many years in the work of making them more readily susceptible to systematic study. Second, there is no clear evidence that a practical definition of any scientific discipline is the most strategic program in the long haul; there is, if anything, evidence in the history of other sciences to suggest that this is a very inefficient procedure and that crucial extensions of our knowledge take place when a disconnection or detachment from the obviously practical takes place. Third, the split allegiance of child psychologists, on one hand to the job of helping parents and teachers, on the other hand of establishing reliable and meaningful general statements about child behavior, has not permitted a sharp definition of our goals. This is not to say that we can or should turn our backs on the realities of child behavior in a free-living state; much of our productive work will grow from a recognition of practical distinctions and systematic attempts to account for them. But it should be equally clear that we cannot stop at the boundaries of "natural" description and explanation; the innovations of Freud, Watson, and Piaget are convincing evidence that the dimensions of child behavior which provide for stable and important prediction need not be the dimensions of common sense. In any case, the work of classification and diagnosis of child behavior will continue to make up a sizable chunk of developmental research; it will be supportive of long-range scientific goals as long as child psychologists are alert to its limitations and keep their sights on statements of regularities and on explanatory notions that do not remain limited by "natural occurrence."

*Selection Based on a Lawful Relationship to Age.* Among the criteria that may be suggested for the selection of observations, there is one which has high standing in the canons of science —the regularity or lawfulness of occurrence. The search for stability in the behavior of children goes beyond the criterion of natural occurrence and puts the question: What behavior is consistently related to age, to some other characteristic of the child, or to some characteristic of the environment? Conceived most broadly, this is a brief statement of the basic scientific aim of establishing supported generalizations and will be seconded by almost all psychologists. Nonetheless, the existence in child psychology of a single, easily determined measure—age—has made the program of research resulting from this fundamental premise somewhat biased. Behavior came under investigation not because of a criterion of significance, whether based on common sense or on general theoretical considerations, but rather because it seemed to have some systematic relationship with age. Take, as an example, the excellent research on grasping patterns by Halverson (1931), in which there is presented in rich detail the sequence of manual positions that children use to pick up small objects. Why were these particular observations chosen for study? The most reasonable answer would seem to be that a steady and consistent progression in these responses can be detected in most children, i.e., the behavior is lawfully related to chronological age. A researcher interested in grasping in young children might alternatively have observed speed of response or success in picking up small objects, or he may have concentrated on subpopulation variation in the behavior of grasping.

Such hypothetical studies may have as much significance as the sequential motor analysis of Halverson, but they would not have the face validity that has come to be ascribed to any child-development research that states a relationship to chronological age. Again, it is a nicely balanced conflict for the researcher looking toward a future systematic child psychology. We should have as much information as can feasibly be had about the regularity of changes in behavior over age, but this is not the same thing as maintaining that the collection of age-response regularities will lead us to a fruitful set of general principles. On the contrary, the existence of a "safe" area of research, in which the psychologist can be relatively certain that most behavior will change with age, may tend to reduce the research commitment to novel or uncertain hypotheses. The trend away from simple age-response research probably indicates a consensus among child psychologists that effective generalizations will not grow automatically from the establishment of lawful relationships with age.

In the field of infant testing it is possible to see in more detail the consequences of depending too exclusively on a criterion of regularity in the selection of observations. It is known that the correlation between tests of early development and later tests of intelligence are remarkably low (Maurer, 1946). An examination of the procedures used in selecting items, i.e., in selecting relevant observations, will show why this negative finding should be no great surprise. Tests of intelligence among school-age children are set up on the basis of their relationship to some external criterion, usually school performance, with an introduction of new observations to ascertain the most effective way of predicting from the test to the external criterion. Infant tests, on the other hand, are built largely on the basis of lawful and reliable relationships with chronological age. This is by no means their sole justification—designers of infant tests certainly mean them to be somehow representative of the child's everyday behavior—but they are different from tests of older children in that they are not usually related to an external criterion. There is, in a word, no school performance that would permit us to judge whether or not the 2-year-old's intellectual development is adequately reflected in his test score, and to include two such different procedures under the descriptive label "test of development" is hardly justified. The point of importance here, however, is the ready-made trap that exists in studies of human development—the face-valid but sometimes misleading dominance of chronological age as a variable. To put the argument in capsule form, a lawful

relationship with age is not a sufficient criterion for the fruitful selection of observations of child behavior; such fundamental description is significant when it is related to variables other than age and to explicit theory.

**Selection on the Basis of Available Instruments.** Still another ground for the selection of observations of child behavior is the availability, usually from general psychology, of particular research instruments. The most obvious example of this criterion is the extension upward and downward of early intelligence tests; an instrument found useful for school-aged children was applied, with more or less sophistication, to adults and to younger children. The result of this particular extension of a technique has been productive of important advances in our knowledge of human development; it is too early to say whether current research with projective tests and lever boxes will also improve our understanding of child behavior. What is relevant in the present context is the recognition that application of a procedure established for the study of adults or animals does not guarantee important findings in children. It goes without saying that there is no legitimate justification for considering extensions of technique improper or unscientific; it does deserve mention that their scientific utility cannot be justified merely because the techniques are available.

**Selection Based on Explicit Hypothesis.** The criteria reviewed in the foregoing paragraphs have the function of putting some definition on the infinite variety of description possible in the observation of children's development. They rarely operate singly, and they certainly are not so "pure" as the present treatment makes them sound, but they outline a rough classification of starting points for the systematic observation of children. Often these criteria are supplemented by yet another—an explicit statement of theoretical principles. This is the ideal goal of systematic study; observations are made not because the behavior happens to be in view but rather because the researcher has an integrated set of general principles, which prescribe in a clear-cut fashion the kinds of observations it would be most strategic to study at any particular moment. Like most human ideals, this one is not often achieved, but it takes only a casual look at the history of child psychology to see the revolutions that were introduced into the field by the speculations of Freud and Watson. Of course, theories are not independent of prior observation, but it is striking what a difference is made in the distribution of energy and the organization of research in a field when the opportunity is presented to test a hypothesis drawn from a wide-reaching set of principles. In child psychology today we are so used to the infusion of psychoanalysis and learning theory that it is difficult to conceive what the discipline would be like without the structure laid down by these two general systems.[1]

[1] There are others, of course; theoretical settings of importance for child study have been proposed by members of the Gestalt group, by Piaget, and by contemporary physiological psychologists, to name only a few.

The technical advantage that comes from explicit hypotheses in delimiting the scope of observation has already been mentioned; it will be seen later that this is no mean gain in solving the practical problems of the developmental researcher. Beyond this, several further supports for theory-directed research can be stated. The first has to do with the broad scientific question of interrelationships among empirical findings. An explicit set of hypotheses permits the researcher to set out on a program of study, with the end in view of bringing his data together in a coherent statement. Traditional studies of child development may be liable to the charge that they lack organization and present a failure to establish linkages between one set of relationships and another. We know a great deal about the development of children; what sometimes appears to be missing is a conceptual framework on which this knowledge can be ordered and extended. Clearly, the achievement of this goal will not occur merely because someone proposes a speculative set of general statements, but such a set does tend to give direction to research, to aid the search for data that can reasonably be related to other data, and to prescribe in a more or less precise way what the appropriate next step in research should be.

Corollary to the chief gain from the organization of study which a set of principles imposes are several somewhat less obvious advantages. Commitment to a particular theory (and it seems at the present stage of child psychology not to matter a great deal which theory) binds a group of researchers together, providing the support of communication and exchange that makes a substantial difference in the probability of doing meaningful research. Shared commitment may also increase the likelihood of replication of observations, with a corresponding increase in the assurance we have about the stability of our findings.

Another gain from theory-directed research in child development lies in the possibility that it will move child psychology more rapidly into a significant relationship with the rest of the behavior sciences. Whether child psychology is a discipline unto itself, requiring its special techniques and special theories, is in large measure an empirical question, but it is a strategy consistent with the usual growth of science to search out the ways in which the study of children may be meaningfully related to the study of animals and human adults. The bridges among the divisions of psychology will be built on general theory; without prejudicing the issue of whether they will take the weight they are constructed to carry, it seems a legitimate part of our job to sketch out working plans.

In short, the selection of observations in the study of children is by no means an automatic or obvious procedure. The researcher will be confined by limitations ranging from the casual to the highly elaborated, and these limitations will determine in part the kind of child psychology he will produce and the decisions he will make in regard to the design and procedures of research. It may reasonably be expected that research presentations would profit from an explicit statement by the investigator of the grounds he has used for the selection of a particular set of observations.

## THE ROLE OF THEORETICAL CONSTRUCTS

Even though there is available no generally accepted and comprehensive theory of child development, child psychologists use a large number of theoretical constructs in their reports and discussions. Terms like "aggression," "dependency," and "emotion" do not merely give names to the investigator's operations; they go beyond simple operational status and become involved in statements of assumed relationships or hypotheses. Two important notions of this sort are widely used in the literature of child psychology—"maturation" and "developmental stage." Although both terms are useful to the psychologist, permitting him to talk about some research findings in an abbreviated fashion, it is important in the present context to note that they are not mere descriptive names, that is, labels for some observable aspect of child behavior. In order to use the terms appropriately, one must know something about the theoretical principles in which the words occur (Hebb, 1958). Much of the contention between the maturational and environmental positions in child psychology does not concern facts but rather the interpretation and use of facts. We know that all normal children smile, but it is a theoretical presupposition that leads us to call the behavior maturational or learned, and we will do different kinds of research on smiling according to this presupposition.

An argument of similar force can be

applied to the construct developmental stage. The issues involved in discussing psychosexual stages (Freud, 1905) or stages of intelligence (Piaget, 1952) are not designed to determine only that child behavior can be categorized into clusters of responses that change with age; there is also at issue an understanding of how the "stage" notion fits into Freud's and Piaget's over-all theory of child behavior (Wolf, 1957).

Briefly, the point under discussion here is that the words a child psychologist uses in talking about his results are not conventional names for aspects of child behavior; they are words which call attention to observations, but they also function in theoretical principles. We shall fully understand the use of maturation, developmental stage, and many other terms in the language of child psychology only when we know their place in hypothetical generalizations as well as their relation to empirical operations. This double aspect of our most important constructs supports once more the need for a public expression of preconception and assumption in the study of children.

## Practical Problems

The psychologist familiar with the realities of child development research will recognize that the distinctions about statement-form and theory elaborated earlier do not represent fairly the workaday business of studying children. At almost every stage of a research project there arise problems of a technical or practical sort, problems that must be tackled and solved before the investigation can be brought to a successful conclusion. In treating some of these problems in the following pages, recourse is often had to psychological lore rather than law, with particular emphasis on the longitudinal method and its sometimes peculiar properties. Moreover, because the line between practical and theoretical is a thin one indeed, there is occasional reference back to some of the questions raised earlier. In general, however, the discussion here assumes that the researcher has solved his theoretical and financial problems and now needs only to collect good data.

## SELECTING AND MAINTAINING A SAMPLE

Beyond the issue of representativeness raised in the treatment of sampling procedures there arise several further problems in setting up and maintaining a group of subjects for developmental research. One of the toughest of these problems lies in determining the characteristics of the subjects who are *not* in the study—the ones who got away. If, for example, a research is set up to study patterns of mother-child interaction in the first years, the researcher will normally recruit from a group of pregnant women or new mothers. Whatever technique is used to enlist a sample, there will almost invariably be some subjects who refuse to participate or who drop out of the study later on. How does this reduction in sample affect one's conclusions? Often there exists no feasible way to tell whether or not such "drop-outs" are different from the maintained sample, but, at the very least, the researcher should keep careful records of the *proportion* of such losses and keep his eyes open for any indication of a systematic variation between the subjects who remain in the study and those who leave it. Occasionally, if his maintained sample shows some apparently unusual characteristic, e.g., a high proportion of feeding problems, he may be able to track down his drop-outs to get at least a superficial picture of how their children have been developing.

When there is a large sample under study and the proportion of drop-outs is low, this problem is probably trivial, but intensive longitudinal study often requires restriction to a relatively small number of cases, so that each refusal or loss may count a great deal. Under these circumstances, it is important in interpreting the results of repeated-measurements research to know as much as possible about the rate and circumstances of attrition in subject population.

The occurrence of attrition in longitudinal study samples poses one of the most interesting questions in developmental research, and one which is of great practical implication: Why do people enter and stay in a long-term child development research project? When no special demands are made on parents or children (e.g., when observations take place in school), there is no difficulty in understanding the cooperation of subjects, but what of those studies in which the parent must bring her child to the researcher, in which home visits are made routinely, or in which the child must be seen for relatively long sessions? No systematic data are available on this point, but several answers can be suggested if it is recognized that wide variation will exist from one group of subjects to another in the weighting of motivations for participation in a research project.

Some parents will agree to enter a longitudinal study because of a conviction that research with children is important. It is unlikely that this is a major argument for more than a small proportion of parents, but the current Zeitgeist clearly supports an interest in the scientific study of development, at least in the community of well-educated parents. At a far remove from such intellectual commitment are the parents who participate in a project because of the gain for them in services. Free pediatric care may be provided, a reduction in nursery school fees, or an opportunity to consult on school problems, but in each case the participating parent gets something from the research that he would not otherwise have had.

Whatever role these two sources of support for participation may play, they clearly do not account for all cases of participation in longitudinal research and may not in themselves be enough to account for more than a few. To understand the willingness of parents to suffer what would normally be intrusions into privacy and to put up with the unusual demands of psychologists, it is necessary to call on another group of factors. Different psychologists will use different terms in discussing these factors, but they seem to turn on some notion of "psychological support" or "rapport." Parents are probably as puzzled by the behavior of their children as psychologists are, and the opportunity to talk to an objective and competent professional about their concerns and their doubts is valuable to many parents. The popularity of books on child care and the range of questions addressed to newspaper and magazine columns about children give a rough estimate of the hesitations and confusions of the American parent. Given a chance to clarify these confusions with a child psychologist or pediatrician, parents are often quite willing to accept the demands of developmental research.

If the foregoing observations are correct, then the successful maintenance of an intensive longitudinal contact depends in large measure on the degree to which the researcher supports the need of the parent for reassurance, advice, and a listening ear. When such a relationship is established, there is reason to believe that parents will not only go along with the researcher but will accept his questions and tests with good grace.[1]

Another practical decision the researcher must make in selecting his sample has to do with the optimal number of cases. It is a fairly good rule of thumb that longitudinal researchers at the outset of their work plan to study more children than they can possibly manage. There are several correctives to this tendency to overestimate one's ability to handle data collection. First,

[1] Apart from the reluctance of parents to participate, a major source of attrition in longitudinal study samples is residential instability. The psychologist with free choice would be wise to work in an area in which there is low geographical mobility among his potential subjects.

it is wise to count, not children, but occasions of observation. A sample of ten babies may not seem very large, but, if one plans to see the child every month or so, to interview and test both parents, and to integrate whatever pediatric information may be available, the number of observations made and the number of problems for data analysis that arise are enormous. Second, insofar as it can be arranged, detailed schedules of observation and of data analysis should be laid out in advance. Only when the psychologist can see who will be available to test babies while someone else is interviewing mothers while someone else is analyzing the data already collected will he be able to make a rational estimate of optimal sample size. As has been the case in so many of the problems raised in this chapter, decisions about the number of cases to be studied are the result of several considerations and no fixed answer can be given. Perhaps the only generalization that all child-development researchers would agree on is that one never overestimates the effort required to collect repeated-measurements data.

## CHANGES IN PROCEDURE DURING LONGITUDINAL STUDY

In considering how to deal with changes in procedure during a longitudinal study of children, it must be remembered that repeated-measurements research can vary widely in scope and duration. For those investigations in which sharply limited aspects of behavior are observed, or in which the time span covered is brief, there usually are no major practical problems involving revision of procedure. Such is not the case in longitudinal research stretching over a long period of the child's life, or that which is designed to study many facets of the child's development. It is into the latter contexts that the present discussion fits; however, the issues raised will apply *mutatis mutandis* to less far-ranging longitudinal investigations.

Among the reasons why a standard set of research procedures cannot be used throughout a developmental research program, one that ranks high on the list is the need for flexibility in following up suggestive relationships as they appear in the course of study. Longitudinal research serves not only as a data-collection device but also as a source of hypotheses for the researcher. Although independent verification will normally be necessary to confirm such hypotheses, one of the ancillary advantages of "big" longitudinal research is the opening up of new areas for fruitful study. To make optimal use of this characteristic, the investigator will often have to leave some ambiguity in the first definition of his procedures.[1]

There is another compelling reason for the occurrence of procedural shifts in repeated-measurements study—the absence of a single observational technique that is applicable across the developmental span. One may want to record general activity or reflex responsiveness in the newborn, but such

observations will not provide adequate measures of variability in the 2-year-old; character of social interaction with peers may be an important dimension of adolescent behavior, but it is less likely to be discriminating in the study of the toddler; and so on. Particularly in the observation of the child from birth to school-age, it is necessary to change techniques used to gather data as the child grows older. This consideration poses a serious problem for the understanding of development— how are we to translate from one observational technique to another? To put the question in another way, what constitutes the "same" behavior at different ages? A 6-month-old is judged to be active on the basis of observations quite different from those used to assign a 5-year-old a "high activity" score. Similarly, the evaluation of quality of mother-child interaction will depend on markedly different criteria when the child is 1 year old and when he is 7. An irreducible problem of developmental research is that we must modify our data-gathering techniques as the child and his environment change. Moreover, it is no solution merely to give the same *name* to the results of different observational procedures; an "anxious" 2-year-old is not similar to an "anxious" third-grader because we use the same word to describe their behavior.

The difficulty underlying shifts in observational procedure is not likely to be easily removed; solution will demand both a sharpening of our conceptualizations of development and a great deal of research comparing different observational modes. Perhaps the potentially most profitable approach to

---

[1] It is necessary in this connection to emphasize the distinction between longitudinal study as an exploratory search for relationships and as a technique of confirmation. See the earlier discussion of goals for developmental research.

this issue is the overlapping of different techniques; at an age at which two or more procedures may be appropriate, they can be used simultaneously or in close succession to evaluate the relationships among them (Bell, 1953). For the area of development testing, there are data of this sort available, and the careful investigation of relationships among tests (Maurer, 1946; Hofstaetter, 1954) has provided leads for a better understanding of what goes on when we modify our devices for collecting data about developmental status or intelligence. Related investigation is in order for establishing correspondence among different ways of assessing social responsiveness, quality of mother-child interaction, emotional development, and many other aspects of children's development. Short of empirical evidence about rules for translating the results of varying observational techniques, the developmental researcher would seem well advised to respect the operationalist's injunction against assuming the equivalence of different procedures. The tangle that results from being forced to change modes of observation in order to keep up with changes in the child will be teased apart only with the help of further empirical examination of research methods.

## THE EFFECT
## OF THE INVESTIGATOR
## ON HIS SUBJECTS

The relationship between a longitudinal researcher and his subjects is not simply an exchange between a source of data and a data-recording system; it is a social interaction that can become,

in long-term studies, fairly intimate and complicated. It was suggested earlier that subjects stay in longitudinal studies at least in part for the support the researcher provides as a competent and attentive professional. If this is the case, he will not remain totally inconsequential in his effect on the participating parent. Some interviewers will be more successful than others in gaining a subject's confidence, some testers will be more frequently asked to "explain" the child's behavior, and so on. Beyond this, child psychologists are probably unable to hide completely their convictions about appropriate rearing techniques behind a screen of impassive neutrality. As the investigator gets to know the child and his parents, and as they get to know him, there arises the possibility that they will change their "normal" behavior or their reports to conform to his position, however mildly expressed. If this kind of distortion occurs at a high rate, then the validity of long-term longitudinal studies of development is in jeopardy.

Yet in a sense the difficulty is insoluble—the researcher cannot avoid asking his questions and making his observations, and a refusal to discuss the parent's problems may weaken the rapport necessary to maintain an informative contact. Some precautions can be taken, nonetheless; rather than pretending to be above or beyond evaluative opinion about his subjects, it would appear wiser for the psychologist to be as explicit as he can to himself and his colleagues in the research about his prejudices and antipathies. In this way, he will be alerted to signs that his subjects are "coming into line" and can take further precautions against apply-ing improper pressure on them. Beyond this, the longitudinal researcher can take whatever comfort is available in the evidence that major changes in parents' rearing practices are unlikely to occur in response to the researcher's weak expression of his attitudes. As Wolf has pointed out in a report on the Yale Child Study Center longitudinal research project,

> People's behavior is not so easily changed in vital matters as some attitude-change studies lead us to believe and as optimistic educators hope for. . . . Only two of our (ten) cases breastfed for any length of time. A number of our study mothers spanked their children during their first year, most of them in the course of the first two years. The toilet-train-ing procedures of our study mothers are certainly not marked by the stamp "ap-proved by child-development experts" (1957, p. 47 f.).

The longitudinal researcher must rec-ognize that he is not seeing his subjects in a perfectly natural state and that they will occasionally be influenced in their behavior as a result of often-repeated interactions with him. But as long as he is tuned to the possibility of distortion and discrete in the social exchange that is part of research on human behavior, it is unlikely that he will seriously re-duce the validity of his findings by mak-ing his subjects too responsive to his own preconceptions.

## THE ANALYSIS OF LONGITUDINAL DATA

After the longitudinal researcher has fought his way through the web of problems that surround the setting up

and execution of an extended study of child development, he faces one last task—the analysis of his data. On occasion, there is nothing in this process special to longitudinal study; when the research is of limited scope and when there are established conventions for handling data analysis, the investigator goes about his work with no more hesitation than is usual for students of human behavior. Once again, examples from the study of test performance (Bayley, 1933) and of physical growth (Stolz and Stolz, 1951) best illustrate this stage of developmental research. But the interest of child psychologists in more intricate aspects of human development leads to the collection of data for which there are no simple rules for analysis and summary. The innova-tor, in particular, setting out to describe and account for behavior that has not been studied in detail before, cannot solve his problems of data analysis by reference to agreed-on principles. This ambiguity, necessary as it is in ex-ploratory phases of study, gives rise to several problems for the longitudinal re-searcher in the midst of his protocols. Two of these issues deserve further comment—the problem of too much information and the problem of con-tamination.

It is somewhat curious to speak of having too much information about a group of subjects, but as the longi-tudinal researcher works over a period of years to collect observations that he considers relevant to his research goals he may find himself in possession of a staggering array of data and with no end in sight. The issue is sometimes further complicated by the fact that the researcher cannot turn to the analysis of the data he has already collected because he is spending full time collecting new material on his subjects. For those studies that extend over decades rather than years, the danger of being overwhelmed by the weight of data is by no means mythical. In a vise like this the researcher may either postpone his report indefinitely or present only a case-historical sample of what he has achieved (Fries and Woolf, 1953; Murphy, 1956).

One corrective to this difficulty is implied in what has already been said about longitudinal research—that the goals of the project must be carefully thought through in the planning stage and careful estimates made of the time and effort that will be required to keep abreast not only of the child and his environment but of one's data as well. This sort of calculation may result in a restriction of the range of behavior observed, in a limitation on duration of the study, in a reduction in the size of anticipated sample, or in an increase in professional personnel scheduled for the project, but it will also make more likely the presentation of a terminal report.

Child psychologists are not seers, however, and the intricacy of children's development demands a good deal of flexibility in the planning of research. Assuming that, in spite of appropriate and considered planning, the researcher finds his data coming in faster than he can analyze them, what can he do? One possibility, which has additional advantages to be mentioned shortly, is to set up a two-team organization for the research. One group of workers collects data and maintains contact with the subjects; the other sets itself the task of coding, summarizing, and analyzing observations. With divided responsibility of this order, some balance will be established between the collection of data and their analysis. Moreover, the occurrence of analysis parallel with observation would provide suggestions to the data-collection team about the kinds of observations that would be relevant to the emerging picture of development.

Finally, the problem of "too much" can be put in better perspective if the double function of longitudinal research is remembered. Extended observation of children with an eye to including a wide range of behavior serves the important purpose of outlining a series of problems for later concentrated study. "Big" longitudinal research has to date primarily served this necessary exploratory function (MacFarlane, 1938; Jones, 1943). It may be most fruitful for child-development research in the long run for psychologists to recognize frankly the preliminary character of current long-term longitudinal research on the development of the child and to accept the data obtained as an unrivaled source of hypotheses rather than as a finished set of observations that must be analyzed in detail. This orientation would reduce our distress at being unable to have in public view all the results of longitudinal research, and it might speed the "second-stage" collection of stable generalizable relationships in child development.

The longitudinal researcher who cannot, because of the exploratory nature of his study, state in advance how he will analyze and present his data runs the risk of another stumbling block—contamination. If, for example, a researcher has observed the development of a child from birth to 4 years and at the end of this period sets about his analysis and summary, he cannot examine his information about the child as an infant free of influence from his knowledge of the child's later behavior. If he knows the 4-year-old to be dependent, anxious, or active, the investigator's appraisal of the child's infancy will be directed in part by this knowledge. Nor are adequate checks always available when a *group* of children is under study because the long-term longitudinal sample will often not be large enough to preclude selective treatment of the data. As was noted in the discussion of *post hoc* analysis, it is often possible to "see" in a mass of protocols the continuing thread of some characteristic. There is enough known about human perception to be certain that contamination will not be avoided simply because the researcher tries to avoid it. In his contacts with his subjects he builds an implicit portrait of them, a set of expectations about their behavior, and it would be surprising if this portrait did not influence the work of analysis and summary. More than that, it is important for the researcher to use his contaminating information *when he is in search of hypotheses;* by moving back and forth through his protocols, he will frequently come up with useful directions for new study. But when the goal of the research is the statement of repeatable relationships, contamination

from the researcher's "theory of the child" is a confusing source of error. The two-team approach to longitudinal study, which permits the analysis of data as they are collected, stands as one technique for reducing contamination of this sort. When the behavior of the 4-year-old is observed, whatever can be said about his infancy has been said some time earlier, and the investigator's response to later behavior cannot influence the report of the child's infancy.

Short of concurrent analysis, the problem of contamination can be dealt with by replication. When a relationship is found in an overview of developmental data collected in longitudinal study, it is usually appropriate to check its generality by an observation of new cases. The creative use of longitudinal observation is an important part of child-development research, and it permits the presentation of an integrated sensible picture of the developing child. However, this exploratory function must be supported by more limited and precise study under circumstances in which contamination does not introduce the possibility of error.

## Summary

The study of child development involves two interlocking goals—the statement of reliable relationships between behavior and age and the analysis of these relationships to provide better prediction and control of child behavior. The achievement of these goals requires the continuing collection of empirical evidence, particularly about age-functional changes in behavior among different subpopulations of children and in response to environmental change, and a refinement of theoretical principles about development.

The intricacy of child development, and the existence of wide individual variation in behavior, has brought to prominence the longitudinal study of child behavior. There is much to recommend longitudinal procedures, both as a source of hypotheses and as a sensitive method of confirmation. There are risks, however, in depending on choice of research design to provide stable answers to our questions about human development. The psychologist studying children must bear in mind the presuppositions of his research, the kind of generalization he is aiming for, and the relevance of his procedures to other research on child development.

## REFERENCES

Bayley, Nancy. 1933. Mental growth during the first three years. *Genet. Psychol. Monogr.*, 14, 1–92.

———. 1955. On the growth of intelligence. *Amer. Psychologist*, 10, 805–18.

Beach, F. A., and J. Jaynes. 1954. Effects of early experience upon the behavior of animals. *Psychol. Bull.*, 51, 239–263.

Bell, R. Q. 1953. Convergence: An accelerated longitudinal approach. *Child Develpm.*, 24, 145–152.

———. 1954. An experimental test of the accelerated longitudinal approach. *Child Develpm.*, 25, 281–286.

Bijou, S. W. 1957. Patterns of reinforcement and resistance to extinction in young children. *Child Develpm.*, 28, 47–55.

Brown, R. 1958. *Words and things.* Glencoe, Ill.: Free Press.

Bühler, K. 1930. *The mental development of the child.* New York: Harcourt, Brace.

Freud, S. 1905. Three contributions to the theory of sex. In A. A. Brill, *Basic writings of Sigmund Freud.* New York: Modern Library, 1938.

Fries, Margaret E., and P. J. Woolf. 1953. Some hypotheses on the role of the congenital activity type in personality development. *Psychoanal. Study Child*, 8, 48–62.

Gesell, A. 1941. *Developmental diagnosis.* New York: Hoeber.

———. 1945. *The embryology of behavior.* New York: Harper.

———, and Helen Thompson. 1929. Twins T and C from infancy to adolescence. *Genet. Psychol. Monogr.*, 24, 1–256.

Goodenough, Florence L. 1931. *Anger in young children.* Minneapolis: Univer. Minnesota Press.

Gordon, J. E. 1957. The validity of Shoben's parent attitude survey. *J. clin. Psychol.*, 13, 154–158.

Halverson, H. M. 1931. An experimental study of prehension in infants by means of systematic cinema records. *Genet. Psychol. Monogr.*, 10, 107–286.

Hebb, D. O. 1958. *A textbook of psychology.* Philadelphia: Saunders.

Hofstaetter, P. R. 1954. The changing composition of intelligence: A study in T-technique. *J. genet. Psychol.*, 85, 159–164.

Hurlock, Elizabeth. 1956. *Child development.* (3rd Ed.) New York: McGraw-Hill.

Jones, H. E. 1943. *Development in adolescence.* New York: Appleton-Century.

Jones, Mary C., and Nancy Bayley. 1950. Physical maturing among boys as related to behavior. *J. educ. Psychol.*, 41, 129–148.

Koffka, K. 1925. *The growth of the mind.* New York: Harcourt, Brace.

MacFarlane, Jean W. 1938. Studies in child guidance. *Monogr. Soc. Res. Child Develpm.*, 3, No. 6.

McGinnis, Esther. 1929. The acquisition and interference of motor-habits in young children. *Genet. Psychol. Monogr.*, 6, 209–311.

McGraw, Myrtle B. 1935. *Growth: A study of Johnny and Jimmy.* New York: Appleton-Century.

Mandler, G., and W. Kessen. 1959. *The language of psychology.* New York: Wiley.

Maurer, Katherine M. 1946. *Intellectual status*

*at maturity as a criterion for selecting items in preschool tests.* Minneapolis: Univer. Minnesota Press.

Morris, D. P., E. Saraker, and G. Burreiss. 1954. Follow-up studies of shy, withdrawn children. *Amer. J. Orthopsychiat.,* **24,** 743–754.

Murphy, Lois B. 1956. *Personality in young children.* Vol. 2. New York: Basic Books.

Mussen, P. H., and J. J. Conger. 1956. *Child development and personality.* New York: Harper.

Piaget, J. 1952. *The origins of intelligence in children.* New York: International Univer. Press.

Scammon, R. E. 1930. The measurement of the body in childhood. In J. A. Harris, et al., *The measurement of man.* Minneapolis: Univer. Minnesota Press.

Sears, R. R., et al. 1957. *Patterns of child rearing.* Evanston, Ill.: Row, Peterson.

Shuttleworth, F. K. 1939. The physical and mental growth of boys and girls age six to nineteen in relation to age at maximum growth. *Monogr. Res. Child Develp.,* **4,** No. 3.

Skinner, B. F. 1957. *Verbal behavior.* New York: Appleton-Century-Crofts.

Smith, Harriet T. 1958. A comparison of interview and observation measures of mother behavior. *J. abnorm. soc. Psychol.,* **57,** 278–82.

Stern, W. 1924. *Psychology of early childhood.* New York: Holt.

Stolz, H. R., and Lois M. Stolz. 1951. *Somatic development of adolescent boys.* New York: Macmillan.

Stone, A. A., and Gloria C. Onqué. 1959. *Longitudinal studies of child personality.* Cambridge, Mass.: Harvard Univer. Press.

Tanner, J. M. 1955. *Growth at adolescence.* Oxford: Blackwell.

Terman, L. M., and Leona E. Tyler. 1954. Psychological sex differences. In L. Carmichael (Ed.), *Manual of child psychology.* (2nd Ed.) New York: Wiley.

Whiting, J. W., and I. L. Child. 1953. *Child training and personality.* New Haven: Yale Univer. Press.

Wolf, Katherine M. 1957. *The origin of individuality.* Unpublished manuscript, Child Study Center, Yale Univer.

chapter 3

# Observational Child Study

Herbert F. Wright
*University of Kansas*

This chapter is about research methods that leave nature and society to their own devices. These methods rest upon direct observation as a scientific practice that includes observing and associated recording and analysis of naturally occurring things and events. *Observational child study* is a collective name for all such methods in psychological research with children.

Observational child study has been complicated at times by facilities that range from notebooks and movie cameras to elaborate check lists and rating scales to designs for experiments in nature. At bottom, though, this must be the simplest way of all to study child behavior. One gets within seeing and hearing distance of a child, observes and records something of his behavior or situation or both, and then scores, classifies, summarizes, freely interprets, or otherwise does something with the recorded observations. A group is some-

Work by Dean H. Kerkman on the bibliography is gratefully acknowledged.

times observed instead of a single child, but the basic routines are the same in either case.

Direct observation here is direct in two ways. (1) No planned arrangements stand between the observer and his target phenomena, and (2) neither does appreciable time: recording closely follows observing. The first of these limitations excludes tests, interviews, and questionnaires as well as manipulative experiments, and the second excludes especially the retrospective descriptions of case studies. What remains is study of spontaneous and ongoing child behavior in the settings of everyday life.

Consider now some data on rate of output in this line of research. Fourteen hundred nine empirical studies whose subjects include children and adolescents have been reported since 1890 in *The Pedagogical Seminary, The Journal of Genetic Psychology, Genetic Psychology Monographs, Child Development,* and *Monographs of the Society for Research in Child Development.* These investigations are classified in Table 3-1, which shows that only 110, or 8 per cent, of them meet the present criteria of observational child study and that this fraction has not been exceeded greatly during any of the seven decades after 1890.

These figures cannot be surprising. They only document the safe generalization that psychology in its every branch has done comparatively little watching and recording and examining of events left to happen as they may. Psychological science began with a leap from the armchair to the laboratory and has since generally preferred to do things with its subjects, to give them

**TABLE 3-1. EMPIRICAL STUDIES IN CHILD PSYCHOLOGY FROM 1890 THROUGH 1958**

| Period | All | Observational | |
|--------|-----|--------|---------|
| | | Number | Per Cent |
| 1890–1899 | 35 | 3 | 9 |
| 1900–1909 | 63 | 8 | 13 |
| 1910–1919 | 48 | 4 | 8 |
| 1920–1929 | 82 | 3 | 4 |
| 1930–1939 | 491 | 53 | 11 |
| 1940–1949 | 328 | 20 | 6 |
| 1950–1958 | 362 | 19 | 5 |
| Total | 1409 | 110 | 8 |

*Note.* The data are from all issues since 1890 of *The Pedagogical Seminary* and the *Journal of Genetic Psychology*, *Genetic Psychology Monographs*, *Child Development*, and *Monographs of the Society for Research in Child Development*. Evident factors contributing to the startling upsurge of studies in the 1930's include the founding then of *Child Development*, with its associated monograph series, and the often noted increase during these years of financial support for behavioral research with children.

tasks or problems, to interrogate them, to test them, or at least to draw them into prearranged situations.

Direct observation, on the other hand, has been a methodological mainstay in many other sciences. It has stood as the basic method of astronomy and the earth sciences, of the natural history disciplines in biology, and of anthropology and sociology. Its contributions may not have been revolutionary so often as procedures that manipulate events; and yet they have been substantial over the long run of progress in science. Purely observational methods have enabled scientists to record

the true appearance and the distribution in nature of countless phenomena, to discover new things from microorganisms to galaxies, to find new problems, to anticipate the needs of theories for hard empirical facts, hence to avoid the vulgarities of easy speculation, and even to test theories where experimental arrangements were difficult or impossible.

These characteristically slow but sure scientific gains alone recommend a review of psychological methods in child development with the common base of direct observation. What differing ways of studying child behavior while leaving it alone have been made available by research in child psychology? And what are the advantages and disadvantages of such methods? The chapter asks these questions.

## Outline of Methods

Two phases of investigation are foremost in our preface to this kind of research in child development: recording of behavior and analyzing the obtained record. A third major phase remains implicit: the beginning one of devising a plan for sampling the universe of child behavior. The sampling plan for a particular investigation generally needs tactics of a statistical nature that suit only its own subjects, measures, and aims. But broader requirements of strategy in sampling that can be generalized as *continuum coverage* and *material coverage* fall on all observational studies of behavior. These requirements are set first by problems of content rather than method, and yet they are bound fast to the task of getting good and sufficient data from an always complex field of study.

The behavior of a person is a lifelong continuum. It is in the nature of a stream that can never be seen in its entirety. To observe it, therefore, one has to divide it into observable lengths. One can look in on the stream, say, once a day for an hour, once an hour for a minute, for as long as a quarrel or a greeting lasts, or from awakening time to bedtime of a day through as many hours, minutes, quarrels, greetings, or days as one may choose. Continuum coverage refers to the lengths or parts into which the stream of behavior is divided for purposes of observation.

The behavior stream is enormously complex. Observing all of its many currents and ripples for the shortest time is so difficult that limits are usually set again. One can look during the hour a day only for such grand current phenomena as taking first steps or saying first words. One can look during the minute once an hour for little ripple phenomena on the order of restless actions in a classroom; or during the greeting for degrees along such a behavior dimension as emotional warmth; or during the day, as precedent truly stands (see p. 83), for everything in sight in the behavior and situation of the person. Material coverage refers to what and how much at a time the observer tries to see in the stream of behavior.

*Through what continuum units are observations made and of what order and scope are the observed phenomena? How are the observations recorded?*

*And what is done with the recorded material?*

Answers made in research to these questions of sampling strategy, recording technique, and analysis procedure give a basis for sorting and describing different methods of observational child study. One can count as a separate method a particular combination of answers to the three questions. Six methods stand out in the literature on this basis. These methods, each conveniently named and identified by an early representative writing, are *diary description* (Tiedemann, 1787), *specimen description* (Dresslar, 1901), *time sampling* (Olson, 1929), *event sampling* (Dawe, 1934), *field unit analysis* (Bishop, 1951), and *trait rating* (Haggerty, Olson, and Wickman, 1930). Another sort of observational investigating in child development will be added later (pp. 114–117). But these six methods accommodate the main findings of our canvass. Table 3-2 may help here. It outlines most of the survey by summarizing the sampling, recording, and analysis provisions of each method.

Both the nature of the target material and the observed lengths of the behavior stream vary definitively from one to another of the different methods. See how this holds by checking the following statements against the entries under Sampling Plan in Table 3-2. Diary description traces developmental changes as these occur at biographically sampled intervals. Specimen description covers intensively and continuously the behavior and situation of the child during more or less extended behavior sequences. Time-sampling records selected aspects of behavior if and as they

TABLE 3-2. A DIGEST OF METHODS IN OBSERVATIONAL CHILD STUDY

| Methods | Sampling Plan | | Recording Technique | Analysis Procedure |
| | Continuum Coverage | Material Coverage | | |
| --- | --- | --- | --- | --- |
| **OPEN** | | | | |
| Diary description | More or less regular day to day intervals | Successive steps in behavioral growth and associated life episodes | Itemization of growth changes and summary narration | Classification and interpretive study |
| Specimen description | Continuous behavior sequences | "Everything" of on-going behavior and situation | Detailed sequential narration | Interpretive study or coding, scoring, and statistical analysis |
| **CLOSED** | | | | |
| Time sampling | Intermittent short and uniform time units | Selected variables of behavior or situation or both | On-the-spot coding or narration or both | Scoring and statistical analysis |
| Event sampling | Event time spans | Behavioral events of a given class (as arguments) | On-the-spot coding or narration or both | Scoring and statistical analysis |
| Trait rating | Continuous behavior sequences | Selected dimensions of behavior | Rating based on cumulative direct observation | Scoring and statistical analysis |
| Field unit analysis | Successive behavior units | Selected variables of behavior or situation or both | On-the-spot coding | Scoring and statistical analysis |

happen within precisely limited time spans. Event sampling singles out naturally segregated behavioral events of one or another class and records these events as they arise and unfold. Field-unit analysis divides the behavior stream into consecutive units as they occur and describes each unit in turn while the iron is still hot. Trait rating selects dimensions of behavior and bases judgments about them on observations during extended sequences of behavior. Recording techniques and analysis procedures, noted in the table, are made to suit these different sampling plans.

Attention is called to the distinction in Table 3-2 between open and closed methods. Field unit analysis is not placed in either of these categories because it is open in some applications and closed in others. Diary description and specimen description are indeed *open* to diverse phenomena. Time and event sampling and trait rating, on the other hand, are *closed* to everything but rather uniform and sharply limited phenomena. The open methods are broadly comparable to those of the biographer, the historian, or the biological field explorer. The closed methods are more like those of the classical experimenter or the field observer in biology with eyes for only one descriptive target. Closed direct observing resembles experimenting in narrowness of observational set.

Some observational techniques of these methods have often been used in manipulative experimental studies. These techniques, as applied in such studies, have pertinence here. However, space limits force nearly complete exclusion of research that does manipulate behavior or

situation. A clear boundary surrounds "purely" observational methods. If one crosses that boundary, stopping becomes difficult.

## Subjects

The change-with-age emphasis of problems in child development makes it important to consider that these methods have not been applied with anything like equal frequency at all age levels. Table 3-3 shows the number and

**TABLE 3-3. NUMBER AND PER CENT OF OBSERVATIONAL AND OTHER EMPIRICAL STUDIES SINCE 1890 WITH PRESCHOOL CHILDREN, SCHOOL CHILDREN, AND ADOLESCENTS AS SUBJECTS**

|  | Observational | | | Other | | |
|---|---|---|---|---|---|---|
|  | Pre | Sch | Ado | Pre | Sch | Ado |
| Number | 104 | 12 | 3 | 643 | 600 | 427 |
| Per Cent | 94 | 11 | 3 | 50 | 46 | 33 |

*Note.* Pre: preschool children, ages under 6. Sch: school children, ages 6–12. Ado: adolescents, ages about 13–19. The N of observational studies is 110. A given study often used subjects of more than one age level with the result that each per cent frame exceeds 100. See Table 3-1 for data sources.

per cent of the studies in our sample of Table 3-1 in which preschool children, school children, and adolescents have been subjects. It may be seen that the percentages at these respective age levels stand at 94, 11, and 3 for observational as against 50, 46, and 33 for every other kind of empirical child study.

In both of these bracketings of research, then, young children and adolescents, respectively, have served most and least often as subjects. The plainest indication here is that methods of studying child behavior by direct observation have been used a good deal more than other methods in child psychology with subjects under 6 years of age. One of the reasons for this may well be an opinion, expressed rather often in the literature, that the younger the child the more natural his behavior in the presence of an observer. Other possible reasons may include institutional policies against frequent participation by younger children in experimental procedures and the popularity among experimenters of research problems calling for knowledge and skills of the older child. It is clear, in any case, that methods of observational child study have been shaped most by research on behavior in early childhood.

## Settings and Situations

Table 3-4 shows the number and per cent of our 110 observational studies in which children have been observed in designated life settings. The figures indicate that, just as preschool children are the preferred subjects, preschools are the favored scenes of this research. Observers have ventured into home settings in less than a fourth of these investigations. They have gone into hospitals and maternity homes in 7 per cent and into elementary schools in 6 per cent of the different studies. In only two of the 110 investigations were children observed as they went about from place to place in entire communities. There are left over finally a miscellany of settings, such as summer camps, clinics, and orphanages, that figured in 13 per cent of the studies.

These scenes of observation have been called interchangeably *settings* and *situations*. We shall go on calling them settings in the meaning of milieu parts that provide time, place, and facilities that are suited to certain kinds of human behavior.[1] At the same time, in re-

TABLE 3-4. NUMBER AND PER CENT OF OBSERVATIONAL STUDIES IN WHICH CHILDREN HAVE BEEN OBSERVED IN SPECIFIED LIFE SETTINGS

| Settings | Studies | |
|---|---|---|
| | Number | Per Cent |
| Nursery schools | 62 | 56 |
| Homes | 24 | 22 |
| Hospitals and maternity homes | 8 | 7 |
| Elementary schools | 7 | 6 |
| Communities-at-large | 2 | 2 |
| Miscellaneous | 14 | 13 |

*Note.* The N of studies is 110. In certain of these investigations children were observed in more than one setting. See Table 3-1 for data sources.

ferring to situations, we shall mean states of affairs that arise within settings and that are made up of the momentary conditions in an individual child and his environment under which the actions of individual behavior episodes occur. A nursery school, again, is a setting. The complex of conditions that includes, in a child X, a present need to have fun and, in the environment, a cheerful teacher, a sandbox, and a toy shovel, all of which make a difference to X while he is digging a hole in

[1] The intention in this statement is only to place a common everyday concept that is used at many points in the chapter. The closely related but more restricted offspring concept of *behavior setting* is represented on pp. 114–117.

the sand, is a situation. A situation, in short, is the relevant person-environment context of a particular action at a particular time. Three assumptions are made here.

1. Certain sorts of situations rather than others tend to arise in a given setting.

2. Yet settings and situations are by no means univocally related. On the contrary, (*a*) very radically differing situations can occur in the same setting, and (*b*) virtually identical situations can occur in different settings.

3. The behavior of the child at a particular time does indeed depend more directly upon the situation than upon the setting in which it takes place.

Now, the present significance of these distinctions is that our six methods and variants of each differ in provisions for observing and recording of settings, situations, and behavior. Aspects of behavior often are described entirely out of context. In these and other instances settings may be barely identified, with nothing recorded as to their distinctive milieu characteristics or associated behavior patterns. In still other cases general comment (Biber et al., 1942; Issacs, 1930) or supplemental methods (Barker and Wright, 1955; Gump and Sutton-Smith, 1955b) point up special characteristics of settings in which the children behave. A few procedures (Olson and Wilkinson, 1932; Baldwin, Kalhorn, and Breese, 1945) focus on the situation of the child while leaving what he does for secondary consideration. Finally, there are some procedures in which situation and behavior are observed, recorded, and examined together. An effort will be made to represent the different methods with enough regard for these dissimilarities and some of their consequences.

It seems a likely guess, meanwhile, that observational methods in child development would now be suited to more problems if they owed less to the American nursery school and more to stores, streets, parks, vacant lots, swimming pools, and other settings that child psychologists rarely visit for research purposes. As for subjects, Gellert (1955, p. 193) points out that most of the children observed in nursery schools have been of "above average intelligence, from high socionomic strata, and of Judean-Christian cultural and ethnic heritage." Consider further that this description applies in a preschool setting, not only to the pupils as subjects, but also to these same children as social behavior objects in the situations of one another. In general, a suggestion by Gellert that methods of direct observation need to be extended more to children of other sorts and ages and to a larger "variety of environments" seems well founded.

## Application Aims

One might expect to find unity of purpose in methods with a common focus on naturally occurring behavior. Outsiders, if no others, could reasonably look here for study of naturally occurring behavior per se. Field historians among biological scientists, for example, might well suppose that the main idea in observing children "in the field" must always be to describe the

natural habitats and behavior of children. But one quickly discovers that
these naturalistic methods have by no
means always served naturalistic purposes.

A natural history objective or *ecological aim* can indeed be found in observational study of relationships between behavior and conditions that
vary from part to part of the real
world. Baldwin, Kalhorn, and Breese
(1945) describe parental behavior patterns in different types of homes and
show some of their consequences for
social and intellectual growth. Barker
and Wright (1949, 1955) survey psychological living conditions and behavior of children in the American
small town of Midwest. Gump and
Schoggen (1955a, 1955b) compare
*home* and *camp* in the life of a single
urban child. Wright and others (1957)
are inquiring into life situations and
behavior of children in communities
differing in size. These studies try to
link child behavior with conditions
anchored in natural habitats. They are
uncommon. Ecological ends as such
have rarely been sought in any field of
psychological research.

A *normative aim* is more prominent
by far in observational child studies.
The research goal here is precisely the
same as in normative applications of
psychological tests and laboratory
measures. Children are classified as to
age or whatever and then observed directly for the purpose of disclosing
central behavior tendencies in 2-year-
olds, 5-year-olds, boys, girls, or the like.
Goodenough (1928), Thomas et al.
(1929, 1933), Arrington (1939), and
others have argued here that norms

based upon direct observation of "spontaneous behavior" may have greater
validity than those established by tests
or other "interference techniques," especially in "the social behavior field."

A *systematic aim* is evident in observational studies of relationships between
universal behavior variables. Theory
steers investigation toward general psychological laws in this research. For example, Lippitt, Polansky, and Rosen, in
"a field study of social influence in
groups of children," contribute to a
"systematic theory of social power in
face-to-face groups." They use sociometric measures to get for each boy of
a camp population an index of attributed power that expresses judgments
by the child's associates of his ability
to influence others. Then, using a time-
sampling method, they observe directly
and count *direct influence attempts* and
instances of *behavioral contagion* in interactions of the children as group
members. Correlations of the sociometric power measures with the observational scores on social influence demonstrate that, among other things:

The group member is more likely to
imitate the behavior of those to whom
he attributes high power in the group.
. . . Members with high attributed power
initiate more social influence attempts
than do low power members . . . (1952,
p. 59).

These are not ecological statements
about "camp behavior" or normative
statements about "boy behavior." They
are generalizations without limiting references to specified habitats or classes
of children. Observational research with
a systematic aim, like so much of labo-

ratory research, turns on such generalizations.

Finally, an *idiographic aim* occurs in observational studies of particular children as individual persons. Virginia Axline introduces such a study with these remarks.

Children in a free play experience tell us many things about themselves. As we observe them . . . we see the expansiveness and restriction in different children. We see the acceptance and rejection of the challenging situation. We notice that the child's way of meeting the new situation is as varied as the personalities of the children (1951, p. 358).

Direct observations of children are used in this study, as in others to be mentioned, much as psychological tests or interviews are often used for diagnostic purposes.

These different aims are not logically foreign to one another. Their end results certainly can overlap. Placing the outcomes of investigation with a normative aim in a separate class by themselves is especially open to question. A developmental norm, for example, is an empirical generalization that connects behavior with age, and, as such, it does not differ strictly from many empirical generalizations of research that we are identifying as systematic in aim. Again, the findings of ecological studies are normative insofar as they reduce to averages that describe designated populations or environments. Practically important differences in emphasis and form of generalization are nevertheless represented by these objectives, which, therefore, we shall take into account in considering each method.

## Survey of Methods

The summaries of Table 3-2 will now be developed.

It would be possible to examine one at a time the separate provisions in Table 3-2 for sampling, recording, and data analysis. Then, with this accomplished, one could re-examine the complete methods. Such a survey plan offers systematic advantages. But severe dismantling of research cases in point is avoided and seeing more of the woods than the trees may be assured by our leaving each method intact as a way to go from start to finish in a research undertaking.

### DIARY DESCRIPTION

This oldest of methods in child development could also be the most simple minded. As the reader is forewarned, however, we believe that it may deserve re-examination and even practical attention by students of child development whose households include young children.[1]

The method is well known. It employs mainly the recording technique of the lay diary to draw a sequential account of growth changes and behavior episodes from the life history of the child. Notations are made from day to day of what happens when development proceeds, and episodes that illustrate various behavioral processes are narratively described. Then, as a rule,

[1] I inject here without delay as respectively great and small *argumenta ad homines* the two facts that Kurt Lewin urged me twenty-one years ago to keep a diary record on my son (now 21) and that I wish I had. Here is something many could do.

the recorded material is treated only by topical classification and characteristically free qualitative analysis. The notations and descriptions necessarily are selective in the face of innumerable events that pass in an endless procession. Yet they are not capriciously selective in the sense that the observer sets down whatever is only arresting. The entries in diary records are ruled on the contrary by a stable and objective principle of limitation, namely, that of recording in sequence *new* behavioral events in the behavior continuum of one subject, usually an infant or a child of preschool age. A special feature of the method has always been close and essentially continuous contact between the subject and the observer, who have invariably lived together as child and parent or other guardian.

The open character of diary description differs in breadth of focus as between the *comprehensive diary*, which records in order as much of everything new as it can, and the *topical diary*, which excludes everything but phenomena in one or a few developmental channels. Beginners in child development read about, although one doubts that many of them have read lately, such comprehensive diary studies as those of Tiedemann (1787), Darwin (1877), Preyer (1888–1889), Sully (1895), Shinn (1900), and the Scupins (1907). Topical diaries include those kept by Taine (1877) and Bateman (1916) on language behavior, Buchner (1909) on emotional behavior, Dearborn (1910) on motor and sensory functions, Brainard (1927) on "learning and instincts," and Navarra (1955) on concept formation.

Diary records are not all products of direct observation alone. There are in many of them reports of casual interview procedures and even of improvised psychological tests (Major, 1906; Hogan, 1898). Some also present such quick experiments as the one reported and interpreted engagingly by Darwin as follows in the diary he kept on his son.

On the seventh day, I touched the naked sole of his foot with a bit of paper, and he jerked it away, curling at the same time his toes, like a much older child when tickled. The perfection of these reflex movements shows that the extreme imperfection of the voluntary ones is not due to the state of the muscles or of the coordinating centers but to that of the seat of the will (1877, p. 285).

Such an experiment barely breaks the rules and would seem to suit the spirit of direct observation.

But most of these records report chiefly (1) such developmental items as "eighty ninth week, running is awkward, but falling rare," from Preyer (1880–1889, p. xxxi), and (2) such occurrences as the one related and interpreted by Sully in the following graphic passage.

One day (end of seventh month [of the third year]) when, after being very naughty, his mother had to carry him upstairs, he broke into a more than usually violent fit of crying. His mother asked him what he meant by making such a noise on being carried upstairs; whereupon he replied, " 'Cause you carry me like a pig.". . . This is significant as showing how . . . the conscious sense of self was developing . . . on its moral side as a sense of personal dignity . . . (1895, p. 452).

Spontaneous growth indices and behavior episodes—these, narratively described, make up the bulk of the child diaries.

Diary records have often been turned to practical account in modern textbooks and journals as object lessons in how not to do psychological research with children. They have been charged with defects which include biased selection, unreliable recording, inefficient gathering and processing of data, and unwarranted interpretation. However, these alleged shortcomings are not bound to the method with any logical necessity; nor would there appear to be insuperable reasons why all of them could not be substantially remedied. In any case, whatever its faults in practice, the basic method has unique advantages in principle. It commands the breadth, richness, subtlety, and permanency of the written word, compared with which the best of check lists and rating scales are limited instruments. It gives a multidimensional picture of simultaneous and successive factors in the behavior and circumstances of an individual child. It saves for later study at any time and for any purpose comparatively intact specimens of behavior with its context. Diary records understandably have not often described in very great detail the situations in single life episodes. Their extended coverage prohibits continuous and unselective moment-to-moment recording of situation and behavior. Yet the method does permit sketchy treatment of situational factors in developmental changes. Finally, diary description takes into account the continuity of behavior as this can be done only by observation of children one by one over extended periods of time.

Some of the early diary keepers made much of the last point. Milicent Shinn,

for example, wrote as follows in introducing the record of development of her niece through the first year.

The biographical method of child study has the inestimable advantage of showing the process of evolution going on, the actual unfolding of one stage after another, and the steps by which the changes come about. No amount of comparative statistics could give this. If I should find out that a thousand babies learned to stand at an average age of forty-six weeks and two days, I should not know as much that is important about standing, as a stage in human progress, as I should after watching a single baby carefully through the whole process . . . (1900, p. 11).

The longitudinal principle in this statement has been endorsed often by contemporary students of child development; and it could be that no method stands to implement the principle better than diary reporting. Other longitudinal methods have generally used large groups of subjects who have been visited or summoned, observed, interviewed, and tested at rather widely separated intervals of time. Because they lack the feature of continuous contact between investigator and subject, these methods inevitably miss much that a diary kept at home stands to reveal of "the actual unfolding of one stage after another" in the life of a child.

The foremost aim of the child diaries has been not the idiographic one of describing and understanding the special behavior of each child subject but the normative one of discovering behavior traits of children by and large at different ages and stages of development. For example, the end results of the classical work by Preyer (1880–1889), which is based upon a record of "mental growth" in his son from birth through age 3, are summarized in a *conspectus* that looks and reads astoundingly like familiar developmental summaries of contemporary child psychology. But the diarists have gathered and worked over their material also with a systematic aim. Many of them theorize often in educing generalizations that relate behavior with its fundamental determinants, as in the instance in the foregoing text note from Darwin.

Diary studies of children have shown little or no explicit regard for the ecological problem. Their preoccupations with universal norms and general laws all but crowd out entirely deliberate attempts to relate behavior with the psychological living conditions of different times, places, and cultures. One thinks, however, of the possibility that the available child diaries, kept as most of them have been over the time span of more than a century on children of Germany, England, Italy, Portugal, France, the United States, and other widely ranging localities (Dennis, 1936), might advantageously be scrutinized for differences across cultures in behavior and its conditions. The chiefly normative study by Dennis and Dennis (1937) of baby biographies from various countries could be extended in this direction.

It may indeed be that some new diary records would be useful. Trained students of child behavior could keep them with new safeguards against bias and error. Colleagues or responsible lay persons could be called in at moot points for tests of observer agreement. New refinements in recording methods could be applied and so also could new ways of coding and quantifying qualitative material. Even standardized tests and minor experiments that threaten only small violence to nature could be worked in at intervals, although some observers might prefer only to make the most of direct observation. The data could be sorted, plumbed, tabled, graphed, Chi-squared, and interpreted with the additional help of descriptive categories and conceptual frameworks that were not available to the early diarists. And each record could be mined with explicit regard for normative, systematic, and ecological problems, to say nothing of idiographic problems with domestic implications for the diarist. Any part of the age span and any one channel or all channels of development could be opened to study.

Psychologists have still done little to lay things and events of the behavior continuum end to end. So much of their research on growth problems has been piecework in the absence of our best assembly line—the growth stages of a single growing child. The Prousts and Twains and Rollands and other literary biographers may well have accomplished more here than scientists in unraveling social and emotional strands in development and in revealing concretely the lines of connection between interdependent factors in the growth process. Diary description has much in common with literary biography. It, too, is well adapted to problems of continuity and interdependency, well enough, perhaps, that this unique way of doing longitudinal research in child development should be renovated and tried again.

Diary description and what can rightly be termed *anecdotal description* have often been given the same names, with each being called either a "diary" method or an "anecdotal" method; and both have been subjected also to much the same criticisms. Both report observed behavior narratively, and each has relied upon qualitative study. But, instead of recording with some regularity the behavioral growth of a single child, anecdotal reports set down at circumstantial times whatever invites attention in the behavior of any child who happens along.

An enchanting model case of this way to investigate child behavior—which it seems incorrect to feature here as a now significant method—is presented by the work of Russell (1892) and some of his students and collaborators, including Burnham, 1891, Brown, 1892, and Haskell, 1906, who, in the time of G. Stanley Hall and with his vigorous encouragement (Hall, 1892), collected and classified under such headings as *imitation, imagination,* and *reasoning* no fewer than *19,000* behavior samples. Here is an example from Brown that is typical in length, style, jocularity, and religious sentiment. The subject is a boy, R, of five years.

R came into the house eating a horse-chestnut. Grandma: "Well, R, if you eat that horse-chestnut you'll die and go to heaven with your mother, and then I shan't have any R." (His mother was dead.) R: "Well, I'll go out and get four horse-chestnuts, one for grandpa, one for you, one for Aunt H, and one for me. I'll eat mine first, then I'll die and go up to heaven first. Then grandpa 'll eat his and he'll die and go to heaven, then Aunt H 'll eat hers, then she'll die, then you'll eat yours and we'll all be up there together. Won't that be nice, grandma?" (1892, p. 383).

In stating a rationale for his amassing of such material, Russell (1892) wrote that ". . . if the science of psychology is to be advanced on the objective side, as

. . . botany and geology, then there is a need for vast masses of facts, which for their multitude can only be collected by an army of investigators working in many quarters, under various conditions, and through a long period of time" (p. 346). At least a corporal's guard of developmental psychologists will agree now that great quantities of facts, straight from nature, assembled from widespread and various life settings, and on the order of many in the Russell anecdotes, are still needed in developmental psychology. But we are concerned here with suitable ways to meet this need.

Anecdotal reports lack the limiting objective principle of observing and recording in sequence new behavioral events as they appear in the life continuum of one child. Nor are they limited by any clear rules. Records that accept anything and everything arresting in the behavior of any child as fair game can yield at most a miscellany of happenings that depend for their content upon spur-of-the-moment interests and implicit theories of the observer. It is for this reason, we suggest, that the proscribing charge of subjective bias, so often brought against narrative records in general, can be sustained against these easy reports.

## SPECIMEN DESCRIPTION

This method begins with the scheduled and continuous observing and narrative recording of a behavior sequence under chosen conditions of time and life setting. A child to observe and a time and particular place in which to observe are selected to suit special interests. But the observer in the field is in no way deliberately selective. He is instead deliberately unselective in the sense that he aims to make a faithful record of "everything" as it comes in the behavior and situation of the child. The obtained record may be exhibited as a behavior documentary. But that seldom is all. The recorded material is usually subjected to study that varies among different applications from ever so free interpretation to somewhat strict and thoroughgoing quantitative analysis.

The end results of specimen description depend upon its field records, which are therefore considered first and independently. These behavior accounts, to add another terminological note, have often been called "diary records." Their narrative form understandably suggests this identification, and enough of them pieced together would make a diary. But they neither select nor span developmental changes in behavior, and, part by part, they are far more intensive than typical diary descriptions. These records have been made and studied, not in the contexts of individual life histories, but in the temporally more limited contexts of particular life settings. They provide lasting *specimens* of the behavior and immediate situations of children in these settings. Accordingly, following Barker and Wright (1949), we shall call them *specimen records,* from which the name of the method as a whole follows. "Let us now get a segment thus-and-so long and as nearly complete as possible from the behavior continuum of child X in habitat Y. Then, later, we shall see what can be done with it." Such is the main idea of the specimen record.

Records of this type have differed a good deal in setting or locale. They have described behavior of children at home (Dresslar, 1901; McFarland, 1938; La-

fore, 1945), in nursery schools (Andrus, 1924; Berne, 1930; Issacs, 1930, 1933; Moore, 1931; Shallit, 1932; Fales, 1937a, b; Slater, 1939; Tucker, 1940; Fite, 1940; Woodcock, 1941; Hartley, Frank, and Goldenson, 1952), in an elementary school (Biber et al., 1942), in a summer camp (Gump, Schoggen, and Redl, 1957), and in communities-at-large (Barker and Wright, 1951, 1955; Gump and Schoggen, 1955b). The recorded sequences have ranged in length from "moments snatched" (in fact, irregularly scheduled periods lasting usually a few minutes: Issacs, 1930, 1933), through the duration of a "baby's morning" (Dresslar, 1901), up to a full day (Barker and Wright, 1951; Gump and Schoggen, 1955a, 1955b). Sequences that span the natural time limits of classroom sessions, parties, and other such come-and-go settings also have been recorded (Barker and Wright, 1949; Gump and Sutton-Smith, 1955).

The recording technique and intended content of specimen records are evident in instructions to observers who have made them. Below, then, is a partial abstract of pooled directives on observing and recording from Stone (1941), Biber and associates (1942), Hartley, Frank, and Goldenson (1952), Barker and Wright (1955), and other investigators.

• Begin in reporting each observed sequence with a description of the scene, the actors, and the ongoing action. Report throughout in everyday language. Describe the situation as fully as the behavior. Thus include "everything the child says and does"; but include also "everything said and done to him."

Describe the larger "adaptive actions"

of the child, but weave in as well the "hows" of these actions as far as possible. "Nonadaptive aspects of behavior" (Stone, 1941) are important on this account. These include hunchings, turnings, twistings, and the like, which often illumine such properties of behavior as intensity, affect, and efficiency.

Do not substitute interpretations that generalize *about* behavior for descriptions *of* behavior, but add such interpretations when they point to possibilities of fact that might otherwise be missed. Segregate every interpretation by some such device as indentation or bracketing. Straight reporting must be left to stand out. •

Procedures in recording that have been followed and recommended offer several possibilities:

• Notes on the scene of observation, which obviously are needed for sufficiently detailed and accurate description, can be kept in improvised shorthand. These field notes can be enlarged in writing immediately after each observation period, or they can serve then as a base for a dictated narration of the observed behavior sequence. Also, a co-worker can hear this account through and at once question the observer where it is thin or unclear. The original dictation plus the interrogation and the observer's responses can be sound recorded. All of the recorded material can then be copied and revised in an improved running account.

Observations can be timed to permit various measures of duration. Timing of the field notes at intervals of approximately one minute or even thirty seconds (Jersild and Fite, 1939; McFarland, 1938; Fite, 1940) has been found practicable. When long records are made, observers can work in rotation; and the time of each observing period can be regulated to minimize effects of fatigue upon ability to see and remember an always fast train of events. •

The following is a part of a *specimen day record* from Gump and Schoggen (1955a), who were joined in the recording process by three others. All five observers took turns of thirty minutes each, in rotation, from 7:23 A.M. to 9:04 P.M. of the recorded day. The observations were recorded by the dictate-interrogate-revise technique, as described above. The setting is a summer camp, and the subject is 9-year-old Wally, whom the first observer finds asleep in his cabin.

*Noting O*

7:23 Wally rolls over in the bed, opens his eyes, props himself up on one elbow, and looks with a sort of bewildered stare at me.

I am across the room from him.

Then he smiles briefly, as if he has caught on to what is going on.

*Telling About Dream*

He says to me, but also to others around, looking at them intermittently, but more at me, "Gee, do you know what happened to me last night?"

He says this again with more earnestness, "Do you know what happened to me last night? I had a dream."

Wally now sits straight up in the bed and begins to tell his dream in a serious, impressed tone of voice.

"I dreamed that my Dad and I were riding in this big truck and we were coming down this hill and the driver, he was knocked out, and we couldn't drive the truck and the truck was going faster and we landed in the river with a big crash! Jeeze!"

I nod but nobody else makes any comment on this dream, which was so vivid in Wally's mind when he awoke.

Specimen records do not all read like this one. Some are less detailed. Others hold back more on partly inferential observing; a few generalize more about whys. But all have the common base of sequential, unselective, plain, narrative description of behavior with some of its conditions.

A researcher who reads one of these running accounts is almost sure to ask whether specimen records are reliable. Several studies have approached this issue via tests that show level of agreement between simultaneous and independent observers. One finds among results of these tests *agreement per cents*[1] of 92 for notation of "social contacts . . . between two or more children" (Jersild and Fite, 1939); 95 for notation of "verbal or physical communication between parent and child" (Lafore, 1945); 90 for notation of "large activities . . . in the . . . development of interests" (Tucker, 1940); 91 to 95 for notation of "major body shifts," "social contacts . . . or attempts at social contacts," and "extraneous or marginal events" (e.g., "departure of the teacher") as factors in "episodes of action" (Biber et al., 1942); 84 for notation of definite "breaks" in the "continuity of . . . play" (Slater, 1939). Comparable observer agreement has been found where specimen narration is used as a recording technique in time sampling studies. Jersild and Markey (1935), Markey (1935), Nesbitt (1943), and Heathers (1955) present examples.

[1] The agreement per cent is a common measure in observational child studies. It has been calculated by formulas that differ some in stringency and yet give comparable values. Examples of these formulas are in Arrington (1932a), Festinger and Katz (1953), Barker and Wright (1955), and Marshall and Mc-Candless (1957a).

So far so good. But these findings do not warrant a broadside conclusion that specimen records are reliable. This is a difficult problem. Such records need as many reliability coefficients as they contain classes of statements about different facets of behavior and situation. Their reliabilities must differ from one to another of such categories as things used, persons encountered, games played, jokes told, tasks undertaken, ideas expressed, dangers met, fears shown, competitions entered, failures suffered, problems solved, successes enjoyed, moods displayed, dreams related, utterances made in "a serious, impressed tone of voice" (see above what is said about what Wally said), and so on through a great list of things that everyone wants to learn about *and* that many investigators ask and write about on the basis of material in specimen records. What this comes to is that the many needed coefficients demand analytical techniques for the identification and measurement of these and other behavior and situation variables. Likely techniques are mentioned later. Each uses a limited number of descriptive categories. Large inroads on this problem can be made only by applying such categories in great number, one by one, in tests of agreement between independent observers. Of course, a choice can be made to use only the parts of a specimen record for which reliability has been firmly established, although it is hard to find a precedent for caution so aseptic, and some would consider this wasteful.

Specimen records cannot now claim direct proof of reliability for all of their applications. Yet some things remain to be said for a generous working trust in them. The balance of social experience indicates that their method of narration in conventional language, the standard method of recording behavior in communications of man with man, can be depended upon as a way to register faithfully many kinds of behavioral data. So, too, does the more immediate experience of reading such a record as the one sampled above through consecutive descriptions by different observers of the same child; for this practical test gives prima facie evidence that these observers were indeed seeing the same child and describing the same stream of behavior. Also, systematic analysis of the recorded observations has shown meaningful and internally consistent relationships between many behavior and situation variables. One would not expect such results from analysis of unreliable material.

Whatever the exact limits of their accuracy, specimen records have assets that encourage making the most of them without shackling anxiety about just how accurate they are. They remind one here of how long scientists made good progress with thumbs and sun dials before they had dependable thermometers and clocks.

First, these records can register almost everything observers can see of behavior. This follows from the range, variety, wealth, and subtlety of plain words—called to attention above by diary description. It does seem doubtful that any instrument short of a sound-movie camera can surpass lay language as a means of recording the range, variety, wealth, and subtlety of behavior itself. This tool has been suited to the purpose by centuries of daily practice. Allport and Odbert (1936) tell us that there are in English 17,953 words for as many ways of behaving. Recording behavior with only a much more limited set of symbols may sometimes gain less in reliability and apparent precision than it loses in validity and genuine refinement.

Specimen records describe behavior in context by recording behavior *with* situation. Try to make one without bringing in situational factors. It is interesting that good sense forbids this. One simply does not report that "John said 'Ouch'" without saying he was stuck with a pin, say, or report that Mary behaved aggressively or submissively or affectionately without identifying the person objects of her aggression or submission or affection or without saying something about their treatment of Mary. Everyone knows, at least intuitively, that the meaning and significance of an action and even its occurrence depend directly (if not primarily, as for Lewin) upon the coexisting situation. So, with no check lists or rating scales or precoded categories to confine him, an observer who makes a specimen record naturally works the situation into his running account, moment by moment and action by action. Specimen records differ here. Some are richer than others on the situation side (on the action side, too, for that matter), but none reports behavior alone, whereas records made by closed methods of direct observation often do this.

For developmental psychology, with its interest in behavioral change over years rather than minutes, hours, or days, specimen records tell less about the continuity of behavior than diaries. Yet continuous accounting for behavior and situation is a first requirement of their recording technique. The result is that these records present for analysis finely woven strands of successive units and conditions of behavior. A further result is that they permit intensive study of sequence relations in behavior. Given S (a child) and O (a mother), what may S do to O at noon if at 11:30 O spanks S? And how may the relations of the two develop and change from moment to moment in the intervening time? Specimen records permit systematic answers to such questions. Here is a much neglected opportunity, although a paper by Barker and others (1955) shows promise in it.

Another possibility is that specimen recording could be done along with diary recording in work on problems of continuity and sequence relations in behavior. A fantasy which the reader may pardon is that of an eight-volume work about a child, C: Volume I, a specimen day record, C's First Day; Volumes II through VII, each a specimen day record made near a birthday (two of which, note, would occur in school years); Volume VIII, a comprehensive diary record, C's First Seven Years. Teachers and students as well as researchers could use the recorded material.

A specimen record preserves much of behavior as it appears without either the omissions of selective observation or the alterations of theory. It therefore goes far to secure whatever advantages theoretically neutral data have to confer upon a discipline with more guesses than facts. One is encouraged here by the fact that about every science but psychology has gone to great pains to store such data. Natural history museums, herbaria, astronomical charts and photographs, and anthropological archives give examples.

Finally, like diary records and like materials in the museums and archives of other sciences, specimen records have permanency. They will keep as long as common words retain their standard meanings, and they can be studied for that long on behalf of innumerable interests. The same cannot be said for the more typical records of closed observational methods. A marked and analyzed check list, for example, may as well be thrown away, whereas a written and analyzed specimen record can be put back in the files and used over and over again. In fact, specimen records increase in value with age. Consider that the older they get the greater the number of possible comparisons between them and other available records for the ecological purpose of studying change from time to time and place to place in children's psychological living conditions and behavior.

Specimen records provide in no way beforehand for quantitative description. Making them must seldom be an efficient way of getting only the data needed to test a particular hypothesis. They are costly in research time and manpower. These can be serious practical drawbacks that one should weigh carefully before undertaking to use specimen records on any considerable scale in a research program. Yet it seems to us that a research tool which records behavior (1) comprehensively, (2) sensitively, (3) in context, (4) in continuous lengths, (5) without theoretical bias, and (6) with permanence ought to meet needs of many problems in child development.

What besides exhibiting them can be done with these records? This is to ask about analysis procedure as a stage in specimen description.

Differing kinds of *qualitative* specimen study are to be found in the literature. One consists in educing from the recorded material chiefly normative generalizations about the behavior of classified children in particular life settings. Biber and associates (1942), for example, draw "pictures" of "seven-year-oldness" from specimen records (in their terminology, "contextual records") on the behavior of 7-year-old children in the settings of "reading, writing, painting, clay, shop, rhythms, and roof play" of an urban school as a "psychological community"; and the same general type of analysis is illustrated by the earlier mentioned research of Woodcock (1941) and Hartley and associates (1952). Another sort of qualitative study here consists in searching among the specimen facts of behavior and situation for properties and laws of basic psychological processes. Susan Issacs has contributed cases in point by using specimen records on the behavior of young children in the daily situations of an experimental school to develop theoretical formulations of interdependencies in intellectual functioning (1930) and social behavior (1933) at different stages of growth.

These measurement-free undertakings give impressions that specimen records are rich in behavioral data and that scrutiny of these data without benefit of numbers reveals much of interest that no presently available techniques of measurement seem likely to pin down. They often support a belief that it would be unfortunate if there were no child psychologists, somewhere between the novelists and the laboratory experimenters, with liking and talent for research that first describes carefully and then only classifies and interprets without the narrowing strictures of quantification. The cited illustrative studies at least document the behavior of children authentically; and it would seem bad policy for child psychology to relinquish this documenting function to literary and journalistic observers.

Efforts to quantify the raw material of specimen description have been made with a number of analytical schemes that yield scores on variables of behavior or situation, or both, from records on individual children. We can merely identify rudiments in some of these schemes as they apply to the single record, which has often spliced together running accounts of sequences observed at different times. Only basal measures are represented.

1. *The record as a whole is scanned as a geologist might study an intact rock specimen.* Then one of two procedures is followed. (*a*) Ratings are made on the prevalence of various ways of behaving, and scale values of these ratings are summed. Andrus (1924), to take a pioneer example, applies to records on children in a nursery school an inventory of 410 questions, such as: Does the child *giggle? Use adverbs? Walk steadily? Try to boss?* Answers of *very often, sometimes, never* to these questions give values of two, one, and zero, which are added in scores on

*emotional, mental, motor,* and *social-moral* divisions of the inventory. (*b*) Straight frequency counts are made on different kinds of behavior. McFarland (1938) tallies the instances per record of *submission, resistance, helping, giving,* and other such responses to one another by 3-to-6-year-old sisters at home. Slater (1939) counts *changes of activity, play materials used, words spoken, nonverbal contacts with other children, contacts with adults,* occurrences of *associative play,* and a number of other interesting things in records of uniform length (125 minutes) on 2-to-3-year-olds of a nursery.

Sarason, Davidson, Lighthall, and Waite (1958) analyze specimen records of a sort by an interesting technique that includes scanning of the intact account. Their subjects are children in classrooms of grades 2 through 5. Each child is observed for one hour, whereupon the observer first records narratively "the major events" in the behavior sequence and then draws "as integrated a personality description as . . . possible" from the summary record. Analysts count the number of children who are characterized thus and so on variables that include *need for achievement* and *academic ability.* Also, tallies are made of references to nail biting and other such behavior in the uninterpreted record. But for making these tallies, the investigators (1) watch behavior for a while, (2) record it in summary fashion, and then (3) extract from the record judgments about the behaving *children.* This seems adventuresome. Reliability of observation is affirmed on the ground that independent observers do very well at blind matching of their total reports on the same subjects. But could such records be so extremely unreliable as not even to give clues that would nearly guarantee success in such matching? What one would like to know is whether the particular observations behind judgments on particular variables, academic ability, say, are reliable.

2. *The record is divided into uniform short time intervals,* much as if the analyst were a time sampler in the field. Different procedures have been followed here also. (*a*) Duration scores are obtained by summing the time spans of selected recurring behavioral phenomena. Thus McFarland adds the thirty-second intervals during which paired sisters of the study just cited engage in such *interaction* as *sharing, dramatic play,* and *cooperation.* (*b*) Frequency scores are obtained by summing the number rather than the time of intervals that encompass certain phenomena, as when Jersild and Fite (1939) count all of the thirty-second lengths during which individual children in a nursery school enter into *social contacts* with their child associates.

3. *The record is divided into natural beginning-to-end units that are anchored to restricted psychological content and are therefore suited to study of phenomena within the chosen content limits.* These units are treated as convenient examination targets; and frequencies, in the total record, of different phenomena which they contain are determined.

Lafore (1945) divides records on preschool children at home into *parent-child contacts* that are delimited by the beginning and end points of "verbal or physical communications." She then counts the instances per record, during these contacts, of such *parental practices* as *bestows affection, blames the child,* and *praises the child* and such acts of the children as *helps the parent* and *cries.* Tucker (1940) divides records on children in a cooperative nursery into *situations* that involve the child and his mother as associates in "the solution of a problem or the development of an interest." She then determines the frequencies per record in these situations of control tactics by the mothers, such as *urges, directs, impedes, warns,* and of *cooperation, resistance, combativeness,* and other such reactions to these tactics by the children.

4. *The record is divided into natural beginning-to-end units that override differences in psychological content, hence are suited to the study of diverse behavior and situation variables and their relationships.* These units are treated as both examination targets and counting integers. Dimensional and discrete-item categories for description of situation and behavior variables are applied to each unit. Scale measures per unit and scores that tell the number of units in which different phenomena occur are derived.

Barker and Wright (1955) divide specimen day records on children in the settings of an American town into *behavior episodes*, defined as units of action and coexisting situation, such that in each the action has a constant direction and falls within the behavior perspective (roughly, evident intention span) of the child. These units are in no way restricted to particular kinds of behavioral content. *Noting O* and *Telling About Dream*, as marked off by brackets in the margin of the record excerpt on p. 85, are examples of episodes. Occurrence rates of these behavior-situation units are studied. So also are their positional or *structural* relations, as when episodes *overlap*, so that the child does two or more things at once (pp. 225–302). In one application of the method (pp. 323–457; Wright, 1956) categories are used to describe various aspects of the social behavior and situation of the child, and a larger set of categories (Wright and Barker, 1950) has also been developed for more comprehensive study of situation and behavior variables. Examples follow shortly.

Space limitations forbid discussion of the ways in which these analytical schemes have been elaborated or of their outcomes in empirical findings. But some things about them which bear on assessment of specimen description in general can be mentioned.

1. Independent analysts make similar discriminations when, as in schemes 3 and 4, records are divided into psychologically defined units.

2. Quite consistently high estimates of accuracy in applications of behavior and situation categories appear generally when judgments of independent analysts are compared.

3. Satisfactory indices of internal consistency are shown by measures of change over time in variables with presumably high stability (Jersild and Fite, 1939; Lafore, 1945).

4. A diversity of behavioral variables usually is accommodated by each scheme. Some of the special advantages in multivariable research designs are represented in these procedures.

5. The reported results meet well the common (and so often final) tests of intelligibility, congruence of independent measures, and agreement with sense.

6. Some of the findings also meet tests of agreement with outside criteria. To illustrate by an early result that may be as exemplary and suggestive in this respect as any, Andrus (1924) reports a correlation of .66 ($\pm$.09) between specimen-record measures of intelligence level in play activities and scores on the 1922 Kuhlmann Revision of the Binet.

We turn now to application aims in specimen recording and analysis. Specimen description, as a method that takes what comes in the field of observation, seems well suited to studies with the ecological aim of exploring and interrelating spontaneous behavior and psychological living conditions of children. Curiously enough, however, the method has not often been applied for quite such a declared purpose. The Midwest research, cited under analysis scheme 4, has made considerable use of specimen records to this end and so have subsequent studies of Gump and his colleagues (Gump and Schoggen 1955a, 1955b; Gump and Sutton-Smith, 1955a; Gump, Schoggen, and Redl, 1957; and Gump, Sutton-Smith, and Redl, 1955). The ecological applications of specimen description to date, however, are only small beginnings whose values can be multiplied by comparative studies in a variety of communities and cultures.

The method has often been adapted to our *systematic* aim by investigators with primarily ecological interests. It offers here the possibility of exploring lawful relations between many and greatly differing variables of behavior and situation that are not easily caught in the same matrix by experiments or closed observational procedures. Laboratory strings, especially, cannot readily be pulled to bring under quantitative assay within, say, a day of a child's life such conditions of psychological situation as bona fide *affection, aggression, dominance, submission, resistance, appeal, nurturance,* and *avoidance* by a mother, father, brother, neighbor friend, or any such associate; waxing and waning in the *social power* of others; varying kinds and degrees of *social pressure, mood,* and *evaluation* by associates, together with concomitant values for all of these in the behavior of the child, plus changes in *cooperation, competition, conflict,* and

related forms of *social interplay* between the child and interacting persons. This has been done after a fashion by the method of specimen description. Relations between simultaneous behavior and situation factors have been investigated, and sequential interdependencies could be studied by the same procedures.

We have referred earlier to normative applications of specimen description. A thing to be considered here is that some arrays of norms in developmental psychology are so characteristically like time tables and other dry civil accounts. Despite their great usefulness, they often look thin against the landscape of child behavior at any age. Work cited earlier here is pertinent. Thus the Biber team's "pictures . . . of seven-year-oldness," Woodcock's similar descriptions in *Life and Ways of the Two Year Old*, and the portrayals of young children at play by Hartley and associates help to fill in, an age level at a time, some enormous gaps in the orderly normative summaries from psychological tests and laboratory measures. These descriptions frequently suggest also that specimen accounts of behavior, even if they were only to be kept on file, should often be good for idiographic purposes; and one finds indeed that they have at times been so applied (Axline, 1951; Reckless, 1929; and Slater, 1939).

## TIME SAMPLING

This closed procedure fixes attention of observer and analyst upon selected aspects of the behavior stream as they occur within uniform and short time intervals. The length, spacing, and number of intervals are intended to secure representative *time samples* of the target phenomena. As a rule with exceptions, descriptive categories are coded in advance for quick and precise judgments in the field and later efficient scoring. The subjects are invariably *assembled* children of a school setting or other institutional environment. Children en masse have been observed in a few studies (Olson, 1929). Usually, however, the observer proceeds in rotation from child to child through the scheduled intervals of time.

Here is a method of some thirty years standing that appears to be indigenous to research in child development. Its applications have indeed been numerous and varied. But we shall be concerned less with differences between these applications than with their common features and with issues that turn upon basic traits of the method. These issues are often clearest in the earlier studies, which, therefore, are featured in the discussion. We believe that getting into these issues would alone justify careful examination of the method.

Groundworkers in time sampling, first named, as here, by John Anderson (in a foreword to Olson, 1929), include Olson (1929), Goodenough (1928), Parten (1932, 1933a, 1933b), Thomas (1929, 1932), and, among associates of Thomas, Barker (1930), Loomis (1931), Beaver (1932), and Arrington (1932a). The method evidently was applied first—to *nervous habits* in school children—by Olson in 1929. Critiques with review of the literature have been made by Olson and Cunningham (1934) and Arrington (1943). See also, for references and appraisal, Goodenough and Anderson (1931), Heyns and Lippitt (1954), Murphy and Murphy (1935), Arrington (1939), Jersild and Meigs (1939), Sells and Ellis (1948, 1951), and Gellert (1955). Applications continue in current journals after reaching a frequency peak in the 1930's.

It will be convenient here to follow routinely the scheme of Table 3-2 for description of observational methods. This scheme is applied to illustrative time sampling studies in Table 3-5, which also presents examples of results from each application.

Consider first that the range of time-sampled behavioral phenomena is wide. So the variables under material coverage in Table 3-5 suggest and so do time samplings of imaginative behavior (Markey, 1935), friendships (Challman, 1932), friendships and quarrels (Green, 1933a), techniques of successful social interaction (Mallay, 1935b), "approach-withdrawal patterns" in intragroup behavior (White and Williams, 1939), responses of teachers to children (Olson and Wilkinson, 1932), resistance and acquiescence in social transactions (Caille, 1933), interactions of *adolescents* in clubs of differing class level (Maas, 1954), thumbsucking in infants (Heering, 1932), and tics or "nervous habits" (Olson, 1929, Koch, 1935). One might expect to come upon the comparatively small units of *molecular* behavior the more often in short time samples. But it turns out otherwise. After Olson's study of nervous habits, time samplers usually have worked with comparatively large phenomena of *molar* behavior. Also, as Table 3-5 suggests, these phenomena are predominantly social in the specific sense of

## TABLE 3-5. ILLUSTRATIVE TIME SAMPLING STUDIES

| Study | Sampling Plan | | Recording Technique | Analysis: Scores | Sample Results |
|---|---|---|---|---|---|
| | Time Units | Material Coverage | | | |
| Parten (1932). *Subjects:* 42, 2–5 years. *Setting:* Outdoor free-play period of nursery school. *Aim:* To describe aspects of the participations by preschool children in activities with one another. Other phases of study in Parten (1933a, 1933b). | *Length:* 1 minute. *Spread:* Mean of 72 units per S over 6 months. No more than 1 unit per S per day. | Social participation levels. With scale weights: -3 unoccupied behavior -2 solitary occupied behavior -1 onlooker behavior 1 "parallel" play 2 merely associative play 3 truly cooperative play | Symbol notation of participation level in each 1-minute interval. Also, narration of general activity and conversation of child. [Narrative material used in illuminating way in phase of study dealing with leadership (Parten, 1933a).] | A. Sum of 1-minute time units in which each participation level occurred. B. Algebraic sum of products obtained by multiplying frequency by scale weight at each participation level. | Parallel play (*beside* but not *with* others) filled over ⅓ of time spent by ⅔ of S's. Rho of age with co-operative play 0.67. Rho of weighted participation score (B) with: age, 0.61; IQ, 0.26; length of nursery attendance, 0.12. |
| Bott (1934; Chapter II main base here). *Subjects:* 28, 2–5 years. *Setting:* Outdoor free-play period of nursery school. *Aim:* To describe "actions toward material objects" and "actions toward persons," in the behavior of preschool children. | *Length:* 15 minutes. *Divided* into 1-minute intervals for present measures. *Spread:* 10 units per S over about 2 months. Rarely more than 1 per S per day. | *Actions toward things:* 1. Aimless or idle behavior. 2. Routine use of things. 3. Constructive activity. *Actions toward persons:* 1. Absent. 2. Watching. 3. With 1 child. 4. With 2 children. 5. With more than 2 children. 6. With adults. | Narrative specimen recording on form with separate space for each minute. Raw records greatly abbreviated on prepared scoring sheet before categories applied. | Sum of minutes during which each of the differing types of action "predominated." | Routine play most frequent among thing actions; play with one child, among social actions. Rho of age with constructive activity and with adult contacts in play high positive. Same for Rho between constructive activity and play with one child. |

**TABLE 3-5. ILLUSTRATIVE TIME SAMPLING STUDIES** (*continued*).

| Study | Sampling Plan | | Recording Technique | Analysis: Scores | Sample Results |
|---|---|---|---|---|---|
| | Time Units | Material Coverage | | | |
| Swan (1938) *Subjects:* 25, 2-4 years. *Settings:* Nursery free-play periods, indoors and outdoors. *Aim:* To investigate the *facial expressive behavior* of preschool children. | *Length:* 5 minutes. *Spread:* 18 units per S, 3 per S per day at monthly intervals. | Types of expression: attentive, vacant; whispering, talking to self, talking to child, talking to adult, shouting; dramatic vocalizing; humming, singing, chanting; smiling, chuckling, laughing; frowning, whimpering, crying; grimacing; "hand-to-face activity." | Each observed expression designated on chart by appropriate symbol. Vertical line drawn for each second through duration of every expression. Seconds ticked off by time marker (Washburn, 1932) with head phone. Retrospective account of behavior in each 5-minute interval. | Percentage per S for each type of expression, E; Duration of E in seconds/total observation time. Independent measures of attendance, height, weight. Ratings by preschool workers of certain personality traits. | Plus Rho of age with talking to persons; minus with crying. Rho of attendance with smiling, plus. Plus Rho of frowning with whimpering, crying. *Weight/height* plus Rho with talking to others; minus with talking to self. Rated hyperactivity positively related with facial motility. |
| Walters, Pearce, and Dahms (1957) *Subjects:* 124, 2-5 years. *Setting:* Nursery free play. *Aim:* To describe and compare affectional and aggressive behavior in social interactions of preschool children. | *Length:* 1 minute. *Spread:* 40 *units* per S, no more than 2 per S per day, over several weeks. Total of 4960 units. | *Physical affection:* 6 items, e.g., helps. *Verbal affection:* 5 items, e.g., compliments. *Physical aggression:* 8 items. *Verbal aggression:* 10 items. *Response* (any action after start of interaction) and *initiation* (any action initiating interaction) differentiated. | All affectional and aggressive items during each 1-minute interval marked on check sheet bearing the total list of 29 items. | A. Sum per S of all affectional and aggressive *responses*. B. Sum per S of all affectional and aggressive *initiations*. | S's more affectionate than aggressive in responses and initiations at all age levels. S's of 3, 4, 5 years more verbally than physically affectionate. Increase in aggression from 2-4 years. Boys more aggressive than girls. |

**TABLE 3-5. ILLUSTRATIVE TIME SAMPLING STUDIES** (*continued*).

| Study | Sampling Plan | | Recording Technique | Analysis: Scores | Sample Results |
|---|---|---|---|---|---|
| | Time Units | Material Coverage | | | |
| Heathers (1955). *Subjects:* 20 2-year-olds and 20 4- to 5-year-olds. *Setting:* Free-play period of nursery school indoors. *Aim:* To test following hypotheses *re* change from 2–5 years in emotional dependence, *D:* (1) *D* on adults declines relative to *D* on children. (2) *D* qua seeking reassurance and affection declines relative to *D* qua seeking attention and approval. | *Length:* 3 minutes. *Spread:* 52–64 units per *S* over 3 weeks. | *Dependence categories:* 1. Seeks affection from teacher, *T.* 2. Seeks affection or approval from child, *C.* 3. Seeks attention or approval from *T.* 4. Seeks attention or approval from *C.* *Independence categories:* 5. Ignores stimuli from *T.* 6. Ignores stimuli from *C.* 7. Plays alone. 8. Structures play of *C.* 9. Interferes with play of *C.* 10. Resists *C's* interference or aggression. (See ref. for secondary categories.) | Narrative specimen recording: a continuous "running account" for each 3-minute unit, timed at minute intervals. | Categories 1–4, 8–9: instances per minute. Categories 5, 6, 10: per cent of instances in which behavior mode occurred. Category 7: per cent of minutes of alone play. | Decreases with age in seeks affection from *T* and seeks attention or approval from *T.* Age increases in seeks attention or approval from *C,* ignores *T,* structures *C* play, alone play. Conclusion: hypotheses supported. Interpretation: in socialization emotional dependence shifts from passive *D* on adults toward active *D* on peers. |

**TABLE 3-5. ILLUSTRATIVE TIME SAMPLING STUDIES** (*continued*).

| Study | Sampling Plan — Time Units | Sampling Plan — Material Coverage | Recording Technique | Analysis: Scores | Sample Results |
|---|---|---|---|---|---|
| Marshall and Mc-Candless (1957b). *Subjects:* 38, 3–5 years, in 2 groups of 19 each. *Settings:* Indoor and outdoor free-play periods of nursery school. *Aim:* To relate social dimensions of spontaneous play with (1) sociometric scores and (2) teacher judgments of social acceptance. | *Length:* 2 minutes. *Spread:* Minimum of 50 units per S over several weeks. | Social participation of S with other children (O's): (1) Associative play (S and O have common activity or interest). (2) Friendly approach (neutral, pleasant, or helpful response to O). (3) Conversation (any conversing with O for ½-minute or more). (4) Hostile action (interfering with, attacking, or "snubbing" O). | Graphic recording of each kind of participation via technique adapted from Hyde and York (1948). Also, scores C and D secured by independent nonobservational methods. Summary notations for every 2-minute unit on setting and ongoing activity. | A. Score for each participation category: sum of unit scores (each the sum of O's with whom category occurred in 2-minute interval) divided by total minutes observation for given S. B. Social acceptance measure derived from categories (1) and (2). Independent measures: C. Sociometric acceptance score. D. Teacher ratings of acceptance. | Observed friendly participation and observed social acceptance positively related to sociometric and teacher-rating acceptance measures. Observed hostile play interactions show some positive relation with ratings but no relation with sociometric scores. |

their involving the child in interactions with peers and adults.

This method is defined primarily by its temporally uniform observation intervals. These time units have varied remarkably in duration from one study to the next. Note among the examples in Table 3-5: *one* minute for recording of solitary through parallel to cooperative play, *five* minutes for facial and vocal expressions, and *three* minutes for emotionally dependent and independent actions. One finds a total range of five seconds (Challman, 1932) to twenty minutes (Manwell and Mengert, 1934) per observation unit. Consistent relationships between length of interval within this range and kind of behavior observed are not apparent. Usually, spacing of the intervals is regulated precisely. Many investigators schedule no more than one unit per child per day and keep all observations within certain diurnal limits. Units in a day rarely exceed two or three, and these are widely separated by observing the subject children in rotation. Periods of five minutes or less are commonest. The typical time sampling schedule is a series of far-between flashes on a behavior stream that otherwise flows in the dark.

Coded observation guides of time sampling characteristically prime and yet restrain the observer with memorized symbols, check lists, rating scales, or graphic recording devices that cannot be reviewed quickly enough to suit this space. Some of these tools present difficult problems in categorizing and scaling that go beyond observational methods in psychology, and others apply only to target phenomena of particular investigations. Narrative specimen recording takes the place of coding on the spot in some applications. The studies of Bott and of Heathers, in Table 3-5, give examples. So also do time samplings of behavior in "artistic and inartistic" children (Dow, 1933), of child-with-child conflicts (Jersild and Markey, 1935; Roff and Roff, 1940), of children's imaginative behavior (Markey, 1935), and of social transactions between teacher and child (Nesbitt, 1943). Parten (1932: Table 3-5) and a few others (Swan, 1938: Table 3-5) have supplemented code recording by brief summary narration.

Scoring operations of the method are usually built into its procedures in data collection. Either the time intervals themselves or the observed phenomena can be used as counting integers; and occurrence time also can serve as a measure. Hence one finds among basal scores (1) the $N$ of intervals in which a target phenomenon occurs, (2) the total $N$ of occurrences, (3) the $N$ of occurrences per interval, (4) the total occurrence time, and (5) the occurrence time per interval. Scale values enter into certain measures. Representative scoring possibilities are exemplified with variations and refinements in Table 3-5. The tabled findings clarify different scores and may also tell enough for present purposes about outcomes of the method.

Circumspect and occasionally prodigious effort (Arrington, 1932a) to test reliability of observation is a mark of time-sampling studies. Several papers (Thomas, 1932; Arrington, 1932b; Bott, 1933; Robinson and Conrad, 1933; Berne and Kelly, 1934) deal primarily with this problem. Investigation of reliability or accuracy of observation by measurement of agreement between simultaneous and independent observers early became a staple phase of this research, with results that indicate two conclusions.

1. The level of interobserver agreement generally has been "good," "acceptable," "adequate," or "satisfactory." Agreement levels are scored by percentages or rank-order coefficients. With allowances made for some categories in a few studies, the obtained values do not fall enough below 90 or .9 to justify serious reservations about the reported data.

2. The agreement percentages and coefficients do not differ with any evident consistency according to size, complexity, sociality-nonsociality, perceivability-with-the-naked-eye, seeming "subjectivity," or any other characteristic of the observed behavior.[1]

Tests of data reliability or consistency over time also fortify most applications of time sampling. Correlations of odd with even interval scores or of scores from different series of intervals generally have shown some measurement stability. Yet most of the reported

[1] See especially for more documentation Olson (1929), VanAlstyne (1932), Beaver (1932), Arrington (1932a), Olson and Wilkinson (1932), Parten (1932), Dow (1933), Green (1933a), Hagman (1933), Robinson and Conrad (1933), Caille (1933), Bott (1934), Jersild and Markey (1935), Markey (1935), Graves (1937), Swan (1938), White and Williams (1939), Nesbitt (1943), Dawe, Ekern, and Berger (1949), Lippitt, Polansky, and Rosen (1952), Maas (1954), Walters, Pearce, and Dahms (1957), and Marshall and McCandless (1957a).

coefficients are not high. They ordinarily stand well below comparable indices of psychological-test reliability. Disparities between the obtained coefficients and 1.0 are commonly ascribed above all to change over time in "situational factors." But steps to find out, sample by sample, what these factors are generally have not been taken. Goodenough (1937) and others stress the importance in this connection of ascertaining "conditions of observation." Time samplers have reacted more often to unstable measures, however, by building up the N's of their samples in ostensible hope of neutralizing these conditions while exhausting the normal range of variability in behavior. Agreement of findings with outside criteria has been demonstrated in some applications (Hagman, 1933); and Marshall and McCandless (1957a: Table 3-5) use the method to validate other measures, namely, sociometric scores and ratings by teachers.

Time sampling has several attractions. It limits with exactitude observed contents as well as temporal lengths of the behavior stream. It permits systematic control by selection of phenomena to be observed and studied. It insures representativeness and reliability by recording large numbers of commensurable observations. It is economical of research time and effort. Its coding schemes minimize equivocal judgments and prescribe definite ways to quantify whatever is observed. It goes far to achieve standardization of observer and analyst as measuring instruments. Yet the method has a number of characteristics that narrow its applications.

First, time sampling is limited to

problems of incidence. Its results show that certain things occur with such and such absolute or relative frequency under specified conditions. These results show little of what the actions or situations of children look like, of how they change from beginning to end, or of how their components are related. Moreover, even when incidence problems are concerned, the method is practicable only for study of events that happen often. Arrington concludes from experience of her own and others that "if the behavior to be observed occurs . . . less than once in 15 minutes on the average . . . some other method than that of short time samples . . . is indicated" (1943, p. 95). This excludes many important phenomena. Schoggen (1954) has analyzed specimen day records to find an occurrence rate of *once* every 32 minutes for *satiation*, every 54 minutes for *success*, every 81 minutes for *frustration*, and every 260 minutes for *failure* over the long run of 156 hours in the lives of 12 Midwest 2-to-10-year-olds. Murphy (1937) rejected time sampling for study of *sympathy* in young children partly because sympathetic behavior proved to be all too infrequent among likely subjects. Goodenough (1930) reports similar experience with one-minute samples of *compliance* by young children. But satiation, success, frustration, failure, sympathy, and compliance are central in child behavior. Possibly there is something of a negative relation between the significance of behavioral events and the rate of their occurrence. Persons are born once, die once, and meanwhile take a billion footsteps.

Time sampling does not honor natural behavior units. Aggressive acts, conversations, quarrels or friendships, and virtually all other segments of behavior in the literature of the method can be ever so long or short, with the outcome that the sampling intervals have to be as found above: arbitrary in length. The loose respect of behavior for time leaves no alternative. But with what consequences? As others have mentioned (Jersild and Meigs, 1939; Murphy and Murphy, 1935), one result here must often be the observation of action fragments. A tally per fragment clearly is legitimate enough for incidence problems as long as each fragment represents what is really going on (aggression, affection, cooperation, or the like) in the complete behavior unit. One can seriously question whether it always does, however, and urge as well that the watching of events through their natural courses must generally be good policy for most research purposes.

Time sampling characteristically severs behavior from its immediate relevant context. It does not often link behavior *with* coexisting situation.

One can find time samplings that record situational factors *and* aspects of child behavior. Nesbitt (1943), for example, gets ten-minute samples of contributions by adults to the social situations of children in a nursery school. She counts such *dominative* adult actions as refusals, postponements, and threats along with such *integrative* adult actions as invitations to activity, participations with the child, and expressions of approval. She also gets measures of how the children behave during the ten-minute intervals. The behavior of each child is rated as to constructive use of play materials, adjustment to routines, social adjustment, and individual well being. Findings of the study show among other things that the adults were more often integrative than dominative and that, on the other hand, the children exhibited more "acceptable and healthy than unacceptable and unhealthy practices." This seems good. But situation and behavior are not aligned here in procedures or results. What did the child do in response to threats or to bring them on? How did he react to expressions of approval? Questions of this order are not asked or answered in such a way as to reveal the give and take of situation and behavior.

Anderson (1939a, 1939b), who introduced and developed the useful concepts of dominative and integrative actions (see also Anderson, 1940), also applied time-sampling procedures in measuring the incidence of these control tactics in behavior of teachers with preschool children while measuring in addition concurrent modes of child behavior. His findings indicate a general relationship over time such that the more integrative the adult contacts the more hygienic the behavior of the child. Again, however, the results do not demonstrate specific behavior-with-situation links. The observed adult actions are distributed among 35 categories that range roughly from extreme directiveness to extreme permissiveness. The reported interesting data do not bear concretely and stepwise on the question of differences from one category to the next in elicited behavior of the children.

What happens in this behavior *plus* situation research can be understood as a function of the method. Common psychological theory now says that for every action (or *response*, for that conceptual matter) there is a corresponding situation (or *stimulus*) and vice versa. It would seem to follow that the way to link actions with situations is to divide the behavior continuum, not into arbitrary time units, but into integral units of behavior with its context. We have seen one way to do this in specimen description. One first records in conventional language the different actions of a child and their conditions as they occur sequentially and then divides the record into behavior-situation units. Or one can single out such units when observations are made, as in event sampling and field-unit analysis. The chances of matching behavior with conditions must be better in either case than when (1) a count is made of behavior items that occur during fixed time intervals and (2) a count *also* is made of situational components that happen to occur during the same uniform lengths of time.

Although data on behavior alone or on situation alone or on one plus the other obviously have value, two points can be urged here. One is that the problem of revealing connections between phenomena and their relevant contexts is the central problem in every science. The second is that the meaning of an action often cannot be established without regard for the situation in which it occurs. Consider some examples that refer to behavior variables of time-sampling studies. *Aggression* (Green, 1933a; Walters et al., 1957) in response to a blow on the head is one thing, whereas aggression in response to indifference or teasing is quite another thing. *Actions toward persons* (Barker,

1930; Beaver, 1932; Bott, 1934) who are hindering you and actions toward persons who are helping you can be no more the same than the hindering and the helping. Among *social approaches* (Mallay, 1935b), *visual regard* for a smile usually differs greatly from visual regard for a frown. Yet all of these and many other kinds of behavior have been time-sampled in situational vacuo. A further limitation is that short and widely separated (cf. p. 98) spans of time must in every case leave the larger continuing situation of a child out of account, which means also that the method can never do much in the light of, or to illumine, the continuity of behavior.

Some time sampling studies have worked at the problem of connecting situation with behavior. In her study of imaginative behavior among preschool children, for example, Markey (1935) records imaginative play of both the child and children who come into contact with the child. She records adult "contributions" toward imaginative activity (as in suggesting things to do) and also examines consequences of change in play-group heterogeneity for imaginative behavior. Jersild and Markey (1935) record "acts of the teacher" and ask how these affect outcomes of conflicts between children in a nursery school. Three procedural features of these two studies are noteworthy.

1. The observation interval lasts fifteen minutes. Fifteen minutes could possibly be near a safe outside limit for capture, intact, of children's conflicts and imaginative-play episodes.
2. Specimen narration is the recording technique.
3. Behavior and situation items are counted, not per integral unit of any kind, but per fifteen-minute interval.

One nevertheless can wonder whether these investigators might have accomplished more with the action-context problem if, in analyzing their narrative specimens, they had first systematically divided each one into action-context units.

There are to be considered, also, tests of relationships between situational factors and behavior in which time sampling and independent measures of specific environmental properties are coordinated. Take the study by Lippitt and associates (cf. p. 78) of behavioral contagion and social influence attempts as they are related to measured social power of the child and his companions. Special measures establish the relative power of each companion, $C$. Direct observations during intervals of five, ten, and fifteen minutes show further that $C$'s power as a situational factor and the behavior of $S$ toward $C$ are related. Here is one indirect way to use time sampling in research to connect behavior with its cotemporaneous conditions.

Body (1955) applies time sampling in a study that aims to get at "situational factors" in the aggressive behavior of children in a "university nursery school" and a "community-supported day school" for young children. The children of the two school settings are found to differ in aggressive behavior. Explanations of the differences are proffered in revealing discussion of dissimilarities between the compared settings in "group composition, intragroup constellations, child-child contacts, direction methods, and school program." But these situational determinants are taken into account ex post facto. They are not measured directly. Only the aggressive *behavior* is time-sampled. The situation of the child action by action is left out of account.

This leaves the question of aims in time sampling. The evident aim of the method in its more typical applications is normative. See for clear examples Bott (1934), Swan (1938), Walters, Pearce, and Dahms (1957)—all in Table 3-5—Arrington (1932a), and Thomas (1932a,b). The investigator in these and other comparable studies records behavior alone for the sake of characterizing the behaving *child*. Attention may be given to individual differences. But these are usually heeded with less regard for the child as an individual than for measurement of deviations from central tendencies. Clearly idiographic applications of the method seem negligible. Most attention is given here to the child of a given class, who nearly always turns out to be the preschool child of a stated age.

Psychological tests are very often applied similarly to the normative problem. Tests to get norms and direct observing of *behavior alone* to get norms seem basically the same in strategy, inasmuch as both use information about behavior to establish common traits of classified children. It is nonetheless true that the two methods differ in important tactics. Paradoxically, direct field observing in this case gives situational factors shorter shrift than psychological testing. Take any representative abilities test or personality test of the inventory type. What every such test does in effect is to score behavior in response to (1) a large number of (2) prototypical situations that are (a) known and (b) standardized. What any observational study of behavior alone does in fact is to score behavior in response to (1) a probably smaller number of (2) local and circumstantial situations that are (a) unknown (where unknown means unrecorded) and (b) not standardized at all. The observational norm seeker generally does identify the activity *setting*, as, for example, preschool X, outdoors, morning, and free-play period. But this leaves much to be said about psychological situations. As for outcomes, the results of the tests tell us what to expect of classified children in situations that present intellectual problems or aggressive acts or affectionate overtures or dangers or whatever at home, at school, on the playground, or the like. On the other hand, to look back on pertinent studies to date, normative observational data on behavior out of context tell us mainly what to expect of children in American preschools. This also is something but it is still not so much as could be hoped. And almost all of these pertinent studies to date are time sampling studies.

At least two issues, which can only be touched on now, are left over here. "Spontaneous behavior" reveals the child in a unique way? Behavior that cannot be elicited by tests can be observed directly? The right answer in each case may well be yes, but we would urge no less that it is more useful to record directly observed behavior in context than out of context for any purpose.

Aims in time sampling have nearly always been systematic when they have not been normative. The study by Heathers in Table 3-5 gives a good example. So also does a demonstration by Marshall and McCandless (1937b) of a negative relation between dependence on adults and social acceptance by peers among preschool children. The study by Lippitt, Polansky, and Rosen (1952) of relationships between power and social behavior in groups of children, which has already been cited, is another case in point (see p. 78 and p. 102). Consider also an investigation by Maas (1954) which tests a number of hypotheses about behavior in lower-class and middle-class groups of adolescents. These hypotheses include, for example, the one that member-to-member actions are more aggressive in the lower-class groups. *One* way to test this hypothesis is to observe intermember behavior in suitable teen-age clubs for brief and constant intervals of time. Maas did as much and thereby gathered efficiently data that upheld the stated expectation and others.

Work begins in these studies with definite ideas about empirical relationships between variables of behavior or of situation and behavior. Time sampling may be at its best in research with such a beginning. It provides *one* efficient way of testing hypotheses or answering questions about how often children behave in given ways in life settings under specified conditions. There are good incidence problems in child development; and the studies at hand show that some of these problems can be met usefully by sampling naturally occurring behavior during fixed intervals of time. But there are other and possibly sounder ways to handle such problems, as discussion to follow may show.

EVENT SAMPLING

Event sampling begins with a plan to study integral behavioral events of a given class. These may be in the nature of anger outbursts, or of arguments, or games. The investigator stations himself where children can be seen and heard, waits for the events to happen, and then describes them if and when they do occur. Each event is a sample of its class in the behavior streams of classified children in selected life settings.

Here in psychological application is the classical method of natural history research in biology. How does a beaver build a dam? what are the nesting habits of geese? and how do frogs prepare for winter? Biological scientists have built up vast stores of knowledge about such events by the straightforward tactic of describing each one as it occurs repeatedly in nature. Child psychologists are comparative novices in this long line of basic descriptive study, and yet they have made some beginnings as event samplers.

Take as a model case a study by Helen Dawe (1934). This modest investigation describes quarrels of preschool children "as they occur spontaneously" during the free-play hour of a nursery school over a period of four autumn and winter months. The subjects are 19 girls and 21 boys of ages 2 to 5 years. Dawe "watched the children from some central spot on the playground or from a doorway between the two main playrooms" of the school. "Immediately upon noting evidences of a struggle" she "moved quickly to the scene of action as unobtrusively as possible" and "devoted her whole attention to the quarrel" until "the issue was settled or the teacher interfered." Each "struggle" was timed from its inception to the outcome. "Running notes" and also entries on prepared forms were recorded immediately after the conclusion of every quarrel. The forms gave space for recording (1) the name, age, and sex of every participant, (2) the duration of the quarrel, (3) what the children were doing at the time of onset, (4) what they quarreled about: contested ownership, physical violence, interference with activity, or other social stress, (5) the role of each participant: precipitator, main aggressor, retaliator, objector, sheer emoter, or passive recipient, (6) specific motor and verbal accompaniments, (7) the outcome: yielding to force, voluntary yielding, compromise, interference by a child spectator, or intervention by a teacher, and (8) the after affects: good cheer or resentment.

What did Dawe learn by waiting for these quarrels to occur and by then describing them one by one? Here are some sample findings.

Two hundred quarrels were observed at the rate of three to four per hour among the 40 children. These quarrels were "amazingly short" indeed. Their average duration was twenty-four seconds, with only 13 lasting more than a minute. The time per quarrel was nearly twice as great outdoors as indoors. Quarrels stopped by teachers were not appreciably shorter than those settled by the children! The boys quarreled more often than the girls. Quarrels involving boys alone or girls alone were the more frequent, but these intrasex quarrels ended with some form of compromise about three times as often as intersex quarrels! So! Retaliative acts increased with age although the number of quarrels declined with age. Such motor activity as pushing or striking was absent

in only three of the 200 quarrels! Truly argumentative quarrels increased with age, as Piaget (1952), for example, would assuredly have expected. Yielding to force was the commonest outcome. Quick and cheerful recoveries outnumbered resentful aftermaths about three to one. (Abstracted from Dawe, 1934.)

Here are data gathered by recording unitary behavioral events as they happen, one by one, in the naturally occurring behavior streams of children; and it is submitted that these data are splendidly intelligible and useful.

Dawe's application of the method does indeed tell something about behavior in context. The quarrel as an integral process with an observable course is described in relation to some of its conditions, included among which there are precipitating states of affairs to quarrel about, opposite-sex and same-sex peers to quarrel with, teachers as interveners, and force or compromise as quarrel enders. The method has not always achieved such description, although several investigators have worked with it in this behavior-in-context vein, as in event samplings of anger or aggressive acts in young children (Goodenough, 1931; Ricketts, 1934; Appel, 1942), children's fears (Jersild and Holmes, 1935) and their "outbreaks" of both anger and fear (Felder, 1932), other "emotional episodes" (in infants, Blatz and Millichamp, 1935; in the child of school age, Blatz, Chant, and Salter, 1937; in Filipino preschool and school children, Inselberg, 1958), sympathetic child behavior (Murphy, 1937), and such other events in children's lives as crying (Landreth, 1941), sleeping (Reese, 1932), laughing and smiling (Ding and Jersild, 1932; Blatz, Allin, and Millichamp, 1936), war play (Bonte and Musgrove, 1943), spontaneous group formations (Chevaleva-Janovskaja, 1927), riding to school with a stranger (Heathers, 1954), the troubles *other* children have with teachers (Kounin and Gump, 1958), and greetings in pedestrian streams of large and small communities (Wright and Dreyer, 1959). Studies of language functions by Fisher (1934), Janus (1943), and Burnham (1956) illustrate similar research on spontaneous verbal behavior. Some of Piaget's observations could also be counted here, even though he generally oversteps the bounds of observational study by interrogating his subjects. See for pleasant examples his descriptions (1932) of how Swiss children play marbles.

This leaves applications with less regard for observed conditions of behavior. Examples include event samplings of classroom recitations (Horn, 1914), misdemeanors at school (Blatz and Bott, 1927), laterality of limb movements in infants (Stubbs and Irwin, 1933), food habits (Vance and Temple, 1933; Campbell, 1933), sleeping habits (Boynton and Goodenough, 1930; Scott, 1931; White, 1931), choice of play materials (McDowell, 1937), and speech elements (Adams, 1932; Stalnaker, 1933; Nice, 1932). These investigations are rather like normative time sampling studies that inquire about the frequency of certain behavior items among children of particular age levels in particular settings. Ames (1949, 1952) and others at Yale have also applied a kind of event sampling toward developmental norms. A procedure that might

appropriately be called "progressive condensation" is followed. The observer begins with detailed notations on selected behavior targets and ends with highly condensed normative summaries. Ames, for example, proceeds in this way to describe the growth of "interpersonal smiling responses" in the preschool years (1949) and to trace developmental change among preschool children in "the sense of self" as expressed or implied by verbal or other behavior (1952).

Event samplers have been like time samplers as a rule in preferring recording techniques that arm them in the field with check lists, category sets, or the like. Yet some have been content just to look, listen, and then describe each event in everyday words. Murphy (1937), Bonte and Musgrove (1943), Ames (1949, 1952), and Kounin and Gump (1958) have done this. A few investigators, also, have combined free narration with coded observation guides. The form used by Jersild and Holmes (1935, p. 351) in their research on children's fears is a clear example. This form includes check lists of items that refer to the child's activity program and physical condition during the day in which each recorded fear occurs, and it also provides white space under each of the subjoined heads.

*Situation in which the child gave signs of being afraid:* place, time, what the child was doing at the time, persons present, apparent cause of fear, *etc.*

*Behavior of the child:* words spoken, cries, other vocalizations, jumping, starting, withdrawing, running away, other physical activity, *etc.*

Perhaps some such directive, yet open-ended provisions for recording both situation and behavior might profitably be made in every event sampling study.

Event samplers generally have worried about the reliability of their observations less than time samplers. One nonetheless finds only reassuring results wherever agreement between simultaneous and independent observers has been tested. See for examples the studies by Dawe (1934), Ding and Jersild (1932), Ricketts (1934), and Landreth (1941). Landreth (1940) compared event ("incident") sampling, time sampling, a class record, and teacher ratings as ways to study crying by preschool children. She reports observer agreement per cents of 97.5 and 95.5, respectively, for the first two methods. The event sampling scores were found to measure this "sporadic" type of behavior best, yet they proved to be low in consistency over time. Dawe and also Ding and Jersild, however, show stability in frequency of their target phenomena (noted above) by getting moderately high correlations between scores from different observation periods.

Others seem to have been little concerned with measurement stability in applications of this method. It is as if most of them had reasoned that (1) psychological events are sure to change in frequency and character over time as their conditions change, in spite of which (2) there will be some stability when the child stays the same, but (3) let us not bother to show this because (4) we are interested in the events more as functions of their momentary conditions than as functions of the transcending child. Students of *personality*, of the *individual*, of the *organism*, of the *child* may not easily get the feel of this position, which is nevertheless as comfortable as an old shoe to some students of social behavior.

Perhaps the most distinctive good point of event sampling is that it structures the field of observation into natural units of behavior and situation. Important resulting advantages have been anticipated, especially in our discussion of time sampling. These advantages amount essentially to a fair chance to study relationships between behavior and its coexisting conditions. Every behavioral event with enough singularity to invite attention is potentially a systematic psychological study in nature. All one has to do to make it actually an experiment of sorts is to control its conditions in effect by keeping track of them and of correlative changes in behavior. Dawe, Jersild and Holmes, Goodenough, and others whose pertinent research we have mentioned show that this can be done.

An important practical asset of the method is that it can be adapted to study of naturally occurring behavioral phenomena that happen only once in a fairly long while. Event sampling is most economical in the face of such phenomena if lay adults who live on the scenes of observation serve as observers. Goodenough (1931) and Jersild and Holmes (1935) have set a precedent here by securing parents and other adult family members as observers in their studies of anger and fear. It is suggested that the possibilities in extensive event sampling of child behavior by resident lay observers in homes, schools, camps, stores, and other such activity settings deserve consideration. There may be no more feasible way to get at key spontaneous behavioral phenomena with low incidence rates.

Possibly the greatest limitation of event sampling is that it breaks up the larger continuity of behavior—as much as time sampling. The method compares unfavorably in this respect with specimen description. Yet any unitary behavioral event has a continuity of its own that can be recorded. Biological naturalists have done so much better here than child psychologists as event samplers. The natural history researcher in biology characteristically describes things, from births to migrations and life cycles, in process as well as in context. Child psychology needs such descriptions. It has only a most pitifully meager stock of beginning-to-end records that describe psychologically significant events in the lives of children. Selective event sampling with some such recording technique as specimen narration could be used to meet this need for descriptions that preserve at least the smaller continuities of behavior.

As for research aims, the evident purpose of the more representative event sampling studies now in the literature is primarily systematic, *not* normative. The studies by Dawe, Goodenough, and many others have contributed toward empirical generalizations that relate behavior to its more or less universal determinants. It may be, however, that the method is suited as well to the ecological aim. Consider as classes of behavioral events in the lives of chil-

dren, all of which have been or might well become targets of event sampling studies: quarrels, anger episodes, fear episodes, frustration episodes, success episodes, failure episodes, competition episodes, cooperation episodes, problem-solving episodes, actions *for* others, actions *against* others, play with pets, play with dolls, solitary play episodes, discipline episodes, illnesses, school recitations, public performances, chores, births, nursing episodes, weaning episodes, car trips, humor episodes, toilet-training episodes, religious-ritual episodes, new-situation episodes (such as first baths, first school days, introductions to strangers), buying things, being the baby sat with, getting-up episodes, and going-to-bed episodes. Here are possible experiments in nature on systematic problems. But here also are possible natural history studies. How do these and other such events in child behavior streams differ, as between differing communities and cultures, primitive and civilized, Soviet and American, Maine and Kansas cultures, and large and small, old and new, central and suburban, rich and poor communities of these cultures, through scores of like variations? Anthropologists and sociologists have worked productively with many facets of this mammoth question, and psychological researchers in child development with an ecological aim have available in event sampling one clear way to do likewise.

## FIELD UNIT ANALYSIS

This method has two phases.

1. A behavior sequence is divided into consecutive units *in the field* on the basis of explicit rules.

2. Descriptive categories are applied to the phenomena of each unit.

Presently ongoing behavior is analyzed here much as narratively recorded behavior has been unitized and examined in the analysis stage of specimen description. Great advantages in a permanent record that can be saved and studied in a hundred ways are lost, but economy is gained; and so also is a special advantage in time sampling and event sampling, namely, close contact through the stage of analysis with behavior in progress.

The method is comparatively new. Partly for this reason, and because it seems uniquely promising, its applications in single studies will be reviewed in some detail.

Consider as one preliminary example a procedure in which Wright and associates (1957) do *on-the-spot episoding*. A child is observed for twenty to thirty minutes as he goes about his business in a community. His behavior throughout this time is divided into episodes on the basis of criteria first developed for discrimination of episodes in specimen records (see p. 91, Barker and Wright, 1955, pp. 225–273). The duration of every episode is recorded. Beyond this, the observer records on the spot only a participial phrase as a title of each episode. *Buying Oranges* and *Discussing Tornado with Banker* are examples. The record for each observation period consists solely in the time notations and a series of participial phrases that identify different episodes and show their structural relations: of sequential position and, at times, of overlapping. Immediately after every observation period, however, categories to describe the behavior and the situation in each episode are applied by the observer. Each recorded participial title serves then to muster in the observer-turned-analyst an image of what the child has just been observed to do and of his situation in the named episode unit. Conclusive statements cannot now be made about the reliability of the substantive outcome of this technique, which may nonetheless show what we mean by field unit analysis.

These same investigators are working similarly with a unit for study of social interaction between children and others of their communities. This part of a behavior sequence is defined only by constancy in number and identity of the child's present associates. Hence it is called an *association unit*. An association unit and a spur-of-the-moment social group that includes the child and any one or more associates are the same. Associates are defined without conceptual or operational ado as individuals with whom the child becomes involved in any way. The subjects, children of 6 through 11 years, are observed individually for periods of one hour. Intervals through which the child is alone become *zero association units*. Different kinds of social action are narratively recorded as they occur in behavior of the child and of every associate. Frequencies of units differing in size and in composition (with respect to sex, age, and role) are determined. Also, different kinds of social action (e.g., aggressive or nurturant) in various sizes of units (e.g., three-person groups) are analyzed on an event sampling basis. Tests show satisfactory levels of observer agreement in identification of associates and actions.

A behavior episode is an integral part of the behavior continuum. It has phenomenal discreteness and some dynamical independence (Barker and Wright, 1955, pp. 225–230). Can the same be said for the association unit? The investigators think so. It is phenomenally discrete insofar as a person knows when others come or go. It has some dynamical independence in that a person's behavior depends in part upon the presence or absence of others. An episode is defined essentially by constancy in direction of behavior. But there obviously are congruencies between behavioral direction and the comings, stayings, and goings of other individuals. Some correspondence between episodes and association units can therefore be predicted. Episoded specimen day records of the Midwest collection (with classroom sequences eliminated) have been used to test this prediction. The resulting data show that 44 per cent of the association units in four day records on as many Midwest 7-to-11-year-olds coincide exactly from beginning to end with behavior episodes. Further, when this correspondence is imperfect, the percentage of association units that *either* start or end where episodes start or end is 95.

The association unit can be seen with the almost naked eye. It is in itself a basic psychosocial phenomenon. It defines precisely as to size and makeup the group context of interpersonal relations. It may have fair integrity for the individual child. These considerations and data coming in encourage belief that the unit offers a good base for on-the-spot study of naturally occurring social behavior. Yet it is crude. One association unit—lasting, for instance,

ten minutes of continuous time that Joe, Tom, and Sue spend together—can span behavior segments in the life of each child that differ greatly as unitary events. Psychologically more refined units are imperative for many research purposes.

Bishop (1951) has contributed a kind of field unit analysis that presents some intriguing tactics. Her technique, which Moustakas and Schalock (1955) and Moustakas, Sigel, and Schalock (1956) have modified, looks at first glance like time sampling.[1] It employs five-second lengths of time both as recording intervals and as counting integers. In the first place, however, these lengths of time are consecutive rather than intermittent, and, in the second place, *the recorded observations account for sequential and complete units of social interaction.* The target phenomena in the research are interactions between preschool children and their mothers in a play setting.

The observer masters sets of categories to describe behavior of the mother and behavior of the child. Each observation period lasts thirty minutes. Symbols of the categories are recorded when they apply during the five-second intervals. Thus, in effect, complete cycles or units of interaction go down in the field protocol as they occur in each period of observation. Further, instigating behavior and responsive behavior on each side in transactions between mother and child are distinguished by the notations. The

[1] Only Bishop's own applications involve appreciable experimental arrangements. See text note on p. 75.

appropriate symbol is carried over from interval to interval when either an instigation or a response lasts longer than five seconds. As we envisage it, a sequence of the field record, kept by devices that cannot be recounted here, might be read off as follows:

Unit 10: instigation : mother *suggests* : : response : child *accepts* (1 interval = 5 seconds)

Unit 11: instigation : mother *restricts* (3 intervals = 15 seconds) : : response : child *resists* (1 interval = 5 seconds)

Unit 12: instigation : child *seeks help* (2 intervals = 10 seconds) : : response : mother *helps* (4 intervals = 20 seconds)

Tests show high observer agreement in application of the categories, and correlations of frequencies from different observation periods show reasonable consistency in the adult and child behavior. A frequency score is obtained per category by summing the five-second intervals in which the social behavior at issue occurs. Proportion scores are also derived to equalize the differences among mother-child pairs in absolute amount of social behavior. Measures on the adult side are correlated with measures on the child side. An $r$ of .70, for instance, shows a clear positive relation between *specific control* by the mother and *reluctant cooperation* by the child.

Each basal frequency count of this procedure expresses well the total *amount* of suggesting or restricting or whatever per child or mother; but the *analysis* procedure could be challenged on the issue of part-to-whole relations in behavior study. These frequency counts add whole actions, specifically, every action that lasts no longer than five seconds, *and* temporally equal action fragments. Some psychological researchers may prefer to add whole actions only, even when these behavior segments differ in temporal length. One might be happier, for example, with a sum of 2 that means "You ought to be more careful, George" (five seconds of *criticizing*), plus a one-minute harangue with the same theme (sixty seconds of *criticizing*), than with a sum of 13 that means "You ought to be more careful, George," plus 12 separate twelfths of the one-minute harangue. Time sampling often adds action fragments perforce. The present technique need not. Perhaps it would do better without the five-second intervals, in which case each categorized action could simply be timed as it comes.

Bishop's action-by-action analysis on the spot nevertheless yields rich findings. Also, the stepwise delineations of behavior that her records give can be mined for many sorts of additional findings. What is the mean duration of each type of action? What are the frequency distributions for different kinds of instigation? Of response? What pairings of instigation by $C$ (the child) and $O$ (the other person) are most to least common? Of instigation by $O$ and response by $C$? What about sequence relations between actions of a series? For example, given any chosen number of consecutive *directing* instigations by $O$, what is the probability of an immediately sequent *noncooperating* response by *C*? Unitary behavior units laid end to end raise hypotheses.

Here is one way to scan systematically the continuous social behavior stream of a child. The technique clearly must be about as good as its main facility: a set of terms for describing social and other behavior. See, with this in view, the categories Bishop has developed and also the categories and refinements in field scoring procedures of Moustakas, Sigel, and Schalock (1956). The latter investigators use no fewer than 97 (memorized) rubrics in analyzing consecutive five-second intervals of therapist-child and parent-child interactions. This staggers a slow-gaited field episoder, but tests show good observer agreement on most of the categories. Practicability and usefulness of this way to unitize and describe behavior on the spot have been clearly demonstrated.

Heinicke (1956) has applied in field procedures a method of analyzing *units of action* that are also called *acts* or *activities*. He compares 2-year-old children of day and residential nurseries, respectively, as subjects of mild and severe separation from parents. His analytical scheme is adapted from the system of Bales (1950; Heinicke and Bales, 1953) for observational study of social interaction. It also has a psychoanalytic base. Certain features of every act are recorded. These are the agent of action: the child or any other person; the object of action: any present or absent recipient of an act—a body part, for example, a toy, or a person; the agent-to-object relation: how the agent relates himself to the object, exemplified

in such kinds of behavior as *nurturance*, *hostility*, and *avoidance;* the mode of expression: how the act is mediated, as by biting or crying; and the intensity of the act: its quantitative force (rated only on hostility as a relation and crying as a mode of expression). A unit of action is defined by constancy in *all* of these variables. Thus a new unit begins with every change in agent, object, relation, mode of expression, or intensity, but for the one qualification that a unit is assigned to every thirty seconds of a continuous act "because on the average about 2 units were scored every minute." Proportions of all action units in which categorized phenomena occur are determined in the final analysis stage. It is found, for example, that the percentage of acts in which the child as agent relates himself with others in a severely hostile way is greater among the residential nursery children.

The unitizing principle here begets a new unit for each of several important changes in behavior or situation. This principle guarantees division of behavior into parts with a certain amount of psychological integrity. The change criteria are so many and varied, however, that the meaning expressed by any sum of these parts is equivocal. We do not find in Heinicke's fascinating report either numerator or denominator for any of his percentages. This is understandable. An absolute *N* of happenings so multiplexly defined as these acts is not interesting. It would be otherwise if, for example, the sole criterion of change in act had been a change in object, perhaps, in some fundamental kind of agent-to-object relation, or in direction of behavior. One would then want to know the number of acts per interval of time under specified conditions. Although variably defined behavior segments must be more legitimate as counting integers than arbitrary time intervals, segments with more nearly univocal meaning can be summed to greater advantage and would seem to give a sounder base for derived measures.

Observational child study may need nothing more than a basic unit of description that (1) can be used in the field, (2) takes in a diversity of behavior and situation variables, (3) has psychological integrity, (4) has clear meaning in terms of some central criterion, and (5) permits study of behavior in context. All of the foregoing descriptive units meet some or all of these specifications. As for application aims, we suggest only that a unit which satisfies each of the five specifications could be made to serve many normative, systematic, ecological, and idiographic purposes. There seems to be much room here for discovery and invention.

A highly specialized analytical scheme, which might be considered a kind of field unit analysis, has been developed by Birdwhistell (1955) for the "systematic study of how human beings communicate through body movement and gesture." Called *kinesics*, this arresting method provides for sequential analysis of "visually perceptible body shifts" and for interpretation of their significance in "nonverbal interpersonal communication." Only pilot applications in research with children (id.) have thus far been reported.

## TRAIT RATING

Essentials of trait rating as an observational method can be seen in its widely familiar routines.

The observer O goes to a school, home, or other setting in which there is at least one child; or perhaps O lives in the setting or works in it, as in the case of a teacher. O has before him or in mind a battery of scales that describe various dimensions of behavior; or, if he is a resident observer, these scales may be unknown to him. The time comes in any event when, after observing the child—possibly on a single occasion but probably on many occasions over days, weeks, or months—O uses the scales to sum up what he has seen in a series of trait ratings. He may do this after consecutive periods of time, so that tests can be made of intrarater consistency or, if the interim periods are very long, so that changes in behavior can be measured. Often, too, someone intercorrelates the ratings to test for behavior syndromes or correlates them with external measures to investigate their validity and psychological bearings. The rated variables have included among others, in great variety, *cheerfulness, jealousy, apprehensiveness, curiosity, planfulness, fancifulness, conformity, friendliness, competitiveness, respect for authority, sense of humor,* and *adjustment to new situations.*

One finds here many skillfully developed instruments. Prominent early and later examples include the behavior scales of Haggerty, Olson, and Wickman (1930), Berne (1930), Conrad

(1933), VanAlstyne (1936), Joël (1936), Roberts and Ball (1938), and Richards and Simons (1941). These and comparable schedules generally have scored well on tests of reliability and on cross validations with other measures. They have been used almost invariably for normative or idiographic study of *the child*. Quite another possibility is the one of using them to compare effects upon behavior of different settings or conditions of life. This possibility has received little attention. What we mean by it is clearly demonstrated, however, in engaging research by Koch (1955a,b and 1955a,b) on consequences for child behavior of sibling position as a property of the family setting.

Each of our other methods deals with behavior in progress. Present actions or conditions are described and observations are recorded when they are made. In applications of trait rating, on the other hand, stable ways of behaving are described and observations are recorded after they are made. These observations are essentially direct in that they are not screened by interference techniques or by passage of enough time to make them fade out considerably. Each rating amounts to a statement that summarizes cumulative direct observation, as indicated in Table 3-2. Yet what the observer records is more an assessment of personality than a description of behavior or its conditions; behavior rating scales are indeed commonly grouped with and even called personality inventories. Accordingly, to save problems in appraisal of personality characteristics for Chapter 17, discussion of the method is limited here to these identifying comments.

## ADDENDUM: ON THE LARGER CONTEXT OF CHILD BEHAVIOR

Methods now at hand are merely added to the foregoing survey of "principal" ways to investigate naturally occurring child behavior only because they exceed the common limits of observational child study. Their importance is another question.

We refer here to methods that bring into focus, not the behavior continuum of the individual child as represented in Table 3-2, but life settings in the larger context of that comparatively slender stream. Thirty years ago Baldwin and others (1930) observed and described one-room schools, country churches, homes, public libraries, and other settings in the larger environment of Iowa farm children. Dennis and Dennis (1940a,b), working in the tradition of cultural anthropology, have used field techniques to depict and relate to child-rearing practices the life settings of the Hopi child. Such examples bring to mind at once a long line of pertinent anthropological studies and also sociological studies of delinquency areas, habitat factors in social class, and the like. We shall review here only some convenient illustrative research in the psychological literature.

A recent concerted attempt to map the environmental penumbra of individual child behavior has been made in a survey of behavior settings in the town of Midwest (Barker and Wright, 1955, pp. 44–176). A *behavior setting* amounts to a special case of the general everyday concept of life setting. This community unit can be defined as a stable part of the physical and social milieu together with an attached standing pattern of human behavior. The milieu part always has its own distinctive characteristics of time, place, things, and personnel that accommodate the behavior pattern. This pattern, too, is always extraindividual in that it stays essentially the same over extended periods of time while different individuals come and go. Examples of behavior settings in Midwest are the Second-Grade Classroom, Hooker's Tavern, the Weekly Meeting of Scout Troop 96, and the Methodist Regular Worship Service. Raising hands, shooting pool, saluting the flag, and singing the Doxology, respectively, are components of the standing behavior patterns attached to these settings.

Behavior settings are common enough as empirical entities that lay persons and social scientists identify them and many of their features and functions with close agreement. This holds, indeed, for the behavior patterns anchored to them. These behavioral wave phenomena in Midwest have been described in terms of such functions as *aesthetics, earning a living, education, recreation, religion,* and *social contact.* Relative weights of these different *action patterns* in settings entered by infants, preschool children, school children, and others of various age, sex, class, and color groups are described. Variations from setting to setting in the incidence of *gross motor activity, listening, talking,* and comparable *behavior mechanisms* are also determined for different population subgroups. Measurements are made as well of the *territorial ranges, occupancy times, degrees of segregation,* and *penetration levels* of children and others in Midwest's behavior settings. The survey data were gathered by participant observers whose sources of information included the local press, public records, and informants. Tests of agreement between independent observers and analysts indicate adequate reliability of the obtained measures.

Watch a child move from home to school to a park to the corner drugstore and so on through a day. His behavior will be seen to change with remarkable speed as he goes from setting to setting. One discovers, then, that behavior settings contain forces that coerce individual behavior; and one can easily believe that these forces must be of critical importance in the processes of socialization and personality growth. Procedures of a behavior setting survey give one way to begin to diagnose and interpret these forces. Communities have behavior settings, indeed, but so have the separate institutions of communities. Koppe (1952) found 71 settings in the grade school of an American town with a population of only 390. A modern hospital has many different behavior settings. So has the average American church. Solution of theoretical problems in child development and of practical problems in child guidance might be helped by application and continuous improvement of ways to identify, catalogue, describe, and assess these stages on which children play their parts in communities and their subordinate institutions.

The persisting larger and more stable context of individual child behavior has a vast reach. It ranges from clothes, family customs and manners, school desks, and school rules to the affairs of nations. Research in this range, which stands nearer to the child than the Midwest setting survey, is found in work with the Fels Parent Behavior Rating Scales. These scales comprise an instrument for appraisal of the child's home environment as a function of enduring parental behavior patterns. First devised by Champney (1941), this instrument has been used extensively in the Fels Home Visit Program. It has been developed and applied in research by Baldwin, Kalhorn, and Breese (1945, 1949). Special studies have also been made of its applications by Roff (1949), Larr and Jenkins (1953), Lasko (1954), and Crandall and Preston (1955). Only supplementing many secondary writings, we want to recount features and applications of this well-known tool with significance from the standpoint of observational method.

Thirty scales make up the rating battery. These scales cover dimensions of the home setting that include such variables as *child-centeredness, protectiveness, readiness of criticism, restrictiveness of regulations, clarity of policy, discord in the home,* and *severity of penalties.* The ratings are based mainly upon information obtained during repeated home visits in the course of which informal interviews or other means of getting pertinent evidence may be added to direct observation. These estimates are not left to stand alone in the Fels applications. They are supplemented at the time of each visit by a clinical summary that records general impressions and cites specific incidents to epitomize important features of the home situation. Satisfactory reliability of the scales is demonstrated by measures of both intrarater consistency and interrater agreement.

Baldwin and associates have prepared a manual (1949, Part II) for use of the Fels Parent Behavior Rating Scales by home visitors. The manual treats the visit, rating techniques, scoring and standardization, administration of a home rating program, and the scales as such. Each scale variable is defined and cue points of every dimension are phrased with abundant references to concrete grounds for high to low ratings.

[A] rating is usually an estimate of the impact of the parent's behavior on the child. This is clearly different from the parent behavior as perceived by the visitor (p. 32).

The Fels ratings and the Midwest setting survey differ here. The Midwest survey does not weigh impacts of standing behavior patterns upon individual children. This is not intended even in ratings by Simpson (1956) on *approval, affectionateness,* and other such variables of *social weather* as a property of a setting. It is here especially that the Fels instrument gets nearer to the behaving child. Yet it does not record discrete parental actions as elements of the child's momentarily changing situations. It does not count or interrelate or connect with ongoing behavior of the child specific rewards, punishments, denials, entreaties, or commands. Instead, it measures conduct resultants in the form of disciplinary policies, warmth of the home, family adjustment mechanisms, and other behavior configurations that have considerable stability as attributes of the enduring home environment.

In one application (Baldwin et al., 1945) ratings of 124 homes are intercorrelated by a method similar to Sanford's technique of syndrone analysis (1943). Resulting groups of related variables permit classification of these homes into such types as the *rejectant-autocratic*, the *casual-indulgent*, and the *acceptant-democratic*. Differences in consequences for child development over a period of three years are found among the several types of homes. Clusters of variables that define *warmth*, *adjustment*, *restrictiveness*, *clarity*, and *interference* as home dimensions are set forth (in Baldwin et al., 1949, pp. 4–17) to guide clinical interpretation of the ratings. Graphic profiles that show the thirty ratings per home in sigma scores also serve this purpose. Crandall and Preston (1955) analyze ratings made with the scales of homes other than and yet comparable in locale and socioeconomic level to those studied by Baldwin and associates (1945). They report intercorrelations that demonstrate considerable similarity in parental behavior patterns between the two samples of homes. Hence their findings suggest that McClelland (1951) and others have been safe in basing theoretical bets on measures secured by the method.

There used to be a wide strip of no-science-at-all land between extremely proximal conditions of human behavior and such distal conditions as economy, political organization, and geography. Sociologists and anthropologists long ago colonized that middle ground to study social classes, primary groups, mores, customs, and even the roles of persons. The studies just sampled suggest that child psychologists can work productively with their preferred tactics of stepwise measurement in the same area of comparatively stable and lasting environmental conditions.

## Common Problems

Some problems that are common to all methods of observational child study need special consideration.

### OBSERVER INFLUENCE

How natural or unnatural is the behavior of a child and his associates in the presence of an observer? What can be done by an observer to minimize his influence, such as it may be, upon the behavior he records? Observational research with children has been up against questions in this vein from the first.

One thinks here at once of observing from behind a one-way vision screen as a way out of the problem. But this is not often practicable if one wants to describe behavior and situations in life settings. So, instead of trying to hide, the observer can take a nearly opposite tack. He can first get acquainted with his subjects and others who are likely to be on the scene and then play his part as a nonevaluating, impartial, non-participating, nondirective, and friendly person with interest in children. Jersild and Meigs (1939, p. 9) write apropos of experience with this tactic that "much-observed children, as well as adults, seem quite readily to become habituated to the presence of an outsider." They add that time has "a tranquilizing effect," and this seems understandable. We suppose that a child or even an adult cannot entirely stop being himself for long because he is being watched. Forces of life settings may always be stronger than induced forces of a detached onlooker.

The observer can do much to dampen his influence upon the child. His part is to fade into the background as much as possible. This obviously requires the set of a neutral bystander, yet it does not call for wooden unresponsiveness. An observer is sure to stand out at times as a stationary figure against a moving ground if he tries to be only a listening post. He had better answer questions, for example, or certainly become a center of uneasy attention. Peripheral vision can sometimes help against the certainty that no one likes to be watched beadily, and some of the advantages in concealed observation often can be gained from skillful "preoccupation with other matters" (Jersild and Meigs, 1939, p. 9). More may be gained by openness and candor. The child and everybody in town or at school, say, is going to know anyhow what is going on.

Such effects of the observer as there may be need not go entirely unmeasured. Teachers, parents, or other adults can be asked to rate deviancies in the child's behavior during periods of observation. Behavior of the child in relations with the observer and with other adults can be compared. At least one attempt has been made to do this quite systematically (Barker and Wright, 1955). Social interactions of eleven Midwest children with a cumulative total of 14 observers during a day in the life of each child are described. The results show, among other things, relatively low frequency of observer-child interplay, less frequent dominance, nurturance, resistance, aggression, and avoidance by the observers than by other adults, and relationships between observer and child that were even-tempered and generally free of extremes in emotive behavior of any kind. Contrary results would of course be startling.

Age of the subject clearly is a factor in sensitivity to an observer. One guesses that observational *adult* study or even observational *adolescent* study would call for very special methods. Probably, the younger the child the fewer the complications, although children up to eleven years of age have served willingly and without symptoms of great stress or self-consciousness as subjects of full day studies.

Human field observers are sure to miss much in child behavior that percipient ghosts would see. Probably their presence attenuates especially the bad extremes of behavior from cuss words on down. But this leaves much that experimenters are never going to see in laboratories at their inestimable best.

Problems in public relations are added to problems in relations with subject children when studies are made outside preschools and other institutions with built-in arrangements for research. This holds especially for community projects. Shall the investigator live where he works? Shall he, in any case, work at least a part of the time as a participant observer? Or shall he keep his distance and look in from the outside? Should he ever pass himself off as John Jones, fellow layman? (One can doubt it, with appreciation for arguments to the contrary.) Whose consent to do this or that ought the investigator to secure? Ought he to keep mothers, fathers, and others who are in on the research informed of his progress? How much and in what ways should lay adults be asked to help? Without pay? With pay? Ought final results to be shared with cooperating lay people? How about press relations? Psychological field projects can stand or fall on answers to these and related questions. But this is a matter in social-science management that can only be raised here. Whyte (1951), among others, has discussed many of the problems helpfully.

## RELIABILITY OF OBSERVATION

Reliability of observation has generally been defined empirically in observational child studies by agreement between simultaneous and independent observers. Tests based upon this definition are included in representative applications of every method in our survey but diary description. These tests have turned out passably well, with few exceptions.

Reported measures of observer agreement in different studies do not clearly favor any principal method over any other. Nor do we find clear differences in trustworthiness of observation as between different sorts of observed phenomena. Yet one clear indication stands out; namely, that many of the bigger and putatively vaguer phenomena pass the standard reliability test of observer agreement. Take from Bishop (field unit analysis: 1951) the example of *noncooperation: ignoring or refusing to comply with or to accept a social approach of another person.* This vari-

able subsumes a multitude of alternative mediating behaviors; and observing it requires some inference. Consider then that Bishop reports an over-all mean agreement percentage of 89 on noncooperation. Similar examples include agreement percentages of 85 to 97 on *friendliness and quarreling* (time sampling: Green, 1933a), *anger-evoking situations* (event sampling: Ricketts, 1934), *episodes of imaginative behavior* (time sampling: Markey, 1935), *verbal or physical parent-child communication* (specimen description: Lafore, 1945), *social conflicts* (time sampling: Jersild and Markey, 1935), and *affection* (field unit analysis: Moustakas, Sigel, and Schalock, 1956).

Arrington reported in 1932 that her efforts to develop accurate techniques for recording children's behavior with things and persons had led her to single out "finer and finer units" and to work toward elimination of "every element capable of different interpretation that might reduce reliability of the data recorded" (Arrington, 1932a, p. 27). Yet her accuracy indices are not remarkably high in present perspective. She does report a median agreement per cent of 99 on physical contacts with such material things as paper towels, cups, chairs, walls, and iron gratings. But she also reports comparable values as low as 72 and no higher than 91 on *gross physical activity* not involving material things, *no overt activity, talking, laughing, crying* and *physical contacts with persons.* Scores from independent observers of Olson's tics (see p. 93) correlate .75. A provocative fact is that, in general, the smaller and more literally objective behaviors have not fared prominently well over the long run in tests of observer agreement.

Some might suppose that the larger behavioral wholes on which independent observers agree acceptably are always defined reductively in terms of subordinate and more directly visible parts. Such is *not* the case. Instead, with exceptions to be noted, the core intended meaning of the target phenomenon is stated without either elaborate conceptual formulation or detailed specifying of "criterion" behavior items. Operational pointing is often done with only a minimum of examples. Moustakas and associates (1956), for instance, define *seeking recognition*, on which they get an agreement per cent of 84, by the following statement, in which *A* and *C*, respectively, are an adult and the child.

> Seeking recognition: Attention to activities, productions, or statements is sought by *A* or *C*. Ex: See what I've made? Ex: Look what I'm doing (p. 113).

This must leave a thousand subordinate behaviors that could be used as criteria for seeking recognition. But these are not even grouped in major classes or so much as sampled studiously. *Seeking recognition is bidding for attention*, as this social act is commonly and confidently known and perceived by socialized man. The target is left to stand right about there for the observer; and this example could be multiplied many times.

Molar phenomena of child behavior evidently can be observed dependably on the basis of definitions that identify these phenomena as objects of common —even if partly inferential—perception.

Nor can this be very surprising. Common perception of the same phenomena works well in everyday life. It *normally* enables us to adapt *most* of our actions with marvelous efficiency to friendliness, anger, fear, affection, seeking recognition, and the like, as these occur all around us hour by hour. So it turns out, moreover, despite the biasing effects of subliminal interests upon ability to see things as they are in real life. Then why should the same ability be unequal to the disinterested observations of science?

Reduction statements here seem generally unpromising. Think again of *seeking recognition*. Listing all of the visible acts and audible words that can mediate this way of behaving obviously is not a serious possibility. One can choose plainly visible items from among these behaviors and, for positivistic surety, make them stand for the bigger and supposedly vaguer target. But an investigator who does this must end up with something less than and different from *bidding for attention* as he would like to understand, predict, and control it in life settings! Such compromising has been going on for a long while in psychology, and it does seem inescapable for some measurement purposes in experimental research. We may have shown, however, that reliability strictures do not demand it in observational studies. Perhaps these studies should build on common perception as a homely base. This would leave plenty of room for conventional scientific operations in the overlapping stages of theory construction, comparative design, data analysis, and integration of findings. Possibly direct observers of children ought to stop being scientists and try to be ordinary citizens while, in the stage of field work, they see as best they can the larger actions and situations of children. Many seem to have done this, and welcoming the practice could be a good thing for work on many problems.

A few child observers have worked hard at reductive definitions of molar behavior variables. Hagman, for example, develops an extended definition of a *companion*, which refers in part to criterion molecular behaviors. Her statement builds on Webster's by asserting that a companion is one who "(1) Comes into physical contact with another ... (2) talks to another ... (3) listens to another ... (4) looks at another ... (5) approaches another within ten seconds ... (6) withdraws from another ... (7) plays with or touches the same unit of apparatus as another ... (8) participates in the same game or project as another ... (9) looks at the unit of apparatus another is playing with ... (10) gets something and immediately gives or shows it to another" (Hagman, 1933, pp. 16–17). We suggest that this statement has two limitations that are likely to hold for others like it. First, it leaves out many behaviors that can mediate companionship. Second, it includes several behaviors that are not necessarily diagnostic of this relation, as witness items (1), (4), (5), (6), (7), and (9). In any case, Hagman reports an observer agreement percentage of 83 for identification of companions. This value is based on 688 judgments of behavior of 39 2-to-4-year-olds.

The research on association units, which is represented above (pp. 109–110), deals in a different way with essentially the same phenomenon. An *associate* of a child, C, is entirely defined in this research as an individual, O, that C gets *involved* with in any direct way under either of two conditions. (1) C and O get together as "companions" and stay together for a while. (2) O does something or says something to C that C "notices," or vice versa. Some examples are added, but the definition is not limited by specific, mediating, subordinate, molecular, literally objective, immediately visible, criterion particulars. Then consider that 30 observer agreement percentages, with a median of 96, are obtained. These percentages are based on thirty hours of observation by 12 lay observers of 30 6-to-11-year-olds.

A consideration that meets concern here for the necessity of *somehow* defining behavior phenomena to be observed is that formal definition can specify conceptual properties without being positivistically reductive. A complex behavior variable often presents to an observer alternative connotations that are sure to leave him confused until a choice is made as to what it shall mean. One is therefore not surprised to find that in a study by King, Erhmann, and Johnson (1952) joint discussion by different observers of the meanings in *cooperation, dominance*, and *hostility* improved their agreement on ratings along these dimensions of the behavior of preschool children. We suppose, too, that it would be impossible in many instances to get along without systematic and carefully disciplined sorting and threshing of alternative ways to construe complex behavior variables, as, for example, in the elaborate definitions by Baldwin and associates (1949) of variables in parent behavior. It does not follow, however, that new meanings are invented in these or other similar cases. A great many definitions of reliably observed behavior would seem to express *elections* of meanings that rule common perception.

Investigators in this line of research have been characteristically conservative about reliability of observation since the years of diary records. It is as if they felt vulnerable outside the laboratory. This conservatism led in some early instances to an apparent policy of reliable observation, first, and significant observation, second. Perhaps the time has come for the reverse policy of significant observation, first, and reliable observation, second. Investigators may prefer to go on getting direct evidence that their observations are dependable and repeatable as best they can. All may want to whenever the services of lay observers or other unusual circumstances would otherwise leave their data in unknown jeopardy. Yet there are circumstances, as in some applications of specimen description, in which putting reliability first could greatly hamper effort to learn something new.

A respectable recourse for the investigator without enough (or any) direct evidence that his observations are reliable remains in any case. He can look at his findings and ask a number of questions about them. Are they internally consistent? Are they in line with tenable theories? May they even fulfill derivations from theory? Do they show relationships that outdo chance? Doubts of the reliability of observation would seem to be legitimately diminished by a yes answer to all or some of these questions. It is hard to see especially how one could start with seriously unreliable data and end with extra-chance relationships.

## INSTRUMENTAL AIDS

The problem of instrumenting observational child study in a material way has been met chiefly with paper and pencil, a timepiece, and the inevitable writing board. Yet considerable work has been done with cinematography and other recording techniques by observers of naturally occurring child behavior. This work is so versatile and so loaded with still new methodological issues and difficult engineering problems that we can comment only briefly upon its accomplishments and promise.

Motion pictures of child behavior in essentially uncontrolled life settings include films that document behavior of the newborn (Spitz, 1947), consequences of social deprivation in early childhood (Spitz, 1949b), changes in behavior over years in the normal growth of individual children (Behrens, 1946–1948; Langmuir, Stone, Buchner, and Bohmer, 1941–1952), neurotic or other pathological trends in development (Fries, 1950; Allen, 1940), the beginnings of emotional life in babies (Spitz, 1951), reactions to the medical visit as a life setting (Fries and Woolf, 1944), and behavior during hospitalization after separation of parent and child (Robertson, 1952). These examples can be grouped with anthropological films that exhibit, among many other behavior samples from the lives of children, sibling rivalry in Bali and New Guinea (Mead, 1951a), bathing of babies in different cultures (Mead, 1951b), family life among the Navajo (Fries, Kluckhohn, and Woolf, 1944), and the first days of a New Guinea infant (Bateson and Mead, 1942). Here are primary and permanent behavior records. These films are reliable, and their visual language has many advantages over the best of other symbols.

Behavior films per se are not finished scientific products. They are similar to specimen records in that each only preserves behavioral raw material. Both document, but, left unanalyzed, neither quite discovers. We suppose that films as well as specimen records become tools of scientific discovery in research on behavior only when (1) they record representative samples of behavior and (2) analytical procedures draw from these samples uniform data which are generalized in the verbal and quantitative language of science.

Beginnings have been made in applications of cinematography that go beyond documentation to inquiry in observational research with children. As early as 1937, for example, Bernhardt, Millichamp, Charles, and McFarland (1937) used motion pictures in a study of *social contacts* by children with their peers in a nursery school. They define a social contact as "any relationship with another child or overt behavior involving other children" (p. 11). A silent-movie camera recorded the action of each subject while paired observers recorded the target phenomena by a time sampling technique. The same observers then used precisely the same technique to record the same phenomena as pictured when the film obtained was projected repeatedly at normal speed until differences between the observers were resolved. Perhaps the

most noteworthy finding of this study now is that the number of observed contacts was increased approximately 70 per cent by addition of what was seen on the screen to what was seen in the field![1] So it turned out, even though the per cent of agreement between the two observers was 82. Note also that the film was silent. One can choose to be discouraged by the indication that observers ordinarily miss a great deal or to be encouraged by the evidence that a motion picture adds much to observations made without its help.

Birdwhistell has made frame analyses of films in describing body movement and gesture by child subjects in his kinesiological research (Birdwhistell, 1955; see also p. 113). Gilmer (1933) has described spontaneous responses of newborn infants on the basis of frame and slow-motion study of films. Mead (1951a, 1951b) and Bateson and Mead (1952) have extended their analyses of cultural factors in personality formation by studying motion pictures (and still photographs) of children in critical life situations of various primitive societies. Bowlby, Robertson, and Rosenbluth (1952) elaborate hypotheses about outcomes for children of parent-child separation by applying psychoanalytic concepts to Robertson's movie of a hospitalized child. Kerkman and Wright (1959) are experimenting with frame analyses of pictures taken by a time-lapse movie camera (with a 10-mm.

[1] It must be considered that the time samples were taken "when the social situation became complex and difficult to record." Otherwise, as the investigators mention, the field observing and the repetitive picture observing might have differed less.

lens) as a way of describing the behavior of children en masse in classrooms and other community behavior settings. Gesell (1934) has long since demonstrated rewarding techniques of *cinemanalysis* as applied to films of child behavior in partially controlled situations. Observational film inquiry into child behavior is in a fairly advanced experimental stage.

Research (and instructional) films with children as subjects usually have been produced without live sound. This leaves silver where there could be gold because vocalizations are lost to a film without a sound track. A sound motion picture of a child in a life setting may be the best of all possible records for observational study. It can capture and preserve indefinitely about all there is to see and hear of a behavior sequence and its immediate conditions. The recorded actions and situations can be observed and analyzed from every conceivable point of view for as long and often as patience lasts. Behavior is hard to study partly because it happens so fast; it comes and goes before one can get a good look at it from even a single point of view. Sound motion pictures can make everyday behavior open to prolonged and intensive observation and study. Good sound movies of child behavior in a wide variety of untrammeled life settings would provide invaluable psychological experiments in nature, and getting them requires neither more nor less than large amounts of research money and technical advancements that are now within reach.

It would be easy to understate present technical difficulties in the filming of children's naturally occurring behavior. See Stone (1952) and Michaelis (1955). Stone finds many obstacles in the way of filming with live sound "observer documentaries" of "real events" in the lives of children. Evidently this is not feasible for the time being if one wants films that are suitable aesthetically for audience presentation. Michaelis indicates, however, that behavior sound films of quality good enough for many inquiry purposes can even now be made under the conditions of field studies. His discussion (pp. 188–204) of anthropological filming is especially interesting in this regard.

Dreger (1955) reports an interesting application of sound recording alone in a study of spontaneous conversation and story-telling by children in a "utterly unarranged" setting. Possibilities in electronic tracking of children's movements in a community via automatic recording of signals delivered from a transistor radio-broadcasting unit (the size of a cigarette pack) borne by the child have been considered at the University of Kansas. The addition of sound to such a system apparently is electronically possible if not otherwise practicable or permissible. Soskin (1951) earlier demonstrated the feasibility of conversation pick-up from radio-broadcasting units on the persons of adults.

Electronic observational child study could boom. It is clear, if one puts engineering and money problems aside, that its progress will depend upon development of analysis procedures to suit the new refinement and fidelity of its records. Consider motion pictures, preferably with sound. Some kind of sequential unit analysis could be most adaptable to their potentialities. Films can be episoded or divided into consecutive integral behavior units of any conceivable sort with the technical help of reruns or slow-motion projection or frame analysis. Adaptations of these procedures to problems of sequence relations in interpersonal action, for example, or to base problems of action-to-situation relationships present an exciting prospect.

## DESCRIPTIVE CATEGORIES

Students of child development who use observational methods are embarrassed by riches. The nearly infinite range and variety of naturally occurring child behavior give almost unlimited chances for categories of description. What categories are to be used? This is a problem in choice of subject matter and conceptual formulation. Its solution for every study depends upon practical and theoretical interests that are out of bounds here. The problem can be brought into account, however, by consideration of three prominent dimensions along which descriptive categories of observational child studies differ. These dimensions are *literal objectivity*, *psychological specificity*, and *theoretical integration*.

The first two of these may be identified well enough by their names and examples to follow. Categories at one extreme of the third, theoretical integration, are taken directly from the unplanned network of everyday notions about behavior. Categories at the opposite extreme on this dimension are tied to statements of developed conceptual schemes, although *they generally are not in themselves conceptually refined*. Take *seeking affection* from the

study by Heinicke (1956; see also pp. 112–113) of children and their associates during separation of the child from his parents. This category refers to a commonly perceived mode of action; and, for purposes of observing and recording, Heinicke does *not* alter its everyday core meaning or reduce it to subordinate, mediating behavior items. Neither does he leave *seeking affection* in the lay network. On the contrary, he subsumes it under the *general relations category* of *succorance*, which, in turn, is derived from a still more general psychoanalytic model. Similar cases will be mentioned.

One can rate the categories of any observational child study on each of our three dimensions. This has been done for illustration in Table 3-6 with the descriptive terms of two studies, the one just considered, by Heinicke, and the study by Arrington (1932a) of play behavior in preschool children. The following seem representative of the categories that observers used in these investigations.

From Arrington: *contacts with material things; verbal contacts with persons* (i.e., "talking"); *physical contacts with persons.*

From Heinicke: *hostility—agent deprives; hostility—agent retaliates; avoidance; seeking attention; seeking affection.*

**TABLE 3-6. RATINGS ON STATED DIMENSIONS OF DESCRIPTIVE CATEGORIES USED by ARRINGTON (1932a) AND HEINICKE (1956)**

| | Arrington Categories | Heinicke Categories |
|---|---|---|
| Literal objectivity | Very high | Low |
| Psychological specificity | Very low | High |
| Theoretical integration | Low | Very high |

The ratings, which obviously can be only suggestive, are relative to the general run of observational research, not all research, in child development.

Several differences and relationships are expressed by these illustrative ratings. Note first that high literal objectivity is combined with low psychological specificity in Arrington's categories. Her *physical contacts with persons,* for example, are as palpable as can be and yet so lacking in psychological discriminativeness, so very general and vague in behavior content, as to make taps on the shoulder, hostile blows, and love pats all one and the same (cf. Murphy and Murphy, 1935). Heinicke's categories are oppositely directed. Seeing either *seeking affection* or *seeking attention,* for example, requires at least "perceptual inference" (Heider, 1944), and yet each of these is a singular kind of social action. Both might involve the child in physical contact with another person but each stands as a particular and unique sort of interpersonal behavior. We have already placed Heinicke's categories on the scale for theoretical integration. Arrington's, by contrast, are linked at most with implicit behavior theories.

Positions on these scales of certain observational methods are fairly clear, as the following spot checks indicate. The categories of specimen description are, in the recording stage, those of common speech. That is to say, they are quite freely inferential, highly specific in psychological content, and in no way bound to explicit constructs. Descriptive terms in the analysis stage

of the same method have run the gamut on each scale. This includes the scale of theoretical integration, on which categories with moorings in psychological field theory have been applied in studies by Gump and associates (see p. 92) and also in the Midwest research (see p. 91). Possibly the remaining clearest examples of theoretical integration are in applications of field unit analysis. Heinicke's research is representative here, and so is the study by Bishop (see pp. 110–112), in which categories to describe mother-child interaction are geared throughout with stimulus-response formulations. The profile in Table 3-6 of Arrington's study seems to fit well many early ventures in time and event sampling. Time sampling especially has moved down on the scale of literal objectivity and up on the scale of specificity, as in going from *verbal contacts with persons* (Arrington, 1932a) to *verbal aggression* (Walters et al., 1957) and *friendly approaches* (Marshall and McCandless, 1957).

Advantages in work with the more specific categories seem clear. To take an extreme example for what it implies in less extreme cases, building a useful theory about *physical contacts with persons* must be nearly impossible, especially when behavior so classified is recorded out of context, as it has been. Such a concept is so broad and equivocal as to mean almost "nothing in particular." It lifts one phenotypical aspect from the whole of behavior and draws into it a multitude of things which, genotypically, belong far apart. On the other hand, one can start to build a theory about *hostility (agent deprives*) or *hostility* (*agent retaliates*) or *avoidance* or *seeking affection* or *seeking attention,* with each singled out as *one* kind of contact with persons. One can indeed begin to build a theory that relates these and other such psychologically specific categories with one another. So one finds on referring to Heinicke's research and to other ventures in current child psychology.

Our discussion of reliability in observation has anticipated a need for partly inferential description in research on molar phenomena of child behavior. Objectivity that rules out everything but palpable facts is unequal to the requirements of observing in such research. Behavioral categories that call for some degree of inference can nevertheless be objective in an important sense if the following is correct.

On the negative side, objective inquiry means correcting against biases and special viewpoints that limit and misrepresent reality. On the positive side, it means describing conditions in the context of whatever one is trying to be objective about as they really are in that context. It follows that, if one is to be objective in describing actions and psychological situations, one must break through a wall of directly observed conditions and events by inference, and must see things as the other person sees them from his viewpoint, and as they really are for that person. If, instead, the student of molar behavior sticks to the facts as he sees them from his own viewpoint, and as they are for him, he will not be objective, but subjective in a bad sense, biased—and wrong (Barker and Wright, 1955, p. 205).

Anyone left with concern about this issue might reconsider the evidence for reliable observing of behavior that no one can see directly.

Blindness of data collection must vary inversely with the degree in which descriptive categories are bound to conceptual models. This is not to propose that good research designs in observational child studies have to be cast in postulate-theorem-demonstration form. Precedent for anything quite like this is meager, which is understandable. The facts of naturally occurring behavior are so numerous, various, widely dispersed, and complex that it is much easier to ask questions about them than to predict them; hypotheses in the true meaning of logical derivations from theory are not easily come by in this jungle area. At the same time, the probability of finding significant relationships between these facts seems sure to be increased by articulating the categories for gathering them with explicit constructs of one sort or another. It may go without saying that these constructs need not belong necessarily to particular psychological "schools," as in our examples.

## On Uses of Observational Methods

Different methods of observational child study have been examined here one by one. Viewing these methods collectively now, I should like to conclude by considering their possibilities in the larger research program in child development. Possible gains of further ecological, normative, idiographic, and systematic applications will be stated in an effort to summarize and develop earlier points and findings. Some proposals apply better to certain methods than to others, but readers can note where this is true.

1. Continued ecological research with these methods can lead to a natural history of child behavior. Like its predecessors in biological science, such a natural history would store plain information. Where do children spend their time away from laboratories, testing rooms, and clinics in different localities and cultures? What life settings do they inhabit and what are the characteristics of these settings? What situations-of-the-moment arise in particular episodes and what behavior of children do these situations engender? Theoretically and practically important problems of maturation and learning, of social behavior, and of personality formation need answers to these questions.

Observational methods do not offer the only approach to natural history problems in child development. Everyday child behavior and its conditions as well can be inquired about in interviews—with children or informants. Both can be similarly explored by questionnaires or reconstructed in part from responses to suitable tests and experimentally contrived settings (Wiest, 1957). Yet direct observation remains the least roundabout way to get data on the natural habitats and behavior of children.

2. Normative applications can produce norms that describe child behavior authentically and also specify its environmental conditions. Norms from psychological tests and laboratory measures quite generally catalogue the abilities or dispositional characteristics of classified children. These potentiality norms are invaluable. But we need as well normative descriptions that make the actual behavior of classified children a matter of scientific record. It is one thing, for example, to look at a table of norms and see that the average 2-year-old is able to walk upstairs alone, to mark time, to turn the leaves of a book, and to open boxes. It is quite another thing to study word pictures or other records that tell concretely how, how often, and in what situations representative 2-year-olds actually walk upstairs alone or the like. Descriptions of this kind can at least round out and vivify the potentiality norms; and observational methods can indeed supply them.

The predictive value of a behavior norm obviously goes up with increase in knowledge about the conditions under which it holds. Hence norms with built-in qualifications that point to environmental conditions of behavior are much to be desired. Here, again, observational methods seem uniquely promising; for parts and properties of the environment are spread out before direct observers of behavior. Not that observational child studies with a normative aim always seize the opportunity in this circumstance! The fact is that some of them short-circuit the environment and connect behavior directly with the child. One could almost consider this an error of omission. Clear chances to describe behavior regularities of 2-year-olds, 10-year-olds, boys, girls, or children of other such groupings with attention to the environmental contexts of these regularities are wide open to research with observational methods. Such description, moreover, can accomplish still more by supplying norms of psychological environments as research products of value in their own right.

3. Idiographic applications stand to test and to supplement other procedures in clinical studies of individual children. The various diagnostic instruments of child clinics are often cross-validated in something of a circle within the clinic setting. Observational methods can breach this circle by validating play sessions, projective tests, and other such devices against descriptions of everyday behavior and its conditions. Research to this end has made only small beginnings. More of it could help clinicians with their difficult problem of seeing children in clinics as children are in real life.

A related possibility is that, beyond testing other means of diagnosis, proven observational methods could be used to advantage in clinical field routines. The main idea here is embodied now in the case worker's diagnostic role, which has been defined traditionally by sensitive interpretation of circumstances in the life settings of children. Good impressionistic and interpretive case reports may always be needed for understanding children's troubles and adjustment patterns. Yet more case *records* of naturally occurring child behavior and its conditions might sharpen greatly and enlarge such understanding. More research to try out, adapt, and improve currently available ways to keep and analyze records of this kind might reasonably be expected to give clinical practice with children a stronger base.

4. Systematic applications stand to fill gaps that would otherwise be left in our knowledge of the laws of child behavior. Experimental child psychologists have shown great inventiveness in profitable tests of hypotheses, and increasingly hard problems of interdependence keep yielding to their manipulative procedures. Direct observers of child behavior have nevertheless worked with independent psychological variables that may overtax the best of Wundtian skill for a long while to come. This holds especially for complex variables of social context that are central in current theories of child behavior and development. Examples include aggressive, nurturant, and restrictive modes of action by associates, spontaneously changing group size and composition, rated power of bona fide companions, and enduring parental acceptance or rejection. Such variables have been subjected to control by selection in observational studies, with the result that relationships between them and significant dimensions of child behavior have been demonstrated. These relationships are usually of a low order. They are generally formulated without elegance, and they seldom have been assimilated explicitly to larger systems. Yet they have good points, which include the important one that lines of connection between their parameters and conditions in the natural milieu of the child have never been broken. This advantage must help to insure validity of implication for the everyday lives of children.

These considerations seem consistent with the larger experience of science. One may suppose on principle that science can ultimately harness experimentally (to its enormous advantage in precision of measurement and control of variables) almost any event that it chooses to investigate. Yet every science has learned that this cannot always be managed in practice. It is impossible now to make experimental arrangements that allow for the full size and complexity of many events, from whirlwinds to wars. Laws of rivers and of ocean currents can be demonstrated in laboratories, but scientists have to follow inland streams or go to sea to get new leads and to learn about important complications of these laws. The strategy in every such case is to capitalize upon experiments in nature by substituting selection for manipulation of variables. This has been done in observational child study, and it can be done better with continuing improvement in comparative designs and in techniques of observing, recording, and analysis.

# REFERENCES

Adams, S. 1932. A study of the growth of language between two and four years. *J. juv. Res.*, 16, 269–277.

Ainsworth, Mary A., and J. Bowlby. 1954. Research strategy in the study of mother-child separation. *Courrier*, of the Centre International de l'Enfance, 4, No. 3.

Allen, D. T. 1940. Film. *The development of Eugene, a 23-year-old boy isolated by 16 years of epileptic seizures*. Children's Hospital, Cincinnati, Ohio.

Allport, G. W., and H. S. Odbert. 1936. Trait-names: A psycho-lexical study. *Psychol. Monogr.*, 47, No. 211.

Ames, Louise B. 1946. Imaginary companions and related phenomena. *J. genet. Psychol.*, 69, 147–167.

———. 1949. Development of interpersonal smiling responses in the preschool years. *J. genet. Psychol.*, 74, 273–291.

———. 1952. The sense of self of nursery school children as manifested by their verbal behavior. *J. genet. Psychol.*, 81, 193–232.

Anderson, Angeline C., and Ruth Staples. 1933. A study of outdoor play, appetite and afternoon sleep of young children. *Child Develpm.*, 4, 191–193.

Anderson, H. H. 1939a. The measurement of domination and of socially integrative behavior in teachers' contacts with children. *Child Develpm.*, 10, 73–89.

———. 1939b. Domination and social integration in the behavior of kindergarten children and teachers. *Genet. Psychol. Monogr.*, 21, 287–385.

———. 1940. An examination of the concepts of domination and integration in relation to dominance and ascendance. *Psychol. Rev.*, 47, 21–37.

Anderson, J. E. 1933. The methods of child psychology. In C. A. Murchison (Ed.), *Handbook of child psychology*. (2nd ed.) Worcester, Mass.: Clark Univer. Press, pp. 3–28.

Andrus, Ruth. 1924. *A tentative inventory of the habits of children from two to four years of age*. New York: Teach. Coll. Contr. Educ., Columbia Univer., No. 160.

Appel, M. H. 1942. Aggressive behavior in nursery school children and adult procedures in dealing with such behavior. *J. exp. Educ.*, 11, 185–199.

Arrington, Ruth E. 1932a. *Interrelations in the behavior of young children*. New York: Columbia Univer. Press. (Child Develpm. Monogr., No. 8.)

———. 1932b. Some technical aspects of observer reliability as indicated in studies of the "talkies." *Amer. J. Sociol.*, 38, 409–417.

———. 1937. An important implication of time sampling in observational studies of behavior. *Amer. J. Sociol.*, 43, 284–295.

———. 1939. Time-sampling studies of child behavior. *Psychol. Monogr.*, 51, No. 2.

———. 1943. Time-sampling in studies of social behavior: A critical review of techniques and results with research suggestions. *Psychol. Bull.*, **40**, 81–124.

Axline, Virginia M. 1951. Observing children at play. *Teach. Coll. Rec.*, **52**, 358–363.

Baldwin, A. L. 1949. The effect of home environment on nursery-school behavior. *Child Develpm.*, **20**, 49–61.

——, Joan Kalhorn, and F. H. Breese. 1945. Patterns of parent behavior. *Psychol. Monogr.*, **58**, No. 5.

——. 1949. The appraisal of parent behavior. *Psychol. Monogr.*, **63**, No. 4.

Baldwin, B. T., E. A. Filmore, and L. Hadley. 1930. *Farm children: An investigation of rural child life in selected areas of Iowa.* New York: Appleton.

Bales, F. 1950. *Interaction process analysis.* Cambridge, Mass.: Addison-Wesley.

Barker, Margaret. 1930. *A technique for studying the social-material activities of young children.* New York: Columbia Univer. Press. (Child Develpm. Monogr., No. 3.)

Barker, R. G., P. Schoggen, and Louise S. Barker. 1955. A hemerography of Mary Ennis. In Arthur Burton and R. E. Benton (Eds.), *Clinical studies of personality.* New York: Harper.

Barker, R. G., and H. F. Wright. 1949. Psychological ecology and the problem of psychosocial development. *Child Develpm.*, **20**, 131–143.

——. 1951. *One boy's day.* New York: Harper.

——. 1955. *Midwest and its children: The psychological ecology of an American town.* New York: Row, Peterson.

Bateman, W. G. 1916. The language status of three children at the same ages. *Pedag. Sem.*, **23**, 211–239.

Bates, M. 1952. *Where winter never comes: A study of man and nature in the tropics.* New York: Scribner.

Bateson, G., and Margaret Mead. 1942. Film. *First days in the life of a New Guinea baby.* New York Univer. Film Library.

Beaver, Alma P. 1932. *Initiation of social contacts by preschool children.* New York: Columbia Univer. Press. (Child Develpm. Monogr., No. 7.)

Behrens, H. D. 1946–1948. Film. *A study in human development.* Parts I, II, III, and IV.

Psychological Cinema Register 90, 91, 92, and 92A. Audio-Visual Aid Library, Pennsylvania State College, State College, Pa.

Belcher, Esther L. 1932. A technique for diary analysis. *Child Develpm.*, **3**, 53–56.

Berne, Esther VanC. 1930. An investigation of the wants of seven children. *Univer. Iowa Stud. Child Welf.*, **4**, No. 2.

——, and Helen G. Kelly. 1934. The adequacy of samples of behavior obtained during short observation periods. *Univer. Iowa Stud. Child Welf.*, **9**, 115–125.

Bernhardt, K. S., Dorothy A. Millichamp, M. W. Charles, and Mary P. McFarland. 1937. An analysis of the social contacts of preschool children with the aid of motion pictures. *Toronto Univer. Stud., Child Develpm. Ser.*, No. 10. Toronto: Univer. Toronto Press.

Biber, Barbara, Lois B. Murphy, Louise P. Woodcock, and Irma S. Black. 1942. *Child life in school: A study of a seven-year-old group.* New York: Dutton.

Birdwhistell, R. L. 1955. Background to kinesics. *Rev. gen. Semant.*, **13**, 10–18.

Bishop, Barbara M. 1951. Mother-child interaction and the social behavior of children. *Psychol. Monogr.*, **65**, No. 11.

Blatz, W. E., Kathleen D. Allin, and Dorothy A. Millichamp. 1936. A study of laughter in the nursery-school child. *Toronto Univer. Stud., Child Develpm. Ser.*, No. 7. Toronto: Univer. Toronto Press.

Blatz, W. E., and E. A. Bott. 1927. Studies in mental hygiene of children. I. Behavior of public school children—a description of method. *J. genet. Psychol.*, **34**, 552–582.

Blatz, W. E., S. N. F. Chant, and M. D. Salter. 1937. Emotional episodes in the child of school age. *Toronto Univer. Stud., Child Develpm. Ser.*, No. 9. Toronto: Univer. Toronto Press.

Blatz, W. E., and Dorothy A. Millichamp. 1935. The development of emotion in the infant. *Toronto Univer. Stud., Child Develpm. Ser.*, No. 4. Toronto: Univer. Toronto Press.

Body, Margaret K. 1955. Patterns of aggression in the nursery school. *Child Develpm.*, **26**, 3–11.

Bonte, Eleanor P., and Mary Musgrove. 1943.

War and children's play. *Child Develpm.*, 14, 179-200.

Bott, Helen M. 1928. Observation of play activities in a nursery school. *Genet. Psychol. Monogr.*, 4, 44-88.

———. 1933. Method in social studies of young children. *Toronto Univer. Stud., Child Develpm. Ser.*, No. 1. Toronto: Univer. Toronto Press.

———. 1934. Personality development in young children. *Toronto Univer. Stud., Child Develpm. Ser.*, No. 2. Toronto: Univer. Toronto Press.

Bowlby, J., J. Robertson, and D. Rosenbluth. 1952. A two-year-old goes to hospital. *Psychoanal. Study Child*, 7, 82-94.

Boynton, M. A., and Florence L. Goodenough. 1930. The posture of nursery school children during sleep. *Amer. J. Psychol.*, 42, 270-278.

Brainard, P. P. 1927. Some observations of infant learning and instincts. *Pedag. Sem.*, 34, 231-254.

Bridges, Katharine M. B. 1932. Emotional development in early infancy. *Child Develpm.*, 3, 324-341.

———. 1933. A study of social development in early infancy. *Child Develpm.*, 4, 36-49.

———. 1936. The development of primary drives in infancy. *Child Develpm.*, 7, 40-56.

Brown, H. W. 1892. Some records of the thoughts and reasonings of children. *Pedag. Sem.*, 2, 358-396.

Brunswik, E. 1947. *Systematic and representative design of psychological experiments.* Berkeley: Univer. California Press.

Buchner, M. 1909. *Die Entwicklung der Gemütsbewegungen im ersten Lebensjahre.* Langensalza: Beyer.

Burnham, Marguerite P. 1956. Imaginative behavior of young children as revealed in their language. Unpublished doctoral dissertation. Columbia Univer.

Burnham, W. H. 1891. The observations of children at the Worcester Normal School. *Pedag. Sem.*, 1, 219-224.

Caille, R. K. 1933. *Resistant behavior of preschool children.* New York: Columbia Univer. Press. (Child Develpm. Monogr., No. 11.)

Campbell, E. H. 1933. The effect of nursery-school training upon the later food habits of the child. *Child Develpm.*, 4, 329-345.

Challman, R. C. 1932. Factors influencing friendships among preschool children. *Child Develpm.*, 3, 146-158.

Champney, H. 1941. Measurement of parent behavior. *Child Develpm.*, 12, 131-166.

Chevaleva-Janovskaja, E. 1927. Les Groupments spontanés d'enfants à l'âge préscolaire. *Arch. Psychol., Genève*, 20, 219-233.

Conrad, H. S. 1933. *The California behavior inventory for nursery school children.* Berkeley: Univer. California Press.

Conrad, H. S. 1934. A statistical study of ratings on the California behavior inventory for nursery school children. *Genet. Psychol. Monogr.*, 16, No. 1.

Crandall, V. J., and Anne Preston. 1955. Patterns and levels of maternal behavior. *Child Develpm.*, 26, 267-277.

Darwin, C. 1877. A biographical sketch of an infant. *Mind*, 2, 285-294.

Dawe, Helen C. 1934. An analysis of two hundred quarrels of preschool children. *Child Develpm.*, 5, 139-157.

———, Dorothy Ekern, and Harriet Berger. 1949. Differences in adult contacts with children. *J. Home Econ.*, 41, 87-88.

Dearborn, G. V. N. 1910. *Moto-sensory development: Observations on the first three years of childhood.* Baltimore: Warwick and York.

DeGuimps, R. 1895. How father Pestalozzi educated and observed his three-and-a-half-year-old son, 1774. In *Pestalozzi.* New York: Appleton.

Dennis, W. 1936. A biography of baby biographies. *Child Develpm.*, 7, 71-73.

———, and Marsena G. Dennis. 1937. Behavioral development in the first year as shown by forty biographies. *Psychol. Rec.*, 1, 349-361.

———. 1940a. *The Hopi child.* New York: Appleton-Century.

———. 1940b. The effect of cradling practices upon the onset of walking in Hopi children. *J. genet. Psychol.*, 56, 77-86.

Ding, G. F., and A. T. Jersild. 1932. A study of the laughing and smiling of preschool children. *J. genet. Psychol.*, 40, 452-472.

Dollard, J. 1935. A method for the sociological study of infancy and preschool childhood. *J. educ. Soc.*, **9**, 88–95.

Dow, Mildred. 1933. Playground behavior differentiating artistic from non-artistic children. *Psychol. Monogr.*, **45**, 82–94.

Dreger, R. M. 1955. Spontaneous conversation and story-telling of children in a naturalistic setting. *J. Psychol.*, **40**, 163–180.

Dresslar, F. B. 1901. A morning's observation of a baby. *Pedag. Sem.*, **8**, 469–481.

Dukes, W. F. 1951. Ecological representativeness in studying perceptual size-constancy in childhood. *Amer. J. Psychol.*, **64**, 87–93.

Escalona, Sibyll, Mary Leitch, and others. 1952. Early phases of personality development: a non-normative study of infant behavior. *Monogr. Soc. Res. Child Develpm.*, **17**, No. 1.

Fales, Evaline. 1937a. A rating scale of the vigorousness of play activities of preschool children. *Child Develpm.*, **8**, 15–45.

———. 1937b. A comparison of the vigorousness of play activities of preschool children. *Child Develpm.*, **8**, 144–158.

Felder, J. G. 1932. Some factors determining the nature and frequency of anger and fear outbreaks in preschool children. *J. juv. Res.*, **16**, 278–290.

Festinger, L., and D. Katz. 1953. *Research methods in the behavioral sciences.* New York: Dryden.

Fisher, Mary S. 1934. *Language patterns of preschool children.* New York: Columbia Univer. Press. (Child Develpm. Monogr., No. 15.)

Fite, M. D. 1940. Aggressive behavior in young children and children's attitudes toward aggression. *Genet. Psychol. Monogr.*, **22**, 151–319.

Friedman, Alice. 1951. Observations in a play group of young children. *Indiv. Psychol. Bull.*, **9**, 25–30.

Fries, Margaret E. 1950. Film. *A character neurosis with depressive and compulsive trends in the making: Life history of Mary from birth to fifteen years.* New York Univer. Film Library. National Film Library.

———, C. Kluckhohn, and P. J. Woolf. 1944. Film. *Family life of the Navajo Indian.* New York Univer. Film Library. National Film Library.

Fries, Margaret E., and P. J. Woolf, 1944. Film. *Psychological implications of behavior during the clinical visit.* New York Univer. Film Library.

Gellert, Elizabeth. 1955. Systematic observation: A method in child study. *Harvard Educ. Rev.*, **25**, 179–195.

Gesell, A. L. 1934. *An atlas of infant behavior.* New Haven: Yale Univer. Press, 2 Vols.

———. 1935. Cinemanalysis: A method of behavior study. *J. genet. Psychol.*, **47**, 3–16.

Gilmer, B. Von H. 1933. An analysis of the spontaneous responses of the newborn infant. *J. genet. Psychol.*, **42**, 392–405.

Goodenough, Florence L. 1928. Measuring behavior traits by means of repeated short samples. *J. juv. Res.*, **12**, 230–235.

———. 1930. Interrelationships in the behavior of young children. *Child Develpm.*, **1**, 29–47.

———. 1931. *Anger in young children.* Minneapolis: Univer. Minn. Press.

———. 1937. The observation of children's behavior as a method in social psychology. *Soc. Forces*, **15**, 476–479.

———. 1938. The use of pronouns by young children: A note on the development of self-awareness. *J. genet. Psychol.*, **52**, 333–345.

———, and J. D. Anderson. 1931. *Experimental child study.* New York: Century.

Graves, E. A. 1937. A study of competitive and cooperative behavior by the short sample technique. *J. abnorm. soc. Psychol.*, **32**, 343–351.

Green, Elsie H. 1933a. Friendships and quarrels among preschool children. *Child Develpm.*, **4**, 237–252.

———. 1933b. Group play and quarreling among preschool children. *Child Develpm.*, **4**, 302–307.

Guetzkow, H. 1950. Unitizing and categorizing problems in coding qualitative data. *J. clin. Psychol.*, **6**, 47–58.

Gump, P. V. 1954. Observational study of activities for disturbed children. In *Group work and community organization, 1953–1954.* New York: Columbia Univer. Press.

———, and P. H. Schoggen. 1955a. *Wally O'Neil at camp.* Wayne Univer.

Gump, P. V. 1955b. *Wally O'Neil at home.* Wayne Univer.

Gump, P. V., P. Schoggen, anl F. Redl. 1957. The camp milieu and its immediate effects. *J. soc. Issues,* 13, No. 1.

Gump, P. V., and B. Sutton-Smith. 1955a. Activity-setting and social interaction: A field study. *Amer. J. Orthopsychiat.,* Oct., 755–760.

———. 1955b. The "it" role in children's games. *The group,* Feb., 3–8.

Gump, P. V., B. Sutton-Smith, and F. Redl. 1955. Influence of camp activities upon camper behavior. Wayne State Univer. Library.

Haggerty, Laura C. G. 1930. What a two-and-one-half-year-old child said in one day. *Pedag. Sem. and J. genet. Psychol.,* 37, 75–100.

Haggerty, M. E., W. C. Olson, and E. K. Wickman. 1930. *Haggerty-Olson-Wickman behavior rating schedules.* Yonkers, New York: World Book.

Hagman, E. P. 1933. The companionships of preschool children. *Univer. Iowa Stud. Child Welf.,* 7, No. 4.

Hall, G. S. 1892. Editorial. *Pedag. Sem.,* 2, 335–342.

Hartley, Ruth E., L. K. Frank, and R. N. Goldenson, 1952. *Understanding children's play.* New York: Columbia Univer. Press.

Haskell, Ellen M. 1906. *Child observations.* 1st series: Imitations and allied activities, with an introduction by E. H. Russell. Boston: D. C. Heath.

Hattwick, Berta Weiss. 1936. Interrelations between the preschool child's behavior and certain factors in the home. *Child Develpm.,* 7, 200–226.

Heathers, G. 1954. The adjustment of two-year-olds in a novel social situation. *Child Develpm.,* 25, 147–158.

———. 1955. Emotional dependence and independence in nursery school play. *J. genet. Psychol.,* 87, 37–57.

Heering, Gertrude A. 1932. A study of thumb-sucking in infants from two to seventeen weeks of age. *Child Develpm.,* 3, 273–277.

Heider, F. 1944. Social perception and phenomenal causality. *Psychol. Rev.,* 51, 358–374.

Heinicke, C. M. 1956. Some effects of separating two-year-old children from their parents: A comparative study. *Hum. Relat.,* 105–176.

———, and R. F. Bales. 1953. Developmental trends in the structure of small groups. *Sociometry,* 16, 7–38.

Heyns, R. W., and R. Lippitt. 1954. Systematic observational techniques. In *Handbook of social psychology,* Vol. 1. Cambridge: Addison-Wesley.

Hogan, Louise E. 1898. *A study of a child.* New York: Harper.

Horn, E. 1914. *Distribution of opportunity for participation among the various pupils in class-room recitation.* New York: Teach. Coll. Contr. Educ., Columbia Univer.

Hulson, Eva L. 1930. An analysis of the free play of ten four-year-old children through consecutive observations. *J. juv. Res.,* 14, 188–208.

Hyde, R. W., and R. H. York. 1948. A technique for investigating interpersonal relationships in a mental hospital. *J. abnorm. soc. Psychol.,* 43, 287–299.

Inselberg, Rachael M. 1958. The causation and manifestations of emotional behavior in Filipino children. *Child Develpm.,* 29, 249–254.

Irwin, O. C., and T. Curry. 1941. Vowel elements in the crying vocalizations of infants under ten days of age. *Child Develpm.,* 12, 99–110.

Issacs, Susan. 1930. *Intellectual growth in young children.* London: Routledge.

———. 1933. *Social development in young children.* London: Routledge.

———. 1949. *The psychological aspects of child development.* London: Evans.

Janus, S. Q. 1943. An investigation of the relationship between children's language and their play. *J. genet. Psychol.,* 62, 3–61.

Jersild, A. T. 1933. The constancy of certain behavior patterns in young children. *Amer. J. Psychol.,* 45, 125–129.

———, and M. D. Fite. 1939. *The influence of nursery school experience on children's social adjustments.* New York: Columbia Univer. Press. (Child Develpm. Monogr., No. 25.)

Jersild, A. T., and F. B. Holmes. 1935. *Chil-*

dren's fears. New York: Columbia Univer. Press. (Child Develpm. Monogr., No. 20).

Jersild, A. T., and F. V. Markey. 1935. Conflicts between preschool children. New York: Columbia Univer. Press. (Child Develpm. Monogr., No. 21.)

Jersild, A. T., and M. F. Meigs. 1939. Direct observation as a research method. Rev. Educ. Res., 9, 472–482.

Joël, W. 1936. "Behavior maturity" of children of nursery school age. Child Develpm., 7, 189–199.

Kerkman, D. H., and H. F. Wright. 1959. Activity settings and behavior of children at school in communities differing in size. Amer. Psychologist, 14, 346. (Abstract)

King, G. F., J. C. Erhmann, and D. M. Johnson. 1952. Experimental analysis of the reliability of observations of social behavior. J. soc. Psychol., 35, 151–160.

Koch, Helen L. 1935. An analysis of certain forms of so-called "nervous habits" in young children. J. genet. Psychol., 46, 139–169.

———. 1955a. The relation of certain family constellation characteristics and the attitudes of children toward adults. Child Develpm., 26, 13–40.

———. 1955b. Some personality correlates of sex, sibling position, and sex of sibling among five- and six-year-old children. Genet. Psychol. Monogr., 52, 3–50.

———. 1956a. Attitudes of young children toward their peers as related to certain characteristics of their siblings. Psychol. Monogr., 70, No. 19.

———. 1956b. Some emotional attitudes of the young child in relation to characteristics of his siblings. Child Develpm., 27, 393–426.

Koppe, W. A. 1952. A behavior setting survey of the small American town of Walker. Unpublished report. Midwest Social Psychology Field Station, Univer. Kansas.

Kounin, J., and P. Gump. 1958. The ripple effect in discipline. Elem. Sch. J., 59, 158–162.

Lafore, Gertrude G. 1945. Practices of parents in dealing with preschool children. New York: Teach. Coll. Contr. Educ. Columbia Univer. Press.

Landreth, Catherine. 1940. Consistency of four methods of measuring on type of sporadic emotional behavior in nursery school. J. gen. Psychol., 57, 101–118.

———. 1941. Factors associated with crying in young children in the nursery school and the home. Child Develpm., 12, 81–97.

Langmuir, Mary S., L. J. Stone, J. Buchner, and J. Bohmer. 1941–1952. Films. Vassar series: studies of normal personality development. New York Univer. Film Library.

Larr, M., and R. L. Jenkins. 1953. Three factors in parent behavior. J. consult. Psychol., 17, 306–308.

Lasko, Joan Kalhorn. 1954. Parent behavior toward first and second children. Genet. Psychol. Monogr., 49–50, 97–138.

Lerner, E., and Lois B. Murphy. 1941. Methods for the study of personality in young children. Monogr. Soc. Res. Child Develpm., 6, No. 4.

Lewin, K. 1946. Behavior and development as a function of the total situation. In L. Carmichael (Ed.), Manual of child psychol. (2nd Ed.) New York: Wiley.

Lippitt, R., N. Polansky, and S. Rosen. 1952. The dynamics of power: A field study of social influence in groups of children. Hum. Relat., 5, 37–64.

Loomis, A. M. 1931. A technique for observing the social behavior of a group of nursery school children. New York: Columbia Univer. Press. (Child Develpm. Monogr., No. 5.)

McCandless, B. R., and Helen R. Marshall. 1957. Sex differences in social acceptance and participation of preschool children. Child Develpm., 28, 421–425.

McCarthy, Dorothea A. 1930. The language development of the preschool child. Inst. Child Welf., Monogr. Ser., No. 4.

McCay, Jeanette B., and Marie B. Fowler. 1941. Some sex differences observed in a group of nursery school children. Child Develpm., 12, 75–79.

McClelland, D. C. 1951. Personality. New York: Dryden.

McDowell, M. S. 1937. Frequency of choice of play material by preschool children. Child Develpm., 8, 305–310.

McFarland, Margaret B. 1938. Relationships between young sisters as revealed in their overt responses. New York: Columbia Univer. Press. (Child Develpm. Monogr., No. 23.)

Maas, H. S. 1954. The role of members in clubs of lower-class and middle-class adolescents. *Child Develpm.*, 25, 241–251.

Major, D. R. 1906. *First steps in mental growth*. New York: Macmillan.

Mallay, Helena. 1935a. Growth in social behavior and mental activity after six months in nursery school. *Child Develpm.*, 6, 303–309.

———. 1935b. A study of some of the techniques underlying the establishment of successful social contacts at the preschool level. *J. genet. Psychol.*, 47, 431–457.

Manwell, Elizabeth M., and Ida G. Mengert. 1934. A study of the development of two- and three-year-old children with respect to play activities. *Univer. Iowa Stud. Child Welf.*, 9, 69–110.

Markey, F. V. 1935. *Imaginative behavior of preschool children*. New York: Columbia Univer. Press. (Child Develpm. Monogr., No. 18.)

Marshall, Helen R., and B. R. McCandless. 1957a. A study in prediction of social behavior of preschool children. *Child Develpm.*, 28, 149–159.

———. 1957b. Relationships between dependence on adults and social acceptance by peers. *Child Develpm.*, 28, 413–419.

Mead, Margaret. 1951a. Film. *Sibling rivalry in Bali and New Guinea*. New York Univer. Film Library.

———. 1951b. Film. *Bathing babies in three cultures*. New York Univer. Film Library.

Michaelis, A. R. 1955. *Research films in biology, anthropology, psychology, and medicine*. New York: Academic Press.

Moore, Elizabeth S. 1931. The development of mental health in a group of young children. *Univer. Iowa Stud. Child Welf.*, 4, No. 6.

Moustakas, C. E., and H. D. Schalock. 1955. An analysis of the therapist-child interaction in play therapy. *Child Develpm.*, 26, 143–157.

Moustakas, C. E., I. E. Sigel, and H. D. Schalock. 1956. An objective method for the measurement and analysis of child-adult interaction. *Child Develpm.*, 27, 109–134.

Muchow, Martha, and H. Muchow. 1935. Der Lebensraum des Grossstadtkindes. From the monograph series: *Der Ertrag der Hamburger Erziehungsbewegung*, No. 2, Hamburg: Martin Riegel.

Murphy, G., and Lois B. Murphy. 1935. The influence of social situations upon the behavior of children. In C. A. Murchison (Ed.), *Handbook of social psychology*. Worcester, Mass.: Clark Univer. Press.

Murphy, Lois B. 1937. *Social behavior and child personality*. New York: Columbia Univer. Press.

Navarra, J. G. 1955. *The development of scientific concepts in a young child: A case study*. New York: Bureau Publ., Teach. Coll., Columbia Univer.

Nesbitt, Margaret. 1943. Student and child relationships in the nursery school. *Child Develpm.*, 14, 143–166.

Nice, Margaret M. 1932. An analysis of the conversation of children and adults. *Child Develpm.*, 3, 240–245.

Olson, W. C. 1929. *The measurement of nervous habits in normal children*. Minneapolis: Univer. Minnesota Press.

———. 1931. A study of classroom behavior. *J. Educ. Psychol.*, 22, 449–454.

———, and Elizabeth M. Cunningham. 1934. Time-sampling techniques. *Child Develpm.*, 5, 41–58.

Olson, W. C., and B. S. Kotzle. 1936. Amount and rate of talk of young children. *J. exp. Educ.*, 5, 175–179.

Olson, W. C., and Muriel M. Wilkinson. 1932. The measurement of child behavior in terms of its social stimulus value. *J. exp. Educ.*, 1, 92–95.

Parten, Mildred A. 1932. Social participation among preschool children. *J. abnorm. soc. Psychol.*, 27, 243–269.

———. 1933a. Leadership among preschool children. *J. abnorm. soc. Psychol.*, 27, 430–440.

———. 1933b. Social play among preschool children. *J. abnorm. soc. Psychol.*, 28, 136–147.

———, and S. M. Newhall. 1943. Social behavior of preschool children. In R. G.

Barker, J. S. Kounin, and H. F. Wright: *Child behavior and development.* New York: McGraw-Hill. Pp. 509–525.

Pasricha, Prem. 1956. Psychological analysis of activities and social behavior of five-year-olds. Unpublished doctoral dissertation, Univer. Minnesota.

Piaget, J. 1932. *The moral judgment of the child.* New York: Harcourt, Brace.

——. 1952. *The origins of intelligence in children.* New York: International Univer. Press.

Preyer, W. 1888–1889. *Die Seele des Kindes.* Leipzig: Fernan, 1882. (tr. H. W. Brown). The mind of the child. Part 1: the senses and the will. Part 2: the development of the intellect. New York: Appleton.

——. 1893. *Die geistige Entwicklung in der ersten Kindheit.* Stuttgart: Union, 1893. (tr. H. W. Brown) Mental development in the child. New York: Appleton.

Read, Katherine H. 1940. Factors affecting agreement in teachers' behavior ratings of nursery school children. *J. exp. Educ.,* 9, 133–138.

Reckless, W. C. 1929. Case studies built around observations of individual foster-children in the playroom of a receiving home. *Papers and Proceedings Amer. Sociol. Soc.,* 24, 170–173.

Reese, Margaret. 1932. A study of the effects of daylight savings time upon the sleep of young children. *Child Develpm.,* 3, 86–89.

Richards, T. W., and Marjorie P. Simons. 1941. The Fels Child Behavior Scale. *Genet. Psychol. Monogr.,* 24, 259–309.

Ricketts, Agnes F. 1934. A study of the behavior of young children in anger. *Univer. Iowa Stud. Child Welf.,* 9, 160–171.

Roberts, Katherine E., and Rachel S. Ball. 1938. A study of personality in young children by means of a series of rating scales. *J. Genet. Psychol.,* 52, 79–149.

Roberts, Mary P. 1934. A study of children's play in the home environment. *Univer. Iowa Stud. Child Welf.,* 8, 35–98.

Robertson, J. 1952. Film. *A two-year-old goes to hospital. A guide to the film, A two-year-old goes to hospital.* London: Tavistock Clinic. New York Univer. Film Library.

Robertson, J., and J. Bowlby. 1952. Responses of young children to separation from their mothers. II. Observations of the sequences of response of children aged 18 to 24 months during the course of separation. *Courrier,* of the Centre International de l'Enfance, 2, 131–142.

Robinson, Esther W., and H. S. Conrad. 1933. The reliability of observations of talkativeness and social contact among nursery school children by the "Short Time Sample" technique. *J. exp. Educ.,* 1, 161–165.

Roff, M. 1949. A factorial study of the Fels Parent Behavior Scales. *Child Develpm.,* 20, 29–45.

——, and L. Roff. 1940. An analysis of the variance of conflict behavior in preschool children. *Child Develpm.,* 11, 43–60.

Russell, E. H. 1892. The study of children at the State Normal School, Worcester, Massachusetts. *Pedag. Sem.,* 2, 343–357.

Sanford, R. N., and others. 1943. Physique, personality, and scholarship. *Monogr. Soc. Res. Child Develpm.,* 8, No. 1.

Sarason, S., K. Davidson, F. Lighthall, and R. R. Waite. 1958. Classroom observation of high and low anxious children. *Child Develpm.,* 29, 287–295.

Schoggen, P. H. 1954. Structural properties of children's behavior based on sixteen daylong specimen records. Unpublished doctoral dissertation. Univer. Kansas.

Scott, Ethel. 1931. A study of the sleeping habits of twenty-nine children of preschool age. *Child Develpm.,* 2, 236–328.

Scupin, E., and G. Scupin. 1907. *Bubis erste Kindheit.* Leipzig: Grieben.

——. 1910. *Bubi im vierten bis sechsten Lebensjahre.* Leipzig: Grieben.

Sears, Pauline S. 1951. Doll play aggression in normal young children: Influence of sex, age, sibling status, father's absence. *Psychol. Monogr.,* 65, No. 6.

Seham, M., and D. V. Boardman. 1934. A study of motor automatisms. *Arch. Neurol. Psychiat.,* 32, 154–173.

Sells, S. B., and R. W. Ellis. 1948. Observational procedures used in research. *Rev. educ. Res.,* 18, 395–407.

——. 1951. Observational procedures used in research. *Rev. educ. Res.,* 21, 432–449.

Shallit, Rebecca. 1932. The dramatic play of ten nursery school children. *Child Develpm.*, 3, 359–362.

Shinn, Milicent W. 1900. *The biography of a baby*. Boston: Houghton Mifflin.

Shirley, Mary M. 1931–1933. *The first two years*, Vol. I, Vol. II, Vol. III. Minneapolis: Univer. Minnesota Press.

——. 1942. Children's adjustments to a strange situation. *J. abnorm. soc. Psychol.*, 37, 201–217.

——, and Lillian Poynts. 1941. The influence of separation from mother on children's emotional responses. *J. Psychol.*, 12, 251–283.

Siegel, Alberta E. 1957. Aggressive behavior of young children in the absence of an adult. *Child Develpm.*, 28, 371–378.

Simpson, J. 1956. Social weather of children in the behavior settings of Midwest. Unpublished doctoral dissertation. Univer. Kansas.

Slater, Eleanor. 1939. Studies from the center for research in child health and development, School of Public Health, Harvard Univer. II. Types, levels, and irregularities of response to a nursery school situation of forty children observed with special reference to the home environment. *Monogr. Soc. Res. Child Develpm.*, 2, 1–148.

Smith, Madorah E. 1933. The influence of age, sex, and situation on the frequency, form and function of questions asked by preschool children. *Child Develpm.*, 4, 201–213.

Smith, M. 1931a. *A study of the unsupervised behavior of a group of institutional children*. Nashville: Marshall and Bruce.

——. 1931b. The agreement of observers concerning groups of behavior traits. *J. juv. Res.*, 15, 246–250.

——. 1933. A method of analyzing the interaction of children. *J. juv. Res.*, 17, 78–88.

Snyder, Alice D. 1914. Notes on the talk of a two-and-a-half-year-old boy. *Pedag. Sem.*, 21, 412–424.

Soskin, W. E. 1951. Unpublished report.

Spitz, R. A. 1945. Hospitalism: An inquiry into the genesis of psychiatric conditions in early childhood. *Psychoanal. Study Child.*, 1, 53–74.

——. 1947. Film. *Birth and the first fifteen minutes of life*. New York Univer. Film Library. National Film Library.

——. 1949a. The role of ecological factors in emotional development. *Child Develpm.*, 20, 145–165.

——. 1949b. Film. *Somatic consequences of emotional starvation*. New York Univer. Film Library.

——. 1951. Film. *Genesis of emotions*. New York Univer. Film Library.

Stalnaker, Elizabeth. 1933. Language of the preschool child. *Child Develpm.*, 4, 229–236.

Stern, W. 1930. *Psychology of early childhood*. New York: Holt.

——, and Clara Stern. 1910. Die zeichnerische Entwicklung eines Knaben vom 4 bis zum 7 Jahre. *Z. angew. Psychol.*, 3, 1–31.

Stone, L. J. 1941. Experiments in group play and readiness for destruction: In methods for the study of personality of young children edited by Eugene Lerner and Lois Barclay Murphy. *Monogr. Soc. Res. Child Develpm.*, 6, No. 4, 100–155.

——. 1952. Some problems of filming children's behavior: A discussion based on experience in the production of studies of normal personality development. *Child Develpm.*, 23, 227–233.

Stubbs, Esther, and O. C. Irwin. 1933. Laterality of limb movements of four newborn infants. *Child Develpm.*, 4, 358–359.

Sully, J. 1895. *Studies of childhood*. New York: Appleton.

Swan, Carla. 1938. Individual differences in facial expressive behavior of preschool children. *Genet. Psychol. Monogr.*, 20, 557–641.

Swinton, R. S. 1934. Analysis of child behavior by intermittent photography. *Child Develpm.*, 5, 292–293.

Taine, M. 1877. On the acquisition of language by children. *Mind*, 2, 252–259.

Thomas, Dorothy S. 1932. An attempt to develop precise measurements in the social behavior field. *Sociologus*, 8, 436–456.

——, A. M. Loomis, and Ruth E. Arrington. 1933. *Observational studies of social be-*

*havior.* New Haven: Inst. Hum. Relat., Yale Univer.

Thomas, Dorothy S., and others. 1929. *Some new techniques for studying social behavior.* New York: Columbia Univer. Press. (Child Develpm. Monogr., No. 1.)

Tiedemann, D. 1927. *Beobachtungen über die Entwicklung der Seelenfähigkeiten bei Kindern.* Altenburg: Oscar Bonde, 1897. First published in 1787. (From Tiedemann's observations on the development of the mental faculties of children. (tr. C. Murchison and S. Langer) *Pedag. Sem. and J. genet. Psychol.,* **34,** 205–230.

Tucker, C. 1940. *A study of mothers' practices and activities of the children in a cooperative nursery school.* New York: Teach. Coll. Contr. Educ., Columbia Univer.

Two Parents. 1928. The scientific interests of a boy in preschool years. *Forum Educ.,* **6,** 17–37.

VanAlstyne, Dorothy. 1932. *Play behavior and choice of play materials of preschool children.* Chicago: Univer. Chicago Press.

———. 1935. Relaxation and some related factors: An exploratory study made in five nursery school units. *Child Develpm.,* **6,** 310–321.

———. 1936. A new scale for rating school behavior and attitude in the elementary school. *J. educ. Psychol.,* **27,** 677–693.

Vance, T. F., and Verna M. Temple. 1933. Food preferences of preschool children: A comparison of rural children with children of the Iowa State Nursery School. *Child Develpm.,* **4,** 222–228.

Walters, J., Doris Pearce, Lucille Dahms. 1957. Affectional and aggressive behavior of preschool children. *Child Develpm.,* **28,** 15–26.

Washburn, Ruth W. 1932. A scheme for grading the reactions of children in a new social situation. *J. genet. Psychol.,* **40,** 84–90.

———. 1936. A simultaneous observation-and-recording method with specimen records of activity patterns in young children. *Psychol. Monogr.,* **47,** No. 2.

Weiss, Berta A. 1931. An experimental investigation of certain factors involved in the preschool child's compliance with com-mands. Master's thesis, State Univer. Iowa.

West, J. Y. 1937. *A technique for appraising certain observable behavior of children in science in elementary school.* New York: Teach. Coll. Contr. Educ., Columbia Univer.

White, M. A., and H. M. Williams. 1939. The approach-withdrawal pattern in the social behavior of young children. *J. genet. Psychol.,* **54,** 73–84.

White, Margaret R. 1931. Some factors affecting the night sleep of children. *Child Develpm.,* **2,** 234–235.

Whiting, J. W. M., and I. L. Child. 1953. *Child training and personality: A cross cultural study.* New Haven: Yale Univer. Press.

Whyte, W. F. 1951. Observational field-work methods. In Marie Jahoda, M. Deutsch, and S. W. Cook (Eds.), *Research methods in social relations: With especial reference to prejudice.* New York: Dryden, 493–513.

Wiest, W. M. 1957. Children's psychological living conditions in communities differing in size as revealed by a projective test of the environment. Unpublished master's thesis, Univer. Kansas.

Woodcock, Louise P. 1941. *Life and ways of the two-year-old.* A teacher's study. New York: Dutton.

Wright, H. F. 1956. Psychological development in Midwest. *Child Develpm.,* **27,** 265–286.

———. 1957. The city-town project: Aims and methods. Unpublished manuscript. Univer. Kansas.

———, and R. G. Barker. 1950. *Methods in psychological ecology.* Lawrence, Kansas: Univer. Kansas.

Wright, H. F., and A. H. Dreyer. 1959. Social transactions of children in pedestrian streams of communities differing in size. Unpublished manuscript. Univer. Kansas.

Wright, H. F., and W. M. Wiest. 1958. Children's miniature constructions of their communities as models of their habitats in communities differing in size. *Amer. Psychologist,* **13,** 328. (Abstract)

Wrightstone, J. W. 1933. Analyzing and measuring democracy in the classroom. *The Nation's Schools,* **11,** 31–35.

# chapter 4

# The Laboratory-
# Experimental Study
# of Child
# Behavior

Sidney W. Bijou
Donald M. Baer
*University of Washington*

The purposes of this chapter are four in number. The first is to define what is meant by an experimental technique of study. The second is to point out the special advantages and limitations of this technique when applied to the problem of child behavior. The third is to describe representative problems and procedures in the experimental investigation of child behavior. It may be that such an analysis will serve to indicate problem areas in which experimental techniques may be applied or re-applied

with fruitfulness. If so, the fourth goal of this chapter is to stimulate further experimental study.

## Meaning of the Experimental Technique

The experimental technique is one of several methods of obtaining information for a science. (Most alternative methods can be collected under the label of *correlational* techniques.) The technique is most commonly applied when the investigator wishes to study a suspected causative relationship holding between a phenomenon of some interest (dependent variable) and one or more other factors (independent variables). A situation is constructed in such a way that the dependent variable is readily observable, the independent variable is introduced and varied in a systematic manner, and all other variables are controlled to prevent them from influencing the dependent variable. Changes in the dependent variables are then stated as a function of the preceding changes in the independent variable.

The essential concept involved in the definition of experimental technique is that of control. In experimental logic phenomena do not change without cause. A statement of cause and effect can be made only when a variation in the supposed effect is coincidental to a preceding variation in the supposed cause, if no other factor has changed. The best guarantee that no other factors have changed is to gain control of them and keep them at fixed values.

This essential need for control over all possible causal factors has conferred upon experimental techniques a secondary characteristic of being *labora-tory* procedures. A laboratory is simply a place in which causal factors may be brought under the investigator's control more easily than elsewhere; it has no other essential characteristics. For the physicist, this may mean a place in which temperature, pressure, or radiation are controllable; for the psychologist, a place in which stimulation to an organism is controllable.

Another secondary characteristic of the experimental technique is that measurement of changes in both the independent and dependent variables is done, whenever possible, by objective (i.e., mechanical) means. Ultimately, of course, observation is done by the human experimenter. The traditional mediation of this process through mechanical instruments is an explicit recognition that (1) the human observer is often (not always) less sensitive than a mechanical device, (2) the human observer is usually less reliable than a mechanical device, and (3) identical mechanical instruments are more readily produced in larger numbers than trained human observers (an important feature if science is to be considered a body of public knowledge).

The use of a laboratory and of objective means of measuring add accuracy and reliability to the logic of the experimental technique. Thus experimentation, well executed, generates relatively precise statements of cause and effect which are remarkably unambiguous. This is its essential attribute. Hence Underwood (1957), speaking of experimental designs, says: ". . . there is only one basic principle, namely, design the experiment so that effects of the independent variable can be evaluated un-

ambiguously." However, it must be noted that even an accurate, reliable, and unambiguous statement of cause and effect is not immune to any broader (or incorrect) meaning that the experimenter may choose to place upon it. Interpretation is a problem outside the present one; but it suggests that experimental technique per se is not a final definition of science. Instead, it is considered here as a technique that is usually efficient in producing unambiguous statements and will frequently prove indispensable for that purpose.

## Application of Experimental Technique

The formula for experimentation in child behavior is simply translated from the general formula. A situation is constructed that allows for the control of all factors affecting a child's behavior; subsequently, one of these factors is introduced as a variable, and objective observations are made of any consequent changes in the child's behavior. The detailed application of this formula involves a recognition of the behaviors that a child exhibits and of the factors that can influence those behaviors. The traditional conceptual scheme for enumerating the sources of all such factors lists three major areas; the limitations of an experimental technique in the study of child behavior become apparent when the experimenter's ability to control factors from these areas is evaluated. The three areas are (1) the child's present environment, (2) the child's history of interaction with his past environments, and (3) the child's genetic endowment.

## THE CHILD'S
## PRESENT ENVIRONMENT

Clearly, the child's present environment will prove the simplest to control. Simply by choosing a well-placed room as a laboratory, the experimenter prevents a large amount of uncontrolled stimulation to the child. Within a room it is practical to wield stimuli in a systematic manner and to observe and record behavior accurately and reliably. The thoroughness with which current environment can be controlled is readily demonstrated on the animal level, where a selected response of an individual animal in a properly engineered experimental situation can easily be shown to vary *only* in response to the experimenter's manipulation of the stimulus environment. The same demonstration with a young child has been achieved, although perhaps not quite so easily. Figure 4-1 represents the bar-pressing behavior of a 4-year-old girl, who, when presented with an amber light, responds in a very uniform manner for reinforcements consisting of trinkets, candy, and cookies delivered on a variable ratio schedule; when presented with a blue light marking a period of no reinforcement, the subject immediately stops responding but just as immediately resumes at her characteristic rate when the amber light returns.

The behavior under study here is a discrimination process. The stability of the behavior and its immediate responsiveness to the manipulated variables show that the experimenter has in hand virtually all factors involved in this situation. Discrimination certainly is one

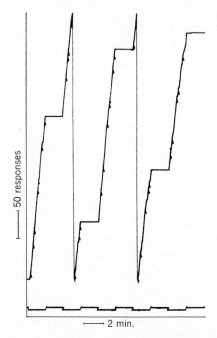

Fig. 4-1. Cumulative response curve of discrimination learning on the ninth experimental day. The subject is a 3-year-old girl. Depressions on the time line indicate two minutes of amber light; elevations, two minutes of blue light. Reinforcements, indicated by pips on the response curve, were delivered on a variable ratio 50 schedule only during the amber-light periods.

of the most important classes of child behavior. These statements in combination lend a great deal of significance to the study described. It is important, nevertheless, to show the limitations of this significance. It would be easy to point to the artificiality of such studies and suggest that the relationships found need not be typical of child behavior in vivo. Certainly it is correct to say that few if any of a child's everyday discriminations will be formed under conditions like those established in the laboratory. Real life discriminations are not made to such regular alternations of stimuli, the cues and the responses are more variable and more complex, the reinforcers differ from occasion to occasion, the reinforcement schedule is more complex, and the entire process is probably not pursued systematically.

A laboratory study of discrimination is ideally suited to a study of any of these variables acting in a pure and simple form. Despite the fact that a child will rarely encounter a pure and simple case of any such variable, this information is of value. The history of science suggests that the complexities of the child's real world are probably only multiple combinations of pure and simple processes. Hence the complexity of child behavior in vivo my result only from the large number of factors involved; yet each factor by itself may operate in a simple manner, readily and completely understandable in a laboratory setting.

Since this supposition has served other sciences well in the past, no other justification will be offered. Its acceptance means that "artificial" laboratory studies of the child's response to his present environment become not only valuable but in fact essential. But by no means are such studies exhaustive. A science of child behavior will require a great deal of additional information that laboratory techniques will prove inadequate to supply. Yet any alternative assumption that the whole child in his whole world may prove to be more than the sum of his and its parts, although conceivably meaningful, is best considered only after a thorough study of the parts has been made.

Terrell reflects this point of view forcefully:

There is some evidence . . . for contending that the likelihood of variables which are known to apply at a simple behavioral level to be relevant also at a more complex level is greater than the probability that variables suggested as relevant in complicated, poorly controlled studies are in fact relevant at that level. The evidence in support of this statement falls into two categories: (a) the application of principles discovered in animal research to more complex human behavior, and (b) the highly inconsistent findings of research in human behavior concerned with such complex phenomena as child rearing variables and their effects on personality development (1958, p. 308).

Whatever the merits of Terrell's position, the attitude expressed appears to be a growing one and may well account for much of the present and future character of experimental studies in child behavior.

Ideally, the highly controlled, artificial laboratory situation is not the final goal of an experimental technique but rather a starting point. When the experimenter can show that the behavior under study varies only in response to his own manipulations of simple factors, then he is assured that he is in a good position, not to generalize about the child's real world, but to investigate more complex factors. These may be added to his highly controlled situation, one at a time, and the effects upon the behavior noted. The culmination of this process may be a very complex variable indeed, with the experimenter in possession of data showing the workings of its components. "The laboratory experiment is a technique for basic and theoretical research and not a goal of an empirical science" (Festinger and Katz, 1953, p. 170).

## THE CHILD'S PAST ENVIRONMENT

An investigator observing a child's behavior in the present may believe that the significant factors affecting this behavior are located in the child's distant past. In this case the possibility of control of the variables is lost, the factors gone forever. Although they cannot be controlled by the experimenter, it may be possible for him to assess and relate them to the child's present behavior. But so doing will rarely qualify as an experimental technique. Any supposed causes of a child's behavior, located in his past history, may themselves be considered effects of some prior cause. Hence it is not clear where in this succession of causes the child's present behavior should be referred. Indeed, there exists the possibility that the child's present behavior is only a manifestation of a long-standing interaction, which is also responsible for the child's history. For example: one may relate current "adjustment" to the feeding schedule adopted by the mother during infancy (Holway, 1949). It is possible that a properly chosen feeding schedule promotes subsequent adjustment; it is possible that the mother's basic attitudes may lead simultaneously to a particular feeding routine and "good" adjustment in the child but that feeding routine itself does not promote adjustment; and it is at least conceivable that early manifestations of a child's subsequent adjustment may influence the mother in her choice of a feeding schedule rather than vice versa. This difficulty is avoided in an experimental approach, basically because it is the experimenter who is the cause of variations in particular factors, if he is careful to avoid bias in his own manipulation of these factors. Yet it cannot be denied that an experimenter will find it difficult to establish experimental control over a variable such as feeding schedule for an appreciable part of an infant's history.

Strategically, the experimenter is in a better position if he can manipulate a "historical" variable in the present, with the intent of observing its effects at some future point. This certainly can qualify as an experimental technique, with a corresponding lack of ambiguity. However, it will often prove difficult to accomplish. Simply the time involved in establishing the variables, waiting the appropriate period, and then making observations of their effects on the child's behavior will prove an expensive deterrent. More important, the experimenter may not be competent to establish many variables in an experimental manner for a reasonable period of time. Children are not cared for by mechanical devices, which apply experimental variables only in the manner they were constructed to do. The human who is the agent responsible for applying many historical variables does so according to his own personality, which is not a product of the experimenter's construction. Hence it will be difficult to set up his behavior according to the experimenter's random number table. Finally, the ethical consequences of manipulating what may prove to be a significant variable in a child's history provides a powerful barrier against such procedures. If a historical variable is under study, it can only be because the experimenter suspects that it will have an effect upon a child's behavior. If the effect is thought to be beneficial, many caretakers will consider it immoral to have their children left in a control group; if the effect is thought to be detrimental, no one, including the experimenter, will care to fill the experimental group with his charges.

Certainly these are severe limitations upon an experimental approach to historical variables. In large part, it is these considerations that have too frequently made experimental studies of child behavior short-term affairs of only mild developmental significance. Yet these limitations, although real, are often magnified beyond their actual effect (Anderson, 1956). Many times, an apparent weakness of experimental techniques in attacking some historical variable represents a practical rather than an inherent difficulty: a shortage of time, personnel, ingenuity, or technology.

The history of experimental studies of children will lend some support to this view. Clearly, the experimental approach has never been the most popular method of study, testifying to the real limitations of experimental techniques in dealing with historical variables. Yet the child's interaction with his past environment traditionally and logically has been the central focus of study, and there have been periods when experimental techniques were attempted with some frequency. The Dennis' (1941)

study of twins reared for a year in relative social isolation, McGraw's six-year pursuit of Jimmy and Johnny (1935), the Kelloggs' willingness to raise Donald with Gua (1933), Dorothy Marquis' discrimination of infants' feeding occasions with a buzzer (1931), and Watson and Raynor's conditioning of Albert to fear the rabbit (1920) are examples of a time when the difficulties of an experimental approach often proved to be more apparent than real.

The most frequent applications of an experimental approach, however, have been applied to the child's present environment. In the 1920's and 1930's a considerable number of experimental studies appeared, which dealt with the sensory and motor capacities of the neonate. Still, interest in postneonatal development for many years centered about topographical and normative development, and although experimental techniques saw some application (Gesell and Thomson, 1929) the basic approach was a field or psychometric one. That is, the investigator essentially restricted himself to observing or asking the child, in a great variety of ways, what he could do.

The concept of manipulating variables to account for the observed variance in what children do saw only slight use. In part, this was because relationships were too often handled only by the use of gross categorization: nature-nurture, reflex-instinct-learning, practice, etc. This approach certainly did not provoke a large number of questions that require an experimental answer. If, for example, a behavior appeared at a characteristic age in average children and if it could not be accelerated in its appearance by direct practice of it, the oversimplified equation of "learning" and "experience" to "practice" led immediately to the conclusion that this behavior was maturational, and "age" was translated immediately into something "neural." It was not until more recent times that a theory such as Hebb's (1949) raised complex (and experimental) questions about the varied nature of "experience" and an experimental study such as Jeffrey's (1958) showed that a behavior might not be accelerated in making its appearance by direct practice but might by practice of a different but related behavior. Indeed, it was the early 1950's that brought a shift in interest to a more realistic analysis of these antecedent categories. The "why" of child development became increasingly pressing; demand for both a practical and theoretical understanding of development grew. The convenience of field and clinical methods brought them into frequent use. The correlations produced by these methods, although subject to a certain ambiguity, were undoubtedly more efficient than an experimental approach in at least producing data about the role of historical variables in the development of personality and social behavior. For example, Mussen and Conger (1956) in their textbook in child development cite approximately six times as many field or clinical studies as experimental studies when dealing with preschool social development. However, the present demand for a "why" to child behavior apparently has accentuated the need for unambiguous statements, too. At any rate, there is growing renaissance in the use of ex-

perimental techniques. The majority of recent experimental studies center upon the child's present rather than past environment. The subjects typically are preschool children, not neonates. The questions commonly considered deal with relationships suggested by some learning or behavior theory. (McCandless and Spiker, 1956; Stevenson, 1954; Gewirtz and Baer, 1958; Bijou, 1957.) There is still much less use of experimental techniques in dealing with the child's history than in the early part of this century.

## THE GENETIC ENDOWMENT OF THE CHILD

The child's inheritance is the most difficult source of variables to bring under adequate experimental control. Current genetic theory ascribes to the genes the power to stimulate development along certain dimensions, including behavioral dimensions. The genes are not directly manipulable.[1] The chromosomes upon which genes are said to be arrayed are not, for practical purposes, directly manipulable. They are manipulable indirectly by the use of selective breeding procedures, but this is a technique explicitly denied in the study of human development.

The child psychologist, then, is left with the possibility of doing something with the children who occasionally come in sets of identical and fraternal twins. A certain experimental logic has grown out of this fact aimed at identifying the degree to which any behavior

[1] Indeed, the existence of genes seems to be established more firmly on logical than on empirical grounds.

is influenced by inherited factors. Identical twins have identical inheritance; hence differences between them may be attributed to environmental action. But similarities between identical twins are much more difficult to refer to genetic endowment. Hebb (1958) argues that this may be done only if the environment of the twins has been systematically contrasted in terms of *all* relevant environmental factors. This immediately returns the experimenter to an exhaustive study of environmental, not genetic, factors. Kallman (1946) has argued from the assumption that identical twins and fraternal twins both share very similar environments; when identical twins are more homogeneous in behavior than fraternal, very likely that difference reflects inherited rather than environmental factors. In response, of course, it can be suggested that fraternal twins do not have an environment so similar as identicals; half of all fraternal twin pairs have different-sexed members, whereas identicals are always same-sexed. Furthermore, fraternals frequently look different; identicals rarely do. Evaluation of this argument again returns the experimenter to a thorough study of the relative similarity of environmental factors, not inherited ones. Both Kallman (1946) and Newman, Freeman, and Holzinger (1937) have suggested the comparison of identical twins reared apart with fraternal twins reared together. The assumption is made that identicals reared apart must have less similar environments than fraternals reared together. Hence greater similarity between identicals than between fraternals must reflect inherited factors. But, again, it can be pointed

out that twins reared apart typically share an environment involving early separation from the mother, a variable considered of great significance but not thoroughly understood.

Both Beach (1955) and Verplanck (1955) have argued that little can be done to study the effects of inherited factors. They maintain that in order to refer a behavior to inheritance it is necessary to show that there is variation in the behavior that cannot be explained by *any* environmental factor. Clearly, this would require an exhaustive knowledge of environmental factors as a prior condition to making any study of a child's inheritance. Acceptance of this position removes the problem of genetic endowment from the field of child study. This attitude is not without opposition, but the extent to which it is accepted will explain to a great degree the paucity of experimental attack upon the child's inheritance.

By way of summary, then, it appears that the virtue of any experimental technique is that it yields a relatively unambiguous conclusion about causal relationships. In an area as complex as child development this virtue is of extreme value: when relationships are ambiguous, too many alternative conclusions of too variegated a nature are possible. However, experimental techniques are most readily applied to controlling the child's present environment; extensive control of the child's interaction with his past environment, although often possible, is more often difficult for both practical and ethical reasons. Since the child's past environment traditionally and logically is a central source of variables in child development, this difficulty constitutes a limitation on the use of experimental techniques in this area. Furthermore, an experimental approach will frequently aim at abstracting a fraction of the child's total environment for study in a controlled setting. Consequently, many of the relationships produced appear devoid of immediate "practical" or "real-life" application.

Current use of experimental techniques, then, seems aimed at three eventualities.

1. The quantification of precise, reliable, and unambiguous laws of child behavior in relation to the present and short-term past environments.

2. The gathering together of such laws into a general system of behavior theory, so that generalized statements about these laws have organizing and unifying value and, perhaps, practical application.

3. The extension of such a body of fact and theory, through the use of other research techniques, to include more variables from the child's long-term past environment and so produce a more comprehensive theory of behavior and its development.

## PLAN OF TREATMENT

What follows is a survey of promising experimental techniques in the area of child behavior. These techniques have no single characteristic apart from their logic; they are almost as varied as the techniques of all psychological experimentation. For present purposes, the logical factor to bring order into this variety is the age (i.e., the develop-

ment) of the child under study. As the child's equipment changes, techniques are modified accordingly. Hence this survey is organized under three main categories of developmental stages:

1. Infancy: the first two years of life, a period of relative physical dependence and a lack of motor competence.

2. Early childhood: from 2 to 5 years of age, a period of decreasing physical dependence, increasing social dependence within a family unit, and rapidly increasing motor and verbal competence.

3. Later childhood and preadolescence: from 6 to 13 years of age, a period of socially structured education in groups, increasing social competence, emotional control, and independence.

In each of these stages the following three common experimental problems will serve as the basis for organizing discussion:

1. Obtaining subjects: Since children are neither purchased nor considered competent to volunteer their services to the experimenter, the problem of obtaining children to observe is a primary one. A number of paths to sources of subjects have been developed by past experience; these are described in terms of the age level of the subjects to be studied.

2. Sampling problems: Since children are not obtained for study in the relatively simple manner that animals are, many problems of biased sampling arise. Sometimes these are unavoidable and can only be recognized; more often, steps can be taken to detect and correct such biases, if important. Again, this

problem varies largely in terms of age.

3. Investigative procedures: This is the actual core of the chapter, a description of the methods of controlling variables and recording responses. A large part of this problem consists in instituting proper controls and developing mechanical devices and instruments. Again, age will explain part of the variety of techniques to be considered, but only a small part. More often, the development of techniques in this field represents a fascinating interaction between the ingenuity of the investigator, the traditional tools of psychology, and current technological development. In general, it will often be found that procedures applicable successfully at one stage of development may be used extensively beyond that stage, and repetition of them will be avoided in the discussion of later stages.

The preceding three problems are common to any experimental undertaking and serve as useful points of reference in organization. However, two other points may be considered as equally common to experimentation but are best dealt with once at the outset. The first of these is the problem of translating a question about child development into an experimental question; the second is the problem of experimental design.

It is common to hear that a particular hypothesis of development (indeed, of behavior) is not adequately represented by the experimental operation in a specific investigation. (This is an especially common statement when the results are negative.) Clearly, no helpful formula can be offered here to re-

solve these occurrences. It can only be noted that experimentation does require a specific and practicable operation that varies some factor of probable relevance to the behavior under study. The meaning of this operation, in broader terms than its own, has nothing to do with laboratory-experimental techniques per se. If experimental techniques seem to promise precision and a lack of ambiguity, it is only if conclusions are stated in terms of the experimental operations used. Statements broader than that proceed at their own risk.

The second problem, that of the statistical design according to which experimental variables are manipulated and responses recorded, is more readily dealt with. To some extent, the ages of the children under study play a role in the choice of an experimental design; to a perhaps larger extent, tradition and training lead the experimenter to certain choices. Yet it may be possible to state particular logical advantages and limitations of the experimental designs available to an investigator, which might in some cases lead to different choices. Since this is one of the objectives of this chapter, a general discussion of experimental designs should prove valuable at this point.

The response of children to experimental variables is commonly studied under any of three general designs: (1) as reflected in randomly composed groups, each group receiving a different degree or level of the experimental variable; (2) as reflected in groups composed of children who are matched, between groups, in terms of relevant variables; and (3) as reflected in the changed behavior of an individual child, relative to a stable baseline of response characteristic of him.

**Random Groups.** The experimenter may establish a degree of control over a child's present environment, yet find that the child's response to an experimental variable in that situation is unstable and/or that children in general show widely varying kinds of response to it. This variance is attributable, in large part, to incomplete control of the present environment and/or the variables the child brings with him to the laboratory (from his history of interaction with past environments and his genetic endowment). The experimenter may not be primarily interested in any but the experimental variable. In this case he will frequently resort to an extensive replication of pairs of observation: one child exposed to the experimental variable, and a control child exposed to a different degree or level of that variable. If enough children are randomly assigned to these groups, the effects of the experimenter's imperfect control of the present situation, and of the variables the child brings with him, will be canceled out. In effect, the experimenter establishes control not over the behavior of a child but over the average behavior of a group of children. In general, the more unstable the behavior of a single child, and/or the more variable the behavior of different children, the larger the required groups.

Furthermore, when large groups are required, the experimenter may, in the end, conclude that he now understands the nature of his experimental variable but may also conclude that he will rarely find a situation in which this variable *alone* will play a major explanatory role.[1]

**Matched Groups.** Again, the investigator may find that the behavior of the child under study is unstable or too different from that of other children. He may believe that he recognizes and can measure the significant variables responsible for this variation, which the child brings with him. In this case he may again resort to replicating pairs of observations (pairs of children) but may *match* the children in each pair so that they are highly similar in terms of these variables responsible for the (irrelevant) variation. *If* the experimenter is correct in his recognition *and* measurement of these variables, then he will be able to study the effect of the experimental variable with relatively small groups of children. Furthermore, he will be better able to state in what situations the experimental variable plays a major role (i.e., in situations closely describable by the matching variables). If the investigator is incorrect in his use of the matching variables, he will find that he has to use larger groups to study the experimental variable, or (following a possibly unexplored confidence in his matching technique) he may conclude (sometimes wrongly) that the experimental variable has no effect by accepting the null hypothesis. But when matching variables may be used with

---

[1] "Randomly composed groups" does not necessarily imply representative groups. All that is meant by this term is that two or more groups of subjects have been formed without bias. Results may be unambiguous as far as the independent variable is concerned, yet not generalizable to all children.

relative confidence, they undoubtedly contribute to the statistical efficiency of the design. Part of this efficiency is lost, however, since a relatively large number of subjects is usually required to find in them a pair of small matched samples. Still, if matching can be accomplished, the experimenter may use fewer subjects, an undoubted saving in experimenter-hours.

*Baseline Techniques.* Adequate control of the child's present environment in the laboratory will often allow use of the child as his own control. It is necessary that the response under study be brought to (or exist at) a stable level that is capable of variation when conditions are changed. If the investigator can rely upon the stability of the response, he may present or remove experimental variables at will, recording the consequent variation in the response. This technique is extremely efficient in many ways. It yields a law of behavior applicable to a particular child, not to a group mean that may correspond to no actual child. If it is easily replicated in a number of individual children, it is a general law. If not, then the changes in experimental technique, which the experimenter must use in order to replicate it in other children, may often give a meaningful clue to the nature of each child's past history. Undoubtedly, this method is economical of subjects. Very often it may not be economical of the experimenter's time: it may take a good deal of pilot work to produce a laboratory situation in which a given response will be suitable for baseline studies. However, this work, once done, should often prove a remarkably gainful investment. The current progress of studies of operant learning in animals, using baseline techniques, bears this out. In general, when child subjects are scarce, an attempt at baseline procedures should often be worth the gamble.

## Infancy

### OBTAINING SUBJECTS

Many avenues for gaining access to infants for study are open to the research psychologist. Babies have been available in child-study clinics, maternity wards, institutions for children, and in the homes of their parents. Each approach presents certain unique advantages and problems.

"Outpatient" research clinics have been the setting for both experimental work and extensive longitudinal studies. The work of Gesell and his colleagues at the former Clinic of Child Development, Yale University, is probably the best-known example. Organizations of this kind are usually part of a medical school and frequently operate in conjunction with a child-care or well-baby clinic. Mothers bring their infants in for observation at regular intervals. In exchange for their cooperation in a study, mothers and babies often receive professional services. The advantage of this approach is that it enables the research staff to design a laboratory with the permanent equipment essential for most experimental studies (e.g., one-way viewing glasses, listening and recording devices, and motion picture cameras) as well as a sufficient number of more flexible devices for specific investigations (e.g., cribs with stablimeter attachments, cribs with adjustable trays, special floor mats, and play pens). Furthermore, by careful scheduling, several investigations can be carried on simultaneously, thus utilizing the facilities to maximum capacity. The obvious limitation is the high cost of establishing such a laboratory, if one does not already exist, and the need for continuing operating funds, if the clinic is an established one.

Most research on the neonate and young infant has been conducted in laboratories in maternity wards. For example, some of the pioneer studies in the 1920's and 1930's on the behavioral equipment of the neonate were done in hospitals at Johns Hopkins University, Ohio State University, and the State University of Iowa. Although these laboratories are not so costly to establish as child-study clinics, they present other problems. Arranging for adequate space, working out relationships with the medical and nursing staffs, and coordinating the investigation with hospital routines are the most important. Another point worthy of mention is that investigations in hospital laboratories must necessarily be limited to study of infants from the time of birth until mothers are discharged, a period that is continually shrinking. In the past mothers were kept in the hospital for two or three weeks after delivery; currently they remain for only three or four days.

Experimental studies in children's institutions, such as foundling homes, children's homes, and orphanages, have been conducted with or without the benefit of a psychological laboratory. Constructing and operating a laboratory in a children's institution pose problems similar to those encountered when working in a maternity ward. Arranging to conduct a single study, however, presents different problems. First, the investigator must obtain permission from the superintendent or the administrative board. Such a request usually takes the form of a letter stating the purpose and nature of the study and assuring the administration that the procedures will not injure the infants. Requests will have to be written in nontechnical language and include information on the amount of floor space required, any encroachment on personnel time, the duration of the study, and its effect on institutional routines. A second problem concerns establishing a working relationship with the members of the staff directly concerned with child care. One way of accomplishing this is to proceed with the experimental program in small steps to give the staff opportunity to understand and gain confidence in the experimenter and his procedures. Third, in many situations of this kind the investigator is expected to reciprocate by giving professional services. The kind and amount rendered are, of course, dependent upon the investigator's competence to give the services requested and his other obligations.

One outstanding advantage of institutional laboratories over hospital laboratories is the opportunity to see infants for longer periods and in later developmental stages. Another is that many studies can be carried out with little disruption of the infant's routines.

The major limitation is that experimental plans may be hampered by the loss of subjects at any time because of adoption. Since current practice is to release infants for adoption at the earliest age possible, infants of this source are becoming increasingly scarce and older subjects quite rare.

Investigations in the homes of parents have usually consisted of intensive studies on one or two infants (Blau and Blau, 1955; Dennis and Dennis, 1935), or relatively brief observations on a larger number of infants, each in a different home (Brackbill, 1958). In studies of the first type making arrangements for performing the study has been obviated by the fact that the investigators have, for the most part, been the parents or guardians of the subjects. In studies of the second type obtaining subjects may produce some difficulties. First, mothers with infants within the desired age range, who are willing and committed to cooperate to the point of "seeing the study through" will have to be found. The work of finding such mothers may often begin profitably through contacts with the community's preschools, schools, and clinics, with mother's groups or clubs, and with local pediatricians. One advantage of working in the child's home is that studies can be conducted with a minimal amount of disturbance to the infant and his routines. Another is that limitations on the number and age range of subjects that can be obtained is less severe. On the other hand, considerable time and money are required for travel and extra research activities. For example, Brackbill (1958), in a study on infant conditioning reported utilizing both individual and group discussions with mothers to introduce her problem and secure cooperation. During the course of the study she gave them simple journal articles on infants, showed graphs, etc. Another limitation of this mode of operation is that it is relatively easy to lose subjects because of changes in the mother's attitudes or circumstances. Finally, conducting studies in private homes precludes the use of any kind of heavy or complicated apparatus.

A procedure used with preschoolers (Bijou, 1958) should also be of value with infants. That is, infant research could be conducted in a mobile laboratory complete with viewing, listening, and response recording devices. The trailer-laboratory could be taken by truck or car to institutions or private homes and remain in a location for an hour, a week, or several months, depending on the study. It would be entirely possible to conduct studies under the constant conditions enjoyed in a traditional laboratory, yet be less costly to establish and operate. Investigative procedures conducted in a trailer would be more disruptive to the baby's routines than in an institution or private home but probably less so than in a child-study clinic.

A particular problem relevant here is that of terminating a study. The relationships uncovered in a particular study are not affected by the procedures that terminate the study, of course; but the probability that these and other subjects in the same area will be available for future study definitely is. This problem is not restricted to the study of infants in their own homes; rather it is common to almost all child research. Probably the most important single factor is to explain to the caretaker (beforehand) the intent, meaning, and procedures of the experiment in understandable terms. Repetition of this, with "progress reports" during the study, is good strategy. Then, a simple announcement of termination, with thanks, should prove adequate, especially if the experimenter can say that the study was a "success" and show reprints and articles. A group address, or a typed letter of thanks and explanation, may be particularly convenient.

SAMPLING

Most methods of obtaining infants for study yield biased samples. For example, when a research clinic opens its doors to mothers who are interested and able to give the required time, energy, and cooperation, it is probable that they would constitute a group that would be above average in education and socioeconomic status. The same thing would probably be true of mothers who would consent to cooperate in a study in their homes. Likewise, samples of mothers and infants drawn from a hospital ward or institution would be biased along other dimensions. This is recognized by most investigators, yet few attempts have been made to obtain random samples. This is partly because of the difficulties of obtaining subjects and partly because many investigations require intensive individual analysis and can handle only a few cases efficiently. If, however, a study requires a representative sample, the research clinic and the mobile laboratory offer the most promising approaches to an approximation. The clinic, because of the large number of cases it can handle efficiently, can see enough cases to extract from them a near-representative sample. The mobile laboratory may be used to approach the many cases whose unwillingness to cooperate is based largely on the distance or expense involved in traveling to the laboratory, the number of other children in the family who then would require a sitter, etc. Whether or not a sampling procedure has been used, it is essential that some account be given of how the subjects were obtained. Too often such information may be critical in resolving otherwise contradictory results.

Not only should there be a description of how the subjects were obtained but also the basis upon which they were eliminated. Some of the criteria are questionable physical status, recent changes in caretaking relationships, and poor health or illness of the mother during pregnancy. For some studies, it may be necessary to eliminate those who do not stay awake for long enough periods to permit study and whose sleeping cycles are markedly irregular. When working in private homes, it may be expedient to eliminate first borns, since new mothers may be tense and overly concerned with the effects of any sort of investigative procedure. When working in institutions, it is recommended that infants over 5 or 6 months of age be excluded, unless the problem concerns behavior that may be related to institutional living.

INVESTIGATIVE PROCEDURES IN EARLY INFANCY

Because of the tremendous equipmental differences of the neonate and the 2-year-old infant, investigative procedures vary widely. It is advantageous, therefore, to discuss this aspect of research in two parts. The first section deals with methodology for full-term babies from the time of birth to the time when the subject can begin to sit for longer periods and can reach and grasp efficiently. In terms of chronological age, this would be about 9 months. The second section extends from the end of early infancy to the age at which basic skills in manipulation, locomotion, and simple verbal behavior are developed. This would be about age 2.

Investigative procedures are viewed as consisting of two parts: (1) manipulating independent variables and measuring responses and (2) controlling the setting conditions affecting the behavior under observation. Since problems of manipulating independent variables and measuring responses are closely tied in with the general experimental area, the specific variables involved, and the age of the subject, they are discussed by the case method, i.e., by describing the relationship between problems and procedures in selected studies. The problems of controlling the setting conditions are discussed in terms of both general considerations and examples. They are also emphasized in some of the studies presented to illustrate manipulative and recording procedures.

The problem of controlling experimental conditions other than the one to be varied is a matter of holding constant the conditions preceding and during sessions. With respect to controlling in-between-sessions conditions, the young infant presents fewer problems than older subjects, since verbal communication is not a factor. The conditions before and during sessions requiring vigilant supervision pertain to the health and behavioral state of the infant. These include colds, sieges of colic, sudden separation from the mother or caretaker, radical changes in living conditions, accidents, emotional experiences, and the like. Such events have to be evaluated to determine whether the consequences would alter the behavior of the infant in the experimental situation.

Reference to controlling conditions during sessions involves the exercise of traditional experimental safeguards. Typically they include conducting sessions at the same hour of the day (thereby avoiding the effects of variations in food elimination, sleep, and fatigue cycles), holding sessions for the same length of time, and keeping physical and social conditions constant. Physical factors of some significance would include constancy in the contraption in which the infant lies and the illumination and temperature of the room. The social conditions would involve standardization of the behavior of the mother (or caretaker) and investigator, if either or both have direct contact with subjects. Control of both sets of these conditions may be facilitated by the use of panels, cabinets, booths, or special experimental rooms. Examples of the specific use of these devices are given in a later section.

Studies illustrating techniques for manipulating variables and measuring responses were selected on the basis of two factors. First, they involve an effective way of presenting and manipulating stimuli or conditions and/or methods for recording and measuring responses, and, second, they are concerned with one of the major problem areas in a stage of development. The categories for major problem areas are as follows:

1. Conditioning.
2. Discriminative processes.
3. Motivation.
4. Frustrating, sudden, or strong stimulation.
5. Changes in complex behavior.

It is recognized that these categories do not include mutually exclusive processes. To a certain extent, any classification system is arbitrary. This chapter must examine many experimental procedures, the labels for which are matters of considerable controversy. It does not seem appropriate to deal with these issues here; consequently, the classifications used are meant simply to allow adequate description and a wide sampling of problems.

*Conditioning.* Because of the difficulty of obtaining stable measures of behavior, experimental work in early infancy poses many problems. One method that has been used to advantage is the classical conditioning technique. Studies have been conducted to determine whether the phenomena observed in animals may be observed in the human infant, to further the analysis of the conditioning process itself, and to evaluate other variables such as ability to discriminate two levels of auditory discrimination. To illustrate some of the investigative procedures for studying the neonate and some of the methodological problems involved, two carefully controlled studies, concerned with at what age and to what stimuli the infant can be conditioned, are considered.

Wenger's study (1936), conducted at the Infant Laboratory at the State University of Iowa, was performed in a Pratt stablimeter (Pratt, Nelson, and Sun, 1930) to control for extraneous noises and variations in temperature and illumination. (See Fig. 4-2.) Onset, duration, and termination of independent variables were controlled by mechanical and electrical devices, and responses were recorded by observers, polygraphic, or photographic techniques. Five experiments were conducted. The first was on three infants twenty-four hours after birth. The unconditioned stimulus was a light from a 100- or 200-watt lamp, eliciting eyelid closure. The conditioned stimulus was a tactual vibrator attached to the plantar surface of the foot. Duration of the conditioned stimulus was 3.4 seconds and came 3 seconds after the light flashed. One experimental session was held a day. Since attempts were made to obtain 30 to 50 pairings per session, the duration of sessions varied from two to three hours. Eye closure responses were recorded by two observers and an interobserver reliability check was made. Experiment I included two control studies, one to determine whether maturation might account for increase in frequency of responses, the other, whether light stimulation might account for it. The first was done by comparing the frequency of reactions to the conditioned stimulus of the experimental subjects to six control subjects 9 days of age. The controls did not have

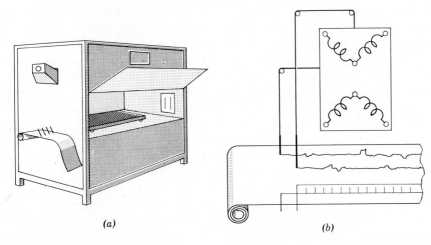

*(a)*          *(b)*

Fig. 4-2. A stablimeter, for measuring reactions of the infant to stimulation. (*a*) shows the experimental cabinet with the platform on which the baby lies. (*b*) shows how motions of the platform are translated into a written record. The two lower lines are signal lines that show when stimuli were presented and provide a time marker (Pratt, Nelson, and Sun, 1930).

any pairings. Wenger concluded that conditioning appeared on the fifth day after 124 pairings. Experiment II was a six-months' continuation study of one of the subjects in Experiment I. Experiments III, IV, and V used an electrotactual stimulation delivered by an electrode fastened to the plantar surface of the left great toe as the unconditioned stimulus and respiratory and electrodermal responses were explored. Experiment III, with one subject, was an exploratory study of a vibratory stimulus as a conditioned stimulus. In Experiment IV a pure tone (frequency of 1084 cycles at 50 decibels above adult human threshold) served as a conditioned stimulus on five subjects. Two control experiments were included, one on the unconditioned responses to the conditioned stimulus and the other on the effects of repeated electrotactual stimulation. The first was on seven infants, who were given only auditory stimulation on their ninth postnatal day, the second, on four subjects who were given 30 shocks per day for seven days and on the ninth day were tested with the tone. Responses were recorded by observational and photographic means. Wenger claimed that three of the five subjects showed conditioning. In Experiment V the conditioned stimulus was a flash of light (3.4 seconds) from a 100-watt lamp. There were four subjects, but complete information was obtained on only two. Three infants served as subjects in a controlled experiment designed to evaluate unconditioned responses to the light flash. Both of the experimental infants showed conditioning of respiratory and withdrawal responses on the ninth day. Experiment VI involved the feeding behavior of two infants. A buzzer, 80–90 decibels above adult human threshold, started about one second before nursing began and lasted ten minutes. It sounded for 0.55 second at intervals of one second. Responses were observed by the investigator and by the parents. No evidence of conditioning was found during eight weeks of study.

Wickens and Wickens (1940) followed up Wenger's study to give special attention to controlling motivation and the effects of the unconditioned stimulus. Their study was conducted in the Ohio State Infant Research Laboratory on 36 infants under 10 days of age, born in the Ohio State University Hospital. Setting conditions were controlled much as in the Wenger study (Dockery and Valentine, 1939). A buzzer served as a conditioned stimulus, and a shock, delivered through an electrode attached to the sole of the right foot, causing foot withdrawal, served as the unconditioned stimulus. Thirty-six infants were divided into three groups. The experimental group was given 12 buzzer-shock pairings a day for three days. Control Group I received 12 shocks a day for three days and never received pairings of buzzer-shock. This group was designed to determine whether repeated presentation of shock would increase response during the test period. Control Group II received the buzzer alone on the first and third days. This was a check on whether any effects observed could be accounted for by maturation. On the third and fourth days all were given the buzzer alone, until three consecutive failures to respond. Tests on the third day were to evaluate conditioning and extinction; on the fourth, spontaneous recovery and extinction. The Experimental Group showed conditioning, extinction, and spontaneous recovery. So did Control Group I. The authors present two theoretical possibilities, one in terms of sensitization and the other in terms of conditioning to a sudden environmental change. The findings have several implications (Underwood, 1949); at any rate, they demonstrate the need for a careful consideration of the experimental conditions used, through control groups representing analyzable components of these conditions. For instance, it follows from Wickens and Wickens' discussion that a study might be done with a control group designed to test the effect of a stimulus other than a buzzer after repeated shock presentations.

The distinction between classical (respondent) conditioning and instrumental (operant) conditioning rests upon identifying the response being conditioned as one that is controlled by eliciting or by consequent stimulation, respectively. Occasionally, a response may seem to fall in both categories, and this may occur more frequently in young infants than in older subjects. In this case it may be a matter of controversy, whether the investigator is studying one kind of conditioning or another. Previously cited studies have cited milk and nipples as eliciting stimuli for the sucking response, and their procedures have been identified as classical conditioning. It is also possible to consider milk as a reinforcing stimulus and the nipple as a cue or discriminative stimulus marking occasions when sucking will be reinforced.

Kantrow's study (1937) of conditioned sucking is an example. Her method was to present a nursing bottle to the infant, having sounded a buzzer 5 seconds before, and to maintain the buzzer during the first 15 seconds of sucking. Then the buzzer stopped, but the child was allowed to continue sucking for 15 to 20 seconds. Preceding the buzzer was a baseline period, during which the infant's sucking was observed, and which varied between 25 and 75 seconds in length. (Initial baseline periods for a session lasted as long as 120 seconds to promote adaptation to the apparatus.) Sucking was recorded on a kymograph by a linen harness placed under the infant's chin and drawn up over his ears by weighted strings running over pulleys. The characteristic chin motions involved in swallowing were transmitted through the strings to the kymograph pen. The subjects were orphanage infants, ranging in age from 1 to 3 months. Observations were made at the 10 A.M. and 2, 6, and 10 P.M. feedings. The conditioning observed may point to classical conditioning of the sucking response to a buzzer, through pairings with the eliciting stimulus of the nursing bottle's nipple, or it may indicate instrumental conditioning of the sucking response to the discriminative stimulus (cue) of the buzzer, through reinforcement of this response by milk on occasions marked by the buzzer. An experimental test will require at least control of milk as a consequence of the conditioned response.

Davis, Sears, Miller, and Brodbeck (1948) exemplify an instrumental conditioning logic in a study of the development of extranutritive sucking in newborn infants. Working in a mater-

nity hospital, they made up three groups of infants, one group being fed at the mother's breast, another group by bottle, and a third by cup. This procedure established a dimension of the frequency of reinforced sucking responses required to satiate the infant for milk (breast-feeding requiring most responses, bottle-feeding an intermediate amount, and cup-feeding least). The experiment lasted ten days, the tenure of the infants in the hospital. Daily tests of extranutritive sucking were made by inserting a rubber-covered finger tip into the infant's mouth at intervals after feeding and measuring the amount of sucking on the finger tip within a fixed time. Differentially increasing responsiveness to this test between groups supported the authors' claim that instrumental conditioning principles could be applied to the sucking response.

Blau and Blau (1955) illustrate an interesting variation in procedures for attacking the same kind of problem. They worked with a sample of one infant (their own) in their home. Observation of behavior and control of feeding conditions were unsurprisingly extensive. The infant was fed from either a two-hole or eight-hole nipple, in a regular alternation of feedings, from age 3 to 7 weeks. Observations were made of extranutritive sucking, crying, restless activity, and general fussiness. The sample necessarily involved a baseline design, which produced reliable data quite efficiently in their single case. Clearly, the method is suitable to the investigator who is also a new parent.

***Discriminative Processes.*** One of the

research problems that has received a good deal of attention is the question of the sensory capacities of the neonate. The major task has been to isolate a response class that will yield definite and reliable records. For the most part, general activity (motility) has served as a measure obtained by a stablimeter and polygraph. Responses have also been recorded by motion pictures and, of course, by observers. Four studies, involving different sense modalities, are described to give a sampling of methodologies employed.

The first one, which was conducted by Stubbs (1934), is concerned with auditory stimulation. Two features of special interest here are that three dimensions of auditory stimuli—pitch, intensity, and duration—were studied over wide ranges and that objective records were obtained by a stablimeter, pneumograph, and polygraph. The study was conducted in an experimental cabinet; stimuli emanated from an oscillator.

Weiss (1934) performed a parallel study involving visual stimulation. Methods were similar, but only the effects of three levels of light intensity were studied (minimal, dim, and moderate). Again, general motility (measured by a stablimeter) was the index of response.

Visual stimulation is very complex. It has, for the adult eye, discriminable components of intensity, color, saturation, and distribution (flux). In a verbal animal these components are readily controllable, but in lower organisms, and in the young child, questions about visual ability become complex and require special experimental procedures.

Some have seen application in infant studies.

For example, sensitivity to color (wavelength) in infants between 2 and 24 months of age was studied by Staples (1932) with a preference method. For younger infants, Staples' method was to have the infant lying on his back in his crib, looking at a framed piece of a cardboard mounted about one foot from his face. On the cardboard were pasted two circles, one colored, the other either colored or gray. The experimenter stood at the foot of the infant's crib, her head and face hidden behind the cardboard, looking at the infant through a small slit in the cardboard. The colored circles were presented for standard lengths of time, and the experimenter recorded on stopwatches held in each hand the duration of the infant's visual fixation on each color. For infants older than $5\frac{1}{2}$ months, a larger cardboard background was used; the infant was placed in a sitting position, with the cardboard held vertically in front of him, and the recorded response was the infant's reaching for or pointing to one of the two disks. (See Fig. 4-3.)

Staples' method included trials on which the brightness of a preferred color was varied or the brightness of its paired gray was varied. The color preferences Staples found were stable for various levels of brightness of the colors and the grays, which is some indication that it was wavelength and not brightness that is preferred by the infant. There always remains the possibility that brightness was not varied over a wide enough range. Assumptions that the infant's eye is similar to the

Fig. 4-3. The Staples' method for studying responses to color involves a large cardboard, to which one of several colored disks has been affixed, and the reaching response of the infant (Staples, 1932).

adult's in matching colors for brightness are probably gratuitous.

Crudden (1937) has made an investigation of the infant's sensitivity to thermal stimulation. His method was to wrap a small hollow cylinder to the infant's calf with a single layer of bandage and to maintain a steady flow of water through this cylinder. Temperatures between 16 and 45°C. were used, always in terms of a temperature change, either from body temperature (33–34°C.) to a higher or lower temperature or from a higher or lower one to body temperature. The response recorded was any change in activity. The recording was accomplished by taking a motion picture of the infant and also a protocol of all observed activities of the infant as they occurred. The obvious advantages of a photographic record are that it can be reviewed many times and also submitted to a panel of judges to determine the reliability of observations.

Thermal stimulation is not so complex in nature as light or sound stimulation.

However, the duration, frequency, and extent of the stimulation are still notable parameters, as in sound and light stimulation. Conceivably, parameters, such as the rate of change of the stimulation (the specific heat of the stimulating object) and the modality of stimulation (contact with solids, liquids, or gases by radiation or by induction) may present problems.

*Motivation.* Studies of motivation usually present points of strong controversy, since this seems to be the nub of dissension between typical behavior theories. Studies of infant motivation do not escape this aura, but here these questions are not of great consequence. The experimenter is often concerned simply with the question: Does a particular stimulus serve as a reinforcer, a reward, or a drive for an infant? Questions concerning why the stimulus is effective or what its proper label should be tend to retreat from central interest; before one can ask why a stimulus is effective in promoting labeling, it must first be identified, and this has proven a difficult enough problem in itself, for the young infant.

A study by Jensen (1932) apparently avoids some of these difficulties and is useful in demonstrating the effectiveness of milk as a stimulus. He constructed a special feeding bottle, from which the infant sucked milk; the pressure changes within the bottle, arising from each sucking response, were transmitted to a kymograph. Milk of the correct temperature (40°C.) gives rise to a steady rate of sucking; variations in the temperature of the milk, or substitution of fluids of differing taste or texture, are reflected in a falling off of the rate or magnitude of response in the same infant. Infants as young as 2 days old are studied with this method.

Jensen's technique is noteworthy in that it measures a response resulting directly from the stimulus under study. Furthermore, the sucking response is one of the few well-organized and precise responses the newborn has available. This response is easily elicited by all sorts of stimulation, especially in the oral region. Despite this difficulty, the use of a baseline technique, in which the infant serves as his own control, allows clear conclusions in single cases. The technique would seem worthy of far wider application than it has seen, especially when the psychologist must adapt his procedures to the requirements of specialists in infant health.

A similar use of baseline technique is made in two other studies of infant motivation. In both the central problem is to identify a stimulus complex that will act as a reinforcing stimulus in operant conditioning. A problem common to both is finding a response

to strengthen that is not too thoroughly tied to eliciting stimuli. Brackbill (1958) chose the smiling response in 4-month-old infants. The reinforcing stimulus was composed of auditory, tactual, movement, and social components. The experimenter, immediately upon observing a smile from the infant lying supine in his crib, smiled in return, began to speak softly to the infant, picked it up, held, jostled, and patted it for thirty seconds (continuing to talk), and then returned it to the crib. The infants were studied in their own homes, with the experimenter serving as a substitute mother during the experimental sessions.

Rheingold, Gewirtz, and Ross (1959) chose vocalization as a response to be conditioned. Again, the reinforcing stimulus was a complex one: the experimenter responded to the infant's vocalization by smiling, clucking, and lightly squeezing the infant's abdomen. The infants were about 3 months old, and during the experimental sessions lay supine in their cribs, the experimenter standing over them and looking down. The study required six daily sessions: the first two constituted a baseline condition, followed by two daily sessions of reinforcement of vocalization; the final two sessions were an extinction period similar to the baseline period.

An essential assumption in both of these studies is that the responses are modifiable by certain kinds of stimulus consequences. However, even casual observation of infants can suggest that a good deal of their behavior is controlled by eliciting (as compared to consequent) stimulation. An operant conditioning session, in which stimuli are offered as consequences of responses in successively closer succession, may also be viewed as a period of increasing elicitation of behavior, if indeed the stimuli being used have any eliciting power. The use of an experimental condition in which these complex stimuli are offered at the same rate, but randomly rather than as consequences of a response, would seem a useful safeguard when conclusions are drawn.

*Frustrating, Sudden, or Strong Stimulation.* Studies considered here are those which ordinarily fall into categories of emotion and emotional behavior. Rather than attempt to give illustrations of the diversified techniques that would have to be included, consideration will be limited to methods of frustration and of presenting sudden and/or strong stimulation. Frustration may consist of the actual prevention of a response by mechanical means, the nonreinforcement of a response that is ordinarily reinforced, or the introduction of conflict by stimulating competitive behavior. Almost all of these categories have been applied to children of some age level, and a considerable number is exemplified in infant studies.

The prevention of responses has been the subject of a surprising number of studies. Some of these were probably stimulated by Watson's early study of infant rage as a response to restraint (1919). Watson's methods were to hold the infant's head steady in his hands, to pin its arms to its sides, or to hold its legs tightly together. Response was observed and passed on as generalized statements of Watson's impressions.

Sherman and Sherman (1925) applied pressure (by hand) to the chins of infants; they recorded (by eye) generalized arm motions. Sherman's later studies (1927) utilized motion-picture recordings of the results of various forms of restraint. Apart from its undoubted superiority in assessing just what infant response is to restraint, this technique also allowed the well-known study in which adults are shown the infant's response but not the stimulus condition giving rise to it; their labeling of the response is less accurate in this condition, a fact that has been given various significance by theorists. Studies by Pratt, Nelson, and Sun (1930) utilized the additional control condition of observing infants only when "asleep and dry."

Nonreinforcement of responses ordinarily being reinforced is the subject of a study by Dorothy P. Marquis (1943). The subjects were newborn infants in a maternity hospital. Marquis' procedure was to interrupt their bottle-feeding sessions for ninety seconds, at points when the infant had consumed one quarter, one half, and three quarters of his ration. Infants were observed twice a day for the first ten days of life. (Some were tested again at the age of 3 months to determine whether individual differences noted at birth had persisted. Mothers brought their children back to the hospital for these observations.) The responses observed were general body activity, recorded by mounting the bassinet as a stablimeter, and also the latency and duration of crying and of mouth activity.

Sudden and/or strong stimulation of an infant has been studied sparingly.

Watson and Raynor (1920) performed a classic experiment by teaching 9-month-old Albert to fear a rat by pairing it with the loud sound produced by striking a steel bar vigorously with a hammer. Recording was done primarily by visual impression. The generalization of Albert's responses to a rabbit, a dog, a sealskin coat, and a mass of white cotton were judged to vary quantitatively, but again, by eye. Lack of response to wooden blocks bespoke a discrimination of these from the rat. An accurate quantitative description of the gradient, however, is not likely by such methods.

A detailed study of the immediate response of infants to the sound of a revolver shot has been made by Landis and Hunt (1937). Their technique utilized motion-picture records of the infant's responses. By employing a camera capable of recording 1500 frames per second, they were able to record the startle response in infants, even in cases in which the Moro reflex effectively concealed the startle response from the naked eye and from conventional camera records (i.e., those taken at 64 frames per second and slowed to quarter speed for slow-motion studies). Crying was also recorded, more readily, of course, but with less useful results. That objective techniques of recording can far surpass the unaided experimenter probably need not be labored in this example.

*Changes in Complex Behavior.* Studies of sequences of responses in the younger infant consist primarily of investigations of the development of reaching, sitting, and similar motor development. This research is devoted to examining the influence of presumably biological variables upon the ability of the infant to perform such instrumental learning. The variable, although labeled "biological," in experimental terms is defined simply as chronological age, and the experimental question, as asked in a study by Dennis (1941), is simply, "Does a restriction of certain types of environmental interaction (with adults) hinder such learning?" The procedure was to rear a pair of fraternal twins from the second month of life through the fourteenth, under conditions of minimal social interaction with each other or with adults and with restricted opportunity for practice of various motor behaviors. Dennis compiled norms from the records of 40 baby biographies and checked the twins' development against these and others.

It should be noted that the labeling of this development as requiring "biological" or "maturational" variables contrasted to simply "learned" is an extension beyond the logic of the experimental design. Certainly it can be concluded that the particular modes of learning restricted for these infants are not the single essential ingredient of development studied (if they were restricted enough); but there is no guarantee resulting from the experimental data that these are the only modes of learning responsible for development.

An example of social learning in 6-to-8-month-old infants is afforded by Rheingold's study (1956). Rheingold served as mother for four infants in an orphanage: she alone was their caretaker for seven and a half hours a day, five days a week, over a two-month period. Otherwise, these infants, and a matched control group, were cared for by many, constantly changing caretakers. Social discrimination or generalization to the experimenter, to a relatively unknown second person, and to a completely unknown third person were tested weekly. The test involved observation of the infant's response to engineered social situations with each of these three persons. These test situations were designed to approximate "natural" social events, such as an adult's approach to the crib, holding the baby, speaking to him ("Hello, baby, how are you?" "You naughty baby, what did you do?"), and returning the baby to the crib.

The experimental techniques devised by Rheingold in this study present some contrast to those of the studies previously cited. One difference is that Rheingold's study of social learning requires an experimental history to be set up, and this history is eminently a social one. Her study goes a long way in demonstrating that experimental techniques can be applied to these problems in the human infant with good results.

### Later Infancy

By the time an infant is 9 months of age, much significant development has taken place. Largely this is a matter of motor competence: the 9-month-old can stand by holding furniture; he has been able to sit unassisted for some weeks; and his hands are becoming increasingly free and adept for manipulation of any loose parts of his environment. Very shortly he will creep. By the end of later infancy (the end of the second year) this motor development will be far advanced. The child will be able to approach and manipulate a great deal of his environment. This will allow the use of many of the experimental techniques developed for adult organisms of various species. However, during this same period, the child's verbal development will increase from a near-zero level to one which will be of considerable use in affecting the child's behavior. From the experiment's point of view, this will prove a mixed blessing as well as an important phenomenon for study.

### INVESTIGATIVE PROCEDURES

The control of pre-experimental conditions presents a few problems differing from those considered for the younger infant. In this age range the child must often enter into the experiment rather than simply be placed in it. Therefore, the use of inducements becomes a factor. Typically, the parent or caretaker will bring the child, after which the experimenter can frequently rely upon curiosity for a continuance of the child in the experiment. Arsenian's study (1943) documents the importance of this problem quite clearly.

Instructions to the subject are a problem even in this age range. Because more complex experimental situations are possible here, some kind of instruction may be necessary, if only to save the experimenter time. The child in his second year frequently can be told what to do, if simple enough words are used in short enough sentences. If successful, this is undoubtedly an efficient technique. Too often, however, the experimenter may find that he promotes misunderstanding in the child by only the use of verbal instructions. Sometimes this can be corrected by simpler instructions. The experimenter may find that an experienced teacher can suggest an optimum wording (Brackbill, 1958). An alternative is simply to demonstrate to the child what he is to do. Imitative behavior may be expected with good probability of success. The child should be given a chance to demonstrate that he understands his instructor before the experiment starts.

Keeping the child free from accidental upsets before the experiment remains a critical problem at this age. Emotional responses are easily elicited, and their consequences may be strong enough to compete successfully with many of the behaviors under study.

The problems of maintaining control over the general setting of the experiment are somewhat different from those described for early infancy. Time of day, in terms of deprivation-satiation cycles, is still important; however, longer cycles between feedings and naps can be expected. Similarly, experimental sessions can often be longer than for the younger infant. The problem of keeping physical stimulation under control is still present. As in the case of the younger infant, the advantages of delimiting the experimental environment by the use of panels, screens, and specially designed rooms can be of critical value. The very definitely increased sensitivity of the child to social stimuli introduces a complex problem, centering about the behavior of the mother (when present) and the experimenter (when observable). These problems are best illustrated by the specific instances in which they arise; some of them are dealt with in the examples that follow. Too often, though, this source of variation is neglected. Merrill's well-known study (1946) demonstrates some of the possibilities involved; even though it deals with older children, its implication is readily applied.

The examples that follow are noteworthy in that they reflect some of these new problems as well as the wider range of stimuli and responses now available to experimental study. Selection has been made essentially on this basis.

*Conditioning.* Studies of conditioning in later infancy frequently exemplify the same lack of distinction between classical and instrumental conditioning noted earlier. This is, of course, largely a historical accident: the law of effect apparently was not widely recognized until relatively recent times, and the studies to be cited are not recent. Much of the confusion arises, as before, from the use of milk as an eliciting stimulus (since milk is an eminent candidate for a reinforcing rather than eliciting stimulus in any instrumental conditioning design involving infants). The studies of Krasnogorski (Mateer, 1918) are an example. Initial experiments utilized the showing of a glass of milk to a 14-month-old, with observation made of the frequency of swallowing responses, essentially by eye. The use of swallowing is based upon the premise that the conditioned secretion of as little as 0.5 cubic centimeters of saliva will induce swallowing in infants of this age. Later studies by Krasnogorski utilized a tambour, placed over the thyroid cartilage or over the hyoid bone, connected to a kymograph by rubber tubing, which differentially recorded both swallowing and mouth-opening responses. In still later studies direct measurement of salivation was made by fitting a cup-shaped receptacle directly over the salivary gland and leading the saliva away through a tube to a receptacle where it could be counted as drops emitted per time interval. This last technique, although admirably direct, also involved an almost prohibitive amount of instrumentation connected directly to the infant and is probably better suited to considerably older children. The age of the children studied apparently ranged from the first 2 or 3 months (where the method was reported as unsuccessful) to 6 years.

The setting of the study is described as an isolated room, in which the child was placed upon a table, usually with his eyes bandaged. Typical trials were spaced at three-minute intervals, the unconditioned stimulus being presented fifteen seconds after the conditioned stimulus, which often was maintained for a full minute.

At least two other studies of infant conditioning are immediate responses to Krasnogorski's publications. Mateer (1918) cited the importance of Krasnogorski's results and set about verification. Much of her technique is a direct reaction to her own criticisms of Krasnogorski's. In particular, she has been at pains to specify in more detail the experimental setting, the relationship between the experimenter and the subject, and the subjects (in terms of sex, IQ, normality or deficiency, and other psychological measures). Her technique involves several interesting variations. The use of an eye bandage was modified to provide the conditioned stimulus. The child wore the bandage on the forehead throughout the experiment, and the conditioned stimulus consisted of the experimenter's sliding down of the bandage over the eyes. The bandage remained over the eyes for twenty seconds, and was then slid up to the forehead again. At the eleventh second of the duration of the conditioned stimulus a bit of sweet chocolate was placed in the child's mouth as the unconditioned stimulus. Recording of swallowing responses was done both by eye and by an apparatus, similar to Krasnogorski's, operating from a tambour over the hyoid bone or thyroid cartilage.

Marinesco and Kreindler (1933) report studies of infant conditioning that also represent a direct reaction to the work of Krasnogorski. Their method is notable in that the unconditioned stimulus used is unavoidable electric shock, so that there can be little question that this study represents classical rather than instrumental conditioning. The infants ranged in age from 25 days (no success) to 3½ years; many were seen on repeated occasions, separated in some cases by several months. Most of the children were normals, but some were identified simply as a spastic idiot, microcephalic idiot, hemiplegiac, or retarded child. Studies were made of the phenomena of conditioning, extinction, retention, spontaneous recovery, inhibition, conditioned inhibition, delayed response, and the chaining of several conditioned stimuli to the unconditioned stimulus.

It is notable that none of these studies includes control over the sort of procedures that Wickens and Wickens label "pseudoconditioning." Hence it is debatable how much of their effects are ascribable simply to repeated presentation of the unconditioned stimuli, independently of any association between the conditioned and unconditioned stimuli. As already stated in the studies of Krasnogorski and Mateer it is debatable how much of the effects are ascribable to operant rather than respondent conditioning. Certainly it seems clear that the entire field of infant conditioning requires a modern replication, making use of newer techniques and attending to findings and concepts that have assumed major significance since these studies were performed. (It remains to be seen, though, whether the psychologist so inclined will find as ready a willingness on the part of parents or institutions today to allow infants to be subjected to some of these rather heroic procedures.) The simple insertion of a pressure-sensitive device into an infant's feeding bottle, which would close a sensitive switch, should allow an easy recording of the rate of the sucking response; the insertion of a simple pressure valve, which would close the nipple in response to the experimenter's actions, should allow control of the supply of milk as a stimulus. This special kind of a bottle converts any crib into a laboratory and invites a study of the sucking response in terms of the scheduling of its consequences.

If any aspect of Mateer's method is in fact instrumental operant rather than classical or respondent conditioning, it is an example of a restricted operant situation, one in which the child may make only a single response per trial and in which trials are necessarily separated somewhat in space and/or time. The free-operant situation, by contrast, is one in which the child's response does not appreciably displace him either in space or in time from his next response; hence behavior may be emitted at a wide range of rates, which may vary freely (Ferster, 1953). This technique is frequently said to be more sensitive and more flexible than the restricted operant situation. However, it apparently has seen no application to the period of late infancy. The studies of Brackbill, and of Rheingold and Gewirtz, represent free-operant situations in early infancy, utilize such responses as smiling or vocalizing. The detailed development of a free-operant technique for older children, characterized by several studies described in the next section, involves a thoroughly ambulatory child in a relatively strange room and uses lever pressing as a response. This technique has been found barely feasible and hardly rewarding below the 2-year level; hence there appears to be a gap in the technology of operant-conditioning procedures for late infancy. The development of techniques and reinforcing stimuli, no doubt by borrowing selectively from the procedures successfully applied to early infancy and early childhood, remains one of the challenging problems of the laboratory-experimental approach to child development.

***Discriminative Processes.*** Studies of

discriminative capacities in the older infant almost invariably make use of his ability to prehend. Ling (1941) has made a study of form discrimination in infants, which exemplifies an efficient technique for this age bracket. The basic method of the study is that of multiple choice. The infant, sitting in an ordinary hospital crib, had placed before him a large gray tray containing a semicircle of five holes, each spaced the same distance from the infant. In these holes form blocks painted a bright yellow (circle, oval, square, triangle, and cross) could be mounted. These blocks might be fastened down or not at the experimenter's option. A one-way vision screen, hung from the ceiling of the small, specially made experimental cubicle, swung out to cover the stimulus objects as they were placed on the child's tray and then swung back to uncover them, allowing the experimenter to observe the child from behind it. Usually, one form was a positive stimulus, and another (or others), negative. The positive form was removable from the tray by the child; the negative form was fixed to the tray. Furthermore, the positive form had previously been dipped into a strong saccharine solution and allowed to dry; if the child brought the form to his mouth (a frequent occurrence), it tasted quite sweet. (The forms were sterilized continuously throughout the experiment.) The usual techniques of randomized order of presentation and position were followed. Responses scored included visual fixation, reaching for a form, reaction time, handedness, mouthing the form, and general "affective attitude," including vocalization. (It is not clear in Ling's report how the form was taken from the infant if he chose to suck on it.) The process was adapted to a study of preference for forms simply by not fastening any form to the tray. (Presumably, all forms were sweetened.)

The technique seems an efficient one and can be applied to infants as young as 6 months. Ling's comments indicate that the motivating power of the entire problem seems to increase as the child approaches about 1 year in age and to decrease after that. In particular, his visual attention to the forms after that age is transitory; however, when he does attend, his performance is coordinated, alert, and controlled.

Munn and Steining (1931) report a variant on this technique, using a single 15-month-old boy as a subject, apparently in his own home, seen daily for well over a month. The discrimination apparatus was a box with two doors on its front face, each door bearing a different figure (circle, triangle, square, etc.) and fronting on a small compartment that would contain a piece of chocolate if the form were the "correct" one. Between trials, while the chocolate and the forms were being arranged, the child played games in an adjoining room (in effect, he "hid" from the experimenter). Close to 400 trials were required for an initial discrimination.

Skeels (1933) has simplified this kind of procedure somewhat by adapting the familiar formboard. In this case the child is presented with a board containing a number of forms, each fitting into its own recess. Under the correct form, when he lifts it, the child will find a cookie. This method is certainly applicable to children of 15 months (the youngest children Skeels tested) and presumably may be applied to children just old enough to lift the form from the board. I. M. L. Hunter (1952) has reduced the technique to its bare rudiments for preverbal infants by simply concealing a raisin under one of two blocks of wood (differing in size) and teaching the child to lift a block to find the raisin underneath.

Most of these studies have used procedures as simplified as possible. Gellermann (1933a) has performed studies of discrimination in children in which he utilized a procedure that, although not complex, is still more cumbersome than many of those described above. However, his procedure, an almost perfect translation of the familiar Yerkes alley technique used in animal experimentation, allows a close comparison of children and animals (in this study, chimpanzees) in the same physical apparatus. The child (or chimpanzee) was seated on a chair facing the forms to be discriminated, which were mounted just behind and just beside doors on a platform, under which the child (or chimpanzee) might find chocolate-covered cookies, bananas, grapes, oranges, or apples. Subjects were handled in a standard way (whether child or chimpanzee) and spoken to in the same formula ("Now sit on the chair").

An interesting feature of Gellermann's study is the use of a special order of stimulus pairs. Gellermann generated a series of orders in which the correct stimulus was to be placed on a particular side (e.g., the left side) designed to minimize the formation of position habits and still yield a chance score of 50 per cent correct. The series consisted of ten trials each; some 44 series were generated (Gellermann, 1933b).

*Motivation.* Only one study of motivation is reported for this age range. The question of evaluating the effectiveness of different stimuli as reinforcers or rewards has had little attention here, and procedures are far from adequate.

Mast (1937) has reported a technique applied to children just below 2 years of age and older. The child was presented with a wooden box with a hinged glass top. Through the glass top, the child could see a toy inside. However, the only way to open the box and get at the toy was to insert a stylus into a small hole in the front of the box; when the stylus contacted the brass plate in which the hole was drilled, a doorbell rang inside the box, and the lid opened, allowing the child access to the toy. The experimenter sat behind the child and timed the response. The only clue afforded to the child in solving the problem lay in the instructions he was given at the outset: "Do you see what is in this box? When you have opened the box you may have it. You must take this in your hand (giving him the stylus) and open the box with it." Questions by the child were answered briefly, without giving any help in the problem. Also, "encouragement" was offered to the child from time to time; since many studies have shown the reinforcing effectiveness of approval, the "motivational" aspects of this procedure seem quite varied. With further experiences with the box, it becomes a question whether the child is motivated primarily by approval, the doorbell, or the toy. (When encouragement is used freely by the experimenter, in a nonstandard manner, it would seem likely that it is used most when the subject is least motivated by other stimuli, is inattentive, or displeased.)

It is doubtful whether this technique could be extended to much younger children without increasing resort to demonstration, which would obviate much of the point of the study. However, the use of a transparent container to present a variety of almost available incentives is probably a useful technique at much younger levels, if coordinated with a different response. Apart from any other direct techniques of comparing reinforcing stimuli, then, there remains a summary of the stimuli used in the studies described above: candy, sweets, cookies, raisins, milk, honey, fruit, toys, and (possibly) the opportunity to manipulate (Ling).

***Frustrating, Sudden, or Strong Stimulation.*** One study classified under this heading is probably typical of an experimental difficulty that is encountered often in this age range, although the population used can hardly be termed typical. Arsenian (1943) has studied the effects of the mother's (or a familiar adult's) absence on the free behavior of a child in a strange room. Her subjects were children from the nursery of the Massachusetts' State Reformatory for Women, many of whom had been born and raised in that relatively restricted environment, with little or no outside experience. In age, they ranged from 11 to 30 months; the youngest could barely walk. Half of them had mothers who worked in the nursery itself; the rest saw their mothers daily but only during visiting hours. Cattell and Gesell IQ scores indicated a normal range. Half of the children were brought to a strange room every other day and left there, alone, for five minutes. There were 11 such sessions. The other half of the children were accompanied into the room either by their mothers or by a familiar adult (a nursery caretaker). Each of the two groups was subdivided, and half of each group was placed in a contrasting condition for the last six of its 11 sessions in the strange room (i.e., some children who had been alone the first five trials were accompanied in the last six and vice versa). The room itself was some distance from the nursery, newly decorated, and filled with new toys and pictures; it was designed to be attractive to the children. The child was observed in the room from behind a one-way screen, and behavior was recorded as a protocol on an electrically timed recording device that yielded behavior in terms of frequency per time interval. Behavior was judged as belonging to one of several categories: crying, autistic gestures, play, locomotion, and vocalization. Patterns of these response categories were synthesized into positively directed and negatively directed sequences. Adaptation to the situation as a function of repeated experiences with it and as a function of mother (familiar adult) presence was readily demonstrated. It may be instructive to experimenters that adaptation (replacement of crying and autistic gestures by play, locomotion, etc.) in children left alone in the room on all trials was not gradual and linear but instead tended to be abrupt. Intelligence and age played little if any role within the range observed.

The technique of this study seems to manipulate an important class of variables for this (and older) age ranges. The response measures used by Arsenian are broad and general (appropriate for an initial investigation); a refinement of these, and a wide use of many other responses and tasks, should prove of great significance in experimental investigations of these children.

## Early Childhood

Before 1950 research with toddlers was devoted mostly to response analyses. With the shift of interest from norms to antecedent and consequent relationships has come a small but increasing number of investigations with laboratory-experimental procedures.

### OBTAINING SUBJECTS

Much of the research on early childhood was made possible not only by the availability of subjects in nursery schools but also by the establishment, about 1920, of laboratory nursery schools. These laboratory schools, part of a college or university (Moustakas and Berson, 1955), have undoubtedly contributed the major portion of children for study. The definite advantages to doing research in a laboratory nursery school are the availability of research facilities and equipment and the stimulation usually provided by staff and students. One frequent disadvantage is the limited number of subjects, which is especially felt when teaching and research needs are heavy. Nevertheless, even then a sufficient number is usually available for pilot studies and intensive individual analyses. In the nursery-school setting two essential integral parts of the investigator's task are to conduct talks and discussions with parents, in which the nature and possible implications of the research are explained, and to develop an understanding and cooperative relationship with the teaching staff, so that children may be taken from groups and returned without hindering the procedures of the study or the routines of the school.

Probably the second largest number of subjects have come from private nursery schools and from private and public day-care centers. Day-care centers are all-day schools for the youngsters of working mothers. Requests for permission to embark upon a study in these two types of school are generally addressed to the owner, head teacher, or chairman of the administrative board. Finding adequate working conditions is probably the problem most frequently encountered here. In most instances little or no space is available. Sometimes there may be a spare room, but rarely will it prove sufficiently isolated from the activities of the school. When space limitations make it impractical to control experimental conditions adequately, conducting research in a nearby research center or a mobile laboratory are possible alternatives. Again, the investigator must assume responsibility for giving talks on his research to teachers and parents.

Subjects are sometimes procured by direct contacts with parents. Lists of parents with children of the required age have been obtained from pediatricians, teachers, clinic waiting lists, mothers' clubs, and students from university housing groups. In all instances personal and written contacts are made; and in many situations transportation is provided to a research center. Under some circumstances psychological service is given in exchange for cooperation.

Residential institutions—orphanages or schools for exceptional children, such as the retarded, blind, emotionally disturbed, and dependent—provide excellent opportunities for experimental analyses. Some have research laboratories in operation; others make facilities available for specific studies on request. Procedures for obtaining permission and establishing working relationships are in substance the same as those described in the section dealing with infants in institutions. In preparing for a relatively short-term study in a residential school, portable or prefabricated observation booths (Gewirtz, 1952) and readily transportable apparatus (Lipsitt, 1958; Norcross, 1958) deserve consideration.

## SAMPLING

Youngsters procured through any of the above procedures are, of course, not random samples of preschool children. For example, a survey by Moustakas and Berson showed that "children enrolled in laboratory nursery schools came largely from middle-class professional and business families" and that "Only 55 per cent of the schools were open to both white and negro children; 3 per cent were for colored children, 42 per cent for white children only" (p. 108). Samples of children from institutions would also be expected to be biased on socioeconomic and racial dimensions as well as others.

Since getting random samples of preschoolers for experimental studies is a difficult, if not an impossible, task, one realistic objective might be to obtain random samples within the available subpopulations. Another might be to work out the specifications of a representative sample, search for parents with youngsters who qualify, and solicit their cooperation.

Unless special status or historical conditions are the major point of interest in a study, it is advisable to eliminate preschoolers characterized by anomalies, emotional disturbances, developmental retardation, and recent changes in living conditions (such as the arrival of another sibling, the addition of a new relative to the household, a separation of the parents, or a move to a new location).

## INVESTIGATIVE PROCEDURES

As in the discussion of infants, investigative procedures here are broken down into manipulating independent variables and measuring responses on the one hand and holding constant setting conditions on the other. The latter, it will be recalled, are subdivided into conditions operating before and during the manipulations of the independent variable. In discussing experimental work with children in this age range and older, it will be helpful to divide further the conditions operating before experimental manipulation into (1) inducements to participate in the research, (2) instructions for performing the experimental task, and (3) influences occurring between sessions.

Since the preschool child often shows reluctance to accompany a comparative stranger, it is common practice to establish a routine to minimize emotional reactions to attempted separations and to reduce the number of refusals. Unfortunately, most reports fail to describe the inducement procedure; some give only a brief statement, such as "the child was asked to come to the adjoining room to play games." Often it is impossible to determine whether variations in the inducing procedures could account for differences in the results of some replicated studies.

In planning the inducement procedure, the following considerations, drawn from common practice, might be taken into account. First, one person, ordinarily a young woman, should take the young child from the school group or home to the laboratory and return him. Second, this person should spend a good deal of time getting acquainted with the child before the study begins if at all possible. Third, whatever the adult says in asking the child to come to the experimental room should be simple, neutral in tone, and repeated each time in the same manner. For example, "Now it is your turn to come and play games." "Would you like to play some games and get some of these (showing toys or edibles)?" Fourth, the relationship between the young woman and the child during the trips to and from the laboratory should be pleasant and nondirective: the caretaker never initiates conversation and responds to questions and comments in a pleasant reflective manner.

It is well established that variations in procedures may produce variations in experimental results. It is therefore standard practice to plan and report instructions with care. There are two special problems in research with children (preschool children in particular). The first concerns comprehension. Does the child understand what is required of him? Inevitably, when a youngster is asked whether he understands his task, he nods his head, smiles, and eagerly says "yes." Later he demonstrates otherwise. The second problem is the applicability of a set of instructions to groups at various maturational levels or with developmental defects. Working out the simplest set of instructions with the aid of a nursery-school teacher and giving the child ample opportunity to show understanding by performance (Brackbill, 1958) will often be useful. Examples of simple sets of instructions are, "Here are two toys. You may turn either one over (like this) and see what is under it. You may keep whatever you find." "Here are some toys. You may play with them as long as you like." House and Zeaman provide an example of a procedure that allows the subject time and opportunity to learn the task in a discrimination problem:

On the first presentation of the stimulus tray, both food cups were left uncovered with candy placed in one of them. The experimenter asked, "Can you find the candy?" and pointed if the subject failed to pick it up. On the next trial, a gray wedge was placed over one of the food cups containing candy, with the other cup left uncovered. Again, S was asked to find the candy and aided by the experimenter if he failed. When the subject picked up the gray wedge without prompting (usually one or two trials), discrimination trials were begun (1958, p. 413).

The third class of conditions that may affect experimental performance includes events between sessions, such as the subjects' receiving information, misinformation, and erroneous instructions from peers, teachers, and parents. Still others are upsetting and interfering conditions and events altering schedules of deprivation related to experimental reinforcers. Birthday parties are a common example. Discussions among the children are another and are one of the most difficult problems in this respect. Since the behavior of children cannot be controlled outside the experimental situation, the investigator may evaluate the significance of such interactions either by setting up a control group with matched subjects from private homes in different parts of the community or by replicating the study using a baseline procedure with each child serving as his own control. Alternatively, unauthorized instructions from parents and teachers may be prevented, at least in part, by discussing the purpose and nature of the research and by telling them what their behavior toward the child should be in order to be helpful. Upsetting conditions usually consist of accidents, fights, or trouble at home just before an experimental session. Mothers and teachers often can

supply enough information on such matters to allow the investigator to evaluate their influence. There are, of course, still other interfering conditions that may compete with the behavior required by the experimental task, e.g., holiday celebrations, special outings, or even the weather. Changes in the living conditions of the child or groups might affect motivation (and may lead to elimination of subjects or modifications in experimental design). Again, reports of teachers and parents and direct observation will provide most of the essential information about these happenings.

If the working situation is adequate in terms of space and physical features and if there is protection from extraneous stimuli, the problem of controlling setting conditions centers upon holding constant nonexperimental social variables. Controlling the interactions of child and adult presents an acute problem in research with preschool children. These youngsters do not like to be alone in a room for the time required by most studies. One solution may be to adapt the child to remaining alone for increasingly longer periods before the experimental run. This approach, however, requires considerable time and may result in the loss of subjects who cannot comply (Warren and Brown, 1943). Another possibility may be to have an adult in the room and attempt to control social interactions. Several studies have followed this course by having the experimenter present, but operating the apparatus from behind a one-way screen on the experimental table (House and Zeaman, 1958), or by having an adult behind an opaque screen in the room while the experimenter operates the apparatus and observes the child from an adjoining room through a one-way screen (Bijou, 1957).

Now we shall turn to a discussion of the ways in which stimuli have been manipulated and responses measured. As in the infancy section, the approach is through representative studies in major problem areas.

*Conditioning.* Classical conditioning with young children has been a problem in early childhood in the sense that many have been interested in whether conditioning principles developed in animal studies apply to young humans and, if they do, what are the differences in the parameters as a function of age. Techniques employed are exemplified in studies by Marinesco and Kreindler (1933), Krasnogorski (1909), and Mateer (1918) described in the preceding section.

One of the basic issues of the conditioning studies previously cited is involved in studies of preschool children as well. Do instrumental or operant conditioning principles, derived from animal studies, apply to children? One study by Warren and Brown (1943) is of particular interest here because methodology was seen as the basic problem. Some effort was made to duplicate the animal situation. Children between the ages of 2 and 5 were taken into a small room. A horizontal bar projected from one wall. Under the bar was a white enameled candy tray. Also in the room were a nursery-school book and a hobby horse. Responses to the bar were recorded on a cumulative marker, and candy pellets made of sugar, corn syrup, and gelatin served as reinforcers. They were delivered through a tube to the tray. Daily sessions were held for fifteen days. For the first few days the parents were urged to come with the child but not to enter the room unless needed. The experimenter, however, entered the room with the child and played with him when it seemed indicated. Finally, the child was left alone. The similarities between these procedures and those in animal studies are apparent, but so are some of the differences. For example, there were differences in motivational operations, in the length and number of sessions, and in the adaptation procedures. Nevertheless, the authors stated that their data indicated that known operant conditioning principles may be validly applied to preschool youngsters.

The development of a method for the analysis of operant behavior in young children was also undertaken by Bijou (1957). The objective was to devise an experimental situation in which a variety of problems indigenous to this age span could be analyzed. The experimental room, equipped with one-way screens, microphones, and speakers, was colorfully decorated like a playroom and contained two tables with a toy on each. One toy was a commercial product consisting of a wooden lever and ball enclosed in a cage. Striking the lever flipped the ball to the top of the cage. As it fell, it automatically rolled to its original position on top of one end of the lever and was in position to be catapulted again by the next response. The child was free to play with this at any time. The other toy was a brightly colored box with blue and amber jewel lights, a metal handle protruding on the front, and a tray at one side for receiving reinforcements. Downward pressure on the handle was always followed by a relay click and now and then by a trinket, a cookie, a piece of dry cereal, or candy. Responses, reinforcements, and outstanding events were recorded on a cumulative marker. A young woman brought the subject into the room, remained with him during the session, and returned him to his school group. She followed a routine for removing the child's coat, taking him to the center of the room, giving simple instructions, and retiring behind an opaque screen to read a book. The experimenter, operating in an adjoining room, observed the child through a one-way glass screen, monitored the apparatus, and gave instructions, through a one-way intercom system and ear-speaker, to the adult in the room. Using this experimental setup (see Fig. 4-4), which was duplicated in a mobile laboratory (Bijou, 1958) investigations have been conducted on reinforcement, extinction, discrimination, escape, and avoidance training.

***Discriminative Processes.*** Studies of discrimination outnumber by far all others in this age period. This fact is even more striking when studies of transposition, learning sets, concept formation, and abstracting behavior are included. A few investigations have employed free operant techniques. Most, however, involve discrete multiple-choice tasks with intervals between trials controlled by the experimenter. Usually the mode of prevent-

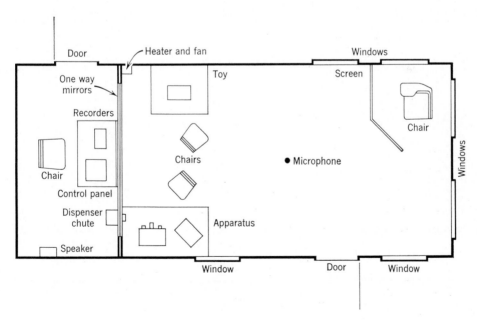

Fig. 4-4. Floor plan of the mobile child study laboratory (Bijou, 1958).

ing stimuli is closely tied in with the required responses to increase the probability of contiguity between attending and choice behavior. For example, subjects have been required to open a drawer under a card with a geometric form (Hunter, 1952), open a door with a distinctive stimulus (Alberts and Ehrenfreund, 1951), press on a glass window showing a stimulus object (Long, 1940), point to an object having a characteristic stimulus dimension (Hicks and Steward, 1935), push a button under a light (Shepard, 1956; Lipsitt, 1958), move a box (Spiker, 1956), point to an inverted cup concealing a toy (Calvin, 1955), or move a stimulus object to see whether there is candy in a hole beneath (House and Zeaman, 1958).

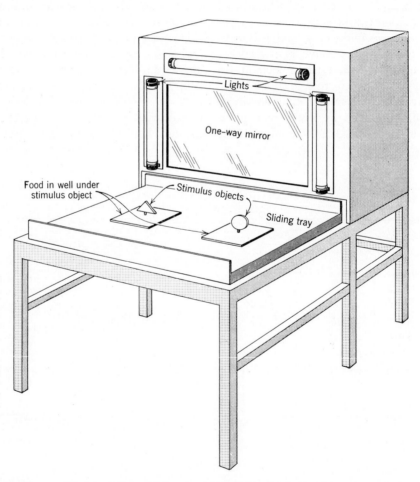

Fig. 4-5. Wisconsin General Test Apparatus (After House and Zeaman, 1958).

In general, discrimination studies have followed virtually every well-known experimental strategy. Subjects have been equated but given different amounts of pretraining; or they have been given the same discrimination training but tested under different conditions. In other studies subjects have been assessed as different in some dimension and have been given the same discrimination task; then they have been tested under different conditions.

An example of study using a controlled multiple-choice technique with good control over adult-child interaction is one by House and Zeaman. Their apparatus was a modification of the Wisconsin General Apparatus Test. (See Fig. 4-5.)

It consisted of a table with a sliding stimulus tray 30 in. by 12 in. with two circular food wells 2 in. in diameter centered 12 in. apart. In the center of the table, separating $S$ from $E$, was a one-way screen. The sliding tray when pulled behind the screen was invisible to $S$. For a trial, the tray was pushed directly in front of $S$ (1958, p. 412).

Five geometric forms were used, each repeated in five colors. Each subject was assigned two stimuli selected at random from among the 25. Correct and incorrect stimuli were designated randomly. Subjects were given pretraining on the task before beginning the training procedure.

For a discrimination trial, $E$ pushed forward the stimulus tray with two stimuli covering the two food cups so that it was directly in front of $S$. The two stimuli were the same on every trial for a given subject with one and only one always correct. The position of the correct stimulus was varied irregularly from left to right according to a Gellermann's series. $E$ recorded $S$'s first response as correct or incorrect (1958, p. 413).

*Serial Learning.* Serial learning is used here to refer to the learning of a behavior-chain or a sequence of stimuli and responses "with only minor variations in the ordinal position of each stimulus or response" (Verplanck, 1957). In a sense, it is a series of linked multiple choices. Learning of this type, sometimes referred to as sensorimotor (Munn, 1954) or multiple responses (Underwood, 1949), is of particular significance in early childhood, since this is the period in which the child characteristically strengthens and extends manipulatory, locomotor, and verbal sequences. Research problems have centered on differences related to age and on conditions that strengthen or weaken chains. Some investigations require manual or locomotor responses, such as finger and alley mazes, others, verbal sequences with numbers or words.

A study by Lambert, Lambert, and Watson of the strengthening and weakening of chains will serve to illustrate a technique with a manual sequence. The apparatus was the Solomon token-reward machine. (See Fig. 4-6.) It consisted of two boxes, one on the other. The top box had a crank on the right side and a chute at the front for delivering tokens; the bottom one, a slot for receiving tokens and a trough below a tube for dispensing candy, both on the front side. The child turned the handle a specific number of turns, received a poker chip, inserted the token in the insert slot, and, after a varying number of these act-sequences, received a small

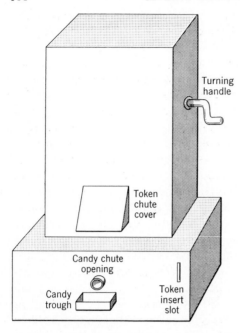

Fig. 4-6. The Solomon token-reward vendor (Lambert, Lambert, and Watson, 1953).

piece of candy. One of the procedures was described as follows:

> The S turned nine turns and this turning was followed by a click which accompanied the automatic ejection of a red token. The S then inserted the red token in the slot of the candy vending machine, and then turned the handle of the work machine nine times. This time a white token was automatically ejected, and insertion of this in the token slot was followed immediately by ejection into the candy trough a small piece of candy (1953, p. 324).

The number of trials per day varied from one to four, and the experiment lasted ten days.

Turning time measures were recorded throughout. This was done by a second E, who sat in an adjoining room and read

the turnings from a dial which led by a flexible cable to the work machine in the experimental room (1953, p. 324).

A serial learning technique involving pictorial and verbal stimuli has been explored with kindergarten children and is described in the serial learning section on later childhood and preadolescence.

*Problem Solving.* Studies of problem solving, reasoning, rational learning, and thinking, taken together, constitute another significant problem area in early childhood. Are children in the initial phase of gaining facility with their behavior equipment capable of such behavior? An oft-recurring question is, "At what age does reasoning behavior start?" Another interest centers around functional problems. If problem-solving behavior starts in early childhood, this is the time, par excellence, to study the conditions that influence it. However, the dimensions of the behavior have not been adequately worked out; consequently, the methods, procedures, approaches, and techniques vary almost as widely as the problems posed. If an empirical definition of the behavior or part of the behavior is adopted, as suggested by Skinner, striking advances could be expected to follow.

Problem solving may be defined as any behavior which, through the manipulation of variables, makes the appearance of a solution more probable (1953, p. 247).

An example of one of the few studies following this lead is that by Kendler, Kendler, Pliskoff, and D'Amato. Their aim was to determine whether inferential behavior resulting from learning is influenced by motivational variables. The equipment was described as follows:

The apparatus is a gray box-like structure with a lever projecting from each of its vertical sides. The face of the apparatus had two rectangular apertures and three transparent windows that could be covered. The levers, painted black or white, when pushed inward, moved small boxes (either a yellow square box or a red triangular box) along a wooden track into the lower aperture. One of these boxes was attached by a hidden string to a translucent circular plastic container mounted on wheels. When this box was pulled down, the plastic container was drawn into the upper aperture (1958, p. 208).

The subjects drawn from nursery schools in the New York metropolitan area were given three training experiences; two led to the attainment of containers with raisins that served as subgoal objects, and the third led to a box with or without the major goal, a gold-colored charm. On test trials the child was confronted with the two sticks. The choice of one led to a box, which, if pulled, would produce the major goal object. The container with the charm could be seen in one of the windows. Motivation was varied during the training and testing trials.

*Motivation.* The term motivation is used here to refer to behavior changes related to differences in reinforcements and operations of satiation and deprivation. The experimental plan of most of the studies in this age group employ one of the techniques described above. Equated groups of children, each of whom receives a different class of reinforcers or a different satiation-deprivation operation, are presented with a task. Differences in performance are compared.

Terrell and Kennedy (1957) and Terrell (1958), for example, studied the effect of different kinds of reinforcement in a discrimination learning and transposition situation. In the Terrell and Kennedy experiment, praise, reproof, candy, and tokens, each accompanied by a flash of light, were compared. The task consisted of button-pushing responses to the larger of two 3-dimensional geometric objects. There were four groups, one for each condition, divided into two age groups, 4 to 5 and 8 to 9. For the praise group, the reinforcement after each correct response was "That's fine. You are doing well." Subjects in the reproof group were told "No, not that. You are wrong," after each incorrect response. The candy group was given a "small piece of candy." The subjects of the token group were allowed to transfer a dried bean from one jar to another and were told that as soon as "enough" of the beans were transferred they could have a "small bag of candy." The control group received only the light flash.

Instructions were given in full at the beginning, and after every tenth trial this sentence was repeated: "Now remember, the game is to see how soon you can learn to make the light go on every time." After reaching the criterion of learning, a four-trial transposition test was given without changing the type of reward. The children in the two age groups, 4 to 5 and 8 to 9, required significantly fewer trials to discriminate and transpose when candy was used.

A study by Brackbill and O'Hara (1957) also attacked a motivational problem dealing with the relative effectiveness of presenting and withdrawing tangible reinforcement. The former was accomplished by giving an M & M candy after a correct response; the latter, by taking away a candy after an error. The procedure was a typical multiple-choice technique. The stimuli were three boxes differing in color and size, and the task was to learn a simple position alternation sequence between the first and the second boxes. At the beginning of the session the subject was "staked" to a box of candy.

*Frustrating, Sudden, or Strong Stimulation.* Despite increasing interest in the concept of anxiety, there have been relatively few experimental studies on the effects of strong and sudden stimulation in early childhood, and follow-up studies on earlier investigations (Landis and Hunt, 1937; Jersild and Holmes, 1935; Jones, 1924; and Hagman, 1932) have yet to be performed. Of the older studies, the Hagman study is described here mainly because of the method used to record responses. Hagman was interested in comparing mothers' reports of their children's fears with the children's behavior in a test situation. Reactions to a phonographic recording of thunder were recorded by means of motion pictures (16 frames per second). The camera and lights were in full view and pictures were taken as the child stood inside the doorway, about 15 feet from the camera. A young woman brought the child into the laboratory, holding his hand throughout. As they stepped inside the room, she said: "We will wait here a minute." The investigator ran the camera for five seconds, started the phonograph, and continued to take pictures for fifteen seconds or longer. Twenty-six days later the child was returned to the laboratory. Just before the camera started, the young woman momentarily let go of the child's hand and backed out of the room. The films were analyzed in terms of behavior changes in eight different parts of the body, right hand, left hand, feet, head, eyes, etc., by running through the film several times forward and backward. Extent of activity in each area was rated on a scale. Findings indicated a decrease in activity and an increase in glancing at the escort.

A well-known study of preschool children consequent to frustration produced by withholding reinforcement is that by Barker, Dembo, and Lewin (1941). Nursery-school children were brought one at a time into a playroom containing run-of-the-mill toys. On the second visit the child found that one partition of the room had been removed, and in the new section was an attractive array of toys. The toys available during the previous session had been mixed with the more alluring objects. After the experimenter was convinced that the child had played with all the new toys, she collected the toys available during the first session and placed them where they had been originally. The child was then told to come and play with these toys. As he left the new toys, a wire-mesh screen was lowered between him and the new toys. Thus he was back with the toys used in the first session but in full view of the more elaborate toys. Observational data were grouped into units of behavior that in turn were quantified on a 7-point constructiveness-of-play scale. It has been pointed out (Underwood, 1957) that the results of the Barker, Dembo, and Lewin study could be accounted for on other grounds and that data on a control group with initial and final play sessions but no intervening frustration would be helpful in clarifying this ambiguity.

*Changes in Complex Behavior.* There is a group of experimental problems centering around the modification of complex physical, social, or emotional behavior at this age level. The experimental design generally consists of equating two groups on some experimental variable and matching them on several other dimensions, giving one training, and retesting both on the experimental variable. A variation may include an additional period in which both groups receive treatment and additional testing.

An example of a study of biological maturation and the learning of motor skills is one by Hilgard (1932). Two groups of children, aged 24 to 36 months, were matched for chronological age, mental age, sex, and approximate initial skill in climbing, cutting with scissors, and buttoning. The climbing task consisted of negotiating a three-step, 2½-foot ladder, stepping on to a table at the top, and then climbing down again. There were toys on the table "to attract and please the child." The score was the average time taken to go up and come down. The buttoning test consisted of buttoning together standard strips containing buttons and button holes. Scores were based on number of successes and time. The cutting-test task required cutting along a straight line. Ratings were based on ability to handle the scissors and accuracy in cutting. One group received twelve weeks of training with retests at two-week intervals. In ladder-climbing training, for example, the experimenter tried to help the child improve his time and quality of performance in a variety of ways, including putting one foot instead of two upon each rung of the ladder. At the end of twelve weeks, the control group received four days of intensive training. At this time the practice group made higher scores than the control group. After a brief period of training, however, the control group reached the level of the practice group.

Covariations in frustration-produced behavior and training are exemplified by the research of Keister and Updegraff (1937) and Keister (1938). In the latter study two groups of children, aged 43 to 72 months, were matched on chronological age, sex, and intelligence. They were contrasted in terms of immature reactions to failure (e.g., retreating or giving up almost at once, crying, sulking) on a difficult puzzle and a task requiring considerable physical strength for their developmental level. Training was restricted to the relatively immature group and consisted of introducing the child in easy stages to a graded series of jigsaw puzzles and block-building tasks. The procedures with the puzzles were flexible and informal. Praise and support were given, but no assistance. In the block-building tasks praise and encouragement were also freely distributed, but the child was left to work the problems himself. Sessions were terminated with praise for the work accomplished. After completion of training both groups were tested again on a difficult puzzle similar to the original one. The trained group made significantly more "attempts to solve alone" and "interest" responses than they had in the original test, and there were less requests for help, less emotional behavior, and less escape behavior. The control group (relatively "mature" to start with) did not show any significant improvement.

A parallel study, except that it dealt with social behavior, was conducted by Jack (1934). Children ranging in age from 45 to 56 months, with the lowest "ascendance" scores in a previous experiment, served as subjects. Their scores were derived from observations of behavior with each of five children in a sandbox with toys. The training group received individual treatment designed "to make their position more secure and to assure them of a certain degree of confidence." Instruction and assistance was given in working on mosaics, picture puzzles, and a picture book. There were seven or more sessions, lasting from ten to fifteen minutes. Following the sessions, each child was observed in four pairings—each time with a different, originally-more-ascendant child—in situations with the material used in training. About ten weeks after the initial ascendance tests the trained children were again paired with the same children as before for a final observation. They showed significantly greater gains in ascendance than the untrained group; the untrained children showed no changes between the initial and the final test.

These three studies obviously involve intricate interactions and a variety of reinforcers. They, and others like them, have explored relationships between performance and training that should now be submitted to more systematic and detailed analysis. Just what specific conditions in the training have or have not had effects? How precisely can these effects be described? What other kinds of reinforcement are effective in promoting such behavior?

## Later Childhood and Pre-adolescence

This section deals with studies of children between 6 and 9 (the first four elementary school grades) and between 10 and 13 (the last four grades). These age spans, sometimes referred to as later childhood and preadolescence or as middle and later childhood, are merged because of the similarity in experimental techniques employed. Differences are discussed as they arise.

Experiments in this age range involve more verbal stimuli and responses, have sessions extending over longer periods, include more situations in which the subject performs alone, and pose many difficulties in controlling verbal behavior between and within sessions. Fewer experimental studies have been conducted on children in this age range. (There seems to be an inverse relationship between stage of development and number of experimental studies.) However, the indications are that this situation gradually is being changed.

## OBTAINING SUBJECTS

As would be expected, most subjects in this age group have been procured in public and private schools. The procedure for obtaining permission to do research varies, but basically it consists of personal or written contact with the principal or superintendent, in which the nature, method, and implications of the investigation, the time required of each child and for the total study, and space needs are described. Frequently time and space problems arise. For example, the time of the sessions may have to be adjusted to class schedules. When a study requires the children to return for a series of sessions, arrangements may have to be worked out to compensate for lost time. This problem would be attenuated when working with preadolescents in a junior high school, in which participation might be limited to study-hour classes. The frequently occurring problem of inadequate working space may be overcome by the use of a mobile laboratory in the schoolyard or by taking the children to a research center. The latter involves the responsibility for transportation, and for that reason is often avoided.

Some investigators have obtained children through parent contacts. Long (1958), for example, wrote letters telling parents that he had received their child's name and address at the school office and asking permission to have the child serve as subject. He described the research and pointed out that it was a part of a university project. He also indicated what was not included. ("Lest you be concerned, let me assure you that the situation involves no competition between children, no psychological tests, or anything else that might be disturbing.") Finally, information was given on appointments and transportation arrangements. Long's approach has particular merit for research conducted during the summer months.

Subjects have also been obtained through organizations such as boys' clubs, community centers for youth, the Boy Scouts, and the Camp Fire Girls. For example, a settlement house was used to study aggressive behavior in experimentally created "social climates" by Lewin, Lippitt, and White (1939) and cooperative behavior in pairs of children by Azrin and Lindsley (1956). Permission to conduct a study is ordinarily obtained both from the person in charge and the parents.

Finally, large numbers of children in residential institutions have served as subjects. As reviews by McPherson (1948, 1958) have shown, many learning experiments on the retarded child have been conducted in these settings. Since the method of requesting permission and the problems encountered in doing research in institutions are similar to those discussed in the parallel section on early childhood, no further comment is necessary.

## SAMPLING

With one exception, problems of sampling are similar to those discussed in the early childhood section. But in studies in which children are obtained in the public schools sampling techniques may be exercised to avoid bias in socioeconomic status, race, intelligence, and the like. Procedures for obtaining random or representative samples under these circumstances have been carefully described (Lindquist, 1940).

## INVESTIGATIVE PROCEDURES

As in the preceding sections, investigative procedures are divided into problems of inducements, instructions, intersession events, and setting conditions. Inducement procedures with children in this age span are as major a source of variance as in early childhood. Some standard procedure is needed simply to deal with misconceptions about the experimenter and the experiment. For example, investigators working in a school or institution have reported that their subjects often believe that the experimenter is a school psychologist and that the study is to find out whether certain children should be in a lower grade. A standard procedure may also prove necessary in explaining the nature of the study and the reason for soliciting the child's cooperation. One workable procedure is to take each subject into a waiting room and discuss all aspects of the study. Children who show persistent negative attitudes can be eliminated at this point if this bias is important.

Some investigators maintain that instructions to children in this age range should be held to a minimum or even eliminated. For example, in a study of cooperation by Azrin and Lindsley instructions consisted merely of telling the subjects that they were going to play a game and showing them how parts of the game worked. The authors believe that an abbreviated procedure has the following advantages:

(*a*) The initial acquisition of cooperation can be studied, (*b* subjects (*S*'s) that learn by demonstration and instruction with difficulty (i.e., infants, certain classes of psychotics, and lower organisms) can be studied, and (*c*) no problems involving the effects of instructions upon the behavior of the *S*'s are involved (1956, p. 100).

However, there are some experimental situations with children that require instructions. In these instances they should be in the simplest possible terms and may well be followed by a period of practice. In a study of stimulus generalization as a function of age Mednick and Lehtinen followed this procedure.

In order to provide a behavior test of *S*'s understanding of the task, two brief demonstration trials were given in which the center lamp and a peripheral lamp were used as test stimuli. It was decided to procure this behavior indication of *S*'s understanding of the task despite the possibility that the older children would learn more from these trials than the other children (1957, p. 180).

It will be recalled that some of the intersession events that have potential effects on experimental behaviors are instructions and admonitions from teachers, supervisors, and parents ("Be a good boy, and do your very best") and discussions among the participants. There are the added possibilities of transitory emotional reactions and variations in satiations and deprivations relative to the experimental reinforcers. In an effort to deal with these factors, some investigators tell the adults in contact with the children what their role should be and how to deal with questions about the study. Individual and group discussions at the end of the study may be used to express appreciation and to show how their cooperation helped carry through the study.

Conversations among the participants may produce erroneous self-instructions, misconceptions, emotional predispositions, and the like, and are indeed difficult to control. Several approaches are possible. First, the experimenter may try to determine whether the child has any preconceptions about the study. For example, in a study of the relative efficacy of various types of stimulus-objects in the discrimination learning of first grade children Calvin and Clifford note:

While walking to the testing room, S was asked such questions as "Do you know where we are going?" and "Do you know what we are going to do?" as a check on possible intercommunication between S's about the experiment. It was found that some of the S's had talked to each other about the game but not about the actual problem involved (1956, p. 104).

Second, at the end of a run the experimenter may ask the child not to tell anyone about the game until it is over, to keep it a secret (Hendrickson and Schroeder, 1941). It is, of course, difficult to estimate the effectiveness of either of these procedures. Third, the experimenter may take these precautions and also run a matched control group with children living in homes separated at some distance one from the other. Fourth, the investigator may replicate the study with a repeated-measures design involving baseline techniques.

Comments from teachers and parents and obvious changes in the child's behavior suggesting an emotional state must be evaluated by the experimenter to determine whether the subject should be continued. The same is true of changes in conditions influencing schedules or cycles of relevant satiations and deprivation.

Holding constant the social aspect of the setting conditions of an experiment is potentially less of a problem with these children than with the younger ones. The problem may be completely eliminated when it is possible for the child to work alone. One deterrent to eliminating the investigator may be the lack of an adjoining room with a one-way screen and listening equipment. Another may be the need for the investigator in the room to set up the problems, observe behavior, and record responses. Under both these conditions it is suggested that inexpensive devices, such as a portable observation booth (Gewirtz, 1952), a one-way screen mounted on a table (House and Zeaman, 1958), or some sort of an opaque screen or partition (Bijou, 1957), be used. If social interactions are curtailed by these or like procedures and all verbal interactions are standardized, at least in tone, a considerable portion of uncontrolled variance will be reduced.

As before, techniques for presenting stimuli and recording responses are discussed in terms of representative studies in problem areas.

*Conditioning.* There are relatively few experiments on classical conditioning problems with children between 6 and 13. A few have been conducted to observe differences in conditioning phenomena as a function of age (e.g., Mateer, 1918; Razran, 1935). Some have involved the classical conditioning method as an approach to other problems. Riess (1940), for example, conditioned the galvanic skin reflex in children of 7 years and older to analyze generalization with respect to dissimilar sounding verbal concepts. One reason for this paucity of studies may be that satisfactory apparatus has not as yet been developed. For instance, there is no technique comparable for children under 12 to the eyelid conditioning method used extensively for young adults (Spence, 1956).

In contrast to the few classical conditioning studies are the numerous investigations on instrumental or operant problems in normal and deviant children. A project by Long (1958) is representative. He and his coworkers (Long, Hammack, May, and Campbell, 1958) have explored methodology and problems of schedule interactions, reinforcement, concurrent operants, and satiation and deprivation. The experimental situation consisted of a console in a 9 x 10 foot soundproof cubicle. The subject sat in front of the console table; directly ahead was a telegraphic key or plunger for responding, colored lights, a translucent screen on which pictures or other stimuli were projected, and a tray for reinforcers. He was shown how to work the apparatus and given an opportunity to obtain reinforcers. When schedules of reinforce-

ment were investigated, the subject was also given an opportunity to respond while reinforcement was being withheld. After the preliminaries, the experimenter told the subject he was leaving and would return in a short time. "During subsequent sessions such instructions were unnecessary, and the child usually went directly to the cubicle, closed the door, and started working" (Long, 1958, p. 5). Responses were obtained in graphic form by a cumulative recorder. Trinkets, pennies, and colored slides served as reinforcers.

Another operant technique study is one by Azrin and Lindsley (1956) on social behavior. Children between the ages of 7 and 12 were paired on the basis of age and sex. Each team of two was taken into the experimental room and asked to sit at opposite sides of a long table. In front of each child were three holes in the table and a stylus with "an extension cord." A wire screen in the center of the table prevented each child from manipulating the stylus of the other. The investigator oriented the children to the apparatus and left the room. Part of their task was to discover that when the styli were placed in opposite holes within 0.04 second of each other a red light flashed and a jelly bean came down a chute, falling into a cup accessible to both children. Recording and programming apparatus was in an adjoining room. The first reinforcement period was followed by an extinction period and a second reinforcement period. All pairs learned the cooperative response and an equitable way to share the candy. Response rate increased during the reinforcement periods and gradually decreased during extinction. The authors give the following reasons for studying cooperative behavior by this technique: "(a) a more continuous record of the cooperative process is obtained, (b) extraneous environmental variables are minimized, and (c) relatively long periods of experimental observation are possible" (p. 100).

**Discriminative Processes.** As in the previous developmental period, most experiments in this age span are concerned with discrimination problems. A study by Carter and Schooler (1949) is taken as an example because of the authors' special emphasis on methodology. The study was concerned with the influence of value on the perception of children from contrasting socioeconomic backgrounds. The apparatus, patterned after Bruner and Goodman (1947), consisted of a metal box with a ground-glass face. At the opposite side of the box was a light source. Between the light and opening was a movable metal plate with a small hole. A turn of the knob on the side of the box moved the plate forward or backward, caused the size of the disk of light on the ground glass to become smaller or larger. The diameter of the illuminated disk could be readily and accurately measured. A "poor" group and a "rich" group between the ages of 9 and 11 served as subjects. Each was seated in front of the apparatus and shown how it operated. Using the method of average error, the investigator instructed the subject (1) to make the illuminated disk the size of a coin of each denomination, (2) to match the size of the disk with a penny

in front of him (and then with a nickel, dime, quarter, and also a half dollar), (3) to match the disk with aluminum disks the size of all five coins, and (4) to match the disk with cardboard disks the size of all five coins. Finally, a series of aluminum disks were shown, one at a time, and the subject was asked to say whether each was larger or smaller than a half dollar. The same procedure was followed for the four other coins. On the basis of their findings and the literature, the authors conclude,

The present results suggest that the value of a disc or the need associated with it is an important determiner of the judged size only when the stimulus object is equivocal or absent, as when judgments are made from memory (p. 207).

**Serial Learning.** Techniques to study serial learning as such include manual, verbal, and temporal mazes, punch boards, and the like. An example of a maze study (Abel, 1936) is found in the section on motivation which follows.

Norcross (1958) has described a device for studying verbal and pictorial material in serial fashion. Her research has been devoted to seeing whether findings on mature subjects apply to children. She has explored procedures and apparatus for comparable experimentation with children. The equipment consisted of a Hunter Card Master,[1] a device which controls exposure and interval between stimuli with high reliability. Since it is also flexible, it permits the investigator to present either or both halves of a stimulus card. Her investigations with kindergarten

[1] Produced by the Hunter Manufacturing Co., 930 So. Linn St., Iowa City, Iowa.

and sixth-grade children demonstrated that the method "is suitable at the pre-reading age level and with elementary-age school children."

**Problem Solving.** An example of a problem-solving study in which performance was related to manipulating verbal instruction is one by Hendrickson and Schroeder (1941). They were interested in varying the degree of explanation of the principle involved in solving a problem. Eighth-grade boys from a suburban junior high school were divided into three groups, designated as the control, experimental A, and experimental B. The task was to hit a standard rifle target with a BB air gun. In the first problem the target was submerged in water at a depth of 6 inches. After three consecutive successful hits, the second task was presented. This time the depth of the water was changed to 2 inches. The boys in the control group were merely told where to stand and the number of consecutive hits they would have to make to show mastery of the problems. Those in experimental groups A and B were given an elementary explanation of refraction involving a diagram and a short text. They were allowed to study the material until they indicated they understood. No questions were permitted. The explanation for group B contained an additional sentence stating the relationship between depth of water and distance between the object under water and the image of the object. Those in group B required fewer trials to learn the first task and to transfer to the second task, whereas those in group A took fewer trials to learn both tasks than the control group.

**Motivation.** As noted earlier, problems of the relative effectiveness of reinforcers and the consequences of satiation and deprivation on performance are usually studied in situations involving conditioning, multiple choice, serial learning, or problem solving. Several examples are given below.

A series of investigations by Screven (1958) utilized the work output of a restricted operant to evaluate various reinforcement conditions. The technique, designed for children between 4 and 7, required the child to sit in a chair and on signal to run down a 15-foot runway, obtain a marble or piece of candy on a table, and return to his seat. On occasions in which there was no reward object, he was to touch the table. By means of timers, measures of reaction time (time between onset of signal and standing up) and running time were obtained. Work output was controlled by fastening a rope to a harness fitted over the child's shoulders so that the subject pulled against a constant weight. Ample opportunity was given the child to learn the task; most were trained in four or five trials. Studies were conducted to compare performances with and without rewards and with increasing and constant work loads.

Another study of motivation in an operant situation by Flanagan, Goldiamond, and Azrin (1958) suggests an interesting approach to aversive and escape training in stuttering behavior. Although the youngest subject was 15 years of age, it is reported here because the same technique may be applied to younger children. The subject was seated at a table and asked to read aloud. Every time he stuttered, the investigator pressed a switch, which activated a marker. "When a curve of stuttering frequency considered smooth was obtained," one of two thirty-minute training periods was begun. In aversive training every depression of the switch produced a one-second blast of a 6000-cycle tone at 105 decibels in the subject's earphones. In escape training the same stimulation was constantly present, and every activation of the switch interrupted the tone for five seconds. Training on either condition was followed by a thirty-minute period without training. A check was made on the reliability of the experimenter's judgments. Each subject was seen on two consecutive days, each day for a different schedule, e.g., on day 1 subject one had a baseline period, an escape training period, and a period of no escape training; on day 2 he had a baseline period, an aversive period, and a period of no aversive training. The order was reversed for the second subject, etc. The findings suggest that escape training increases the rate of stuttering and aversive training decreases it.

Few studies are concerned with the operations of satiation and deprivation on the performance of children, especially in relation to social reinforcement. Hence a study by Gewirtz and Baer (1958) is of particular interest. Their objective was to study the two operations in relation to approval ("Good," "Hm-hmm," "Fine") given by a young woman experimenter. The subjects were first-grade boys and girls from a laboratory elementary school. They were divided into three groups. Subjects in the deprivation group were left alone in the experimental room for twenty minutes before starting the task. Those in the nondeprivation group started the experiment without delay, and those in the satiation group received considerable praise and admiration while drawing pictures and cutting out designs during the twenty-minute waiting period. (An attempt was made to give exactly 30 reinforcers during that period.) The experimental task was to drop marbles into either of two holes of a toy while the experimenter sat alongside and observed. "The E observed S's play for a 'baseline' period of 4 minutes during which no reinforcers were dispensed." Immediately after this there was a ten-minute period in which social reinforcers were given in successively higher fixed ratios following a "correct response" (which was defined as that preferred least during the last minute of the baseline period). They found that the reinforcing effectiveness of approval was greatest after deprivation and least after satiation.

A well-known serial-learning study on the relative efficacy of classes of reinforcers is one by Abel (1936). Her subjects were boys between the ages of 9 and 10 from lower middle-class homes, whose fathers were in the occupational classes of skilled laborers, small shopkeepers, etc. They were divided into five groups, each to receive different rewards in the learning of a finger maze with ten-choice points. After instructions and practice on a simpler maze of the same kind, differential training was initiated. Group 1 received no experimental reward at the end of each run. Group 2 received a penny each time. Group 3 received social reinforcement and were encouraged to improve their scores. ("Good," "Very good," "Let me see if you can make even fewer mistakes this time.") Group 4 received no experimental reward during the first 15 trials and a penny after each one thereafter. Group 5 received the same kind of social reinforcement given group 3 during the first 15 trials and a penny after each completion of trial 16. Analysis was made of the number of errors as a function of trials and incentive. Material reward (pennies) alone or in combination with earlier training of no reward or verbal reward resulted in fewer errors than verbal reward or no experimental reward conditions.

Examples of motivational studies in which multiple-choice techniques were used, such as Terrell and Kennedy's (1957) and problem-solving procedures, such as Kendler, Kendler, Pliskoff, and D'Amato (1958), could be cited. For a review of the use of tangible positive reinforcers with a variety of techniques with young children, see Bijou and Sturges (1959).

*Frustrating, Sudden, or Strong Stimulation.* A technique for studying the physiological consequences of frustration was performed by Jost (1941). His subjects were normal children from an elementary school and children with adjustment problems from a special school. The task was to learn a series of numbers by the anticipation method. Numbers with digits from 1 to 5 were flashed on a lighted panel, and the subject was allowed to learn two series successfully. Then a series apparently like the others was presented but was too difficult to recall. Frustration was said to occur when the subject discovered that he could not learn a series that was very similar to the one he had formerly learned easily. The measures taken were galvanic skin response, respiration, pulse rate, blood pressure, hand tremor, gross movements, and brain potentials. Brain-potential measures were taken by a crystalline recording method; the others were recorded photographically.

A method for analyzing conflict behavior is described by Barker (1942). The experiment was concerned with time factors and vicarious trial-and-error behavior (VTE) produced by forced choices between liquids of similar and dissimilar desirability and with real (the subject had to drink the liquid chosen) and hypothetical consequences (the subject indicated the one he would drink if required). Seven liquids were used: (1) orange juice, (2) pineapple juice, (3) tomato juice, (4) water, (5) lemon juice, (6) vinegar, and (7) saturated solution of salt water. The liquids were placed, by the method of paired comparisons, in a preference series for each subject individually. The subjects were boys, 9 to 11 years old, all of whom could read the names of and were familiar with the seven liquids. Each received some money for participating in the study. The apparatus and procedure were as follows: each subject was seated in a chair at a small table. "At a suitable distance and height," the names of the liquids were exposed side by side at the same height in an exposure apparatus; "at a convenient reaching distance," a lever was mounted 2 inches below the surface of the table and extended 6 inches above the top of the table and was so placed and weighted that it came to rest in a vertical position on a line midway between the cards in the exposure apparatus. The lever could be moved easily to the right or left from the vertical position in arcs of 5 inches. When moved as far as possible to either side, a circuit operating a buzzer was automatically closed. The subject indicated the liquid of his choice by moving the lever to the appropriate side. Movements of the lever from the vertical of less than the 5-inch maximum that sounded the buzzer did not "count," and the subject was free to reverse the movement at any point within the limits of these arcs. The lever was returned to the central position before each exposure. On a continuously moving tape, a record was made of the time of exposure of the cards and of all the movements of the lever, thus providing a record of the time from the moment of the occurrence of the conflict until its resolution and of the VTE behavior occurring. Every pair of cards was presented twice in each sequence of conflicts; their positions were reversed on the two exposures to avoid the influence of position. The data for a particular choice in a sequence consisted of the average of the two determinations.

A study concerned with the physiological reactions to the sudden stimulation resulting from a loss of support was conducted by Ray (1932). The subjects were boys selected "at random" by their teachers and the principal. They ranged in age from 7 to 12 years and in IQ from 73 to 144. Loss of support was accomplished by a 2-to-3-inch vertical drop in the seat of a chair. The procedure involved (1) seating the child in the experimental chair and giving him a Stanford-Binet Intelligence Test, (2) adjusting the apparatus for obtaining circulatory and respiratory measures, (3) making two or three preliminary runs to check on the functioning of the apparatus, and (4) making the test run after a baseline period of five minutes. Reactions were recorded by a Summer pneumograph and a modified form of the Erlanger sphygmomanometer connected with Marey tambours to record on smoked paper. Analysis was made by comparing performance during the baseline period and following the sudden drop. Regarding the feasibility of the method, Ray said,

Experiments on the physiological reactions of children of school age can be carried on, although under greater difficulties than are encountered with adults (1932, p. 116).

## REFERENCES

Abel, L. B. 1936. Effects of shifts in motivation upon the learning of a sensori-motor task. *Arch. Psychol., N. Y.,* **29**, No. 205.

Alberts, E., and D. Ehrenfreund. 1951. Transposition of children as a function of age. *J. exp. Psychol.,* **41**, 30–38.

Anderson, J. E. 1956. Child development: An historical prospective. *Child Develpm.,* **27**, 181–196.

Arsenian, Jean M. 1943. Young children in an insecure situation. *J. abnorm. soc. Psychol.*, 38, 225–249.

Azrin, N. H., and O. R. Lindsley. 1956. The reinforcement of cooperation between children. *J. abnorm. soc. Psychol.*, 52, 100–102.

Barker, R. G. 1942. An experimental study of the resolution of conflict by children: Time elapsing and the amount of vicarious trial-and-error behavior occurring. Cited by Q. McUlman and M. H. Merrell (Eds.). *Studies in personality*, New York: McGraw-Hill.

———, Temara Dembo, and K. Lewin. 1941. Studies in topological and vector psychology, II: Frustration and regression: An experiment with young children. *Univer. Iowa Stud. Child Welf.*, 18, No. 1.

Beach, F. A. 1955. The descent of instinct. *Psychol. Rev.*, 62, 401–410.

Bijou, S. W. 1957. Methodology for an experimental analysis of child behavior. *Psychol. Rep.*, 3, 243–250.

———. 1958. A child study laboratory on wheels. *Child Develpm.*, 29, 425–427.

———, and Persis T. Sturges. 1959. Positive reinforcers for experimental studies with children—consumables and manipulatables. *Child Develpm.*, 30, 151–170.

Blau, T. H., and Lili R. Blau. 1955. The sucking reflex: The effects of long feeding vs. short feeding of the behavior of a human infant. *J. abnorm. soc. Psychol.*, 51, 123–125.

Brackbill, Yvonne. 1958. Extinction of the smiling response in infants as a function of reinforcement schedule. *Child Develpm.*, 29, 115–124.

———. 1958. Personal communication.

———, and J. O'Hara. 1957. Discrimination learning in children as a function of reward and punishment. Paper read at Western Psychol. Ass., Eugene, Oregon.

Bruner, J. S., and Cecile C. Goodman. 1947. Value and need as organizing factors in perception. *J. abnorm. soc. Psychol.*, 42, 33–44.

Calvin, A. D. 1955. Configurational learning in children. *J. educ. Psychol.*, 46, 117–120.

———, and L. T. Clifford. 1956. The relative efficacy of various types of stimulus objects in discriminative learning in children. *Amer. J. Psychol.*, 69, 103–106.

Carter, L. F., and K. Schooler. 1949. Value, need, and other factors in perception. *Psychol. Rev.*, 56, 200–207.

Crudden, C. H. 1937. Reactions of newborn infants to thermal stimuli under constant tactual conditions. *J. exp. Psychol.*, 20, 350–370.

Davis, H. V., R. R. Sears, H. C. Miller, and A. J. Brodbeck. 1948. Effects of cup, bottle, and breast feeding in oral activities of newborn infants. *Pediatrics*, 3, 549–558.

Dennis, W. 1941. Infant development under conditions of restricted practice and of minimum social stimulation. *Genet. Psychol. Monogr.*, 23, 143–189.

———. 1951. Infant reaction to restraint. In W. Dennis (Ed.), *Reading in child psychology*. New York: Prentice-Hall. Pp. 393–407.

———, and Marsena G. Dennis. 1935. The effect of restricted practice upon the reaching, sitting, and standing of two infants. *J. genet. Psychol.*, 47, 17–32.

Dockery, F. C., and W. L. Valentine. 1939. A new isolation cabinet for infant research. *J. exp. Psychol.*, 24, 211–214.

Ferster, C. B. 1953. The use of the free operant in the analysis of behavior. *Psychol. Bull.*, 50, 263–274.

Festinger, L., and D. Katz. 1953. *Research methods in the behavioral sciences*. New York: Dryden.

Flanagan, B., I. Goldiamond, and N. Azrin. 1958. Operant stuttering: The control of stuttering through response contingent consequences. *J. exp. anal. Behav.*, 2, 173–178.

Gellermann, L. W. 1933a. Form discrimination in chimpanzees and two-year-old children. I. Form (triangularity) per se. *J. genet. Psychol.*, 42, 3–27.

———. 1933b. Chance orders of alternating stimuli in visual discrimination experiments. *J. genet. Psychol.*, 42, 206–208.

———. 1933c. II. Forms vs. background. *J. genet. Psychol.*, 42, 28–50.

Gesell, A., and Helen Thompson. 1929. Learning and growth in identical infant twins: An experimental study by the method of co-twin control. *Genet. Psychol. Monogr.*, 6, 1–124.

Gewirtz, J. L. 1952. Plans for the construction

of a one-way portable observation booth. *Child Develpm.*, 23, 307–314.

Gewirtz, J. L., and D. M. Baer. 1958. Deprivation and satiation of social reinforcers as drive conditions. *J. abnorm. soc. Psychol.*, 56, 165–172.

Hagman, S. R. 1932. A study of fears of children of preschool age. *J. exp. Educ.*, 1, 110–130.

Hebb, D. O. 1949. *The organization of behavior.* New York: Wiley.

———. 1958. *A textbook of psychology.* Philadelphia: Saunders.

Hendrickson, G., and W. H. Schroeder. 1941. Transfer of training in learning to hit a submerged target. *J. educ. Psychol.*, 32, 205–213.

Hicks, J. A., and F. D. Steward. 1935. The learning of abstract concepts of size. *Child Develpm.*, 6, 120–140.

Hilgard, Josephine R. 1932. Learning and motivation in preschool children. *J. genet. Psychol.*, 41, 40–53.

Holway, Amy R. 1949. Early self-regulation of infants and later behavior in play interviews. *Amer. J. Orthopsychiat.*, 19, 612–623.

House, Betty J., and D. Zeaman. 1958. A comparison of discrimination learning in normal and mentally defective children. *Child Develpm.*, 29, 411–416.

Hunter, I. M. L. 1952. An experimental investigation of the absolute and relative theories of transpositional behaviour in children. *Brit. J. Psychol.*, 43, 113–128.

Hunter, W. S. 1917. The delayed reaction in a child. *Psychol. Rev.*, 24, 74–87.

Jack, Lois M. 1934. An experimental study of ascendent behavior in preschool children. Cited by Lois M. Jack, E. M. Maxwell, I. G. Mengert et al. Behavior of the preschool child. *Univer. Iowa Stud. Child Welf.*, 9, No. 3, 7–65.

Jeffrey, W. E. 1958. Variables in early discrimination learning: I. Motor responses in the training of left-right discrimination. *Child Develpm.*, 29, 269–275.

Jensen, K. 1932. Differential reactions to taste and temperature stimuli in newborn infants. *Genet. Psychol. Monogr.*, 12, 361–479.

Jersild, A. T., and F. B. Holmes. 1935. *Children's Fears.* New York: Teachers Coll., Columbia Univer.

Jost, H. 1941. Some physiological changes during frustration. *Child Develpm.*, 12, 9–15.

Kallmann, F. J. 1946. The genetic theory of schizophrenia. *Amer. J. Psychiat.*, 101, 309–322.

Kantrow, Ruth W. 1937. An investigation of conditioned feeding responses and concomitant adaptive behavior in young infants. *Univer. Iowa Stud. Child Welf.*, 13, No. 3.

Keister, Mary E. 1938. The behavior of young children in failure: An experimental attempt to discover and to modify undesirable responses of preschool children to failure. *Univer. Iowa Stud. Child Welf.*, 14, 27–82.

———, and Ruth Updegraff. 1937. A study of children's reactions to failure and an experimental attempt to modify them. *Child Develpm.*, 8, 241–248.

Kellogg, W. N., and Louella A. Kellogg. 1933. *The ape and the child.* New York: McGraw-Hill.

Kendler, H. H., Tracy S. Kendler, S. S. Pliskoff, and M. F. D'Amato. 1958. Inferential behavior in children: 1. The influence of reinforcement and incentive motivation. *J. exp. Psychol.*, 55, 207–212.

Krasnogorski, N. J. 1909. Über die Bedingungsreflexe im Kindesalter. *Jahrb. Kinderheilk*, 69, 1–24.

Lambert, W. W., Elizabeth C. Lambert, and P. D. Watson. 1953. Acquisition and extinction of an instrumental response sequence in the token-reward situation. *J. exp. Psychol.*, 45, 321–326.

Landis, C., and W. A. Hunt. 1937. Magnification of time as a research technique in the study of behavior. *Science*, 85, 384–385.

Lewin, K., R. Lippitt, and R. K. White. 1939. Patterns of aggressive behavior in experimentally created "social climates." *J. soc. Psychol.*, 10, 271–299.

Lindquist, E. F. 1940. *Statistical analysis in educational research.* Boston: Houghton Mifflin.

Ling, B-C. 1941. Form discrimination as a learning cue in infants. *Comp. Psychol. Monogr.*, 17, No. 2.

Lipsitt, L. P. 1958. The systematic study of variables affecting children's discrimination learning. Paper read at APA, Washington, D. C.

Long, E. R. 1958. *An investigation of operant conditioning techniques for children.* Terminal Progress Report, Small Grant No. M-2007, U.S.P.H.S.

Long, E. R., J. T. Hammack, F. May, and B. J. Campbell. 1958. Intermittent reinforcement of operant behavior in children. *J. exp. anal. Behav.* 1, 315–340.

Long, L. 1940. Conceptual relationships in children: The concept of roundness. *J. genet. Psychol.,* 57, 289–315.

McCandless, B. R., and C. C. Spiker. 1956. Experimental research in child psychology. *Child Develpm.,* 27, 75–80.

McGraw, Myrtle B. 1935. *The growth: A study of Johnny and Jimmy.* New York: Appleton-Century.

McPherson, Marion W. 1948. A survey of experimental studies of learning in individuals who achieve subnormal ratings on standardized psychometric measures. *Amer. J. ment. Defic.,* 52, 232–252.

———. 1958. Learning and mental deficiency. *Amer. J. ment. Defic.,* 62, 870–877.

Marinesco, G., and A. Kreindler. 1933. Des Réflexes conditionnels: I. L'Organisation des réflexes conditionnels chez l'enfant. *J. Psychol.,* 30, 855–886.

Marquis, Dorothy P. 1931. Can conditioned responses be established in the newborn infant? *J. genet. Psychol.,* 39, 479–492.

———. 1941. Learning in the neonate: The modification of behavior under three feeding schedules. *J. exp. Psychol.,* 29, 213–282.

———. 1943. A study of frustration in newborn infants. *J. exp. Psychol.,* 32, 123–138.

Mast, Elizabeth T. 1937. Motivating factors in child learning. *Child Develpm.,* 8, 273–278.

Mateer, Florence. 1918. *Child behavior.* Boston: Badga.

Mednick, S. A., and L. E. Lehtinen. 1957. Stimulus generalization as a function of age of children. *J. exp. Psychol.,* 53, 180–183.

Merrill, Barbara. 1946. The measurement of mother-child interaction. *J. abnorm. soc. Psychol.,* 41, 37–49.

Moustakas, C. E., and Minnie P. Berson. 1955. *The nursery school and child care center.* New York: Whiteside & Morrow.

Munn, N. L., and B. R. Steining. 1931. The relative efficacy of form and background in a child's discrimination of visual patterns. *J. genet., Psychol.,* 39, 73–90.

———. 1954. Learning in children. In L. Carmichael (Ed.), *Manual of child psychology.* (2nd ed.), New York: Wiley. Pp. 374–458.

Mussen, P. H., and J. J. Conger. 1956. *Child development and personality.* New York: Harper.

Newman, H. H., R. N. Freeman, and K. J. Holzinger. 1937. *Twins: A study of heredity and environment.* Chicago: Univer. Chicago Press.

Norcross, Kathryn J. 1958. Verbal paired associates research with children. Paper delivered at APA, Washington, D. C.

Pratt, K. C., Amalie K. Nelson, and K. H. Sun. 1930. *The behavior of the newborn infant.* Columbus: Ohio State Univer. Press.

Ray, W. S. 1932. A study of the emotions of children with particular reference to circulatory and respiratory changes. *J. genet. Psychol.,* 40, 100–117.

Razran, G. H. S. 1935. Conditioned responses: An experimental study and a theoretical analysis. *Arch. Psychol., N. Y.,* 28, No. 191.

Rheingold, Harriet L. 1956. The modification of social responsiveness in institutional babies. *Monogr. Soc. Res. Child Develpm.,* 21, No. 2 (Whole No. 63).

———, J. L. Gewirtz, and Helen W. Ross. 1959. Social conditioning of vocalizations in the infant. *J. comp. physiol. Psychol.,* 52, 68–73.

Riess, B. F. 1940. Semantic conditioning involving the galvanic skin reflex. *J. exp. Psychol.,* 26, 238–240.

Screven, C. G. 1958. Research on running time and physical work of children under various reinforcement conditions. Paper delivered at the 1958 meeting of the APA.

Shepard, Winifred O. 1956. The effect of verbal training on initial generalization tendencies. *Child Develpm.,* 27, 311–316.

Sherman, M. 1927. The differentiation of emotional response in infants. *J. comp. Psychol.*, 7, 265–284.

———, and Irene C. Sherman. 1925. Sensori-motor responses in infants. *J. comp. Psychol.*, 5, 53–68.

Skeels, H. M. 1933. A study of some factors in form board accomplishments of pre-school children. *Univer. Iowa Stud. Child Welf.*, 7, No. 2.

Skinner, B. F. 1953. *Science and human behavior.* New York: Macmillan.

Spence, K. W. 1956. *Behavior theory and conditioning.* New Haven: Yale Univer. Press.

Spiker, C. C. 1956. The effects of number of reinforcements on the strength of a generalized instrumental response. *Child Develpm.*, 27, 37–44.

Staples, R. 1932. The responses of infants to color. *J. exp. Psychol.*, 15, 119–141.

Stevenson, H. W. 1954. Latent learning in children. *J. exp. Psychol.*, 47, 17–21.

Stubbs, Esther M. 1934. The effect of the factors of duration, intensity, and pitch of sound stimuli on responses of new-born infants. *Univer. Iowa Stud. Child Welf.*, 9, No. 4.

Taylor, J. H. 1934. Innate emotional responses in infants. *Ohio State Univer. Contrib. in Psychol.: Studies in infant behavior.* No. 12, 69–93.

Terrell, G. 1958. The need for simplicity in research in child psychology. *Child Develpm.*, 29, 303–310.

———, and W. A. Kennedy. 1957. Discrimination learning and transposition in children as a function of the nature of the reward. *J. exp. Psychol.*, 52, 257–260.

Underwood, B. J. 1949. *Experimental psychology.* New York: Appleton-Century-Crofts.

———. 1957. *Psychological research.* New York: Appleton-Century-Crofts.

Verplanck, W. S. 1955. Since learned behavior is innate, and *vice versa*, what now? *Psychol. Rev.*, 62, 139–144.

———. 1957. *A glossary of some terms used in the objective science of behavior.* Washington, D. C.: Amer. Psychol. Ass.

Warren, A. B., and R. H. Brown. 1943. Conditioned operant response phenomenon in children. *J. gen. Psychol.*, 28, 181–207.

Watson, J. B. 1919. *Psychology from the point of view of a behaviorist.* Philadelphia: Lippincott.

Watson, J. B. and Rosalie A. Raynor. 1920. Conditioned emotional reactions. *J. exp. Psychol.*, 3, 1–4.

Wenger, M. A. 1936. An investigation of conditioned responses in human infants. In M. A. Wenger, Josephine M. Smith, C. Hazard, and O. C. Irwin. Studies in infant behavior III. *Univer. Iowa Stud. Child Welf.*, 12, No. 19.

Weiss, La Berta A. 1934. Differential variations in the amount of activity of the newborn infants under continuous light and sound stimulation. *Univer. Iowa Stud. Child Welf.*, 9, No. 4.

Wickens, D. D., and C. D. Wickens. 1940. A study of conditioning in the neonate. *J. exp. Psychol.*, 26, 94–102.

# part II

# The Study of Biological Growth and Development

chapter 5

# Methods of Studying Physical Growth

Howard V. Meredith
*State University of Iowa*

"Physical growth" is a commonplace synonym for anatomic ontogenesis. Anatomic ontogenesis encompasses all of the structural modifications that a biologic organism undergoes during ontogeny. It includes the gamut of changes sometimes subgrouped under such captions as morphologic differentiation, dimensional growth, proportional development, and structural maturation (Meredith, 1957a).

As a facet of the field of child development, anatomic ontogenesis pertains to study of the human organism during the first two decades of its individual life span. Exploration of this facet involves studying the child from zygote to young adult with regard to sequential changes in the kind, number, size, shape, position, and composition of his body components.

At the laboratory level, investigators of anatomic ontogenesis are seen identifying the structural components of organisms by kind, measuring their size, describing their form, counting their number, observing their location, and examining their constituents. Why are these tasks undertaken and how are they performed? Although this chapter is written to deal principally with the *how* part of the question, the *why* part should be recognized as of prime importance. In responsible research a clear purpose is the star to which a wagon of efficient method is hitched.

Research methods should subserve the general objectives of studying anatomic ontogenesis in children. Among the broad purposes of scholars working in this field are the following: (1) description of specific aspects of structural change in different cells, tissues, organs, and body regions, (2) systematization of accumulated series of morphologic findings in ways to reveal principles of human ontogenesis, (3) discovery of variables that modify physical growth and exploration of each variable with respect to time of impact, direction of influence, and magnitude of depressing or accelerating effect, (4) investigation of relationships between sectors of the structural facet of child development and sectors of other facets of child development, (5) comparison of the developmental anatomy of children and other animal organisms, (6) provision of normative materials on physical growth to meet clinical, health education and other service needs, and (7) contribution to a cumulative understanding of the attributes of desirable anatomic ontogenesis and of the conditions that will produce them (Meredith, 1953b).

Methods should also subserve the particular aims of a given investigation.

At its growing edge, research centers upon well-formulated and pertinent questions, explicitly expressed and testable hypotheses, clearly specified and solvable problems. Methods have the function of high-grade tools that may be devised, modified, and utilized to answer thoughtfully considered propositions relating to the anatomic development of children. Ontogenetic knowledge increases in fitting stride as techniques are kept subordinate to ideas, as methods play a supporting role to problem perspicacity.

The foregoing paragraphs deliberately emphasize the perspective that adequate qualification as an investigator of physical growth entails far more than a reasonable mastery of the methods used in the area. It comprises continuing re-examination of what anatomic ontogenesis encompasses, the reasons it should be studied, and the ways it can be explored with greater effectiveness. The competent investigator engages in day-by-day integration of activities in the library and the laboratory. These integrative efforts ferment an ongoing interplay of creative thinking about frontier problems and selective utilization of promising methods for their study.

From here forward, the scope of this chapter is delimited to a discussion of *research methods* in the study of anatomic ontogenesis during the first twenty years of the human life cycle. It would be unrealistic to expect the discussion to achieve the feat of dealing with the topic comprehensively and exhaustively. This follows from no more than cursory contemplation of the task of colligating all relevant methodology with respect to anthropometry, radiography, photography, vital staining and implanting, preparation of histologic slides, preservation of nonliving organisms, anatomic dissection, cast preparation, apparatus construction and calibration, sampling theory, biostatistics, experimental design, and the preparation of scientific reports. Although the treatment necessarily is selective, it aims at representative breadth and meaning.

Primary consideration is given to the *acquisition of data* for investigating structural development in children. The following questions indicate the range of subtopics chosen for inclusion. From what *sources* are data drawn? For what purpose is a given source unique or superior to alternative sources? What *types* of data are gathered; what types, derived? What instrumental aids are available for use in obtaining source materials and securing data? How much training is required to obtain satisfactory proficiency in various methods of data collection? What factors influence the validities of different series of data? In what ways do research on procedures in obtaining data and standardization of method facilitate the study of problems of structural change?

The substantial treatment of data collection is augmented by a brief section on the *subdivision of data* for statistical analysis. This section illustrates the different ways in which subgroups are formed and shows the interdependence of grouping procedure and research outcome.

## SOURCES OF DATA

The data employed in studying ontogenetic changes in body structure are drawn from a variety of sources, e.g., from living subjects and cadavers, from photographs and roentgenograms, from silhouettes and contour tracings, and from histologic slides and plaster casts.

It is a principle of scientific method that research data should be amassed, using the most parsimonious medium for attaining the needed degree of exactitude. This is a basic reason for studying many problems in terms of data obtained directly on the living or the nonliving child. If it were an investigator's purpose to describe variability of head width for children of a given age, measuring the subjects' heads directly would be more economical, and for most purposes no less valid, than obtaining roentgenograms of the head and measuring them (Potter and Meredith, 1948). Similarly, the principle of parsimony would require direct inspection of the oral cavity (in preference to dental cast preparation and inspection) when an investigator's problem called solely for data from counting the number of erupted teeth and direct observation of the axillary region (in preference to photographic reproduction and observation) when the problem called solely for data from rating the quantity of pigmented hair in this region.

Indirect sources (plaster casts, roentgenograms, and so forth) supply the only data sufficiently valid for the study of certain problems, e.g., determining the extent to which rate of change in width of the lower face dur-ing childhood shows oscillation and individual variation (Newman and Meredith, 1956). With respect to other problems, indirect source materials constitute the sole avenue of investigation available. An example is the study of childhood differences in increase of muscle tissue in selected body regions (Stuart, Hill and Shaw, 1940; Maresh, 1948).

In research programs in which, for purposeful reasons, roentgenograms, photographs and/or casts are being obtained, the investigator may have a choice of sources that will yield identical data. For instance, when dental casts are being made as a source of tooth measurements that cannot be taken in the mouth conveniently or with satisfactory reliability, one has the option of accumulating data on tooth eruption either by direct examination of each child's dental arches or by inspection of the casts.

***The Living Child.*** Human anatomic ontogenesis takes place in individuals who live and move and acquire standards of modesty. Respiratory and digestive functions, postural changes, and reluctance to submit some parts of the body for examination all give rise to methodologic problems in using the living child as a source of research data. Problems pertaining to the child's willingness to cooperate usually can be resolved by taking sufficient time to develop rapport, remaining sensitive during examinations to cues from the child, and exercising professional tact in the collection of data. Some of the problems that arise from involuntary physiologic functioning can be only partly surmounted. In determining the body weight of a child, for instance, it is considerably more feasible to remove or standardize the extraneous material carried as clothing (Clark, 1930; Sumner and Whitacre, 1931) than to remove or standardize the extraneous material carried as urine and feces.

Townsend (1887) reported (1) weighing the contents of the bladder and bowels of a stillborn infant and (2) weighing four live infants immediately following birth and again after washing. He estimated that the extraneous urine, meconium, and vernix caseosa added 0.1 kilogram[1] to the weight of the neonatal organism. Griffith (1899) listed as factors that may spuriously influence weekly weight gains in infancy the time and quantity of feeding, the emptying of the bladder and bowels, the amount of exercise and respiration, and the metabolic changes going on during sleep.

Three preschool children were weighed by Palmer (1930) at approximate hourly intervals during the day for periods of three to five days. He found that children typically gain in weight during the day, attain a maximum weight after the evening meal, lose weight during the night, and reach a minimum weight in the morning after discharge of the accumulated excreta. Diurnal fluctuation varied for different children and for the same child on different days. Sumner and Whitacre (1931) weighed 58 elementary school children nude and then reweighed them following the request that they

[1] It is customary to use the metric system in biologic research: 1.0 kilogram = 2.20 pounds; 1.0 centimeter = 0.39 inch.

urinate. After urination, 50 per cent were 0.1 kilogram or more lighter and 17 per cent were 0.2 to 0.5 kilogram lighter. During a six-month period Curtiss (1898) obtained nude weights for three young adults just before they retired at night and as soon as they arose in the morning. There was no food intake and no urination or defecation between the two weighings. Average loss during the night was 0.4 kilogram, with variation in loss extending from 0.2 to 0.7 kilogram.

McKay and Patton (1935), in a study on food habits and physical development of preschool children, obtained nude weights at monthly intervals, always having the child empty his bladder and always weighing at the same hour of the day. Clayton (1944), in a study on food habits and physical conditions of elementary-school children, requested each subject to urinate before being weighed, determined weight with the subject wearing only a one-piece gown, and subtracted the weight of the gown.

Beyond the methodologic difficulties of obtaining the weight of a living organism lies the biologic perspective of body weight as a gross over-all measure that aggregates varying tissue representations in slender, muscular, and obese children of a given age (Stuart, Hill, and Shaw, 1940) and disregards change in tissue proportions with age (Reynolds, 1948). In the phraseology of Scammon (1929), a weight increase of 1.0 kilogram in an infant represents a gain in brain substance and viscera, together with some enlargement of other parts of the body; in an adolescent, it is primarily an increase in bone and muscle; whereas in the middle-aged it is often an accumulation of adipose tissue.

Next to body weight, the structural trait most frequently studied on the living child is stature. Before stature can be determined, the head and lower limbs must be placed in fixed positions with reference to the trunk. The head is positioned so that the lowest point on the border of the bone socket of the left eye and the highest point on the anterior margin of the tragus of each ear[1] lie in a plane at right angles to the long axis of the trunk; the lower limbs are extended and parallel, with the feet at right angles to the long axes of the limbs. When the head, trunk, and lower limbs are in this relationship, stature is the projected (straight-line) distance from the top of the head to the plantar surfaces of the feet.

Before the child is able to stand, stature is taken with the body supine; at later ages, it is obtained with the body erect and/or supine. It is common to refer to stature in the erect orientation as standing height, or body height, and stature in the recumbent orientation as crown-heels length, vertex-soles length, or total length (Krogman, 1950).[2]

[1] The tragus is the cartilaginous projection before the entrance of the external acoustic meatus.

[2] Stature and total length are not equivalent terms in early prenatal life. From the time a long axis of the organism is apparent (approximately two weeks after fertilization) until the middle of the second prenatal month the largest rectilinear dimension of the body is stem length (length of the head, neck, and trunk). It is not until the second half of the second month that the heels form and the lower limbs increase sufficiently for stature to surpass stem length.

Early studies of individual children by Bradford (1883), Shinn (1893) and Hall (1896) found stature "horizontal" to exceed stature "vertical" by 1.1 centimeter in a girl aged 1 year, 1.5 centimeter in a boy aged 1.5 years, 1.8 centimeter in a child aged 3.5 years, and 2.3 centimeters in an adolescent aged 15 years. Studies of the same problem on large samples of children have been made by Wilson et al. (1930), Palmer (1932), and Vickers and Stuart (1943). The Vickers-Stuart investigation, based on more than 2000 children between the ages of 2 and 10 years, shows that on the average stature erect is 1.5 centimeter less than stature supine. The Palmer report, covering the postnatal period of 18 months to 20 years and utilizing over 1000 subjects, includes tables of erect and supine equivalents for each centimeter of stature from 80 to 180 centimeters.

From measurement of a young adult, it was discovered prior to 1780 that stature is greatest following recumbent sleep and decreases after arising and with prolonged exertion (Scammon, 1927a). About a century later, Malling-Hanson (1886) studied a group of 70 boys and confirmed diurnal stature variation for the school-age segment of the human life cycle. Investigations on preschool children have been made in the present century. Taken collectively, the accumulated studies support the generalization that at all ages beyond 2 years ambulant human beings typically are 2.0 centimeters taller when they assume the erect position in the morning than when they return to the recumbent position at night (Redfield and Meredith, 1938).

Greater reduction in stature occurs during the first hour after arising than during any succeeding hour. On infants 6 months to 1 year of age, Hejinian and Hatt (1929) found an average decrease in body length of 0.8 centimeter after sitting for one hour and 1.1 centimeter after standing for one hour. Similar losses on children of preschool age have been found by Palmer (1930) during the first hour after getting up in the morning and by Redfield and Meredith (1938) during the first hour after an afternoon nap. In the former study the average losses were 0.7 centimeter over the first hour and 0.4 centimeter over the second hour, making a combined loss during the first two hours of fully one half the daily total. The Redfield-Meredith study obtained an average gain from a two-hour afternoon nap period of 1.2 centimeter and an average loss for the first hour after arising from the nap of 0.8 centimeter.

It follows that in investigating growth problems pertaining to stature diurnal and postural variation should be controlled and the controls specified. To disregard whether a child in nursery school is measured sometimes before his rest period and sometimes immediately following a nap (assuming comparable orientation for measurement) is to confound his seriate record with artifacts as large as the mean increase in stature for two months. Macy and Kelly (1957), in a study of chemical and anatomic ontogenesis, measured children supine immediately on their waking in the morning. Whitacre (1935), in a study of seasonal variation in stature, measured each subject on successive occasions in the erect position and at a constant hour of the school day. Newcomer and Meredith (1951), in a study of body size of adolescent boys, measured stature erect in the afternoon between 1:00 P.M. and 3:00 P.M.

Why is stature influenced by the orientation and condition of the ambulant child's body? The increase with change from a standing position to dorsal recumbency seemingly is brought about by the reduction of body curvatures (particularly those of the upper and lower back) and muscular relaxation. The decrease with sustained assumption of erect and sitting positions probably results from compression of the intervertebral disks, closer apposition of the bones of the lower limbs, and reduction of muscle tonus.

Another group of kinesiological and physiological problems is faced in using the living child as a direct source for measures of shoulder breadth and girth of the trunk and limbs. Maximum girth of the leg in the calf region is not the same (1) as a child stands with his weight distributed equally in both lower limbs and (2) as he sits with his legs hanging over the edge of a table. Girth of the upper limb midway between the shoulder and the elbow is not the same (1) when a child's arm is raised and his biceps muscle contracted and (2) when the arm hangs at his side in a relaxed state. The human shoulder girdle is highly mobile and not readily placed in the same position on successive occasions. Girth of the thorax alters with inspiration and expiration, elevation of the shoulders, tipping of the head, and orientation of the trunk to the force of gravity. Girth of the abdomen varies with time and quantity of food intake, especially in infancy, and is difficult to bring under control, since children are able to produce marked fluctuations by voluntary contraction of abdominal muscles.

Far more data for studying anatomic ontogenesis have been obtained from direct measurement of the living child than from any other source. This is shown readily by reference to research bibliographies, reviews, and syntheses. Krogman (1941), in displaying the extent to which body size and form are related to racial, geographic, socioeconomic, dietary, and other variables, assembled more than 1000 tables based on direct study of children. A Children's Bureau (1927) publication lists over 500 studies on age changes in body weight. More than 60 investigations, employing data obtained directly on children, are colligated in a review of North American research for the period 1850–1900 (Meredith, 1936).[1] There are syntheses of direct measurement research drawing from 130 studies on growth in stature during infancy (Meredith, 1943), 70 studies on the association between body size and birth order (Meredith, 1950), and 30 to 50 studies each on the development of head width (Meredith, 1953a), head girth (Meredith, 1946b), face width (Meredith, 1954), upper limb length

[1] Research on the physical growth of children began prior to this time. A development of scientific activity similar to that in America during the last half of the nineteenth century occurred in Europe during the last half of the eighteenth century (Scammon, 1927b).

(Meredith, 1947) and foot length (Meredith, 1944). Multitrait investigations, each extending from early childhood to early adulthood and utilizing direct measurement data, have been reported by Herskovits (1930), Gray and Ayres (1931), Meredith (1935), Boynton (1936), Goldstein (1936), O'Brien et al. (1941), and Simmons (1944).

Cadavers and indirect source materials portray fixed ontogenetic states; they can be kept for future reference. The living subject is an ephemeral source; it cannot be retained in a given state for later study. This sets the living child considerably apart from the other sources on two methodologic counts, one largely surmountable and the other restricting. A record for number of erupted teeth obtained from direct examination of an infant one year after birth cannot be confirmed six months later nor can a record for width of hips taken on a child 10 years of age be verified some years later. It is possible, however, to cancel effectively the need for confirmation by providing that original independent records for each trait and subject studied shall be made by two or more trained workers. The second count pertains to the study of additional traits at a later date, i.e., the investigator may in time wish to extend his research with data for more traits in order to analyze relationships not initially projected for study. These could not be obtained from the living sample (since this would have become a source for data representing a later stage), whereas they might be accessible if nonliving or indirect sources were used. The one way to minimize this limitation is by increasing the thoroughness with which research programs originally are planned.

**The Child Cadaver.** Compared with the living child, the child cadaver has methodologic advantages from being more rigid, more amenable to anatomic study, and more permanent. There are no rapport requirements, no voluntary movements, and no oscillations due to ongoing contraction and expansion of respiratory, circulatory, or digestive systems. Segments and organs may be removed for examination, and tissues may be dissected for macroscopic study or sectioned for microscopic study. Although in investigating some problems it is necessary to correct for structural changes produced by the medium or media employed in specimen preservation, cadavers can be preserved over long periods. A major disadvantage of the child cadaver lies in the fact that it is not changing ontogenetically and cannot be utilized as a source for longitudinal records. It may be drawn upon for a wide range of observations and measures representing structural status at the time of death, but it can give no data on topics such as intra-individual increment relationships for sets of traits or interindividual trend differences for a given trait.

Child cadavers are difficult to obtain for study. Their scarcity explains why students preparing to do research on structural development in children get much of their anatomical laboratory training with specimens of human adults and young mammals of other species. It also explains why far more research has been done on phases of anatomic ontogenesis open to investigation on the

living child (e.g., postnatal change in stature and body weight) than on phases open only to investigation on the cadaver, e.g., postnatal change of internal organs with respect to weight, volume, surface area, and tissue components.

The difficulty of securing prenatal human specimens tends to be related inversely to stage of development. For ages below one week, when the organism is as small as a grain of sand and placentation has not begun, less than a dozen normal specimens have been recovered for study (Hertig et al., 1954).[1] Many of the research publications on human ontogenesis up to the age of one month deal with the procurement and description of single embryos (Bremer, 1906; Dandy, 1910; Ingalls, 1918; Greenhill, 1927; West, 1930; Litzenburg, 1933; Odgers, 1937; Brewer, 1938; George, 1942; Wilson, 1945). For the period between the third month and birth, there are investigations based on samples of several hundred fetuses (Streeter, 1920; Schultz, 1926; Scammon and Calkins, 1929).

Of the child cadavers that become available for study, many cannot be accepted as anatomically normal. The diseases that cause death, and the injuries that precede or follow death, inflict varying types and degrees of damage; an organ may be hypertrophied, a tissue dehydrated, a segment distorted; the modifications may be

[1] This does not imply that little is known regarding early stages of ontogenesis. Embryologists have amassed a large amount of applicable research on animals of the vertebrate phylum and mammalian order (Witschi, 1956).

slight or severe, localized or widespread. Investigators of normal anatomic ontogenesis utilize cadaver samples appraised as nonpathologic for specific purposes, i.e., appraisal of cadavers for normality is made with reference to the anatomic item projected for study. Fewer rejections would be made in selecting a sample to obtain weight of the osseous skeleton than in selecting a sample to obtain weight of the heart or liver. Boyd (1933), in a well-controlled study of normal variability in weight of the spleen, selected cadavers that met the following criteria: (1) death caused by a violent accident, (2) ill less than twenty-four hours following the accident, (3) no symptoms of relevant disease either at the time of the accident or at necropsy, (4) no gross hemorrhage prior to death, and (5) death not caused by poisons likely to affect spleen weight, i.e., compounds of mercury, arsenic or bismuth, and the strong acids and caustics.

The time during which cadavers can be studied in the fresh state is short. For more extended study, they must be fixed with a preservative. It is known that preservation media can produce changes in the size and form of the body; these changes may take the direction of shrinkage or expansion, become more marked with time, and vary for different tissues. Consequently, a methodologic requirement in the use of child cadavers as a source for quantitative data is the control or correction for preservation effects. Rasmussen (1947), in studying the weight of the pituitary gland and its components, achieved good control by using the glands of children deceased less than one hour, hence only slightly fixed. Since in many studies the collection of data at necropsy is not practicable, considerable technical attention has been given to preservation media. To the extent that the ideal of preserving cadavers in true biologic size, form, and composition cannot be attained, it is necessary to know what corrections should be made.

Jackson (1909), Schultz (1919), and Scammon and Calkins (1929) investigated the influence of formalin fixation on human fetuses during periods of three to eight months. Using a solution one part 40 per cent formalin and nine parts distilled water, they found enlargements approximating 1 per cent for stature and head dimensions, 13 per cent for total volume of the body, and 20 per cent for thickness of the abdomen. Other workers have reported shrinkages from immersing soft tissues in alcohol and from embedding young embryos in paraffin matrices for sectioning. A highly developed program of laboratory procedures for preparing and sectioning young embryos has been described by Heard (1957).

For the study of human ontogenesis during prenatal life, a large number of the specimens judged to be satisfactory with respect to normality and preservation are of limited usefulness because information on age is lacking. A cadaver cannot be used in investigating trait distributions at successive ages in the absence of direct data pertaining to age. Consider a series of 17 embryos, two of known age and 15 of unknown age. The two of known age (say 4 prenatal weeks) have stem lengths of 0.3 and 0.6 centimeter, respectively. Each of the

15 others, on the basis of a series of observations for presence, number, and size of body structures, is estimated to approximate 4 weeks of age. For the study of individual differences *at age 4 weeks*, in stem length or in any other trait, the group of 17 embryos can contribute two subjects only.

The earlier the stage of development under investigation the more important does precise information on age become. Changes are so rapid in the early weeks of life that to age a 2-week-old embryo incorrectly by three days is more serious than incorrectly aging a 2-year-old child by three weeks. Notwithstanding, information leading to close determination of age for embryos is difficult to secure. It is not possible to obtain data for the exact time of fertilization; rarely is information available from which the day of fruitful copulation can be determined with reasonable dependability; and not uncommonly the date of the beginning of the menses preceding fertilization is unobtainable. In consequence, primary identification and subgrouping of prenatal specimens is not usually in terms of true age: in studies on embryos it is in terms of stage of preparation for implantation (Hertig and Rock, 1944), number of somites (Bartelmez and Evans, 1926; Heuser, 1930), or the developmental categories defined by Streeter (1942); in studies on fetuses it is in terms of body length (Scammon and Calkins, 1929) or menstrual age (Streeter, 1920).[1]

---

[1] Menstrual age is equivalent to the true age of the organism plus the time between commencement of the mother's last menses before pregnancy and formation of the zygote (roughly, true age plus a fortnight).

The following list illustrates aspects of anatomic ontogenesis that have been investigated using child cadavers as the direct source for data. During the prenatal period developmental changes in number of ossification centers (Mall, 1906), composition of the tailbud (Kunitomo, 1918), position of the larynx and lungs (Noback, 1923), linear dimensions of the head and trunk (Scammon and Calkins, 1929), areal measures of the upper and lower limbs (Boyd, 1935), ponderal measures of the hands and feet (Scammon, 1930), and body proportions (Schultz, 1926). For infancy and early childhood, developmental changes in weight of the brain and its subdivisions (Scammon, 1936), calcification of the permanent teeth (Logan and Kronfeld, 1933), and weight of the kidneys, liver, and spleen (Coppoletta and Wolbach, 1933). Over the first two decades of life, developmental changes in volume and surface area of the cerebrum (Scammon and Hesdorffer, 1935), surface area and weight of the stomach (Scammon, 1919), weight of the thymus gland and its component parts (Boyd, 1936), and total area of the external body surface (Boyd, 1935).

*Roentgenograms (Radiographs).* With the discovery of the X-ray by Wilhelm Roentgen in 1895, many facets of anatomic ontogenesis previously accessible to study only by the cross-sectional approach (using different cadavers for each stage) were opened to study by the longitudinal approach. Roentgenograms could be made depicting the same child at successive stages with respect to ossification of the skeleton (Pyle and Sontag, 1943), calcification of the dentition (Gleiser and Hunt, 1955), thickness of the skeletal musculature (Reynolds, 1944), and shape of the viscera (Lincoln and Spillman, 1928).

The roentgenogram has become the most broadly used of the several indirect sources of research data on human structural development. Seriate, or time series, radiographs have been accumulated for all regions of the body (Stuart, 1939). Beginning with Pryor's publication (1905), reported investigations on child growth have utilized radiographs of the head (Young, 1957), face (Woods, 1950), thorax (Maresh, 1948), abdomen (Bakwin and Bakwin, 1935), pelvis (Reynolds, 1947), arm and forearm (Maresh, 1955), wrist and hand (Baldwin, Busby, and Garside, 1928), knee (Pyle and Hoerr, 1955), leg (Stuart and Dwinell, 1942), and foot (Wallis, 1931).

One easily underestimates the technical aspects of obtaining roentgenograms suitable for research purposes and adequately interpreting them as datum sources. A radiographic film, once exposed and developed, is a permanent record, a fixed exhibit pertaining to some part of the child's body. This tangibility should not be confused with anatomic validity. In order to study developmental changes in the form of a structure, the consecutive roentgenograms must be secured with the structure in a similar position on each occasion. For studying developmental changes in the size of a structure, there must be standardized positioning and also adjustment of the radiographically obtained measures to "life-size" meas-

ures. For investigating developmental changes in tissue density, it is necessary to hold the degree of X-ray penetration in good control and detect deviations from control with a densimeter (Garn and Shamir, 1958). In short, the extent to which data derived from radiographs are valid depends upon the purpose(s) for which they are used and numerous methodologic considerations.

The object to be radiographed is placed between the X-ray tube and the cassette (film holder) in a location near the cassette and some distance from the tube. Exposure is made for $x$ time (seconds) at $y$ milliamperes and $z$ kilovolts, the values for these three factors varying with the mass, composition, and location of the object (Stunz, 1934; Stuart, 1939; Cartwright and Harvold, 1954). Exposure time increases with the distance of the object from the tube; the higher the milliampere-seconds the greater the density (blackness) of the image; kilovolts control contrast, higher kilovoltage being required for the penetration of hard tissues than soft tissues (Franklin, 1957). X-rays emanate from a small area termed the focal spot and travel in straight lines; the zone they radiate increases with distance from the focal spot and diaphragm (diaphragms are used to constrict the beam of radiation). Marked improvements have been made in radiological equipment and procedure. The trend in recent years is toward the use of fast film, small focal spot, intensifying screens, and the highest kilovoltage compatible with adequate contrast (Krogman and Sassouni, 1957). Intensifying screens (calcium–tungstate-impregnated bristol board placed in contact with each side of the film) make it possible to reduce exposure time with little increase in the granular appearance of the image.

It is a methodologic objective to place the structure under study in a defined, reproducible, and anatomically adequate position with respect to the plane of the cassette and the path of the central ray emanating from the tube. Positioning for an anteroposterior view of the child's leg has been studied by Stuart, Hill and Shaw (1940) and by Reynolds (1944). In the former investigation the child was placed in a supine position on a flat surface with the lower limbs extended, both ischium of the pelvis resting evenly on the surface, the dorsal aspect of the right leg in relaxed contact with the cassette, and the right foot perpendicular. An assistant supported the foot and applied sufficient pressure over the lower right thigh to prevent flexion at the knee joint. The focal spot was centered over the greatest thickness of the calf at a distance 90 centimeters from the film. Roentgenograms from two independent positionings for each of 26 children showed the tissue components of the leg to be highly reproducible by this procedure.

Reynolds obtained roentgenograms on 107 children, using the same supine position and also an erect position. The latter required the child to stand with his weight evenly distributed through the lower limbs, his feet pointing directly forward, and his calf touching the cassette without pressure. Breadth of bone was identical in the two series, but breadth of muscle was greater for the supine series than the erect.

Reynolds suggested that although the supine procedure can be defined and duplicated satisfactorily it is inadequate anatomically, since the amount of spreading of the calf on the cassette tends to vary directly with age and inversely with firmness of the leg musculature and/or adipose tissue. Anatomic adequacy could be enhanced further by setting the mid-point of the calf at a constant distance from the focal spot (say 100 centimeters) and at a fixed distance from the cassette sufficient to allow for age increases in calf thickness.

Studies relating to placement of the child's manus (wrist and hand) for a posteroanterior roentgenogram have been made by Bayer and Gray (1933), Baldwin, Busby, and Garside (1928), and Flory (1936). On the basis of a broad historical and experimental investigation on positioning the manus for research purposes, Bayer and Gray recommended the following standard orientation: (1) child seated on a low stool so that his armpits approximate the height of a table carrying a horizontally placed cassette; (2) arm in 90 degrees abduction, forearm in 90 degrees flexion, and hand in complete pronation; (3) axis of the middle metacarpal parallel with the axis of the forearm; and (4) fingers moderately fanned, each in line with its metacarpal. The hands of a child and a young adult positioned on cassettes in this manner were radiographed by Baldwin, Busby, and Garside at film-tube distances of 50 and 100 centimeters. Bone areas on the radiographs taken at the shorter distance were found to be larger than corresponding areas at the greater distance by almost 1 per cent. Using similar film-tube distances, Flory radiographed metal blocks 2.5 centimeters square and graduated in thickness 1.2 to 5 centimeters. The blocks were placed on the cassette to simulate thickness variations for different parts of the manus and suspended 1.2 centimeter above the cassette to simulate increase in thickness of the manus with age. At the 100-centimeter film-tube distance, radiographic area was 7 per cent less for the block 1.2 centimeter thick than for the block 5 centimeters thick. Areal enlargement from raising the blocks 1.2 centimeter was around 2 per cent.

In general, a standard prone position for the manus can be specified and duplicated. Placement of the manus in contact with the cassette, although an anatomically adequate procedure for ossification studies based on inspectional data (Stuart, 1934; Greulich and Pyle, 1950), is not a fully adequate procedure for research on bone size. For the latter purpose, it would be preferable to orient the median plane of the manus 5 centimeters from the film and approximately 100 centimeters from the focal spot.

Except as research problems necessitate deviation (Popovich, 1957), it is common laboratory practice when radiographically studying the head (calvaria and face) to work from the *norma lateralis* roentgenogram (Björk, 1947; Brodie, 1953; Higley, 1954) and/or the *norma posteroanterior* roentgenogram (Woods, 1950; Newman and Meredith, 1956). In obtaining both, the head is placed with the lowest point of the external margin of the left orbit, and the highest point of the ex-

ternal margin of each acoustic meatus, in a plane at right angles to the long axis of the trunk. For the lateral view, the central roentgen ray passes through the child's acoustic meatuses at right angles to the cassette; for the anteroposterior view, the central ray passes through the mid-point of the trans-meatal line at right angles to the cassette. The head is oriented and supported with the aid of a cephalostat. There are several varieties of this instrument (Krogman and Sassouni, 1957); all require painstaking use and full subject cooperation. Björk (1947) meticulously positioned the child's head in a cephalo-stat and maintained it with a short rod in each acoustic meatus and a chin rest. Using fixed distances of 155 centimeters from the focal spot to the midsagittal plane of the head and 9 centimeters from the midsagittal plane to the film, he obtained two independent *norma lateralis* roentgenograms on each of 20 boys. His positioning procedure was found to give roentgenograms sufficiently dependable for measurement to the nearest 0.01 centimeter.

Björk (1955) described a method involving the combined use of radiographs and metallic implants for the study of human osteogenesis. Employing an especially designed instrument, he placed a small number of vitallium pins 0.2 centimeter long in the right jaws of five children between the ages of 4 and 14 years. A local anesthetic was used and the pins instantaneously inserted to a controlled depth. Radiographs were made at the time of insertion and successively for a period of two years. Björk's report indicates that the method has promise as a means of investigating the sites of bone deposition and resorption during childhood.

A roentgenogram transposes anatomic structures that are three-dimensional to two-dimensional surfaces. This telescoping to a plane gives rise to a class of methodologic problems. Some anatomic structures and/or structural components are difficult to locate by roentgenogram inspection, and, conversely, some features of the roentgenogram are difficult to identify on the basis of training in anatomic dissection. For the most part the technical task of resolving such problems is not complicated. In locating anatomic points, one may attach small radiopaque markers to cadaveric or living tissue at desired points and then reproduce the designations radiographically (Potter and Meredith, 1948). In determining the anatomic basis of radiographic shadows, one may use the method employed by Etter (1955). Etter disarticulated the component bones of dry skulls and radiographed them separately and in groups. Intercomparison was made of radiographs for (1) single bones posed in skull position, (2) skulls with one or more bones removed, (3) skulls with all components replaced, and (4) heads of living subjects.

Anatomic structures cannot be reproduced radiographically in correct size. This is inconsequential when roentgenograms are used as a source for observational data (Greulich and Pyle, 1950), angle measurements (Higley, 1954), and ratios (Meredith, Knott and Hixon, 1958). In the use of roentgenograms for the study of absolute dimensions. the matter should

always receive consideration and adjustments must usually be made (Ritt and Sawtell, 1930; Adams, 1940; Woods, 1950; Newman and Meredith, 1956). Thurow (1951) has systematized the corrections that may be necessary under three captions: enlargement, distortion, and blurring. Enlargement is a methodologic variable specific to single structural planes. For example, skeletal nose height is a dimension in the midsagittal plane (Meredith, 1958). Enlargement of this dimension (1) increases with distance from the midsagittal plane to the film, (2) decreases with distance from the focal spot to the film, and (3) increases with size of the dimension.

Distortion pertains to radiographic magnification when the termini for a measurement lie in different anatomic planes. To illustrate: if the length of the lower left jaw were required from a *norma lateralis* roentgenogram, the end of the dimension lying in the midsagittal plane would be magnified differently than the end lying more laterally. Adjustment for distortion is correction for such differential magnification. Enlargement and distortion corrections are calculated on the assumption that the X-rays emanate from a point. In fact, X-rays emanate from a small area and add a slight blurring variable. Blurring (1) increases with the size of the focal spot, (2) decreases with distance between the focal spot and plane of the object, and (3) increases with distance from the plane of the object to the film.

In accumulating seriate roentgenograms as a source for data on anatomic development, the responsible investigator takes steps to minimize radiation exposure (Stanford and Vance, 1955; Schubert and Lapp, 1957). He does this through efficient research design, selection of radiological equipment, and protective laboratory procedures. Radiation exposure is reduced by using filters to absorb extraneous radiation, diaphragms to restrict the width of the roentgen beam, fast films and intensifying screens to reduce exposure time, and leaded aprons to shield critical tissues (Blackman and Greening, 1957; Graber, 1958; Tanner, Whitehouse and Powell, 1958; Hixon, 1960).

*Photographs and Silhouettes.* Photographic methods make possible the permanent visualization of anatomic structures from chosen viewpoints. This sometimes is advantageous for both cross-sectional and longitudinal investigations. To assemble several hundred children of a given age for intercomparison with respect to one or more body features is not practicable; it is practicable, however, to amass and compare silhouettes on such a sample. Photographs of individual children taken at a series of developmental stages have unique value in supplying time-free panoramas on the ontogenesis of surface anatomy.

A far greater variety of photographic source materials is accessible on child cadavers than on the living organism. To date, investigations utilizing data derived from photographing the live child have dealt largely with individual and age differences in (1) postural variables, such as lumbar lordosis, knee hyperextension, and foot pronation, (2) circumpuberal variables, such as breast contour, scrotum size, and dis-

tribution of pubic hair, and (3) body form[1] variables, such as limb and trunk stockiness, shoulders–hips relationship, and bulgings of adipose and muscle tissue.

Investigators of anatomic ontogenesis employ photographs and/or silhouettes in a number of separable roles. In some studies the role is that of providing illustrative examples of the phenomenon under discussion; in others photographs are utilized to define, or help define, the categories of rating scales; and in still others they are the sole source, or a primary source, of data on a growth problem.

Shuttleworth (1951) assembled photographs to illustrate (1) sequential modifications in over-all appearance of the external body during childhood and adolescence, and (2) individual differences at selected circumpuberal ages in appearance of the breast region, pubic region, and body as a whole. Others have used photographs to illustrate such matters as changes in location and composition of the deciduous teeth during prenatal life (Diamond, 1944); variability of physique in infancy (Bayley and Davis, 1935); changes in the facial profiles of children brought about by orthodontic treatment (Hellman, 1935); body build of siblings and of parents and offspring (Reynolds, 1951); association between precocious puberty and ossification of the manus (Greulich and Pyle, 1950); circumpuberal breast development in boys (Greulich et al., 1942); and variations in the relation between breast develop-

[1] Alternative terms are body shape, physique, body build, morphologic type, body proportion, physical constitution, and somatotype.

ment and pubic-hair development in girls (Reynolds, 1948).

Posture-rating scales for use with children 2 to 10 years of age were constructed by Robinow, Leonard, and Anderson (1943). The scales, derived from examination of several hundred photographs, are for five regional posture variables: rear-view photographs define scale points for knock-knees and foot pronation; lateral-view photographs define scale points for hyperextended knees, lumbar lordosis, and slumped back. Kubitschek (1932), drawing from direct observations on 730 boys, developed a three-category photographic rating scale for each annual age, 11 to 18 years. These scales are front-view photographs showing moderately early, typical, and moderately late development of the scrotum, penis, and pubic hair. Reynolds and Wines (1948) used front-view photographs of girls to define partly the categories for rating circumpuberal growth in the breast and pubic regions: photographs complement verbal descriptions for four stages of breast shape, three stages of breast size, five stages of breast-areola-papilla relationship, and three stages of pubic-hair distribution.

From direct and photographic examination of 757 boys, 10 to 19 years of age, Greulich et al. (1942) developed a scale for subgrouping boys on the basis of development of the external genitalia and the pubic, axillary, facial, and perineal hair. Here, verbal definitions for five developmental stages are supplemented with front-view photographs of the full body and of the pubic region. Bayley and Bayer (1946) used photographs to illustrate a set of definitions for rating androgyny in young adults: rear-view photographs supplement verbal description of a five-step masculinity-femininity scale for each of eight variates of limb and trunk contour. From photographs of 4000 young adult males (front, side, and rear views), Sheldon, Stevens, and Tucker (1940) drew three samples of 100 considered extreme in predominance of subcutaneous fat, predominance of voluntary musculature, and paucity of muscle and fat. These were used to obtain rating criteria; i.e., three deviant categories were verbally defined by enumerating the distinguishing features of each group of photographs.

Profile silhouettes were the sole source materials utilized by Crook (1937) for studying variation of erect posture in 76 children between 2 and 5 years of age. Robinow, Leonard, and Anderson (1943) used rear-view and profile photographs on 170 children for studying age trends in five posture variables over the period 2 to 12 years of age. Profile or side-view photographs also were employed by Schwartz, Britten, and Thompson (1928) for determining the effect of systematic exercise on five posture variables in a group of boys 12 to 18 years of age.

Photographs and silhouettes, in conjunction with roentgenograms, direct observations, family-history records, and health-care protocols, were used by Stuart (1939) in a developmental and comparative study of six related children covering the early years of postnatal life. Front-view photographs were employed by Seckel, Scott, and Benditt (1949) as one of several media for describing precocious sexual development in six children between 2 and 9 years of age. Tracings of anterior and posterior photographs at ages between 4 and 19 years were utilized by Boyd (1955) in a longitudinal study of body size and form combining data from the living child, the roentgenogram, and the photograph. In a study of 112 boys 9 to 19 years of age, many of whom were examined at semiannual intervals over a seven-year period, Stolz and Stolz (1951) made joint use of data from front, side and rear photographs, medical examinations, and direct measurement of the body.

Photographs were the primary source materials utilized by Sheldon, Stevens, and Tucker (1940) in an investigation of physique variations among 4000 young adult males and by Bullen and Hardy (1946) in an investigation of physique variations among 175 young adult females. For samples of young adults of both sexes, photographs were used by Bayley and Bayer (1946) in a study of androgyny and by Dupertuis, Atkinson, and Elftman (1945) in a study of patterns of pubic-hair distribution.

In obtaining photographic source materials, as elsewhere, procedural requirements vary with research purposes (Meredith, 1955b). The extent to which such matters as precise positioning of the subject, controlled lighting, constant subject-lens distance, standardized processing, and waterproof-base printing paper are methodologic requisites depends upon the investigator's problem. For some inspectional and illustrative purposes, fairly crude photographic technic is adequate; as a source for measurement data, photographs must meet exacting specifications (Tanner and Weiner, 1949; Geoghegan, 1953).

Clough and Murlin (1928) described an installation designed to produce photographs of school-age children suitable for the extraction of metric data. Their apparatus and method held constant the subject-film distance, camera height, light arrangement, and type of exposure. By mirror photography and a stereoscopic camera, two lateral-view images and two anterior-view images were secured simultaneously. Centimeter scales, cemented to iron posts, were at the child's right and rear. The child was positioned with his heels separated by 12 centimeters, his sacrum and upper back against the rear scale, and his eyes in a horizontal plane passing through the external acoustic meatuses.

A procedure whereby photographs could be used as a source of measurements of the posture of preschool children was developed by Sweeny et al. (1929). Following laboratory experimentation with various body markings, photographic backgrounds, and scaling devices, they recommended (1) using a flesh pencil to spot the acromion processes, inner and lower borders of the scapulae, spinous processes of the vertebrae from the seventh cervical to the sacrum, posterior superior iliac spines, xiphisternal junction, center of the patellae, external malleoli, and head of the fibulae, (2) photographing the child against a dull walnut-brown background marked with a white line along its lower edge and another down one side, (3) photographing a grid of horizontal and vertical lines 5 centimeters apart, with a mid-vertical line heavier than the others, and (4) printing simultaneously a negative of the grid and a negative of the child. Superimposition of the negatives was made so that their horizontal lines were parallel and the mid-line of the grid passed through the cleft of the buttocks in the rear view, the left patella in the front view, and the external malleolus in the side view.

Halverson (1936) discussed a double-exposure method for deriving face measurements in infancy. He recommended photographing the infant during sleep, then adding to the negative a centimeter grid exposed at the same distance.

Gavan, Washburn, and Lewis (1952) published an experimentally based study on the technical aspects of procuring a scaled photograph of such excellence as to constitute an adequate source for metric data on body size and form. They treated lighting and positioning, reduction and distortion, and selection of film and printing paper. Their recommendations, made with reference to photographing subjects in the erect position, include (1) using a long focal-length lens and a minimum lens-subject distance of 600 centimeters, (2) varying the floor-lens distance with the height of the subject, (3) marking needed skeletal points with gummed stickers (the type used to reinforce holes in loose-leaf paper), (4) lighting the subject with a single high-speed strobe light mounted directly above the camera and also lighting the backdrop, (5) including in the photograph a size scale and a scale with ten graduations

from white to black,[1] and (6) using moderately fast, fine-grained film and nonshrinkable printing paper. Dupertuis and Tanner (1950) gave particular attention to the positioning of the subject for erect front-, side-, and rear-view photographs. They considered orientation of the head, posture of the limbs and trunk, and placement of the feet. Regarding foot placement, it was recommended that the subject stand on a turntable with his heels separated by 4 centimeters and his feet turned outwards at angles of 10 degrees each from the midsagittal plane. Geoghegan (1953) discussed a number of additional body positions and demonstrated the usefulness of some of them in estimating the surface area of the body.

Hunt and Giles (1956) described a commercial photographic installation manufactured by the Photo-Metric Corporation. This assembly includes camera, mirrors, and electronic flash units so arranged that one exposure records four views of the subject: front, left side, back, and overhead. A projector and mirror enlarge the obtained glass positives to one half life size. A photographic method that gives a contour map of body surfaces has been described by Sassouni (1957). He recommends securing a view of the conformation of face depth as follows: (1) place the subject's head in *norma lateralis;* (2) from a distance 250 centimeters in front of the subject, project a millimetric grid upon his face; and (3) with a camera at right angles to the midsagittal plane and 150 centi-

---

[1] In the adequately exposed and developed negative each graduation is distinguishable.

meters from the mid-point of the transmeatal axis, photograph the contour-lined face.

Stuart (1939) discussed photography of the nude child with respect to allaying apprehension, obtaining naturalness of pose, dealing with modesty, and counteracting fatigue. Dupertuis and Tanner (1950) emphasized the need for training in positioning the child. Shuttleworth (1951) stressed the importance of preserving anonymity in the use of nude photographs, e.g., by masking the eyes or blocking out the face.

*Molds and Casts.* In the study of anatomic ontogenesis molds (impressions, negatives) and casts (models, positives) have been made for the palate, viscera, voluntary musculature, and entire body of the child cadaver (Boyd, 1935; Freiband, 1937; Wilmer and Scammon, 1945) and for the maxillary and mandibular dental arches, face, and entire body of the living child (Boyd, Scammon, and Lawrence, 1930; Cohen, 1940; Schwarz, 1933).

For what sorts of datum is the mold or cast a uniquely valuable source? It is more fatiguing and time-consuming for a child to serve directly as a source of measurement of the surface area of the body than for him to submit to the preparation of a body mold (Boyd, 1935). Data for height of the palate (Channing and Wissler, 1908), depth of the dental arches (Meredith and Cox, 1954), and width of the crowns of the molar teeth (Moorrees et al., 1957) can be obtained more precisely and conveniently on a cast than by measurement directly in the mouth.

Being three-dimensional, the cast is superior to photographs as a source of data on the surface area of body segments and superior to roentgenograms as a source of data on the form of the dental arches. Although the cast has no advantage over direct inspection as a source of data on age or order of tooth eruption, when casts are obtained for other purposes (e.g., studying age changes in tooth position), they constitute an alternative source for securing tooth-eruption data. The cast, in common with the roentgenogram and photograph, fixes a structural state and makes it possible for the investigator to accumulate series of such states for large-scale intercomparison and extended study.

As sources for determining the area of the external body surface, molds and casts have been used by Sawyer, Stone, and DuBois (1916) and by Boyd, Scammon, and Lawrence (1930). The former made a mold for a boy 12 years of age. After covering the boy's entire body with cloth (union suit, thin gloves, and cotton bandage), the gloves were infiltrated with paraffin, and all other parts, except the area of the anterior nares, were wrapped with gummed paper tape. The resultant firm mold was cut to permit removal, and additional study was made of those surfaces not contacted by the mold, i.e., the cutaneous areas between the toes, behind the ears, and around the scrotum and penis.

Boyd, Scammon, and Lawrence obtained nine cast reproductions of children between the ages of 3 and 5 years. Plaster of Paris was used for mold and model, the mold being made on a large galvanized-iron tray. To prevent sticking, each child's body was greased with stearine (stearic acid and kerosene); his eyelids were closed, coated with vaseline, and covered with soft paper, and his head hair was protected with a snugly fitting silk cap. The mold was made in three stages: (1) semi-solid plaster was placed in the tray, and a mold of the dorsal half of the body was made by having the child assume a supine position—his feet were about 10 centimeters apart, his hands about 10 centimeters from the body, and his fingers moderately spread; (2) the following day the child returned to this dorsal half-shell and a mold was made of the ventral portion of the body from soles to neck; (3) the ventral mold was removed, a small segment near the neck was replaced, and a mold was obtained for the remainder of the head and the face, excluding, of course, the anterior nares region. Several casting procedures were tried before a satisfactory one was devised. It was found necessary to grease the mold generously, to reinforce the limb and finger regions with iron rods, to allow the assembled and well-clamped mold to dry for several days, to place the mold in the upright position and pour liquid casting plaster through a hole at the vertex, and to use exceptional care in removing the mold.

Employing materials that eliminated the need for greasing either the subject or the mold, Hixon (1958) made facial casts for three young adults. In mold preparation, tubes were placed in the nares, an alginate-base hydrocolloid (Jeltrate) was applied on the face to a depth of approximately 1.5 cm., and the flexible Jeltrate was then covered with a fast-setting plaster for reinforcement. After removal of the mold from the face, a hydrocal cast was poured.[1]

The reported findings on child growth derived from casts of the dental arches are in part the outcome of planned research and in part the by-products of dental practice. Many of the by-products of dental practice have the value inherent in the individual instance but lack the generalization possibilities attainable by purposeful sampling and statistical tests. Johnson (1937) reported eight childhood instances of dental malocclusions associated with thumb-sucking, lip-biting, lip-sucking, tongue-thrusting, and abnormal swallowing. Instances of medial and lateral tooth movements in the absence of orthodontic treatment were reported by Ainsworth (1935) and Spiller (1913). Ainsworth's subject showed change between ages 6 and 10 years from crowded mandibular incisors to regular spacing; Spiller's subject showed change between ages 7 and 16 years from widely separated mandibular incisors to regular spacing. Rogers (1922) reported two childhood instances of increase in dental-arch width associated with a period of special exercise of the masseter-temporal muscles. Seriate measures of dental-arch width were reported by Colyer (1920) on three normal, healthy children examined seven or eight times between ages 4 and 12 years.

[1] Hydrocolloid and hydrocal are discussed on p. 222, together with recommended procedures in their use.

In cross-sectional investigations casts of the gum pads or dental arches have been used by Freiband (1937) in determining size and shape of the palate at different ages between the third prenatal month and term; Clinch and Young (1934), in determining size and relationship of the maxillary and mandibular gum pads at birth; Goldberg (1929), in comparing size of the tooth crowns in identical twins at 3 years to early adulthood; Cohen (1935), in comparing volume and surface area of the tooth crowns in the deciduous and permanent dentitions; Meredith and Hixon (1954), in determining frequency, size, and bilateralism of Carabelli's tubercle in children 9 years of age; Channing and Wissler (1908), in determining dimensions of the palate in feeble-minded children, adolescents, and young adults; Moorrees and Reed (1954), in studying crowding and spacing of the teeth in young adult females; and Koski and Hautala (1952), in studying incidence of shovel-shaped incisors in young adults of both sexes.[1]

In longitudinal investigations casts of the dental arches have been utilized by Lewis and Lehman (1932) and Moorrees et al. (1957) for investigating relationships between deciduous and succedaneous teeth; Cohen (1940) and Sillman (1951), for investigating lateral development of the dental arches; Barrow and White (1952), for studying age changes in dental occlusion; Goldstein and Stanton (1936a, 1938), for

studying associations between dental occlusion and movements of the teeth anteroposteriorly and laterally; Holcomb and Meredith (1956) and Meredith and Hopp (1956), for studying individual differences in size and growth rate of the dental arches. All of these research publications deal with dental ontogenesis during the first two decades of postnatal life, four of them using seriate casts covering periods of more than a decade.

The validity with which molds and casts reproduce anatomic structures depends upon the materials and methods used and, with the living organism, upon the cooperation of the subject. In the study of the gum pads and dental arches molds have been made from plaster of Paris (Goldstein and Stanton, 1936a), modeling compound (Burson, 1952), wax (Bakwin and Bakwin, 1936), and hydrocolloid (Barrow and White, 1952); casts have been prepared from plaster of Paris (Goldberg, 1929) and hydrocal (Freiband, 1937).

Wax is used acceptably to obtain molds of the gum pads on infants; it lends itself to rapid use, and the gum pads are not complicated topographically. When undercuts and complex formations are to be reproduced, as in securing molds of the dental arches, the elasticity of the newer hydrocolloids is needed. Skinner and Hoblit (1956) have found that the agar-base and alginate-base hydrocolloids, used in conformity with manufacturer's specifications, each give highly accurate results. For obtaining molds of the dental arches on children, alginate-base hydrocolloid is preferable, since its setting

---

[1] Hixon and Oldfather (1958) made joint use of casts and roentgenograms in developing a procedure for predicting the size of the crowns of the permanent canine and premolar teeth.

time is shorter (Skinner and Carlisle, 1956). Alginate-base hydrocolloid is a powder which, on the addition of water, becomes a plastic material and, within a period of ten minutes, passes from the plastic state through an elastic state to a fairly rigid state.

After hydrocolloid has been mixed with water, it is carried to the mouth in a dental impression tray. Impression trays are made in a variety of shapes and sizes; the one chosen for making a particular mold should be well suited to the child's dental arch. Phillips and Ito (1951), on the basis of extensive experimental work, conclude that in the use of alginate-base hydrocolloid (1) the impression tray should be centered on the teeth, (2) the mold should be removed from the teeth with more of a jerking than a teasing movement, and (3) the cast should be poured within fifteen minutes after withdrawal of the mold from the mouth.

As sources of measurement data, hydrocal (dental stone) casts are superior to plaster of Paris casts, since, when set, they are much harder (Skinner, 1954). At the time hydrocal is poured the mold should be vibrated to assist in removal of trapped air and the pouring should proceed at a slow rate and with approximately even dispersion (Phillips, Price, and Reinking, 1953). The dimensional change of hydrocal casts during setting is less than 0.1 per cent, and under ordinary conditions of temperature and humidity there is no change once the setting reaction is completed (Skinner, 1954).

Using alginate-base hydrocolloid for molding, hydrocal for casting, and the procedural stipulations listed above, it is possible to produce casts that are highly satisfactory as sources for metric data representing the dental arches and their units. Meredith and Cox (1954) measured the minimum distance between the maxillary first molars (1) on casts of this type and (2) directly in the mouth. Their subjects were five children, 9 years of age. Both investigators took series of measurements on each child and each cast, measuring to the nearest 0.01 cm. The ten averages for direct measurement did not differ systematically from those for cast measurement.

On several occasions source materials have been devised in which photography complemented molding and casting. Sawyer, Stone, and DuBois (1916) flattened pieces of a cloth-paper mold on photographic paper, exposed the paper to the sun, and obtained areal duplicates less difficult to measure than the mold areas. Goldberg (1929) derived a source for measuring tooth size by photographing plaster casts and imposing a millimeter grid on the prints. A combination of casting, photography, and tracing was used by Speck (1950). Casts of the mandibular dental arch were photographed, the negatives projected to a common enlargement (3X), and tracings made of the enlarged tooth images. The number of steps from the teeth of the child to Speck's indirect source for metric data is seen on specifying the sequence, child to mold to cast to photographic enlargement to tracing.

This section has discussed five sources of data: the living child, the child cadaver, the roentgenogram, the photograph, and the cast. For each, in turn, an attempt has been made to indicate both the usefulness of the source and the methodologic problems confronted in its use. It should be clear that no source is satisfactory for all purposes; conversely, each source has pre-eminence in the study of some aspects of anatomic ontogenesis.

## TYPES OF DATA

Whatever source or combination of sources is employed, the investigator may obtain ratings and/or measurements. Ratings are made with a descriptive scale and measurements with a metric scale. For some purposes, inspectional judgments and/or metric readings are analyzed directly; for other purposes, these data are utilized to derive composite ratings, ratios, or increments.

An important function of the investigator is to decide upon the kind of scale to be used in a particular study. Sometimes, as in designing an investigation on anatomic form, there is an early planning stage in which the feasibility of a rating approach is clear, while the practicability of a measurement alternative is obscure. It is wise to act on the principle that ordinal data should not be gathered without thoughtfully considering a way to study the problem metrically (Thorndike, 1951). In the event a choice exists, metric data should be amassed in preference to inspectional data. This follows from regarding maximization of objectivity and mathematic adaptability as *desiderata* in science (Wilson, 1952).

*Ratings.* A rating is a datum obtained with the aid of a descriptive criterion or scale. If a scale is used, two or more categories are defined, and each subject is assigned the symbol of the category he best fits; if a criterion is used, a single category is defined, and each subject is assigned a symbol denoting the time at which the criterion occurs. The latter is illustrated by defining the category "erupted" with the criterion: a tooth is considered erupted at the time it has ruptured the gingiva sufficiently to expose an area of tooth enamel o.1 centimeter in diameter.[1]

The number of classes or categories employed in studies of human structural variation has extended from the single class (Pyle and Sontag, 1943), through the partitioning of a continuum into as many as 20 classes (Schonfeld and Beebe, 1942), to a set of tricomponent categories numbering more than 70 (Sheldon, Stevens, and Tucker, 1940). Identified in inverse order, the three illustrative references deal with varieties of external body form, differences in volume of the testes, and differences in age at which a specified stage of ossification is reached.

Criterion ratings have been used widely in estimating the time of occurrence of specific anatomic events. They facilitate investigation of ontogenetic sequences for the acquisition and resorption of tissues, the addition and discard of organs, and the appear-

[1] In rating by a sole criterion a three-category scale is implied. There is a middle "age of occurrence" category (for which records are made), and there are two unused bordering categories representing ages "earlier" and "later" (Crampton, 1908a).

ance and loss of structures (Garn, Lewis, and Shoemaker, 1956). They help provide answers to questions such as when is mesoderm derived, the liver differentiated, the pronephros obliterated? When are the limb buds acquired, the fingers individuated, the touch pads lost? In what order are muscles formed, bone centers deposited, deciduous teeth shed?

Multicategory ratings have been utilized in studying the number, size, and form of structures. Examples are counts of the number of ossified carpal and tarsal centers (Wallis, 1931); counts of the number of permanent third molar teeth congenitally missing, impacted, and erupted (Hellman, 1936); estimates of the number of pigmented axillary and pubic hairs as few, moderate, and many (Pryor, 1936); ratings of the vertebral border of the scapula as convex, straight, and concave (Graves, 1925); ratings of the male genitalia as small, average, and large (Kubitschek, 1932); and classification of mammary hypertrophy in adolescent boys as absent, slight, moderate, and marked (Jung and Shafton, 1935).

Rating categories have been defined verbally, pictorially, and by samples or models. Three classes of dental occlusion were described verbally and pictorially by Angle (1900), three stages of pubic-hair growth were described verbally by Crampton (1908a), four stages of female breast development were defined verbally and pictorially by Stratz (1909), five categories of lumbar lordosis were defined pictorially by Robinow, Leonard and Anderson (1943), and five stages of genital and body-hair growth were described ver-

bally and pictorially by Greulich, et al. (1942). Thirty samples of head hair were arranged in a *Haarfarbentafel* by Eugen Fischer (Martin, 1928), 20 glass specimens simulating eyes were set in an *Augenfarbentafel* by Rudolf Martin and Bruno Schultz (Martin and Saller, 1956), and 23 hard-rubber models simulating testes were graded in an orchidometer by Schonfeld and Beebe (1942).

The Schonfeld-Beebe orchidometer was used to estimate testis volume at successive ages from birth to early adulthood. Estimates were made on the living child by palpating a testis with one hand and, with the other hand, selecting the model judged to have the same volume. The validity of this rating procedure was investigated with respect to reliability and relevance.[1] In studying relevance, the volume of each of 400 clay models made to simulate testes of varying size was (1) rated with the orchidometer and (2) measured by water displacement. There was a slight tendency for small volumes to be overestimated and large volumes, underestimated. Reliability was studied from two series of ratings for 65 boys, 11 and 12 years of age; in a few instances the estimates were in error by as much as 20 per cent.

The number of categories used in investigating a given growth phenomenon has varied in different studies. In studies of metaphyseal obliteration four categories were used by Stevenson (1924) and nine categories by Todd (1937). In studies of tooth calcification four stages of root development

---

[1] A datum is valid to the extent that chance error is minimized (reliability) and systematic error eliminated (relevance).

were defined by Bengston (1935) and eight stages by Gleiser and Hunt (1955). Greenwood (1891) employed a four-category scale for rating hair color; the scale developed by Eugen Fischer has 30 classes.

Category variation has occurred particularly in the investigation of tooth eruption. There have been numerous studies based on the age at which a criterion stage is attained (Meredith, 1946a; Falkner, 1957; Hurme, 1948; Leslie, 1951). Suk (1919) utilized three categories: gingiva not ruptured, tooth erupting, and tooth fully erupted. Four categories were used by Cattell (1928): gingiva not pierced, crown less than one-third exposed, crown between one- and two-thirds exposed, and crown more than two-thirds exposed. James and Pitts (1912) employed a six-step scale: gingiva not ruptured, tooth just erupting, crown less than half erupted, crown more than half erupted, crown almost fully erupted, and tooth in occlusion. On roentgenograms, Bengston (1935) made use of five categories: morsal surface of crown more than 0.20 centimeter beneath the alveolar crest, 0.20 to 0.05 centimeter beneath crest, breaking through crest, midway between gingival crest and line of occlusion, and in occlusion.[1]

Careful attention must be given to the definition of categories. Crampton (1908a, 1908b) devised a three-stage classification of pubic-hair development. His intermediate category is defined in the first paper to include children with any amount of pigmented hair less than a dense covering; in the second paper it is defined to include children with heavy down and those with nonkinky pigmented hair. An earlier ontogenetic period is encompassed by the second definition than by the first. Several months elapse, sometimes more than a year, between the time a child has some pigmented hairs with the characteristic kink or twist, and the time he shows a dense covering of hair.

Single category ratings for tooth emergence were used by Gleiser and Hunt (1955) and Leslie (1951). In the first study the criterion was the initial piercing of the alveolar bone, in the second it was the initial piercing of the gingival tissue. McKern and Stewart (1957) noted similar systematic differences in criterion definitions of diaphyso-epiphyseal union. Meredith (1940) called attention to the need for explicit definition of portions of three scales used in a study by Sheldon, Stevens, and Tucker (1940).[2]

The procedure in defining categories and testing their objectivity can be illustrated by reference to a study by Meredith and Hixon (1954). Major steps in this study included (1) examining 100 maxillary permanent first-molar teeth and making notations on the furrows, pits, and protuberances in the region of Carabelli's tubercle, (2) using these notations to derive a six-

---

[1] Gleiser and Hunt (1955), in an investigation of the mandibular permanent first molar teeth, found alveolar eruption to precede gingival eruption by an average of ten months. In a study of the permanent canine, premolar, and second molar teeth Hellman (1930) found gingival emergence to antedate full eruption by periods of seven months (maxillary second premolar) to fourteen months (maxillary canine).

[2] See also Humphreys (1957).

category descriptive scale, (3) testing the usability of this scale, (4) altering the number of categories and revising the definitions, and (5) determining the reliability of the revised four-category scale. Two investigators, working independently, rated a series of 200 teeth; there was 73 per cent agreement on category placement, and all of the discrepancies except one were between adjacent categories.

Categories that have been defined precisely may not yield dependable ratings. Robinow, Leonard, and Anderson (1943) used rear-view photographs to define a six-stage scale for knock-knees and side-view photographs to define a five-stage scale for slumped-back. Ratings were found to be considerably more reliable for knock-knees than for slumped-back. Seemingly, the child assumed much the same lower-limb posture on different occasions, whereas his trunk posture varied appreciably.

Ratings frequently involve interpolation (Pyle and Sontag, 1943). Assume that a criterion for appearance of ossification centers has been defined in an unambiguous and precise manner, e.g., a center is considered present at the time its density makes it clearly identifiable on the roentgenogram and its diameter approximates 0.1 centimeter. Further, assume that roentgenograms have been obtained at semiannual ages, and a particular center has been found absent at one age and 0.3 centimeter in diameter at the succeeding age. An estimate for age of appearance of the center can be derived only by interpolation. It follows that estimates of this type become more de-

pendable as the interval between examinations is decreased. Garn, Lewis, and Shoemaker (1956), in a study of the sequence of calcification for mandibular teeth, noted that interpolation is less difficult in estimating the *order* in which teeth begin to calcify than in making close estimates of the *time* at which they begin to calcify.

Many problems investigated initially by means of ratings have been subjected at a later time to metric investigation. These transitions from inspectional data to measurement data constitute a major expression of methodologic advancement in the study of anatomic ontogenesis. Schwartz, Britten, and Thompson (1928) replaced ratings with measurements in a study of posture. By measuring selected angles and distances on lateral-view photographs, they secured quantitative data for posterior extension of the shoulders beyond the hips, anterior extension of the abdomen beyond the thorax, relation between the long axes of the trunk and lower limbs, and stoop of the shoulders. A procedure for quantitatively expressing the amount of flat-footedness in children was developed by Irwin (1937). He found the procedure to be highly reliable and recommended its substitution for ratings of flat-footedness.

A metric method of studying mandibular tooth eruption in childhood was devised by Carlson (1944). Curves indicating the amount and rate of eruption for different teeth during a ten-year period were derived from seriate radiographs by measuring the distance from the highest point of a tooth to the lowest point of the mandible directly beneath the tooth. Continuing in the area of dentition, procedures have been developed by Goldstein and Stanton (1936b) for measuring the amount of dental overbite and by Moorrees and Reed (1954) for measuring crowding and spacing of the teeth.

In the area of ossification Kelly (1937), Meredith (1957b), and others have developed methods of data collection that substitute measurements for ratings. Meredith developed a quantitative method of studying change in the profile of the osseous chin during childhood. Kelly (1) reviewed and appraised several metric approaches to osseous growth of the manus developed during the period 1920–1935 and (2) devised a practical and highly reliable measure designated the CM/WD index. The CM/WD index expresses the attained size of 14 carpal and epiphyseal diameters in relation to a measure of wrist size.

Similarly, in the area of physique numerous measurement proposals have been made. Many of those made prior to 1935 have been colligated and evaluated by McCloy (1936). Davenport (1925) computed an index of over-all build (chest girth/stature) at successive ages from birth to early adulthood. He found that the typical child becomes slenderer with age, during infancy and childhood, then increases slightly in stockiness throughout adolescence.

Meredith and Culp (1951) and Meredith and Sherbina (1951) studied three slender-to-stocky continua representing the upper limb (arm girth/upper limb length), lower limb (leg girth/lower limb length), and body stem (chest girth/stem length). They found that in childhood there is a low relationship between stockiness of the body stem and stockiness of each limb ($r$'s ca. 0.4), and no more than a moderate association between upper-limb stockiness and lower-limb stockiness ($r$'s ca. 0.7).

The same three ratios, plus two ratios portraying shoulder width in relation to hip width and chest girth in relation to abdomen girth, were studied by Trim and Meredith (1952) and Meredith and Meredith (1953) on girls 7, 9, and 11 years of age and boys 7, 10, and 15 years of age. After finding that the shoulder-hip and chest-abdomen ratios were not highly associated, five-variable frames of reference were constructed for the different age-sex groups[1] and illustrations were given of their usability in securing physique profiles for individual children. It was recommended that these frames of reference be lengthened to include more aspects of body form and that additional frames be developed in order to provide metrically based normative distributions for each consecutive annual age during childhood and adolescence. Other variables suggested for inclusion were ratios depicting head form (Bayley, 1936), face form (Goldstein, 1936), chest form (Meredith and Knott, 1937),

[1] It will suffice to describe this construction with respect to one variable and a single age-sex group. A reference frame was developed by determining the tenth, thirtieth, seventieth, and ninetieth percentiles of the distribution for the upper-limb index on 4-year-old boys and then employing these percentiles to subdivide the distribution into five successive parts named Slender, Moderately Slender, Average, Moderately Stocky, Stocky.

and the relation of lower-limb length to stem length (Meredith and Knott, 1938). Heath (1945), in a study of young adult males, derived profiles of body form based on a somewhat different selection of ratios.

*Measurements.* A measurement is a datum obtained by means of an instrument or apparatus having a scale graduated in equal intervals. Nearly all of the instruments used in the study of anatomic ontogenesis have scales that begin at an absolute zero point and are graduated in units of the metric system.

Instruments of many kinds and varieties are available for measuring body structures. These include slide-type and spread-type calipers[1] for measuring diameters (Steggerda, 1949[2]), metric tapes for measuring girths (McCloy, 1936), planimeters for measuring areas (Baldwin, Busby, and Garside, 1928), platform-type scales for measuring weights (Goldstein, 1937), scaled tanks for measuring volumes (Tilton, 1930), and variously named instruments for measuring angles (Schultz, 1929; Salzmann, 1945).

The development of anthropometric precision instruments has occurred largely in the period since 1830. Platform-type weighing scales were produced first in 1831 (Goldstein, 1937), and spread-type calipers, a few years later (Woodbury, 1952). Between 1850

[1] Slide calipers have parallel arms, one fixed at right angles to a calibrated scale and the other movable along the scale. Spread calipers have hinged arms, with the scale attached to one and crossing the other at a set level.

[2] See also the catalog of "GPM Anthropological Instruments" available from Siber Hegner and Company, 183 Madison Avenue, New York 16, N. Y.

and 1870 a number of metrically scaled boards, rods, and calipers were designed for anthropological research on skeletal material and living adults; Paul Broca was a leading contributor to this improvement of the equipment armamentorium (Hrdlicka, 1920). The development of instruments especially adapted for measuring fetuses and young children began shortly before the end of the nineteenth century (Chapin, 1894) but received scant attention prior to 1920. In the period 1920–1940 a variety of these instruments was described by Schultz (1920), Baldwin (1921), Thompson (1929), Wilson et al. (1930), Carey (1936), Cates and Goodwin (1936), Stuart (1939) and Knott (1941).

The design and production of improved measurement tools continues. During the last decade Tanner and Weiner (1949) have described spread calipers with a scale × 5 enlargement; Woodbury (1952) and Tanner and Whitehouse (1955) have described dial-type spread calipers; Tanner and Whitehouse (1957) have described counter-type slide calipers; and Karpovich (1951) has described a modified tape for measuring trunk girths.

Research pertaining to the selection of instruments has been reported by Whitacre (1934) and Gray (1935). Two laboratory instruments commonly used in measuring stature are the fixed vertical rod and the fixed vertical board. Whitacre measured 400 children by each method in succession and 25 children by each method on two different days. All positioning was the same except that when the rod was used the child "stood free" and when the board was used his heels, buttocks, and shoulders were in contact with it. Compared with the measures by rod, the measures by board were systematically larger and considerably more reliable. This study illustrates the principle that one way to increase reliability is by controlling the posture of each body segment included in a dimension.

Gray's investigation shows how instrument selection can be related to what is measured anatomically. Depth (anteroposterior diameter) of the chest was determined on 370 adult males by using both slide and outside-spread calipers.[1] The readings were larger for the slide calipers than for the spread calipers by an average of 10 per cent. This systematic discrepancy was a function of the contour of the chest and the manner in which the instruments made contact with it. The ends of the spread calipers contacted points in the midsagittal plane; the arms of the slide calipers contacted points in more lateral planes on the posterior and anterior chest walls. Succinctly, the one instrument measured chest depth in the mid-line and the other measured maximum chest depth.

Prior to research use, every piece of metric equipment should be sent to the Bureau of Standards for testing or checked against a scale that has been sent for testing. It is courting bias to assume that commercially available

products arrive at the laboratory in correct calibration; this is especially true of linen tapes, wood meter sticks, and inexpensive metal calipers. Nor should the testing of instruments made or modified in the laboratory be overlooked.

Instrument maintenance is no less important than initial testing. This includes careful handling, protective storage when not in use, and re-testing. In particular, there should be frequent checking of weighing scales, tapes, and instruments with slender arms or pointed ends. Meticulous attention to measuring equipment is one of the principal avenues by which investigators can seek to exclude systematic error from metric data.

Diameters of body structures are obtained between specified termini, angles are determined by reference to selected lines, and girths are taken in chosen planes. The points that define these termini and lines and planes are called landmarks.

The importance of landmarks is attested by the fact that they are given primary emphasis in two international agreements. These agreements, adopted at Monaco in 1906 and Geneva in 1912, list approximately 100 body dimensions and recommend landmarks for securing them (Hrdlicka, 1920). The Monaco document pertains to landmarks in the head region, the Geneva document to landmarks on the trunk and limbs. Those who investigate anatomic ontogenesis are obligated to become familiar with these agreements and to follow their recommendations except as departures are indicated by methodologic advances and/or problem requirements.

[1] Outside-spread calipers have arms that are curved first outwardly and then inwardly to facilitate contact with external points. There are also inward-spread calipers that are curved to facilitate contact with internal points and slide calipers with special adaptations for contacting both internal and external points (Ashley-Montagu and Trevor, 1937).

Landmarks are defined in several ways. The landmark "vertex" is defined in terms of an orientation: it is the highest point of the skull when the lowest point on the external border of the left orbit and the highest points on the external borders of the right and left acoustic meatuses are in a plane at right angles to the long axis of the body (Tildesley, 1931). Many landmarks are defined in terms of skeletal projections, margins, or appositions; e.g., menton is the lowest point on the mandible in the mid-line, iliocristale is the most lateral point on the crest of an ilium of the pelvis, bregma is the point of juncture of the coronal and sagittal sutures on the external skull, and nasion is the external point of junction of the nasal and nasofrontal skull sutures. These definitions serve useful purposes in that they (1) specify sites for instrument application and (2) lead to terse identification of dimensions. Notice the abridgment, without loss of specificity, in stating that measures were made for vertex-menton diameter, bregma-nasion diameter, and bi-iliocristal diameter.

Some measurement sites are defined instrumentally. In measuring leg girth (calf circumference) a tape is passed around the leg at right angles to its long axis and a number of applications are made at different levels until the largest girth is found. In measuring maximum head width, the ends of outside-spread calipers are placed against the sides of the head and moved about horizontally until the greatest transverse diameter is found. To assign names to sites that are instrumentally located is needlessly encumbering; e.g.,

it is more parsimonious to state that maximum head width was measured than to assign the name "euryon" to an end-point of this dimension (Martin, 1928) and state that bi-euryon diameter was measured.

Nasion is one of the commonly used landmarks. It serves as a terminus for many vertical, anteroposterior, and oblique dimensions obtained on the roentgenogram and skull. Although it cannot be directly located on the living child or photograph, its *estimated* site is employed in measuring nose height, face height, and other facial diameters. A highly valid procedure for estimating the location of nasion was discovered by Ashley-Montagu (1937): preliminary experimental work suggested that nasion, considered with respect to its placement vertically and transversely, is situated at the point at which a line tangent to the highest points of the superior palpebral sulci intersects the midsagittal plane. This hypothesis was tested on ten adolescent boys and 115 adult cadavers of both sexes. The method with the cadavers was to bore a hole 0.2 centimeter in diameter through the soft tissues at the point postulated, dissect the nasofrontal region, and observe whether the hole penetrated nasion. With the living subjects, a piece of wire was placed at the level stipulated, and a *norma lateralis* roentgenogram taken. Nasion was found to be located correctly on 98 per cent of the cadavers and all of the living subjects. From studying soft tissue and skeletal relationships in the region of the external ear, Ashley-Montagu (1938) also provided experimental support for a procedure used in estimating the location of vertex on the living subject.[1] Further research on the determination of these and other landmarks is needed; for example, the associations found by Ashley-Montagu should be investigated, using young children as subjects.

Not infrequently bilateral structures are of unequal size. One shoulder may be higher than the other, one arm thinner than the other, one hand broader than the other, one leg shorter than the other, one ankle thicker than the other, one foot longer than the other (Davenport, Steggerda, and Drager, 1934). Studies of corresponding dimensions on the right and left limbs have shown both individual and group differences (Morton, 1886; Bjelke-Petersen, 1902; Van Dusen, 1939). Consequently, it is necessary to identify the side on which a measurement is taken. The Geneva agreement recommends that whenever plans are made to collect data on one side only the left side should be measured.

In applying calipers and tapes to nonrigid structures, the anthropometrist is confronted with the task of controlling the degree to which tissues are compressed. Hall (1895), in an early description of methods of measuring girths of the trunk and limbs on schoolboys, emphasized that special effort must be made to avoid the introduction of error caused by variation in the amount of tension applied to the tape. Steggerda (1942), in a comparative investigation of the measurement techniques being used at ten labora-

[1] This procedure is specified on page 205.

tories, found wide deviation in the pressure exerted in measuring width of shoulders, width of hips, and other diameters of the body stem.

The first step toward control of the compression variable is clarification of purpose. If the investigator's purpose were to measure *maximum* width of hips at the bi-iliocristal level, the arms of the calipers would be brought into light contact with the skin; if his purpose were to approximate closely a *skeletal* measurement of bi-iliocristal diameter, firm pressure would be applied in order to reduce the thickness of the overlying soft tissues as much as practicable. Having a clear purpose, the compression decided upon should be specified as objectively as possible, and the measurer(s) well trained to the criterion as defined. Illustrative definitions are (1) the tape is brought into sufficiently light contact with the skin that there is no indentation of the tissues, (2) the headpiece is moved down until it crushes the hair and makes firm contact with the head at the vertex, and (3) heavy pressure is applied to the arms of the calipers in an attempt to approximate maximum compression of the skin and subcutaneous adipose tissue (Meredith, 1951b). Laboratory utilization of these definitions necessitates painstaking effort and care. For many dimensions on the living child, reduction of variation in application of the instrument is a large part of attaining technical competence.

There are many sources of measurement error. In fact, each step in a measurement procedure involves one or more possibilities for the occurrence of uncontrolled variation. The investigator has the responsibility of minimizing these multiple sources of extraneous variation to the extent necessary for satisfactorily studying particular problems. What must be considered? Position of the subject: is this described in sufficient detail, is the description clear to the measurer(s), and does each child appear to meet the position specifications at the time of measurement? Instrument: is this suitably designed for the task, is it adequately engineered and calibrated, and have the measurers developed proficiency in handling it? Landmarks: are these precisely defined, are the definitions clear to each measurer, and is each measurer skilled in locating the landmarks and applying the instrument to them? Other facets of method: does the pressure or tension approximate that stipulated, is the correct limb being measured, and are there obstacles to correct measurement, e.g., hair fasteners or braids, a limb inflamation or scab, fatigue or lack of cooperation? Reading and recording: is the scale of the instrument being read at the proper place, does the measurer exercise care in reading the scale, and does the recorder give close attention first to registering correctly the values that are called and then to announcing what has been recorded for approval by the measurer?

It follows that measurement data for studies of anatomic ontogenesis should be collected only when the following criteria are satisfied: (1) a written statement specifying each technique employed is prepared; (2) those who participate in amassing the data are trained to meet stipulated standards of dependability; and (3) there is frequent checking to assure that these standards are maintained. Meredith and Goodman (1941) gathered neonatal stature measures under these conditions. The written statement required (1) placing the nude infant in dorsal recumbency on a specially constructed metric board, (2) standardizing the position of the head, (3) bringing the knees together and extending the lower limbs, and (4) setting the two uprights of the apparatus in firm contact with the head and soles.[1] A high level of training and its sustenance were demonstrated as follows: two measurers, working independently over a period of eight weeks, measured 100 full-term neonates on the day of birth, obtaining (1) a reliability coefficient of $r = .97$ and (2) agreement within 0.5 centimeter for 92 per cent of the infants. Comparison was made of the stature distribution from these records, and the stature distribution from routine hospital records for the same 100 neonates. Although the two means were alike, the magnitude of chance error differed so markedly that the standard deviations were 1.6 and 2.4 centimeter, respectively. This manifestation of different operational levels indicates how widely measurement efficiency can vary and sounds an alert on any tendency to underestimate the importance of proce-

[1] An assistant maintained the head position while the measurer used one hand to maintain the position of the knees and the other to bring the sliding upright of the instrument snugly against the heels. The indispensability of an assistant in securing this measurement is one example of the importance of the assistant's role in many measuring situations (Knott, 1941).

dural design, adequate training, and sustained attention to method.

Knott (1941), in a major monograph on measurement of the child, (1) reviewed reliability studies made prior to 1940 on fetuses, infants, and older children and (2) investigated reliability for 35 external body measurements on children 3 to 6 years of age. Other reports on the reliability of measurements taken on the living child were made by Goodman (1941), O'Brien, Girshick, and Hunt (1941), Newcomer and Meredith (1951), Stolz and Stolz (1951), and Edwards et al. (1955). Collectively, these studies are based on samples of children at different ages, from birth to early adulthood, and encompass numerous lengths, widths, girths, and measures of thickness. They show that many traits of body size can be measured by competent anthropometrists with high dependability, e.g., paired series of independent measures on children homogeneous in age, sex, race, region, and secular period yield reliability coefficients above .95 for about 50 per cent of the dimensions studied and above .90 for over 80 per cent of the dimensions studied.

Reliability investigations were reported by Björk (1947) for measurements on roentgenograms, by Tanner and Weiner (1949) for measurements on photographs, and by Boyd (1935) and Meredith and Hopp (1956) for measurements on casts. Potter and Meredith (1948) compared reliabilities for measurements taken on the roentgenogram and the living subject; Geoghegan (1953) compared reliabilities for measurements taken on the photograph and the living subject. Among

other findings, these studies report standard errors of measurements below 0.10 centimeter for several facial diameters obtained from roentgenograms and below 0.02 centimeter for some dental diameters obtained from casts.

The comparability of measurements obtained from the photograph and the living subject was studied by Tanner and Weiner (1949) and Gavan, Washburn, and Lewis (1952). Ritt and Sawtell (1930), Clarke, Geser, and Hunsdon (1956), Garn (1956), and Newman and Meredith (1956) studied the comparability of measurements obtained from the roentgenogram and the living subject.

When different laboratories and individual investigators employ the same measurement procedure in collecting data for a given trait, the procedure is referred to as "standardized." The importance of standardization of method was recognized in drafting the international agreements of 1906 and 1912, and it has been stressed less formally in papers of more recent date (Hrdlicka, 1936; Steggerda, 1942).

Standardization is seen in correct perspective as an ongoing process with advantages to be sought and excesses to be avoided. It functions effectively in (1) facilitating comparative and composite use of findings on anatomic ontogenesis (Meredith, 1943), yet (2) must not stifle the development of new techniques and the adoption of procedural improvements.

Standardization is not always a straightforward matter; there are ontogenetic, phylogenetic, methodologic, anatomic, and historic considerations to be weighed. Sometimes, as the following questions indicate, these considerations are difficult to harmonize and implement. Since stature must be obtained in the recumbent position on infants, should this position be continued throughout ontogeny? Should the measurement of stature be replaced by stem length, since the latter is the longest diameter that can be measured in early prenatal life and on most mammals other than man? Is it preferable to adopt the hip width that can be determined most reliably on children (biiliocristal diameter) or a hip width that is obtainable on most young mammals (interspinous diameter or bitrochanteric diameter)? Should lower face width be taken on the living child, continuing historic practice, or should the greater precision of the radiographic approach outweigh precedent?

Having commented on the intricacies and tentativeness of standardization, it remains to give due emphasis to its research significance. For any selected trait, the aggregate knowledge accessible from a group of studies is directly related to the comparability of the measurement procedures utilized. This is illustrated in syntheses of research for head width (Meredith, 1953a) and upper-limb length (Meredith, 1947). The standardization of head width has led to a substantial body of knowledge, whereas the unnecessary variation in method of measuring upper-limb length has produced a relatively small scientific yield. In 12 investigations of upper-limb length use was made of three different limb orientations, three proximal landmarks, and two distal landmarks.

*Derived Measures.* A derived measure is a datum obtained from joint utilization of two or more measurements. Examples of data of this type are a weight increment for the first postnatal year, derived by subtracting a weight measurement secured at birth from a weight measurement secured on the same child one year later (Simmons and Todd, 1938); a facial index at age 7 years, derived from dividing a measurement for face length by a measurement for face width (Goldstein, 1936); and a measure of length of the head and neck at age 17 years, derived by subtracting a measurement for trunk length from a measurement for stem length (Meredith, 1939a).

Before use is made of derived measures, it should be shown that they meet *high* reliability standards. The special need for this becomes apparent on recognizing an important difference between measurements and derived measures. Associated with any measurement there is probability of chance error; associated with any derived measure there is an error probability arising from no less than two measurements. The way in which these probabilities express themselves in reliability coefficients is indicated by the following example. On a sample of 100 boys 15 years of age, two sets of data were obtained for chest girth, abdomen girth, and the ratio of chest girth to abdomen girth. The coefficients of reliability were $r = .98$ for each of the measurements (Newcomer and Meredith, 1951) and $r = .85$ for the derived measure (Trim and Meredith, 1952).

A procedure for increasing the dependability of ratio data was described by Trim and Meredith (1952). Each subject was measured by four anthropometrists designated $T$, $N$, $S$ and $P$. The "single record" method of data collection was compared with a "team record" method. The dependability of the former was symbolized by correlating series of ratios derived from the measurements of $T$ and $N$; that of the latter by correlating ratios derived from averaging the measurements of $T$ and $S$ and those of $N$ and $P$. For the ratio of chest girth to abdomen girth, the obtained $r$'s were .85 for the "single record" method and .96 for the "team record" method. Corresponding $r$'s for the ratio of shoulder width to hip width were .91 and .98, respectively. In each instance the change represents a 20 per cent improvement in reliability. For the study of many problems pertaining to the body form of individuals, a procedure whereby the consistency of ratio data can be increased by 20 per cent merits adoption.

There is no more demanding task in the collection of data for studying anatomic ontogenesis than that of amassing adequate increment data. The validity and research usefulness of increment data are related to the growth rate for the trait under investigation, the length of the ontogenetic interval covered, and the magnitude of the error component for the data.

The validity of an increment datum varies directly with the reduction of chance error in the measurements used to derive it. For a given period of childhood, it is more difficult to attain adequate reduction of error in an increment of chest girth than head girth, stem length than stature, arm girth than leg girth, shoulder width than hip width, hip width than dental arch width (Knott, 1941; Meredith and Cox, 1954). Even so, the error component of increment data cannot be controlled satisfactorily for any trait except through rigorous procedures and constant vigilance (Meredith, 1955b). In all increment studies made in the writer's laboratory over the past twenty years the basic measurements have been obtained by two anthropometrists and required to meet explicit standards, i.e., whenever the two records fail to satisfy an adopted criterion for "close agreement," each anthropometrist takes another measurement. Examples of the criteria for "close agreement" are as follows: agreement within 0.02 centimeter on skeletal nose height, skeletal width of the lower face, and dental arch widths; 0.1 centimeter on head width, upper face width, bi-iliocristal width of hips, and leg girth; 0.2 centimeter on stature, arm girth, and foot length; 0.4 centimeter on biacromial width of shoulders, stem length, upperlimb length, and chest girth.

Given a procedure for which the probability of error is known, and specifying an ontogenetic interval, the validity of an increment datum varies directly with the velocity at which a trait is increasing or decreasing. Since many dimensions change more rapidly during early postnatal life than later, it is often practicable to use smaller increment periods in infancy (Kasius et al., 1957) than in childhood (Meredith and Meredith, 1950). Again, since over the childhood years some dimensions change more slowly than others (e.g., head width more slowly than lower limb length), increment analyses sometimes are tenable for periods of shorter duration on one trait (Meredith, 1955a) than another (Holcomb and Meredith, 1956).

Given a trait that is changing at a constant velocity and a measurement procedure for which the probability of error is known, the validity of an increment datum varies directly with the length of the temporal period. To illustrate: the same amount of error may be 40 per cent of an obtained increment for one month, 5 per cent of an annual increment, and 1 per cent of a quinquennial increment. Frequently, because numerous anatomic traits do not change at a constant velocity, the use of long periods is contraindicated.

Efficient procedure in the accumulation of increment data requires close correspondence between the ontogenetic interval selected for study and that studied; i.e., when a problem calls for increments representing the period between the fourth and fifth birth anniversaries, or between menarche and the first anniversary of menarche, the obtained data become less valid as the examination ages (or stages) vary for different subjects. In ongoing research programs the *desideratum* of regularity is almost attainable by a person delegated to maintain an appointment register and to strive for precise timing of examinations. Under the writer's direction, increment studies have been carried out to cover quarterly, semiannual and annual intervals all defined with reference to date of birth. Sustained effort has been made to schedule examinations within three days of the exact age termini decided upon. This standard has been found practicable;

deviations have been few, except for occasions of illness or travel.

It follows from the contents of the foregoing paragraphs that the investigator's opportunities for amassing highly valid increment data lie in trait selection, interval selection, interval precision, and the reduction of measurement error.

Derived measures have been used in investigating variability of aspects of body form at different ages (Freeman, 1933), changes in body form with age (Meredith and Sherbina, 1951), associations between components of body form (Trim and Meredith, 1952), intragroup variation in index trends (Kelly, 1937), interindividual variation in index trends (Meredith, 1955a), and the influence of environmental variables on index trends (Meredith, Knott, and Hixon, 1958). They also have been employed in studies of relationship between size at a given age and growth rate over an ensuing period (Meredith and Meredith, 1958), relationship between growth rate and illness history (Evans, 1944), associations between age of menarche and growth rate (Shuttleworth, 1937), variability of absolute and percentage increments for different ontogenetic periods (Meredith and Carl, 1946), interindividual variation in absolute increment trends (Meredith, 1939b), intraindividual variation in percentage increment trends (Nanda, 1955), subgroup intercomparison of absolute increment trends (Shuttleworth, 1939), subgroup intercomparison of percentage increment trends (Meredith, 1958), relationship between increments for adjacent age intervals (Simmons and Todd, 1938), associations among increments for different traits during a given period (Newman and Meredith, 1956), and construction of increment norms for infancy (Kasius et al., 1957) and childhood (Meredith and Meredith, 1950).

## SUBDIVISION OF DATA

After the data for a study of anatomic ontogenesis have been accumulated, they are usually subdivided in some manner prior to statistical analysis. For any given trait, the data may be classified ontogenetically and/or subgrouped with respect to one or more other variables. The purpose of ontogenetic classification is to partition ontogenesis into segments appropriate for determining sequential modifications in the distribution of a trait. The purpose of subgrouping in terms of additional variables is to discover, or control for, differences in trait distribution associated with these variables.

The writer of a research report who omits specification of the basis of data subdivision, or describes subgroup formation ambiguously, forfeits part of the potential value of his investigation. Correspondingly, the reader of a research report who fails to give close attention to subgrouping procedures foregoes background that is pertinent to an understanding of the findings of the study and to making comparative use of them. There is ambiguity when, in the absence of reference to the particular methods used in subgroup formation, findings are presented for subgroups designated "malnourished" and "well nourished" or "underweight" and "overweight" (Jenss and Souther,

1940). Apparent contradictions arise from detaching findings on "prepubescent" and "postpubescent" subgroups from explicit notations on whether these subgroups were formed in terms of age of menarche, growth of pubic hair, breast development, or other criteria (Meredith, 1939b). Misinterpretation is fostered when a subgroup is given an evaluation caption such as "retarded" and nothing is presented to support the tenability of regarding the subgroup as anything other than a descriptive class fitly captioned "small" (Meredith, 1955c).

*Ontogenetic Grouping.* Studying change during ontogenesis in the distribution of anatomic traits has been a major interest of investigators of human physical development. In the research literature this is expressed by the frequency with which data are subgrouped in order to describe the central tendency and variability of a trait at consecutive stages or in successive periods. The stages or periods employed are chosen with reference to events that occur during ontogenesis or are related to ontogenesis.

Classification of data on fetuses according to "menstrual age" illustrates grouping in terms of an event related to ontogenesis (Streeter, 1920). Another example is placing data on newborn infants into "premature" and "full-term" categories, using the menstrual age 37 weeks (true age ca. 35 weeks) as the lower limit of the older group (Meredith, 1943).

Grouping on the basis of ontogenetic events includes subdivision of data with regard to birth, menarche, and structural attainments. Under structural attainments, previous reference has been made to the grouping of prenatal data for dimensions of the head, trunk, and limbs in terms of stature classes (Scammon and Calkins, 1929). Data on new-born infants have been grouped in "premature" and "full-term" categories on the basis of attained body weight and/or stature; common partitioning values have been 2.0 and 2.5 kilograms for weight and 45.0 and 47.0 centimeters for stature (Meredith, 1943). In childhood ontogenetic grouping has been based on attained stage of tooth eruption. Hellman (1932) and Krogman (1951) subdivided data for facial dimensions with respect to a series of ten selected dental stages beginning with eruption of the deciduous teeth and extending to full eruption of the permanent dentition. A similar grouping procedure, using seven odontic classes, was utilized by Zuckerman (1955).

It will be recognized that grouping according to attained stature, or weight or dental stage, is classification by the use of different anatomic scales. Although each scale provides groups that are ontogenetically progressive, the scales are neither perfectly intercorrelated nor rectilinearly related to chronologic age.

Several ontogenetic events have been used as reference points in grouping to obtain statistics representing equally spaced time intervals. Shuttleworth (1937) chose the occurrence of menarche as the focal event and studied increments in a variety of dimensions during several years prior to and following it. Burson (1952) chose eruption of a tooth and its antimere (the permanent mandibular central incisors)

as the point of reference and studied changes in dental-arch width during several years immediately preceding and subsequent to it.

The reference event most commonly utilized is birth. Before 1890 it was customary to form postnatal age groups by the "last birthday" method: (1) each child was asked to state his age, and (2) those replying "6" constituted one group, those replying "7" another, and so forth (Meredith, 1936). In contemporary research it is commoner to form annual age groups by the "nearest birthday" method: (1) the age of each child is calculated from records for date of birth and date of examination, and (2) children are grouped according to their closest birth anniversary. The means for data subdivided in these ways differ systematically; e.g., on a sample of boys each within six months of his eighth birth anniversary the age mid-point is 8 years; on a sample of boys each giving his age as "8" the mid-point is 8.5 years.

Every investigator should define his ontogenetic grouping precisely. This is necessary for reasons pertaining to the clear communication of findings and the synthesis of findings from different studies. The means for an anatomic trait listed in the tables of two investigations at age "10 years" are not directly comparable when in the one investigation this figure symbolizes the lower limit of a "last birthday" age group (O'Brien, Girshick, and Hunt, 1941) and in the other it symbolizes the mid-point of a "nearest birthday" age group (Gray and Ayres, 1931). Measures of variability, for any trait that is changing progressively with age, increase with increase in the distance between the upper and lower limits of age groups. There is also a relationship between the range for ontogenetic groups and the magnitude of correlation coefficients (Demisch and Wartmann, 1956).

*Bivariate Subgrouping.* Another broad interest of investigators of human physical growth has been the study of the extent to which the distribution of anatomic traits varies conjointly with ontogenetic time and a second variable. This interest is expressed in the research literature by the extensive assortment of investigations employing subgroups for birth order and chronologic age (Meredith and Brown, 1939), birth weight and chronologic age (Hammett, 1918), diet and chronologic age (Slyker, et al., 1937), chronologic age and ethnic group (Lloyd-Jones, 1941), chronologic age and secular period (Meredith, 1941), chronologic age and appearance of axillary hair (Richey, 1937), dental stage and orthodontic class (Hellman, 1931), osseous stage and dental stage (Demisch and Wartman, 1956), and so forth.

There is considerable variation in the way nonontogenetic variables are subdivided. Menarcheal groups have been formed by sectioning the continuum for age of menarche into three segments, the middle one including first menses between 12.5 and 13.5 years (Goldstein, 1939); three segments, the middle one including first menses between 13.0 and 14.0 years (Richey, 1937); seven segments, five consecutive half years between two open-end tails (Greulich and Pyle, 1950); and eight segments, six consecutive half years between two open-end tails (Shuttle-

worth, 1937). Socioeconomic groups have been formed by drawing from schools in the "wealthy" and "poor" sections of cities (Hopkins, 1947), dividing into two parts the distribution for "occupation of the principal wage earner of the family" (O'Brien, Girshick, and Hunt, 1941), excluding the middle portion of the occupational distribution and comparing the "professional and managerial" section with the "semiskilled and unskilled" section (Meredith, 1951a), and selecting for comparison the "professional" and "unskilled" segments only (Bowditch, 1879). "Tall" and "short" groups have been constituted at a particular age, using the upper and lower halves of the stature distribution (Baldwin, 1921), the upper and lower quarters (Van Dyke, 1930), the upper and lower fifths (Meredith, 1939b), and the upper and lower tenths (Meredith, 1949). When the trait under study varies with the nonontogenetic trait utilized for grouping, it must be expected that the magnitude of the difference between subgroup means for a given age, or stage, will increase as one progresses from comparison of the two halves of a continuum to comparison of its terminal segments.

In several studies "tall" and "short" groups have been formed at selected ages and then followed for a number of years. From one trio of studies it has been found that tall girls, in comparison with short girls, attain menarche earlier (Shuttleworth, 1934), later (Van Dyke, 1930), and at the same time (Barker and Stone, 1936). These seeming discrepancies are a function of the ontogenetic variable; the tall and short groups were constituted, using stature distributions at age 13 years, two years before menarche, and at age 17 years, respectively.

From the foregoing introductory treatment of data subdivision, it becomes apparent that (1) there are intimate connections between the findings of a study and the procedures used in subgrouping, and (2) as subgrouping practices become standardized the intercomparison of different studies on a given topic is facilitated.

It is beyond the scope of this chapter to discuss the investigation of anatomic ontogenesis with respect to the statistical methods employed in analyzing data or the tabular, graphic and other methods utilized in reporting findings. Notwithstanding, attention is directed to the desirability of complementing textbook readings on these topics with readings of illustrative applications in research and proposed applications in the further study of growth problems. Selected references are as follows: Boucher (1957), Boyd (1955), Deming (1957), Garn (1955), Geoghegan (1953), Hunt, Cocke, and Gallagher (1958), Kavanagh and Richards (1942), Kihlberg and Koski (1956), Koch and Kaplan (1950), Mainland (1955), Meredith (1935, 1943, 1955a), Newman and Meredith (1956), Quo (1953), Sholl (1954), Tanner (1951, 1952), Tyler (1954), Wilmer and Scammon (1945), and Yates (1950).

## REFERENCES

Adams, J. W. 1940. Correction of error in cephalometric roentgenograms. *Angle Orthodont.*, **10**, 3–13.

Ainsworth, N. J. 1935. Some problems of treatment. *Int. J. Orthodont.*, **21**, 625–637.

Angle, E. H. 1900. *Treatment of malocclusion of the teeth*. Philadelphia: White.

Ashley-Montagu, M. F. 1937. The determination of the naso-frontal suture and the nasion in the living. *Radiology*, **28**, 473–476.

——. 1938. The location of porion in the living. *Amer. J. phys. Anthrop.*, **23**, 492.

——, and J. C. Trevor. 1937. Note on a new sliding calipers for cranial measurements. *Hum. Biol.*, **9**, 417–418.

Bakwin, H., and Ruth M. Bakwin. 1935. Body build in infants: VI. Growth of the cardiac silhouette and the thoraco-abdominal cavity. *Amer. J. Dis. Child.*, **49**, 861–869.

——. 1936. Form and dimensions of the palate during the first year of life. *Int. J. Orthodont.*, **22**, 1018–1024.

Baldwin, B. T. 1921. Physical growth of children from birth to maturity. *Univer. Iowa Stud. Child Wel.* **1**, No. 1.

——, Laura M. Busby, and Helen V. Garside. 1928. Anatomic growth of children. *Univer. Iowa Stud. Child Wel.* **4**, No. 1.

Barker, R. G., and C. P. Stone. 1936. Physical development in relation to menarcheal age in university women. *Hum. Biol.*, **8**, 198–222.

Barrow, G. V., and J. R. White. 1952. Developmental changes of the maxillary and mandibular dental arches. *Angle Orthodont.*, **22**, 41–46.

Bartelmez, G. W., and H. M. Evans. 1926. Development of the human embryo during the period of somite formation. *Contr. Embryol., Carnegie Inst. Wash.*, No. 85, 1–67.

Bayer, Leona M., and H. Gray. 1933. The hand: Method of measurement. *Amer. J. phys. Anthrop.*, **17**, 379–415.

Bayley, Nancy. 1936. Growth changes in the cephalic index during the first five years of life. *Hum. Biol.*, **8**, 1–18.

——, and Leona M. Bayer. 1946. The assessment of somatic androgyny. *Amer. J. phys. Anthrop.*, **4**, n.s., 433–461.

Bayley, Nancy, and F. C. Davis. 1935. Growth changes in bodily size and proportions during the first three years. *Biometrika*, **27**, 26–87.

Bengston, R. T. 1935. A study of the time of eruption and root development of the permanent teeth between 6 and 13 years. *Northwestern Univer. Dent. Res. Quart.*, 36, No. 8, 3–9.

Bjelke-Petersen, C. 1902. Measurements of boys at each year of age from 8 to 15 years. *Rep. Australian Assoc. Adv. Sci.*, 823.

Björk, A. 1947. The face in profile. *Svenska Tandlakare Tidskri.* 40, No. 5B.

——. 1955. Facial growth in man, studied with the aid of metallic implants. *Acta odont. scand.*, 13, 9–34.

Blackman, S., and J. R. Greening. 1957. Radiation hazards in dental radiography. *Brit. dent. J.*, 102, 167–172.

Boucher, Barbara J. 1957. Sex differences in the foetal pelvis. *Amer. J. phys. Anthrop.*, 15 n.s., 581–600.

Bowditch, H. P. 1879. The growth of children. *Rep. Bd. Hlth Massachusetts*, 10, 35–62.

Boyd, Edith. 1933. Normal variability in weight of the adult human liver and spleen. *Arch. Path.*, 16, 350–372.

——. 1935. *The growth of the surface area of the human body*. Minneapolis: Univer. Minnesota Press.

——. 1936. Weight of the thymus and its component parts. *Amer. J. Dis. Child.*, 51, 313–335.

——. 1955. Pictorial and graphic analysis of the body build of one boy. *Amer. J. Dis. Child.*, 89, 322–340.

——, R. E. Scammon, and D. Lawrence. 1930. The determination of surface area of living children. *Proc. Soc. exp. Biol.*, 27, 445–449.

Boynton, Bernice. 1936. The physical growth of girls. *Univer. Iowa Stud. Child Welfare*, 12, No. 4.

Bradford, E. H. 1883. The effect of recumbency on the length of the spine. *Boston med. surg. J.*, 109, 245–246.

Bremer, J. L. 1906. Description of a four millimeter human embryo. *Amer. J. Anat.*, 5, 459–480.

Brewer, J. I. 1938. A human embryo in the bilaminar blastodisc stage (The Edwards-Jones-Brewer Ovum). *Contr. Embryol., Carnegie Inst. Wash.*, No. 162, 85–93.

Brodie, A. G. 1953. Late growth changes in the human face. *Angle Orthodont.*, 23, 146–157.

Bullen, Adelaide K., and Harriet L. Hardy. 1946. Analysis of body build photographs of 175 college women. *Amer. J. phys. Anthrop.*, 4 n.s., 37–68.

Burson, C. E. 1952. A study of individual variation in mandibular bicanine dimension during growth. *Amer. J. Orthodont.*, 38, 848–865.

Carey, T. F. 1936. An anthropometric measuring board. *Child Develpm.*, 7, 57–59.

Carlson, H. 1944. Studies on the rate and amount of eruption of certain human teeth. *Amer. J. Orthodont.*, 30, 575–588.

Cartwright, L. J., and E. Harvold. 1954. Improved radiographic results in cephalometry through the use of high kilovoltage. *J. Canad. dent. Ass.*, 20, 261–262.

Cates, H. A., and J. C. Goodwin. 1936. The twelve-day old baby. *Hum. Biol.*, 8, 433–450.

Cattell, Psyche. 1928. Dentition as a measure of maturity. *Harv. Monogr. Educ.*, No. 9.

Channing, W., and C. Wissler. 1908. The hard palate in normal and feeble-minded individuals. *Anthrop. Pap. Amer. Mus.*, 1, Part V, 283–349.

Chapin, H. D. 1894. A plan of infantile measurements. *Med. Rec.*, 46, 649–651.

Children's Bureau. 1927. References on the physical growth and development of the normal child. *U. S. Dept. Labor, Children's Bureau*, No. 179.

Clark, Grace. 1930. Differences in measurements made in the nude and clothed for children between 7 and 9 years of age. *Child Develpm.*, 1, 343–345.

Clarke, H. H., L. R. Geser, and S. B. Hunsdon. 1956. Comparison of upper arm measurements by use of roentgenogram and anthropometric techniques. *Res. Quart.*, 27, 379–385.

Clayton, Mary M. 1944. A four-year study of the food habits and physical condition of grade-school children in Newport, Maine. *Univer. Maine Bull.*, 430.

Clinch, Lilah, and M. Young. 1934. Variations in the mutual relationships of the maxillary and mandibular gum pads in the newborn child. *Int. J. Orthodont.*, 20, 359–372.

Clough, H. D., and J. R. Murlin. 1928. Permanent records of growth and nutrition of children. *Amer. J. Dis. Child.*, 36, 425–433.

Cohen, J. T. 1935. The width, the enamel surface area, and the volume of the crown of the deciduous and the permanent teeth. *Int. J. Orthodont.*, 21, 477–482.

———. 1940. Growth and development of the dental arches in children. *J. Amer. dent. Ass.*, 27, 1250–1260.

Colyer, F. 1920. A note on the changes in the dental arch during childhood. *Dent. Rec.*, 40, 273–281.

Coppoletta, J. M., and S. B. Wolbach. 1933. Body length and organ weights of infants and children. *Amer. J. Path.*, 9, 55–70.

Crampton, C. W. 1908a. Anatomical or physiological age: Versus chronological age. *Pedag. Sem.*, 15, 230–237.

———. 1908b. Physiological age-a fundamental principle. *Amer. phys. Educ. Rev.*, 13, 141–154.

Crook, Billie L. 1937. Posture of the young child. *Childh. Educ.*, 13, 317–321.

Curtiss, F. H. 1898. Some investigations regarding loss in weight and gain in height during sleep. *Amer. phys. Educ. Rev.*, 3, 270–273.

Dandy, W. E. 1910. A human embryo with seven pairs of somites. *Amer. J. Anat.*, 10, 85–108.

Davenport, C. B. 1925. Body build: Its development and inheritance. *Eugenics Rec. Office, Carnegie Inst. Wash.*, Bull 24.

———, M. Steggerda, and W. Drager. 1934. Critical examination of physical anthropometry on the living. *Proc. Am. Acad. Arts Sci.*, 69, 265–284.

Deming, Jean. 1957. Application of the Gompertz curve to the observed pattern of growth in length of 48 individual boys and girls during the adolescent cycle of growth. *Hum. Biol.*, 29, 83–122.

Demisch, A., and P. Wartmann. 1956. Calcification of the mandibular third molar and its relation to skeletal and chronological age in children. *Child Develpm.*, 27, 459–473.

Diamond, M. 1944. The patterns of growth and development of the human teeth and jaws. *J. dent. Res.*, 23, 273–303.

Dupertuis, C. W., W. B. Atkinson, and H. Elftman. 1945. Sex differences in pubic hair distribution. *Hum. Biol.*, 17, 137–142.

———, and J. M. Tanner. 1950. The pose of the subject for photogrammetric anthropometry. *Amer. J. phys. Anthrop.*, 8 n.s., 27–47.

Edwards, D. A. W., W. H. Hammond, M.. J. R. Healy, J. M. Tanner, and R. H. Whitehouse. 1955. Design and accuracy of calipers for measuring subcutaneous tissue thickness. *Brit. J. Nutr.*, 9, 133–143.

Etter, L. E. 1955. *Atlas of roentgen anatomy of the skull. Springfield*, Illinois: Thomas.

Evans, Mary E. 1944. Illness history and physical growth. *Amer. J. Dis. Child.*, 68, 390–394.

Falkner, F. 1957. Deciduous tooth eruption. *Arch. Dis. Childh.*, 32, 386–391.

Flory, C. D. 1936. Osseous development in the hand as an index of skeletal development. *Monogr. Soc. Res. Child Develpm.*, 1, No. 3.

Franklin, J. B. 1957. Radiographic phenomena in cephalometric roentgenography. *Angle Orthodont.*, 27, 162–170.

Freeman, R. G. 1933. Skeletentwicklung und Wachstum im Alter von 2 bis 18 Monaten, von 2 bis 7½ en Jahren und von 8 bis 14½ Jahren. *Anthrop. Anz.*, 10, 185–208.

Freiband, B. 1937. Growth of the palate in the human fetus. *J. dent. Res.*, 16, 103–122.

Garn, S. M. 1955. Applications of pattern analysis to anthropometric data. *Ann. N. Y. Acad. Sci.*, 63, 537–552.

———. 1956. Comparison of pinch-caliper and X-ray measurements of skin plus subcutaneous fat. *Science*, 124, 178–179.

———, A. B. Lewis, and Dorothy W. Shoemaker. 1956. The sequence of calcification of the mandibular molar and permolar teeth. *J. dent. Res.*, 35, 555–561.

Garn, S. M., and Z. Shamir. 1958. *Methods for Research in Human Growth.* Springfield: Thomas.

Gavan, J. A., S. L. Washburn, and P. H. Lewis. 1952. Photography: An anthropometric tool. *Amer. J. phys. Anthrop.*, 10 n.s., 331–353.

Geoghegan, B. 1953. The determination of

body measurements, surface area and body volume by photography. *Amer. J. phys. Anthrop.*, 11 n.s., 97–120.

George, W. C. 1942. A presomite human embryo with chorda canal and prochordal plate. *Contr. Embryol., Carnegie Inst. Wash.*, No. 187, 1–7.

Gleiser, I., and E. E. Hunt. 1955. The permanent mandibular first molar; Its calcification, eruption and decay. *Amer. J. phys. Anthrop.*, 13, n.s., 253–283.

Goldberg, S. 1929. Biometrics of identical twins from the dental viewpoint. *J. dent. Res.*, 9, 363–409.

Goldstein, M. S. 1936. Changes in dimensions and form of the face and head with age. *Amer. J. phys. Anthrop.*, 22, 37–89.

———. 1937. Weight: A survey of differences of method, instruments. *Amer. J. phys. Anthrop.*, 22, 437–465.

———. 1939. Development of the head in the same individuals. *Hum. Biol.*, 11, 197–219.

———, and F. L. Stanton. 1936a. Anteroposterior movements of the teeth between 2 and 10 years. *Hum. Biol.*, 8, 161–197.

———. 1936b. Various types of occlusion and amounts of overbite in normal and abnormal occlusion between 2 and 12 years. *Int. J. Orthodont.*, 22, 549–569.

———. 1938. Development of the alveolar arches in normal and abnormal occlusion. *Hum. Biol.*, 10, 327–335.

Goodman, J. L. 1941. Physical growth of infants from birth to 3 months. Unpublished M. A. thesis, State Univer. Iowa.

Graber, T. M. 1958. Implementation of the roentgenographic cephalometric technique. *Amer. J. Orthodont.*, 44, 906–932.

Graves, W. W. 1925. *The relations of shoulder blade types to problems of mental and physical adaptability*. Edinburgh: Oliver and Boyd.

Gray, H. 1935. Chest depth. *Amer. J. phys. Anthrop.*, 20, 1–4.

———, and J. G. Ayres. 1931. *Growth in private school children*. Chicago: Univer. Chicago Press.

Greenhill, J. P. 1927. A human ovum approximately nineteen days old. *Surg., Gynec. Obstet.*, 45, 493–501.

Greenwood, J. M. 1891. Heights and weights of children. *Twentieth Ann. Rep. Bd. Educ. Kansas City Pub. Sch.*, 48–56.

Greulich, W. W. 1938. Anthropometry. In a handbook of methods for the study of adolescent children. *Monogr. Soc. Res. Child Develpm.*, 3, No. 2, 1–27.

———, R. I. Dorfman, H. R. Catchpole, C. I. Solomon, and C. S. Culotta. 1942. Somatic and endocrine studies of puberal and adolescent boys *Monogr. Soc. Res. Child Develpm.*, 7, No. 3.

Greulich, W. W., and S. Idell Pyle. 1950. *Radiographic atlas of skeletal development of the hand and wrist*. Stanford: Stanford Univer. Press.

Griffith, J. P. C. 1899. The weight in the first two years of life, with a description of a new weight chart. *N. Y. med. J.*, 69, 292–297.

Hall, W. S. 1895. The changes in the proportions of the human body during the period of growth. *J. R. anthrop. Inst.* 25, 21–46.

———. 1896. The first 500 days of a child's life. *Child-Study Monthly*, 2, 330–342.

Halverson, H. M. 1936. A photo-anthropometric method for the study of cranio-facial contour growth in infancy. *Amer. J. phys. Anthrop.*, 21, Supplement, 4.

Hammett, F. S. 1918. The relation between growth capacity and weight at birth. *Amer. J. Physiol.*, 45, 396–405.

Heard, O. O. 1957. Methods used in preparing and sectioning early embryos. *Contr. Embryol., Carnegie Inst. Wash.*, No. 242, 1–18.

Heath, C. W. 1945. *What people are: A study of normal young men*. Cambridge; Harvard Univer. Press.

Hejinian, Lucea, and Elise Hatt. 1929. The stem-length: Recumbent-length ratio as an index of body type in young children. *Amer. J. phys. Anthrop.*, 13, 287–307.

Hellman, M. 1930. Physiological treatment. *Dent. Cosmos*, 72, 578–595.

———. 1931. What about diagnosis and treatment of Class II malocclusion of the teeth? *Int. J. Orthodont.*, 17, 113–152.

———. 1932. An introduction to growth of

the human face from infancy to adulthood. *Int. J. Orthodont.*, **18**, 777–798.

Hellman, M. 1935. The face in its developmental career. *Dent. Cosmos*, 77, 685–699, 777–787.

———. 1936. Our third molar teeth; their eruption, presence and absence. *Dent. Cosmos*, 78, 750–762.

Herskovits, M. J. 1930. The anthropometry of the American Negro. *Columbia Univer. Contr. Anthrop.*, 11.

Hertig, A. T., and J. Rock. 1944. On the development of the early human ovum, with special reference to the trophoblast of the previllous stage: A description of 7 normal and 5 pathologic human ova. *Amer. J. Obstet. Gynec.*, 47, 149–184.

———, E. C. Adams, and W. J. Mulligan. 1954. On the preimplantation stages of the human ovum: A description of 4 normal and 4 abnormal specimens ranging from the second to the fifth day of development. *Contr. Embryol., Carnegie Inst. Wash.*, No. 240, 199–220.

Heuser, C. H. 1930. A human embryo of 14 pairs of somites. *Contr. Embryol., Carnegie Inst. Wash.*, No. 131, 135–154.

Higley, L. B. 1954. Cephalometric standards for children 4 to 8 years of age. *Amer. J. Orthodont.*, **40**, 51–59.

Hixon, E. H. 1958. Personal communication.

———. 1960. Cephalometrics and longitudinal research. *Amer. J. Orthodont.*, **46**, 36–42.

———, and R. E. Oldfather. 1958. Estimation of the sizes of unerupted cuspid and bicuspid teeth. *Angle Orthodont.*, **28**, 236–240.

Holcomb, A. E., and H. V. Meredith. 1956. Width of the dental arches at the deciduous canines in white children 4 to 8 years of age. *Growth*, **20**, 159–177.

Hopkins, J. W. 1947. Height and weight of Ottawa elementary school children of two socio-economic strata. *Hum. Biol.*, **19**, 68–82.

Hrdlicka, A. 1920. *Anthropometry*. Philadelphia: Wistar Institute.

———. 1936. The anthropometric committee of the American Association of Physical Anthropologists. *Amer. J. phys. Anthrop.*, 21, 287–300.

Humphreys, L. G. 1957. Characteristics of type concepts with special reference to Sheldon's typology. *Psychol. Bull.*, **54**, 218–228.

Hunt, E. E., Grace Cocke, and J. R. Gallagher. 1958. Somatotype and sexual maturation in boys: A method of developmental analysis. *Hum. Biol.*, **30**, 73–91.

———, and E. Giles. 1956. An evaluation of the photo-metric camera. *Amer. J. phys. Anthrop.*, **14** n.s., 429–436.

Hurme, V. O. 1948. Standards of variation in the eruption of the first six permanent teeth. *Child Develpm.*, **19**, 213–231.

Ingalls, N. W. 1918. A human embryo before the appearance of the myotomes. *Contr. Embryol., Carnegie Inst. Wash.*, No. 23, 111–134.

Irwin, L. W. 1937. A study of the tendency of school children to develop flat-footedness. *Res. Quart.*, **8**, 46–53.

Jackson, C. M. 1909. On the prenatal growth of the human body and the relative growth of the various organs and parts. *Amer. J. Anat.*, **9**, 119–165.

James, W. W., and A. T. Pitts. 1912. Some notes on the dates of eruption in 4,850 children, aged under 12. *Proc. Roy. Soc. Med.*, **5**, 80–98.

Jenss, Rachel M., and Susan P. Souther. 1940. Methods of assessing the physical fitness of children. *U. S. Dept. Labor, Children's Bureau*, No. 263.

Johnson, L. R. 1937. Habits and their control during childhood. *J. Amer. dent. Ass.*, **24**, 1409–1421.

Jung, F. T., and A. L. Shafton. 1935. The mammary gland in the normal adolescent male. *Proc. Soc. exp. Biol.*, **33**, 455–458.

Karpovich, P. V. 1951. An improved tape for measuring the chest girth. *Res. Quart.*, **22**, 334–336.

Kasius, R. V., A. Randall, W. T. Tompkins, and Dorothy G. Wiehl. 1957. Maternal and newborn nutrition studies at Philadelphia Lying-in Hospital. *Milbank mem. Fd. quart. Bull.*, **35**, 323–372.

Kavanagh, A. J., and O. W. Richards. 1942. Mathematical analysis of the relative growth of organisms. *Proc. Rochester Acad. Sci.*, **8**, 150–174.

Kelly, Harriet J. 1937. Anatomic age and its relation to stature. *Univer. Iowa Stud. Child Welf.*, 12, No. 5.

Kihlberg, J., and Koski, K. 1956. On basic principles in dental statistics. *Hum. Biol.*, 28, 365–375.

Knott, Virginia B. 1941. Physical measurement of young children. *Univer. Iowa Stud. Child Welf.*, 18, No. 3.

Koch, W., and Deborah Kaplan. 1950. Testing of trend in bodily development of school children. *Amer. J. Dis. Child.*, 80, 541–544.

Koski, K., and Eeva Hautala. 1952. On the frequency of shovel-shaped incisors in the Finns. *Amer. J. phys. Anthrop.*, 10 n.s., 127–132.

Krogman, W. M. 1941. *Growth of man*. Den Haag: Uitgeverij Junk.

———. 1950. A handbook of the measurement and interpretation of height and weight in the growing child. *Monogr. Soc. Res. Child Develpm.*, 13, No. 3.

———. 1951. The problem of "timing" in facial growth, with special reference to the period of the changing dentition. *Amer. J. Orthodont.*, 37, 253–276.

———, and V. Sassouni. 1957. *A syllabus in roentgenographic cephalometry*. Philadelphia: Center Res. Child Growth.

Kubitschek, P. E. 1932. Sexual development of boys. *J. nerv. ment. Dis.*, 76, 425–451.

Kunitomo, K. 1918. The development and reduction of the tail and of the caudal end of the spinal cord. *Contr. Embryol., Carnegie Inst. Wash.*, No. 26, 161–198.

Leslie, G. H. 1951. A biometrical study of the eruption of the permanent dentition of New Zealand children. *Monogr. Ministry Health New Zealand.*

Lewis, S. J., and I. A. Lehman. 1932. A quantitative study of the relation between certain factors in the development of the dental arch and the occlusion of the teeth. *Int. J. Orthodont.*, 18, 1015–1035.

Lincoln, Edith M., and R. Spillman. 1928. Studies on the hearts of normal children. *Amer. J. Dis. Child.*, 35, 791–810.

Litzenburg, J. C. 1933. A young human embryo of the early somite period. *Amer. J. Obstet. Gynec.*, 26, 519–529.

Lloyd-Jones, O. 1941. Race and stature: A study of Los Angeles school children. *Res. Quart.*, 12, 83–97.

Logan, W. H. G., and R. Kronfeld. 1933. Development of the human jaws and surrounding structures from birth to the age of 15 years. *J. Amer. dent. Ass.*, 20, 379–427.

McCloy, C. H. 1936. Appraising physical status: The selection of measurements. *Univer. Iowa Stud. Child Welfare*, 12, No. 2.

McKay, Hughina, and Mary B. Patton. 1935. A study of the food habits and physical development of preschool children over a two-year period. *Ohio Agri. Exp. Sta.*, Bull. 549.

McKern, T. W., and T. D. Stewart. 1957. Skeletal age changes in young American males. *Quartermaster Res. and Develpm. Command, Technical Report*, EP-45.

Macy, Icie G., and Harriet J. Kelly. 1957. *Chemical anthropology: A new approach to growth in children*. Chicago: Univer. Chicago Press.

Mainland, D. 1955. An experimental statistician looks at anthropometry. *Ann. N. Y. Acad. Scl.*, 63, 474–483.

Mall, F. P. 1906. On ossification centers in human embryos less than 100 days old. *Amer. J. Anat.*, 5, 433–458.

Malling-Hansen, R. 1886. *Perioden im Gewicht der Kinder und in der Sonnenwärme.* Kopenhagen: Tryde.

Maresh, Marion M. 1948. Growth of the heart related to bodily growth during childhood and adolescence. *Pediatrics*, 2, 382–404.

———. 1955. Linear growth of long bones of extremities from infancy through adolescence. *Amer. J. Dis. Child.*, 89, 725–742.

Martin, R. 1928. *Lehrbuch der Anthropologie: I.* Jena: Fischer.

———, and K. Saller. 1956. *Lehrbuch der Anthropologie in systematischer Darstellung*. Stuttgart: Fischer.

Meredith, H. V. 1935. The rhythm of physical growth. *Univer. Iowa Stud. Child Welf.*, 11, No. 3.

———. 1936. Physical growth of white children: A review of American research prior to 1900. *Monogr. Soc. Res. Child Develpm.*, 1, No. 2.

Meredith, H. V. 1939a. Length of head and neck, trunk, and lower extremities on Iowa City children aged 7 to 17 years. *Child Develpm.*, 10, 129–144.

———. 1939b. Stature of Massachusetts children of North European and Italian ancestry. *Amer. J. phys. Anthrop.*, 24, 301–346.

———. 1940. Comments on "The varieties of human physique." *Child Develpm.*, 11, 301–309.

———. 1941. Stature and weight of private school children in two successive decades. *Amer. J. phys. Anthrop.*, 28, 1–40.

———. 1943. Physical growth from birth to two years: I. Stature. *Univer. Iowa Stud. Child Welf.*, 19.

———. 1944. Human foot length from embryo to adult. *Hum. Biol.*, 16, 207–282.

———. 1946a. Order and age of eruption for the deciduous dentition. *J. dent. Res.*, 25, 43–66.

———. 1946b. Physical growth from birth to two years: II. Head circumference. *Child Develpm.*, 17, 1–61.

———. 1947. Length of upper extremities in Homo sapiens from birth through adolescence. *Growth*, 11, 1–50.

———. 1949. A "physical growth record" for use in elementary and high schools. *Amer. J. publ. Hlth*, 39, 878–885.

———. 1950. Birth order and body size. *Amer. J. phys. Anthrop.*, 8 n.s., 195–224.

———. 1951a. Relation between socioeconomic status and body size. *Amer. J. Dis. Child.*, 82, 702–709.

———. 1951b. Size and form of boys of U.S.A.-North European ancestry born and reared in Oregon. *Growth*, 15, 39–55.

———. 1953a. Growth in head width during the first twelve years of life. *Pediatrics*, 12, 411–429.

———. 1953b. Growth, physical. *Encyclopedia Americana*, 13, 499–502b.

———. 1954. Growth in bizygomatic face breadth during childhood. *Growth*, 18, 111–134.

———. 1955a. A longitudinal study of change in size and form of the lower limbs. *Growth*, 19, 89–106.

———. 1955b. Longitudinal anthropometric data in the study of individual growth. *Ann. N. Y. Acad. Sci.*, 63, 510–527.

Meredith, H. V. 1955c. Measuring the growth characteristics of school children. *J. Sch. Health*, 25, 267–277.

———. 1957a. A descriptive concept of physical development. In D. B. Harris (Ed.), *The concept of development*. Minneapolis: Univer. Minnesota Press, 109–122.

———. 1957b. Change in the profile of the osseous chin during childhood. *Amer. J. phys. Anthrop.*, 15 n.s., 247–252.

———. 1958. A time series analysis of growth in nose height during childhood. *Child Develpm.*, 29, 19–34.

———, and A. W. Brown. 1939. Growth in body weight during the first 10 days of postnatal life. *Hum. Biol.*, 11, 24–77.

Meredith, H. V., and Lois J. Carl. 1946. Individual growth in hip width. *Child Develpm.*, 17, 157–172.

Meredith, H. V., and G. C. Cox. 1954. Widths of the dental arches at the permanent first molars in children 9 years of age. *Amer. J. Orthodont.*, 40, 134–144.

Meredith, H. V., and S. S. Culp. 1951. Body form in childhood: Ratios quantitatively describing four slender-to-stocky continua on boys 4 to 8 years of age. *Child Develpm.*, 22, 3–14.

Meredith, H. V., and J. L. Goodman. 1941. A comparison of routine hospital records of birth stature with measurements of birth stature obtained for longitudinal research. *Child Develpm.*, 12, 175–181.

Meredith, H. V., and E. H. Hixon. 1954. Frequency, size, and bilateralism of Carabelli's tubercle. *J. dent. Res.*, 33, 435–440.

Meredith, H. V., and W. M. Hopp. 1956. A longitudinal study of dental arch width at the deciduous second molars. *J. dent. Res.*, 35, 879–889.

Meredith, H. V., and Virginia B. Knott. 1937. Changes in body proportions during infancy and the preschool years: I. The thoracic index. *Child Develpm.*, 8, 173–190.

———. 1938. Changes in body proportions during infancy and the preschool years: III. The skelic index. *Child Develpm.*, 9, 49–62.

———, and E. H. Hixon. 1958. Relation of the nasal and subnasal components of facial height in childhood. *Amer. J. Orthodont.*, **44**, 285–294.

Meredith, H. V., and E. Matilda Meredith. 1950. Annual increment norms for 10 measures of physical growth on children 4 to 8 years of age. *Child Develpm.*, **21**, 141–147.

———. 1953. The body size and form of present-day white elementary school children residing in west-central Oregon. *Child Develpm.*, **24**, 83–102.

———. 1958. Concomitant variation of measures of body size on boys 5 years of age and measures of growth rate for the ensuing sexennium. *Growth*, **22**, 1–8.

Meredith, H. V., and P. R. Sherbina. 1951. Body form in childhood: Ratios quantitatively describing three slender-to-stocky continua on girls 4 to 8 years of age. *Child Develpm.*, **22**, 275–283.

Moorrees, C. F. A., and R. B. Reed. 1954. Biometrics of crowding and spacing of the teeth in the mandible. *Amer. J. phys. Anthrop.*, **12**, n.s., 77–88.

———, S. O. Thomsen, E. Jensen, and P. K. Yen. 1957. Mesiodistal crown diameters of the deciduous and permanent teeth in individuals. *J. dent. Res.*, **36**, 39–47.

Morton, T. G. 1886. On unrecognized asymmetry of the lower limbs as a cause of lateral spinal curvature. *Philadelphia med. Times*, **16**, 743–746.

Nanda, R. S. 1955. The rates of growth of several facial components measured from serial cephalometric roentgenograms. *Amer. J. Orthodont.*, **41**, 658–673.

Newcomer, E. O., and H. V. Meredith. 1951. Eleven measures of body size on a 1950 sample of 15-year-old white schoolboys at Eugene, Oregon. *Hum. Biol.*, **23**, 24–40.

Newman, Katherine J., and H. V. Meredith. 1956. Individual growth in skeletal bigonial diameter during the childhood period from 5 to 11 years of age. *Amer. J. Anat.*, **99**, 157–187.

Noback, G. J. 1923. The developmental topography of the larynx, trachea and lungs in the fetus, new-born, infant and child. *Amer. J. Dis. Child.*, **26**, 515–533.

O'Brien, Ruth, M. A. Girshick, and Eleanor P. Hunt. 1941. Body measurements of American boys and girls for garment and pattern construction. *U. S. Bureau Home Econ.*, Misc. Pub. No. 366.

Odgers, P. N. B. 1937. An early human ovum (Thompson) in situ. *J. Anat.*, **71**, 161–168.

Palmer, C. E. 1930. Diurnal variations of height and weight in the human body during growth. *Anat. Rec.*, **45**, 234–235.

———. 1932. The relationship of erect body length to supine body length. *Hum. Biol.*, **4**, 262–271.

Phillips, R. W., and B. Y. Ito. 1951. Factors influencing the accuracy of reversible hydrocolloid impressions. *J. Amer. dent. Ass.*, **43**, 1–17.

Phillips, R. W., R. R. Price, and R. H. Reinking. 1953. The use of alginate for indirect restorations. *J. Amer. dent. Ass.*, **46**, 393–403.

Popovich, F. 1957. The Burlington orthodontic research center. *Amer. J. Orthodont.*, **43**, 291–293.

Potter, J. W., and H. V. Meredith. 1948. A comparison of two methods of obtaining biparietal and bigonial measurements. *J. dent. Res.*, **27**, 459–466.

Pryor, Helen B. 1936. Certain physical and physiological aspects of adolescent development in girls. *J. Pediat.*, **8**, 52–62.

Pryor, J. W. 1905. Development of the bones of the hand as shown by the x-ray method. *Bull. State College Kentucky*, Series 2, No. 5.

Pyle, S. Idell, and L. W. Sontag. 1943. Variability in onset of ossification in epiphyses and short bones of the extremities. *Amer. J. Roentgenol.* **49**, 795–798.

Pyle, S. Idell, and N. L. Hoerr. 1955. *Radiographic atlas of skeletal development of the knee*. Springfield, Illinois: Thomas.

Quo, Sung-Ken. 1953. Mathematical analysis of the growth of man. *Hum. Biol.*, **25**, 333–358.

Rasmussen, A. T. 1947. The growth of the hypophysis cerebri (pituitary gland) and its major subdivisions during childhood. *Amer. J. Anat.*, **80**, 95–116.

Redfield, Janet E., and H. V. Meredith. 1938. Changes in the stature and sitting height of preschool children in relation to rest in the recumbent position and activity following rest. *Child Develpm.*, **3**, 293–302.

Reynolds, E. E. 1944. Differential tissue growth in the leg during childhood. *Child Develpm.*, 15, 181–205.

———. 1947. The bony pelvis in prepuberal childhood. *Amer. J. phys. Anthrop.*, 5 n.s., 165–200.

———. 1948. Distribution of tissue components in the female leg from birth to maturity. *Anat. Rec.*, 100, 621–630.

———. 1951. The distribution of subcutaneous fat in childhood and adolescence. *Monogr. Soc. Res. Child Develpm.*, 15, No. 2.

———, and Janet V. Wines. 1948. Individual differences in physical changes associated with adolescence in girls. *Amer. J. Dis. Child.*, 75, 329–350.

Richey, H. G. 1937. The relation of accelerated, normal and retarded puberty to the height and weight of school children. *Monogr. Soc. Res. Child Develpm.*, 2, No. 1.

Ritt, Estelle F., and Ruth O. Sawtell. 1930. Growth studies by roentgen ray. *Amer. J. phys. Anthrop.*, 14, 1–8.

Robinow, M., Verna L. Leonard, and Margaret Anderson. 1943. A new approach to the quantitative analysis of children's posture. *J. Pediat.*, 22, 655–663.

Rogers, A. P. 1922. Stimulating arch development by the exercise of the masseter-temporal group of muscles. *Int. J. Orthodont.*, 8, 61–64.

Salzmann, J. A. 1945. The Maxillator: A new instrument for measuring the Frankfort-mandibular base angle, the incisor-mandibular base angle, and other component parts of the face and jaws. *Amer. J. Orthodont.*, 31, 608–617.

Sassouni, V. 1957. Palatoprint, physioprint, and roentgenographic cephalometry, as new methods in human identification. *J. Forensic Sci.*, 2, 429–443.

Sawyer, M., R. H. Stone, and E. F. DuBois. 1916. Clinical calorimetry: Further measurements of the surface area of adults and children. *Arch. intern. Med.*, 17, 855–862.

Scammon, R. E. 1919. Some graphs and tables illustrating the growth of the human stomach. *Amer. J. Dis. Child.*, 17, 395–422.

———. 1927a. The first seriatim study of human growth. *Amer. J. phys. Anthrop.*, 10, 329–336.

Scammon, R. E. 1927b. The literature on the growth and physical development of the fetus, infant, and child. *Anat. Rec.*, 35, 241–267.

———. 1929. The measurement and analysis of human growth. *Proc. Third Conf. Res. Child Develpm.*, 1–24.

———. 1930. The ponderal growth of the extremities of the human fetus. *Amer. J. phys. Anthrop.*, 15, 111–121.

———. 1936. Interpolation formulae for the growth of the human brain and its major parts in the first year of postnatal life. *Child Develpm.*, 7, 149–160.

———, and L. A. Calkins. 1929. *The development and growth of the external dimensions of the human body in the fetal period.* Minneapolis: Univer. Minn. Press.

Scammon, R. E., and M. B. Hesdorffer. 1935. Growth of human nervous system. II. Indices of relation of cerebral volume to surface in developmental period. *Proc. Soc. exp. Biol.*, 33, 418–421.

Schonfeld, W. A., and G. W. Beebe. 1942. Normal growth and variation in the male genitalia from birth to maturity. *J. Urol.*, 48, 759–777.

Schubert, J., and R. E. Lapp. 1957. *Radiation: What it is and how it affects you.* New York: Viking.

Schultz, A. H. 1919. Changes in fetuses due to formalin preservation. *Amer. J. phys. Anthrop.*, 2, 35–41.

———. 1920. An apparatus for measuring the newborn. *Johns Hopk. Hosp. Bull.*, 31, 131–132.

———. 1926. Fetal growth of man and other primates. *Quart. Rev. Biol.*, 1, 465–521.

———. 1929. The technique of measuring the outer body of human fetuses and of primates in general. *Contr. Embryol., Carnegie Inst. Wash.*, No. 117, 213–257.

Schwartz, L., R. H. Britten, and L. R. Thompson. 1928. Studies in physical development and posture. *U. S. Publ. Hlth Bull.*, No. 179.

Schwarz, R. 1933. Individual measurements of the face and jaws before and during orthodontic treatment. *Int. J. Orthodont.*, 19, 22–54.

Seckel, H. P. G., W. W. Scott, and E. P. Benditt. 1949. Six examples of precocious sexual development. *Amer. J. Dis. Child.*, 78, 484–515.

Sheldon, W. H., S. S. Stevens, and W. B. Tucker. 1940. *The varieties of human physique.* New York: Harper.

Shinn, Milicent W. 1893. Notes on the development of a child. *Univer. California Stud.*, 1, Nos. 1 and 2.

Sholl, D. A. 1954. "Regularities in growth curves, including rhythms and allometry." In E. J. Boell (Ed.), *Dynamics of growth processes.* Princeton: Princeton Univer. Press. Pp. 224–241.

Shuttleworth, F. K. 1934. Van Dyke's data on the relation of menstruation to growth of girls. *Sch. Rev.*, 42, 210–212.

———. 1937. Sexual maturation and the physical growth of girls age 6 to 19. *Monogr. Soc. Res. Child Develpm.*, 2, No. 5.

———. 1939. The physical and mental growth of girls and boys age 6 to 19 in relation to age at maximum growth. *Monogr. Soc. Res. Child Develpm.*, 4, No. 3.

———. 1951. The adolescent period: A pictorial atlas. *Monogr. Soc. Res. Child Develpm.*, 14, No. 2.

Sillman, J. H. 1951. Serial study of good occlusion from birth to 12 years of age. *Amer. J. Orthodont.*, 37, 481–507.

Simmons, Katherine. 1944. The Brush Foundation study of child growth and development. II. Physical growth. *Monogr. Soc. Res. Child Develpm.*, 9, No. 37.

———, and T. W. Todd. 1938. Growth of well children: Analysis of stature and weight. *Growth*, 2, 93–134.

Skinner, E. W. 1954. *The science of dental materials.* Philadelphia: Saunders.

———, and F. B. Carlisle. 1956. The use of alginate impression materials in the Sears' hydrocolloid impression technique. *J. pros. Dent.*, 6, 405–411.

Skinner, E. W., and N. E. Hoblit. 1956. A study of the accuracy of hydrocolloid impressions. *J. pros. Dent.*, 6, 80–86.

Slyker, F., B. M. Hammil, M. W. Poole, T. B. Cooley, and Icie G. Macy. 1937. Relationship between vitamin D intake and linear growth in infants. *Proc. Soc. exp. Biol.*, 37, 499–502.

Speck, N. T. 1950. A longitudinal study of developmental changes in human lower dental arches. *Angle Orthodont.*, 20, 215–228.

Spiller, J. E. 1913. A case showing expansion of the upper arch without treatment. *Dent. Rec.*, 33, 393–394.

Stanford, R. W., and J. Vance. 1955. The quantity of radiation received by the reproductive organs of patients during routine diagnostic X-ray examinations. *Brit. J. Radiol.*, 28, 266–273.

Steggerda, M. 1942. Anthropometry of the living: A study on checking of techniques. *Anthrop. Briefs*, No. 2, 7–15.

———. 1949. Anthropometric instruments. *Amer. J. phys. Anthrop.*, 7 n.s., 473–474.

Stevenson, P. H. 1924. Age order of epipyseal union in man. *Amer. J. phys. Anthrop.*, 7, 53–93.

Stolz, H. R., and Lois M. Stolz. 1951. *Somatic development of adolescent boys.* New York: Macmillan.

Stratz, C. H. 1909. *Der Körper des Kindes und seine Pflege.* Stuttgart: Enke.

Streeter, G. L. 1920. Weight, sitting height, head size, foot length, and menstrual age of the human embryo. *Contr. Embryol., Carnegie Inst. Wash.*, No. 55, 143–170.

———. 1942. Developmental horizons in human embryos. *Contr. Embryol., Carnegie Inst. Wash.*, No. 197, 211–245.

Stuart, H. C. 1934. Standards of physical development for reference in clinical appraisement. *J. Pediat.*, 5, 194–209.

———. 1939. Studies from the Center for Research in Child Health and Development, Harvard Univer. *Monogr. Soc. Res. Child Develpm.*, 4, No. 1.

———, and Penelope H. Dwinell. 1942. The growth of bone, muscle and overlying tissues in children 6 to 10 years of age as revealed by studies of roentgenograms of the leg area. *Child Develpm.*, 13, 195–213.

Stuart, H. C., Penelope Hill, and Constance Shaw. 1940. The growth of bone, muscle and overlying tissues as revealed by studies of roentgenograms of the leg area. *Monogr. Soc. Res. Child Develpm.*, 5, No. 3.

Stunz, Dorothy I. 1934. X-ray technic for children. *Radiology*, 22, 694–700.

Suk, V. 1919. Eruption and decay of permanent teeth in whites and Negroes. *Amer. J. phys. Anthrop.*, 2, 351–388.

Sumner, Emma E., and Jessie Whitacre. 1931. Some factors affecting accuracy in the collection of data on the growth in weight of school children. *J. Nutr.*, 4, 15–23.

Sweeny, Mary E., Helen King, C. A. Wilson, and Lucea Hejinian. 1929. *A method of recording the posture of preschool children.* Detroit: Merrill-Palmer.

Tanner, J. M. 1951. Some notes on the reporting of growth data. *Hum. Biol.*, 23, 93–159.

———. 1952. The assessment of growth and development in children. *Arch. Dis. Childh.*, 27, 10–33.

———, and J. S. Weiner. 1949. The reliability of the photogrammetric method of anthropometry. *Amer. J. phys. Anthrop.*, 7 n.s., 145–186.

Tanner, J. M., and R. H. Whitehouse. 1955. The Harpenden skinfold caliper. *Amer. J. phys. Anthrop.*, 13 n.s., 743–746.

———. 1957. The Harpenden anthropometer. *Amer. J. phys. Anthrop.*, 15 n.s., 277–280.

———, and J. H. Powell. 1958. Armadillo: A protective clothing as a shield from X-radiation. *Lancet*, 2, 779–780.

Thompson, Helen. 1929. A measuring-board for infants. *Amer. J. phys. Anthrop.*, 13, 281–286.

Thorndike, R. L. 1951. Reliability. In E. F. Lindquist (Ed.), *Educational Measurement.* Washington, D. C.: American Council on Education, 560–620.

Thurow, R. C. 1951. Cephalometric methods in research and private practice. *Angle Orthodont.*, 21, 104–116.

Tildesley, Miriam L. 1931. Orthodontic standards. *Int. J. Orthodont.*, 17, 656–671.

Tilton, J. P., 1930. Volume measurement as an aid to the study of body build. *J. genet. Psychol.*, 37, 536–540.

Todd, T. W. 1937. *Atlas of skeletal maturation.* St. Louis: Mosby.

Townsend, C. W. 1887. The so-called physi-

ological loss in infants. *Boston med. surg. J.*, 116, 157–160.

Trim, P. T., and H. V. Meredith. 1952. Body form in Homo sapiens: A study of five anthropometric ratios on white boys 15 years of age. *Growth*, 16, 1–14.

Tyler, F. T. 1954. Organismic growth: P-technique in the analysis of longitudinal growth data. *Child Develpm.*, 25, 83–88.

Van Dusen, C. R. 1939. An anthropometric study of the upper extremities of children. *Hum. Biol.*, 11, 277–284.

Van Dyke, G. E. 1930. The effect of the advent of puberty on the growth in height and weight of girls. *Sch. Rev.*, 38, 211–221.

Vickers, Vernette S., and H. C. Stuart. 1943. Anthropometry in the pediatrician's office. *J. Pediat.*, 22, 115–170.

Wallis, Ruth S. 1931. How children grow. *Univer. Iowa Stud. Child Welf.*, 5, No. 1.

West, C. M. 1930. Description of an embryo of eight somites. *Contr. Embryol., Carnegie Inst. Wash.*, No. 119, 25–35.

Whitacre, Jessie. 1934. Standing heights of school children as determined by two techniques. *Amer. J. phys. Anthrop.*, 18, 457–465.

———. 1935. Seasonal variations of growth in weight and height of Texas school children. *Texas Agri. Exp. Sta. Bull.*, No. 510.

Wilmer, H. A., and R. E. Scammon. 1945. The use of iconometrography in graphic exposition. *Hum. Biol.*, 17, 314–339.

Wilson, C. A., Mary E. Sweeny, Rachel Stutsman, Leone E. Chesire, and Elise Hatt. 1930. *The Merrill-Palmer standards of physical and mental growth.* Detroit: Merrill-Palmer.

Wilson, E. B. 1952. *An introduction to scientific research.* New York: McGraw-Hill.

Wilson, K. M. 1945. A normal human ovum of 16 days development (the Rochester Ovum). *Contr. Embryol., Carnegie Inst. Wash.*, No. 202, 101–106.

Witschi, E. 1956. *Development of vertebrates.* Philadelphia: Saunders.

Woodbury, N. F. S. 1952. Dial spreading caliper. *Amer. J. phys. Anthrop.*, 10 n.s., 223–226.

Woods, G. A. 1950. Changes in width dimensions between certain teeth and facial points during growth. *Amer. J. Orthodont.*, 36, 676–700.

Yates, F. 1950. The place of statistics in the study of growth and form. *Proc. Roy. Soc., London*, 137, 479–488.

Young, R. W. 1957. Postnatal growth of the frontal and parietal bones in white males. *Amer. J. phys. Anthrop.*, 15 n.s., 367–386.

Zuckerman, S. 1955. Age changes in the basicranial axis of the human skull. *Amer. J. phys. Anthrop.*, 13 n.s., 521–539.

chapter 6

# Chemical
# and
# Physiologic Growth

Icie G. Macy
Harriet J. Kelly
*Merrill-Palmer Institute*

One of the great mysteries of life is the power of growth, that harmonious development of composite organs and tissues from simple protoplasmic cells, with the ultimate formation of a complex organism with its orderly adjustment of structure and function. Equally mysterious is that wonderful power of rehabilitation by which the cells of the body are able to renew their living substance and to maintain their ceaseless activity through a period, it may be of fourscore years, before succumbing to the inevitable fate that awaits all organic structure. This bodily activity, visible and invisible, is the result of a third mysterious process, more or less continuous as long as life endures, of chemical disintegration, decomposition, and oxidation, by which arises the evolution of energy to maintain the heat of the body and the power of mental and physical work. These three main functions constitute the purpose of nutrition. . . . Development, growth, and vital activity all depend upon the availability of food in proper amounts and proper quality.
Chittenden (1907)

Life is a chemical function. Lavoisier, the pioneering chemist, brought together the isolated chemical, biologic, and physical discoveries leading to this concept more than a century ago. The chemistry of life and growth may be studied in the laboratory or in living organisms. Both methods are of fundamental significance to the study of biologic growth of man.

Child development includes two types of growth, the one being visible, the other invisible. *Visible growth* is characterized by increase in the body size and change in its shape and proportions. Chemical and physiologic growth, on the other hand, is described as *invisible growth*, since it results from a sequence of biochemical and physiologic adjustments involving integrated chemical, metabolic, and functional reactions by which the incorporation of foodstuff as new tissues, or as renewal of the body, may take place. Invisible growth, therefore, is concerned with the subtler chemical, metabolic, and physiologic functions and adaptations of the enlarging organs and tissues and fundamental changes in body structure and composition—it is the bulwark of physical growth. Visible and invisible growth coexist—neither can exist in isolation.

In spite of the great complexities of chemical and physiologic growth, many aspects of which are only partially understood, it is a basic and integral part of child development and a

Recent explorations of chemical and physiologic growth were supported in part by grants from the Williams-Waterman Fund, The Nutrition Foundation, Inc., The Kresge Foundation, Swift and Company, and the National Institute of Health for the Study of Rheumatic Diseases.

necessary function to a rational program of improvement of health, growth, and development. Methods of assessment, therefore, are of great consequence and significance. The purpose of this chapter is to present a brief consideration of the importance of methods in the study of child development concerned with chemical and physiologic growth together with some illustrative chemical, metabolic, and functional reactions involved therein and factors affecting them.

The massive scientific literature records results from carefully designed research endeavors embracing a majority of the chemical, biologic, physiologic, and medical fields and is available to those desiring all the facts; therefore, only a few references pertinent to this discussion are cited here. Our insight into the processes of life may be enriched by many noteworthy communications pertaining to the chemical aspects of life (Hopkins, 1933; Mendel, 1923; Needham, 1942), to growth (Brody, 1945; Forbes, 1952; Macy, 1942, 1946, 1951; Moulton, 1923) and development (Willier, Weiss, and Hamburger, 1955), to the physiologic adjustment of the body to inherent biologic function (Adolph, 1943; Barcroft, 1934; Benedict, 1938; Bernard, 1865; Cannon, 1932; Haldane, 1931), to biochemical individuality (Loeb, 1947; Williams, 1956), to the dynamic hormonal, nutritional, and biochemical changes characterizing the progressive stages in the life cycle (Macy and Kelly, 1957; Mitchell et al., 1945; Spray and Widdowson, 1950; Widdowson et al., 1951), and to body composition (Behnke, 1941–1942, 1953; Brozek,

Mori, and Keys, 1958; Cowgill, 1958; Friis-Hansen et al., 1951; Hunt and Giles, 1956; Keys and Brozek, 1953; Keys et al., 1950; McCance and Widdowson, 1951) and the structure of the body (Reynolds, 1950; Stuart and Sobel, 1946; Tanner, 1953, 1955; Todd, 1937) as it grows and matures.

## CHEMICAL BASIS OF LIVING GROWTH

Living growth is a process characterized by the utilization of nutrient substances differing more or less from those composing the body. The organism must be capable of taking the relatively complex components of foodstuffs, converting them into smaller and simpler molecules, selecting those required, and then synthesizing or refashioning the simpler molecules into complex chemical units that are characteristic of the organism itself. By the processes of digestion, food is first broken down and changed to a suitable form for active participation in body chemistry and is then assimilated. Each of the nutrients absorbed, retained, and utilized contributes to the formation, maintenance, and function of parts of the body or the whole of the organism. Living growth constitutes the increase in mass of communities of cells in the tissues and organs that form the mosaic of the different metabolizing systems by which the intricate biologic processes take place.

The last century was enriched by many epoch-making discoveries leading to the energy concept of foods, to the evaluation of different foods on the basis of their chemical and biological properties, and to the modern theory that foodstuffs must furnish not one but more than 60 different kinds of nutrient substances known to be present in the body and necessary for the maintenance of life and support of growth and health. Concurrently, biochemical discoveries led to a new concept, which envisions a dynamic state of the body constituents (replacing the classic picture of a fixed system), to extensive knowledge concerning increased dietary requirements and adjustment of body composition with growth, and to the metabolic mechanisms involved in changing physiologic functions, adaptations, and needs during succeeding phases in the life cycle.

Modern biology envisions the living tissues to be in a dynamic state of building and tearing down (Schoenheimer, 1942). This interchanging of elements is an essential feature of physiologic and chemical growth, since it permits the young organism to change in biochemical complexity and organization and to progress towards chemical maturity of body composition (Moulton, 1923) and maturity of structure and function. The degree of difference in the quality and intensity of the irreproducible biologic reactions due to environmental change, such as diet, however, depends in large measure on the inheritance, the physiologic and biochemical state, and the nutritive background of the individual.

The proper application of existing methods and the development of new and more precise ones for fundamental studies of chemical and physiologic growth and nutritional adequacy is of public health concern and the basis for extending knowledge of the interrelated processes of growth. The interpretation of the data collected in such methodologic studies must take into consideration many factors, such as nutritive growth requirements, food intake, nutritional chemistry, hormonal and other factors.

***Growth Requirements.*** World-wide observations have established the fact that inadequate diets and malnutrition may warp body and mind and retard growth. Growth increases nutritive requirements, and its progress is influenced by nutritional state, hormonal activities, and other factors.

*Food factors* are basic to growth and developmental progress. The first requisite for optimal inherent growth is an adequate food supply. A nutritionally adequate diet provides the essential elements and compounds, in proper proportion, for the manufacture of new body tissues, for maintenance of nutritional stability with a "steady state" of internal environment, for rebuilding existing body structures, and for the energy requirements of basic metabolic processes and activity.

*Nutritional factors* determine how the body uses the individual nutrients in the construction of new organs and body tissues and at the same time maintains the physiologic functions commensurate with biologic age and increasing body size. Hence inquiries into physical, chemical, and physiologic growth cannot be satisfied alone by the study of the food eaten but must take into consideration nutritional factors.

The development and maintenance of healthy body structures depend on the supply of many food substances and the fate of the individual nutrients as they pass through the metabolic processes of digestion, absorption, and excretion or utilization. In fulfillment of growth and developmental needs, there must be sufficient energy present in the diet to meet the requirements of activity, of maintenance of body temperature and basal heat production, and of full utilization of the essential amino acids, vitamins, and minerals in the metabolic enzyme systems for the synthesis of protoplasm—true living growth. If the diet is short in supply of energy, the protein or its constituent amino acids cannot be utilized to the fullest extent, and this condition may lead to the sacrifice of protein of the body for fuel to provide for activity requirements, thus depriving the enzyme, hormonal, and other essential metabolic activities of essential protein.

Prolonged use of marginal diets may force the body into a lowered nutritional and functional state. Depressed nutritional states may develop during any epoch in the life cycle and influence the health, growth, and dietary requirements in subsequent periods. Lowered levels of metabolic performance in the body involve food intake, the processes of utilization, body functions, endocrine and vitamin balances, physical environment, attitudes, and social conditions. A relatively slight change in the nature of one of many chemical reactions proceeding in the body may result in an alteration of digestion, absorption, or utilization of the food factors and thereby change the course and intensity of inherent growth by failure to nourish the body adequately. Each individual, therefore, has a biochemical individuality with a characteristic physiologic capacity to utilize and store chemical substances from ingested foodstuff determined by heredity, nutritional state, eating and elimination habits, and physical and mental state; and these factors must be considered in the interpretation of data obtained for the assessment of chemical and physiologic growth.

*Hormonal factors* influence different steps in metabolism either directly or indirectly by enzyme production and interaction of individual vitamins, amino acids, and minerals. The growth hormone produced during infancy and childhood increases nitrogen metabolism in the body in the form of protein and is an integral part of growth and synthesis of protoplasm. It aids in nitrogen or protein conservation when dietary protein and carbohydrates are in short supply. The basal metabolic rate and protein synthesis (Sokoloff and Kaufman, 1959) are influenced by thyroid function. Other hormones play equally essential roles in nutrition and growth. It is significant that vitamins and amino acids are used as precursors of the hormones.

*Other factors* influence the requirements for growth. The chemical composition of the body changes from rich protoplasmic growth during infancy to relatively more equalized skeletal and protoplasmic growth with changing fat deposition during childhood. Young infants retain a higher percentage of protein fed and are more efficient in their utilization of it than older infants and children. New physiologic mechanisms are continually coming into activity, while others are receding, so that the child may cope with changing internal and external conditions as developmental alterations take place. As the child grows, his organs and body systems are unremitting in their progress toward full performance of physiologic activities peculiar to them in mature or adult life, some developing at a faster rate than others (Scammon, 1930). The composition of protoplasmic growth reaches chemical maturity (Moulton, 1923) and mature hydration (Hunt and Giles, 1956) during childhood and remains more or less constant thereafter.

Increase in visible size is not self-contained but occurs amid a multitude of chemical changes and additions for enlargement of tissues, organs, and the body structure as a whole. These are accompanied by modifications in functional capacity and alterations in internal environment that permit full realization of the inherent capacity of the child for growth and development commensurate with his nutritional status and stage of development in the life cycle. If the nutritive requirements for growth and activity are not met in full measure, the link between harmonious blending of chemical growth and physiologic functioning is disturbed, and the inherent healthy pattern of growth and body composition cannot be maintained. Excess of some nutrients may also cause untoward results. Biochemical individuality is exhibited in food intake and nutritional needs, in blood composition, body structure and composition, in hormonal activity and enzyme levels, and in digestive, absorptive, and excretory activities.

As the methodologies for assessing chemical and physiologic growth reach greater precision and scope, cumulative evidence is emerging to explain in part some of the underlying individual differences that anthropologists, physiologists, and social scientists have observed to exist among boys and girls of the same race, of comparable chronologic and anatomic age, with similar activity, and mental and intellectual acumen, and living in similar economic and social conditions or circumstances.

**Relation between Internal and External Environment.** The organism is ultimately dependent on external conditions and on the integrative processes mediating the relationship between the organism and external environment. Although the blood provides a homeostatic internal environment, it bears to actual cell environment a relation similar to that of the external environment but of a much closer and well-defined sort.

The cells within the body are bathed by fluids that constitute an internal environment, the *milieu interieur* of Claude Bernard (1865). Life and growth of cells are possible only if the composition of these fluids varies within narrow limits. Haldane (1931) emphasized the maintenance of body structure and the fact that structure and activity cannot be separated, a phenomenon that is the active manifestation of the persistent whole life of the organism. Barcroft (1934) observed that gross variations in internal environment do not result in devastating disturbances in such body functions as heart action, muscular efficiency, and kidney function; rather, variations in the internal environment may result in subtle mental disturbances and lack of ability to concentrate and to think logically. The implications are that we can expect to find normal physiologic function and intellectual development only in an organism whose blood and lymph, bathing all the living cells in the body, are able through vital biological mechanisms to preserve constant the conditions of life in the internal environment and a high level of nutritional state.

## Methodologies

Knowledge of the chemistry of the body rests on measurements of the concentration of organic and inorganic components in the body fluids: the food intake, the absorption and retention of nutrients in the body, primarily by the metabolic balance procedure, and the major chemical components of the body (protoplasm, fat, and water). Some procedures (Brozek, 1956, 1957; Jolliffe et al., 1950; Sinclair, 1948; Spector et al., 1954) used to study nutritional status and chemical and physiological growth in relation to physical growth and health are presented in Table 6-1. These procedures are based on the application of clinical, dietary, biochemical, physiologic, and metabolic techniques. Some are direct and others are indirect measurements, which, either singly or in combination, give an evaluation of nutriture, invisible growth, and physiologic function.

### RESEARCH DESIGN

*Purpose and Degree of Accuracy Desired.* There are many phases of chemical and physiologic growth research, each of which may be approached by a variety of different scientific routes, by procedures and methods of varying degrees of accuracy, and by involving a few or large number of subjects for short or long periods of time. The first requisite, therefore, for designing an investigation is to establish a clearly delineated purpose and the degree of accuracy necessary to accomplish the objectives. The requirements must be reconciled with proper application within the framework of the available resources of time, finances, space, trained personnel, facilities, and equipment. As a matter of fact, this initial state is the most challenging one in research, inasmuch as it requires an appraisal of existing attacks and current procedures in use, an evaluation of available facilities and resources, and the development of new, more specific, and accurate methods that will accomplish an unequivocal solution to the problem undertaken with the least expenditure of time, effort, and cost.

### CHEMICAL AND PHYSIOLOGICAL INVISIBLE GROWTH

The metabolic balance method is the core procedure in a comprehensive study of nutrition and chemical growth. The description of the method and the use of the knowledge gained (Macy, 1942, p. 5–6) is presented thus:

The sole means of determining total nutritive requirement of the vital functions of a living body is the metabolic balance, in which are determined the actual amounts of nitrogen, calcium,

**TABLE 6-1. METHODOLOGIES FOR ASSESSING INVISIBLE GROWTH AND NUTRITURE**

I. Assessment of Chemical and Physiological Growth
 A. Cumulative chemical growth determined by the metabolic balance method.
  1. Determination of difference between analyzed nutrients in the food consumed and their outgo in urine and feces over successive five-day balance periods. These may include proteins (nitrogen or amino acids), heat of combustion of carbohydrates, fats, and total energy; total electropositive minerals (calcium, magnesium, sodium, and potassium); total electronegative minerals (phosphorus, chlorine, and sulfur); and any one of a number of vitamins.
  2. Relationship of nutrients in metabolism: ratios of calcium to phosphorus, nitrogen to phosphorus, nitrogen to potassium, nitrogen to sulfur, phosphorus to potassium; excess anions or cations stored; protein as related to energy, or energy from carbohydrate and fat.
 B. Physiological growth.
  1. Basal oxygen consumption and basal heat production.
  2. Nitrogen distribution in twenty-four hour samples of urine.
   a. Urinary nitrogen partition: total nitrogen, urea nitrogen, creatinine nitrogen, creatine nitrogen, uric acid nitrogen, ammonia nitrogen, and estimated basal nitrogen.
   b. Relationship of total nitrogen excretion to creatinine, to the creatinine coefficient, to sulfur, and to carbon.
II. Assessment of Body Composition
 A. In vivo analysis.
  1. Total body water and its component parts, intracellular and extracellular water; protoplasmic mass; and total body fat.
  2. Evaluation from basal heat production, specific gravity, creatinine excretion, nitrogen and mineral metabolic balances; nitrogen and mineral content of blood serum and erythrocytes.
 B. In vitro analysis.
  Direct chemical analysis of whole cadavers or parts.
III. Assessments of Nutritional Adequacy and Status (Nutriture)
 A. Nutritional status surveys—application of integrated clinical, dietary, and biochemical observations.
 B. Nutritional anthropology—application of body measurements with emphasis on body composition.
 C. Chemical anthropology—evaluation of nutrient metabolism, absorption, retention, and metabolite excretion in relation to physical growth and physiological function.
 D. Nutritional status as it relates to fundamental problems of behavior.
IV. Physical Measurements
 A. Anthropometric measurements including body weight, length, width, circumference, and subcutaneous tissue.
 B. Estimation of body build.

phosphorus, and other equally essential dietary constituents retained in the body. This procedure includes quantitative chemical analyses for components of all food, urine, and feces; the difference between the ingesta and egesta, over a definite period of time, is the quantity apparently retained in the body for its physiological activity. The mineral metabolic balance, so-called, is not a true balance, inasmuch as losses through the skin are unmeasurable over long periods of time or under usual environmental conditions. Tears, sweat, oral and nasal secretions constitute an additional potential source of mineral losses, mainly of chlorine, sodium, potassium, and sulfur. From the relatively more accurate retention values for calcium, phosphorus, and magnesium, the excretion of chlorine, sodium, and potassium through the skin can be approximated.

Further it is stated:

The greater the number of dietary components determined, the greater the knowledge obtained about the relative proportions of the different substances being incorporated into the body, and the greater the opportunity for determining the controlling factors in the mechanisms by which the materials are being used. It is possible to predict, from a knowledge of the amount of sodium, potassium, and chloride retained in a given time, the distribution of body water between its two constituent forms, extracellular and intracellular water; from the amount or relative proportions of calcium and phosphorus stored, the bone or hard tissue can be estimated; from the amount and proportions of nitrogen, sulfur, phosphorus, and potassium retained, we can estimate the relative amount of soft tissues being formed. . . . From a knowledge of the retention of positive and negative minerals, it is possible to determine with considerable accuracy whether the physiological tendency is in the direction of soft or hard tissue formation.

*In planning a balance study*, the investigator must choose the methods, the nutrients, and the procedures of analysis that will provide data most pertinent to the objectives of his research. Since restrictions due to limitations of staff, equipment, facilities, and finanical resources frequently are encountered in metabolic work, these considerations should be met in the planning stage rather than after initiation of the routine of the investigation.

*The metabolic balance type of study* does not have the *accuracy* that chemistry or physics may have, yet it furnishes significant information on current metabolic performance, efficiency of food utilization, and biochemical and metabolic responses to the physiologic stress of growth with its changing nutritive needs. A detailed study of the paths of excretion provides additional information concerning the utilization of several chemical elements and serves as an integral part of the study of nutrition and growth. An investigation may involve three or four nutrients, or in a more comprehensive study of growth there may be included the study of the intake and excretion of as many as a dozen or more chemical substances by a number of children, supplemented by observations and determinations that may be classified as pediatric, anatomic, psychometric, physiologic, anthropometric, roentgenologic, and chemical (Macy, 1942; Macy and Kelly, 1957).

Isotopically and radioactive labeled elements are being used in biochemical tracer research to extend biological knowledge and to define more clearly the metabolic pathways in the body. Isotopes may exist in nature or may be created artificially by splitting the atom by physical force and thereby changing the neutron-proton composition of the nuclei. Although the variation in the composition of the nucleus does not affect the chemical properties of the element, it does introduce important differences in physical properties that serve as the basis of identification or determination of these substances in metabolic materials, such as food, urine, and feces. By separation in pure form the isotopic labeled portions of the material may be determined quantitatively, whereas the radioactive isotopes may be determined in smaller quantities by measuring their radiations by actual counting devices. Radioactive substances, however, must be used with caution.

As an illustration of the use of the metabolic balance method in the study of growth, let us consider nitrogen balance. The retention of nitrogen by a child who is provided with adequate energy to meet the demands of activity and growth is evidence of increasing protoplasmic tissue, the center of metabolically active living growth. The construction of protoplasmic tissue involves particularly the assimilation of nitrogen, sulfur, phosphorus, calcium, magnesium, potassium, sodium, and chlorine. The nitrogen, the sulfur, and part of the phosphorus are used largely as structural components in the protein combinations of body cells, whereas potassium, sodium, chlorine, and some of the phosphorus serve a functional purpose in maintaining the electroneutrality of the tissues and an equitable osmotic environment for the proper distribution of intracellular and extracellular fluids. On the other hand, calcium, magnesium, and the remaining phosphorus are associated with other elements, functioning largely in the growth and maintenance of the skeleton. Beyond a small amount of essential lipids for cellular structure and function, the accumulation of fat in the body is an additive but does not constitute metabolically active true living growth.

In a consideration of physical growth, it has been stated that the study of growth is a study of a moving point,

and no measurement which does not allow us to measure the movement in time in relation to other values can be thoroughly successful (White House Conference, 1932). A study of growth, therefore, is enhanced by multiple periodic measures. This holds true also in the chemistry of growth, in which single and multiple measurements of several elements at succeeding levels of growth provide results which permit the study of the movement of growth through the relationship of one element to another, thus revealing more clearly the changes taking place (Allison, 1958; Macy and Kelly, 1957).

In children there is a delicate balance between the dynamics of energy and protein metabolism during protoplasmic growth as demonstrated by the metabolic balance method of nitrogen retention, by the twenty-four hour urinary excretion of total nitrogen and creatinine, and by the determination of the basal metabolic rate. Basal metabolism and urinary creatinine have been associated in one way or another with the protoplasmic mass contained in the body. Records of oxygen consumption, urinary creatinine excretion, and nitrogen storage, singly or together, are integral parts in the evaluation of growth and nutrition; they serve to validate observations on the movement of protoplasm during growth. By combining these methods, it has been demonstrated that as few as ten calories per kilogram of body weight per day may determine success or failure in making satisfactory growth progress (Macy, 1952). The individual food components that serve as structural and functional constituents of invisible growth of protoplasmic tissue are measured by the metabolic balance. The difference between the total food intake and total outgo of major nutrients, such as calcium and nitrogen, over a given period of time represents the amount that the body retains for its structural and functional purposes.

The metabolic balance method provides valuable information on the nutritional status of the individual. This nutritional status markedly influences the amount and rate at which nutriments are used or rejected by the body. When the plane of nutrition is lowered, the malnourished individual will tend to store larger amounts of nutriments when his diet is improved. When a surplus of nutrients is supplied to body cells and tissues which have been deprived of adequate protein or calcium, for instance, the cells gradually improve their nutritive condition until they reach an optimum, at which point they lose their power to attract additional protein and calcium. There is provision in the tissues for deposit of certain elements in excess of current needs, a bodily reserve to meet the stress of sudden increased demands. The metabolic balance method is useful in a wide variety of studies of both visible and invisible growth and nutrition. The various types of results obtained by the metabolic balance procedure, including the evaluation of nutrient metabolism, absorption, retention, and metabolite excretion in relation to physical growth and physiologic function, contribute basic data to the development of nutritional anthropology (Brozek, 1956) and chemical anthropology (Macy and Kelly, 1957).

The value of the metabolic balance method depends on the length of the study interval, the accuracy with which representative homogeneous samples of food, urine, and feces are collected, and the precision of the chemical determinations. Existing chemical methods for some elements have greater sensitivity than others; some procedures are more satisfactorily applied than others. One fact cannot be too strongly emphasized in the pursuit of knowledge of invisible growth, namely, that a few data from coordinated procedures carefully executed, recorded, interpreted, and clearly presented are of far greater value than a large number of less reliable figures (Macy, 1942).

An adequate diet is the first requisite in the study of the normal processes of nutrition and of chemical and physiologic growth and function. Such a diet contains the essential nutrients in the desired amounts and proportions. It furnishes a generous supply of protein with its components of essential and other amino acids and of the various minerals and vitamins for the synthesis and maintenance of protoplasmic and skeletal tissues. To suppress growth in childhood by depleted or minimal food intake, judged essential by some investigators for determining food requirements, may be unwise. The normal pattern of growth may be disturbed or even thwarted, since the body receiving an inadequate food supply is required to make other physiologic adjustments to attain homeostasis at a lower plane of nutrition.

*Criteria for Selecting Experimental Subjects.* It is difficult to make detailed observations on a child, especially when experimental control and conditions require regulation of his existence and environment beyond a few days. A study of the chemistry of tissue replacement and growth, and the establishment of chemicophysiologic criteria for identifying and evaluating progress in the child, requires the maintenance and observation of the subjects under consistent environmental conditions at regular intervals; at the same time, a battery of biochemical, physical, clinical, and nutritional tests should be given (Nutrition for National Defense, 1957; Jolliffe, Tisdall, and Cannon, 1950; Lowry, 1952; Wohl and Goodhart, 1955).

In selecting experimental subjects, we cannot separate physical and mental characteristics of an individual and attribute them to their respective causations; therefore, it is necessary to accept normal individuals who conform to accepted standards of growth, development, nutrition, and behavior and who possess no detectable manifestation commonly considered abnormal.

By repeated observations and measurements under controlled conditions favorable to growth and development, an estimation may be made of the subject's progress in biologic time, though we cannot determine the relation between the actual change and the capacity for change.

**Consistent Control of Experimental Subjects.** Consistent control is important in a study of the intricate chemical and physiologic processes of invisible growth, and equal consideration should be given to emotional and physiologic factors, for they are deeply intertwined and each is directly influenced by the other. Cardinal requirements include wholesome diet, good habits of hygiene, regular periods of sleep and exercise, wholesome companionship and constructive entertainment, and sympathetic understanding and security, thus inducing joy and happiness in living. These factors contribute to the interest and well-being of the subject and the successful organization and conclusion of the study. An adequate dietary intake is basic to the study of normal growth processes. The Recommended Dietary Allowances of the Food and Nutrition Board of the National Research Council (1958) is a useful guide in planning a satisfactory intake for children of different age levels (Table 6-2).

**Cooperation of Experimental Subjects.** Cooperation is essential in all metabolic procedures and observations. The children should be protected from fear, for emotional stress may, in itself, disturb natural chemicophysiologic functioning. It is desirable to try out each possible subject with a few simple tests to determine his qualifications for, and adaptability to, intensive training in metabolic balance procedures. Should the subject prove unsuitable, large expenditures of time, effort, and money in collecting unreliable data can be avoided. Each study should be continued as long as possible, unless extended observation is not compatible with unhampered physiologic and psychologic functioning.

**Nutrients Studied.** Some sixty nutrients participate in the structure and functioning of the human body. Many are known to be essential for life and health and must be obtained directly

**TABLE 6.2. RECOMMENDED DIETARY ALLOWANCES FOR CHILDREN, FOOD AND NUTRITION BOARD OF THE NATIONAL RESEARCH COUNCIL**

Designed for the Maintenance of Good Nutrition of Healthy Persons in the United States
(Allowances are intended for persons normally active in a temperate climate)

| | Age Years | Weight kg. | Weight lb. | Height cm. | Height in. | Calories | Protein gm. | Calcium gm. | Iron mg. | Vitamin A I.U. | Thiam. mg. | Ribo. mg. | Niacin[2] mg. equiv. | Asc. Acid mg. | Vitamin D I.U. |
|---|---|---|---|---|---|---|---|---|---|---|---|---|---|---|---|
| Infants[3] | 2–6 mo | 6 | 13 | 60 | 24 | kg. × 120 | | 0.6 | 5 | 1500 | 0.4 | 0.5 | 6 | 30 | 400 |
| | 7–12 mo | 9 | 20 | 70 | 28 | kg. × 100 | | 0.8 | 7 | 1500 | 0.5 | 0.8 | 7 | 30 | 400 |
| Children | 1–3 | 12 | 27 | 87 | 34 | 1300 | 40 | 1.0 | 7 | 2000 | 0.7 | 1.0 | 8 | 35 | 400 |
| | 4–6 | 18 | 40 | 109 | 43 | 1700 | 50 | 1.0 | 8 | 2500 | 0.9 | 1.3 | 11 | 50 | 400 |
| | 7–9 | 27 | 60 | 129 | 51 | 2100 | 60 | 1.0 | 10 | 3500 | 1.1 | 1.5 | 14 | 60 | 400 |
| | 10–12 | 36 | 79 | 144 | 57 | 2500 | 70 | 1.2 | 12 | 4500 | 1.3 | 1.8 | 17 | 75 | 400 |
| Boys | 13–15 | 49 | 108 | 163 | 64 | 3100 | 85 | 1.4 | 15 | 5000 | 1.6 | 2.1 | 21 | 90 | 400 |
| | 16–19 | 63 | 139 | 175 | 69 | 3600 | 100 | 1.4 | 15 | 5000 | 1.8 | 2.5 | 25 | 100 | 400 |
| Girls | 13–15 | 49 | 108 | 160 | 63 | 2600 | 80 | 1.3 | 15 | 5000 | 1.3 | 2.0 | 17 | 80 | 400 |
| | 16–19 | 54 | 120 | 162 | 64 | 2400 | 75 | 1.3 | 15 | 5000 | 1.2 | 1.9 | 16 | 80 | 400 |

Adapted from the Food and Nutrition Board, National Research Council Recommended Daily Dietary Allowances,[1] Revised 1958.

[1] The allowance levels are intended to cover individual variations among most normal persons as they live in the United States under usual environmental stresses. The recommended allowances can be attained with a variety of common foods, providing other nutrients for which human requirements have been less well defined.

[2] Niacin equivalents include dietary sources of the preformed vitamin and the precursor, tryptophan, 60 milligrams tryptophan equals 1 milligram niacin.

[3] The Board recognizes that human milk is the natural food for infants and feels that breast feeding is the best and desired procedure for meeting nutrient requirements in the first months of life. No allowances are stated for the first month of life. Breast feeding is particularly indicated during the first month when infants show handicaps in homeostasis due to different rates of maturation of digestive, excretory, and endocrine functions. Recommendations as listed pertain to nutrient intake as afforded by cow's milk formulas and supplementary foods given the infant when breast feeding is terminated. Allowances are not given for protein during infancy.

from the food eaten. Each essential nutrient plays a specific role in metabolic and enzymatic processes and physiologic function. Because the opportunity for study is so great, an investigator must choose carefully the area within which to work. For detailed methods of chemical analysis and the collecting and handling of the metabolic materials, specific texts should be consulted (Macy, 1942, 1946, 1951). New chemical procedures should also be sought out.

*Subjects of metabolic balance studies can be standardized* to some extent, preliminary to actual study of chemical and physiologic growth. They can be established in the environment in which the observations are to be carried out, the routine of the study can be initiated, and diets can be given which will insure ample quantities of all essential food constituents. Even after all these efforts, further standardization may occur during the course of metabolic studies over extended periods of time. Figure 6-1 illustrates the use of the metabolic balance method in studying calcium nutriture and growth and progressive standardization of children, 4 to 8 years of age, over six successive months.

The children received diets composed of the same foods, in daily quantities considered adequate, and containing an average of 0.9 gm. of calcium per day. As the study proceeded, the children,

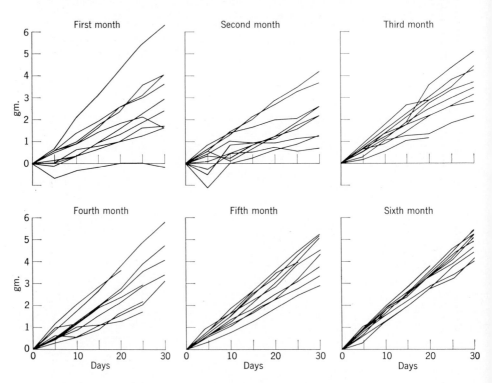

Fig. 6-1. Cumulated calcium retentions for six consecutive months (Macy, 1942, p. 40).

regardless of age or size, exhibited less variation from each other, and they became more alike in the amount of calcium they were able to retain.

The accretions of the chemical units of nitrogen and calcium determined by the metabolic balance procedure have been used as a measure of cellular and skeletal formation and as a means of observing the metabolic patterns of protoplasmic and skeletal activities as the body adapts to growth and development or reacts to injury or processes of regeneration.

## PHYSIOLOGIC METHODS

Growth and nutrition may be studied by physiologic methods arising from different sources and following different metabolic routes. They are equally useful, accurate, and readily applied. These methods include measurement of oxygen consumption and urinary creatinine excretion. Since the results of these methods have long been associated with the amount of metabolically active protoplasmic tissue present in the body at a given time, they contribute supplementary and related data to those obtained by the nitrogen metabolic balance method.

*Determination of Oxygen Consumption.* The rate at which an individual is utilizing oxygen without the influence of food or muscular work is the basis for computing the basal metabolic rate (BMR), a measure of the energy required for the fundamental processes which must go on in the body to maintain life.

The assessment of oxygen consumption and basal heat production measures the metabolically active protoplasmic tissue in the body and therefore is an integral part of the problem of the evaluation of growth and nutrition (Lewis, Kinsman, and Iliff, 1937; Nylin, 1929). The determination of the basal energy expended by the protoplasmic tissues when the modifying factors of activity, food intake, and environmental temperature are producing their minimal effect gives the minimal heat production of the energy metabolism of muscles and internal organs of the body, including the involuntary muscular activity of breathing, of the heart in the resting state, and of the smooth muscles of the alimentary canal. The test records the performance of the body at a specific time under a given set of conditions. The relative proportion of active and inactive tissue varies greatly with different individuals and may vary considerably in any one individual at different times. The protoplasmic tissue is metabolically active and influences oxygen consumption, whereas the fat (neutral) and water of the body composition are inactive.

The Benedict-Roth closed-circuit portable apparatus (Kleiner and Orten, 1958) or a comparable instrument may be used. The subject breathes pure oxygen from a closed system through a face mask or some similar device, and the air returned by the patient passes through soda-lime, which removes the carbon dioxide produced. The apparatus consists of a device that contains oxygen and records changes in its volume. From the rate of oxygen consumption, the rate of heat production is computed.

The test is made in the postabsorptive state, no food having been consumed since the evening before. For accurate results, the child should be carefully trained in the technique until he is unafraid, is emotionally stable, and will remain quiet and relaxed during the test. He should be kept warm and comfortable but awake and should rest a half hour before the test is made. Coincident with the determination of basal metabolic rate, records of pulse rate, body temperature, respiratory rate, and blood pressure are tabulated.

**Determination of Urinary Creatinine Excretion.** Urinary creatinine excretion per twenty-four hours is considered an index of the amount of active protoplasmic tissue in the body. Early investigators showed that endogenous protein metabolism, which results in the constant, even production of creatinine, is a manifestation of cell metabolism (Folin, 1905) or an index of muscular mass (Shaffer, 1908). There is an increase in both the absolute and relative excretion of creatinine from birth to puberty (Clark and Thompson, 1949; Stearns et al., 1958). Creatine, likewise, increases in early childhood but levels off at about 4 years of age and decreases during puberty. Figure 6-2, illustrating the relationship of urinary creatinine and creatine excretion of children from birth to age 18, has been furnished through the courtesy of Dr. Genevieve Stearns.

Urinary creatinine and basal heat production are associated with the amount and activity of the protoplasmic

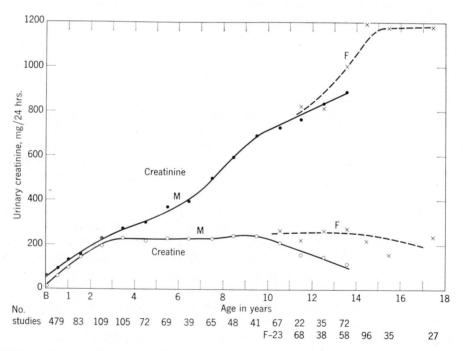

Fig. 6-2. Urinary creatinine and creatine excretion of children with age (courtesy of Dr. Stearns).

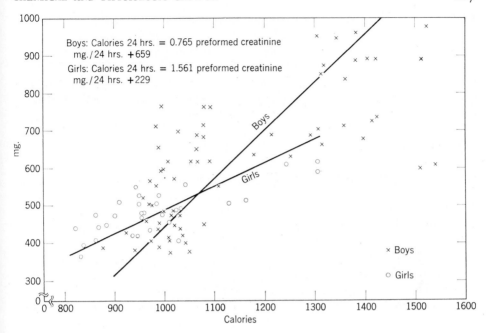

Boys: Calories 24 hrs. = 0.765 preformed creatinine
    mg./24 hrs. +659
Girls: Calories 24 hrs. = 1.561 preformed creatinine
    mg./24 hrs. +229

Fig. 6-3. Creatinine excretion versus basal heat production (Macy, 1942, p. 146).

tissue present in the body and with the rapidity of growth and maintenance of protoplasm. Basal heat production and creatinine excretion are related and increase with body size and age (Fig. 6-3). Both result from the metabolic activity of all the individual body organs and tissues. The fact that measurements of oxygen consumption and creatinine excretion are derived from different sources may account for the various patterns of growth when considered on the basis of different standards, such as height, weight, and body surface area.

The protoplasmic cellular component, which is an essential element of all normal body mass of a given species, is the center of metabolic activity. The oxygen consumption and the urinary creatinine excretion are directly associated with the amount of active protoplasmic tissue present in the body and also may be greatly influenced by the rapidity with which protoplasm is forming. Although it increases with growth in physical size, metabolic activity varies also with the amount, stage, and rapidity of development of various organs and tissues, since on a unit basis some tissues have greater metabolic activity than others, as shown by the studies of oxygen consumption of isolated organs and tissues. These methods are useful in assessing chemical growth and physiologic function and nutritional adequacy and status (Macy and Kelly, 1957).

In the assessment of nutritional adequacy and chemical and physiologic growth of children, the metabolic balance and the physiologic procedures of determining oxygen consumption and urinary creatinine excretion can be used successfully in evaluation of chemical growth.

## COMPOSITION
## OF THE HUMAN BODY

There are two methods of acquiring knowledge on the composition of the human body with respect to its major components of total water, fat, and solids-not-fat. The direct in vitro method is based on the chemical analysis of whole corpses or parts of bodies obtained at autopsy. The in vivo analysis of the living human being is concerned with various procedures, used singly or together, in breaking down the body composition into water, fat, and protoplasmic mass of nonfat solids and assessing the relative quantities of each. The concentrations of the major constituents change with age and nutritive state. Therefore, the assessment of the composition of the body and of the gain or loss in body weight has special significance during growth and development.

*In vitro chemical analysis* has been applied to a few human bodies. The individuals reaching autopsy and made available to the biochemist for chemical analysis too frequently have had questionable health records, and consequently the data resulting from the determinations may not represent normal body composition values. They are helpful, however, as guides and for general interest.

More data have been accumulated on the composition of fetuses and young infants than on adults. Only one male child, aged 4½ years, possessing a body weight of 14.0 kilograms and height of 107 centimeters, has been analyzed. Figure 6-4, adapted from the data of Widdowson, McCance, and Spray (1951), illustrates the changes that may occur in body composition with age. These investigators state that "many more bodies will have to be analyzed to establish reliable figures for the normal average and its variation."

Allometry is a mathematical technique for characterizing the relationships of size or concentration of two parts or constituents of the body. Hunt and Giles (1956), using selected chemical analyses in the literature, made a valuable study of the allometric growth of body composition in man and other mammals. Describing in detail the various allometric equations by which developmental trends in body composition of man were determined, they appraised the normative composition of a 10-year-old boy to be about 24 per cent fat, 55 per cent water, and 21 per cent nonfat solids, as compared with 14 per cent fat, 61 per cent water, and 25 per cent nonfat solids in the adult reference man.

*In vivo assessments of body composition* are indirect estimates. Although estimates are based on certain assumptions, if a number of assessments made independently display the same trend, it would justify the use of these estimates for observing growth and development. A major advantage of in vivo assessments, other than their feasibility, is that they can be used for longitudinal studies.

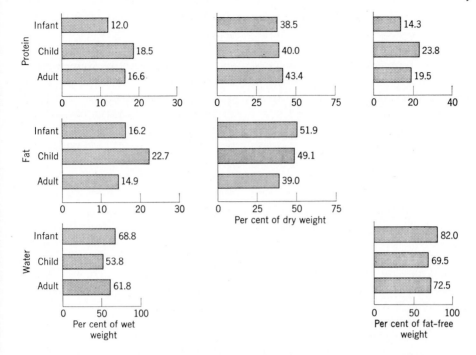

Fig. 6-4. Protein, water, and fat composition of the body during infancy, childhood, and adulthood, as adapted from the data of Widdowson et al. (Macy and Kelly, 1957, p. 71).

***Fat.*** Physical anthropologists estimate over- and underweight with varying degrees of control; for example, in addition to sex, a single factor, such as age or height; two factors, such as age and height; three factors, such as age, height, and hip width; four factors, such as age, height, width of hip, and chest breadth (Pryor, 1943); five factors, such as age, height, width of hip and knee, and chest circumference, with chest and hip measurements corrected for fat (McCloy, 1938). In each case the standard weight used as a reference point is an average of a group of individuals similar in one or more factors. The addition of some measure of body type to that of age and height

increases the value of the estimated standard weight. The ratio of observed to standard weight is a measure of the amount of weight over or under the reference point, but it may be the result of fat, muscle, or water.

Other kinds of fat assessments have been used, as from skin fold or roentgenographic measurements (Reynolds, 1950; Stuart and Sobel, 1956). With the roentgenographic technique, it has been observed that the thickness of subcutaneous fat (calf breadth) shows a rise in infancy, some decrement in childhood, and another rise in adolescence and that the early-maturing child showed a greater mean relative thickness of fat (calf breadth) than late-maturing children. These estimates are for specific areas and are not over-all estimates.

*Specific Gravity.* Two substances of equal size may have very different weights. For example, a bar of aluminum weighs less than a bar of equal size made of iron. Similarly equal portions of fat, water, and body solids differ in weight. Equal portions of fat weigh less than water, which in turn weighs less than other substances, such as muscle, bone, and minerals. Density or the ratio of mass (or weight) to volume serves as a measure for comparing weight on a unit volume basis. Specific gravity or the ratio of the density of a substance to the density of water at a specified temperature is a more refined measure for comparing substances of equal size on a unit weight basis as it is corrected for temperature changes.

On the assumption that the specific gravity of the nonfat portion of the body remains fairly constant, the person with the lowest specific gravity would have the greatest percentage of fat. However, there are exceptions. Edema would alter the rating, but corrections, when edema is suspected, could be made. Other factors, such as the changing specific gravity of the skeleton due to ossification during growth, may influence the estimate. In order to determine the specific gravity of a person, the only difficult measure to obtain is the volume. The weight can be obtained by the usual methods under controlled conditions, such as nude values for a specified room temperature, and the density of water for specified temperatures has been recorded in chemistry and physics handbooks. The volume of a person can be obtained by means of water displacement; that is, a body submerged in a tank of water displaces a portion of water equal to the volume of the body. It is necessary, however, to have a tank constructed in such a manner that water displacement can be accurately measured under controlled temperature conditions by trained personnel. Zook (1932) used the method of submersion of the body to determine the specific gravity as a measure of body composition. Boyd (1933) has reported formulas for estimating specific gravity from height and surface area that check the specific gravity values for children obtained by Zook with the submersion technique. Most values reported in the literature have been for adults.

Formulas have been derived for estimating body fat by specific gravity, but at the present time the available values for the specific gravity of children when applied to this formula give unusually high results. The specific gravity values of Zook and Boyd give fat percentage values of 38 to 51 per cent for children 4 to 12 years of age; these values are based on the fat-prediction equations of either Pace and Rathbun (1945) or Keys and Brozek (1953). The latter investigators suggested that the reported submersion values for children may not have been corrected for air in the lungs and respiratory passages and for gas in the gastro-intestinal tract.

*Body water* can be estimated by the *dilution method*. A substance of known quantity is injected into the blood stream, and by the process of osmosis it permeates the body fluids. After allowing sufficient time for the concentrations of the substance to equalize throughout the body fluids, the concentration level of the substance is determined in the blood sample and from it the total volume of body fluid can be calculated. The substances that have proved most satisfactory have been deuterium (heavy) water, antipyrine, and urea. Friis-Hansen et al. (1951) used the deuterium oxide and antipyrine dilution methods for determining the body water for children up to 11 years of age. Using total water estimates and physical measurements, they derived formulas for estimating body water from weight and also from surface area. Studies on animals on different planes of nutrition support the theory that the fat-free body has a fixed composition. On the basis of this assumption, it would be possible to estimate the fat-free portion of the body from body water by simply dividing the body water value by the percentage of water in the lean body mass (fat-free). We have used the value 73.2 as the percentage of water in the lean body mass for children. This value is slightly higher than that of adults as a result of analysis made on young and adult bodies (Macy and Kelly, 1956, 1957).

Water can be separated into *extracellular* and *intracellular* water. Extracellular fluid volume (McCance and Widdowson, 1951) can be obtained from a measure of the thiocyanate space. The subject, having emptied his bladder, is given intravenously a solution of sodium thiocyanate. After a period of time, during which the subject moves about the room, about 10 milli-

liters of venous blood, as well as the urine excreted during the period, is collected. The concentration of thiocyanate in the serum and in the urine is measured, and the thiocyanate space is determined. The measure of thiocyanate space should be corrected for the water in the red cells. Although the thiocyanate space may be larger than the true volume of extracellular fluid, at present it provides the most practical way of measuring extracellular fluid.

Basal metabolism and creatinine excretion have long been associated with *active protoplasmic tissue.* Behnke (1953) and Miller and Blyth (1952), using the specific gravity value obtained from underwater weighings to calculate lean body mass, derived formulas for estimating the lean body weight of adults from basal oxygen consumption. Miller also derived formulas for estimating lean body mass from urinary creatinine. The formulas are for adults. No similar studies have been made for children, though formulas can be adapted for children on the assumption that the relative lean body mass is on the average the same during childhood and adulthood (Macy and Kelly, 1956, 1957).

## NUTRITIONAL ADEQUACY AND STATUS

Although we have no objective method of estimating the influence of an individual's genetic inheritance, nutritional investigations during and after World War II produced ample experimental evidence to demonstrate that the food eaten may enhance or distort the growth potentialities conferred by heredity (Toverud, Stearns, and Macy, 1950). It is believed that biochemical, nutritional, and pathologic studies focused on cells, organs, and tissue systems, as well as on the organism as a whole, will detect some nutritional deficiencies at their source (Jolliffe, Tisdall, and Cannon, 1950; Wohl and Goodhart, 1955).

*Nutritional adequacy* and status (nutriture) may be studied in one of several ways: by the nutritional-status survey technique of applying integrated clinical, dietary, and biochemical procedures (Nutrition for National Defense, 1957; Spector, Peterson, and Friedemann, 1954), by nutritional anthropology (Brozek, 1956), in which body measurements with emphasis on body composition are applied, and by chemical anthropology (Macy and Kelly, 1957), in which chemical analysis applied to food eaten and metabolites excreted yields an evaluation of the nutrients absorbed and retained in relation to physical growth and physiologic function.

Nutritional status assessments have varying degrees of accuracy and value, depending on the methods used in obtaining the results and the precision with which they are applied. They range from qualitative to quantitative, used singly or in combination. Some measurements have the advantage of being direct determinations; others are indirect.

Not all measurements of nutritional status are equally practicable or equally informative at all ages from birth through maturity. Some determinations require little equipment; some require expensive equipment less readily available and skilled personnel; others are practical in the laboratory but rarely practical in the field. Nutritional status may be determined in different ways within the framework and scope determined by the objectives of each investigation.

Good nutrition depends on selection of a balanced diet and a knowledge of nutritive value of foods. It does not necessarily depend on economic factors, although a higher economic status may permit a higher nutritional level. The serious effects of nutritional deficiencies may be greatly increased by growth needs. The nutritional status of the individual markedly influences the amount and the rate at which nutrients are used by the body. Tissue nutrition depends on the relation between the supply of nutrients to the tissue and the tissue requirement. The tissue essential and the dietary essential are different. Kruse (1955) comments that the dietary essential must be present in the diet if nutrition is to be successful—a tissue essential is a nutrient that a tissue must receive for its nutrition.

*Field nutritional surveys*, which are organized to indicate the presence or absence of relationships between nutritional status and health, employ a tripart combination of clinical inspection and medical history, dietary history, and biochemical determination of sera blood components (Nutrition for National Defense, 1957; Jolliffe, Tisdall, and Cannon, 1950; Spector, Peterson, and Friedemann, 1954). In other studies the nutritional spectrum for any single nutrient may be based on response to dietary therapy and urinary excretion of the metabolite of that nutrient.

Assessment of nutritional status is a separate problem for each nutrient. A test that is appropriate for one nutrient may be of no value for another. Each nutrient has a specific type of measurement suited to one purpose and not to another. The essential components determined in the blood may represent various developmental, functional, and metabolic processes and involve several body systems.

*The clinical and physical* examinations include signs of malnutrition and consist in a thorough medical examination to detect other diseases or conditioning factors that may influence nutritional status and special examination to detect clinical signs in identification of deficiency diseases.

The purpose of the *dietary history* is to detect unsatisfactory dietary patterns that may cause deficiency diseases or malnutrition. If a deficiency disease exists, an indication to its etiology may be discovered; if disease is not detected, the connection with an unsatisfactory nutritional state may give direction for improvement of the diet. Dietary histories may be qualitative or quantitative, depending on the purpose of the study.

*Biochemistry* is an aid in the study of nutritional status. Information now available concerning the chemical structure and function of essential nutritive factors permits the application of biochemical procedures for measuring the levels of these substances in the blood and urine, and for detecting metabolic abnormalities that occur when the supply of these nutrients is too low for health. With an adequate intake of a particular nutrient, it is possible to establish the corresponding parameters

for tissue, blood, and urine, which may be used in nutritional assessment. When the food intake or tissue level is inadequate, the enzymatic capacity of that tissue or the nutritional adequacy of the whole body is diminished; under these conditions, it becomes easier to assess that intake or tissue level.

Specific nutrients studied with the aid of biochemical methods are hemoglobin, sera total protein, ascorbic acid, vitamin A, carotenoids, thiamine, riboflavin, and niacin. Others depend on the worker's interest. Many recent publications are ready and reliable sources of helpful information on methods of sampling, on clinical appraisal of nuriture, on biochemical procedures for collecting, storing, and analyzing samples of blood and urine, on dietary evaluations, and on suggested methods of interpretation. For the investigator who wishes specific details, the original publications should be consulted. The integrated results of the clinical, dietary, and biochemical surveys indicate the presence or absence of relationships between nutritional status and health. The method can be used in the study of population groups or as a supplementary aid in other types of studies, such as growth.

Dietary intake studies may be qualitative or quantitative and of varying duration, depending on the requirement of the investigation. Records taken for seven successive days or longer on the quality of food eaten at intervals of time are informative. When supplemented by carefully taken dietary histories and twenty-four-hour recall records of the food intake, a broad qualitative estimate of the dietary pattern may be obtained for comparison with the Recommended Dietary Allowance of the Food and Nutrition Board, National Research Council (National Academy of Sciences, 1958). Regardless of the limitations attributed to evaluation methods based on dietary histories and records, carefully taken and skillfully evaluated qualitative estimations for large population groups provide information on food intake and dietary habits that otherwise could not be recorded quantitatively (Burke, 1947; Hunscher and Macy, 1951). Approximations of nutrient intake for groups possessing racial, socioeconomic, and other differentiating characteristics indicate the need for public health measures and individual instruction aimed at desirable improvements in diet.

*Biochemical studies* of the blood and urine are helpful in the measurement of levels of essential nutrients for detecting metabolic abnormalities. Compounds in serum vary in their behavior: some, such as carotenoids and ascorbic acid (vitamin C), tend to reflect the immediate past dietary intake; others, such as proteins, may remain at concentrations that are within the statistically normal range, even though clinical malnutrition may be present.

*Blood Methods.* Peripheral blood samples may be collected and analyzed by microchemical methods developed by Bessey and Lowry (Lowry, 1952; Moyer et al., 1948). Approximately 0.3 milliliter of blood is drawn from the child by finger puncture after cleansing the skin with alcohol. Hemoglobin and total serum protein are determined immediately after collection and preparation of the samples. Samples and pro-

tein-free filtrates of serum are prepared and measured into microtubes and stored in deep freeze for later determinations of ascorbic acid, alkaline phosphatase, vitamin A, and carotenoids. Accuracy of the results may be attained by taking the sample in the morning, preferably representative of the fasting state. Variations caused by anxiety, fatigue, recent food consumption, and diurnal influences should be decreased to a minimum. Some investigators may prefer collecting samples of blood by venipuncture for use in macrochemical determinations. Venous samples should be collected with the minimum stasis, and capillary samples should be obtained from a free-flowing puncture. Each investigator may choose the methods best suited to the fulfillment of the objectives of the investigation that can be carried out with available personnel, facilities, and funds. A large number of analyses may be made in a routine manner with reasonably simple equipment and a high degree of accuracy.

*An illustrative application* of the tripart clinical, biochemical, and dietary intake evaluation of the ascorbic-acid nutritional status of underprivileged children during a stay of eight weeks in a health camp is presented in Fig. 6-5. Successive determinations of ascorbic acid in the blood serum were made during the first week, in the third and fourth weeks, and after four weeks of residence in the camp (Cooperstock et al., 1948). Clinical and dietary assessments accompanied the biochemical determinations of blood vitamin C. The results demonstrate the beneficial physiologic effect of an adequate diet

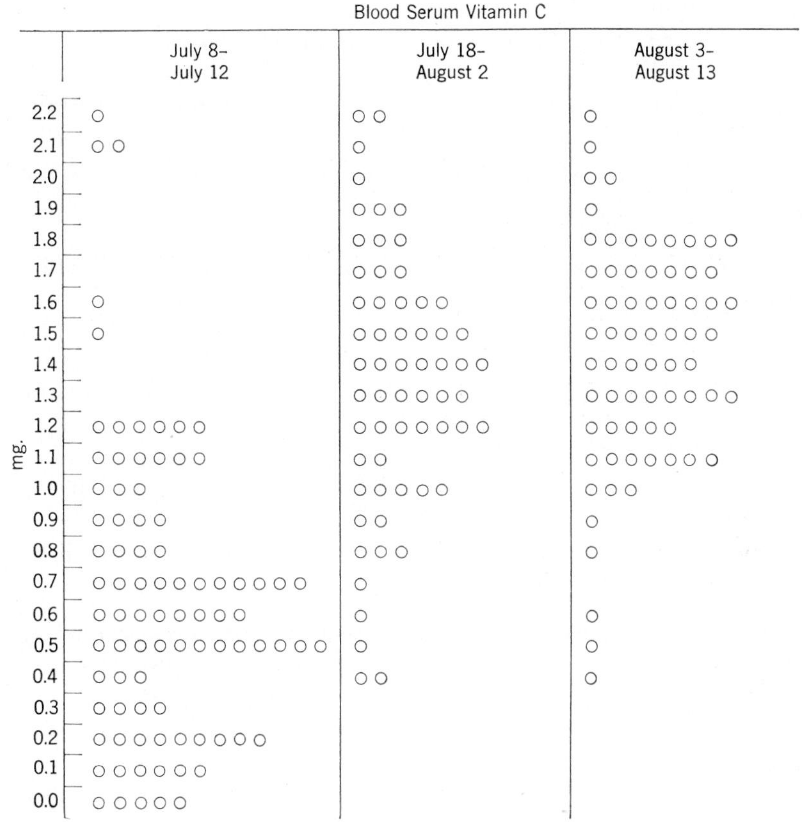

Blood Serum Vitamin C

| mg. | July 8–July 12 | July 18–August 2 | August 3–August 13 |
|---|---|---|---|
| 2.2 | O | O O | O |
| 2.1 | O O | O | O |
| 2.0 | | O | O O |
| 1.9 | | O O O | O |
| 1.8 | | O O O | O O O O O O O |
| 1.7 | | O O O | O O O O O O O |
| 1.6 | O | O O O O O | O O O O O O O O |
| 1.5 | O | O O O O O O | O O O O O O O |
| 1.4 | | O O O O O O O | O O O O O O |
| 1.3 | | O O O O O O | O O O O O O O O |
| 1.2 | O O O O O O | O O O O O O O | O O O O O |
| 1.1 | O O O O O O | O O | O O O O O O O |
| 1.0 | O O O | O O O O O | O O O |
| 0.9 | O O O O | O O | O |
| 0.8 | O O O O | O O O | O |
| 0.7 | O O O O O O O O O O O | O | |
| 0.6 | O O O O O O O O | O | O |
| 0.5 | O O O O O O O O O O O O O | O | O |
| 0.4 | O O O | O O | O |
| 0.3 | O O O O | | |
| 0.2 | O O O O O O O O O | | |
| 0.1 | O O O O O O | | |
| 0.0 | O O O O O | | |

Fig. 6-5. Fasting blood serum vitamin C levels of children during first week, in third and fourth weeks, and after four weeks residence in a health camp (Cooperstock et al., p. 207).

and healthful environment on improved health and vitamin C nutriture. They demonstrate also that nutritional conditioning may be rapidly achieved by the majority of the poorly nourished children. Clinically, the 99 children, aged 6 to 16 years, improved and increased their body weights 0.1 to 25.1 per cent during the camp experience. Vitamin C is one of the nutrients most likely to be low in the diets of underprivileged populations.

Ascorbic acid is important in the regulation of normal cell function, in the formation of intercellular cement substances, and in the formation of the steroid hormones of the adrenal cortex under the stimulus of the adrenotropic hormone of the pituitary gland. It is especially necessary for the growing child because young tissues are richer in vitamin C than adult tissues, and the tissues of highest metabolic activities are characterized by high concentration of this nutrient. Since blood levels of ascorbic acid reflect the immediate past dietary intake, nutritional reconditioning of the children at the health camp would be expected in this group living under improved diet, medical care, and living conditions.

Nutritional status surveys are useful as a guide in the improvement of the environment of so-called healthy children, for such children are often subject to the untutored whims of adults in whose care they fall. For example, children living in a modern child-caring institution with devoted housemothers may be subjected unwittingly to health hazards caused by misconceptions in food values (Harrington et al., 1950). The same type of experience may arise in the home. Table 6-3 shows the aver-

cause of her impression that its bulk prevented the consumption of a more desirable and larger intake of milk. By failing to give the citrus fruit, which provided for the largest source of ascorbic acid in the daily diet, she forced the children to a lowered level of vitamin C nutriture.

In comparing the children of two cottages, the highest and lowest consumptions of ascorbic acid are associated, respectively, with maximum and minimum ascorbic acid concentrations in the blood. The normal level in healthy children ranges from 0.7 milligram and above of ascorbic acid per 100 milliliters of blood, whereas 0.4 and 0.6 milligram per 100 milliliters is the

**TABLE 6-3. FASTING BLOOD SERUM VITAMIN C LEVELS FOR TWO GROUPS OF 10 CHILDREN EACH LIVING IN AN INDIVIDUAL COTTAGE, ON THREE SUCCESSIVE DAYS**

Values in milligrams per 100 milliliters

| Day | Cottage A | | Cottage B | |
|---|---|---|---|---|
| | Mean | Range | Mean | Range |
| 1 | 1.13 | 0.92–1.33 | 0.12 | 0.02–0.28 |
| 2 | 1.06 | 0.54–1.52 | 0.17 | 0.00–0.34 |
| 3 | 1.05 | 0.66–1.51 | 0.12 | 0.05–0.23 |

age blood levels of ascorbic acid of ten children in each of two cottages on three successive days. Each cottage was provided with a generous supply of carefully selected foods from which adequate diets could be formulated and served by the housemothers. In one cottage the well-meaning housemother knew that milk was good for growing children, so she did not serve the citrus fruit provided by the institution be-

range in borderline cases and below 0.4 milligram per 100 milliliters in deficient subjects. The children unwittingly deprived of an adequate dietary intake had deficient blood levels; indeed, in some cases the vitamin C blood levels were comparable to those in children with scurvy. Although the clinical examinations revealed no obvious disease, the discovery of consistent low blood levels led to an investigation of the diet, which revealed the cause. Immediate improvement of the diet by restoring the citrus fruit brought the blood levels back to normal, thus improving ascorbic acid nutriture rapidly and preventing malnutrition and suppression of growth.

The scatter of the results of blood vitamin C shown in Fig. 6-5 demonstrates that the individual child has a characteristic physiologic capacity to respond to improved dietary intake, predetermined by his health and the extent of his nutritional impairment. With but few exceptions, normal vitamin C nutriture was attained by most underprivileged children within six weeks. The so-called healthy children within the cottage receiving inadequate intake of this essential nutrient responded even more quickly. Other types of nutritional deficiencies, however, may respond more gradually over a longer period of time.

## OTHER SURVEYS

*Electrophoretic studies* for separating the plasma proteins into their true chemical entities constitute one of the major advances of modern biochemistry. The method is based on the migration of charged colloidal particles in a solution or suspension when electromotive force is applied. In electrophoresis all negatively charged particles migrate toward the positive electrode; positively charged particles move in the opposite direction to the negative electrode. The particles migrate with different speeds dependent on the number of charges each carries—the greater the number of charges, the faster the migration.

*Blood proteins* in health and disease have primary significance in the metabolism of the organism. The amount and distribution of the blood proteins at any time may reflect diverse processes concerned with the synthesis, maintenance, and dissolution of different body constituents; and the protein structure of this fluid, which nurtures all tissues, seems to depend more on the physiologic state of the individual as a whole than does any other tissue.

Changes in the blood proteins with age are of great interest and should be investigated thoroughly. Electrophoretic analysis of the proteins of the serum or plasma provides a more detailed and reliable picture of this labile biologic system than other methods. It permits accurate estimation of the ratio of albumin to globulin, the two major protein fractions, and also provides quantitative data for the $alpha_1$, $alpha_2$, beta, and gamma components of plasma globulin, in addition to fibrinogen (phi globulin). Albumin normally represents the largest fraction of the total blood (plasma) protein and has three important functions: (1) maintenance and stabilization of blood volume and equilibrium of fluid exchange between the intravascular and extravascular fluid compartments of the body, (2) carrying of organic and inorganic substances, and (3) providing nutrients for the tissues and possibly supplies for the formation of blood (plasma) globulins. An outstanding characteristic of the globulin group is the ability to act as carriers for other substances, notably lipids, lipoproteins, and metals such as copper and iron. Fibrinogen is important for its well-known role in blood coagulation and in the phenomenon of erythrocyte sedimentation. Gamma globulins are the carriers of immune bodies so important in the defense of the body against infectious disease. The breakdown of alpha into the alpha$_1$ and alpha$_2$ fractions and the fractionation of blood proteins into albumin, alpha, beta, gamma, and fibrinogen portions are especially useful in disease and during the reproductive period.

Twenty milliliters of blood are needed for the chemical analysis of total protein and for electrophoresis; this amount is drawn from a vein in the antecubital fossa (depression or pit in front of the elbow) with minimum stasis that will affect the proteins. Each sample must be handled carefully and determined with the greatest care by the most accurate procedures and equipment described in the latest scientific literature. It is beyond the scope of this chapter to discuss in detail procedures and application of results.

*Hemoglobin* and other blood proteins are of primary significance in maintaining health, and dietary proteins must be relied on to furnish the essential amino acids of which blood proteins are composed. Concentration of hemoglobin and total serum protein are among the most commonly used measures of nutritional status. Many types of hemoglobin exist (National Academy of Sciences, 1958), however, and they, too, may be separated and studied electrophoretically.

*Other nutritional status* studies related to growth may consider the mineral nutrients and lipid distribution of blood cells and plasma or be based on quantitatively analyzed diets for a number of nutrients, to name but a few types of study that give valuable information on the relation of nutritional status to growth.

At a Conference on the Role of Body Measurements in Evaluation of Human Nutrition, *nutritional anthropometry* came into being (Brozek, 1956). It refers to the

. . . application of body measurements for the purpose of characterizing man's nutritional status (nutriture), with emphasis on body composition. Somatic measurements, properly made and properly interpreted, are useful in several nutritional contexts. These include evaluation of caloric requirements, assessment of nutriture of a given school child or patient, description of the present nutritional status of different populations and the demonstration of improvement resulting from better economic, agricultural or dietary practices, and a continuous assessment of the biological adequacy of the caloric supply during periods of food restriction and food shortages. While starvation is a continuous threat in some parts of the world, elsewhere obesity has been considered as a serious health hazard. For the study of this problem a clearer differentiation between gross underweight-overweight and leanness-fatness is desirable. In the description of man's body build the separation of the contribution of the skeletal frame from the amount and distribution of specific soft tissues will increase the precision of the portrait (p. iii).

Further, it was stated:

Through contact with the science of human nutrition, the trends toward a more functional, "dynamic" orientation in physical anthropology are strengthened. The biological significance of human somatic variations at a given time is measured in terms of association with physiological functions and biochemical characteristics, while morbidity and mortality constitute the long-range criteria of the importance of differences in human physique (p. iv).

*Chemical anthropology*, likewise, has arisen in the biochemical field (Macy and Kelly, 1957). It is concerned with the evaluation of nutrient intake and of absorption and retention and metabolite excretion in relation to physical growth and physiologic function, body metabolism (Williams, 1956), and physiologic efficiency. Nutritional status is being explored as one of the fundamental processes of behavior. In discussing the impact of diet on behavior, MacLeod (Brozek, 1957), speaking for the psychologists present at a Symposium on Nutrition and Behavior held in 1957, said,

. . . this symposium is a welcome indicator of the growing realization not only that psychologic research has something to contribute to the science of nutrition but also, and more important for us, that nutritional studies can help to clarify some of the fundamental problems of behavior (p. 5).

Body weight, so often used as an index of nutrition and growth, may not be so reliable as a criterion of satisfactory growth conditions for children as a thorough-going evaluation of nutritional status, for, even with food intake sufficient to allay hunger and produce weight gain, the diet may not contain essential substances in amounts sufficient to maintain in the blood and body tissues the levels requisite to healthy body composition. If the body has become conditioned to an inadequate diet and a lowered nutritional state exists, weeks may be required for nutritional reconditioning on an adequate diet with the necessary physiologic adjustment of the body tissues and fluids.

*Quality of Survival.* Constitutional and environmental factors that arrest or distort development have significant implications in the rate and quality of growth taking place at any period in infancy and childhood. The tempo and dynamic quality of growth and development are influenced by the interplay of chemical processes and their response to different internal and external environments, to the metabolic performance, and to the rate of excretion of nutrients and waste. When unhampered, all the physiologic and metabolic processes concerned with growth flow in an orderly fashion in physiologic time toward maturity of structure and function. If interrupted by an inadequate diet and a lowered plane of nutritional state for a time, growth will return in its original proportions or in some altered form of progression and symmetry when an adequate diet is provided. Maintenance of a healthy chemical structure depends on the presence in the food of many nutrients and on an environment favoring full utilization.

Evidence indicates that many children do not receive enough of the essential nutrients to satisfy their usual body needs, to acquire reserves sufficient to meet sudden and unexpected periods of physiologic and pathologic stress arising from ineffective fulfillment of biologic demands, and to meet growth and other structural and functional requirements. Children whose plane of nutrition has been lowered because of insufficient calories in the diet will respond by a slower growth rate. Children who are malnourished because of disease or are undernourished because of chronic inadequate food consumption will require an enlarged nutrient intake to make up the deficits and to condition or recondition their bodies before a normal growth rate can be attained. Stearns et al. (1958) observed that children whose plane of nutrition is always high and who have been largely free from illness tend to be taller and heavier for their age than children whose diet and environment are poor.

There is a basic progression and symmetry of life and growth in accordance with the individual's biologic time that links the many physical, chemical, metabolic, and developmental processes into a functioning unit. The inherent physical, chemical, and physiologic growth changes taking place as the body matures are accomplished by an increase in body size and changes in visceral organs and body composition. Functional changes accompanying dimensional and ponderal growth are attained by the enlargement and functional maturation of the energy-releasing organs (i.e., the nervous, endocrine, and digestive systems) and the cardiac, respiratory, and renal systems. All these components are integral parts of growth and differentiational processes, each advancing in its own way and at a different rate. Cellular changes, synergy of growth rates for all systems, and proportionate functioning among them permit developmental differentiation to proceed in a normal fashion.

In summarizing the epoch-making experimental chemical and biological enlightenment of the last half century, Sherman (1952), the renowned chemical nutritionist, says,

. . . the activities upon which the life of the body depends involve a continuous expenditure of energy and also a never-ceasing exchange of material. Body substances may be, and often are, drawn upon to meet temporary deficiencies of the nutrient intake; but ultimately the body is dependent upon food for the fuel substances (oxidizable organic nutrients) which supply energy; for the substances which make good the exchange of body material; and (either by supplying actual substances or their precursors) for all those regulatory factors which keep the reactions running at the right rates, and keep the internal conditions of the body within the zones of delicate adjustment which the life processes requires (p. 7).

The body is an organized, coordinated whole, which may behave as something more than a mere summation of its parts.

The new and increasing numbers of methodologies for more precise study of chemical and physiological growth will continue to add new knowledge to the chemistry of life. Challenging and fertile opportunities await those with imaginative and creative minds who apply these methods and develop other procedures to broaden the scope and contribute greater depth and meaning to child development. New methods may arise in any field of science, for there are no real boundaries between the increasing numbers of branches of science that have to do with man. Each overlaps with the other.

## REFERENCES

Adolph, E. F. 1943. *Physiological regulations.* Lancaster, Pa.: Jacques Cattell.

Allison, J. B. 1958. Calories and protein nutrition. *Ann. N. Y. Acad. Sci.*, **69**, 1009–1024.

Barcroft, J. 1934. *Features in the Architecture of physiological function.* New York: Macmillan.

Behnke, A. R. 1941–1942. Physiologic studies pertaining to deep sea diving and aviation especially in relation to the fat content and composition of the body. *Harvey Lect.*, **37**, 198–226.

———. 1953. The relation of lean body weight to metabolism and some consequent systematizations. *Ann. N. Y. Acad. Sci.*, **56**, 1095–1142.

Benedict, F. G. 1938. Vital energetics: A study of comparative basal metabolism. *Carnegie Inst. Wash., Pub. No. 503.*

Bernard, C. 1865. Introduction, a l'étude de la Medicine Experimentale. Bailliere, Paris. (Tr. H. C. Green, 1927.) New York: Macmillan.

Boyd, Edith. 1933. The specific gravity of the human body. *Hum. Biol.*, **5**, 646–672.

Brody, S. 1945. *Bioenergetics and growth, with special reference to the efficiency complex in domestic animals.* New York: Reinhold.

Brozek, J. (Ed.) 1956. *Body measurements and human nutrition.* Detroit: Wayne Univer. Press.

———. 1957. *Symposium on nutrition and behavior.* Nutrition Symposium Series No. 14. New York: The National Vitamin Foundation.

———, H. Mori, and A. Keys. 1958. Estimation of total body fat from roentgenograms. *Science*, **128**, 901.

Burke, B. S. 1947. The dietary history as a tool in research. *J. Amer. Diet. Ass.*, **23**, 1041.

Cannon, W. B. 1932. *The wisdom of the body.* New York: Norton.

Chittenden, R. H. 1907. *The nutrition of man.* New York: Stokes.

Clark, L. C., Jr., and H. L. Thompson. 1949. Determination of creatine and creatinine in urine. *Analy. Chem.*, **21**, 1218–1221.

Cooperstock, M., Elba Morse, Elsie Z. Moyer, and I. G. Macy. 1948. Nutritional status of children. IV. Nutritional conditioning in a health camp. *J. Amer. Diet. Ass.*, **24**, 205–211.

Cowgill, G. R. 1957. A formula for estimating the specific gravity of the human body with a consideration of its possible uses. *Amer. J. Clin. Nutr.*, **5**, 601–611.

———. 1958. Evaluating body composition. *Bordens' Rev.*, **19**, #1, 1–17.

Folin, O. 1905. Laws governing the chemical composition of urine. *Amer. J. Physiol.*, **13**, 66–115.

Forbes, G. B. 1952. Chemical growth in man. *Pediatrics*, **9**, 58–68.

Friis-Hansen, B. J., M. Holiday, T. Stapleton, and W. M. Wallace. 1951. Total body water in children. *Pediatrics*, **7**, 321–27.

Haudane, J. S. 1931. *The philosophical basis of biology.* London: Hodder and Stoughton.

Harrington, Mary Margaret, Ruth Cumbow, Ruth Uhler Thomas, Hazel Metz, Marjorie Macy Rutledge, and Icie G. Macy. 1950. Nutritional status of children. IX. Feeding practices in child-caring agencies. A cottage-plan home. *J. Amer. Diet. Ass.*, **26**, 241–247.

Hopkins, Sir F. G. 1933. Some chemical aspects of life. *Science*, **78**, 219.

Hunscher, Helen A., and Icie G. Macy. 1951. Dietary study methods. 1. Uses and abuses of dietary study methods. *J. Amer. Diet. Ass.*, **27**, 558–563.

Hunt, E. E., Jr., and E. Giles. 1956. Allometric growth of body composition in man and other mammals. In Brozek, Josef (Ed.), *Body measurements and human nutrition.* Detroit: Wayne Univer. Press.

Interdepartmental Committee on Nutrition for National Defense. 1957. *Manual for nutrition surveys.* Supt. of Documents, U. S. Government Printing Office, Washington, D. C.

Jolliffe, N., F. F. Tisdall, and P. R. Cannon (Eds.). 1950. *Clinical nutrition.* For the Food and Nutrition Board of the National Research Council. New York: Harper.

Keys, A., and J. Brozek. 1953. Body fat in adult man. *Physiol. Rev.*, **33**, 245–325.

———, A. Henschel, O. Mickelsen, and H. L. Taylor. 1950. *The biology of human starva-*

*tion.* Minneapolis: Univer. Minnesota Press. 2 vols.

Kleiner, I. S., and J. M. Orten, 1958. *Human biochemistry.* St. Louis: Mosby. Pp. 614.

Kruse, H. D. In M. G. Wohl, and R. S. Goodhart. 1955. *Modern nutrition in health and disease,* Philadelphia: Lea and Febiger. Pp. 483.

Lewis, R. C., Gladys M. Kinsman, and Alberta Iliff. 1937. The basal metabolism of normal boys and girls from two to twelve years old, inclusive. *Amer. J. Dis. Child.,* 53, 348–428.

Loeb, L. 1947. *The biological basis of individuality.* Springfield, Ill.: Thomas.

Lowry, O. H. 1952. Biochemical evidence of nutritional status. *Physiol. Rev.,* 32, 431–448.

McCance, R. A., and E. M. Widdowson. 1951. A method of breaking down the body weights of living persons into terms of extracellular fluid, cell mass and fat, and some applications of it to physiology and medicine. *Proc. Royal Soc.,* London, B138, 115–130.

McCloy, C. H. 1938. Appraising physical status: Methods and norms. *Univer. Iowa Stud. Child Welf.,* 15, No. 2, n.s. no. 356.

Macy, Icie G. 1942. *Nutrition and chemical growth in childhood.* Vol. I: Evaluation. Springfield, Ill.: Thomas.

———. 1946. *Nutrition and chemical growth in childhood.* Vol. II: Original data. Springfield, Ill.: Thomas.

———. 1951. *Nutrition and chemical growth in childhood.* Vol. III: Calculated data. Springfield, Ill.: Thomas.

———. 1952. Importance of calories in the growth of children. *Ann. N. Y. Acad. Sci.,* 56, 122–126.

Macy, Icie G., and Harriet J. Kelly. 1956. Body composition in childhood with reference to in vivo chemical analysis of water, fat, and protoplasmic mass. *Hum. Biol.,* 28, 289–308.

———. 1957. *Chemical anthropology: A new approach to growth in children.* Chicago: Univer. Chicago Press.

Mendel, L. B. 1923. *Nutrition: The chemistry of life.* New Haven: Yale Univer. Press.

Miller, A. T., Jr., and C. S. Blyth. 1952. Estimation of lean body mass and body fat from basal oxygen consumption and creatinine excretion. *J. appl. Physiol.,* 5, 73–78.

Mitchell, H. H., T. S. Hamilton, F. R. Steggerda, and H. W. Bearn. 1945. The chemical composition of the adult human body and its bearing on the biochemistry of growth. *J. biol. Chem.,* 158, 625–637.

Moyer, Elsie Z., E. F. Beach, A. Robinson, Margaret N. Coryell, S. Miller, Charlotte Roderuck, Marjorie Lesher, and Icie G. Macy, 1948. Nutritional status of children. II. The organization of a survey of child-caring agencies. *J. Amer. Diet. Ass.,* 24, 85–90.

Moulton, C. R. 1923. Age and chemical development in mammals. *J. biol. Chem.,* 57, 79–97.

National Academy of Sciences. 1958. *Conference on hemoglobin. Nat. Research Council Pub. No. 557.*

National Academy of Sciences. 1958. *Recommended dietary allowances. Nat. Research Council Pub. No. 589.*

Needham, J. 1942. *Biochemistry and morphogenesis.* Cambridge: Cambridge Univer. Press.

Nylin, G. 1929. Periodical variations in growth, standard metabolism and oxygen capacity of the blood in children. *Acta med. scand. Suppl. XXXI.*

Pace, N. and Edith N. Rathbun. 1945. Studies on body composition. III. The body water and chemically combined nitrogen content in relation to fat content. *J. biol. Chem.,* 158, 685–691.

Pryor, Helen Brenton. 1943. *As the child grows.* New York: Silver Burdett.

Reynolds, E. L. 1950. The distribution of subcutaneous fat in childhood and adolescence. *Monogr. Soc. Res. Child Develpm.* 15, serial #50, #2.

Scammon, R. E. 1930. The measurement of the body in childhood. In J. A. Harris, C. M. Jackson, D. G. Paterson, and R. E. Scammon, *Measurement of man.* Minneapolis: Univer. Minnesota Press.

Schoenheimer, R. 1942. *The Dynamic state of body constituents.* (Harvard University Monographs in Medicine and Public Health.) Cambridge, Mass.: Harvard Univer. Press.

Shaffer, P. 1908. The excretion of kreatinin and kreatin in health and disease. *Amer. J. Physiol.*, **23**, 1–22.

Sherman, H. C. 1952. *Chemistry of food and nutrition.* 8th. ed. New York: Macmillan.

Sinclair, H. M. 1948. The assessment of human nutriture. In *Vitamins and hormones.* New York: Academic VI. P. 101.

Sokoloff, L. and S. Kaufman. 1959. Effects of thyroxin on amino acid incorporation into protein, *Science*, **129**, 569.

Spector, H., M. S. Peterson, and T. E. Friedemann. (Eds.) 1954. *Methods for evaluation of nutritional adequacy and status.* A symposium. Chicago: Quartermaster Food and Container Institute for the Armed Forces.

Spray, Christine M., and Elsie M. Widdowson. 1950. The effect of growth and development on the composition of mammals. *Brit. J. Nutr.* **4**, 332–53.

Stearns, Genevieve, Katherine J. Newman, J. B. McKinley, and P. C. Jeans. 1958. The protein requirements of children from one to ten Years of age. *Ann. N. Y. Acad. Sci.*, **69**, 857–868.

Stuart, H. C., and E. H. Sobel. 1946. The thickness of the skin and subcutaneous tissue by age and sex in childhood. *J. Pediat.*, **28**, 637–647.

Tanner, J. M. 1953. Growth and constitution. In Kroeber, A. L. (Ed.) *Anthropology today: An encyclopedic inventory.* Chicago: Univer. Chicago Press, Pp. 750–70.

Tanner, J. M. 1955. *Growth at adolescence.* Springfield, Ill.: Thomas.

Todd, T. W. 1937. *Atlas of skeletal maturation.* St. Louis: Mosby.

Toverud, Kirsten Utheim, Genevieve Stearns, and Icie G. Macy. 1950. Maternal nutrition and child health. An interpretative review. *Nat. Research Council Bull.*, **123**, Nat. Acad. Sci.

White House Conference on Child Health and Protection. 1932. *Growth and development of the child. Part IV: Appraisement of the child.* New York: Century.

Widdowson, E. M., R. A. McCance, and C. M. Spray. 1951. The chemical composition of the human body. *Clin. Sci.*, **10**, 113–25.

Williams, R. J. 1956. *Biochemical individuality. The basis for the genetotrophic concept.* New York: Wiley.

Willier, B. H., P. A. Weiss, and Viktor Hamburger. (Eds.) 1955. *Analysis of development.* Philadelphia: Saunders.

Wohl, M. G., and R. S. Goodhart. 1955. *Modern nutrition in health and disease.* Philadelphia: Lea and Febiger.

Zook, D. Earl. 1932. The Physical growth of boys: A study by means of water displacement. *Amer. J. Dis. Child.*, **43**, 1347–1432.

chapter 7

# Receptor Functions

Austin H. Riesen
*The University of Chicago*

When the functions of receptors are studied in the intact organism, the effects of stimulation are typically measured after neural mediation and by means of some response indicator. An isolated sensory cell of the skin, cochlea, or retina may be activated by energy from the external environment, yet contribute nothing to neural processes or behavior. When it does, its contribution is relative to that of other receptor cells and highly dependent upon a background of concurrent neural activity. Hence, the effect of an afferent process may range from a relatively constant to a highly variable one, depending in part on the extent of intervening neural mediation that is involved. To understand the consequences of stimulation for behavior of the living organism, the investigator measures physiological or behavioral response at the level or levels appropriate to the particular problem of his interest. In developmental studies special care is necessary to avoid equating or confusing the different levels.

The present chapter is aimed at a review of those methods of investigation that are useful for the measurement of sensory capacities by behavioral effects of stimulation. When it is clear that data are relevant to a restricted behavioral class or level of response, such restricted applicability is pointed out. For example, when the human infant moves its eyes laterally in response to the sweeping motion of a series of vertical stripes across the field of vision, the observer concludes rightly that receptors of the eye are activated and that a complex neuromuscular system is brought into action by the visual stimulation. With only this much information, however, the psychologist exercises caution in drawing conclusions about visual acuity or the general adequacy of form vision. He knows that in mammalian phylogeny this response occurs in the absence of the visual cortex (Smith, 1937) and conceivably reflects strictly midbrain integrations when observed in the newborn infant.

For developmental psychology, the problems of distinguishing receptor from neural developmental stages, and of separating levels within the nervous system, are no less significant than the problems of diagnosing sensory and neural disorders selectively. The initial discovery of a deficiency is often only the beginning of a prolonged series of diagnostic observations. An apparent deafness may turn out to be unrelated to the organ of hearing, except insofar as a cortical integrating process, which may not be functioning effectively (Myklebust, 1954), is involved. Presumably, both auditory and extra-auditory cortical regions would be under suspicion. A demonstration that auditory reflexes can be elicited at normal thresholds places the site of impairment or developmental failure farther along in the neural network.

The use of so-called "objective" methods (e.g., the optokinetic reflex, galvanic skin response, and tympanic reflex) for testing receptor functions typically involves responses that are integrated at lower levels than the "subjective" methods, which call for the voluntary cooperation of the subject. In work with infants and children advantages of involuntary behavioral indicators are often very great, but there is also danger in overlooking possible absence of correlation between these and other standard tests. More "objective" methods are needed, nevertheless. Developmental norms can be greatly improved by their use, for their reproducibility is a distinct gain. Relations between various methods will also have to be worked out before interpretations based on the use of some of the newer methods can rest on firm ground. Regardless of the level or objectivity of the methods, certain principles of systematic experimental investigation must be observed if data of permanent value in a science of behavioral development are to be obtained.

## Quantification in Receptor Sensitivity

### THE DETERMINATION OF THRESHOLDS

**Psychophysical Experimentation.** Much of what an investigator does in sensory psychophysiology depends upon his ability to control and reproduce the physical stimuli to which his subject may respond. This problem will vary with the sense mode and is solved differently for each dimension of stimulation and for each technique within a dimension. In the present section of this chapter the more general question of procedural standardization is treated; in later sections the instrumentation necessary for controlled presentation of the stimulus is discussed in specific terms for each type of energy and its appropriate receptor.

Psychophysics deals with the experimental and statistical methods needed for obtaining quantitative and reproducible sets of responses to standard stimuli. Both average response values and variability are determined from any systematic study of absolute and differential thresholds. The number and specific quantitative values of stimulation to be used in a study are selected after appropriate preliminary investigation. A sequence of trials is planned, and the basic numerical computations follow logically from the set of values that a method produces. This set of values will reflect a stimulus dimension and two or more categories of responses to each value along that stimulus dimension. For the reader with little experience in psychophysical theory and experimentation, an excellent discussion of basic principles, with examples of appropriate methods of tabulation and statistical treatment, is available in Chapters 8 and 9 of Woodworth and Schlosberg (1954). More advanced presentations are available in textbooks on psychometrics.

*Sequences of Stimulus-Presentation.* Three standard methods for ordering the stimuli and then arriving at values of the physical stimulus that are correlated with a change in response (threshold values) have long been in standard use. The final statistical statement will vary in detail with the method, as is true for measurements in science generally. Fundamentally, there is good agreement between the various methods in the quantitative relationships expressed. The method of choice is often indicated by the nature of the stimuli to be presented in conjunction with the response required of the subject. Since responses may shift somewhat as a consequence of a sequence of stimulation, these effects themselves are sometimes made the central interest of experimental investigation.

The most straightforward approach to the determination of a threshold, one which gives an initial approximation on the first set of observations, is known as the *method of limits*, or method of serial exploration. For obtaining a lower threshold (RL, or Reiz Limen), the intensity of the stimulus may be increased by small steps until the first response is obtained or decreased until the response is first absent or both. Exploratory work with animal or infant human subjects is often done by the descending method of limits if the response has been developed through training (to provide some assurance that the response is still possible) or by the ascending method of limits if an innate response to the stimulus is utilized (to minimize negative adaptation or habituation). Many investigators prefer to obtain an average value

compounded from both ascending and descending series of trials in order to reduce the effects of constant errors that come from a unidirectional approach to the threshold. Whichever approach is used, psychologists understand the result to be an approximation or calculated value. They accept the concept of *limen* as a statistical entity, varying somewhat with the method of determination and not to be regarded as an absolute.

For the measurement of transition zones, through which a subject varies in his response to fixed values of the stimulus, two additional methods are available and are more satisfactory statistically than the method of limits. These methods may also be more satisfying to the subject if he is being asked to make judgments of which he feels unsure. Guilford (1954) may profitably be consulted by the student who is seriously engaged in designing an experimental investigation of this nature.

The first of these methods, the *method of average error*, is peculiarly suited for use with an apparatus that can be constructed to allow the subject to vary the stimulus values himself until he becomes aware of the stipulated change (presence, absence, just noticeable difference, or just not noticeable difference). This method has proved highly satisfactory for the measurement of loudness and brightness discriminations. The PSE (point of subjective equality) or the RL are simply an average value of the settings obtained. Although an experimenter may in the method of average error move the stimulus value until the subject gives a response, this destroys one of its main advantages and essentially converts it into a method of limits. In fact, this is just what such a procedure does when the lower threshold is under investigation.

The most refined procedures in psychophysics, as well as the most generally applicable, are the *constant methods*. These share the advantage of eliminating constant errors that stem from series effects. They are applied to lower, upper, and difference limens (DL's) and to interval scaling problems. Variations in these methods have been devised to fit special procedural or computing requirements, but the essential approach is that the experimenter selects a limited number of stimulus values for each of which he then obtains a frequency of response. To do this $E$ presents the selected stimuli in a random or prearranged mixed order until each stimulus has been presented an equal and reasonably large number of times. A plotting is thus obtained of the transition between values which give very few responses of a given category to those for which response approaches 100 per cent. The threshold is typically taken as the point (determined by interpolation or curve fitting) at which the function passes through the 50 per cent frequency of response value. Two curves rather than one are obtained in studies of the DL when "equals" judgments are permitted. Their separation at the 50 per cent frequency level is referred to as the interval of uncertainty, which is taken as twice the DL.

Many exploratory experiments with infants and children end at the point of giving preliminary values for absolute thresholds, the RL's. The experimenters could have proceeded from the base of information so provided to plan a psychophysical experiment. This knowledge is needed before the selection of stimulus values is attempted for use with a constant method, and, with this much accomplished, psychophysical studies can proceed.

## Measuring Visual Functions

### THRESHOLDS OF SENSITIVITY

**Sensitivity Thresholds and Innate Response Indicators.** In the newborn infant visual responsiveness is unmistakably present but limited. Neither end-organ nor central nervous pathways are sufficiently developed for more than rudimentary activity. The nature and exact locus of functional deficiencies are only partially understood. By an electrophysiological technique limited responsiveness of the retina can be measured. This technique, the electroretinographic, gives a record of the changes in potential at the eye as measured in relation to a neutral electrode placed on a convenient skin surface. Zetterström (1955–1956) used flicker electroretinography to show a maturation of function during the first eight weeks after birth, which correlates well *in time* with the histological maturation of the macular portion of the retina. Cortical on- and off-responses (Heck and Zetterström, 1958) to single light stimuli, when measured electroencephalographically through scalp and bone over occipital cortex, were first clearly evident only after the age of 6 months. Ellingson (1958) reports an earlier appearance of evoked potentials, with latencies that were much longer than in adults.

The pupillary reflex is functional before birth and has been used to measure increasing sensitivity with age (Sherman and Sherman, 1925). Sudden increases in illumination also produce innate responses of the neck and head. A light of sufficient intensity produces a dorsal head movement. This response, the "eye reflex on the neck," has been used by a number of investigators (Sherman and Sherman, 1925, Peiper, 1926, Trincker and Trincker, 1955) to study the relative sensitivity of the newborn infant to light from different spectral regions and for determining increasing sensitivity with age. It is useful only during the early months, since the response weakens and dies away or becomes suppressed between the second and the sixth month after birth (Trincker and Trincker, 1955). Thresholds are measured with light from narrow wave-band filters (1) for various selected regions of the spectrum and (2) for the light-adapted as compared to the dark-adapted eye. In premature and newborn infants the sensitivity maximum lies close to that of the light-adapted adult eye. By the age of 1 month the curve of relative sensitivity under dark adaptation has shifted to give the typical scotopic (rod receptor) curve.

Another response that has found use is the reduction in general motility induced by increasing the level of illumination (Smith, 1936). Automatic recording by a device known as a sta-bilimeter is employed to obtain quantitative measurements. This method is heavily dependent upon a proper control or evaluation of the level of activity of the subject when the visual change is introduced. Methods employing pupillary reflexes or head movement are somewhat less variable but even these are not free of this problem.

Missing from the literature thus far is a study of the differential thresholds for young infants. The objective methods described above are either poorly adapted to this task, or, what seems more likely, no investigator has applied them with sufficient skill and patience to work out a psychophysical function. Even for older children, from whom sufficient comprehension of the task and cooperation for its accomplishment might be expected, this research has not been completed.

An innate response to movement of a large portion of the visual field, the optokinetic nystagmus, forms the basis of a method that we shall consider further in connection with techniques for measuring acuity. The eyes are induced to move horizontally in an involuntary pursuit of the moving field, wherein each slower pursuit phase is interrupted by a quick return in the opposite direction. This method has possibilities for the measurement of absolute and differential intensity thresholds. It has not been systematically exploited for this purpose nor for the purpose of studying the development of color vision. Theoretically, it would be suited to these purposes if the problems of simultaneously controlling hue and brightness could be solved in conjunction with the requirement that successive bands of light of uniform width be made to move at some optimal speed across the field of vision.

An apparatus that proved quite satisfactory for these purposes was described by Meesman (1944). The image of a small sector of a rotating wheel bearing a translucent spiral design was projected onto a screen, and the luminous intensity of the projected image was controlled by means of light filters and a variable lamp voltage. The image, projected in a field of total darkness, was 56 by 34 centimeters, viewing distance, 30 centimeters, and the widths of the moving stripes, 6 centimeters. These values were justified by Meesman on theoretical grounds and are said to have worked out well in practice. Data are given in his report to show the correspondence between curves of dark adaptation obtained by this method and by subjective (judgmental) responses. Average absolute values and variability are closely parallel over the course of progressive increase in sensitivity, but the "objective" threshold is consistently above that measured by the subjective method.

*Measuring Thresholds in Older Children.* Methods for testing visual sensitivity in older children and adults employ careful psychophysical procedures with accurately calibrated instruments. The best of these give valid and highly reliable measurements when calibration requirements and procedural standards are carefully adhered to. An adaptometer designed by Hecht and Shlaer (1938) for systematically varying the intensity of a test figure was used by Hunt (1941) with children 12 to 19 years of age. A violet test figure, 3 degrees in diameter, is viewed with off-center fixation 7 degrees toward the nasal side of the visual field. Exposure is for $\frac{1}{5}$ second and $S$ must report presence or absence of the figure. This instrument and its procedural requirements have been given careful evaluation. Hunt and Palmer (1940) found some variation between three commercial units of the adaptometer and made recommendations for their calibration. They also evaluated the degree and sources of variation in data obtained from a representative group of inexperienced subjects. They concluded that even with this highly standardized procedure and well-calibrated instrument, "Variation in the subjective criteria of perceptible light flashes may be of sufficient magnitude to account for a considerable proportion of the variation among different individuals in final threshold values obtained after 30 minutes of dark adaptation" (p. 424). The method was sufficiently reliable, nevertheless, to demonstrate differences between groups whose nutritional requirements were being met with different degrees of adequacy (Hunt, 1941).

An earlier instrument described by Ferree and Rand (1931) has been used with children 9 years old to adulthood. Some have taken the data from the Hunt study and from one by Ferree, Rand, and Stoll (1934) to indicate a lesser sensitivity after dark adaptation in preadolescents than in young adults (Zubek and Solberg, p. 179). The data are not extensive enough to justify confidence in this conclusion in view of the variation found and in consideration of the statement quoted concerning possible differences in the criteria of judgment. Given a group of subjects with somewhat more experience as observers and carefully standardized instrumentation, an investigator might obtain data with a minimum of these sources of error, which would settle the question of possible age differences among older children.

In the hands of an expert the instrument of Ferree and Rand has certain advantages. It provides greater flexibility than the Hecht-Schlaer adaptometer for exploratory studies with varied sizes of test fields, largely eliminates effects of the size of the subject's pupil, and minimizes effects of ocular refractive errors and accommodation. An advantage of simplicity of operation and procedure, once calibrations have been made, is held by the Hecht and Shlaer apparatus.

*Critical Flicker Frequency (CFF).* The frequency at which a flashing light can just be discriminated from a steady light of apparently equal luminosity constitutes a threshold of great usefulness in psychophysiological studies of the eye and the visual system. A standard procedure employs a single small luminous area upon which intermittent illumination can be altered in a controlled cycle of light versus dark at a frequency that can be varied continuously over a range above and below the fusion threshold. Subjects are asked to judge when flashes appear to give way to steady light and when steady luminosity changes to flicker. These

judgments are not difficult for older children, but they seem not to have been used at younger ages when the method should be distinctly useful.

For age groups beginning at 13–19, compared with those for each decade thereafter, up to 80–89 years, McFarland et al. (1958) have shown steadily decreasing average CFF's. This study is a distinct contribution to the development of a method that is sensitive to the effects of aging. The authors demonstrated that light flashes should be of short duration, i.e., under 10 per cent of the light-dark cycle, if the method is to be best suited to the measurement of loss of discriminating power as a function of age. McFarland and co-workers used an instrument designed by W. B. Fisher, which produces light flashes of a square waveform. Flash rate could be varied 1 to 125 per second, and the duty cycle (ratio of light to dark) could be varied between 2 and 98 per cent. This instrument is a distinct advance over the episcotister and earlier electronic methods for presenting controlled variations in the parameters known to influence the CFF.

For studying the development of visual sensitivity through thresholds for flicker, a method employing the optokinetic response should be useful in infants and young children. Its chief drawbacks would include some lack of direct comparability with standard CFF procedures and other problems common to the use of innate response indicators. The essential measure would have to be in terms of the speed at which moving striations could no longer be followed, as very effectively

employed in studies of the visual neu-
rophysiology of animals (Crozier and
Wolf, 1941).

## THE DEVELOPMENT
## OF COLOR DISCRIMINATION

*Differential Responses to Wave-
length.* The studies of Peiper and of
Trincker and Trincker, discussed
above, were conceived in terms of the
duplicity theory of retinal sensitivity.
They were designed to ascertain
whether both photopic and scotopic
luminosity curves could be shown to
exist for the newborn infant, and therefore the results have significance for
both the achromatic and the chromatic
aspects of visual function. The results
imply that the newborn infant has receptors that are ready to mediate cone-
like activity in the retina when the eye
is *light-adapted*. Together, these studies
show that the neck reflex provides an
index of the *relative* luminosity curve
of infants, which corresponds to that
of the photopic curve of the adult eye
for wavelengths between 430 and 680
millimicrons. This reflex gives results
that appear to be more valid than those
obtained from a general measure of
body motility and its inhibition (Smith,
1936).

*Hue Discrimination.* To ask whether
infants discriminate one color from another is to pose a more difficult question than the one just considered. At
five spectral regions Trincker and
Trincker (1955) measured the relative
energy required to produce a neck reflex, confirming Peiper's earlier finding
that the newborn infant exhibits the

luminosity curve of *cone* vision. The
result also tells us that the intensity
dimension is alone effective in eliciting
the neck reflex. Some other technique
is required to ascertain whether hues
are discriminable.

Chase (1937) used a method whose
validity is now well supported by the
evidence that under conditions of light
adaptation brightness values can be
equated for infants when we use the
relative sensitivity to different wavelengths of the adult eye. By moving a
small area of colored light within a
colorless field of equivalent brightness
or within a field of a contrasting hue,
Chase was able to obtain visual pursuit
in a high percentage of trials. The
method served well for infants ranging
from 15 to 70 days of age. Control
trials in which the hue of figure and
ground was the same but brightness
differed by as much as 25 per cent gave
negative results. The study indicates
that each of four hues were discriminated one from the other.

To equate luminosity over the entire screen, an area of 24 by 17½ inches,
Chase projected light through Wratten
filters. A square hole was punched
through the center of the gelatin of
the surround, and the test hue was inserted. The projected light flooded the
entire translucent screen, and a Bodine
variable speed motor served to drive
the filter holder back and forth on a
small track. Two observers were used
to obtain independent records of the
infant's eye movements.

For infants of 60 days to 2 years,
Staples (1932) found a preference
method for testing hue discrimination

to be increasingly effective with increasing age. Again equating for brightness, she presented a pair of colored disks or a colored versus a gray disk and observed fixation times. In the youngest group (60 to 143 days) only yellow attracted significantly longer fixation times than grays, although for other colors the direction of difference was always in favor of the colored over the colorless disk. For older groups of children, there were reliable preferences for some colors over others and some shifts of preferences with age. Red was markedly preferred by preschool children but later gave way to blue.

Other techniques that give evidence of color discrimination require matching of objects on the basis of color, the tracing of colored forms, or the naming of forms whose outline is imbedded in discontinuous background figures. Munn (1955, pp. 242–243) has reviewed these studies and comments on the marked improvement found with increasing age of the subject. Negative results with a younger child may not represent an absence of color sensitivity: "All that can be said with assurance is that, as they become older, children improve in color naming and in their discrimination of the figures in pseudo-isochromatic charts like those in the Ishihara and Dvorine tests."

## THE DEVELOPMENT
## OF VISUAL ACUITY

Measurement of the resolving power of the visual system requires accurate specification both of the nature of the test figure and of the background conditions under which it is used. The several classes of acuity can be compared if each is expressed in terms of the visual angle subtended by an object or the visual angle of a gap that can just be perceived. Any test of a threshold of acuity shows some change in the minimum resolvable visual angle with variation in illumination or brightness. For a bright line or a dot that is made narrower and narrower within a dark field, the effect of luminosity is so strong that it can always be made to compensate for a reduction in size of the test object. Control of luminosity and of the adaptation of the eye are so critical as to be impractical for routine or large scale testing. Measures of acuity therefore usually rely on a determination of the *minimum separable*, as distinguished from the minimum visible. When the minimum separable is expressed in seconds or minutes, a direct measure is given of the arc of the visual angle subtended by the distance between test bars at the threshold. *Visual acuity* is defined as the reciprocal of this angle, the angle being measured in minutes. Under good conditions of testing, acuity reaches a value of 2.0, corresponding to a visual angle of one half minute. The conventional Snellen fraction represents "normal" acuity as 20/20, which corresponds to a visual acuity of 1 or a resolution of one minute of visual angle (Bartley, 1958, Ch. 7).

*Innate ("Objective") Indicators of Acuity.* Ohm, who in 1922 originally described the use of optokinetic nystagmus as a method of examining the excitability of the human visual system, has more recently (Ohm, 1952) commented on several European variations of this "objective" indicator. He also reiterates a warning against the uncritical application of this technique. One limitation of considerable importance lies in the relative contribution of the peripheral retina, which is more active in mediating the response to motion of a large portion of the visual field than the fovea. This means that optokinetic nystagmus measures something less than maximum resolving power when the striations have been reduced in width to the point at which eye movements are no longer elicited. All words of caution notwithstanding, the promise of this method for studying visual development during infancy and early childhood should have been recognized sooner and exploited more extensively than is yet the case.

McGinnis (1930) demonstrated that the response can be elicited on the day of birth. A proper level of alertness is necessary, as shown by the fact that the eye movements do not occur when the eyes of a sleeping infant are gently separated during movement of the optokinetic drum. Gorman, Cogan, and Gellis (1957) have applied a simplified version of the McGinnis technique to the measurement of 100 infants under 5 days of age. They used a field that moved at a rate of 8.5 degrees per second, with either of two widths for the alternating lines and spaces. When each line and space subtended 33.5 minutes, they found nystagmus occurred in 93 of the infants, but with widths of 11.1 minutes of visual angle the response generally failed. The larger width is equivalent to a Snellen notation of 20/670. Without intervening steps for testing purposes, these authors were unable to find any change in acuity between days 1 and 5 and concluded that more work with this method is needed to determine the acuity of young infants. Warkentin and Smith (1937) have given us a more precise developmental study, using this technique with kittens between birth and 30 days of age, and report that the first response to stripe widths of eleven minutes occurs between days 23 and 30.

Using children as subjects, Reinecke and Cogan (1958) compared acuities determined by the optokinetic method with those obtained from Snellen charts. Snellen acuity was frequently higher than the index obtained with the optokinetic drum. The correlation between the measures was +.66 for 100 subjects. These experimenters used lines and spaces that were equal in width, and they had series of widths ranging from 0.333 to 0.028 inch, presented at 1 meter from the eye. For those subjects who still showed response to the narrowest stripes at 1 meter, the distance was increased to 2.5 meters.

For infants older than 6 weeks, McGinnis (1930) reported that visual pursuit of a single line moving slowly across the visual field could be elicited reliably, and the response was easily recorded by him on motion-picture film. If we assume that fixation and pursuit of such a visual stimulus depends, as it almost certainly does, on foveal vision, this method could furnish the basis for a developmental study of foveal acuity.

*Judgmental Tests of Acuity.* For

subjects capable of voluntary cooperation and compliance with instructions, a more complex form of visual stimulus is used for the acuity target. The Snellen illiterate E test is such a standard instrument for use with preschool children. Stern (1953) suggests that instead of relying on the chart and a verbal description by the child of the position of the E it helps to use a series of solid plastic E's. The child is given such an E and is shown how he can turn it to match the position of the examiner's E. Then the examiner places smaller E's in varying orientation against a viewing screen and the child continues to turn his E to correspond. "Children as young as 2 years old have been tested to 20/30 vision in each eye by this method."

Allen (1957) offers a new picture test, which he claims often works when the illiterate E test is unsatisfactory, as is sometimes the case with 3- and 4-year-olds. Eight broken-line black-on-white pictures are used in this test. Most normal 3-year-olds recognized the pictures at 15 feet and 4-year-olds, at 20 feet. Using the illiterate E test for validation, Allen found that 20/40 vision did not permit recognition of the pictures at 20 feet. Approximate norms and Snellen equivalents are indicated, as is also the manufacturer of the test equipment, Ophthalmix, Inc., Brookfield, Illinois. Comparing the variability of five different types of chart figures in common use (letters, figures, pictures, Landolt rings, and E-hooks), Jonkers (1958) reports standard deviations between .04 (for letters) and .15 (for pictures). His data are derived from children aged 5 years and over.

For children of school age, several commercially available tests of acuity are in use. These are offered in combination with tests for stereopsis or binocular fusion and for measures of the degree to which the eyes orient in parallel along the line of sight. Such combined "screening" tests are much used in schools and in industrial establishments. The Massachusetts Vision Test was given by Leverett (1957) to children from kindergarten age through the twelfth grade. A consistent increase in the proportion of children showing less than 20/20 vision was found with increase in grade level. The phoria test showed that there was a similar trend toward deviating positions of the eyes. In one study of children from grades 1 through 12 (Kelley, 1957) the Keystone Telebinocular was selected "because it proved better adapted to testing very young children, and it was desired that the same instrument be used with all grades." The basic principle of the Keystone instrument, like that of the Bausch and Lomb Ortho-Rater, is that of the older and familiar Brewster stereoscope. Tests for acuity at near and at far (about 20 to 25 feet), for monocular and binocular performance, fusion, and degrees of phoria are provided in the Ortho-Rater or the Keystone. One compact instrument with a series of precision-constructed test plates can be used for the battery of interrelated tests (Robinson, 1953).

*Pattern Discrimination.* The problem of more complex visual pattern discrimination is beyond the scope of this chapter. However, the transition between acuity measurements and pattern vision is not one with a sharp cut-off. Pattern preferences in infants under 6 months of age have been demonstrated by Fantz (1958), who proposes also to use such preferences as a method for measuring acuity. The technique involves a comparison between relative fixation times exhibited by the infant to one of two simultaneously presented visual patterns. Horizontal stripes were found to be preferred over concentric circles. As in the training technique used by Riesen (1958) with infant chimpanzees, the evaluation of acuity can be made by using stripes of varying widths.

Ling (1941) found a training method satisfactory for the study of learned form discriminations in babies of 6 to 12 months. The technique is reported to give an initial discrimination between forms such as circle versus cross or circle versus triangle in 40 training trials to a criterion of four out of five correct responses. The method Ling used was to fasten one form down and leave the other free to be picked up and brought to the mouth, whereupon the child found it sweet to the taste. The circle versus oval blocks method was most difficult, which suggests immediately that it would lend itself to a measurement of differential thresholds for form acuity.

## Measuring Auditory Receptivity

For detecting a sensitivity of the ear in newborn infants, some reflex responses are useful but not so readily observed as in vision. Pure tones produce little or no response of any kind. High intensity noise is quite often reported to startle or to produce an increase in general bodily activity. For anatomical reasons, it is usually presumed that hearing in the newborn is interfered with by external and middle-ear impediments, especially by amnionic fluid remaining in the middle ear, where it impedes motion of the ossicles. Authors have sometimes erroneously asserted that newborn babies hear nothing.

## SENSITIVITY TO NOISE IN THE FETUS AND NEWBORN

*Sound Induced Reflexes.* The generalized muscular contraction often referred to as the "startle response" has been used to test the sensitivity of the fetus and newborn infant. Forbes and Forbes (1927) reported observations of this response through the mother's abdominal wall thirty-one days before term. Froeschels and Beebe (1946) looked for any or all movements that infants might make to the sound of tuning forks or whistles. Tuning forks proved ineffective in 33 newborn to 9-day-old infants, but the noisy onset of whistles produced responses in 29 of these. An acoustopalpebral reflex was the most frequent positive indicator observed.

Whereas newborn chimpanzees, some other infrahuman primates, and many laboratory mammals reliably exhibit a pinna reflex to a bell or whistle, this response is only occasionally reported by those who study human infants. Forbes and Forbes (1927, pp. 354–355) cite their observation of an 8-day-old infant who was stimulated with "soft notes from a gong coming from behind. . . . The baby's ear at once flattened against the side of its head and for a few seconds it stopped nursing, then the ear relaxed again and nursing continued." What may be the same response and was called "ad concham" is reported for four of the 33 subjects of Froeschels and Beebe (1946). A reflex of the tensor tympani has also been used to indicate the presence of hearing. Kobrak (1957) describes in detail a technique for making this response visible through a system of mirrors and a reflected light beam that moves with motion of the eardrum.

The galvanic skin response of young adults has been shown to vary directly in magnitude with the intensity of a pure tone (Hovland and Riesen, 1940). Stimuli near the lower limits of audibility were not used in this study. The use of sound-induced reflexes shares the common disadvantage that useful data on thresholds are seldom obtained because all of these indicators require at least moderately intense stimulation if the reflex mechanism is to be activated. Lower limits of stimulus intensity and response could, however, prove diagnostic if careful quantification on normal populations were first carried out.

For evaluating the hearing of babies between 3 and 5 weeks of age, Haller (1932) made observations of general somatic responses to pure tones. She varied these along both intensity and pitch dimensions. This represents an attempt to do a very rough kind of audiometry and might be improved upon somewhat by the use of better controlled conditions. The Dockeray and Valentine (1939) isolation cabinet was proposed for such purposes. The main conclusion of Haller's study is that tones of high frequency and high intensity produce restlessness. There was also the suggestion that low-frequency tones have a quieting effect.

*Electrophysiological Methods.* The electrical response at the cortex to clicks of varying intensity can give an estimate of hearing impairment (Perl, Galambos, and Glorig, 1953). As compared with subjective thresholds, the EEG threshold determined by visual inspection of the EEG records is higher. Newer electronic summators could be employed to reduce the amount of discrepancy between psychophysical limens and those taken by electroencephalography. With pure tone audiometry and evaluations of the effects of pure tones on EEG patterns with respect to onset, continuation, termination and delayed arousal reactions, Derbyshire et al. (1956) reported statistical comparisons of thresholds obtained from 22 children (aged 4 to 13 years) with normal and impaired hearing. Average differences between standard audiometric and EEG thresholds ranged from 4 to 40 decibels. The EEG responses were interpreted as reflecting activation of a diffuse arousal system. This conclusion was based on the authors' experience with a much larger sample of subjects for whom no effect of age from 3 months to 27 years was seen in the records and in whom similar responses were obtained by stimulation of other sensory modalities. Derbyshire and co-authors state that they obtained audiometric and EEG records in which these two sources of information were for diagnostic purposes more useful taken together than either would have been alone.

***Special Evaluative Procedures for Infants and Children.*** Those specialists who must evaluate the hearing of infants and younger children agree that pure tones have little interest value and that the standard audiometric procedure is unsatisfactory with most children up to 5 years of age. Myklebust (1954) urges that the mental and emotional status of the child be appraised as preliminary steps to auditory tests for the reason that "failure to respond to an auditory stimulus does not necessarily mean inability to hear" (Myklebust, p. 242).

Several authors (Ewing and Ewing, 1944; Myklebust, 1954) find that the use of whispered speech often brings good response when louder sounds do not. Other meaningful sounds, some of which are learned as early as 2 months, serve in the assessment of receptive and interpretive capacity. These and other methods were evaluated in a survey study done on 91 presumably normal children and 170 children suspected of deafness (Ewing and Ewing, 1944). For children 3 to 6 years old, Bloomer (1942) utilized pictures of objects that children associate with sound to obtain responses in pure tone audiometry. The verbal instructions and required behavior are simple. The child is asked to listen for a sound that will be a "train whistle" or a "bird song." They are to touch the pictured object or animal as soon as they hear it and to remove their hands from the picture as soon as it stops. Bloomer suggests that

only three or four frequencies be tested during a given session and that for a complete audiogram a second session be scheduled for another day.

Techniques for conditioning infants or children to give responses to sound stimuli by pairing them with a reinforcing stimulus have been described and evaluated by several investigators. Hirsh (1952, Ch. 10) discussed the varieties of such methods and compared them with standard audiometric procedures, which he regarded as not fundamentally different in that they have in common the utilization of learned responses as indicators of auditory sensitivity. However, conditioning procedures that are based on the classical conditioning of involuntary (autonomic) responses have the possible advantage of placing fewer demands on the voluntary cooperation of the subject. For this reason, they have sometimes been especially advocated for testing infants and younger children.

A study whose primary objective was the determination of the conditionability of very young infants (Wickens and Wickens, 1940) successfully demonstrated auditory sensitivity of babies aged 10 days or under. These investigators paired buzzer and shock 12 times daily for three days, the shock being applied to the foot to produce a withdrawal movement. In a control group it was found that applying the shock alone was as effective as the pairing, for in the total of 24 subjects 20 gave foot withdrawal movements to the sound alone, nine of these having received paired stimulation and 11 only the shock. The pseudo-conditioning was thus as capable of bringing out the auditory responsivity of these very young infants as the classical conditioning procedure.

The conditioned galvanic skin response was found effective in screening hundreds of children for hearing defects at the Johns Hopkins Hospital (Bordley and Hardy, 1949; Bordley, 1952). These authors report that in children of 1 and 2 years of age a tone and shock need be paired only a few times. Thereafter, response continues for many trials over a wide frequency range. Results were checked against a standard audiometry test in slightly older children, who gave sufficient cooperation to permit this procedure. Still another standard conditioning technique has paired pure tones (the CS) with air-puff stimulation of the cornea (Galloway and Butler, 1956). For 20 subjects, the difference between thresholds obtained by audiometric tests and those measured by this conditioned eyelid response averaged approximately 5 decibels.

Hirsh (1952) and others have reported considerable interest in the instrumental (operant) conditioning technique of Dix and Hallpike (1947). A pure tone sounded for short intervals of time is made the occasion for reinforcement during a "peep-show" game. After a training session, the young child who can hear demonstrates this capacity by turning promptly after the onset of the tone to the peep-show window and pressing the button to illuminate the interesting picture or object. During silent periods the button is ineffective. This technique differs from standard audiometry primarily in that it minimizes any need for the understanding of instructions and for the child's giving verbal reports of what he hears.

Older children can tolerate the repetition necessary for a thorough psychophysical procedure in the audiometric measurement of thresholds over a wide range of frequencies. Nevertheless, there is something to be said for the time-saving advantages of an audiometer in which the subject adjusts the tonal intensities over his threshold range rather than having to make judgments in an arbitrary prearranged series or in a series that the examiner adjusts as he gradually rules out the more extreme and less useful settings. The Békésy (1947) audiometer produces a continuous increase of intensity as long as the subject holds down a button, a continuous decrease after release. The absolute threshold and difference limens can be recorded over a wide range of frequencies (500 to 15,000 cycles per second). Corso (1955) determined that an attenuation rate of 0.5 decibel per second was optimal; i.e., it produces the best test-retest reliability for threshold determinations at 1000 cycles per second.

It is clear from the writings of the clinically oriented specialists that if all children at various ages and presenting abnormal as well as normal hearing capacities are to be evaluated several techniques must be available. A systematic study of a normal population of very young children could be done with a specific technique and would have the merits of reproducibility as well as contributing to further validation of that procedure.

## Testing the Chemoreceptors

### TASTE SENSITIVITY

***Taste in the Newborn.*** For studying gustatory and olfactory sensitivity in the infant, there are more methods than there are developmental data described in the literature. There is need for further refinement in methodology, but much could be learned by the application of currently available procedures. In addition to general problems of improving thresholds, the question of the possible differential development of the several receptor areas within the mouth needs investigation, and this would require a method of controlling the cite of stimulation more adequately than any currently in use.

For studying taste sensitivity in newborn infants, the standard stimuli, sweet, sour, salt, and bitter and occasionally more complex stimuli, such as human versus cow's milk, have been used. The solutions have been applied with cotton applicators or through a nipple. Pulse, breathing, body movement, and sucking responses have been observed or recorded automatically. Change from base-line scores or contrast scores are used as a measure of differential sensitivity.

Pratt, Nelson, and Sun (1930) used the applicators and measured changes in general activity, as recorded on the stabilimeter-polygraph. Citric acid and quinine were about equally effective in raising the level of activity. To sugar and salt the newborn infant was much more likely to show increased sucking movements than changes in general bodily activity. These were not part of the records taken on the polygraph. It

remained for Jensen (1932) to develop a technique that permitted analysis of detailed records of sucking responses. Momentary changes in pressure and volume consumed as a function of time were recorded on cumulative curves from his elaborate manometer system, timer, and polygraph. Temperature of the fluid stimulant was held constant (except when he studied it as the independent variable). Nipples were calibrated carefully for rate of flow, matched pairs of nipples being used for the experimental and control feedings. The chief inadequacy of this method lies in the absence of control over the area that is stimulated within the mouth. That it employs a most natural and a discriminative indicator response is attested to by results obtained, and it is to be regretted that the method has not been applied to infants other than Jensen's group of 2-to-16-day-old hospital babies.

Jensen used five concentrations of salt solution for determining differential reactions compared with milk. Apparently a descending method of limits gave him the results in his Table 4, which showed that no infant discriminated the 0.200 per cent salt solution and that 13 of 14 discriminated the 0.900 per cent solution. All are weaker solutions than those recommended by Börnstein (1940–1941) for the detection of taste impairment in man.

***Techniques with Older Subjects.*** Taste-testing the anthropoid apes (Fisher, Ford, and Huxley, 1939) has been accomplished by a procedure that also employs a behavioral sign of reluctance or strong aversion. It would be applicable to human subjects over a wide range of ages. About 30 per cent of a chimpanzee population was found to be clearly distinguished from the remainder of the group on the basis of refusal or willingness to drink a 2 per cent sucrose solution containing 50 parts per million of phenyl-thio-carbamide. Threshold work could easily be done by a method of constant stimuli. Fisher and co-workers, for example, used two other concentrations and found that nontasters were unable to detect even 400 parts per million, whereas some tasters refused a solution containing only 6¼ parts per million. The use of quinine for determining changes in threshold for the sensory quality of *bitter* is standard practice. Here, again, rejection is used as a criterion (Moncrieff, 1946) when verbal judgments are not possible.

Very young children and animals are found to accept solutions having a sweet taste in preference to distilled water. This was the basis on which sucrose taste thresholds were compared in rats, school children, adults up to 50 years of age, and elderly subjects, 52 to 85 years old (Richter and Campbell, 1940). For the rats, the criterion was in terms of relative quantity of fluid consumed. The human subjects judged first when a difference between the sucrose solution and distilled water could be detected and then reported at what point they recognized a sweet taste. An ascending method of limits was used, the concentrations being increased from a value of 0.01 per cent in a standard series of steps. Rats and young adult humans exhibited nearly equivalent sucrose (sweet) taste thresholds of approxi-

mately 0.5 and 0.4 per cent. The 58 children averaged 0.68 per cent, and the 52 elderly individuals, 1.23 per cent. In making their judgments, the human subjects were permitted to taste the sucrose solution and the distilled water, contained in glasses held in either hand, as often as they wished before giving their statements.

## OLFACTORY SENSITIVITY

Even fewer developmental studies of odor thresholds than of taste are in the literature. Methods applicable specifically to infants and children are sparse, indeed, and depend exclusively upon signs of aversion, irritation, or pleasure, the last of these being the most difficult to evaluate. Lack of adequate methods has produced contradictory statements by different investigators, some of whom deny that newborn infants exhibit any sense of smell.

Disher (1934) made no claim that her method differentiated smell from taste. With a syringe she pushed air or samples of gas from collecting tubes and mixed with air into the nostrils of infants. Two observers and a motion-picture record gave her the data on face and mouth movements, movements of extremities, breathing changes, eye movements, head movements, and vocalizations. Movements of face and mouth are reported to have been 25 per cent more frequent after use of an odorous substance than after the use of air. Other parts of the body gave lesser degrees of increase in activity. There was no clear indication of differential effects from different odors. The extent and frequency of responses did show increase with higher concentrations of the olfactory stimuli.

Other investigations (Pratt, Nelson, and Sun, 1930; Stirnimann, 1936) used automatic recording apparatus for measuring general bodily motility or graphic recording of respiratory and circulatory changes. When such strong stimuli as ammonia or acetic acid have been used, the interpretation of the results is confused by the question whether pain, gustatory, or olfactory receptors are involved.

*Pain Sensitivity.* Cutaneous pain is clearly a distinct sensory process, having separate receptors and central pathways. Relations between this mode and the responses to intense stimulation of receptors for temperature and pressure and the distance receptors have not been clearly determined. Central physiological correlates of pain need further study before the common factor of extreme discomfort from mechanical, thermal, light, vibratory, and chemical irritants can be understood (Morgan and Stellar, 1950, Ch. 11).

For the study of the young organism, a frequently used method has been to observe motor and autonomic response to pinprick. Most observers express some degree of surprise at the mildness of reactions elicited in fetal and newborn mammals, including man. Carmichael expresses this for the guinea pig, as observed approximately five days prenatally or at 63 days postcopulation age. Needle stimulation produced flexion or extension, including in many cases rhythmic limb movements, but "no indication of violent response or of the behavioral signs of pain were noted" (Carmichael, 1934,

p. 413). The newborn human infant responds inconsistently or not at all to pinprick (McGraw, 1943, p. 102). A week or so later crying and general bodily movements occur, with sometimes a local flexion of the member stimulated. McGraw interprets this as a reflex movement, for there is a subsequent phase in which no localization of the stimulation, little crying, and only a widening of the eyes and some facial muscle activity give evidence that neural activation occurs. The infant at 150 days first shows deliberate withdrawal and a visual search for the spot being irritated. Perhaps this is the time of onset of an adult type of painful experience, prior reactions having been largely reflex or subcortical in their mediation.

Painful cold and heat presumably involve receptors other than or in addition to those mediating temperature sensitivity. Failure to react to painful burns and cuts is sometimes observed as a congenital anomaly and is not necessarily associated with other sensory incapacities (Boyd and Nie, 1949). Evidence obtained does not tell us whether peripheral sensory or central neural dysfunction is involved. However, this independence of function is not crucial to the question of a receptor for thermal pain. In Carmichael's study of the prenatal guinea-pig (1934, p. 436) he was not certain whether true temperature stimulation or pain stimulation or both were involved in the extremes of heat and cold used.

The studies by Dockeray and Rice (1934), Sherman, Sherman, and Flory (1936), and McGraw (1941) all agree in their demonstration of marked changes in response to pinprick or electric-shock stimulation as a function of age and experience between birth and 6 months. More work is needed on the anatomical and neurophysiological maturation of pain receptors (Bishop, 1944), conduction pathways, and neural centers that are involved in pain. The problem of a behavioral criterion plagues workers with adult subjects almost as seriously as those studying infants. Beecher (1957, p. 115), who has nothing to say about this for infants, indicates in his voluminous review that the problem is difficult: "Unfortunately there is no bodily reaction in man which occurs only in response to pain."

Apparently, no specific methods for infant or child studies of other kinds of pain have been systematically developed. Deep somatic pain and visceral pain must be regarded as distinct from cutaneous pain but are even more difficult to study experimentally.

## Vestibular and Somesthetic Receptivity

### MECHANISMS OF EQUILIBRIUM OF THE INNER EAR

The so-called "sense" of equilibrium is usually specifically identified with sensory activity from the semicircular canals and vestibular sacs of the inner ear. Ordinarily a person also uses cues from vision and kinesthesis to maintain bodily equilibrium. The functions of the labyrinthine receptors are consequently more difficult to isolate and study than are either the auditory or visual functions. In other words, as Geldard (1953,

p. 249) has pointed out, the subject is unaware of any direct sensations from the labyrinths. A sense of motion, loss of equilibrium, or dizziness are pure indicators of activity of the labyrinths only when visual, kinesthetic, and other organic receptors are held in a steady state. This is a problem that must be faced when techniques for study are being developed.

***Reflex Response Thresholds.*** Except for simple reflex indicators of gross responsivity within the vestibular mechanisms, there are no studies on infants and children that attempt to solve methodological problems and obtain normative developmental data for this system. Animal experimentation has been more extensive, but the methods are in many instances inapplicable for use with human subjects. Changes in rate of bodily motion are the normal physical correlates of labyrinthine stimulation. Temperature and mechanical stimuli can be used to indicate the presence of sensory processes, but these we will ignore in the discussion of the developmental study of this system, useful as they are for physiological investigation.

Asking the child for a judgment of linear or rotary motion or nonmotion is a potentially useful approach. It seems not to have been exploited systematically except, however, with adults (Dodge, 1923). A more sensitive indicator and perhaps a much easier judgment for a young subject is the *oculogyral illusion*, as employed in studies of adults by Graybiel, Kerr, and Bartley (1948). This illusion depends upon sensitivity to rotary motion. The chief technical problem is that of control and accurate measurement of rotary acceleration or deceleration. The subject sits in a specially mounted chair. A tachometer is typically used to measure rotation rates, which are themselves produced under only approximate control. Either a throttle or voltage regulator, depending upon the source of power, may be used to govern changes in speed of rotation. Many trials are given to explore the responses in the region of the absolute threshold and to provide continuous response curves from an average value of no apparent movement to consistent apparent movement in one direction or the other (to right or to left).

Judgment of the oculo-gyral illusion is made in three categories, the chief requirement being that the subject understand the instructions to report whether the single visual target exposed between periods of darkness is seen to move to the right or the left or to remain still. Graybiel et al. used a six-pointed collimated star whose three-dimensional properties are said to have reduced the difficulty otherwise encountered from the autokinetic illusion. They permitted judgments by exposing the star at intervals of twenty seconds. Less difficulty with nystagmoid after-effects of motion would be encountered if trials were spaced at intervals of sixty seconds, permitting the attainment of a steady state during the period of constant rate of rotation between trials. This method gives the slowest rates of angular acceleration thresholds in adult subjects obtained: on the order of 0.12 degrees per sec.$^2$

A method for the direct measurement of vestibular nystagmus by recording eye movements was devised by Dohlmann (1935). Neither this method nor the more modern photographic methods for recording eye movements have been used for developmental studies of vestibular sensitivity. Since they would require only the passive cooperation of the subject, these methods would be highly feasible for studies of younger children. Threshold values are typically about 1.0 degree per sec.$^2$ when this method is used in adults, which compares favorably with values of nearly 2.0 degrees per sec.$^2$ when the judgment of perceived motion is required.

***Other Potential Methods.*** It is clear from the verbal judgments that children can make with respect to rotational and postrotational effects that learned responses could be used in this sense mode as in hearing and vision. Further confirmation of such possibilities comes from the successful conditioning of animals with angular acceleration as the conditioned stimulus (Spiegel and Oppenheimer, 1939).

## Temperature, Contact, and Pressure Sensitivity

Although there has been some work on the first appearance of temperature, touch, and pressure sensitivity in the developing fetus and some demonstrations of sensitivity in the newborn, studies of these receptor modalities are conspicuously absent from the literature on infant and child development. Pratt,

Nelson, and Sun (1930) elicited vigorous bodily responses to cold by using a temperature cylinder. More satisfactory control of tactual conditions was obtained by Crudden (1937), who left capsules in contact with the skin. These had inflow and outflow tubes to permit the prompt alteration of temperature by fluid interchange. Motion-picture and protocol records were taken of respiration and movement. Indications from a few records taken with three older infants encouraged Crudden to conclude that local responses increased with age. Respiratory changes were the promptest and most consistent responses noted.

Carmichael and Lehner (1937) used a method of constant stimuli to study the development of sensitivity in fetal animals. Their criterion of response to temperature was based on a comparison with the effect of tactual stimulation from drops of fluid of 37.5°C., the physiological neutral point.

Jensen (1932) reports threshold values in newborn infants for hot and for cold in the mouth. His technique has been described in connection with his work on taste thresholds (see p. 299).

For touch and/or pressure, our information includes some rough comparisons of different bodily surfaces. About the only firm conclusion is that the region about the mouth is one of the earliest to develop sensitivity and retains priority thereafter as one of the more sensitive areas (Fitzgerald and Windle, 1942; Hooker, 1952). Touch, pressure, and somesthesis are each greatly in need of methodological advancement and developmental study.

## REFERENCES

Allen, H. F. 1957. Testing of visual acuity in preschool children. *Pediatrics*, 19, 1093–1100.

Bartley, S. H. 1958. *Principles of perception.* New York: Harper.

Beecher, H. K. 1957. The measurement of pain. *Pharmacol. Rev.*, 9, 59–209.

Békésy, G. von 1947. A new audiometer. *Acta Otolaryng., Stockh.*, 35, 411–422.

Bishop, G. H. 1944. The structural identity of the pain spot in human skin. *J. Neurophysiol.*, 7, 184–198.

Bloomer, H. 1942. A simple method for testing the hearing of small children. *J. Speech Dis.* 7, 311–312.

Bordley, J. E. 1952. The problem of the preschool deaf child. *Laryngoscope*, 62, 514–520.

———, and W. G. Hardy. 1949. A study in objective audiometry with the use of a psychogalvanometric response. *Ann. Otol., Rhinol. Laryng.*, 58, 751–760.

Börnstein, W. S. 1940–1941. The localization of the cortical taste area in man and a method for measuring impairment of taste in man. *Yale J. Biol. Med.*, 13, 133–136.

Boyd, D. A., Jr., and L. W. Nie. 1949. Congenital universal indifference to pain. *Arch. Neurol. Psychiat.*, 61, 402–412.

Carmichael, L. 1934. An experimental study in the prenatal guinea-pig of the origin and development of reflexes and patterns of behavior in relation to the stimulation of specific receptor areas during the period of active fetal life. *Genet. Psychol. Monogr.*, 16, 337–491.

———, and G. F. J. Lehner. 1937. The development of temperature sensitivity during the fetal period. *J. genet. Psychol.*, 50, 217–227.

Chase, W. P. 1937. Color vision in infants. *J. exp. Psychol.*, 20, 203–222.

Corso, J. F. 1955. Evaluation of operating conditions on a Békésy-type audiometer. *Arch Otolaryng.*, 61, 649–653.

Crane, M. M., F. M. Foote, R. G. Scobee, and E. L. Green. 1954. Screening school children for visual defects. Children's Bureau Publication Number 345, Washington: U. S. Government Printing Office.

Crozier, W. J., and E. Wolf. 1941. Theory and measurement of visual mechanisms. *J. gen. Physiol.*, **24**, 635–654.

Crudden, C. H. 1937. Reactions of newborn infants to thermal stimuli under constant tactual conditions. *J. exp. Psychol.*, **20**, 350–370.

Derbyshire, A. J., A. A. Fraser, M. McDermott, and A. Bridge. 1956. Audiometric measurements by electroencephalography. *EEG Clin. Neurophysiol.*, **8**, 467–478.

Disher, D. R. 1934. The reactions of newborn infants to chemical stimuli administered nasally. *Ohio State Univer. Stud., Contr. Psychol.*, **12**, 1–52.

Dix, M. R., and C. S. Hallpike. 1947. The peep-show: a new technique for pure-tone audiometry in young children. *Brit. med. J.*, **2**, 719–731.

Dockeray, F. C., and C. Rice. 1934. Responses of newborn infants to pain stimulation. *Ohio State Univer. Stud., Contrib. Psychol.*, **12**, 82–93.

———, and W. L. Valentine. 1939. A new isolation cabinet for infant research. *J. exp. Psychol.*, **24**, 211–214.

Dodge, R. 1923. Thresholds of rotation. *J. exp. Psychol.*, **6**, 107–137.

Dohlmann, G. 1935. Towards a method for quantitative measurement of the functional capacity of the vestibular apparatus. *Acta Otolaryng., Stockh.*, **23**, 50–62.

Ellingson, R. J. 1958. Electroencephalograms of normal, full-term newborns immediately after birth with observations on arousal and visual evoked responses. *EEG Clin. Neurophysiol.*, **10**, 31–50.

Ewing, I. R., and A. W. G. Ewing. 1944. The ascertainment of deafness in infancy and early childhood. *J. Laryng.* **59**, 309–333.

Fantz, R. L. 1958. Pattern vision in young infants. *Psychol. Rec.*, **8**, 43–47.

Ferree, C. E., and G. Rand. 1931. A new type of instrument for testing the light and color sense. *Amer. J. Ophthal.*, **14**, 325–333.

———, and M. R. Stoll. 1934. Critical values for the light minimum and for the amount and rapidity of dark adaptation. *Brit. J. Ophthal.*, **18**, 673–687.

Fisher, R. A., E. B. Ford, and J. Huxley. 1939. Taste-testing the anthropoid apes. *Nature*, **144**, 750.

Fitzgerald, J. E., and W. F. Windle. 1942. Some observations on early human fetal activity. *J. comp. Neurol.*, **76**, 159–167.

Forbes, H. S., and H. B. Forbes. 1927. Fetal sense reaction: Hearing. *J. comp. Psychol.*, **7**, 353–355.

Froeschels, E., and H. Beebe. 1946. Testing the hearing of newborn infants. *Arch. Otolaryng.*, **44**, 710–714.

Galloway, F. T., and R. A. Butler. 1956. Conditioned eyelid response to tone as an objective test of hearing. *J. Speech Dis.* **21**, 47–55.

Geldard, F. A. 1953. *The human senses.* New York: Wiley.

Gorman, J. J., D. G. Cogan, and S. S. Gellis. 1957. An apparatus for grading the visual acuity of infants on the basis of opticokinetic nystagmus. *Pediatrics*, **19**, 1088–1092.

Graybiel, A., W. A. Kerr, and S. H. Bartley. 1948. Stimulus thresholds of the semicircular canals as a function of angular acceleration. *Amer. J. Psychol.*, **61**, 21–36.

Guilford, J. P. 1954. *Psychometric methods.* (2nd Ed.) New York: McGraw-Hill.

Haller, Mary W. 1932. The reactions of infants to changes in the intensity and pitch of pure tone. *J. genet. Psychol.*, **40**, 162–180.

Hecht, S., and S. Shlaer. 1938. An adaptometer for measuring dark adaptation. *J. opt. Soc. Amer.*, **28**, 269–275.

Heck, J., and Birgitta Zetterström. 1958. Electroencephalographic recording of the on-and-off response from the human visual cortex. *Ophthalmologica*, **136**, 258–265.

Hellström, B., and Birgitta Zetterström. 1956. The effect of light on the manifestation of the electroretinogram and on histochemically demonstrable SH-groups in the retina. *Exp. Cell Res.* **10**, 248–251.

Hirsh, I. 1952. *The measurement of hearing.* New York: McGraw-Hill.

Hooker, D. 1952. *The prenatal origin of behavior.* Lawrence: Univer. Kansas Press.

Hovland, C. I., and A. H. Riesen. 1940. Magnitude of galvanic and vasomotor response as a function of stimulus intensity. *J. gen. Psychol.*, **23**, 103–121.

Hunt, Eleanor P. 1941. Dark adaptation of high school children at different income levels. *Milbank mem. Fd. quart. Bull.*, 19, 252–281.

———, and C. E. Palmer. 1940. Medical evaluation of nutritional status. II. Measurement of visual dark adaptation with the adaptometer. *Milbank. mem. Fd. quart. Bull.*, 18, 403–424.

Jensen, K. 1932. Differential reactions to taste and temperature stimuli in newborn infants. *Genet. Psychol. Monogr.*, 12, 367–479.

Jonkers, G. H. 1958. The examination of the visual acuity of children. *Ophthalmologica*, 136, 140–144.

Kelley, C. R. 1957. *Visual screening and child development: the North Carolina study*. Raleigh: North Carolina State College.

Kobrak, H. G. 1957. Utilization of an unconscious muscle reflex for the determination of sound perception. *Arch. Otolaryng.*, 65, 26–31.

Lange, Fr. 1952. Untersuchungen zur normalen Verteilung des Lichtsinns in der Netzhaut und ihrer Altersabhängigkeit. *Albr. v. Graefes Arch. Ophthal.*, 153, 93–104.

Leverett, H. M. 1957. Vision test performance of school children. *Amer. J. Ophthal.* 44, 508–519.

Ling, Bing-Chung, 1941. Form discrimination as a learning cue in infants. *Comp. Psychol. Monogr.*, 17, No. 2, 66 pp.

McFarland, R. A., A. B. Warren, and C. Karis. 1958. Alterations in critical flicker frequency as a function of age and light-dark ratio. *J. exp. Psychol.*, 56, 529–538.

McGinnis, J. M. 1930. Eye-movements and optic nystagmus in early infancy. *Genet. Psychol. Monogr.*, 8, No. 4, 321–430.

McGraw, Myrtle B. 1941. Neural maturation as exemplified in the changing reactions of the infant to pin prick. *Child Develp.*, 12, 31–41.

———. 1943. *The neuromuscular maturation of the human infant*. New York: Columbia Univer. Press.

Meesmann, A. 1944. Über ein Projections-adaptometer zur subjektiven und objektiven Adaptometrie (Rieken). *Klin. Mbl. Augenheilk.*, 110, 446–459.

Moncrieff, R. W. 1946. *The chemical senses*. New York: Wiley.

Morgan, C. T., and E. Stellar. 1950. *Physiological psychology*. (2nd Ed.) New York: McGraw-Hill.

Munn, N. L. 1955. *The evolution and growth of human behavior*. Boston: Houghton-Mifflin.

Myklebust, H. R. 1954. *Auditory disorders in children*. New York: Grune and Stratton.

Ohm, J. 1952. Über die Anwendung bewegter Spiegelmarken in Verbindung mit dem optokinetischen Nystagmus zwecks objektiver Sehschärfenbestimmung. *Klin. Mbl. Augenheilk.*, 120, 144–150.

Peiper, A. 1926. Über die Helligkeits- und Farbenempfindungen der Frühgeburten. *Arch. Kinderheilk.*, 80, 1–20.

Perl, E. R., R. Galambos, and A. Glorig. 1953. The estimation of hearing threshold by electroencephalography. *Electroenceph. clin. Neurophysiol.*, 5, 501–512.

Pratt, K. C., A. K. Nelson, and K. H. Sun. 1930. *The behavior of the newborn infant*. Columbus: Ohio State Univer. Press.

Reinecke, R. D., and D. G. Cogan. 1958. Standardization of objective visual acuity measurements. *Arch. Ophthal.*, 60, 418–421.

Richter, C. P., and K. H. Campbell. 1940. Sucrose taste thresholds of rats and humans. *Amer. J. Physiol.*, 128, 291–297.

Riesen, A. H. 1958. Plasticity of behavior: Psychological aspects. In H. F. Harlow and C. N. Woolsey. (Eds.) *Biological and biochemical bases of behavior*. Madison: Univer. Wisconsin Press.

Robinson, Helen M. 1953. An analysis of four visual screening tests at grades four and seven. *Amer. J. Optom. and Arch. Amer. Acad. Optom.*, 30, No. 4, 177–187.

Sherman, M. C., and I. C. Sherman. 1925. Sensorimotor responses in infants. *J. comp. Psychol.*, 5, 53–68.

Sherman, M. C., I. C. Sherman, and C. D. Flory. 1936. Infant behavior. *Comp. Psychol. Monogr.*, 12, No. 4.

Smith, J. M. 1936. The relative brightness values of three hues for newborn infants. *Univer. Iowa Stud. Child Welfare*, 12, No. 1, 91–140.

Smith, Karl U. 1937. The postoperative effects of removal of the striate cortex upon certain unlearned visually controlled reactions in the cat. *J. genet. Psychol.*, 50, 137–156.

Spiegel, E. A., and M. J. Oppenheimer. 1939. Conditioned reactions to position and angular acceleration. *Amer. J. Physiol.*, 125, 265–275.

Staples, Ruth. 1932. The responses of infants to color. *J. exp. Psychol.*, 15, 119–141.

Stern, R. U. 1953. Method of testing visual acuity in children. *Trans. Amer. Acad. Ophthal., Otolaryng.* 57, 686.

Stirnimann, F. 1936. Le Goût et l'odorat du nouveau-né. *Rev. franç. Pédiat.*, 12, 453–485.

Trincker, D., and Ingeborg Trincker. 1955. Die ontogenetische Entwicklung des Helligkeits- und Farbensehens beim Menschen. I. Die Entwicklung des Helligkeitssehens.

*Albr. v. Graefes Arch. Ophthal.*, 156, 519–534.

Warkentin, J., and K. U. Smith. 1937. The development of visual acuity in the cat. *J. genet. Psychol.*, 50, 371–399.

Wickens, D. D., and C. Wickens. 1940. A study of conditioning in the neonate. *J. exp. Psychol.*, 25, 94–102.

Woodworth, R. S. and H. A. Schlosberg. 1954. *Experimental Psychology.* (Rev. Ed.) New York: Holt.

Zetterström, Birgitta. 1955. Flicker electroretinography in newborn infants. *Acta ophthal.*, 33, 157–166.

———. 1955–1956. The effect of light on the appearance and development of the electroretinogram in newborn kittens. *Acta physiol. scand.* 35, 272–279.

Zubek, J. P., and P. A. Solberg. 1954. *Human development.* New York: McGraw-Hill.

part III

# The
# Study
# of
# Cognitive
# Processes

chapter 8

# Experimental Methods of Studying Perception in Children

Eleanor J. Gibson
Vivian Olum
*Cornell University*

"Look at it through the eyes of the child" is a favorite maxim of popular writers on child psychology. What, actually, does the child see? American child psychologists have seldom asked this question, though in Europe research on perception, even in children, has always flourished. Development of perception was studied in Peters' laboratory in Germany, in the Bühlers' in Vienna,

Dr. Gibson was a member of The Institute for Advanced Study, Princeton, N. J., 1958–1959, during the preparation of this chapter.
Dr. Olum was a Public Health Service Research Fellow of the National Institute of Mental Health during the preparation of this chapter.

and continues in Piaget's in Geneva. This background contrasts with the normative approach of American child psychologists during the comparable era. In our mental tests are many tasks that could be classified as perceptual: formboards, matching pictures, copying figures, and so on. By inspecting the test norms, it is possible to compare performances at different ages on these tests and thus gain some rough notion of perceptual development. But the time is ripe for a direct experimental approach to the problem. With the advent of the "new look" in perception, research with children on the effects of need and value on perception began to appear. The present trend toward empiricism ("effects of early experience") has stimulated interest in the developmental course of perceptual functions as such.

The psychologist about to undertake such research would do well to look first at the general sources on methods of studying perception; Guilford's *Psychometric Methods* (1954), the chapters on psychophysical measurement in Woodworth and Schlosberg's *Experimental Psychology* (1954), Gibson's chapter, "Studying Perceptual Phenomena," in Andrews' *Methods of Psychology* (1948), and Thurstone's *A Factorial Study of Perception* (1944).

Choice of a specific method will always depend on the investigator's problem. The question asked in a sense dictates the method. We shall consider first, therefore, the principal questions that a psychologist interested in perception might ask and then discuss the methods available and appropriate for each when the subjects are children of varying ages.

## Theoretical Issues and General Methodology

What do we want to know about perception? Three major questions can be asked.

1. What are the basic correlations between physical events and the perceiving organism's discrimination of them? For the child psychologist, the question becomes whether or not the basic correlations show some developmental course or evolution.

2. The second question concerns the phenomenal qualities of experience; what are they for the child and how do they change with age?

3. The third question asks how the basic correlations between physical events and discrimination or phenomenal experience are affected when other factors (e.g., attitudinal ones) are introduced. This question has been of special interest to some child psychologists because of the possibility that children's perceptions may be more subject than adults' to distortion from complicating factors.

Not all psychologists are equally interested in all three questions; choice of a problem is bound to be a matter of individual preference and systematic bias as well as expediency.

### THE FIRST QUESTION

What is the developmental course or evolution of discrimination? How precise and accurate is the relationship between physical events and the person's differential reaction to them? Does precision increase with growth and exercise? (In other words, the two dimensions, physical and "experiential," are thought of as correlated in some degree.) Does this correlation show an increase with age? In answering this question, it is assumed that the stimulus-experience correlations characteristic of the adult are known and can tell us what dimensions to vary and to measure in the child. The question then becomes, to what extent have adult patterns of discrimination developed at each age level?

What is an adequate criterion of discrimination? An index of discrimination must be differential—that is, behavior must show a change that can be definitely correlated with a change in stimulation. In addition, a measure of the degree of specificity of response to the stimuli is needed. *How wide a range of stimuli along a given dimension will produce the same response?* An index of precision is needed for any study to be useful in a comparative sense. We can actually pose our first question just this way. What is the class of stimuli that will produce a given judgment? What happens to this class of stimuli genetically? Does it increase or decrease, become more general or more specific? The psychophysical methods were developed especially to provide adequate measures of discrimination.

*The Psychophysical Methods.* For the older child, the psychophysical methods can be employed much as they would be for the adult. The least modification necessary is the best for a comparative approach. Detailed descriptions of the methods and statistical procedures are best found in such a book as Guilford's (1954). Some useful ones are mentioned briefly here for the sake of establishing a terminology.

The method of *reproduction* or *adjustment* is a psychophysical method often used with children. The traditional method of adjustment varies only one dimension of the stimulus. The *S* sets a variable stimulus to reproduce, as exactly as possible, the degree of some specified dimension of the standard. The average error over a series of trials yields an indication of the precision of *S*'s discrimination of small differences in the dimension measured. The Galton bar is a classic apparatus for demonstration of the method. The *S* sets the length of the variable side to match the length of the standard.

Many experimenters, using a method of adjustment with children, have assumed that the manipulation would be difficult for the child and have therefore done it for him, asking him to signal when the right point is reached. This procedure introduces a possibility of bias, since *E* usually knows when the adjustment is right and may give *S* cues by his facial expression or his speed of varying the stimulus. Unconsciously given cues from *E* must be guarded against in these experiments just as carefully as they would be in animal experimentation. We do not actually know to what extent a child may be influenced by cues from *E*'s expression or behavior; research on this problem with children of different ages would be useful methodologically and also interesting per se for social perception.

An example of reproduction by copying and by adjustment is found in research on the discrimination of parallelism of lines by Wursten (1947, p. 112ff.). In one series children were given a sheet of paper containing a straight line or an oblique one and were asked to draw ten lines like it. All ten lines were drawn on the same sheet. Departure from the vertical, or from the angle given, was measured afterward. The drawing was done in a group situation, and demonstration with a blackboard preceded it. In such a situation the earlier drawings may influence the later ones. Also, *S*'s motor skill can play a large role. To minimize motor skill, Wursten ran, individually, another series in which a needle was presented, vertical, horizontal, or at an angle, and *S* adjusted 11 other needles to the same position as the model. The needles could be rotated to a desired position, somewhat like the hands of a clock, but all could be viewed simultaneously, so that the first objection above was not met. The child was frequently reminded to take account of the position of the standard and to compare with it the position given each new needle. Average errors and constant errors were calculated for both techniques. Errors were least for the vertical and horizontal positions at all ages. Progressive shift of the needle's position, as the series progressed was observed with the oblique lines—a greater and greater departure from the standard. For all measures, the older the child the better the performance, though differences in the vertical lines were small.

The *method of limits* is useful for determining absolute as well as differential thresholds. In this case *S* is usually not given a pair of stimuli to compare. Instead, he is instructed to *detect a change* in some indicated dimension of the variable stimulus. The stimulus is gradually changed in this aspect, and *S* reports when the change is first detected. The stimulus is varied in both increasing and decreasing orders, so that an upper and lower limit is obtained. The "zone of uncertainty" is the area between these limits and provides a measure of precision. Some measure (e.g., the mean) between them may be taken as the actual threshold. The traditional example of the use of this method is the two-point limen on the skin. The *S*, with this method, must keep in mind some concept of the change to be detected. This concept may itself shift with practice and perhaps with age. Friedmann (1927) investigated the development of the two-point limen in children, combining the method of limits with a constant method.

Upper and lower thresholds are usually investigated by a method of limits. Zwaardemaker (reported in Peters, 1927) measured the upper tonal threshold, using a Galton whistle, in three age groups, one below 10, one 10–12, and one 20–30.

*The constant method* (right and wrong cases) is often used with adult *S*'s and is widely applicable. It yields the typical psychophysical curves or psychometric functions. Such a method (in getting differential limens) calls for a judgment of more, equal, or less when a standard and a comparison stimulus are presented (either successively or together). The "equal" category is often prohibited so as to force *S* to make a differential judgment. Variation of the stimulus is accomplished by randomly presenting comparison stimuli whose values differ by scale steps along the critical dimension. Each value of the variable stimulus must be presented many times with the standard, since *S* may guess; the measure of *S*'s variability indicates his precision of judgment. Order and other intraserial effects (e.g., the time error and the space error) must be compensated for in the procedure. The method is necessarily long and may fatigue and bore a child. Motivation may therefore become considerably important. The Seashore tests provide familiar examples of the constant method used to measure discrimination of pitch and loudness differences (Saetvit et al., 1940). The tests have often been used with school children.

The method of *recognition* is frequently used with children when a constant method might be used with adults, since the procedure seems easier for the child to follow. The task is simply to say whether a given variable stimulus is the same as or different from a standard stimulus, or whether it is "equal" or "not equal," if these words are more easily comprehended. Gilbert (1894), investigating thresholds for lifted weights in children, presented the child with a series of comparison stimuli and asked him to say which one or ones were equal to the standard. Requiring the child to make a "heavier" or "lighter" judgment for each pair would, presumably, have been more exacting.

The standard and the variable stimulus may be presented successively, or they may be presented together.

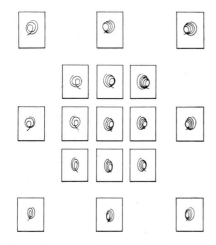

Fig. 8-1. Nonsense items differing in three dimensions of variation.

There may be only one comparison object present for a given judgment, or there may be a series. Control of position is necessary when simultaneous comparison is used, since children are very susceptible to place habits. If the child is to choose from a group of samples the one that is the same as the standard, there is the question of how the group or series is to be arranged— in some kind of order or randomly? And how extended is the series to be? If the series is scaled, how large is the step in the scale from one member to the other? These problems are considered with specific examples under *constancy*, since the method has been widely used with children in this case.

An experiment by Gibson and Gibson (1955) is an example of the method of recognition used to study development of form perception in children and adults. The increase in specificity of identification or recognition was the essential comparison. The *S* was pre-sented with a sample item, a scribble drawn on a card, which served as the standard. His recognition of it was tested when it was interspersed in a series of 17 similar scribbles, each of which varied in one of three ways (number of coils, horizontal compression, and orientation) from the standard. Twelve other items, more easily distinguishable, were included. The items are shown in Figs. 8-1 and 8-2. The *S* was shown the standard for five seconds and told that some of the items to be shown would be exactly like it. The series of items (including four identical copies of the standard) was then presented one at a time for three seconds each, and *S* was asked to report which of them were the same as the standard. He was not told when his identification was correct or incorrect. At the end of the series *S* was again shown the standard, and another series, in a different random order, was run through. This procedure continued until *S* made only the four correct identifications in one trial. Three groups of *S*'s, adults, older children (8½ to 11

Fig. 8-2. Nonsense items differing in many dimensions of variation.

years) and younger children (6 to 8 years) took part. Scores available were the mean number of trials required for a completely specific response, the mean number of undifferentiated items on the first trial, and the analysis of false recognitions by the dimensions of variation. Differences in the three age groups were apparent by all criteria. Comprehension of the task and control of cues from the E, as well as the prevention of flaws or marks on the cards that would permit identification of particular cards, are the main problems to be faced with this technique. Photographic reproduction of the patterns and duplication of the series should take care of the latter difficulty.

Many modifications of the methods so far described have been devised to suit the requirements of the problem and the subjects to be tested. In Piaget's laboratory a variation of the method of limits that can be used either with constant stimuli or adjustment has been devised especially for children. It is known as the *"concentric clinical method"* (méthode concentrique clinique) and can be used with adults as well. It is a shortened procedure, "clinical" in the sense that it is modified to suit the individual S. It is "concentric" in that extreme values of the comparison stimulus are presented first to get the child's range, roughly, and then smaller differences are introduced, working in toward the limen. Alternate presentations of values above and below the standard are given to determine, as precisely as possible, upper and lower thresholds. Median values are used to get threshold width, or area of un-

certainty, and their average is used as a point of equivalence. Many descriptions of the method are available [see, for instance, Lambercier (1946, p. 141ff.)]. Wursten (1947) used this method, with constant stimuli, in his experiments on discrimination of the parallelism of lines. He used cards on which two lines were drawn. One, at the left, was vertical. The other, 2 centimeters to the right of it and extending obliquely downward from the base of the vertical line, was at an angle varying from 151 to 119 degrees by steps of 2 degrees. On the standard card the oblique line was always at an angle of 135 degrees. The standard card was presented on the left and the variable card on the right (see Fig. 8-3). The subjects were asked to judge if the oblique lines had the same inclination; if one was straighter or more leaning than the other. From the results were calculated thresholds of equality (the average distance in degrees between the extremes accepted by the S's), average error, and constant error for different age groups from 5 years to adult. All show a very consistent development. The spread of the threshold varied from 18.3 degrees in 5-year-olds to 2.3 degrees in adults. Usually, with a constant method, the variable and the standard would be shifted from right to left to compensate for a possible "space error." More attention to the standard, or fixation of it, may be responsible for another systematic error called by Piaget the "error of the standard" (Piaget and Lambercier, 1943). Overestimation of the standard, whatever its position, whatever the temporal

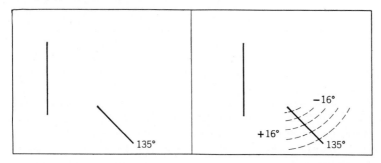

Fig. 8-3. Cards used for testing discrimination of the parallelism of lines (from Wursten, 1947).

order of standard and variable, or whatever the stimulus dimension, is characteristic of this systematic error. It is a unique type and was apparently discovered in Piaget's laboratory.

*Fractionation* (ratio judgments) is one of the methods used with adults for psychological scaling. On the whole, such methods are too complicated for children. But Piaget (1949) has studied the perception of the size of angles, in three age groups, with a method of ratio judgments. He wished to investigate the overestimation of acute angles and the underestimation of obtuse angles as a function of age. He used as measures the doubling of an acute angle and the halving, or taking a third of, an obtuse angle. The method was not applicable under 7 years, and "taking a third of" was impossible at 7 and 8 years. The S was given a standard angle (60 degrees for the acute, 120 degrees for the obtuse) and then presented with a series of variables, one by one, varying by 5 degrees, from which he was to choose the double, the half, or the third, as the case might be. A "concentric" method was used (alternate increase and decrease). Constant and average

errors were calculated, the average errors showing a clear decrease with age. The role of "the error of the standard" in ratio judgments is discussed in some detail.

The method of *absolute judgment* (single stimuli) involves the assigning of specified categories or names to stimuli presented singly to the S. As a rule, these categories would be similar to those in the number of yards on a scale of yards, differing quantitatively along a defined continuum. But conceptual scales such as yards, inches, or pounds, are not available before the educational process is well underway. Less abstract categories might be tried —easy rating scales such as long-medium-short. If simple scales were used, with a small number of categories, the amount of information transmitted for different age groups could be compared for stimulus dimensions such as brightness, length, and numerosity.

Categories that are not successive or scalar can, of course, be assigned to stimuli presented. Such a method is not usually classified as a psychophysical method, but it would nevertheless yield information about discrimination. Such a method can be called *identification.* Naming objects or other stimuli presented—for instance, color naming—would be an example. Cook (1931) investigated color naming in children and found that it increased in accuracy (for a given sample of colors) from 25 per cent at 2 years to 62 per cent at 6 years. Vocabulary obviously plays a big role in performance in such a task.

It should be clear that different thresholds and consequently different developmental curves can be obtained, depending on the psychophysical method chosen. Concrete instances of such divergence are presented in a later section. Other methods than these mentioned, although infrequently used with children, are described in the general sources referred to and may suggest to an experimenter a modification especially appropriate for an attack on his problem. If the requirements of good psychophysical measurement are understood, there is no reason why a particular textbook method must be rigidly adhered to.

"Adapting" a technique to suit a given age level should be cautious, however. A developmental study can be defeated by too free adaptation for different ages. Instructions should be kept essentially the same. Frequently, experimenters have varied their instructions to conform to the child's vocabulary at different age levels, thus biasing their results. Failure to understand the task by a younger child is equally disastrous.

***Substitutes for Psychophysical Methods.*** For very young children, the psychophysical methods must be supplemented by methods suited to the abilities of the child. Verbal judgments can be replaced by other *indicator responses,*[1] as they are in animal experimentation. Instructions can be replaced by demonstration and example, training procedures, or, ideally, by responses having spontaneous motivation. In any case, the stimuli should be varied dimensionally, as they would be in the customary psychophysical procedure. Substitutes for those psychophysical methods used with older children and adults must be carefully validated if they are to be compared from age to age with other methods.

The crudest tests of discrimination in an infant are those that simply measure the *gross amount* or *change* of activity when the critical stimulus is presented. That is, differential responses are not singled out and measured, but any change in *degree of responsiveness* at the onset of stimulation (e.g., magnitude of response, latency, duration, rate of emission) is noted. The general activity technique used by Pratt, Nelson, and Sun (1930) is a good example of this. The infant is placed on a "stabilimeter" platform, which wobbles whenever he moves. The movement is transmitted by string and pulley mechanisms to writing pens of a polygraph, so that amount and change of activity can be recorded for a control interval and after the onset of a prepared stimulus. The infant's repertory of activity is small, but such

[1] Munn (1955, Ch. 8) has an excellent discussion of methods of studying sensory processes in infants and young children. K. U. Smith's (1951) chapter on discriminative behavior in animals is also extremely relevant, since the problems of measuring discriminative behavior in animals are much the same as in preverbal children.

responses as crying, breathing rate, and startle can be observed directly and measured in various aspects when critical stimuli are introduced. When there is no specific indicator response, it must be inferred that any change in whatever aspect of the response is being measured is due to the stimulation $E$ is interested in and not to some other cause. Even if $E$ is satisfied that he has adequately controlled other stimuli and that the increase or decrease in response is caused by the stimulation he has presented, he has only this crude fact. The child's discriminative ability cannot be measured precisely by such a method.

Even with young infants, it is often possible to do a little better than observation of mere amount or change of general activity, since a few *differential responses* exist from birth or appear soon afterward. (Presence or absence of the reaction to alternative stimuli or differential orientation to them can then be looked for.) Crying, sucking, smiling, following with the eyes, and rejecting substances from the mouth are relatively selective, i.e., correlated with certain stimulus categories and not others. They have been used extensively in studying perception in the infant. Jensen (1932) studied differential reactions to taste and temperature stimuli in newborn infants by measuring differential sucking to various experimental stimuli and comparing it with response to a control stimulus. The best-known example is perhaps the developmental study of vision by Gesell, Ilg, and Bullis (1949). A description of their techniques is given in their appendix A. For the infant, observation of fixation,

eye-hand coordination, and direction of regard provide the data. Fixation *preference* has been used systematically with very young infants for evidence of color discrimination (Staples, 1932) and pattern discrimination (Fantz, 1958). Staples' experiments are well known; she measured the amount of time a colored disk was fixated when two disks were placed 6 inches apart on a piece of cardboard. They were of equal area, equidistant, and of equal brightness. The technique is similar to that of paired comparisons (Woodworth and Schlosberg, 1954, p. 252ff.) and requires the usual controls, such as randomized sequence, compensation for possible space errors, and equalization of other possible variables, such as movement. Berlyne (1959) points out that the $E$ holding the cards should not know which ones are present, lest his manner of holding the cards or recording fixation time be biased.

A response that is sufficiently specific, such as sucking, may be used in the manner of the ethologists to discover what they would term the *"innate releaser."* Their method gives evidence at a very early age of certain stimuli that are discriminated from a complex or from other presumably similar stimuli. Gunther (1955), looking for the "sign stimulus" for sucking, found that tactile stimuli within the mouth provided by the nipple and the protractile tissues behind it, were the critical releasers for sucking in the neonate. But such innate mechanisms are few in the human infant and besides are quickly replaced or added to by learned stimuli.

Although certain responses (sucking, smiling, fixation, etc.) are to some extent differential, specificity is by no means complete, so that the validity of assessing discrimination by means of them is questionable. If an infant smiles equally at two different objects or looks equally long at two colors presented side by side, it does not insure that he cannot discriminate them. Only in case of positive evidence of discrimination, the occurrence of a response known to be specific, can we draw a firm conclusion.

Another problem of validation with unlearned differential responses is the necessity of assuming that maturation of motor functions antedates perceptual maturation. It is often assumed, for instance, that space perception in an infant is inaccurate because he makes errors in reaching for objects. It could be equally possible that the motor functions alone are unskilled or that coordination of perceptual and motor functioning is incomplete.

In animals the comparative study of discrimination has most often been carried out by a *learning* method; the animal is reinforced or rewarded for response to one situation and not to another. Conditioning techniques have yielded much information about precision of discrimination and even perceptual organization (Smith, 1951) in animals. Actually, the formation of any conditioned response is evidence of some discrimination, for the conditioned stimulus must be detected in the total flow of stimulation in the environment and responded to; and suitable controls ought always to be made to show that the CS was neutral (not responded to with the CR) before conditioning. For evidence of more precise discrimination

in conditioning, what Pavlov called the "method of contrasts" must be resorted to. After the CR is established, generalization will occur to similar stimuli; the critical one is then presented alternately with one or another stimulus designed to be negative. The positive stimulus is consistently reinforced, the negative one is not. Differentiation is best established by starting with a negative stimulus not too close on a similarity dimension with the positive and progressing, after a successful differentiation, to more similar stimuli and a finer discrimination. Conditioning techniques have been used widely with children and infants in Russia. Razran (1933) reports a number of these. Control of the stimulus is very careful in the Russian experiments, and the S is usually isolated from E. The youngest S's appear to have been infants 13 to 73 days old. Levikova and Nevymakova studied differential auditory conditioning to food (nursing and food-seeking responses). The positive CS was $B^4$ on an organ pipe; an electric bell and $B^5$ on an organ pipe were to be differentiated. The infants were blindfolded during the experiment. Differential CR's were found at 110–122 days, simple CR's, earlier.

Conditioning techniques traditionally present one stimulus at a time only. A simultaneous choice with differential reward from the beginning is, of course, possible and may be quicker. Food is generally the reinforcing agent in such an experiment. It can be quite literally *in* the stimulus object; for instance, by sweetening an object of one shape but not one of another shape or coloring liquids in a bottle and sweetening some colors but not others. Ling (1941) studied form discrimination in infants as young as 6 months. Two or more blocks differing in shape were presented on a board. The "correct" form was sweetened with saccharine and could be lifted to the mouth. The "incorrect" forms were fixed to the board. Difficulty was increased by increasing the number of blocks.

Welch (1939) used a technique intermediate between conditioning and simultaneous choice (he refers to it as "conditioning") to study size discrimination. Children learned to find candy under a small box by repeated presentation of it; no language was used. When discrimination testing began, however, two boxes were presented simultaneously. The biggest contrast (largest and smallest) was presented first, until the child chose correctly. Thereafter, the difficulty of the choice was increased step by step until $S$ reached his limit of discrimination. A good deal of pretraining is generally required before the critical stimuli are introduced. Munn and Stiening (1931), using a two-choice discrimination apparatus with doors, allowed $S$ to examine the apparatus and find chocolate behind both doors before patterns to be discriminated were put on the doors.

With choice-learning techniques, controls must be made for irrelevant cues that are potentially differential—olfactory cues, for instance, when food is the incentive. Unconsciously given cues from $E$ and systematic errors caused by position and order are important. Children often develop a tendency, for instance, to choose the side that was "right" last time. Geller-

mann (1933a,b) has a good discussion of irrelevant cues in discrimination-learning experiments. It is important to remember, also, that the experimenter can make two kinds of error—one by concluding that there is evidence of discrimination when some other factor may really be responsible and another by denying it when it was actually present.

With slightly older children, the potential irrelevant cues rising from use of food as a lure may be avoided by putting a tiny toy within the correct choice box or compartment. If the child is allowed to keep the toys or play with them, this may be sufficient incentive. Motivation, as well as irrelevant cues, is a big problem to be faced in establishing the validity of discrimination-learning techniques.

*Matching* methods, if the child is old enough to be instructed by example or by a few simple words, have a certain advantage over discrimination-learning techniques. It is possible to test many more comparison stimuli against the standard or "correct" one in a short time. Weinstein (1941) used the matching of a sample to study form and object discrimination in rhesus monkeys and in young children. Stimulus objects were presented on a tray that had a sample-object-area on the right and a choice-object-area on the left. Training was carried on with two choice objects, one identical with the sample. Food wells holding a piece of candy or other food were under the forms. No language was used in the training. The children were later able to transfer the matching principle to a four-choice situation and to series of new stimulus objects. A control series was introduced to test for secondary cues in which the E was concealed during the experiment.

*Identification learning* is another technique that, if successful, reveals discrimination in a group or series of stimulus objects. It entails learning different responses to each of the stimulus objects. When verbal responses are not easily available, it is not a frequent choice. But it may be the only possibility in getting at a secondary problem, such as the effect of similar and dissimilar learned responses on development of discrimination. Dietze (1955) used such a method with 4- and 5-year-old children who learned nonsense syllable names to sets of forms (three in a set). The forms were discriminated faster when the names were dissimilar. The reward here was a tiny toy when each set was learned, and E later made S a bracelet of the toys.

The identification-learning method, obviously, would compare unfavorably with simpler techniques, such as matching, if time to complete the discrimination were taken as a criterion. Needless to say, different learning techniques may yield different thresholds, as do the psychophysical techniques. A developmental study, therefore, has the necessity of choosing the most appropriate technique and sticking to it for all age levels.

## THE SECOND QUESTION

What is the nature of the phenomenal world of the child and how does it change with age? This question has been asked primarily by Gestalt psychologists (Koffka, 1931), but the phenomenological approach has been taken by others as well, notably Piaget.

At each stage of development, Gestalt theorists assume that the behavior of the child is in large part a function of the phenomenal world in which he lives, that is, the world of his experience. Very little is known about the perceptual world of the child. Unfortunately, we cannot look at the world through the eyes of the child, and we do not really know what the child sees and in what respect it differs from what we see. It is necessary to discover the nature of the perceptual phenomena that the child experiences. By comparing the different stages of development, we can determine to what extent and in what respect the phenomenal world changes as the child matures. However, "phenomenology in psychology can never be a substitute for psychophysics and psychophysiology. Its function is rather to set the initial problem, to define the psychological datum which must then be envisaged in the setting of its physical and physiological correlates." (MacLeod, 1958, p. 34).

***Method of Research: Description of Experience.*** The phenomenological method requires of the subject a naïve description of his experience. Rather than having him make a perceptual discrimination, he is asked simply to tell the experimenter what he sees. To do this in a systematic way, we can set up controlled experiments touching on various aspects of perceptual experience, such as size, shape, movement, and depth. These experiments must be as carefully performed as the psychophysical experiments already discussed.

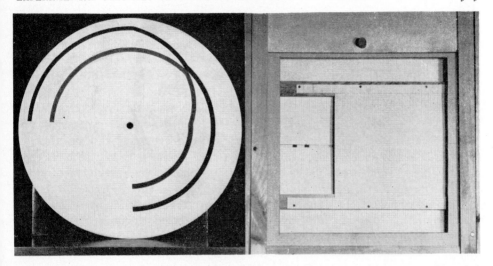

Fig. 8-4. Michotte apparatus. The figure on the left shows the disk. The figure on the right shows the subject's view, with the disk now behind the screen.

The primary difference is in the instructions given the subject. Since the aim is the qualitative nature of the child's experience, the experimenter presents the child with a given stimulus situation and asks, "What does it look like?" "What seems to be going on?" "What do you see?" The child is not directed to report on any particular aspect of his percept but just to tell how it appears to him.

This method, frequently used with adults and older children, can be effective with younger children as well. Olum (1956) used it with 7-year-olds in an experiment on developmental differences in the perception of causality by means of the Michotte disk technique. When the disk (in Fig. 8-4) is rotated counterclockwise behind a screen containing a narrow horizontal slit, the S is presented with two small rectangles, one black and one red, moving from left to right. Under certain conditions of movement, e.g., rate or beginning and ending of the two movements, an adult S perceives a black object, which hits or bumps a red object and causes it to move. This is the "causal effect." Under somewhat different stimulus conditions this effect is destroyed. In the Olum study stimulus conditions were used to represent both of these situations, i.e., the expected response in one situation was a definite causal experience, whereas the expected response in another situation was a definite noncausal experience. Two groups were used, adults and 7-year-old children, each S taken individually. The S was told to watch the little blocks and then the experimenter said: "What does it look like to you? . . . What do they seem to be doing? . . . Tell me what is happening." For each presentation, the S took as long as he wished, describing what he saw while he was still observing the phenomenon.

The results of this experiment demonstrated that stimulus conditions that produce in adults only the causal or the standard noncausal responses evoke in a large percentage of young children responses never reported by adults. These were of two types: *mutual approach*, in which both objects hit or push each other, and *passing*, in which the black rectangle passes the red one, the red passes the black, or both pass each other. The passing response is of special interest, since children clearly experience an overlapping of the moving objects when physically such an overlapping never occurs. One child verbalized the passing experience: "One runs past the other. The black runs past the red. It passes somehow, over or under. The red really runs away. It looks like the black keeps on going but it doesn't . . . it stops and the red keeps on going."

The descriptions were classified into four groups: (1) causal responses, (2) standard noncausal responses, (3) mutual approach, (4) passing. The differences between children and adults were clearly significant.

This method of description of perceptual experience is particularly valuable in areas of research such as the perception of causality, which have not previously been studied in children, since we cannot assume that children will perceive things in the same way as adults. It should be pointed out, however, that when using this method the younger the subject the more concerned the experimenter must be with problems of validity. The experimenter must be certain that rapport is good and motivation high, that the child fully understands what is required of him, and that he has the verbal ability to describe his experiences.

**Substitutes for the Direct Method.** Below the age of verbal communication, the child is, of course, not able to describe his perceptual experience. The best that the psychologist can do is to examine the child's behavior as carefully as he can in as many situations as possible, both in the laboratory (see Substitutes for Psychophysical Methods, p. 318) and in everyday life, and from this behavior to deduce what the child's world must be like. Of course, such an approach is essentially a "best guess," the primary criterion of validity being that of consistency. Koffka states this position:

> How shall we proceed to reconstruct the phenomenal world of a newborn baby? . . . Our reconstruction of the infant's consciousness must "fit" the observed events and conduct which constitute its "objective" behaviour. That is to say, the infant's consciousness and behaviour must fit together in the same way in which the phenomenal world of the adult fits his objective behaviour (1931, pp. 142–143).

Another way of deducing the characteristics of the phenomenal world of the preverbal child is to study perceptual experiences at as many stages of development as possible in an attempt to discover whether there are definite developmental trends. When this is the case, the assumption can be made that the variable under consideration has evolved in the same direction from infancy. A picture of the world of the infant is arrived at by extrapolation from the available data, as the necessary prior state of a known developmental sequence.

Piaget's work is the most striking application of these two deductive approaches. From repeated observations of the behavior of children, both in spontaneous situations as well as in those initiated by the experimenter, Piaget reconstructs the phenomenal world of the child at each developmental stage; and, by looking at the developmental stages in sequence, he attempts to deduce the nature of the phenomenal world of the infant.

An example of this is Piaget's study of babies' reactions to the disappearance of an object. In the early stages of infancy the baby acts as if an object had no existence when not directly perceived. When the object vanishes, the baby makes no attempt to look for it. From a study of the changes in behavior from this stage to the final one, in which the child searches for the vanished object, Piaget reconstructed at each point what the child's experience of objects must be and deduced from the total series that the object as we experience it, the "object concept," is achieved only little by little. Initially, he said, "The infantile universe is formed of pictures that can be recognized but that have no substantial permanence or spatial organization" (1954, p. 4).

## THE THIRD QUESTION

Our first question concerned the basic correspondences between the physical world and dimensions of perceptual experience, with special reference to development. Now, we are ready to ask how such correspondence is affected when other factors are introduced.

"Other" factors include complicating stimuli, practice, attention, and affective and social factors. Are the basic correlations made more precise, less precise, or are they distorted? How is an experiment designed to study the role of such factors? We can, of course, also ask how phenomenal experience (our second question) is affected in the same experiments.

The kind of experiments discussed under the first question employed the classical methods of psychophysics, modified as necessary for the age of the child. Only one dimension of the stimuli to be compared was varied and that was the dimension to be judged (length, for instance, with the Galton bar). The variable was isolated, and constant errors inherent in the procedure were controlled by balancing them in the experimental design. Measures of precision (variability or threshold) rather than constant errors were sought, and the conditions for judgment were typically optimal. Such cases are referred to now as *Type 1* experiments.

Experiments deriving from question 3 depart from this classic tradition by permitting more than one dimension of variation. We shall call these *Type 2* experiments. Many illusion experiments are in this group. In measuring the Müller-Lyer illusion, the length of the horizontal line is variable, as it is with the Galton bar. But, together with length, there is added a variable of form—the direction of the arrowheads or wings at the ends of the line. In the size-weight illusion the stimuli vary not only in weight, which is to be judged, but also in size (although no size judgment is requested). In these experiments it is the constant error that is of interest to the experimenter. He has compounded two stimulus variables, and he is looking for a *distortion* in the dimension judged as compared to the simple case in which one dimension is isolated. The psychophysical methods are still used to obtain judgments, but it is *departure* from the basic correspondence that has become of interest.

Constancy experiments fall into this classification. Size with distance variant (size constancy) implies variation of both objective size (to be judged) and distance. Whether *S* tends to underestimate as the object is placed farther away is of interest; if he does, he is making a constant error. In the size constancy experiment the second variable, distance, can be altered dimensionally. But sometimes the second variable can be altered only categorically, as is often the case with illusions.

Some of the so-called "value" experiments likewise vary the stimuli in more than one aspect so as to contain or not contain the "value." In the coin experiments, for instance (Bruner and Goodman, 1947; Carter and Schooler, 1949), coins are matched with a neutral disk for size. But it is not only size that varies, since the coin contains a dollar sign or some other designation of value. In an experiment by Dukes and Bevan (1952) children were asked to compare the weights of jars visibly filled with candy and jars visibly filled with sand. The standard and variable stimulus objects could vary, therefore, not only in weight but in various stimulus aspects associated with their contents. In this experiment the constant error was of principal interest; the children over-

estimated the weight of the jars of candy, compared with jars of sand. But the constant method used in this experiment also permitted measurements of precision. The precision of judgment was significantly greater when both jars were filled with candy than when both were filled with sand or one with sand and one with candy. Tajfel (1957) has pointed out the theoretical importance of this *increase* in precision, and future experiments of this type should be set up to secure data on precision as well as constant errors.

Sometimes these experiments (which vary in more than one aspect of the stimulus at the same time) are interpreted as showing that a personality variable has affected perception, but such a conclusion is not justified when the "value" is represented in the stimulus. It is possible, however, to control the stimulus variables so that only one is changed while varying some factor within the organism. The standard and variable differ along one stimulus dimension, that to be judged, and a second variable, such as need (e.g., degree of hunger), degree of practice, or amount of reinforcement, is introduced as well. Ideally, both variables would be altered dimensionally, but there are obvious difficulties in scaling variables within the organism.

An experiment by Beams (1954) varied like and dislike by using pictures of food that *S*'s had already rated for preference. The same pictures were used for all, but preferences for any given food pictured varied among the *S*'s. In a test series *S* looked at the actual food object in a stimulus box through a peephole. Then he looked at a projected color photograph of the object in another box and adjusted it (by moving the picture back and forth) until he judged it to be the same size as the object. A majority of S's made the pictures of preferred food objects larger than those of nonpreferred ones. Here the standard and variable stimulus were similar, except for the dimension that changed when S moved the projected image.

Lambert, Solomon, and Watson (1949) created "value" for poker chips by letting children drop them into a slot machine in return for a candy reward. Before and after this reinforcement, S matched the size of the poker chips with a luminous disk by adjusting a diaphragm. In this case the poker chips and the light spot differed in more than one dimension (color, etc.), but the other stimulus variables were controlled by securing the same matches before and after reinforcement as well as after an extinction series. Since S's matches of the same standard and variable showed an increase and then a decrease in apparent size with reinforcement and withdrawal of it, it can properly be inferred that the difference is due to the reinforcing conditions.

The effect of *practice* on discrimination of form and area was investigated by Welch (1939) with children 12 months to 5 years of age. The child was trained to choose a standard rectangle of given proportions and area by rewarding him with candy when it was chosen. Then it was paired with other rectangles of differing form and area that were never rewarded. There were 32 different rectangles of varying dimensions. A rough threshold was ob-

tained by using a technique resembling Piaget's clinical concentric procedure. Further practice and new tests were given an experimental group from month to month for varying intervals. Practice improved the discrimination, for children in the experimental group discriminated as well at 27 months as those in a control group at 4½ and 5 years being tested for the first time.

A *third* type of experiment might be singled out in which standard and variable differ in stimulus characteristics in many ways that cannot be specified. Judging different faces for prettiness or intelligence would fall under such a classification. Neither variable nor constant errors are meaningful here, since the experimenter does not know exactly what he is varying or what an "error" would be. He may pick out some measurable aspect, such as height of forehead, and see if it correlates with the dimension judged. But it is always possible that some other feature is being systematically varied and consistently responded to, even though E does not know what it is. Since stimulus dimensions cannot be exactly specified, the standard psychophysical techniques are not applicable, and a rating procedure or categorizing must be employed. Elaborate rating methods are not appropriate for children, but a simple scale with only a few categories can generally be used. The number of categories or points on a scale that could be employed would probably be a function of age.

Some experiments aimed at investigating the effects of internal variables on perception belong to Type 3 because the stimulus objects presented for judgment vary in a number of indefinable ways and only categorizing or rating methods can be employed. A relevant example is Murray's experiment (1933) on the "maliciousness" of faces. A group of children at a summer camp rated pictures of faces for maliciousness. Later they played a game of "murder" and again performed the ratings. The ratings were raised (more "malicious" faces were perceived), presumably because of the fear aroused.

***Impoverishment Experiments.*** Cutting across these three types of experiments, a number of special techniques have been devised for investigating the effects of internal variables on perception. They have been referred to as "impoverishment" experiments (Gibson, 1948). They have in common some method of reducing the "power" of the stimulus and thus enhancing the role of the internal variable.[1]

Short interval presentation is a time-honored method of reducing the stimulus. Early tachistoscopes,[2] such as Dodge's, were not especially suitable for use with children, but present-day instruments, which can be used in combination with a projector and a screen, make tachistoscopic presentation much less cumbersome for E and less awkward for S. Tachistoscopic experiments with children have been mostly devoted to work on reading and have so

far yielded little information about other kinds of perception (Tinker, 1958). Much more might be done with projection tachistoscopes. The frequency and word recognition studies (Solomon and Postman, 1952) might, for instance, be approached developmentally with profit. Something analogous to a threshold may be obtained by gradually increasing exposure time by using a sort of method of limits and arriving at a criterion time for correct recognition. The effect on this threshold of internal variables can be investigated.

A variety of other ways of impoverishing the stimulus has been employed with adults, but not all are suitable for use with children (ones requiring steady fixation, for instance). Visual stimulation can be reduced by cutting down the contrast between figure and ground, by altering focus so as to produce blur, by reducing size of a figure, or by displaying the material at a distance. All of these are familiar methods for measuring acuity; a kind of threshold measure can be expressed in terms of the amount of reduction that can be tolerated by the S, yet give rise to an accurate recognition. The methods could equally well be used for studying the effects of internal variables.

A "noisy" background against which the relevant stimulus is presented is a method suitable for creating auditory impoverishment. Recognition of speech against a background of noise is difficult; thus guessing, which permits the influence of factors within the S, is encouraged. Skinner's "verbal summator"

[1] "Given less than optimal stimulus-conditions, certain factors of past experience may play a determinative part in perceptual organization" (Bruner, Postman, and Rodrigues, 1951, p. 227).

[2] See Woodworth and Schlosberg, 1954, p. 92ff., for a good discussion of tachistoscopes.

(1957) is such a technique. The S hears "liminal" sounds, such as mumbled, faint vowels, and tries to make sense of them. A vague pattern of speech sounds at low intensity or against a noisy background is recorded on tape and repeated until S makes some response. Skinner reports that in children the responses evoked are "heavily determined by the conditions of the experiment" (p. 263). Effects of practice and especially created needs could well be studied with this method.

The "verbal summator" is closely related to the projective techniques. These techniques do not reduce the stimula-tion, as does the tachistoscope, but instead present the S with a stimulus configuration that is *ambiguous*. Figures that are not literal representations of anything, such as ink blots, or incomplete pictures, such as the Street figures (see Fig. 8-5), would be examples. These methods yield nothing akin to a threshold, but more or less objective measurements are still available: time to give a response can be taken; approximation to the most probable identification (with Street figures, for instance); and classification of responses as "whole," "part," etc.

Other kinds of ambiguous stimula-

Fig. 8-5. An incomplete picture taken from Street's Gestalt Completion Test.

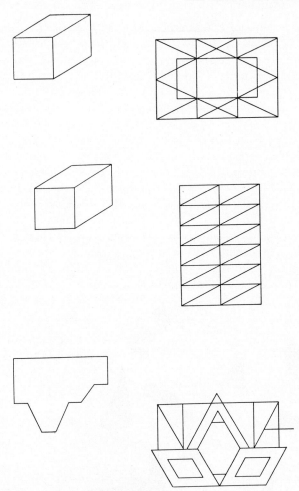

Fig. 8-6. An example of hidden figures used by Gottschaldt (from W. D. Ellis, *A Source Book of Gestalt Psychology*, Harcourt, Brace, 1938).

tion with more fidelity of representation are *hidden* figures and *reversible* figures. The Gottschaldt figures are examples of hidden or camouflaged figures (see Fig. 8-6).

Reversible figures are those which place two representations in conflict. The staircase figure and the Necker cube are well-known examples. The

effects on report of suggestion, past experience, reinforcement, etc., can be studied with them. Solley and Sommer (1957) performed an experiment of this type with an ambiguous figure, which could be seen as either of two faces whose profiles joined. Children were shown the two faces separately, with a ⅓ second exposure, five times. Half the children were given nickels whenever one was presented, half when the other was. Afterward the faces were exposed together in the ambiguous figure twenty times, and S was asked to name which he saw. The children named the rewarded profile more often. Other children looked at the test figure until they reported both figures, and then were asked which looked biggest, closest, etc. The rewarded profile was said to be happiest, brightest, and closest (not biggest). When naming is used as an indicator of S's percept, as it is here, it is open to the obvious objection that reward may have affected merely the verbal naming habit. The reports of brighter, nearer, etc., under continuous exposure were intended to provide a second criterion to meet this objection.

Ames' rotating trapezoidal window, a three-dimensional conflicting stimulus, has been used by Allport and Pettigrew (1957) to compare children of different cultures. A phenomenological report of what the children actually "saw" was sought, and the children used their hands, as well as speech, to indicate whether they saw a swaying rectangular window or a rotating trapezoid. The rotating trapezoid was presented at different distances and under both monocular and binocular conditions to urban children (white European and Zulu) and to rural children (Zulu). Under monocular conditions and at the greatest distance (20 feet) there was no difference between the groups; all tended to see the "illusion," even if they did not recognize the frame as a window. Under binocular conditions and close up (10 feet) the urban

children reported the illusion (the window) more often than the rural children. The authors attribute this difference to more frequent experience with windows and straight lines.

The methodological problems in studying the effect of internal variables on perception are many. First, there is the difficulty of controlling and then of scaling the internal variable. Hunger, thirst, and, to a lesser extent, anger and fear are possible to manipulate. Interests, likes, and dislikes can be rated in various ways, depending on the experimenter's ingenuity. But some control of the internal variable is essential if it is to be isolated and its effect studied. To scale one of these variables and alter it dimensionally in an experiment is still more difficult; most experimenters have been satisfied with categories, such as like and dislike. It is often assumed that a relevant experience has or has not taken place (e.g., absence of straight lines in the environment of rural Zulus); but it is obviously desirable to "build" the experience as part of the experiment.

Control of other variables than the one presumably being studied should be mentioned again. If the relevant variable is to be a "personality" variable, then it should *not* be accompanied by an alteration in the stimulus in such a way as to confound the two. This is a simple axiom of experimental design, but it is often violated.

The design of an experiment, in which a stimulus dimension or category is varied for measurement, as well as an internal variable, might well be set up so that interactions of the variables, and the contribution of each, can be measured. An experiment by Gilchrist and Nesberg (1952) varied need, degree of need, and relevance of stimulus and was designed in such a way that the triple interaction could be tested. Since interactions were significant, the example seems valuable.

Finally, validity—the relevance of the behavioral criterion chosen—should be mentioned. If $S$ overestimates the size of poker chips when they are exchangeable for candy, how do we interpret the overestimation? A very interesting case among the experiments considered is the Beams experiment already described. Pictures of both liked and disliked food-objects were presented by means of a slide projector, and $S$ was asked to adjust the size of the picture by moving the slide nearer or farther away to match the size of the real object. The pictures of liked foods were overestimated as compared with disliked ones. Was the judgment really one of size? When a picture is enlarged or reduced, $S$ normally sees not a change in size but a change in the *distance* of the object. Perhaps these $S$'s were unwittingly trying to move the liked foods closer and push the unliked foods away. Interpretation of the results of these experiments demands a careful analysis of what $S$ is really perceiving as he makes his adjustment. The experiment is not worth the trouble if the criterion measure is not a valid indicator of the variable that $E$ hopes he is isolating. An experiment must be interpreted as well as performed.

The effect of complicating variables on the perception of infants is obviously especially difficult to study, since measurement of discrimination under optimal conditions of stimulus presentation is difficult enough with them. It would seem that such questions might best be postponed until many experimental studies of the development of discrimination have been made available. The effect of deprivation and enrichment of environment might be an exception here and is discussed later.

## Problems of Perception

### DISCRIMINATION OF SENSORY QUALITIES

To what extent the child can respond differentially to physical dimensions of stimulation is a problem in the realm of psychophysics. The methods have been described, in general terms, under our first question. But a few cases deserve further mention, either because there has been special interest in the problem or because available research is of methodological value. It is important to keep in mind that the method used and the difficulty of the task required will affect the results, as Peters (1927) concluded in his review of developmental studies of this type.

*Color.* Color discrimination in infants and children has received much study, and the research is instructive because of the variety of methods that have been tried. Evidence for discrimination of the four primary hues was found by Staples (1932), using a simple fixation-preference method, in very young infants (see p. 319). Chase (1937), using as a criterion pursuit movements of the eyes in following a spot differing from its background only in hue, also found evidence of early discrimination of hues at well-separated points of the spectrum. These studies, although indicating presence of some color discrimination, yielded little information about exact sensitivity. A differential conditioning technique (Figurin and Denisova in Razran, 1933) also gave evidence of early discrimination of primary colors, but it is likewise not very useful for threshold determinations.

When a child is old enough to use a matching procedure, the number of variable stimuli can be increased easily, but the task is more difficult, the younger the child. Cook (1931) found that children of 2 years could match hues (red, green, blue, and yellow) that varied in saturation and brightness with 45 per cent accuracy, whereas successes increased to 97 per cent at 6 years. The improvement may or may not be attributable to an increase in differential sensitivity. Matching for brightness and saturation was less successful than matching for hue. Gilbert (1894) investigated discrimination of saturation by a matching technique in school children, 6 to 17. Cloth of different saturations with red as the hue was used. The least saturated item, the standard, was compared with ten variables. The child was told to pick all the shades of red that were exactly like the standard. The number of shades chosen as the same decreased steadily as age increased. At 6 years 57 per cent of the children did not discriminate at all. At that time the median number of shades picked as being exactly alike was 9.6, but the number decreased to 3.9 at 17 years. A somewhat similar procedure was used by the Heiders (1940) with deaf and hearing children of different ages. They also found that the younger children selected matches over a wider range than the older ones.

Discrimination of colors by naming develops even later than discrimination by matching and is only 62 per cent accurate (for red, green, blue, and yellow) at 6 years (Cook, 1931). Koffka (1931, p. 280f.) has discussed methods of studying color discrimination and has related differences in the results to phenomenological descriptions of the tasks required by the different methods.

Prepared color-blindness tests, such as the Ishihara and Dvorine, which demand tracing of a pattern differentiated only by hue, have also been used with children (Synolds and Pronko, 1949). Since they are aimed at detecting abnormalities, rather than studying development of discrimination, they are less relevant here.

A more accurate technique, such as a constant method or a method of limits, can be used with older children. One such study by Jones is reported in Peters (1927). Children 4 to 14 and adults were the subjects. A sector in a gray disk of a color wheel was increased gradually until the color was named correctly. Sensitivity increased markedly; adults, with a method of limits, were 118 per cent more sensitive than 6-year-olds.

*Pitch.* Pitch discrimination, like color, has always been of interest, particularly because of its importance in musical appreciation and production. When the task is difficult, e.g., a constant method with very small differences between the tones to be compared, discrimination typically improves with age (Peters, 1927, Werner, 1948, p. 101f.). Gilbert

(1893), using a method of limits combined with a same-different judgment, likewise found that sensitivity increased rapidly from 6 to 10 years. Whether the improvement is attributable to practice, to superior comprehension and attention to the task, or to some aspect of physical maturation or to all of these is still a problem. Wyatt (1945) has shown that improvement *can* be the result of training.

**Weight.** Gilbert (1894) investigated differential sensitivity to lifted weights in school children by using the method he employed with saturation. The S was given a standard weight and asked to choose from a group of comparison weights those that were exactly the same. The size of the group judged to be the same decreased with age, and the measures of differential sensitivity showed an increase (sensitivity was $2\frac{1}{2}$ times greater at 17 years than at 6). The absolute amount of improvement in such studies cannot be taken as meaningful, for it can be shown to be a function of such factors as the scale-steps of the group of variable stimuli.

A curious contrast to the typical finding of increased "veridicality" of perception with development is the judgment of weight in the size-weight illusion. When information is coming from more than one channel (visual and tactual-kinesthetic here), the prediction of performance in relation to age may be difficult. Sensitivity to a more complex, intersensory variable (specific gravity or density in this case) apparently increases; but if only the weight judgment is measured, it appears that veridicality decreases. Jenkin and West (1958) have shown that mental defec-

tives are less susceptible to the size-weight illusion than a normal control group. But, as they point out, it would be wrong to conclude that the defective group is perceiving more accurately. They are failing to discriminate a more complex stimulus variable (density), which is a synthesis of information from several senses. The importance of analyzing the information in the stimuli presented is brought out rather strikingly in this example.

**Skin Senses.** Friedmann (1927) found that the two point limen, using a constant method, decreased with age; but the curve of increased sensitivity was different with small separations than with larger ones, again showing that results with a constant method may be dependent on the step-size between the comparison stimuli. Developmental differences were enhanced with smaller differences between standard and variable.

## SPACE PERCEPTION

Independent measurements of discrimination of single dimensions of space, such as distance and length, are very much complicated by the fact that spatial dimensions are naturally interdependent. Distance is a "cue" to the real size of an object; but size is also a "cue" to distance, or so it has been asserted. This seeming paradox has been responsible for much confusion and many experiments on "constancy." The separate dimensions are often abstracted from their background and studied separately.

**Visual Size.** Sensitivity to length (linear size) has been studied in children of 6 years on; in one study it was found to increase, but in another it did not appear to change significantly (Lobsien, and Giering, reported in Peters, 1927). Welch (1939a) studied discrimination of visually perceived area (two-dimensional) in younger children (12 to 60 months) and found improvement with age. A conditioning method was used (see p. 321). Welch employed parallelograms of different area, varying in form (from a square to a thin rectangle) as well as in size. An attempt to separate the form from the size aspect of the stimuli seemed to indicate that fine discriminations of form came later than size. Some form difference was discriminated very early, and the two dimensions are hardly commensurable.

In another experiment Welch (1939b) used boxes of different areas (three-dimensional stimuli), under one of which a piece of candy was hidden. There were nine sizes. Ten children of 22 to 32 months, without special practice, differentiated the area significantly better than a younger group (16 months or under). The discrimination of size of solid objects may be easier than of plane figures.

*Depth and Distance.* Updegraff (1930) studied visual perception of distance in 4-year-olds and adults. The main experiment took place in a dark room 10 meters long. Relative judgments (nearer, farther) were obtained by using a constant method. The markers were illuminated circles, which moved on an invisible track. Five comparison distances (two farther, two nearer, one the same) were presented with the standard distance, the range

predetermined for each *S*. The standard and variable distances were presented simultaneously. Nine series were run (monocular, binocular, size of marker varied, displacement of marker to the side or downward, etc.). The discriminative ability was much alike for children and adults. There was no difference in accuracy between the binocular and monocular series. Another experiment took place outdoors over a long range. The ground was a pasture with a slight rise. The stimuli were large beaverboard disks fastened to poles 2.5 meters high. A pair of stimuli was presented, and *S* was asked to indicate the nearer. The disks were 3.31 meters apart. The standard distance was 0.195 meter. The children were asked "to put up the hand in front of the one that is nearer to you." The children could discriminate correctly 6 meters on either side of the standard. Visual angle was said to be the important cue here. Judgment of the height of the tops of the disks undoubtedly played a big role. Experiments of this type might better be done with the stimuli on the ground, rather than raised, and separated horizontally by a wider angle.

Stereoscopic vision in preschool children (2 to 6 years) was studied by Johnson and Beck (1941). Two polarized images were projected on a screen. The child wore polarized spectacles. The stereoscopic slide was a color photograph of a doll. Disparity was such that an adult would localize the doll midway between himself and the screen. The child was invited to touch the doll. His localization was noted by measuring his reach against a scale ruled on the floor. Then one image was blocked out, and the child was again allowed to "touch." In this case the children touched the screen. With stereoscopic projection, they reached 10 to 12 inches in front of the screen. Furthermore, many reported that the doll seemed to move back and grow larger when one image was withdrawn. The authors concluded that 2-year-old children have well-developed stereoscopic vision.

Visual depth discrimination in 36 infants 6½ to 14 months old has recently been studied by Walk and Gibson (1959) by a technique called the "visual cliff." The infant was placed in crawling position on a board in the center

of a large table. The surface of the table was heavy plate glass, and a low fence surrounded it. Directly under the glass on one side was a patterned linoleum surface. Four feet below the glass on the other side was the same linoleum surface. The child's mother stood alternately on one side and then the other for two 2-minute intervals, twirling a toy and urging the infant to come to her (Fig. 8-7). When the mother beckoned at the side with a floor directly under the glass, 75 per cent of the babies left the board and crawled to her. The others stayed on the center board. When she beckoned at the side with the floor 4 feet below the glass, only 8 per cent of the infants went to

Fig. 8-7. A "visual cliff" used to test perception of depth in infants (photo by Cornell University).

her, 62 per cent stayed on the board, and 30 per cent actually crawled off in the opposite direction. It was concluded that by the time locomotion is possible human infants can discriminate a "drop-off" visually.

*Discrimination of Tilt.* Reproduction of visually perceived vertical and horizontal lines has been studied by Wursten with children (see p. 316). More elaborate research on apparent verticality as affected by body tilt and starting position has been performed by Witkin (1954) and by Wapner and Werner (1957), using a method of adjustment. Wapner and Werner's subjects (6 to 19 years) sat in a tilt chair in a dark room. Their task was to adjust a luminous rod so that it appeared vertical. The rod was adjusted by *E*, at *S*'s instruction, at first in steps of 2 degrees and finally in smaller ones. There were 12 different conditions; three conditions of body tilt (erect, 30 degrees left, 30 degrees right), in combination with four starting positions of the rod (10 degrees left, 30 degrees left, 10 degrees right, and 30 degrees right). There was a reversal of constant errors in relation to age. For younger *S*'s, the position of the apparent vertical was tilted toward the same side as body tilt; for older *S*'s it was tilted opposite the body tilt.

*Tactual Space.* Investigations of space perception, other than visual, are rare in children. Renshaw (1930) has studied localization on the skin in children and adults. A 30-millimeter square area on the back of the hand or the forearm was marked with 30 spots. Stimulation of one of these was followed by *S*'s attempt at localizing it

with a pointed wooden stick. The *S* was blindfolded and given no knowledge of results. The children (8 to 11 years) were superior to the adults both before and after practice. Practice effects were large. These results are unusual, especially since the 2-point limen apparently shows a growth curve of developing sensitivity. Renshaw, Wherry, and Newlin (1930) tested a congenitally blind group of children and adults and found improvement in localizing with age. They concluded that the seeing individual shifts with age from tactual to visual localization, thus explaining the children's superiority in the first experiment.

Tactual perception of form was studied by Benton and Schultz (1949) in 3-, 4-, and 5-year-old children by an identification method. Familiar objects, such as a ball, fork, or pencil, were first shown to the child, and he was asked to name them. Then the objects were put in the child's hand inside a screened box, and the child tried to identify the object by name. The ability to identify objects in this manner increased with age but was nearly perfect in most 5-year-olds.

## FORM PERCEPTION

Form perception is generally treated as a separate topic, but it must be remembered that the dimensions of form are spatial. Although form has most frequently been studied in two-dimensional drawings, the forms of natural objects are three-dimensional and are perceived in a three-dimensional space. It cannot be assumed that findings in the first case can simply be carried over to the other.

Methods of measuring form discrimination have included drawing, formboards, discrimination learning, matching a sample, and recognition. Drawings are easy to obtain but have some obvious defects as a method. They are affected by motor skill and are difficult to score objectively. Form boards also require some manipulatory skill. Skeels (1933), using a conditioning technique, found that differently shaped blocks could be discriminated by children 15 to 46 months old before the children could perform adequately with a formboard. She concealed a reward under one of a number of differently shaped blocks (cubes, spheres, crosses, etc.), and the child learned to choose the block that was consistently paired with the reward. Ling (1941) found that infants between 6 and 15 months could learn to choose one of two blocks differing in shape when the "correct" one was sweetened and the other fastened to the board on which it was presented. Change in spatial orientation and size of the blocks had little effect on the discrimination, suggesting that form per se was discriminated. Difficulty was increased by increasing the number of blocks presented. It should be noted that these studies made use of three-dimensional shapes—i.e., objects. Discrimination of two-dimensional shapes or drawings is a different and harder task. Stevenson and McBee (1958) gave children aged 3.4 to 6.8 years a pair of stereometric objects, a pair of planometric objects, or a pair of painted patterns to discriminate by a rewarded-choice method. Discrimination was faster for stereometric objects.

*Transposability.* Whether discrimination of one form from another is discrimination of form per se or is specific to the particular background and the identical stimulus conditions has been the subject of much discussion and is related to the "transposability" problem. Munn and Stiening (1931) investigated the influence of background and the discrimination of form per se in a 15-month-old child. A two-choice situation with a reward concealed behind one of two doors was used. The patterns (cross, square, diamond, etc.) were placed on the doors. After learning to discriminate two patterns, the child still responded to a positive stimulus with 45 or 90 degrees' rotation, with changes in background, and with different negative stimuli.

Gellermann (1933a,b) has a discussion of criteria for the discrimination of form. He maintains that a learned discrimination of a triangle, say, must persist when the form is rotated, be independent of size, generalize to other types of triangle and to outline figures, and be independent of background. He found generalization of these types with 2-year-old children and with chimpanzees by using a choice situation with food reward. He found, as well, keen sensitivity to small changes in shape when he varied the positive and negative stimulus by small steps so as to approach one another in form. The inference was that the subjects were discriminating form as such and that the response to form was transposable. The children were superior to the apes, perhaps because they could verbalize to some extent. In the course of mastering a difficult discrimination, it was noted that all the *S*'s at one time or another traced the outline of the forms with a finger.

Transposition along a dimension, such as brightness or size, is a related problem, studied first by Köhler (1918). He demonstrated transposition of brightness in a 3-year-old child. An experiment by Hunter (1952) may serve as an example. The subjects were children (23 months and older). The stimulus objects were square hollow wooden blocks varying in area. The child was first taught to lift a block to secure a currant hidden beneath it. He was then trained to choose the larger (or smaller) of a pair and later tested with other pairs of different absolute sizes. Transposition is generally the result in such experiments, but its interpretation is a matter of argument (see Chapter 9 on learning). The relationship of language to transposition along a dimension, or to a central position along a dimension (the "middle-size" problem), has been the subject of considerable experiment (Kuenne, 1946; Spiker and Terrell, 1955).

*Recognition of Inversion.* Discrimination of changing orientations of a plane form is of great importance when the child begins to read. That plane figures on paper can be identified by children 3 to 5 years old despite changing orientation has been shown by various methods, such as drawing and recognition by matching (Rice, 1930; Newhall, 1937). This is, indeed, a case of "transposition" similar to that just discussed. It is not so clear that the child *cannot* discriminate a change in orientation. In these two studies (Rice and Newhall) the ability appeared to be a function of age, as it did in a study

by Davidson (1935). He studied discrimination of the letter-shapes b, d, p, and q in kindergarten and first-grade children by a matching method. He found four stages in development of the discrimination, beginning with the confusion of all four letters. The children identified d and b as the same letter in different orientations before they identified them as different letters.

Two other studies point in a somewhat different direction. Hanfmann (1933) had children 4 to 7 years old copy triangles in varying orientations and found that predominance of vertical and horizontal orientations was already strong at 4 years. Shifts and reversals occurred in copying because the child changed the figure to a "natural" position. The implication was that transposability was present and also that change of position on the child's part was motivated.

Hunton (1955) showed children 22 months to 14 years old pictures of objects, such as people and trees, in different orientations and recorded their verbal comments. She reported that as early as 2 years children recognized pictures as disoriented. Head movements often occurred with recognition of inversion. It is possible that the identification of originally meaningless abstract forms, as in the reading process, may develop differently from identification of the forms of natural objects. Experimental materials might be planned with this distinction in mind.

*Acuity.* A special problem related to form perception is the measurement of acuity. The usual Snellen chart has been modified in various ways for children. One is described—the Bailey visual perception test—in Peckham (1933) and involves matching forms on a chart placed at a standard distance. The child is given a tray of cutout figures and asked to match one indicated on the chart. Sizes of figures asked for are progressively reduced. The group of cutouts from which the child is to choose can be reduced to make the task less difficult for younger children.

A method similar to the E chart was used by Cohn (reported in Peters, 1927) with 50,000 school children. He used an E turned to face North, South, East, or West at different distances from the child, beginning at 20 meters. The child had a similar E in his hand, which he turned to match. Cohn reported a slow rise in acuity up to 13 years. Measurement of acuity with Landolt rings presents no difficulties by the time a child reaches kindergarten and perhaps before.

**Gestalt Factors in Form Perception.** The Gestalt psychologists have emphasized the importance of the *figure-ground* relationship in form perception. An early study by Schroff is reported in Meili (1931). Schroff presented children with line drawings of rows of cups or teapots. But instead of perceiving cups or teapots, the children reported perception of forms that corresponded to the intervals between the figures. In other words, they saw as a figure that which was intended as ground.

More recently Meister (1949) compared the figure-ground discrimination of preschool children with that of adults, using eight series of cards (each series composed of seven cards) differing in respect either to figure or to ground. In each of the first four series

the size of the figures used varied, whereas the ground (diagonal, vertical, or horizontal lines) was kept constant. In each of the last four series the figure was constant, and the background lines varied in density.

After a preliminary practice series (on other cards), a test card was presented for 0.5 second and then removed. The S was asked to pick the card he had just seen from the series before him. In the preliminary series the test card was actually present in the choice display, but in the experimental series it was absent. The adults were told to choose a card "most like" the test card (which was to them obviously absent), but this instruction was omitted for children on the grounds that it was too complex. The author felt that this deception did not affect the results. (The desirability of keeping instructions comparable when two groups are to be compared has been pointed out before.) Adults chose a figure either slightly larger or slightly smaller as most like the test card, whereas children chose a larger figure than that on the test card. Adults chose very dense grounds, and children tended in this direction but not so strongly. Meister concluded that children and adults differ in their perception of figure and ground.

The problem of whether children perceive *globally*, that is, the *whole* at the expense of the *part*, or *analytically*, the parts or details at the expense of the whole, is a controversy of long standing. In some situations children seem unable to differentiate the parts of a perceptual whole, and in others they apparently perceive details when an adult would have a unified percept. Meili in 1931 summarized the research up to that time.

In an experiment of Heiss and Sander (reported in Meili), children 3 to 19 years old had to complete a figure that lacked a piece by finding the missing piece either in a random collection of pieces or embedded in another figure. When the piece was embedded, the task took longer for subjects of all ages, but the time was much greater for young children than for adults. A study, using Gottschalt figures (see p. 330), was done by Witkin (1950) with adults and 10-year-olds. The task was to locate a simple figure embedded in a complex figure. In each trial first the complex, then the simple, and then the complex figure was presented, with instructions to locate the simple figure in the complex one. Children had much greater difficulty than adults and often had to trace the simple figure in order to find it in the complex one. It took the children much longer.

Crudden (1941), working with children 5½ to 6½ years old, first trained the child to select one of a pair of simple figures in a standard learning situation. The two figures were drawn on cards and set in a large screen in such a way that when the child pushed the correct one a bell, chime, or siren sounded ("an auditory reward"). Discrimination by size alone was prevented by altering the relative size during the learning period. When the S had made five correct successive responses, he was told that the E was going to hide the pictures by drawing lines around them and that he had to find the one that rang the bell, i.e., the figure to which he had been trained. Then the child was presented with complex pairs of figures in which the training figures were embedded. Crudden compared the ease of finding embedded symmetrical or asymmetrical figures and found that an asymmetrical figure was much more difficult for a young child to find than a corresponding symmetrical figure, although individual differences were very great.

The most recent experiment of this type is Ghent's (1956) with children between the ages of 4 and 13. She used overlapping line drawings of realistic and geometric figures, as well as embedded figures, and asked the child to tell her what he saw in the picture. When the child pointed to an object, he was asked to trace it. In the case of the overlapping geometric figures, the S was asked to pick the form he saw from a display of various forms. Ghent found that children had difficulty perceiving figures that were not clearly set apart from each other, especially when they shared a contour, as in the case of embedded figures; the younger the child, the greater the difficulty.

A somewhat different approach to the problem of embeddedness was taken by Leuba (1940). In his main experiment nursery-school children 1½ to 5½ years old were seated about 10 feet away from an arrangement of small round pillboxes. Each child was given a small piece of chocolate to eat and shown one of the pillboxes, which he practiced opening and shutting. The child then watched while the E arranged the boxes (in a circle, square, or triangle) and placed a piece of chocolate in one of them. The child was told that he could have the chocolate if, after a minute, he could pick up the box it was in without touching any of the other boxes. Then for 1 minute a screen was placed between the child and the pattern, and the child's attention was diverted. The children were unable, in their first choice, to find the correct box when it was a part of a configuration. When the box was placed just outside, but touching, the configuration, the choices were almost always correct. Leuba asserted, however, that the children did not completely react to these configurations as unanalyzed wholes, since the results appeared to depend in large measure on where in the configuration the chocolate was placed. Success was much more frequent when it was at the ends of the line, at the corners of the square, or at the points of the triangle; and even the positions adjacent to these led frequently to success.

The child's perception of the part *rather* than the whole has been reported by many psychologists. Binet (in Meili) pointed out that the child enumerates details at an age younger than that at which he describes a total picture. Cramaussel (in Meili), studying kindergarten children, used two identical mosaics and two other mosaics, identical to each other but differing from the first two in some small detail. The child, given one of the first mosaics, was asked to choose the one of the three remaining that was the same. That the young child was able to do this was interpreted as evidence that children have no syncretic perception. Segers (1926), working with children 4 to 10 years old, used a technique like the game of lotto. The child was given

a large cardboard on which were drawn 16 pictures of houses. Each house was identical to the others except in some small detail. The child also had 16 small corresponding pictures, which he was to match to the pictures on the large cardboard. In this study the youngest group had the greatest difficulty perceiving the differences.

Children's descriptions of pictures have also been considered as evidence for whole-versus-part perception. Cramaussel (1924) showed two children in their second and third year, respectively, pictures in art magazines and recorded their comments. He found that the children did not use the whole picture as a basis for their comments. Attention went from one to another object in a picture but not to the relations between them. An attempt at giving a response to the whole was based on a detail and was rather like caricature; a distinctive detail was seized on and brought the rest with it, in spite of incongruities. The material used was highly complex; simple pictures of familiar objects might have produced something different.

The results in these studies appear to depend to a large extent on the material used. Meaningless, relatively unstructured forms (such as mosaics) may well give different results from simple familiar forms, such as pictures, or a complex painting in an art magazine.

Two studies of developmental differences in response to the Rorschach ink blots are relevant to this whole-versus-part controversy. Hemmendinger (1953), working with adults and 3-to-11-year-old boys, found that the youngest children responded globally by giving whole responses and few details. By ages 6, 7, and 8, however, there was an increase in detailed responses, but these details were not integrated into larger wholes until ages 9 and 10. In a longitudinal study of children 2 to 10, Ames et al. (1953), have reported these same general trends, although they differ somewhat from Hemmendinger in respect to the ages at which these shifts occur.

Studies of *closure* (completion of incomplete forms) have generally shown that children are less able than adults to recognize a form when it is incomplete. The technique used is often simply that of naming the objects portrayed in incomplete pictures. Sometimes a series of pictures of increasing completeness has been used to determine age differences in degrees of completeness necessary for recognition. Results vary somewhat, depending on whether the whole picture is gradually built up in the series by adding details or whether the outer contour of the object is filled in by adding details. For early studies using these techniques, see Meili (1931).

Siegel and Ozkaptan (1953) studied closure by means of 16 geometrical forms, cut in two. The subjects (children 4 to 7 and adults), given the two halves, were asked to make whatever they liked out of them. Although "minimal perimetry" occurred in 87.6 per cent of the adults, it occurred in only 58.4 per cent of the children. The authors concluded that closure is a function of past conditioning and familiarity.

Mooney (1957) studied the relation of age and ability in closure. He tested school children (7 through 13) and adults. Forty incomplete black-and-white representations of the heads and faces of people were used, together with additional similar but nonsensical items. These pictures were made up into packs of cards, each pack containing 40 real and 20 false (nonsensical) items. The task for the child was to sort his pack of cards into seven categories—six types of people (e.g., boy, old woman) and a leftover category. The results showed a positive and significant association between ability to achieve closure and age. The nature of the task (discrimination and categorizing as well as closure are called for in sorting) may account in part for the age differences found. Street (1931), using his well-known Gestalt completion test (see p. 329), found no differences between scores of third-grade, sixth-grade, and high-school students.

Piaget and von Albertini (1954) did an elaborate study of the perception of intersecting and incomplete forms. They found that, with increasing accuracy from 4 years up, children could recognize intersecting forms; but the recognition of incomplete forms was much more difficult. These forms were made by cutting or tearing out a piece of the original figure. The E showed S the seven pieces of cardboard, each representing a good form with something cut out, and said, "Here are some forms out of which something is cut." Then the E took a rectangular paper and cut out a corner, saying, "Here too, something is cut out. Show me how it looked before being cut." The child was to show the complete form by tracing with his finger or by drawing.

The easiest gaps for the child to fill were those that required a straight line without corners, as in prolonging an actual line; arcs of circles were still more difficult, and oblique lines and corners were the hardest. A 75 per cent level of success was not achieved under 7 years. Gaps were perceived, but they were filled with scribbles, straight lines joining the actual lines, or bumps drawn from one of the actual lines to the other. Very young children tried to make empirical forms (boats, men) out of the cut forms, apparently not perceiving them as incomplete wholes. Under 6 years the child also had trouble recognizing dotted-line figures (circle, square, triangle, rectangle); and when several dotted-line figures overlapped, even the 6-year-olds could find only the simplest of them. Only at age 9 could all of them be recognized. Piaget and von Albertini interpreted these results in terms of primary good Gestalten due to field effects and secondary good Gestalten that were the result of perceptual activity during the course of development.

## PERCEPTUAL CONSTANCY

It has already been pointed out that the dimensions of space and the forms of objects are interdependent. The so-called constancy problem is a reflection of this fact. The psychologist asks how it is that an object is usually perceived in its real size or shape when it lies at various distances or at various angles with respect to the observer. Two opposed explanations have been suggested to account for the apparent constancy of the dimensions of an object. Since developmental trends in constancy experiments are thought to be relevant to these explanations, the theories are outlined before dealing with the research itself.

The Gestalt psychologists have taken the stand that perception is organized within a framework and that an invariant relation between certain aspects of stimulation, along with the framework, accounts for constancy. They demonstrated constancy in animals (Köhler, 1915) and considered it a primary feature of perceptual organization, even at a simple level. Koffka's statement is representative:

Since, however, constancy of any kind presupposes dynamic intercourse between the segregated object and the whole field, constancy itself should under favorable conditions appear from the start, since progress consists not in creating or increasing but in decreasing the mutual interdependence of the parts (1935, p. 240).

N. M. Locke (1938) took a radical position of this sort, arguing that constancy was especially characteristic of more primitive organisms, animals and children. He believed that "as we ascend the phylogenetic scale, the organism increases in intelligence and at the same time decreases in degree of perceptual constancy" (p. 336).

On the other hand, some psychologists, following the Helmholtzian view, have argued that constancy is a result of learning; the retinal image (projected size of an object, for instance) is "corrected" by motor and other kinds of experience with the objects providing stimulation. The young child, for instance, learns to "allow" for the distance of an object in estimating its size because he has reached for it or walked to it. The views of Piaget and of Brunswik are both of this kind. They have led to a number of developmental studies, for it is predicted, from this view, that constancy should increase with age and that lack of constancy should be characteristic of the young child for any given judgment.

The results of the developmental studies are not easy to interpret in this light because they are highly dependent on variations in the experimental methods employed.

*Methodological Variables.* Lambercier (1946) has written a very detailed history of work on size constancy in children in which he emphasizes the methodological procedures that have varied in the studies and that may account for the wide differences in results. Some of these conditions are (1) single comparison versus comparison with a series or group of stimuli; (2) arrangement and scale level of the series (a "central tendency" or leveling effect may occur); (3) placing the standard nearer than the comparison object or placing it farther; (4) different types of stimulus objects (meaningful-meaningless, flat-solid, filled-empty, etc.); (5) distance of the objects from one another and from $S$; (6) the background (size, nature of surfaces visible, whether objects lie on a ground surface or are seen against a vertical background, presence or absence of other objects); (7) the lateral and vertical displacement of the objects; (8)

the $S$'s height of regard; (9) the method of comparison (distance can be constant and size varied or size can be constant and distance varied); (10) the $S$'s attitude (is he trying to match "real," "apparent," or "projective" size); (11) instructions; (12) repetition and practice; (13) treatment of results; and (14) the psychophysical method chosen.

*Size Constancy.* Lambercier undertook a series of studies of size constancy with different age groups that is especially instructive for its methodological implications. One of these (1946) compared a method of successive single presentation with two methods of simultaneous "serial" presentation in order to determine the effect of the constitution of the series on size constancy. The objects used were thin wire rods varying in height. The standard (at 1 meter from $S$) was 10 centimeters high. The variable (at 4 meters from $S$) was from 3.5 to 21 centimeters high in steps of 0.5 centimeter. In the method of single comparison the variable rods were presented successively, either in a regular order or by the concentric clinical method. One method of serial presentation ("fixed serial") presented an ordered series of variable rods simultaneously (3, 7, 15, or 31 at once). The median height of the series varied from trial to trial. The series was immobile for any one judgment, and $S$ chose the rod "equal" to the standard. The other serial method (mobile serial presentation) involved moving the series progressively so as to expose a fraction of the rods in a window before $S$'s eyes until the whole scale had

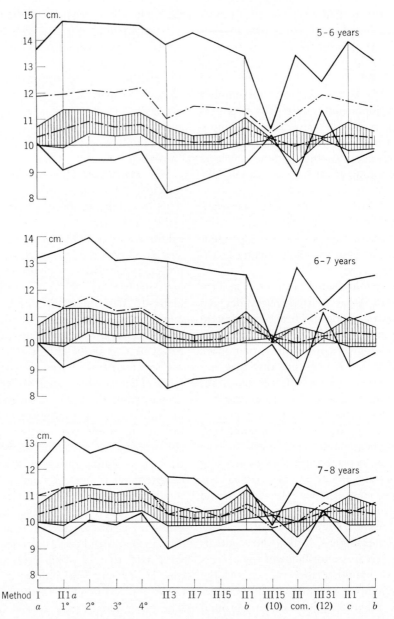

Fig. 8-8. Graphs taken from Lambercier (1946, p. 195) showing the upper and lower limits of the threshold (top and bottom line in each graph) and the median (dotted line) for three age groups (5 to 6 years, 6 to 7 years, and 7 to 8 years) and for adults (the cross-hatched section in the center of the graph). The different methods of comparison are

been shown. The fraction exposed at any moment included 3, 7, or 15 rods. S was to say when the middle rod of this exposed fraction was equal to the standard.

The results for *single comparison* and *mobile serial comparison* were similar and showed a decrease in constant error with age (combined means were 11.6 centimeters for the youngest age group and 10.3 centimeters for adults). The precision of judgments increased markedly from the youngest children to the adults. The results for *fixed serial comparisons* were quite different. The precision was greatly increased, compared to the other techniques, for all ages. The constant error for any series shifted with the level of the series. If the middle of the series was 10 centimeters, the same as the standard, perfect constancy resulted, but if the middle of the series was 8 centimeters, the mean judgment was lowered; if it was 12 centimeters, the mean judgment was raised accordingly. In other words, what looked like over- or under-constancy occurred if the middle of the series of variables presented was under or over the standard. Lambercier felt that the absence of any

evidence for the growth of constancy with age, found by certain experimenters (Burzlaff, 1931), might be explained by their use of a fixed series of comparison stimuli having a middle stimulus that was equal to the standard. The children were actually more susceptible to the series effect ("central tendency" or leveling) than the adults. Figure 8-8 from Lambercier shows the wide variation in precision, depending on the method. Note the apparent precision, with a fixed series of variables for comparison, especially series III 15, where the middle of the comparison series coincided in size with the standard. Note also the difference in variability (width of threshold) with age.

The best measure of constancy, Lambercier thought (the freest from effects of the scale), was the "mobile serial" comparison. One can, he showed, choose a series of variables of such composition, and presented by such a method, as to obtain any desired degree of "constancy" for any age group. Even with single comparison there is not really an isolated variable—the scale of the variables presented will still be influential.

Another methodological variable re-

---

indicated below the horizontal axis in order of presentation. A key to the notation of methods follows: I *a*. Single comparison, concentric clinical method. II 1*a*. Single comparison, in regular order; 1st, 2nd, 3rd, and 4th indicate four successive repetitions. II 3, II 7, and II 15. Mobile serial comparison; the arabic numerals indicate the number of elements presented simultaneously in a series. II 1*b*. A repetition of II 1*a*. III. Fixed serial comparison: III 15 represents the result for a series of 15 elements, with its middle at 10 cm. (equal to the standard); III com. represents the over-all (combined) result of all the fixed series; III 31 represents the result for a series of 31 elements, with its middle at 12 cm. II 1*c*. A repetition of II 1*a*. I *b*. A repetition of I *a*.

sponsible for apparent over- or under-constancy is the position of the standard. Piaget and Lambercier (1943) investigated its effects for size constancy, using wire rods, but with a method of adjustment rather than a constant method. In one experiment the standard rod, i.e., the one to be matched, was placed 1 meter from S and the variable (raised and lowered by E until S judged it to be equal) at 4 meters. In another experiment the positions of standard and variable were reversed. The measure of apparent constancy obtained under these two conditions was different because of what Piaget terms the "error of the standard." The standard tends to be overestimated; thus, if it is placed close at hand, the variable, farther away, will be made greater than the standard's 10 centimeters and apparent under-constancy results. If the standard is farther away, the overestimation of it automatically produces a trend toward "over-constancy." Such results were obtained. Even the youngest age group had a mean of 104 (slight over-constancy) when the standard was farther away than the variable. But their mean judgment showed "under-constancy" when the standard was nearer. A comparable shift occurred for all age groups. From a developmental point of view, the results appear paradoxical, for there was a decrease with age in the constant error when the standard was near and variable far but an increase in error with age when the standard was far and the variable near (the trend is toward greater over-constancy).

One of the biggest sources of confusion and criticism in constancy ex-periments has been the instructions given S. Sometimes he is clearly asked to match "real" size. Sometimes a "projective" size match seems to be suggested (though seldom clearly). Often the instructions speak of "apparent" size, not making clear what is meant by that term. Piaget and Lambercier (1951, 1956) conducted two experiments in an investigation of projective size matches and compared them developmentally with real size matches. They had the hypothesis that projective size matches would be more readily made by younger children because, they thought, objective perception (constancy) resulted from a learned correction of projected size on the retina. They first got real size matches from all S's (five age groups, youngest 6 to 8 years) with an adjustable variable rod. The concentric clinical method was used. This was an easy task for all the S's. Projective size matches followed and required very elaborate instruction and practice. (E began with teaching S how to make a perspective drawing of two lines at different distances. Then he was questioned about his understanding of the drawing. If S did not understand, he was shown a window behind which cartoon figures could be placed at different distances. The S was shown two figures of the same height at different distances and two of such height that their images were projected on the window at the same level when one was farther away. If the S still did not understand, he was eliminated.) The S's retained made three sets of projective estimations, with tests following the first two to check their understanding.

One check involved putting a window with a horizontal grid on the experimental table in front of S and having him verify his results by indicating on the window the projections of the standard and the variable he had chosen.

Some of the results from these two experiments are presented in Table 8-1.

but since practice was essential for performing the task at all the conclusion is dubious. Lack of precision, especially for the youngest age group, was very evident. In one of the experiments more than half of the youngest age group was eliminated before the projective judgments were taken. Such elimina-

**TABLE 8-1**

Mean objective and projective size matches in mm. made by different age groups with standard near and standard far. The projective matches given were made after practice. (From Piaget and Lambercier, 1951 and 1956)

| Age | | 7-8 | 8-10 | 10-12 | 12-14 | Adults |
|---|---|---|---|---|---|---|
| Standard | Objective | 102 | 97 | 94 | 91 | 90 |
| Near* | Projective | 297 | 217 | 206 | 219 | 280 |
| Standard | Objective | 104 | 118 | | 116 | 124 |
| Far† | Projective | 161 | 150 | | 150 | 143 |

\* When standard is near, a perfect *projective* match would be 400 cm.; for an *objective* match, a number less than 100 indicates over-constancy.

† When standard is far, a perfect *projective* match would be 100 cm.; for an *objective* match, a number greater than 100 indicates over-constancy. Note that objective matches are made more accurately by the children than by the adults.

The most striking fact is the extreme inaccuracy of the projective size matches for all age groups, even after practice. (The figures given for projective size matches represent the third set of judgments. The two prior sets were less accurate.) Age differences in projective estimation were found, but they were not consistent in the two experiments. When the standard was near, the youngest age group actually made better projective matches than the other groups; but in the second experiment it did not. The authors thought that practice had covered up such a trend,

tion could have resulted in a group selected for intelligence compared to the other age groups. When complicated instructions are involved in an experiment used for comparative purposes, some method of equating intelligence of the groups is desirable. Possible interactions of age, practice, and intelligence make these experiments difficult to interpret.

An older experiment by Weber and Bicknell (1935) might be compared with the foregoing. Weber and Bicknell photographed disks of different sizes, at three different distances, and presented them in a stereoscope with 3 degrees of disparity as well as to the S's unaided eye. The S was asked to take a "phenomenal" attitude rather than an "object-directed" attitude; that is, to judge the *photographic* size of the disk, i.e., the projected size. To do this he selected a disk from a set of 30 comparison-circles varying in area, after gauging the phenomenal area of the photographed disk. All of the S's (children 9 to 12 and adults) showed a tendency to see the disks closer to their real sizes than the photographic size would warrant. Age differences were small, but the children showed by one measure a greater tendency to see the photographed object as larger than its stimulus-size. The tendency became larger with practice. These results appear contradictory to those of Piaget and Lambercier, but the point to be made is rather that differences in experimental conditions can alter results profoundly. The use of photographs, the comparison with a series of objects, and the stereoscopic situation might all make a difference, despite the fact that the attitude invoked was similar.

Studies of size constancy in infants have been made by using the response of reaching instead of verbal judgments. Cruikshank's (1941) study employed infants 10 to 50 weeks old. She had two rattles of similar appearance, one three times as large as the other. A rattle was presented in front of the infant at a distance of either 25 or 75 centimeters, and the infant's facial and reaching movements were noted. There were three situations: (1) the small rattle at 25 centimeters; (2) the small rattle at 75 centimeters; (3) the large rattle at

75 centimeters, making its retinal image the same as that for the smaller at a distance of 25 centimeters. Reaching in situation (1) would be an adaptive response, but it would not be so in (2) or (3), since the rattle was too far away to be grasped. Reaching only in (1) would presumably indicate the presence of size constancy and distance perception. The same response in situation (1) and (3) would indicate that projective size was perceived, without discrimination of distance. At about 14 weeks, positive responses occurred 62 per cent of the time in (1), 31 per cent in (2), and 35 per cent in (3). By 24 weeks, response was 99 per cent in (1), and only 13 per cent in (2) and in (3). Cruikshank concluded that infants of 6 months distinguished between objects of different size, even when the retinal extents were equal; in other words, size was perceived in relation to distance.

A methodologically very different study was made by Dukes (1951) on a 6-year-old boy. He was randomly interrupted during his ordinary daily activities and asked what he was looking at; then he was asked to make a size judgment of the object by designating size equivalents in terms of other objects in his environment, at different distances, which he chose himself. A high degree of constancy was shown. This experiment was inspired by Brunswik (1956) and is an example of "representative design."

*Constancy of Interspaces.* A different type of size judgment was studied in an experiment by Costa (1949). S was asked to match the size of empty intervals between pairs of horizontally grouped objects seen at different distances against a neutral background. The objects delimiting the intervals were suspended in air so that S could not relate them to a ground surface. The standard interval between two objects (20 centimeters) was 1 meter distant from S. The variable interval between two similar objects was always at 4 meters. In one series S judged an interval marked by sticks, in a second, one marked by small cubes, and in a third the interval was filled by a solid stick. A concentric clinical technique was used. Adults made good objective matches even for the empty intervals. Children tended toward under-constancy for the empty intervals, but there was no steady progression from the youngest group to the oldest. For the solid intervals the tendency of the younger groups toward under-constancy was less apparent (the median judgment in this case for the youngest group was 22.5 millimeters, compared with a standard of 20 millimeters).

*Color Constancy.* Constancy of color and shape have also been studied developmentally but less frequently than size. Brunswik (1956) studied brightness constancy in children by using a graded series of papers (black to white) with a standard presented at different distances from a light source. A method of single comparison was used (one variable at a time compared with the standard). He found a developmental curve, with constancy increasing up to age 10 and showing a decline later at about 16. Another study by Burzlaff (1931) employed a group of comparison shades of gray presented simultaneously and found no developmental curve whatsoever; children of four showed complete constancy. From these two studies it might be suspected that all the variables that affect the results in size constancy experiments would do so for color—that is, such factors as instructions and attitude, method of presentation (single or simultaneous grouping), or psychophysical method. As an example of the last, Burzlaff found different results when a method of adjustment (with a color wheel) was used than when a group of variables was offered for simultaneous comparison.

*Shape Constancy.* An experiment by Klimpfinger (reported in Brunswik, 1956) on shape constancy obtained a developmental curve similar to Brunswik's for color. Ellipses tilted at varying degrees were compared with a standard, again with single presentation. No comparable developmental study with groups of comparison stimuli presented simultaneously appears to be available. That results for shape constancy should vary with the experimental conditions, as in size constancy, is to be expected.

In conclusion, it should be re-emphasized that developmental experiments on the constancies face extremely difficult problems of control and interpretation. The number of variables that may influence results is large, and every one may alone produce effects varying with age and development. Interpretation of any particular developmental curve of constancy must therefore be cautious, since it is almost certainly only one of many possible ones.

It does not seem possible at the present time to claim exclusive support for either of the two theories described from the developmental data available. What does seem fairly clear, however, is a trend toward greater precision of judgments with age, when the relevant data are furnished. One more experiment, which emphasizes this trend, might be cited. Cohen, Hershkowitz, and Chodack (1958) studied size constancy with different distances of the standard in subjects 5 to 17 years old. The comparison stimulus was always at a distance of 8 meters from *S*, whereas the standard was at 2 or 6 meters. Only one of the thirteen comparison stimuli was presented at a time. Ascending and descending series of judgments were obtained so that a measure of precision (interval of uncertainty) could be obtained. Three sizes of standard were employed. There was no difference in constant error for the age groups when the standard was at 6 meters. When the standard was at 2 meters, the 17-year-old group was significantly more accurate, but there was no difference in accuracy between the other age groups. Thus constancy, as it is usually defined, did not show a clear trend with age. Precision showed more consistent differences with age, the interval of uncertainty tending to decrease. The authors suggest that the performance of the younger children can be interpreted as a "reflection of their greater diffuseness in perception."

A trend toward greater *over-constancy* with age has appeared in a number of experiments. This finding is sometimes interpreted as evidence for the learning theory of constancy. Such an interpretation is not valid, however, for the only prediction that could reasonably be made from the learning theory is that judgments should become more accurate with increasing amounts of experience with objects. A clearer formulation of the concept of constancy and a stricter logic in deducing the experimental outcome to be predicted will have to precede use of developmental trends as crucial evidence for either theory.

## PERCEPTION OF MOVEMENT

*Lower Threshold.* The lower threshold for visually perceived movement was studied by Carpenter and Carpenter (1958) with a moving belt. The *S*'s were two children (81 and 101 months old), two chimpanzees, and adults. A training situation with reward was used to instruct the children and chimpanzees. The threshold was determined by a method of limits. The data consistently supported the conclusion that the threshold is lowered with maturity.

*Perception of Velocity.* Fraisse and Vautrey (1952a) studied the perception of velocity (speed of movement) in a group of school children aged 4 years 6 months to 5 years 6 months. Two toy cyclists (one blue, one red) were moved on parallel tracks by *E*'s hand and perpendicular to the child's line of regard. Fourteen different experimental arrangements were used, in which spatial, temporal, and movement factors were systematically varied. Sometimes the cyclists disappeared into tunnels at the end of the course, and sometimes the child could witness their arrivals at the finish. The child compared the space covered, the speed, and the time taken (duration). Here are two sample courses:

Test I

$m_1 \longrightarrow$
$m_2 \longrightarrow$

The space covered is equal, arrival is simultaneous, but $m_2$ leaves later than $m_1$, goes twice as fast, and overtakes him.

Test II

$m_1 \longrightarrow$
$m_2 \longrightarrow$

This is the tortoise and the hare. $m_1$ leaves after $m_2$. $m_2$ is less rapid, but still keeps ahead of $m_1$. They arrive simultaneously.

The child was told before the test to note the speed of the cyclists, and afterward he was asked, "Did they go at the same speed?" If he answered no, he was asked which went faster. Similar questions were asked about space and time but not at the same test. In all the situations, including the tunnel ones, at least half the children compared the velocities correctly. Of those errors that occurred, passing or preceding during the run was sometimes the cause. When the slower preceded throughout, there were errors, but nearly 75 per cent of the children judged correctly. The authors concluded that there was no single systematic error. Perception of velocity is relative to the spatial situation in which the movement is presented, and passing, preceding, and overtaking are "perceptual data" by which velocity is manifested. But the child could compare velocities even when the greater speed did not correspond with passing. They concluded that there was "direct perception of velocity."

*Perception of Apparent Movement.* Meili and Tobler (1931) studied stroboscopic (apparent) movement in children 5 to 12 years old and adults. They used a technique that projected on a

screen two luminous vertical dashes. The time between the appearance of the first dash, A, and the second dash, B, was variable. As the time interval was decreased the percept changed from one of succession (A then B) to optimal movement (a single object moved from the position of A to that of B) and finally to simultaneity (A and B). The range of time intervals was such that only children reported simultaneity.

Initially, two little cartoon figures were projected in succession, and the child was asked to describe them. Then the figures were presented at an interval that produced optimal movement, i.e., the child said that one figure ran or jumped from one place to the other. When the child understood the stages of succession and movement, the figures were replaced by dashes, and the child was asked if he saw two dashes or a single dash going from one place to the other. In addition, a real movement was projected below the stroboscopic movement and in the opposite direction. In order for a movement response to be acceptable, the S had to say that the apparent and real movements looked the same, except for direction. For each S, the threshold was determined at which succession gave way to movement with decreasing time intervals and movement gave way to succession with increasing time intervals. The authors found that in the descending series (time interval decreasing) succession perseverated to values for which in the ascending series there was movement. Despite great individual differences, the results showed that stroboscopic movement appeared in children under the same conditions as in adults but at time intervals greater than those needed for adults, i.e., children saw movement when adults saw succession.

Gantenbein (1952), working with the same age range, used a similar technique but varied the lengths of time of presentation of A and B, the light intensity, and the point of fixation, as well as the time interval between the presentation of A and B. Her apparatus allowed for a variation in the conditions so that developmental differences in the perception of simultaneity could be determined. She used the concentric clinical method. Gantenbein found, at all ages, that greater exposure time of A and B, low intensity, fixation on A, a smaller time interval between A and B, and increase of distance between stimuli all favored the perception of movement and simultaneity. The younger the S, the more easily was the perception of movement and simultaneity produced, with children experiencing movement over a larger range between succession and simultaneity than adults.

*Perception of Complex Movement Relationships: The Causal Effect.* By determining the conditions of motion that produce the causal effect, Michotte established the perception of causality as a special case of perception of movement. Olum, using the Michotte technique, studied the perception of causality in children. This experiment employed the phenomenological method as discussed (see p. 322). The same experiment was also performed with two other groups (one adult and one child) and used a different experimental method, namely, under conditions of specific instructions related to the expected causal and noncausal responses (Olum, 1958). The notions of *shove* and *tag* were chosen, after considerable pretest of possible instructions, as the best translation, into terms understandable to a child, of the expected causal and noncausal experiences.[1] Before proceeding with the experiment, the *E* explained to each child the differences between the motions involved in tag and shove, in an attempt to make certain that the child knew what to look for in the perceptual situation.

The number of shove (causal) responses and tag (noncausal) responses for adults and children were compared, and it was found that there were significant differences between children and adults. Stimulus conditions to which the adult response was noncausal evoked in children a significantly greater number of causal responses. When these two groups were compared to the two groups that were not given specific instructions, differences were also found. Especially striking were the differences between the two child groups. Under conditions of specific instruction, no passing or mutual approach responses were given. It is not clear whether the instructions actually changed the percept for the children or merely in-

[1] The phrasing of instructions in meaningful terms is especially important when working with young children, since they will often try to perform for the experimenter, whether or not they completely grasp the instructions. Even after terms are chosen that are meaningful to the age group, it is necessary to make sure that each child understands what is required.

hibited their verbal report. This situation illustrates again the influence of the method chosen on the results obtained.

Other work in this area has recently been reported from Piaget's laboratory in Geneva. Piaget and Lambercier (1958) studied a large number of causal effects with children (4 to 8 years old) and adults, also using the Michotte disk technique but with different stimulus conditions than those used by Olum. One problem studied intensively was the effect on the perception of causality of changes in the spatio-temporal interval between the two objects at the place of their expected causal interaction. Results from this study indicated that (1) children perceive a contact between the two objects in motion when there is, in fact, no contact and when adults perceive none; and (2) when children fail to perceive such a contact they also do not experience the causal effect, whereas when adults fail to perceive such contact they continue to perceive causality but across a perceived gap, that is, causality at a distance.

A modification of the phenomenological method discussed (p. 322) was used by Piaget and Lambercier. Since they were interested in certain specific aspects of S's experience (e.g., the perception of contact between A and B), if S failed to report on these spontaneously, E helped by asking relevant questions and by introducing stimulus variations that would call S's attention to these aspects. Such a modification of the phenomenological method may often be unavoidable when working with

very young children, but it has obvious dangers. The E is actually instructing S to concentrate on aspects of the situation that may or may not have been previously present for him. Since, as already noted, instructions may often change the percept itself, or at least S's response, it is important to keep the instructions explicit and identical for all S's.

A device, worth noting for work with the very young, was used in these experiments. Cubes of wood, painted to represent the moving objects in the apparatus, were placed on the table at which the child sat during the experiment. The child, by moving these cubes, could demonstrate how the objects in the apparatus appeared to him to be moving. This is an excellent way to check on the young child's verbal descriptions.

A second study, by Piaget and Maroun (1958), was concerned with developmental differences in the perception of tactile-kinesthetic impressions of causality and the influence on these impressions of visual perception.

The S, holding a special type of rake, felt-padded to eliminate any sound when it came into contact with another object, stood at the end of a long table on which there was a track containing a number of felt-padded boxes, placed one ahead of the other. The rake, pushed along the track, struck the first box. As the S continued to push the rake, the first box struck the second, and so on. The purpose of the experiment was to determine (1) where the feeling of impact was experienced, that is, was it localized in some part of the rake or in some part of the body or was it delegated beyond the pushing-end of the rake; (2) were there developmental differences; and (3) were these localizations or delegations influenced by vision.

Adults and children (6 to 7 years old) were studied under two conditions: (1) the *S*'s started with their eyes open and then repeated the task with their eyes closed; (2) the *S*'s started with their eyes closed and then proceeded with eyes open.

The results indicated (1) that when the rake comes in contact with the first box the impact is located at the end of the rake; when the rake pushes a box, which then pushes another ahead of it, there is a delegation of the impact from box to box. (2) Such impressions of location and delegation increased in frequency with age. (3) These impressions were stronger if *S* worked with his eyes open; and there was a strong influence of the visual on the tactual-kinesthetic, the groups working first with eyes open showing stronger impressions of localization and delegation in the eyes-closed situation than the groups working initially with eyes closed.

## PERCEPTION OF COMPLEX QUALITIES

*Qualities of Objects.* The perception of objects in terms of their expressive or physiognomic qualities is sometimes said to be more characteristic of the child's perception than of the perception of the adult (Werner, 1948, p. 67f.). Wapner and Werner (1957) studied the effect of the physiognomic quality of motion inherent in a static figure on perceived velocity when this figure was actually moved along a trajectory. Four sets of pictures, each set consisting of a standard, showing a static figure (e.g., a grazing horse), and a variable, showing a dynamic figure (e.g., a running horse), were used with children 6 to 19 years old. An additional set consisted of a triangle with apex pointing away from the direction of movement as standard and the identical triangle pointing in the direction of movement as variable. Standard and variable were drawn on belts of white paper and moved independently, each behind its own stationary window. The *S*, seated in front of the two windows, had the task of adjusting the speed of the variable to that of the standard. There were four trials for each set of figures, two trials in which the speed of the variable was initially set at less than that of the standard and two in which the speed was initially greater than that of the standard (see Fig. 8-9).

The results indicated that for the youngest age group (6–7) the dynamic figure was perceived as moving faster (i.e., adjusted to a slower speed) than the static figure. This effect decreased with age and held for all five sets of figures.

*Qualities of People.* The perception of expressive qualities of human faces, sometimes called social perception, is of increasing interest to psychologists today. For an overview of this area, see Bruner and Tagiuri (1954). Murphy and Murphy (1931, Ch. 6) have an excellent discussion of the early experimental work with children on the development of responses to social stimuli. Among these early studies,

Fig. 8-9. Static and dynamic figures (from Wapner and Werner 1957, p. 32).

many were concerned with the smiling response. The more recent study by Spitz and Wolf (1946) is the most thorough on this subject.

This study was designed to determine the stimulus conditions necessary to evoke the smiling response, its developmental pattern, and its universality. The S's were 251 children (White, Negro, Indian) from five different environments (private homes, nursery, foundling home, delivery clinic, Indian village) and ranged in age from birth to 1 year. A number of experiments were performed on each child to exclude the possibility of accidental results, and each experiment was done independently by both a male and a female experimenter, who neither talked to nor touched the child. The mother was never present in the child's visual field. The technique was to present the child with a nodding or smiling face, in full-face. When the child smiled, the face was slowly turned into profile, continuing to nod or smile. If the child stopped smiling, the face was turned back to full-face. In the standard smiling situation, the *E* smiled or nodded pleasantly at the child. In addition three other conditions were used: (1) the *E* assumed an expression of a savage beast baring its fangs, thus conserving the configurational aspects of the stimulus but removing the pleasant emotional quality; (2) the *E* wore a Halloween mask and rhythmically stuck out his tongue, thus retaining configurational aspects but removing all human attributes; and (3) a life-size puppet with a nodding head was used, with the *E* out of sight.

Results showed that although the motor pattern for smiling was present in the baby from the first few days of life, without an environmental stimulus, the social responses of smiling did not begin until about three weeks. In the 3-to-6-month group it was almost unfailingly present in *all* of the conditions discussed when presented in full-face. When the face was turned to profile, the child stopped smiling. In the second half of the first year the child no longer smiled indiscriminately but only at certain people.

A control series, consisting of many objects of varying intensity, surface structure, shape, size, familiarity and emotional significance (e.g., bottle, doll, or block with funny face on it) but lacking the configurational aspects, was also used. At no age did the children tested smile in response to these objects.

These findings held for all groups tested, despite differences in racial origin and background. Spitz maintained that this pattern is established by the child's experience with the mother, whose face is seen full-face in emotionally positive situations of feeding and child-care.

Gates (1923) studied the growth of the ability to identify specific emotions by facial expression in photographs in children 3 to 14 years old. Six photographs, representing joy, pain, anger, fear, scorn, and surprise, were used as stimuli. For each picture, she asked, "What is this lady doing?" "How does she feel?" There was a gradual increase with age in the ability to interpret each picture correctly. Laughter was the only emotion recognized by over half of the children at age three. It was not until age six that half of the children recognized pain; and anger, fear, and surprise came later than that, with scorn the most difficult of all. Only 43 per cent of the 11-year-olds judged scorn correctly, although adults had no difficulty with it.

Dashiell (1927) modified this method somewhat by first telling the child a story and then asking him to pick from a series of pictures the appropriate one for each incident in the story. This method has the advantage of depending less upon the available vocabulary of the child. Consequently, it proved to be a more discriminating tool for use with very young children, especially in studying recognition of the subtler emotions.

Gates (1927) studied the child's ability to identify expressive qualities in the human voice and related this to his ability to identify emotions in facial expression, using children in grades 3 through 8. A recording was made of an actress repeating the letters of the alphabet in tones of happiness, unhappiness, anger, fear, surprise, scorn, defiance, pity, and suspicion. Gates' results showed a developmental increase of correct judgments, although there was a greater number of correct responses to the visual than to the auditory situation.

Harlow's (1958) recent study of the stimulus properties of a love object is a new approach to social perception. Although Harlow worked with baby monkeys, his research has relevance for child development. The question was, what perceptual qualities must an object have to be accepted by the baby monkey as an adequate mother-object (i.e., the mother-object must evoke in the baby the characteristic baby-mother affectional responses). Two surrogate mothers were constructed, one of wire mesh and the other of wood covered with sponge rubber and sheathed in tan cotton terry cloth, both radiating heat. Eight newborn monkeys had both surrogates equally available, but for four of the monkeys the cloth mother lactated and the wire mother did not, whereas for four others the condition was reversed. In order to determine the relative importance of nursing comfort and contact comfort, the time each monkey spent on each surrogate mother was recorded for 165 consecutive days. The physiognomic qualities (tactual and visual) of the cloth mother won out, since regardless of whether the monkeys nursed from the cloth or wire mother they clearly preferred the cloth

mother, spending much more time on her and running to her as a haven of refuge when they were frightened. This was nicely underlined when the monkeys were put in the "love machine," a dimly lighted box with a little door which the monkey could open in order to look out. The strength of affectional responsiveness to an object was measured by the rate with which the monkey opened the door to look at the object outside. The cloth mother, wire mother, another baby monkey, and an empty box were presented for a thirty-minute period on successive days. The monkeys responded equally to the cloth mother and another baby monkey but showed no greater responsiveness to the wire mother than to an empty box.

Attempts to identify the critical stimuli for physiognomic qualities will doubtless increase in the near future, but methods in this area are still in their infancy.

## PERCEPTION OF QUANTITY

Although the growth of number *concepts* has received much study (see Chapter 10), there have been few experiments with children on the perception of quantity or numerosity. Long and Welch (1941) studied the development of ability to discriminate and match for quantity. Three kinds of test were used.

1. Discrimination of ten marbles from a varying quantity of them, beginning with one and progressing to nine by a modified method of limits. The child was told to look for a toy under the box with most marbles.

2. A number matching test. Two marbles were placed in front of the child. He was then given ten to fifteen marbles and told to make a pile just as big. If he succeeded, the standard pile was increased.

3. A group matching test. Four groups of marbles were placed within a radius of 6 inches. Two groups contained two marbles, two contained three. The child was asked to point to the groups containing most marbles and then to the groups containing least. The numbers were increased following a success.

The performance on all three tests increased with age (30 months to 7 years), but the tests were not of the same degree of difficulty. The authors concluded that they were measuring different things, not a single trait of "quantitative perceptual ability." A concept of "larger" was needed for test 1 (the easiest), of "sameness" for test 2, and both for test 3 (the hardest).

Several studies have been performed to discover the factors that aid the child to apprehend numbers as a group rather than to count individual items. Carper (1942) varied context (e.g., embedding of objects in a group), form (geometric as opposed to familiar objects), and pattern arrangement (regular versus irregular) in pictures drawn on cards. The subjects (kindergarten children) drew as many objects as they perceived. Apprehension by groups was apparently hindered by complex embedding, "poor" form units, and irregular patterns. Dawson (1953) also showed children cards on which objects were differently arranged and asked

them to say how many there were as rapidly as possible. Apprehension by grouping was hindered by complexity (lack of symmetry, heterogeneity of elements, poor figure-ground relations, etc.). First graders could not apprehend more than four or five elements as a group. With more, they tended to count.

## TIME PERCEPTION

Fraisse and his co-workers have studied perception of duration in children with both visual and auditory presentation of intervals. In the same situation used to investigate velocity Fraisse and Vautrey (1952b) secured comparative judgments of duration for two toy cyclists running courses of variable lengths and at variable speeds. The children (5 years old) were asked which took longer to run its course. The judgments averaged 50 per cent correct. Correctness depended on whether the factors on which the children based their judgments corresponded to the actual duration. There was no "intuition of the duration as such." Time, the authors thought, is perceived by adults in terms of succession of events and is thus simply a constituent of the structure given by these events. Children of 5 estimated duration by the quantity of work apparently done, i.e., whether the cyclist went farther or faster, or by the quantity of "effort," i.e., taking longer to do the same work (the children referred to the cyclist in this case as "tired"). The situation permitted identification of the child with the cyclist, and he responded by estimating time in terms of action.

Fraisse and Orsini (1958) used an adjustment technique with children of three age groups (6, 8, and 10 years). The task was to match the duration (thirty seconds) of a noise made by a synchronous motor. When the noise stopped, the motor was started again, and S was to stop it when it had lasted equally long. Three lights of different color gave S knowledge of results (right, too long, or too short). Accuracy increased with age. All the children improved, the youngest most. The 6-year-olds tended to overestimate, whereas the 10-year-olds had a tendency to underestimate.

Smythe and Goldstone (1957) used a different technique with auditory duration. The S's were children, 6 to 14, and adults. The S was asked to report whether a tone heard was more or less than a second. Runs of ascending and descending duration, starting at 1 second, were given. Then S was given five runs of 1 second duration and told to use them as a standard; then he was tested again. All the S's overestimated a second. Variability decreased with increasing age. The 6- and 7-year-olds were unable to profit from the information given, perhaps because of their very inadequate concepts of a second, but the others became more accurate.

# PERCEPTION
# OF SYMBOLIC FORMS
# AND PICTURES

*Symbols.* Perception of speech sounds and written words are specialized topics, better considered under speech and reading. It should be pointed out that the perceptual problems in learning to read are closely related to the discrimination of meaningless or abstract forms drawn on pieces of paper. Discrimination of such forms by matching techniques has been used as part of reading readiness programs, on the assumption that practice in the task will facilitate progress in reading. How discrimination of such forms can be improved is a problem of interest. Will the learning of identifying names for certain forms, for instance, make discrimination faster and more accurate? Spiker (1956) has reviewed some relevant experiments performed on children and given some rules for good methodology to be followed in experiments on "acquired distinctiveness."

*Pictures.* Although pictures of objects have been used in intelligence tests and as material for the study of personality, there has been relatively little research on the development of this kind of perception as compared with "real" objects. Research with a group of native African children (Nissen, Machover, and Kinder, 1935) indicated that these children whose culture included few if any pictures performed relatively poorly on tests that had pictorially representative content. Experimental research might well follow up this lead.

Some of the material discussed under form perception is relevant here, since two-dimensional drawings are in many cases pictures, though of varying degrees of fidelity. Some attempt to dimensionalize fidelity might be of use in organizing the rather hit-or-miss collection of facts in this area. There is no systematic research on children's perception of photographs, as compared with line drawings, abstract geometrical forms, and (at the other end of the scale) the real objects.

One attempt to grade pictorial material can be cited. Vernon (1940) showed a graded series of pictures presented for 1.8 seconds in a tachistoscope to children of various ages. The series progressed from a clearly "meaningful" picture with sharp contours to one similar in design but drawn with blurred, crosshatched outlines. The children's descriptions of the "meaningful" pictures were accurate, but the blurred ones produced a great deal of invention.

Recognition of incongruity in a picture of a building (photographed so that it appeared to have only one side) was studied by Behar and Bevan (1956). Age was an important factor in sensitivity to this incongruity. The authors related this fact to the child's ability to respond to the representation of a three-dimensional world in two-dimensional space, pointing out the lack of perspective in children's drawings. But children's judgments of space in photographs does not appear to have been studied where there is good fidelity. Some other factor may have been responsible for failure to notice the incongruity. Methods other than drawing and free report are indicated.

## ATTITUDE AND PERCEPTION

Techniques appropriate for studying the influence of attitudinal factors (need, set, emotion, etc.) have been discussed under question 3 (see p. 325). Two rather specialized problems within this area might be given further mention: the effect of attention on perception and the relationship between perception and personality.

*Attention.* That perception is selective—that one can attend or not attend —is a generally accepted proposition. It is also commonly understood that children's capacity for attending increases with age (e.g., as shown by digit span on intelligence tests, for instance). Here might lie a factor of great importance in the understanding of perceptual development, as indicated by increase in precision and ability to differentiate. Yet there seems to be little research on attention in children, at least in regard to perceiving. Experiments by Dallenbach (1914) with second graders, aged 7 to 10 years, gave drill in "apprehending" nine figures presented for five seconds on a card (numbers, letters, geometrical figures, etc., in a 3 by 3 matrix). Practice over a period of weeks resulted in apparently lasting improvement on similar tests, as compared with unpracticed schoolmates.

That training with tachistoscopic devices ("flashmeters," for instance) results in improved performance in the same situation has often been demonstrated (Gates, 1925; Freeburne, 1949). Whether this improvement transfers to more complex perceptual skills, such as reading, is a matter that has caused much controversy. Goins (1958) recently summarized the controversy and presented fresh experimental evidence that tachistoscopic training does not transfer to reading skill. Research on the problem obviously requires control of many factors, such as teacher differences and motivation of control groups. Validity of results of such experiments must be sought in transfer situations; is it merely specific eye-movement habits or fixations that are being trained or is it something more general?

What an infant will attend to spontaneously was the subject of an experiment by Berlyne (1959). He used a fixation preference technique, like Staples, with paired comparisons of stimuli varying in albedo and in "complexity" of figures. Differences in albedo did not affect fixation, but "complexity" may have, since the preferred patterns were described as ones with more contour. Fantz (1958) used a similar technique. Infants as young as 2 months showed some consistent preferences. They tended to fixate a checker pattern in preference to a square and a bull's-eye in preference to stripes.

*Perception and Personality.* It has become a popular tenet in the last decade that personality affects perception and also that personality can be studied by way of perception. It is therefore of considerable importance to clinicians to discover whether differences in personality are correlated with differences in perception. The method of such experiments is to give a battery of personality tests and then to seek some measures of perception, later correlating individual differences in the two. Witkin et al. (1954) made such a study. Personality was assessed by the Rorschach, TAT, figure-drawing tests, and by miniature-toy play. Perception was measured by a rod and frame test, tilting room and tilting chair, and embedded figures. What to correlate here is a very complex matter. The authors were interested in "in-

dependence of the field" in perception and thought that differences could be correlated with such aspects of personality as self-concept, organization in play, control of impulses, "coping" ability, and so on. The methodology of correlational experiments is unavoidably much concerned with statistics, not the concern of this chapter. But the validity and meaning of the individual test scores correlated is obviously important and must be independently determined. Furthermore, results are bound to depend to some extent on the choice of tests. Post hoc selection of differentiating scores as a basis for analysis is a dubious procedure sometimes employed. Postman (1955) has pointed out some of the logical and technical weaknesses of this work.

## ILLUSIONS

In recent years there has been considerable interest in the development of perception of illusions (Inhelder, 1957). Piaget and his collaborators systematically studied a great number of them. He divides illusions into three types: those that decrease with age, such as the Müller-Lyer illusion, those that increase with age, such as the size-weight illusion, and a third type that increases up to about age 10 and then decreases, as does one form of the vertical-horizontal illusion.[1]

The various techniques used to study illusions can be illustrated by the work done on the Müller-Lyer illusion with children. Binet (1895) made a system-

[1] See Piaget's *Recherches sur le développement des perceptions. Archives de Psychologie, Genève,* from 1942 on.

atic study of illusions in children. Children 7 through 14 were seated individually at a table on which was a booklet with the standard, Figure A, on the right-hand margin. The comparison figures, B, in varying sizes made up the pages of the booklet. Instructions to the S were to disregard the oblique lines and to compare the lengths of the straight lines, choosing the variable figure that looked equal in length to the standard.

In one booklet A was 10 centimeters, the B's varied from 9 to 15 centimeters, and the oblique lines were 4 centimeters. In another booklet A was 2 centimeters, the B's were 1.8 to 4 centimeters, and the oblique lines were 0.8 centimeter. The distance between A and B, kept constant at 20 centimeters, required the S to move his eyes for purposes of comparison. The variable figures were presented in increasing and decreasing order. All the S's chose a larger B as equal to A, but the illusion was stronger in the younger children. It was also found to be greater for the smaller figure and in the decreasing rather than the increasing order.

In another experiment Binet had S's compare Figure A to a series of straight lines and Figure B to a series of straight lines in order to separate the double effect of the different types of oblique lines. He found that the illusion of A is stronger than that of B.

Van Biervliet (1896), working with children 12 to 16 years old and adults,

used a method similar to Binet's, but he varied the angles of the oblique lines as well as the length of the vertical lines. Taking Binet's large Figure A as the standard (with oblique lines at 30 degrees) he had five series of type A comparison figures. In all of the series the figures varied in length, but the angles of the oblique lines differed from series to series (60, 90, up to 180 degrees). He found the illusion stronger in children than in adults, but in all cases the more obtuse the angle, the less the illusion.

Piaget and von Albertini (1950), working with children 5 to 9 years old and adults, systematically varied both the angle of the oblique lines and their length, while keeping the standard figure constant at 15 millimeters. Both types of Müller-Lyer figures were used independently. All figures were placed horizontally, with comparison figures presented successively at the right of the standard and in concentric order (first a figure much larger than the standard, then one much smaller, etc.). The authors found that (1) as the height of the oblique lines increased, the illusion decreased; (2) in type A figures, as the length of the oblique lines increased, the illusion first increased, then decreased, and for children even became negative; (3) in figures of type B, as the length of the oblique lines increased, the illusion increased; (4) in all cases the illusion decreased with age.

A somewhat different technique was used by Wapner and Werner (1957), working with children between 6 and 19 years. They combined into one horizontal pattern both types of Müller-Lyer figures (←——→——→). The part on the left was the standard and was 75 milli-meters long. The S, who sat 3 feet from the pattern, could adjust the part on the right (by means of a knob) until it looked equal to the standard. Four trials were used (two with the initial setting of the variable at 25 millimeters and two with the initial setting of the variable at 125 millimeters). The order of the settings was small, large, large, small.

In this study, as in all the others, the results show a considerable decrease of the illusion with age.

## DEVELOPMENT AND ENVIRONMENTAL OPPORTUNITY

Development under controlled en-vironmental conditions has often been the subject of study, especially in ani-mals. Generally, the behavior observed has been locomotor, emotional, or social. The development of perception under such conditions is no less interesting and instructive. When human infants are to be the subjects, it is not feasible, as a rule, to create special types of en-vironmental deprivation, but nature provides such cases occasionally and it is important that good methods should be followed in studying them.

*Deprivation of Stimulation.* The most spectacular cases of deprivation are those of the blind-born restored to sight by surgery. Extensive reports of these cases are found in Bourdon (1902, Ch. 13) and Senden (1932). Since very different conclusions have been drawn from studying these reports, caution is necessary in interpreting them. Many of them are very old, and the testing procedures were informal and not re-ported in detail. Dennis (1934) dis-cussed the inadequacies of the research procedures. One source of disagreement may lie in the use of verbal identifica-tion (naming) as an indicator of dis-crimination. It is not reasonable to sup-pose that a word learned to identify stimulation coming from other senses would automatically transfer to visual stimulation present for the first time (i.e., the fact that a child can identify a marble by touch does not mean that he could name it when it is shown him for the first time). The most suitable methods of testing discrimination would probably be those that have been used successfully with young children, such as matching methods. The task in-volved should be as easy as possible because of the emotional upsets, inter-ference from old habits, and nystagmus that are characteristic of these cases.

Experimental production of depriva-tion, such as dark-rearing, is possible with animals. Riesen's (1958) experi-ments with infant chimpanzees are the most relevant here and should be con-sulted for methods of control and testing (see Chapter 7).

A few studies of the effect of a restricted environment on human in-fants are available, though they contain little information about discrimination. Dennis and Dennis (1941) raised a pair of twins from the beginning of the second month to the end of the four-teenth in relative confinement. The in-fants never left the nursery (except for medical check-up), were cared for solely by two adults, and remained in their cribs except for necessary care. There were no pictures or decoration, a screen was placed between the two cribs, and they were given no toys until the forty-ninth week. For the most part their development was normal, as far as could be observed, but they were retarded in visually directed reaching. This ability developed very rapidly when practice was allowed. The authors thought that learning played a part in the development of "autogenous" responses—those that appear without training but are practiced by the child himself.

Spitz's study (1945) of "hospitalism" compared children in two institutions during the first year. Again, there is little information in regard to discriminatory abilities. It is not clear how much of the children's retardation was caused by inadequate "mothering" and how much by the restricted environment.

A recent report by Dennis and Najarian (1957) of infants reared in a foundling home in Beirut in a very limited environment discusses the problems of testing these subjects and interpretation of the results. Restriction of learning opportunities resulted in a depressed developmental index in the last 9 months of the first year but apparently did not result in a generally poor performance by 4½ to 6 years. It is to be hoped that future studies of such groups can be planned to study perceptual development with specialized laboratory methods as well as a routine test schedule.

Another type of environmental restriction is found in children with organic impairment of sight and hearing. Education and development of blind and deaf children has long been a subject of special study and is too voluminous to treat in detail. It was at one time supposed that deprivation of one sense brought about "compensation" or extraordinary superiority of discrimination by means of others. That any such compensation is probably the result of training is now a general opinion (Hayes, 1934). How superior acuity is achieved in such cases is a matter of extreme interest for perceptual development and deserves further study. The studies of obstacle avoidance in the blind by echolocation (Griffin, 1958, Ch. 12) are an impressive example of the knowledge to be obtained by expertly planned research in this area.

Cases of early blindness, later blindness (occurring after four years), and sighted S's were compared by Drever (1955) to discover whether early deprivation is a more serious handicap than later. The S's were tested in tactual recognition of shapes, orientation and forms on a peg board, and perception of straightness of a curved rule. Results differed for the tests. Sighted S's and, next, late blind were better at recognition of shapes, but the blind S's had a more objective perception of tactual straightness.

***Enrichment of Stimulation.*** The effect of a specially enriched environment or extra opportunities for practice on the development of discrimination is not only interesting theoretically but of obvious importance educationally. The idea of developing "sensitivity" by providing special opportunities for practice is an old one. The "Montessori Method" specialized in such practice, and an account of it is instructive to those interested in perceptual learning, though it was a teaching not a research program. The basis of the program was the "education of the senses," which had as its aim "the refinement of the differential perception of stimuli by means of repeated exercises" (Montessori, 1912, p. 173). The exercises consisted of observing and ordering series of graded stimuli, such as sandpapers of graduated roughness, weights, pieces of wood of varying thickness and height.

The color series was most interesting. It consisted of eight "tints" (black, red, orange, yellow, green, blue, violet, and brown), with eight gradations of intensity for each. First the child was asked to find duplicates for only three "strong colors." Later, he found matches for all eight. Then the lighter tones would be presented, and the child was shown how to arrange them in order of gradation. The procedure was continued until the child could order all 64 samples. Children of three were said to be able to "put all of the tints into gradation." Some of the principles given are interesting in the light of current research. The procedure was always from "few stimuli, strongly contrasting, to many stimuli in gradual differentiation, always more fine and imperceptible" (p. 184). Activity and self-correction on the part of the child were thought very important. Transfer from simple kinds of preliminary training was stressed; when forms and letters were taught, for instance, the child began by following the contours with his finger before attempting visual recognition. The importance of *early* experience, so much stressed nowadays, was also emphasized. "It is necessary to

begin the education of the senses in the formative period" (p. 221).

The validity of these techniques was not tested with controlled experiments, but such experiments can be done and are beginning to be. An example of an experiment on transfer from pretraining is one by Jeffrey (1958) with tonal frequencies. His criterion task was learning to press a button on the left in response to a low tone (128 cycles per second), one on the right to a high tone (1152 cycles per second), and, after mastering this problem, to do the same for a closer pair (256 and 384 cycles per second). Three groups of kindergarten children took part. Group I did only the criterion task, Group II had pretraining consisting of trying to sing the two tones and were then passed to the criterion task. Group III had pretraining by striking the appropriate key on a piano (the two keys were marked with red tape) and were then passed to the criterion task. Only one of the seven S's in Group I was able to learn the criterion task in 72 trials. In Group II five of seven learned it, and in Group III all did. One S in Group II and one in Group III transferred to the closer pair of tones. None in Group I did. The immediate comparison between a response-produced tone and the stimulus tone accentuates the correctness of a response and also helps "define the continuum," Jeffrey thought.

Research in this area will certainly increase. It is to be hoped that future experiments will include tests of discrimination other than learning or naming. It would be interesting, in fact, to compare the effects of various types of training on discrimination measured in a number of different ways. Ordering tests are a promising possibility, since they can be extended to almost any length and degree of difficulty. One problem to be pondered by the investigator is, as always, whether he is actually measuring discriminative ability or whether the real variable is the child's comprehension of the task.

## Summary and Evaluation

A brief final appraisal of methods for studying perception in children leads to the conclusion that there is no dearth of techniques or proper conventions for using them. Looking at the area as a whole, one is struck by the fact that its weaknesses are not methodological; they seem to arise, rather, from a theoretical lack. The methods are rich enough; sometimes an experimenter's ingenuity in devising substitutes for too "adult" methods is astonishing.

With the simpler discriminations, such as color comparisons, there is a good array of facts, derived from a variety of methods. Success is already notable or is just around the corner. With the more complex discriminations, such as physiognomic qualities and interpersonal relations, methods are needed. The difficulty of describing the stimuli in these cases makes the problem very hard. Good research will have to cope with this difficulty.

As for the real faults in this field, we might place first the rarity of the truly

developmental approach. At least half the studies the writers have been through were just experiments that happened to have been done with children —perhaps because the children were conveniently at hand in a nursery school or institution. The methods employed in such cases are not tools for the solution of a problem in development. The choice instead is likely to be merely opportunistic. Often, in a given area of research, there are many facts and interesting methods, but they seem to add up to a motley, rather hit-or-miss collection. This is obviously not the fault of any one person who made a contribution. However, it warns the would-be experimenter that a careful and systematic definition of his problem should come first, lest another bit of unrelated information be the result.

Finally, this field would benefit very much by programmatic research. Long-range planning of a program in which the experiments are related and the designs thought out in terms of all the significant variables and dimensions would begin to solve problems not just create them. Piaget's laboratory, with its long series of integrated studies, one developing from another and yet stemming from a prearranged pattern, is an impressive example here. The experiments have their faults, no doubt. One wishes for fewer words, more data, and an occasional test of significance, but developmental psychologists in this country should certainly let themselves profit from the systematic nature of his program in planning their own research.

# REFERENCES

Allport, G. W., and T. F. Pettigrew. 1957. Cultural influence on the perception of movement: the trapezoidal illusion among Zulus. *J. abnorm. soc. Psychol.*, **55**, 104–113.

Ames, Louise B., Janet Learned, Ruth Metraux, and R. Walker. 1953. Development of perception in the young child as observed in responses to the Rorschach test blots. *J. genet. Psychol.*, **82**, 183–204.

Beams, H. L. 1954. Affectivity as a factor in the apparent size of pictured food objects. *J. exp. Psychol.*, **47**, 197–200.

Behar, I., and W. Bevan. 1956. The perception of incongruity by young children. *Acta Psychol.* **12**, 342–348.

Benton, A. L., and L. M. Schultz. 1949. Observations on tactual form perception (stereognosis) in preschool children. *J. clin. Psychol.*, **5**, 359–364.

Berlyne, D. E. 1959. Albedo and complexity of stimuli and visual fixation in the human infant. *Brit. J. Psychol.* In press.

Binet, A. 1895. La Mesure des illusions visuelles chez les enfants. *Rev. philos. de la France et de l'étranger*, **40**, 11–25.

Bourdon, B. 1902. *La Perception visuelle de l'espace.* Paris: Schleicher Frères.

Bruner, J. S., and Cecile C. Goodman. 1947. Value and need as organizing factors in perception. *J. abnorm. soc. Psychol.* **42**, 33–44.

Bruner, J. S., L. Postman, and J. Rodrigues. 1951. Expectation and the perception of color. *Amer. J. Psychol.*, **64**, 216–227.

Bruner, J. S., and R. Tagiuri. 1954. The perception of people. In G. Lindzey (Ed.), *Handbook of Social Psychology.* Cambridge: Addison-Wesley, Ch. 17.

Brunswik, E. 1956. *Perception and the representative design of psychological experiments.* Berkeley: Univer. California Press.

Burzlaff, W. 1931. Methodologische Beiträge zum Problem der Farbenkonstanz. *Z. Psychol.*, **119**, 177–235.

Carpenter, B., and Janeth T. Carpenter. 1958. The perception of movement by young chimpanzees and human children. *J. comp. physiol. Psychol.*, **51**, 782–784.

Carper, Doris. 1942. Seeing numbers as groups in primary-grade arithmetic. *Elem. Sch. J.*, **43**, 166–170.

Carter, L., and E. Schooler. 1949. Value, and other factors in perception. *Psychol. Rev.*, **56**, 200–208.

Chase, W. P. 1937. Color vision in infants. *J. exp. Psychol.*, **20**, 203–222.

Cohen, W., A. Hershkowitz, and Marie Chodak. 1958. Size judgment at different distances as a function of age level. *Child Develpm.* **29**, 473–479.

Cook, W. M. 1931. Ability of children in color discrimination. *Child Develpm.*, **2**, 303–320.

Costa, A. M. 1949. Constanza percettiva di intervalli vuoti. *Arch. Psicol. Neur. Psich.*, **10**, 377–388.

Cramaussel, E. 1924. Ce que voient des yeux d'enfants. *J. Psychol.*, **21**, 161–170.

Crudden, C. H. 1941. Form abstraction by children. *J. genet. Psychol.*, **58**, 113–129.

Cruikshank, Ruth M. 1941. The development of visual size constancy in early infancy. *J. genet. Psychol.*, **58**, 327–351.

Dallenbach, K. M. 1914. The effect of practice upon visual apprehension in school children. Part I and Part II. *J educ. Psychol.*, **5**, 321–334 and 387–404.

Dashiell, J. F. 1927. A new method of measuring reactions to facial expression of emotion. *Psychol. Bull.*, **24**, 174–175.

Davidson, H. P. 1935. A study of the confusing letters b, d, p and q. *J. genet. Psychol.*, **47**, 458–468.

Dawson, D. T. 1953. Number grouping as a function of complexity. *Elem. Sch. J.*, **54**, 35–42.

Dennis, W. 1934. Congenital cataract and unlearned behavior. *J. genet. Psychol.*, **44**, 340–351.

———, and Marsena G. Dennis. 1941. Infant development under conditions of restricted practice and minimum social stimulations. *Genet. Psychol. Monogr.*, **23**, 149–155.

Dennis, W., and P. Najarian. 1957. Infant development under environmental handicap. *Psychol. Monogr.*, **71**, No. 7, 1–13.

Dietze, D. 1955. The facilitating effect of words on discrimination and generalization. *J. exp. Psychol.*, **50**, 255–260.

Drever, J. 1955. Early learning and the perception of space. *Amer. J. Psychol.*, 68, 605–614.

Dukes, W. F. 1951. Ecological representiveness in studying perceptual size-constancy in childhood. *Amer. J. Psychol.*, 64, 87–93.

Dukes, W. F., and W. Bevan. 1952. Accentuation and response variability in the perception of personally relevant objects. *J. Pers.*, 20, 457–465.

Fantz, R. L. 1958. Pattern vision in young infants. *Psychol. Record*, 8, 43–47.

Fraisse, P., and P. Vautrey. 1952a. La Perception de l'espace, de la vitesse, et du temps chez l'enfant de cinq ans. *Enfance*, 5, 1–20.

———. 1952b. La Perception de l'espace, de la vitesse et du temps chez l'enfant de cinq ans. II. Le Temps. *Enfance*, 5, 102–119.

Fraisse, P. and F. Orsini. 1958. Étude expérimentale des conduites temporelles. III. Étude genétique de l'estimation de la durée. *Année psychol.*, 58, 1–6.

Freeburne, C. M. 1949. The influence of training in perceptual span and perceptual speed upon reading ability. *J. educ. Psychol.*, 40, 321–352.

Friedmann, P. 1927. Die Raumschwelle der Haut beim Kinde. *Z. Psychol.*, 103, 185–202.

Gantenbein, Maria-Martha. 1952. Recherches sur le développement de la perception du mouvement avec l'âge (mouvement apparent, dit stroboscopique). *Arch. Psychol. Genève*, 33, 197–294.

Gates, A. I. 1925. Functions of Flashcard exercises in reading: An experimental study. *Teach. Coll. Rec.*, 27, 311–327.

Gates, Georgina S. 1923. An experimental study of the growth of social perception. *J. educ. Psychol.*, 14, 449–462.

———. 1927. The role of the auditory element in the interpretation of emotion. *Psychol. Bull.*, 24, 175.

Ghent, Lila. 1956. Perception of overlapping and embedded figures by children of different ages. *Amer. J. Psychol.*, 69, 575–587.

Gellermann, L. W. 1933a. Form discrimination in chimpanzees and two-year-old children: I. Form (triangularity) per se. *J. genet. Psychol.*, 42, 3–29.

———. 1933b. Form discrimination in chimpanzees and two-year-old children: II. Form

versus background. *J. genet. Psychol.*, 42, 29–50.

Gesell, A., Frances L. Ilg, and Glenna E. Bullis. 1949. *Vision: Its development in infant and child.* New York: Hoeber.

Gibson, J. J. 1948. Studying perceptual phenomena. In T. G. Andrews (Ed.), *Methods of Psychology.* New York: Wiley. Ch. 6. Pp. 158–188.

Gibson, J. J., and Eleanor J. Gibson. 1955. Perceptual learning: Differentiation or enrichment? *Psychol. Rev.*, 62, 32–41.

Gilbert, J. A. 1893. Experiments on the musical sensitiveness of school children. *Stud. Yale Psychol. Lab.*, 1, 80–87.

———. 1894. Researches on the mental and physical development of school children. *Stud. Yale Psychol. Lab.*, 2, 40–100.

Gilchrist, J. C., and L. S. Nesberg. 1952. Need and perceptual change in need-related objects. *J. exp. Psychol.*, 44, 369–377.

Goins, Jean T. 1958. *Visual perceptual abilities and early reading progress.* Suppl. educ. Monogr., No. 87. Chicago: Univer. Chicago Press.

Griffin, D. R. 1958. *Listening in the dark,* New Haven: Yale Univer. Press.

Guilford, J. P. 1954. *Psychometric methods.* (2nd ed.) New York: McGraw-Hill.

Gunther, M. 1955. Instinct and the nursing couple. *Lancet*, I, 575–78.

Hanfmann, Eugenia. 1933. Some experiments on spacial position as a factor in children's perception and reproduction of simple figures. *Psychol. Forsch.*, 17, 319–329.

Harlow, H. F. 1958. The nature of love. *Amer. Psychol.*, 13, 673–685.

Hayes, S. P. 1934. Sensory compensation, or the vicariate of the senses. *Quart. Blind.*, 28, 122–129.

Heider, F. and Grace M. Heider. 1940. A comparison of color sorting behavior of deaf and hearing children. *Psychol. Monogr.*, 52, No. 2, 6–22.

Hemmendinger, L. 1953. Perceptual organization and development as reflected in the structure of Rorschach test responses. *J. proj. Tech.*, 17, 162–170.

Hunton, Vera D. 1955. The recognition of inverted pictures by children. *J. genet. Psychol.*, 86, 281–288.

Inhelder, Bärbel. 1957. Developmental psychology. In P. R. Farnsworth and Q. McNemar (Eds.), *Annu. Rev. Psych.* Palo Alto: Annual Reviews, 8, pp. 139–163.

Jeffrey, W. E. 1958. Variables in early discrimination learning: II. Mode of response and stimulus difference in the discrimination of tonal frequencies. *Child Develpm.*, 29, 531–538.

Jenkin, N., and N. West. 1958. Perception in organic mental defectives: An exploratory study. I. The size-weight illusion. *The Training School Bulletin*, 55, 5–10.

Jensen, K. 1932. Differential reactions to taste and temperature stimuli in newborn infants. *Genet. Psychol. Monogr.* 12, 361–479.

Johnson, B., and F. L. Beck. 1941. The development of space perception: I. Stereoscopic vision in preschool children. *J. genet. Psychol.*, 58, 247–254.

Hunter, I. M. L. 1952. An experimental investigation of the absolute and relative theories of transposition behaviour in children. *Brit. J. Psychol.*, 43, 113–128.

Koffka, K. 1931. *The growth of the mind.* New York: Harcourt, Brace.

———. 1935. *Principles of Gestalt psychology.* New York: Harcourt, Brace.

Köhler, W. 1915. Optische Untersuchungen am Schimpansen und am Haushuhn. *Abh. preuss. Akad. Wiss.*, Phys.-Math. Kl., Nr. 3.

———. 1918. Nachweis einfacher Strukturfunktionen beim Schimpansen und beim Haushuhn. Über eine neue Methode zur Untersuchung des bunten Farben-systems. *Abh. preuss. Akad. Wiss.*, Nr. 2.

Kuenne, M. R. 1946. Experimental investigation of the relation of language to transposition behavior in young children. *J. exp. Psychol.*, 36, 471–490.

Lambercier, M. 1946. La Constance des grandeurs en comparaisons sériales. *Arch. Psychol.*, Genève, 31, 79–282.

Lambert, W. W., R. L. Solomon, and P. D. Watson. 1949. Reinforcement and extinction as factors in size estimation. *J. exp. Psychol.*, 39, 637–641.

Leuba, C. 1940. Children's reactions to elements of simple geometric patterns. *Amer. J. Psychol.*, 53, 575–578.

Ling, B. C. 1941. Form discrimination as a learning cue in infants. *Comp. Psychol. Monogr.*, 17, No. 2.

Locke, N. M. 1938. Perception and intelligence: Their phylogenetic relation. *Psychol. Rev.*, 45, 335–345.

Long, L., and L. Welch. 1941. The development of the ability to discriminate and match numbers. *J. genet. Psychol.*, 59, 377–387.

MacLeod, R. B. 1958. The phenomenological approach to social psychology. In R. Tagiuri and L. Petrullo. (Eds.) *Person perception and interpersonal behavior.* Stanford: Stanford Univer. Press. Ch. 4. Pp. 33–54.

Meili, R. 1931. Les Perceptions des enfants et la psychologie de la Gestalt. *Arch. Psychol. Genève*, 23, 25–45.

———, and E. Tobler. 1931. Les Mouvements stroboscopiques chez les enfants. *Arch. Psychol. Genève*, 23, 131–157.

Meister, D. 1949. A comparative study of figure-ground discrimination in preschool children and adults. *J. genet. Psychol.* 74, 311–323.

Mooney, C. M. 1957. Age in the development of closure ability in children. *Canad. J. Psychol.*, 11, 219–226.

Montessori, Marie. 1912. *Montessori method.* (Trans. by A. S. George.) New York: Stokes.

Munn, N. L. 1955. *The evolution and growth of human behavior.* Boston: Houghton-Mifflin.

———, and B. R. Stiening. 1931. The relative efficacy of form and background in a child's discrimination of visual patterns. *J. genet. Psychol.*, 39, 73–88.

Murray, H. A. 1933. The effect of fear upon estimates of the maliciousness of other personalities. *J. soc. Psychol.*, 4, 310–329.

Murphy, G., and Lois B. Murphy. 1931. *Experimental social psychology.* New York: Harper.

Newhall, S. M. 1937. Identification by young children of differently oriented visual forms. *Child Develpm.* 8, 105–111.

Nissen, H. W., S. Machover, and Elaine F. Kinder. 1935. A study of performance tests given to a group of native African Negro children. *Brit. J. Psychol.*, 25, 308–355.

Olum, Vivian. 1956. Developmental differences in the perception of causality. *Amer. J. Psychol.*, 69, 417–423.

——. 1958. Developmental differences in the perception of causality under conditions of specific instructions. *Vita Humana*, 1, 191–203.

Peckham, R. H. 1933. Visual discrimination in preschool children. *Child Develpm.*, 4, 292–297.

Peters, W. 1927. Die Entwicklung von Wahrnehmungsleistungen beim Kind. *Z. Psychol. Physiol. Sinnesorg.*, 103, 129–184.

Piaget, J. 1949. Recherches sur le développement des perceptions. X. Les illusions relatives aux angles et à la longueur de leurs cotés. *Arch. Psychol.*, *Genève*, 32, 281–307.

——. 1954. *The construction of reality in the child.* New York: Basic Books.

——, and Barbara von Albertini. 1950. Recherches sur le développement des perceptions. XI. L'Illusion de Müller-Lyer. *Arch. Psychol.*, *Genève*, 33, 1–48.

——. 1954. Recherches sur le développement des perceptions. XIX. Observations sur la perception des bonnes formes chez l'enfant par actualization des lignes virtuelles. *Arch. Psychol.*, *Genève*, 34, 203–243.

Piaget, J., and M. Lambercier. 1943. Recherches sur le développement des perceptions. III. Le problème de la comparaison visuelle en profondeur et l'erreur systematique de l'étalon. *Arch. Psychol.*, *Genève*, 29, 205–308.

——. 1951. Recherches sur le développement des perceptions. XII. La comparaison des grandeurs projectives chez l'enfant et chez l'adulte. *Arch. Psychol.*, *Genève*, 33, 81–130.

——. 1956. Recherches sur le développement des perceptions. XXIX. Grandeurs projectives et grandeurs réeles avec étalon éloigné. *Arch. Psychol.*, *Genève*, 35, 257–280.

——. 1958. Recherches sur le développement des perceptions. XXXIII. La causalité perceptive visuelle chez l'enfant et chez l'adulte. *Arch. Psychol. Genève*, 36, 77–202.

Piaget, J., and J. Maroun. 1958. Recherches sur le développement des perceptions. XXXIV. La Localisation des impressions d'impact dans la causalité perceptive tactilo-kinesthésique. *Arch. Psychol. Genève*, 36, 202–236.

Postman, L. 1955. Review of *Personality through perception* (H. A. Witkin et al.). *Psychol. Bull.*, 51, 79–83.

Pratt, K. C., A. K. Nelson, and K. H. Sun. 1930. The behavior of the newborn infant. Columbus: Ohio State Univer. Press.

Razran, G. H. S. 1933. Conditioned responses in children. *Arch. Psychol.*, 23, No. 148.

Renshaw, S. 1930. The errors of cutaneous localization and the effect of practice on the localizing movement in children and adults. *J. genet. Psychol.*, 38, 223–238.

——, R. J. Wherry, and J. C. Newlin. 1930. Cutaneous localization in congenitally blind versus seeing children and adults. *J. genet. Psychol.*, 38, 239–248.

Rice, C. 1930. The orientation of plane figures as a factor in their perception by children. *Child Develpm.*, 1, 111–143.

Riesen, A. H. 1958. Plasticity of behavior: Psychological aspects. In H. F. Harlow and C. N. Woolsey. (Eds.), *Biological and biochemical bases of behavior.* Madison: Univer. Wisconsin Press. Pp. 425–450.

Saetvit, J. G., D. Lewis, and C. E. Seashore. 1940. *Revision of The Seashore measures of musical talent.* Iowa City: Univer. Iowa Press.

Segers, J. E. La perception visuelle et la fonction de globalisation chez les enfants. *Documents Pédotechniques*, 1926. 5me Année, No. 2, Bruxelles.

Senden, M. v. 1932. *Raum-und Gestaltauffassung des operierten Blindgeborenen vor und nach der Operation.* Leipzig: Barth.

Siegel, A. I., and H. Ozkaptan. 1953. Manipulative completion of bisected geometrical forms by nursery school children. *Amer. J. Psychol.*, 66, 626–628.

Skeels, H. M. 1933. The use of conditioning techniques in the study of form discrimination of young children. *J. exp. Educ.*, 2, 127–137.

Skinner, B. F. 1957. *Verbal behavior.* New York: Appleton-Century-Crofts.

Smith, K. U. 1951. Discriminative behavior in animals. In C. P. Stone, *Comparative Psychology.* (3rd ed.) New York: Prentice-Hall. Ch. 10. Pp. 316–362.

Smythe, E. J., and S. Goldstone. 1957. The time sense: A normative genetic study of the development of time perception. *Percept. mot. Skills*, 7, 49–59.

Solley, C. M., and R. Sommer. 1957. Perceptual autism in children. *J. genet. Psychol.*, 56, 3–13.

Solomon, R. L., and L. Postman. 1952. Frequency of usage as a determinant of recognition thresholds for words. *J. exp. Psychol.*, 43, 195–201.

Spiker, C. C. 1956. Experiments with children on the hypotheses of acquired distinctiveness and equivalence of cues. *Child Develpm.* 27, 253–263.

———, and G. Terrell. 1955. Factors associated with transposition behavior of preschool children. *J. genet. Psychol.*, 86, 143–158.

Spitz, R. A. 1945. Hospitalism. An inquiry into the genesis of psychiatric conditions in early childhood. *Psychoanal. Study Child*, 1. New York: International Univer. Press. Pp. 53–74.

———, and Katherine M. Wolf. 1946. The smiling response: A contribution to the ontogenesis of social relations. *Genet. Psychol. Monogr.*, 34, 57–125.

Staples, Ruth. 1932. The responses of infants to color. *J. exp. Psychol.*, 15, 119–141.

Stevenson, H. W., and G. McBee. 1958. The learning of object and pattern discriminations by children. *J. comp. physiol. Psychol.*, 51, 752–754.

Street, R. F. 1931. *A Gestalt completion test.* New York: Teachers College, Columbia Univer.

Synolds, D. L., and N. H. Pronko. 1949. An exploratory study of color discrimination of children. *J. genet. Psychol.*, 74, 17–21.

Tajfel, H. 1957. Value and the perceptual judgment of magnitude. *Psychol. Rev.*, 64, 192–204.

Thurstone, L. L. 1944. *A factorial study of perception.* Psychometric Monogr. No. 4. Chicago: Univer. Chicago Press.

Tinker, M. A. 1958. Recent studies of eye movements in reading. *Psychol. Bull.*, 55, 215–231.

Updegraff, Ruth. 1930. The visual perception of distance in young children and adults. A comparative study. *Univer. Iowa Stud. Child Welfare*, 4, No. 4.

Van Biervliet, J. J. 1896. Nouvelles mesures des illusions visuelles chez les adultes et les enfants. *Rev. Philos. de la France et de l'étranger.* 41, 169–182.

Vernon, Magdalen D. 1940. The relation of cognition and phantasy in children. *Brit. J. Psychol.*, 30, 273–294.

Walk, R. D., and Eleanor J. Gibson. 1959. A study of visual depth perception in the human infant with a visual cliff. Paper read at EPA in April.

Wapner, S., and H. Werner. 1957. *Perceptual development: An investigation within the framework of sensory-tonic field theory.* Worcester: Clark Univer. Press.

Weber, C. O., and N. Bicknell. 1935. The size-constancy phenomenon in stereoscopic space. *Amer. J. Psychol.*, 47, 436–448.

Weinstein, B. 1941. Matching-from-sample by Rhesus monkeys and by children. *J. comp. physiol. Psychol.*, 31, 195–213.

Welch, L. 1939a. The development of discrimination of form and area. *J. Psychol.*, 1, 37–54.

———. 1939b. The development of size discrimination between the ages of 12 to 40 months. *J. genet. Psychol.*, 55, 243–268.

Werner, H. 1948. *Comparative Psychology of Mental Development.* (Rev. ed.) Chicago: Follett.

Witkin, H. A. 1950. Individual differences in the ease of perception of embedded figures. *J. Pers.*, 19, 1–16.

Witkin, H. A. and Helen B. Lewis, M. Hertzman, Karen Machover, P. Bretnall Meissner, and S. Wapner. 1954. *Personality through perception.* New York: Harper.

Woodworth, R. S. and H. Schlosberg. 1954. *Experimental Psychology.* (Rev. Ed.) New York: Henry Holt.

Wursten, H. 1947. L'Evolution des comparaisons de longueurs de l'enfant à l'adulte. *Arch. Psychol., Genève*, 32, 1–144.

Wyatt, Ruth F. 1945. Improvability of pitch discrimination. *Psychol. Monogr.*, 58, No. 2.

# chapter 9

# Research Methods in Children's Learning

Charles C. Spiker
*State University of Iowa*

After nearly two decades of neglect, child psychologists currently recognize the empirical study of learning in children as one of the urgent needs for an understanding of child behavior and for the advance of general psychology. The lack of emphasis on children's learning, from the 1930's to the 1950's, resulted from several factors. The most decisive was surely the difficulty in developing and adapting appropriate apparatus, methods, and procedures. It is to be hoped that an anthology of techniques, which have been used in such studies, will alleviate some of the problems of potential investigators and indirectly stimulate further research in this area.

Although the purpose of the present chapter is not to extoll the significance of research on the learning of children, perhaps it is not entirely inappropriate to summarize the main concerns of previous investigators. Their primary interest was to provide normative, developmental data on children's learning. These investigators recognized that behavior changes resulting from learning are among the most obvious phenomena accompanying growth and development. They subscribed to the belief that any serious attempt to describe the behavioral changes accompanying increase in chronological age must include behavioral changes resulting from learning. Perhaps the immensity of the task they set for themselves discouraged continuation of this approach to children's learning. At any rate, the literature contains data on only a few of the vast number of tasks that children normally learn. Principles governing the learning of children are still required to fill in the developmental picture.

Somewhat later the belief that childhood learning has profound effects on adult behavior and personality became prevalent among general and child psychologists. This assumption has been crucial not only in the comprehensive accounts of human behavior advanced by psychoanalytic writers but also in the more restricted formulations of stimulus-response behavior theorists. Although this conviction did not lead to immediate investigations of children's learning, it has contributed to the recent renewal of interest in the area.

Many recent experiments in children's learning have been concerned with attempts to extend theories of behavior based primarily on infrahuman and adult human behavior. Some investigators appear to have selected children for subjects because the study of children enables them to test certain principles of the theories to which they adhere. They do not assume that their task is merely to demonstrate that principles derived from studies of other subjects are applicable to children. Rather, they seek to discover additional variables and laws, and new combinations of old laws, which are required for a more complete understanding of behavior. · They are simultaneously concerned with discovering the limitations of principles based on infrahuman behavior and with methods of extending these principles to human behavior. This approach promises to place the study of children's learning within a framework that extends beyond that of traditional child psychology to include that of general psychology.

## PROBLEMS
## IN DEFINING LEARNING

Whether one discusses the methodology for studying learning or the results of learning studies, some consideration must be given to the meaning of "learning." The term appears both as a "chapter heading" and as a technical term. As a chapter-heading word, it provides a convenient name for the variety of phenomena that the textbook writer, for reasons of his own, has decided to discuss in a single place. As a technical, "theoretical" concept, its meaning is usually about as explicit as are those of the other concepts that appear in the theory. Its meaning will vary somewhat from one theory to another, and a definition acceptable to one theorist will probably be unacceptable to others. Contiguity theorists, for example, prefer to define learning as the strengthening of a stimulus-response association, which results when the response is made in the presence of the stimulus. Reinforcement theorists define learning as the strengthening of the association when the response is made in the presence of the stimulus and is followed by a reward. Other theorists (e.g., Lewin, 1954, p. 931) consider learning a lay concept that has no place in psychological theory and even consider its use as a chapter heading more misleading than helpful. The different meanings that have been given learning in different theories result also in disagreement about the classification of empirical phenomena. Insightful or sudden solution of a problem, for example, would be considered new learning by some psychologists; others would explain it as the transfer of previous learning to relatively new situations.

Evaluation of the methodology of a given study is made difficult by the different theoretical meanings of learning. Consider the following situation. The learning concept in Hullian theory (Hull, 1943) is "habit strength"—defined in classical conditioning as a positive function of the number of paired presentations of the conditioned (CS) and unconditioned stimulus (US). Habit strength is assumed to be positively related to the relative frequency of conditioned responses (CR's) to the CS. But the theory also asserts that other variables, such as drive and inhibitory potential, affect the relative frequency of CR's. Consequently, a Hullian investigator is required to control the other theoretical variables if he wishes to determine the exact relationship between habit strength and frequency of CR's. The implication is that at present a study of learning can be methodologically sound within the framework of one theory but methodologically faulty within the framework of others.

The learning concept has been used in many different ways in psychological literature, and this lack of agreement has been inconvenient. Of far more serious consequence than this inconvenience are the fruitless controversies that have arisen from a writer's failure to state explicitly how the term was to be used in a given context.

Despite the disagreement about the *exact* meaning that "learning" ought to have, there is a considerable commonality of meaning. Most psychologists agree that learning involves a change in behavior, but they exclude changes resulting from drugs, fatigue, increase in age, and changes in external stimulation. Fortunately, this commonality makes possible a useful discussion of learning without a precise preliminary definition. The present writer has adopted a statement by McGeoch and Irion (1952, p. 5): "Learning, as we measure it, is a change in performance which occurs under the conditions of practice." Although this statement justifies the inclusion of each study mentioned in the present chapter, it does not provide criteria for evaluating these studies within each of the several theoretical frames of reference. But then no reasonable allotment of space would be adequate for such a task. Such methodological treatment must be left for articles specifically concerned with theory construction and evaluation.

## SCOPE OF THE CHAPTER

This chapter is concerned with methods that have been used in researches on children's learning. "Methods" has been interpreted to include procedures, apparatus, materials, and, in some cases, the experimental designs. To conserve space, without unduly restricting the number of methods treated, three principles were used to govern the selection of material. First, methods that are highly similar to those used with adults and infrahuman subjects are discussed primarily with respect to their adaptations to children, and the reader is referred to other methodological discussions already available (Hilgard and Marquis, 1940; McGeoch and Irion, 1952; Hovland, 1951; Brogden, 1951; Spence, 1956; and Hilgard, 1951). Second, minor variations are not extensively treated. References to articles in which such variations were used are included, however, and the reader is urged to examine them carefully. Finally, many details of apparatus and procedure have been omitted. Although no detail of method is too minor to warrant careful consideration, a complete description of the methods utilized in each study would seriously restrict the number of learning situations examined.

As in other areas of science, the simpler situations have received the most careful attention. Methods for studying classical and instrumental conditioning, discrimination learning, and rote learning are more advanced and more rigorous than those for the study of complex motor learning, the learning of academic content, and reasoning. The present discussion emphasizes the stabler procedures, on the assumption that rapid development of new methods for the study of complex learning will soon make present procedures obsolete.

## Conditioning

Conditioning is generally regarded as the simplest form of learning. Although several types and subtypes have been distinguished, all have one characteristic in common: during the course of conditioning, the subject begins to make a response, the CR, to a stimulus, the CS, which did not previously elicit that response. The conditions under which the association between the CS and the CR is established provide the criteria for distinguishing among different types of conditioning experiments. Hilgard and Marquis (1940, p. 27) distinguished between classical conditioning and instrumental conditioning. In classical conditioning the CS is presented to the subject, followed shortly by the unconditioned stimulus (US). Thus in eyelid conditioning a flash of light (CS) is presented approximately one half second before an air puff (US) is delivered to the eye. The air puff elicits an eyelid closure, the unconditioned response (UR). After several CS-US presentations, the eyeblink begins to occur after the CS onset but before the US onset; that is, the response begins to occur during the CS-US interval. The anticipatory eyeblink is called a conditioned response (CR). The interval between the CS and US is usually held constant, with both stimuli occurring on each trial. The occurrence of the CR does not result in any change in procedure.

In instrumental conditioning the CS is presented, and, *if* the subject makes the CR, he is given a reward or is permitted to escape or avoid a noxious stimulus. A conventional example concerns the rat in a box containing a lever, near which is a food cup. The sight of the lever constitutes the CS and pushing the lever is the CR. If the rat pushes the lever, a pellet of food is delivered into the food cup. Thus the CR is instrumental in obtaining the food reward. An analogous situation may be arranged for children. The child may be placed in a room in which there is a lever that can be pressed in order to obtain a toy, a piece of candy, or some other attractive object.

The experimenter ordinarily arranges the instrumental situation so that the initial occurrence of the CR to the CS is highly probable. Thus the experimenter may place food on the lever to increase the likelihood that the rat will press the lever. An attractive toy may be tied to the child's lever to speed the child's manipulation of the lever, or the experimenter may simply instruct the child to push the lever "to see what happens." These procedures serve a function analogous to that of the US in the classical conditioning experiment. The difference is mainly one of degree—the US of classical conditioning is selected because it elicits the UR with a high reliability; the experimenter's techniques in instrumental conditioning are not usually so effective in eliciting the response at the beginning of the experiment.

Both classical and instrumental conditioning have been further subdivided, according to whether the stimulus that follows the CR satisfies an appetitional need or is a noxious stimulus (Spence, 1956, p. 38ff.). Thus classical conditioning is called *classical reward conditioning* if the US is food or some other goal object needed by the subject and *classical defense conditioning* if the US is a noxious stimulus. Similarly, instrumental conditioning is called *instrumental reward conditioning* if the CR is followed by a goal object, *instrumental escape conditioning* if the CR permits the subject to escape a noxious stimulus, and *instrumental avoidance conditioning* if the CR results in the subject's avoidance of the noxious stimulus.

All conditioning involves the establishment of an association between the CS and the CR if the CS is a stimulus that did not originally elicit the CR. At first glance, it might appear that it would be easy to demonstrate conditioning in a given situation. For example, in the classical conditioning of the eyeblink the CS could be presented to the subject and followed by an air puff to the eye. If the subject began to make anticipatory eyeblinks after several trials, one might be tempted to conclude conditioning had been established. The demonstration would not be conclusive, however. It is conceivable that the subject might begin to blink at the CS after a series of presentations of the CS alone. The subject might also blink at the CS after a succession of presentations of the air puff alone. Neither of these results would be at-

tributed to conditioning. Some of the earlier studies of conditioning failed to control for pseudo-conditioning. It is now customary to provide such a control. In classical conditioning, for example, one group receives the experimental conditions, a second group may receive the CS alone, and a third group, the US alone. The "backward conditioning" control is also frequently applied. With this procedure, the control group receives the CS and US on each trial, but the US is presented first. This temporal arrangement of the stimuli results in little or no conditioning, and it controls simultaneously for the two factors that otherwise require two groups of subjects. Regardless of the method of control used, the experimental group must be compared to the control group in order to ascertain that conditioning was established. The comparison requires the application of statistical procedures.

Analogous controls for instrumental conditioning are not as readily attained. Indeed, one of the present concerns of students of instrumental conditioning is whether the increase with trials in the relative frequency of the CR (or in the speed of the CR) represents conditioning or an increase in motivation. Consider a child who pushes a button when a light (CS) is presented in order to obtain a reward. Does the increase in his speed of button-pushing reflect a strengthening of the association between the CS and the button-pushing response? Or does it reflect an increase in the child's motivation as he becomes more certain that the reward follows the button-pushing? Since learning is involved in either case, the question is not whether learning occurs; it has to do with *what* is learned. The question, therefore, is not merely methodological; it is a matter for empirical research.

## CLASSICAL CONDITIONING

The first investigations of conditioning in children were those of Krasnogorski (1925) in which he used a modification of the Pavlovian procedures. He observed the motor component of the total reaction to food (swallowing and mouth movements) as well as the glandular reactions (salivation). The early American interest in classical conditioning in children centered around the question of the conditionability of neonates (Marquis, 1931; Wenger, 1936). Many of the methods that have been developed are more appropriate for infants than for older children. Although the early studies provide many useful methodological suggestions, few of them would serve as models for contemporary conditioning experiments.

*General Considerations.* There are some general requirements for classical conditioning that obtain, regardless of the specific experiment. One of the more important of these requirements concerns the selection of the US. As previously noted, the US determines whether the experiment is to be classical reward or classical defense. Care should be taken to select a US that will elicit the UR consistently and that will not permit the subject to adapt to it in the later stages of conditioning. The most frequently used US's in classical conditioning experiments have been such potent stimuli as food for hungry

subjects, air puffs to the eye, acids or salts in the mouth, and electric shock. The selection of the US also affects the selection of the CR. The response to the US is rarely a single, discrete response; usually it is a constellation of responses, and the experimenter must decide which of these components of the UR he wishes to observe and record as CR's. For example, presentation of food to the infant elicits salivation, chewing movements, lip and mouth movements, swallowing, and sucking. It may also bring about a reduction in the frequency and intensity of crying, general bodily activity, and orienting behavior (Kantrow, 1937). The experimenter must decide which of these behavioral changes he wishes to observe and record. His decision will be governed in part by the type of apparatus and materials he has available and by the degree of precision his purpose requires. It will also be governed by psychological considerations. He will note that all behavioral changes that occur to food in the mouth are not possible as *anticipatory* responses to food. The subject cannot literally swallow or chew food or suck milk into his mouth in the absence of food or milk, although he may make swallowing, chewing, and sucking movements similar to those made with food. The experimenter will also note that some responses are more sensitive to change than others. For example, since infants do not cry incessantly, even when hungry, noncrying would not be a sensitive measure of conditioning.

The selection of the CS is also important and is made only after consideration of type of subject to be used.

Assurance that the subjects normally perceive the CS can be obtained from preliminary evidence that they make consistent responses to it. This is not always easily demonstrated in the case of inarticulate subjects such as infants. The CS is also selected so that it does not initially elicit that aspect of the UR which is recorded as the CR. The elicitation of all or part of the UR by the CS is particularly likely if the CS has one or more dimensions in common with the US. For example, if the CS is a tactile vibrator and the US is a moderate shock, there could be some question as to whether anticipatory responses to the CS represented conditioning or merely generalization of the UR from the shock to the vibrator.

Although the interval between the onset of the CS and the onset of the US (the CS-US interval) affects the rate of conditioning, the exact relationship is not known for each type of conditioning situation (Hovland, 1951, p. 615; Brogden, 1951, p. 575). Since one ordinarily wishes to select the interval that is optimal for conditioning, the choice of the appropriate interval poses a problem. The interval that is optimal for conditioning, as evidenced by the subsequent resistance of the CR to extinction or by the promptness with which it begins to appear on test trials when the US is omitted or delayed, may not maximize the probability of obtaining anticipatory CR's on each trial. This is to say that a CS-US interval that maximizes the rate of conditioning may be shorter than the normal latency of the CR. Current evidence suggests that the shorter CS-US intervals generally produce faster conditioning (Brogden,

1951, pp. 575ff.). However, if the typical latency of the CR is longer than the selected CS-US interval, it is necessary to obtain measures of the CR on trials other than the conditioning trials; e.g., by presenting the CS alone periodically during the conditioning phase, by interspersing trials in which the US is delayed, or by determining resistance to extinction following conditioning.

The type of subject used in classical conditioning is undoubtedly of great importance. Classical conditioning of human subjects has not been extensive thus far, except for conditioning of the galvanic skin response (GSR) and the eyeblink. The GSR is regarded as involuntary, meaning that its occurrence or nonoccurrence is not normally subject to instructional control. The eyeblink is classified as semivoluntary, since it is subject to instructional control under some conditions but not under others. Numerous complications arise in the conditioning of voluntary responses in articulate subjects. Even in eyelid-conditioning experiments, complex criteria have been devised to eliminate voluntary responses and voluntary responders.

The deliberate study of the effects of verbal processes on conditioning is, of course, a legitimate problem. But if one wishes to study human conditioning in order to formulate laws comparable to those obtained from infrahuman subjects, one must attempt to prevent the contamination of the data by the verbal processes. There are several possibilities for accomplishing such control. The experimenter may use human infants, on the assumption that they do not have extensive verbal control over their responses. He may also use older subjects but must restrict his observations to responses that are normally involuntary (e.g., GSR, salivation, pupillary reflex, and heart rate). He may also observe responses in older subjects, which, although voluntary, have a minimal proprioceptive feedback (e.g., minor movements of the fingers, measures of muscle potential, and eyeblink). The latter possibility requires the use of highly refined methods for measuring the responses. The writer's experience with preschool children suggests that when such responses as button-pushing, lever-pulling, and bulb-squeezing occur as anticipatory responses they tend to be viewed as erroneous by the subjects and inhibited. This voluntary inhibition masks the development of conditioned responses that can be observed under more subtle experimental arrangements.

*Response Measures.* One of the most frequently used response measures in classical conditioning is the number of CR's that occur during the CS-US interval. In some cases it is desirable to correct this measure for spontaneous occurrences of the response. Thus, if the experimenter has recorded the number of sucking responses that occur in a CS-US interval of five seconds, it is advisable to compare this measure with the number of sucking responses that occur in five-second intervals during which the CS is not presented (Kantrow, 1937). This procedure is particularly appropriate when different experimental conditions result in different probabilities of spontaneous responding. Thus, in a study designed to compare the effects of different CS-

US intervals on conditioning, the number of "CR's" for subjects given the longer intervals may be inflated by spontaneous responses (McAllister, 1953).

The latencies of anticipatory responses have also been used as measures of the strength of conditioning (Hilgard and Campbell, 1936). The practice is apparently based on the finding that the latencies of anticipatory responses that occur late in conditioning are shorter than those that occur early. Pavlov's work, however, indicated that the latency of the anticipatory response is dependent on the length of the CS-US interval. The subject learns to delay the anticipatory response until the end of the CS-US interval if the interval is relatively long (Pavlov, 1928, p. 149). Perhaps, then, the latency of the anticipatory response should be considered an index of the strength of conditioning only if the CS-US interval is slightly longer than the average latency of the CR. Even under this restricted condition, Spence (1956, p. 70ff.) reports latency data from eyelid conditioning that show marked irregularities as a function of the number of conditioning trials.

Response magnitude, measured by scales of such quantities as volume of saliva secreted, length of a movement, amount of electrical resistance generated, and amount of pressure exerted, has also been used as an index of strength of conditioning. Studies of GSR conditioning have also relied heavily on amplitude measures of some type. Since most eyelid conditioning experiments report the results in terms of frequency of the CR's, the amplitude measure has apparently not been found highly useful. It is obvious that the amount of instrumentation required to obtain reliable indices of either response latency or response amplitude is greater than that required to determine the occurrence or nonoccurrence of the response. This fact probably has contributed to the greater popularity of the response frequency measure.

If the experiment is designed to relate the strength of conditioning to the number of conditioning trials, one of the aforementioned measures may be used. For each trial, or block of trials, the average of the number, latencies, or amplitudes of the CR's may be computed and plotted to obtain a conditioning curve for all subjects combined. If interest is in the exact form of the conditioning curve, however, care must be taken not to average individual curves so heterogeneous that the group curve will not represent the individual curves on which it is based. One useful procedure is to divide the subjects into subgroups, which condition at slow, fast, and medium rates, and to examine the curves for these subgroups (Spence, 1956, p. 60ff.).

Another measure of the strength of conditioning is the degree to which the conditioned subject resists extinction during a period when the CS is presented without the US. Following conditioning, the experimenter presents the CS alone and counts the number of trials necessary before the CR fails to occur or the number of CR's the subject makes in a set number of trials. Resistance to extinction measures are often used when it is undesirable or impractical to obtain measures of anticipatory responses during the conditioning phase. Since the number of conditioning trials is generally positively related to the number of responses during extinction, the latter is taken to be an index of the strength of conditioning. The extinction measure does not permit assessment of the growth of conditioning during the administration of the paired CS-US presentations, since extinction is not begun until all conditioning trials have been given. For this reason, the experimenter will often intersperse single presentations of the CS (test-trials) among paired CS-US presentations during conditioning. The test-trials provide an index of the growth of the CR during conditioning. The extinction measure and the test-trial procedure may be used when the different experimental conditions result in different probabilities of anticipatory CR's; for example, when the experimental conditions differ in the length of the CS-US interval (McAllister, 1953). Recent practice in eyelid conditioning provides an extra long CS-US interval on test trials rather than an omission of the US altogether. This procedure presumably maintains the level of motivation and minimizes the development of extinction effects.

*Classical Reward Conditioning.* The Pavlovian experiments are the prototype of classical reward conditioning. Classical reward conditioning in older children has been studied by Krasnogorski, by Chuchmarev, and by Lenz. The elaborate laboratories, methods, and procedures of these investigators have been described in detail by Razran (1935) and are not repeated here. Razran also gives an extensive review of the findings of these experiments. In general, the procedures do not differ markedly from those used by Kantrow (1937), except that in many experiments measures of salivation were directly obtained. Her methods and procedures may still serve as a useful model for this type of conditioning. Kantrow used infants ranging in age from 1½ to 4 months at the beginning of the experiment. The US was the presentation of the nipple of the feeding bottle into the infant's mouth, and the CS was the onset of a buzzer. The CS was presented for five seconds before the feeding bottle, and the CS and US overlapped for fifteen seconds. The infants were fed on a four-hour schedule, but the experiment was conducted only during the four daytime feedings. Several paired presentations of the CS and US were given at each feeding.

A linen harness was placed under the infant's chin and was mechanically connected by strings to a recording polygraph pen. A second pen recorded the onset and duration of the CS. The experimenter manually recorded on the polygraph tape the time of administering the bottle. Thus each movement of the infant's chin during sucking was recorded graphically, with its temporal position designated in terms of the onset of the CS and US.

Kantrow's measure of conditioning was the number of sucking responses made in the CS-US interval, corrected by subtracting the number of sucking responses occurring during a five-second critical control period immediately preceding the conditioning trial. The critical control period was that period of five consecutive seconds, in the 25

to 75 seconds immediately preceding the onset of the CS, which contained the largest number of sucking responses. The critical control period was designed to control for random or spontaneous sucking responses. Since the period selected was the one having the maximum number of sucking responses, the control seems to be a conservative one.

Kantrow did not use a group to control for increase in sucking behavior to the CS, which might have occurred without the CS-US pairings. The decline in the anticipatory responses that occurred during extinction suggests that the paired presentations of the CS and US were essential to their development and maintenance. The use of the critical control period provides some control for pseudo-conditioning, but her design would have been more convincing if a pseudo-conditioning control group had been included.

Investigators seeking to extend the findings of Kantrow's study would probably wish to consider shorter CS-US intervals. Research by Krasnogorski, summarized by Razran (1935), compared the secretory and the motor responses (swallowing and sucking). The latencies of the motor responses were found to be somewhat less than one second, whereas the salivary responses had average latencies of about five seconds. Thus the use of shorter CS-US intervals would still permit the swallowing and sucking responses to occur as anticipatory responses. It might also be the case that the rate of conditioning would be faster, and the final level more stable, if shorter intervals were used.

***Classical Defense Conditioning.*** The

procedures used in defense conditioning in the classical situation have been more varied than those in appetitional conditioning. Classical defense conditioning should be distinguished from instrumental escape or instrumental avoidance, which is discussed in a later section. In classical defense conditioning the subject receives the noxious US on each trial except test trials, and the UR does not result in escape from the noxious stimulus. Moreover, if the CR begins to appear anticipatorily, it does not result in avoidance of the US.

Aversive conditioning procedures with children have not been popular. The US must be noxious enough to elicit the UR reliably. On the other hand, since experimenters prefer the subject's voluntary cooperation, the US must not be so noxious as to arouse strong fear reactions and tendencies to escape the experimental situation. The delicate balance of these two factors is difficult to achieve. With older children and adults, cooperation of the majority of subjects can be achieved even though relatively noxious stimuli are utilized. With infants, it is possible to select a US that is noxious enough to promote conditioning without harming the child or arousing emotional reactions that interfere unduly with the purpose of the experiment.

An investigation of classical defense conditioning in infants was reported by Wickens and Wickens (1940). An electric shock was applied to the foot of the infant. Approximately 250 milliseconds prior to the application of the shock the CS (buzzer) was sounded. The paired CS-US presentations were given 12 times a day for three days.

On the third day 12 presentations of the buzzer were also administered without shock. The experimenters observed the number of leg flexions that occurred on the test trials. Two control groups were included. In one group the CS was presented without shock for the same number of trials given the experimental group. In the second control group the US was presented without the CS. Both control groups then received 12 test trials on the third day. The results verify the need to control pseudo-conditioning, since the group given only shock gave as many leg flexions to the buzzer as the group given paired CS-US presentations. The control group given only the CS made significantly fewer responses than either of the other two groups.

Wickens and Wickens depended for their basic data on the observations of the experimenters. Wenger (1936) developed methods for the graphic recording of the onset of the CS and US and of the infants' CR's. His records permitted the study of foot and toe movements as well as the grosser limb withdrawal. The Wickens' methodology would have been considerably improved had they used the recording techniques developed earlier by Wenger.

Eyelid conditioning procedures, comparable to those used so successfully with adults, have not been developed for children. Although the adult procedures could be adapted rather easily to upper elementary and high-school children, special problems may be involved with younger children. Modern techniques utilize sensitive potentiometers fastened to the eyelid, and best results are obtained when the subject remains quiet with the head relatively immobile (Spence, 1953). The adaptation of such procedures to younger children entails obvious difficulties.

One study of eyelid conditioning with older infants, however, suggests that if proper conditions can be achieved this type of defense conditioning will be profitable. Morgan and Morgan (1944) presented as the US a puff of air to the eye, administered manually with a hand syringe. The CS was the sight of the syringe being brought to the infant's eye. The experimenters did not use any graphic or other mechanical means of recording, depending on the experimenter's judgment to determine whether the blink was anticipatory or random. They report a fairly high level of conditioning as having been obtained in a considerable number of infants between the ages of 6 and 10 weeks. Unfortunately, adequate controls for random or spontaneous blinking were not included.

An early study of the conditioning of the GSR was reported by Jones (1930). He was able to demonstrate sizable increases in the magnitude of the GSR to stimuli after they had been paired with shock. Effective use of the GSR procedure requires elaborate apparatus as well as unusually good control over extraneous stimulation. The GSR has been found to be sensitive to a wide variety of stimuli and produces reliable stable measures only when the subject is relatively inactive. Adapting the procedure to unselected samples of younger children poses some technical problems that remain to be solved.

The conditioning of "overt emotional responses" in young children has been investigated by Watson and Rayner (1920) and Jones (1931). These experimenters paired neutral stimuli with noxious stimuli that elicited crying and escape responses and noted the subsequent tendencies for these responses to occur with neutral stimuli. Extensive laboratory investigations of such conditioning have not been made. Further investigation seems warranted only if response measures are developed that are sufficiently precise to permit fruitful study of such variables as intensity of the US, length of temporal intervals, intensity of the CS, range of generalization, and the like. If these variables can be as satisfactorily studied with the GSR, the elicitation of overt emotional responses in young children appears unnecessary.

Although the study of aversive conditioning in the classical framework would undoubtedly add considerably to our knowledge of learning in children, particularly to our understanding of the learning of fear and anxiety, the practical difficulties of developing adequate procedures are not to be underestimated. It is likely that fruitful study of this type of conditioning in children must be preceded by a thorough understanding of the phenomenon in infrahuman organisms.

## INSTRUMENTAL CONDITIONING

Historically, instrumental conditioning is probably an outgrowth of the trial-and-error experiments of C. L. Morgan and E. L. Thorndike (Hilgard and Marquis, 1940, p. 53). Indeed, Spence (1956, p. 37ff.) characterizes instrumental conditioning as a limiting case of trial-and-error learning in which the occurrence of competing responses is minimized. It is convenient to discuss the methodology of classical and instrumental conditioning separately because different apparatus and procedures have been employed. The separate discussion, however, does not necessarily imply a conviction that different laws govern behavior in the two types of situations.

**General Considerations.** Two procedures for instrumental conditioning, distinguished by the manner in which a trial is defined, are currently recognized and applied. The free-operant method, developed and intensively studied by Skinner (1938), places the subject in a situation in which occurrence of a given response results in a reward. The subject is free to make as many of these responses as the time allows. The course of conditioning is measured by an increase with successive periods in the rate of responding in the conditioning situation. The "trial" is thus an arbitrary period of time set by the experimenter. The CS presumably includes internal cues, arising from processes inside the organism, and the external situation, particularly the response manipulandum.

The discrete-trial method resembles classical conditioning. The trial is defined in terms of the presentation of the CS. The subject is ordinarily allowed an arbitrary maximum time for the response to occur. The trial is terminated when the CR occurs or when the maximum time has elapsed. The CS is specified as it is in classical conditioning and is equally subject to experimental control. The free-operant and discrete-trial methods have also been combined to develop the "controlled-operant" method. The CS is presented on each trial for a set period of time during which the subject is free to respond repeatedly. Here, the usual response measure is the number of CR's per trial.

Free-operant and discrete-trial conditioning have been employed in the investigation of somewhat different types of problems. Free-operant conditioning has been widely used in the study of motivational and incentive variables as well as in the study of reinforcement schedules. The discrete-trial method has been preferred in the study of those problems having to do with characteristics of the CS, such as stimulus generalization, variation in CS intensity, and differential conditioning. The discrete-trial procedure has also been preferred by psychologists concerned with the development of S-R learning theories, since the manner of specifying a conditioning trial is more consistent with learning principles in these theories.

One of the major problems of the investigator of instrumental conditioning is the selection of an appropriate response to be conditioned. Before conditioning can occur, the CR must be elicited. After it occurs in the presence of the CS, the experimenter may increase its probability of occurrence on the next trial by an immediate administration of a reward. It is usually desirable to select a response that has a high probability of occurring in the experimental situation. Several procedures have been used to elicit the CR. The bar-pressing response in rats has been facilitated by increasing the distinctiveness of the response mechanism, differentiating it from the background stimuli. Usually, food is smeared on the bar during the early trials to elicit approach and manipulative responses. The normal exploratory behavior of rats is exploited in the instrumental conditioning of a running or approach response in the simple runway situation. With children, instructions to pull a lever, press a button, squeeze a bulb, etc., have been given to increase the probability of occurrence of the CR. As noted previously, these arrangements of the experimenter serve as a substitute for the US of the classical conditioning experiment. It is, of course, desirable to select a response that can be observed and recorded with a high degree of reliability.

*Response Measures.* The response measures available in instrumental conditioning vary somewhat from one procedure to another. Several measures based on the frequency of the CR have been used. In discrete-trial conditioning the number of subjects responding on each trial or the number of CR's given by each subject in a block of trials may be determined. With the usual procedures for instrumental conditioning, however, neither of these measures proves to be highly satisfactory. The experimenter ordinarily attempts to arrange the situation so that the subject responds on each trial. As noted earlier, this is accomplished by pretraining, by instructing human subjects, or by arranging the experimental situation so that there is a high probability of occurrence of the response. Thus a conditioning curve based on

frequency of CR's would begin at or near 100 per cent and show little change thereafter. Spence (1956, p. 77) has shown that a frequency measure reflecting the course of conditioning can be obtained whenever the latencies of the CR's are also recorded. By his procedure, an arbitrary latency criterion may be set so that a response is counted as a CR only if its latency is equal to or less than the criterion. In tests of generalization the standard frequency of response measure may still be a satisfactory index of the strength of generalized conditioning (Shepard, 1956).

The free-operant conditioning procedure typically provides the rate-of-response measure. The total time that the subject is in the conditioning situation may be divided into a number of time intervals. The rate of responding in any interval is given by dividing the number of responses by the amount of time. The controlled-operant procedure provides the number of responses occurring during each CS presentation.

Several time measures may profitably be used to show the course of conditioning. In the discrete-trial method the time between the onset of the CS and the occurrence of the response is often designated as the response latency. Strictly speaking, this measure will approximate the response latency only if the response has a very short duration. The distinction between *response latency* and *response duration* can be exemplified in the runway situation in which the rat is placed in the starting box behind an opaque door leading into the alley. The time between the opening of the opaque door (the CS presentation) and the rat's *beginning* to traverse the alley is the latency of the CR. After the rat has started, the time taken to traverse the alley and enter the goal box may be designated the response duration. A measure that includes the time between the opening of the door and the rat's entry into the goal box is composed of the response latency and duration. The reciprocal of the response latency is called the *response evocation speed*, whereas the reciprocal of the response duration is the *response speed*. It is, of course, quite possible that experimental variables may affect these two measures differently, with the consequence that they are not highly correlated. Response evocation speeds, for example, seem to be more sensitive to distracting stimuli and to variations in the subject's orienting behavior than response speeds. Therefore, it is advisable to analyze the total response time into the two components unless the response duration is quite brief.

The free-operant procedure does not permit the determination of response latencies, since the CS is not under the experimenter's control. If the responses are graphically recorded, however, response-duration times may be obtained in either the free-operant or controlled-operant situations. In the controlled-operant situation the time between the onset of the CS and the occurrence of the first response may also be obtained.

Several measures of resistance to extinction have been developed, all of which are obtained during nonreinforced trials following conditioning. Two measures are typical of the discrete-trial method. The experimenter may count the number of CR's made in a set number of extinction trials. Or he may administer the nonreinforced CS until the subject fails to respond, on one or more successive trials, within a predetermined period of time; his measure, then, is the number of CS presentations required to reach the criterion. The same general procedures apply in the controlled-operant situation, in which the number of responses per trial is the basic measure. Free-operant conditioning, of course, provides the rate of responding measure during extinction as well as in conditioning. Furthermore, the experimenter may record the total number of responses the subject makes before failing to respond in a predetermined period of time.

Although amplitude of the CR has been used as an index of response strength (Holton, 1956; Haner and Brown, 1955), it is questionable whether or not these measures provide a good index of strength of conditioning in the instrumental situation. Hull (1943, p. 304ff.) cites evidence that a rat learned to respond with a particular amount of pressure on a bar. Holton's experiment showed no consistent increase with practice in the pressure preschool children applied to the response mechanism. For these reasons, response amplitude in instrumental situations should be carefully explored before it is assumed that it reflects the strength of conditioning.

***Instrumental Reward Conditioning: Discrete-Trial Method.*** One of the simpler arrangements for instrumental reward conditioning has been described by Shepard (1956) in connection with her study of stimulus generalization. The apparatus and procedure were adapted to children of preschool ages (3½ to 6 years). The apparatus consisted of a box with an aperture in which a colored light (the CS) was presented, a push-button on a small panel as the response mechanism, and an interval timer to control the duration of the CS. The CS was presented for four seconds and the subject was required to respond within that time. Shepard used verbal praise as rewards for responses that occurred within the interval.

Unfortunately, the only response measure available with this procedure is the frequency of occurrence of the CR. The rapid learning of preschool children under these conditions makes this measure relatively insensitive to variations in the experimental variables. Although the number of responses that occur during an extinction session could be obtained, this measure tends to be quite variable for children when the reward has been experimenter approval and the experimenter remains in the room during extinction. Two modifications of the Shepard apparatus would overcome these difficulties. First, a reward dispensing unit may be incorporated into the apparatus so that the experimenter need not remain in the room. Second, an electric clock may be wired into the circuit so that it will start with the onset of the CS and be stopped by the subject's response. This provides a measure of response latency, since response duration is brief, that may be used to obtain evocation speeds or to derive a response frequency measure based on an arbitrary latency criterion.

Stimuli other than lights may be used; other visual stimuli may be presented in a visual stimulus presentation device (e.g., a memory drum), and auditory stimuli may be employed. Similarly, any objective instrumental response may be substituted for the button pushing. The only requirement is that the response be simple, discrete, and capable of operating an electric switch. Responses requiring the development of a complex motor skill are probably to be avoided, since measures of such responses reflect the development of the skill rather than simple conditioning. Anything that appeals to the subjects may be given as a reward if it can be reliably dispensed automatically.

Longstreth (1957) adapted to preschool children the instrumental runway situation frequently used with rats. At one end of a large room he placed a wooden screen, approximately 6 feet high and 4 feet wide, behind which were located the controls and recording equipment. During the experiment the experimenter remained behind the screen viewing the child through a one-way mirror. On the subject's side of the screen was a small door with spring hinges arranged so that the pushing of a button under the door caused the door to spring open to expose a reward compartment. Directly above the door was a single stimulus aperture through which colored lights could be filtered. On the floor at the base of the screen was a switch-mat. Extending away from the screen was a rubber hall-carpet approximately 12 feet long. A small chair was placed at the end of the carpet. Two electric clocks were wired into circuits, so that the first clock started when the CS was presented. When the child rose from the chair, he activated a switch that stopped the first clock and started the second. Finally, when he stepped on the switch-mat at the end of the "alley," he stopped the second clock. The first clock thus recorded the response latency and the second, the running time.

Although Longstreth studied the effects of incentives on the children's behavior, his procedure may also prove fruitful in the study of such variables as amount of training, generalization, stimulus intensity, etc. It is necessary in this situation, as in others involving time measures, to minimize extraneous distracting stimuli and/or to present dynamic stimuli (e.g., change in room illumination, flashing lights, raucous buzzers) in order to obtain reliable response measures.

*Instrumental Reward Conditioning: Controlled-Operant Method.* The modified operant procedure used with infrahuman subjects (e.g., Guttman and Kalish, 1956) has been adapted to preschool children (Spiker, 1956a, 1956b). The controlled-operant method provides the experimenter with better control of the CS than the free-operant method and at the same time retains much of the latter's reliability of response measure. Spiker's procedure involved the presentation of a stimulus light in a flashed opal glass aperture for a three-second period. The subject was required to pull a lever. Each pull of the lever resulted in the automatic delivery of a marble and was recorded on an electric impulse counter. Responses made between presentations of

the CS were neither rewarded nor recorded. The response measure was the number of responses occurring during each CS presentation (trial). White (1958) used a similar procedure, except that visual stimuli (colored patches) were presented by means of a device serving the same function as a memory drum.

An interesting fact concerning this type of conditioning is that if the subjects are pretrained to pull the lever, without presentation of the CS, the rate of responding to the CS during conditioning shows little increase. This fact suggests that change in the rate of responding that occurs without such pretraining largely represents skill learning rather than an increase in the strength of conditioning. Essentially, the same thing may be true of the free-operant situation. A disadvantage of both free-operant and controlled-operant methods is that the experimenter has no direct control over the rate of responding and thus has no control over the amount of fatigue developed by the individual subject.

*Instrumental Reward Conditioning: Free-Operant Method.* In an exploratory study, Warren and Brown (1943) adapted the free-operant method to children of preschool ages. The apparatus consisted of a mechanism to deliver a piece of candy down a chute when the lever projecting into the experimental room was depressed. After adaptation sessions, the subjects were placed in the room with the door closed and with two or three toys in addition to the lever. A kymographic record of each response was obtained, providing the data to determine the rate of lever pressing. Acquisition under continuous and partial reinforcement and extinction were studied. The acquisition curves generally indicated that the children responded at relatively constant rates after the first few trials.

Whereas Warren and Brown left the child to discover the lever and the consequences of pressing it, Siegel and Foshee (1953) oriented their subjects to the lever by instructions. They counted the number of nonrewarded responses during extinction as the measure of the strength of the conditioning and reported a positive correlation between number of previously reinforced responses and resistance to extinction.

An experiment by Screven (1954) qualifies as a free-operant study. The turning of a crank by the subject energized in succession 12 jeweled lights placed on a vertical panel. When the lights reached the top of the column, a marble was automatically ejected to the subject, ending the trial. The response measure was the rate of crank turning—number of turns per second—in each trial. Although the rate of crank turning had no effect on the rate of progression of the lights, there were significant increases in the rate of turning as a function of the number of preceding trials. The speed of turning was read directly from a speed indicator. In a second study by Screven and Nunis (1954) the crank was attached to a small generator, and the voltage produced by crank turning was recorded by the sweep-pen of a voltmeter on a polygraph tape. The crank-turning response in the free-responding situation was also utilized by Lambert, Lambert and Watson (1953) in the study of the effects on behavior of reward cessation.

Another type of operant conditioning has been described in detail by Bijou (1955, 1957a) and utilized in the study of patterns of reinforcement (1957b). In its simplest form it is probably best adapted to children of preschool and kindergarten ages, although older children might be used for certain types of problems. The child takes a ball from a receptacle and places it in a hole in the front face of the apparatus. A motor-driven bicycle chain with small trinkets attached is arranged so that a trinket may be released into a chute and delivered to the child. Placing the ball into the hole activates a polygraph pen that records the number of responses and the rate of their emission. Depending on the reinforcement schedule prearranged by the experimenter, the response may also activate the reward dispenser.

Bijou (1958) also describes a "laboratory on wheels," which was devised to circumvent some of the difficulties inherent in experimenting with children in immobile laboratories. The mobile laboratory, constructed in a house-trailer, can be taken by the experimenter to the children's homes or schools. It thereby eliminates the problems involved in transporting the children to and from the laboratory, and, if the subjects are to be drawn from several different schools, it provides the experimenter with the same experimental situation in which to run the subjects.

Operant conditioning of infants approximately 12 weeks of age has been reported by Rheingold and Gewirtz (1957). First, the experimenters obtained a baseline of vocalization by recording the number of vocalized responses occurring in set periods of time during which the experimenter would bend over the infant's crib with an expressionless face. After the baseline was established, each vocalization by an infant was followed by a clucking sound, a smile, and a patting of the infant's abdomen by the experimenter. Finally, an extinction period was begun during which the experimenter reverted to the procedure of the baseline period. The investigators report significant increase in rate of vocalization during the conditioning phase, followed during extinction by a significant decrease toward the level of the baseline. The use of this procedure to reinforce those sounds that are relatively rare in young infants (Irwin, 1947) would provide some interesting results for the development of speech sounds.

One of the major advantages of free-operant conditioning is that it provides a reliable, objective response measure. The measure has proved to be sensitive to variations in the number of previous rewarded responses, in the value of the incentives given, in the motivational level of the subject, and in the reinforcement schedule. The difficulties of the free-operant situation include the lack of experimental control over the administration of the CS, the complications of response chaining, and the inability of the experimenter to control the amount of work done by the subject.

*Instrumental Escape Conditioning.* Since instrumental escape conditioning with child subjects has not been reported, the method is illustrated with an infrahuman study. A rat may be placed in one of two compartments with a low barrier between them. The floors of each compartment contain grids through which shock to the animal's feet may be administered. The onset of shock stimulates activity on the part of the rat, in which jumping over the barrier is the terminal response. The grid of the second compartment is not activated, so the subject escapes the shock. He remains in the second compartment until shock is administered again, eliciting a sequence of behaviors until the barrier is jumped again. A repeated series of trials results in the gradual reduction in the time between the onset of shock and the jumping of the barrier. The latency of the jumping response constitutes the primary measure of conditioning.

The difficulties encountered in administering noxious stimulation to children probably account for the paucity of research in this type of learning. Moreover, the most convenient experimental arrangements for children, such as shock to a limb, would probably not result in changes in the latencies of simple withdrawal responses. It should be noted that in instrumental escape conditioning there is no CS preceding the noxious stimulus. The onset of the noxious stimulus is the subject's first cue to perform the escape response.

*Instrumental Avoidance Conditioning.* Instrumental avoidance conditioning is similar to escape conditioning, except that a CS precedes the noxious stimulus, and if the subject makes the CR prior to the onset of the noxious stimulus there is complete avoidance of the effects. Frequently, to produce avoidance conditioning, preliminary training in escape conditioning is given to establish the response to the noxious stimulus at a high level. Instrumental avoidance conditioning starts out as identical to classical defense conditioning. As the subject begins to make anticipatory CR's, however, the procedure changes from classical defense conditioning to a partial reinforcement or extinction condition of classical defense conditioning.

Razran (1935) summarized the results of several studies of conditioned finger withdrawal in children conducted in the laboratory of Bekhterev. A similar procedure has been used by Wickens (1938, 1939, 1943) with adults. The selection of highly voluntary responses as CR's complicates the interpretation of results. Instructions designed to prevent subjects from inhibiting or deliberately making anticipatory responses are given. It is questionable whether laws obtained from such situations will resemble those obtained from conditioning studies in which the subject is unaware of interrelations of the stimuli and the response.

*Higher-Order Instrumental Conditioning.* The procedure originally developed by Ivanov-Smolensky (1927) for use with children is an example of higher-order instrumental conditioning. It involves the setting up, by training or instruction, of an instrumental response to a stimulus ($S_1$) which did not originally elicit that response. After this preliminary training or instruction,

$S_1$ serves in a role analogous to that of the US in classical conditioning. A second stimulus ($S_2$) is then introduced in a role analogous to the CS of classical conditioning. That is, $S_2$ is presented prior to the onset of $S_1$, and the basic measure is the number of times that the response occurs anticipatorily to $S_2$.

Ivanov-Smolensky's procedure has been described in considerable detail by Razran (1935) and Munn (1954). The experimenter arranges a sloping tube extending from the experimenter's compartment into the subject's compartment. On the top surface of the subject's end of the tube is a glass window. When the experimenter releases a piece of candy into his end of the tube, the subject sees the candy as it rolls past the window. The subject is instructed to squeeze a bulb in order to eject the candy from his end of the tube. Thus the sight of the candy moving down the tube serves as the US eliciting the squeezing response. The experimenter precedes the insertion of the candy into the tube by presenting the CS—a bell, buzzer, or flash of light. After a few trials, the subject begins to anticipate the sight of the candy in the tube by squeezing the bulb at the onset of the CS. The time of occurrence of the CS, the US, and the subject's response are recorded for each trial on a polygraph tape.

Dernowa-Yarmolenko (1933) followed essentially the same procedure in the conditioning of a voluntary hand movement. The experimenter instructed the subjects, as a group in the classroom, to raise their hands when the experimenter raised his (US). The experimenter would then tap a pencil on the desk (CS) two seconds before raising his hand. Anticipatory hand-raising to the pencil tap was noted.

Dernowa-Yarmolenko's finding that the number of anticipatory responses decreased with age of the subjects suggests that the occurrence of anticipatory voluntary responses is viewed as incorrect by the subject and the responses tend to be voluntarily inhibited. A decrease in the time interval between the CS and US might serve to reduce the subject's sensitivity to the "false" responses.

## GENERALIZATION OF CONDITIONING

The simplest form of transfer of training has been studied in the context of classical and instrumental conditioning. Although the basic idea is simple, the methodological problems are numerous. When a response has been conditioned to a given stimulus ($S_1$), it is often found to occur when some other stimulus ($S_2$) is presented, even though the response has never been conditioned to $S_2$. If the response occurs to the new ($S_2$) stimulus, it is said to have generalized. Generalization is studied by presenting generalized or test stimuli (GS) to the subject following conditioning. Suppose, for example, the experimenter has trained a group of children to get a reward by pulling a lever each time a light is presented with a brightness of 5000 footcandles (f.c.). The subjects have received 25 conditioning trials, and they now pull the lever promptly each time the CS is presented. Suppose the test

stimuli are lights of 500, 50, and 5 f.c. When the experimenter presents one of the GS's, he must either reward or not reward the child if the latter pulls the lever. If the reward is given, then a conditioning trial has been administered, and the child's subsequent tendency to pull the lever to that GS has been strengthened. If the reward is not given, an extinction trial has been administered, and the tendency to make the response subsequently has been weakened. If the experimenter wishes to determine the relation between the strength of the response tendency and the similarity of the GS to the CS, following a certain amount of conditioning, then a GS can be presented to a given child only once. From available evidence (e.g., Hovland, 1937a,b), it seems safe to conclude that the amount of generalization is an increasing function of the similarity of the CS and GS.

It also appears that the extinction effects built up to a stimulus through nonreinforcement generalize to similar stimuli (Hovland, 1937c; Bass and Hull, 1934). This fact further complicates the study of the generalization gradient. If a given subject is presented with more than one GS, the extinction effects that result from the nonreinforcement of one GS will generalize to others, thereby distorting the gradient of generalized conditioning. Hence, if one wishes to obtain a reliable measure of generalized conditioning, uncontaminated by extinction effects and the generalization of these effects, it is necessary to administer each GS to a sizable group of subjects and to test each subject only once.

The typical practice has been to sacrifice some precision in estimating the shape of the gradient. Sometimes each GS is repeatedly administered to a different group of subjects, and sometimes each GS is repeatedly administered to each subject. There are many problems that can be attacked with these approximate procedures, but the law relating generalized response strength to the similarity of the GS and the CS must await a highly precise experiment.

Generalization can be assessed by any response measure that is sensitive to change or conditioning. The shape of the obtained generalization gradient may well depend on the particular response measures employed in the experiment. Because the experimenter does not have adequate control of the CS in free-operant conditioning, the study of stimulus generalization in this situation is difficult.

Experimental study of stimulus generalization in instrumental conditioning is reported by Mednick and Lehtinen (1957) and by Spiker (1956a,b). White (1958) reported generalization data with variation in two dimensions of the CS. Systematic investigation of children's generalization tendencies in classical conditioning remains to be conducted.

## Discrimination Learning

Discrimination-learning problems require the subject to respond differentially to different simultaneously or successively presented stimuli. A subject responds differentially when he makes a response to one stimulus and does not make that response to others,

as well as when he makes a different response to each stimulus. He may be rewarded for making the correct response and punished and/or nonrewarded for making the incorrect response to a stimulus. The discrimination may be developed in other ways, however. For example, the subject may be given a large reward if he responds to one stimulus and a small one if he responds to the other. Or, responding to the "correct" stimulus may result in immediate reward, whereas responding to the "incorrect" stimulus may result in reward only after considerable delay.

Discrimination-learning situations may be classified in several ways. The theoretical commitments of a writer often seem to dictate his preference for a given classificatory schema. In the present chapter the different types of discrimination-learning problems will be labeled according to conventional usage, a practice that pleases no theorist but wears the cloak of custom. *Differential conditioning*, also called conditioned discrimination, involves conditioning the subject to make a response to a given stimulus and extinguishing his tendency to make that response to other stimuli presented at other times. *Simultaneous discrimination learning* requires the subject to select or respond to a given one of two or more simultaneously presented stimuli. *Successive* or *patterned discrimination learning* requires the subject to respond in one manner to a given stimulus and in a different manner to other stimuli presented at other times. One of the major concerns of present discrimination-learning theories is to provide a satisfactory account of the empirical phenomena that have been observed in each of these situations.

## DIFFERENTIAL CONDITIONING

Since differential conditioning may be studied in any of the conditioning situations previously described, there is no need for a detailed summary of the experimental arrangements necessary for its study. Differential conditioning involves the successive presentation of at least two different stimuli, to one of which the subject is rewarded for responding, whereas response to the other is not rewarded or at least is followed by a less attractive reward. The discrimination is developed in one of two ways. With the *successive phase,* the subject is first consistently rewarded for responding to the positive stimulus until he responds to it each time. Then, for the first time, the negative stimulus is introduced without reward, and both stimuli are presented in a random sequence until the subject consistently responds differentially to them. In the *mixed phase* both stimuli are presented alternately from the beginning. The mixed phase procedure, in its pure form, is rarely used with infrahuman subjects because the extinction effects generated from presentations of the negative stimulus generalize and make difficult the establishment of the response to the positive stimulus. With children, and especially older children, response to the positive stimulus may be satisfactorily established by instructions so that the mixed-phase procedure does not result in the complete extinction of the response.

In differential conditioning the ex-perimenter may obtain separate measures for responses made to the positive and to the negative stimuli. He may record whether or not the response occurs to each stimulus, as well as the speed and magnitude of the response. The development of the discrimination with successive trials is reflected by the divergence of response curves for the positive and negative stimulus presentations. A single curve reflecting the development of the discrimination may be obtained by plotting, for each block of trials, that percentage of the total responses made to the positive stimulus. This measure will reach 100 per cent when the subject responds only to the positive stimulus. For controlled-operant conditioning, in which multiple responses are permitted on each trial, the number of responses to each stimulus presentation may be obtained as a measure of the differentiation between the positive and negative stimuli (Spiker and White, 1959).

Whereas differential conditioning has been extensively studied with infrahuman subjects, particularly in instrumental situations, comparable studies of children are not yet available in the literature. Kasatkin and Levikova (1935a,b) differentially conditioned the sucking response in infants to visual and auditory stimuli. Spiker and White report an experiment in which preschool children were differentially conditioned in the controlled-operant situation.

Although the preceding paragraphs have referred to appetitional conditioning situations, differential conditioning could be carried out in aversive conditioning situations as well. In this case the subject would learn to make a defense, escape, or avoidance reaction to the reinforced stimulus and not to make such a response to the nonreinforced stimulus.

There is one important advantage of differential conditioning in the study of discrimination learning. Since the positive stimulus is presented alone, the subject's response to it is not immediately affected by his tendency to respond to the negative stimulus and vice versa. Thus conditioning to the positive stimulus and extinction to the negative stimulus may be studied without their being confounded by the necessity for the subject to choose between the two stimuli. The next section contains a discussion of differential conditioning in simultaneous discrimination problems. When differential conditioning and simultaneous discrimination learning are studied in the same situation, it is possible to investigate the relationship between the relative strengths of response tendencies to different stimuli and the choice behavior that occurs when the different response tendencies are simultaneously aroused.

## SIMULTANEOUS DISCRIMINATION LEARNING

The positive and negative stimuli are presented at the same time in simultaneous discrimination learning. The subject must choose among the two or more stimuli presented on each trial. The choice of a given stimulus, therefore, does not simply reflect the absolute strength of the tendency to respond to that stimulus; it reflects the strength of that tendency *relative* to the strength of tendencies to respond

to the other simultaneously presented stimuli. The typical response measures are the number of choices of the positive or correct stimulus or, conversely, the number of errors in selecting the negative stimulus. If the subject is allowed to correct on each stimulus setting, two different error measures are frequent. One is the total number of errors made in reaching a performance criterion and the other is the number of trials or settings on which the first response was an error.

The simplest simultaneous problem involves a spatial discrimination. Thus the subject may learn to select consistently the left one of two identical boxes. In more complex spatial discriminations the subject may, for example, learn to select the box fourth from the left in an array of nine identical boxes. Stevenson and Zigler (1958) used a three-choice problem for preschool children. Three response knobs were placed on the front of the apparatus. A signal light was above the knobs, and an aperture through which rewards (marbles) were delivered to the subjects was below the knobs. The left, right, or middle knob was assigned as correct to a given subject. From the Stevenson and Zigler results, it is apparent that this problem is quite easy for preschool children, unless it is made more difficult by a partial reinforcement of the correct response.

Gewirtz and Baer (1958a,b) have developed a procedure for the study of spatial discrimination that resembles the free-operant conditioning procedure described by Bijou (1955, 1957a). The subject is placed before an apparatus that contains two holes into which the subject can put marbles. The experimenter arbitrarily designates one of the two holes as correct; he rewards the subject for placing marbles in that hole and gives no reward for marbles placed in the other hole. The total session is divided into equal time units, and the response measure is the ratio of correct responses to total responses per unit of time. The problems studied by Gewirtz and Baer required them to administer social rewards (verbal approval), but the apparatus could readily be adapted to the administration of material rewards.

A more difficult simultaneous problem utilizes both spatial and nonspatial cues. The procedure is nicely illustrated in an experiment by Kuenne (1946). In this experiment the nonspatial cues were two stimulus plaques, differing in size, placed on the fronts of two goal compartments. The child found a reward in the compartment behind the small plaque, regardless of the compartment on which it was placed. On half the trials the positive cue was placed on the right compartment, and on the other half, on the left compartment. The problem could not be solved satisfactorily on the basis of position.

Schaeffer and Gerjuoy (1955) devised a simpler arrangement. Rewards (marbles) were hidden in wooden cubes with holes in their bases. The subject was simply required to pick up the cube of the correct hue in order to receive the reward consistently. Jeffrey (1958) and Terrell and Kennedy (1957) place push-buttons directly in front of their three-dimensional stimuli. The subject then signals his choice by pushing the correspond-

ing button. This technique has the advantage that a discrete response permits graphic or other relatively permanent recording.

The simultaneous problem can be adapted to children of different ages by varying certain parameters that determine problem difficulty. Problem difficulty can be increased by increasing the similarity of the stimuli to be discriminated. Thus a black-white discrimination can be made more difficult by using light-gray and dark-gray stimuli. An increase in the number of stimuli to be discriminated will also increase problem difficulty. The subject might be required to choose one of five rather than one of two discriminable stimuli, regardless of spatial position. The difficulty of the task may also be increased by increasing the number of simultaneous discriminations the subject is required to learn concurrently. For example, the subject might be required to choose the white stimulus of a pair of black and white circles and to choose the red stimulus if a red and a green circle were presented. In this case he would be learning concurrently a brightness and a hue discrimination, although on different trials of the task.

An experiment by Weiss (1954) demonstrated that the preliminary instructions given the subjects also affect the difficulty of the task. He found that preschool children who had been told that one of the stimulus boxes *always* contained the reward learned significantly faster than children who had not been apprised of the experimenter's consistency. His experiment also suggested that calling the children's attention to the relevant dimensions of the discriminanda subsequently facilitated their learning. The marked differences between the rates of learning in the Kuenne experiment and in a similar one by Alberts and Ehrenfreund (1951) may be the result, in part, of differences in instructions.

Logan (1952) developed a useful procedure in which differential conditioning was studied within the framework of a simultaneous discrimination problem. Although Logan studied rats, Lipsitt and Castaneda (1958) used a similar procedure with preschool children. Each block of trials contains some on which only the positive stimulus is presented and some on which only the negative stimulus is presented. Each block also contains at least one trial on which both stimuli are presented. The latter constitutes a free-choice trial. In this way, the subject's choice behavior can be related to the relative speeds of his response to the positive and negative stimuli when they are presented alone. The procedure has been used successfully in the study of theoretical problems dealing with the competition or conflict of habits in the choice situation. If it is feasible for the positive and negative stimuli to be presented both separately and simultaneously and if the subjects can respond in the same manner to the single and to the joint presentations, the Logan procedure may be profitably employed.

## SUCCESSIVE DISCRIMINATION LEARNING

If the child were required to select the left one of two white boxes and the right one of two black boxes, were each pair of boxes presented on a different trial, the problem would be called a successive or patterned discrimination problem. Thus the successive problem can be described as one in which the nonspatial cues are never present at the same time and the subject must choose the response to make on each trial. Regardless of current theoretical attempts to integrate the simultaneous and successive types of discrimination learning (e.g., Spence, 1952; Weise and Bitterman, 1951), the performances of subjects on the two types of task differ markedly. It is therefore important to analyze each discrimination task to determine which of the two it represents. Auditory, gustatory, and olfactory discriminations, of course, can be studied satisfactorily only in successive discrimination situations.

The literature does not yet contain many examples of the learning by children of successive problems. Perkins, Banks, and Calvin (1954) arranged a successive problem by presenting one of two discriminanda between two identical cups on each trial. The location of the correct cup on each trial depended on which of the two discriminanda was in place. This attempt to isolate one of the variables that affects the relative difficulty of the simultaneous and successive problems is typical of the current theoretical and research interest in discrimination learning.

Gerjuoy (1953) used a successive discrimination problem with elementary-school children. In this case the stimuli were three lights, differing only in their positions on a stimulus panel. The responses involved pushing one of three buttons to each presentation of a light. Pushing the correct button turned out the stimulus light, and the subject was told that the object of the task was to learn to turn out the stimulus light with the first response on each trial. This type of task may also be referred to as motor paired-associate learning. The fact that it can be conceptualized either as successive discrimination or paired-associate learning suggests the possibility of integrating the extensive findings in each of these two areas. A more detailed discussion of these tasks is given in a later section on motor paired-associate learning (see p. 408).

The difficulty of the successive discrimination problem may be varied in much the same way as that of the simultaneous. The number of stimuli to be discriminated may be varied, the similarity of these stimuli may be increased or decreased, the time allowed for the choice may be varied, the subject may be allowed to correct on each trial or he may be informed only that his first choice is right or wrong, and so on. The number of stimuli may be varied with the number of response choices held constant, the number of response choices may be varied with the number of stimuli held constant, or the number of stimuli and response choices may be varied. The findings of Perkins, Banks, and Calvin (1954) suggest that the successive problem is quite difficult for children. However, this apparent difficulty may be largely the result of peculiarities of instructions and procedures, which may be eliminated upon further study of the problem.

It is apparent that successive discrimination is a common occurrence in the everyday lives of children. Learning to read, for example, requires the child to make a different verbal response to each of several similar words without having all the words simultaneously presented. The need to study this type of discrimination in relatively simple, well-controlled situations is obvious.

## RELATIONAL DISCRIMINATION LEARNING

A subject could perform correctly in both simultaneous and successive problems without attending to all stimuli on every trial. In the simultaneous problem he could select the white stimulus (positive) without having observed the black stimulus on that trial. Although the subject cannot observe both white and black on the same trial in the successive problem, he can observe "white on the left" and approach this compound without observing the other compound, "white on the right."

Relational discrimination learning is to be distinguished from these by the fact that the subject, if he is to perform perfectly, must observe all discriminanda on each trial. Consider the following arrangement: choice of the circle is rewarded when it is presented with a triangle, choice of the triangle is rewarded when it is presented with a square, and choice of the square is rewarded when it is presented with the circle. If the spatial arrangements of the pairs of stimuli were systematically counterbalanced, the reward would not be consistently associated with any given form, with either position, or even with any given combination of position and form. This type of learning has also been called "transverse patterning" (Spence, 1952). Only if the subject attends to the negative stimulus, as well as to the positive one, can he receive adequate information to make correct choices consistently. The problem thus demands a *comparative* orienting response on each trial. Research indicates that such a problem is difficult for preschool children. For example, in a problem requiring the subjects to select the middle-sized of three stimuli on each trial, in which the absolute size of the stimuli varied from trial to trial, only subjects for whom a test had indicated understanding of the concept "middle-sizedness" showed any evidence of learning in 30 trials (Spiker, Gerjuoy, and Shepard, 1956).

It is likely that experienced preschool children often solve even the simultaneous discrimination problems by using a comparative orienting response. For example, if two stimuli differing in size are presented on each trial and the reward is consistently associated with the larger, the preschool child who has had considerable experience in such problems often is observed to turn first to one, then to the other, and to repeat this sequence one or more times before making a choice. It is likely that once a subject has developed this type of orienting behavior the relational problem can be solved with relative ease. In their study of monkeys' solutions of the oddity problems Moon and Harlow (1955) demonstrate that infrahuman subjects can solve problems requiring observation of all stimuli simultaneously presented. Subjects possessing a high level of verbal facility could learn a preliminary set of instructions that would permit errorless performance on the relational problems, even without preliminary practice on the problem.

## TRANSFER OF TRAINING IN DISCRIMINATION LEARNING

The transfer of discrimination learning has been studied in several different contexts. Harlow (1949) reports evidence for the development of learning-to-learn or discrimination-learning set in preschool children as a function of the number of previous simultaneous discrimination problems they had learned. The rate of learning improved with the number of previous problems solved, even when the stimuli in the series of problems were unrelated. The same finding was reported by Shepard (1957) when her preschool subjects learned a series of successive discrimination problems.

The transfer of discrimination learning within the context of the transposition experiment provides another example of transfer of training. Kuenne (1946) showed that preschool-aged children transpose on a size discrimination. That is, after the subjects had learned to select the smaller of two stimuli, they would select the smaller of another pair of stimuli differing in size from the original pair. Whether such transfer is positive or negative depends on which stimulus of the second problem is correct. Similar findings were reported in the study of Alberts and Ehrenfreund (1951).

Cantor (1955) demonstrated that preliminary training involving learning names for the stimuli will facilitate subsequent discrimination of the same stimuli in a simultaneous problem. Norcross and Spiker (1957) confirmed Cantor's results in a similar experiment. Norcross (1958) showed facilitation, resulting from previous name-learning, in a successive discrimination-learning problem. The study by Lipsitt and Castaneda (1958), mentioned previously, demonstrated transfer from previous differential conditioning to a simultaneous problem involving the same stimuli.

## GENERAL CONSIDERATIONS IN DISCRIMINATION LEARNING

Although it is not difficult to devise discrimination-learning problems for children that are analogous to those used with infrahuman subjects, it is probably a serious error to assume that children learn such problems in the same way as infrahuman subjects. Differences in the performance of children in discrimination learning after they have learned names for the stimuli (Cantor, 1955; Gerjuoy, 1953; Shepard, 1954; Norcross, 1958; and Smith and Goss, 1955) demonstrate conclusively that the language abilities of the subjects play an important role in their solution of discrimination problems. Although the restricted motility of preverbal children makes difficult the comparison of their discrimination learning with that of infrahuman subjects, such comparative studies would provide much information on the role of language in simple learning.

The preschool child's ability to conceptualize the goal of a discrimination problem probably plays a crucial role in his reactions to a nonrewarded response. If the child has been instructed and understands that the goal is to get a reward on each trial, a nonreward seems to serve as a punishment. This can be concluded from the fact that numerous nonrewarded trials early in learning result in a marked negative attitude toward the task, a result that also occurs when punishments and/or criticisms are given for early errors. On the other hand, if the goal of "perfection" is not mentioned or is deemphasized by the experimenter, the child will often settle for a reward on only a fraction of the trials. In the latter case learning may not occur unless the rewards are highly pertinent to the child's current needs. This ability to conceptualize a perfect performance may prove to be one of the factors that critically distinguish children's discrimination performance from that of infrahuman subjects. However, reactions to failure, similar to those of children, have been observed in monkeys and chimpanzees who have had considerable prior experience in discrimination learning tasks. Indeed, recent studies with rats suggest that the omission of a customary ("expected") reward results in marked evidence of emotional reactions (Amsel and Roussell, 1952; Roussell, 1952).

## Rote Learning

Certain types of learning problems are customarily referred to as rote-learning tasks. This practice, of course, is no evidence that the laws governing rote learning are fundamentally different from those governing other types of learning. Research on learning is not yet adequate to answer this question.

If a task requires a subject to make a different response to each of several stimuli and if there is no principle or set of principles that systematically determines which response goes with which stimulus, the task is usually labeled a rote-learning task. If the responses the subject makes are verbal, the task is called a rote-verbal-learning task; if the responses are motor, it is called a rote-motor-learning task.

On the other hand, if a task, for example, requires the subject to learn to respond to each stimulus word with its antonym, it would not be called a rote-learning task. In this case a single principle determines the stimulus-response pairs, and the subject's discovery and use of this principle will greatly simplify the learning task. Similarly, a concept-formation task in which the subject is required to learn to make the same verbal response to each member of a class of stimulus items, in which the members of a class have common features (e.g., common functions, common elements, and similar shapes), would also be distinguished from rote-learning tasks (Metzger, 1958).

Discrimination-learning tasks, in which the subject learns to select one stimulus that is arbitrarily designated as correct by the experimenter, are not ordinarily referred to as rote-learning tasks. Except for convention, however, there appears to be no reason to distinguish such tasks from those that are called rote-learning tasks. The laws that govern the learning of rote tasks and discrimination tasks may ultimately be found to be similar or overlapping.

Although convention is not entirely consistent on this point, the learning of prose and poetry is not ordinarily classified as rote learning. This seems to be especially true if the subject "understands" the prose or poetry that he learns. On the other hand, learning to associate pairs of meaningful words is usually called rote learning, even when the pairs of words are highly associated to begin with. It is probably not surprising that psychologists do not agree perfectly on the tasks to be classified as rote-learning tasks. The distinction between rote learning and more insightful types of learning is based on the degree to which the subject understands (or is likely to understand) the principles inherent in the task. The discovery of just how well the subject understands such principles is the object of many studies of learning.

## ROTE VERBAL LEARNING

The use of rote-verbal-learning tasks in experimental psychology dates back to the early work of Ebbinghaus (1885). There are several types of verbal tasks that have been used with adult subjects as well as several different procedures for the study of each. Three types of rote verbal tasks are described here—list learning, serial learning, and paired-associate learning.

*List Learning.* For this task, the subject is presented with a list of items (e.g., words, nonsense syllables, and numbers), is allowed to study them, and is then asked to reproduce the list in its absence. The subject is not required to reproduce the list in the order in which it was originally presented. The list-learning procedure was used by Lahey (1937) to study the extent to which the learning of new lists affected elementary-school children's recall of previously learned lists.

There are two major techniques of presenting the list. In the complete presentation method the entire list is given to the subject, and he is allowed to study it for a specified period of time. After the list has been removed, the subject is asked to recall as many of the items as possible. Either the amount of study time or the number of study periods may be varied to determine the effect of practice on recall. With the second technique, each item is presented separately for a constant length of time on each trial. The second procedure is preferred, since it provides better control over the amount of time the subject spends on each item.

For prereading subjects, a series of pictures or objects can be presented, which the subject is asked to recall in the same way as words, nonsense syllables, or digits (Bayley, 1926; McGeoch, 1928). Auditory presentation of the materials permits the use of words, nonsense syllables, and digits with prereading subjects (Bayley, 1926; Hurlock and Newmark, 1931). Although most studies involving such procedures have been concerned with recall following a single presentation of the list (memory span), the procedures seem entirely appropriate for repeated presentation in the study of learning.

Manual methods of presenting the items may be used, but current practice prefers the automatic presentation procedures whenever possible. For verbal materials (words, nonsense syllables, digits, pictures, figures, and letters), automatic presentation may be accomplished by use of the memory drum, or similar devices, which permit a constant exposure time for each item as well as a constant between-item interval. Control of this interval is considered important, since it is known that the between-item intervals are often used for rehearsal. The auditory presentation of verbal materials can be accomplished by tape-recordings, in which each item is equally spaced with respect to time.

*Serial Verbal Learning.* The major difference between list learning and serial verbal learning is that the latter requires the subject to reproduce the list in the order in which it was presented to him. Serial-learning tasks have been given to children primarily to study their memory spans. Whereas the literature on serial verbal learning in adults is massive, the research with children is less impressive. It may be that the reading ability of elementary-school children usually has been considered inadequate for the efficient study of verbal learning.

Serial verbal learning has been presented by two methods. The method of complete presentation involves, as in list learning, the presentation of the entire list to the subject, followed by a test trial in which the subject is asked to reproduce the list in the proper order. Lepley (1934) conducted an extensive study of the serial learning of elementary-school children with the complete-presentation method. The serial-verbal learning of adults is currently studied primarily by the serial-anticipation method (Hilgard, 1951). The materials are typically presented in a memory drum. The items in the list appear at a constant rate, and the subject is required to attempt to call out the next item in the list before it appears in the drum. Once through the list is considered a trial, and the response measure is usually the number of correct anticipations per trial. The progress of learning is represented by a plot of the number of correct anticipations per trial or per block of trials. Andrews, Shapiro, and Cofer (1954) report the successful study of serial learning in elementary-school children (9 to 13 years of age) by the serial-anticipation method. Their anticipation interval was the usual two seconds provided for adult subjects. It seems likely that the serial-anticipation method could also be used with prereading subjects if auditory or pictorial presentation of the materials were used and if relatively long anticipation intervals were provided.

One of the major limitations of serial learning is that it is impossible to vary the stimulus and response items independently. Each item serves both as a stimulus item and as a response item. The study of the effect of stimulus similarity on rate of learning, holding response similarity constant, could not be accomplished with a serial task. The study of the effect of response familiarity on rate of learning, holding constant stimulus familiarity, likewise would not be possible. Since there is a number of important problems concerned with the manipulation of stimulus and response factors independently, it is fortunate that the method of paired-associate verbal learning has been developed.

*Paired-Associate Verbal Learning.* In paired-associate verbal learning the subject is presented with several pairs of words and is asked to associate the pairs in such a way that, upon presentation of the first member, he will be able to call out the second. Two techniques for presenting the materials have been used. In the first, called the complete-presentation method, the pairs of words are exposed together, one pair at a time, until the list has been completely presented. Then the first member of each pair is presented, and the subject is asked to respond with the second member. The amount of time given for the recall of each item varies from experiment to experiment. In some experiments the subject is prompted if he fails to recall; in others, he is not prompted. The order of presenting the pairs is varied from trial to trial to prevent serial learning. The paired-associate learning of elementary-school children was successfully studied by Postman and Murphy (1943) with the complete-presentation method. Formerly, verbal paired-associate learning was studied almost exclusively by this method. Currently, the paired-associate anticipation method is most frequently used. With this method, the first member of a pair is presented alone for a set period of time. It is followed immediately by the joint presentation of both members. The subject is asked to call out the response member before it appears. The usual rate of presentation to adult subjects is such that the subject has approximately two seconds in which to anticipate the response. Thus, on each presentation of a pair, the stimulus word is immediately followed by information as to which word is correct for that stimulus.[1]

It is probable that the development and increasingly prevalent use of the paired-associate method in recent years has been due, in part, to certain limitations of the serial learning method. With the paired-associate method, the stimulus and response items can be independently manipulated. Paired-associate procedures also permit an extensive analysis of the various types of error that occur during learning. When the anticipation procedure is used, the experimenter may obtain the number of intralist errors, extralist errors, and omissions, in addition to the number of correct anticipations. Intralist errors, which occur when the subject responds to one stimulus with a word that is correct for another, are particularly sensitive to variations in the similarity of the stimulus items. Intruded errors —response words that are not in the list—may be of particular interest when the experiment is concerned with the effects of interpolated learning tasks. Failures to respond within the anticipation interval (omissions) constitute

another major source of error which may be of interest in investigations of negative transfer or interference due to blocking.

Several procedures have been devised to adapt paired-associate learning to subjects who either do not read well or do not read at all. Lund (1927) used a task in which 5-year-old children were required to say the names of color stimuli as rapidly as possible. Failures to respond or erroneous responses were followed by oral prompting. Jersild (1932) used a similar task for 7- and 8-year-old children.

Norcross and Spiker (1958) adapted the paired-associate anticipation method to kindergarten and first-grade children. These investigators presented pictures of single objects for both stimulus and response items. The subjects were instructed to call out the names of the pictured objects. Anticipation intervals considerably longer than those used for adults were selected in order to avoid too frequent failures. The between-item intervals were kept relatively brief to avoid boredom and lack of attention. The between-trial intervals were somewhat lengthened to prevent the development of excessive fatigue.

Still a different method of presenting paired-associate materials by the anticipation procedure was used by Reese (1958). He studied children from the fourth, fifth, and sixth grades whose reading ability was relatively poor. The stimulus items were lights differing in hue and/or brightness and the response items were nonsense words. A bell signaled the end of the anticipation interval, at which time the experimenter orally prompted the subject, whether

[1] It may be noted that the paired-associate anticipation method resembles the procedure in classical conditioning. The stimulus word may be thought of as the CS, the response word as the US, the anticipation interval as the CS-US interval, the subject's reading of the response word when it is exposed as the UR, and his overt anticipation of this word as the CR. It is tempting to describe paired-associate verbal learning as the concurrent classical conditioning of several responses.

or not the subject had correctly anticipated. Reese's procedure should also be useful with older elementary-school children if the response items were nonsense syllables that were difficult to read and pronounce.

The paired-associate verbal task is nicely suited to the study of children's learning because of the ease with which its difficulty can be adapted. The task is made much easier if one- or two-syllable nouns naming familiar, concrete objects are used. The subject's attention to the materials can be improved if he is required to pronounce both the stimulus item and the response item on each presentation. It may also be desirable to present independently the stimulus and response items prior to administering the paired list in order to determine any individual idiosyncrasies in pronunciation and to familiarize the child with the response items (Norcross and Spiker, 1958). Finally, the number of pairs in the list can be reduced or increased to adapt the difficulty of the tasks to the subjects used. Paired-associate verbal learning has been studied in elementary-school children of intermediate grades with essentially the same procedures used with college undergraduates (Andrews et al., 1954; Spiker, 1960).

## ROTE MOTOR LEARNING

The sharp distinction that is often made between "verbal" and "motor" learning tasks would be difficult to defend. It is difficult to conceive of a motor task for human subjects, the learning of which is not subject to the influence of verbal processes. At one extreme, consider a task in which the subject is required to press a different response button to each of several stimulus lights differing in hue. If the buttons can be identified by distinctive names, e.g., by numbers, an adult could conceivably learn the task without touching a single button. That is, he could learn "yellow-button 1," "blue-button 2," etc., prior to any practice on the task. Following the verbal learning, he could perform on the "motor" task without error, although subsequent practice might show improvement in speed of the responses, the smoothness with which they were executed, etc. (Baker and Wylie, 1950). It is likely that most adult human subjects, even if not given the prior verbal practice, would soon introduce verbalizations to facilitate learning. At the other extreme, there are tasks that do not seem to be so subject to verbal control. Throwing a basketball through the hoop with the consistency of the professional basketball player is a skill that is not acquired merely by memorizing verbal instructions. Improvement in such a skill is dependent on the individual's attention to the proprioceptive feedback from his responses. There is presently no language that permits the description and discussion of the proprioceptive stimuli that are crucial in the development of this type of skill. Nevertheless, many of the preparatory responses that facilitate the development of the skill are subject to instructional control. The prospective basketball player can be instructed as to the angle at which he should face the hoop; he may be told the height at which he should hold the basketball, and so on.

Despite these considerations, tasks requiring the subject to make nonverbal, skeletal responses are frequently designated as "motor tasks." But, once again, it is well to remember that performances on differently named tasks are not necessarily governed by different laws. Indeed, one of the most important endeavors of the student of human learning is to determine whether or not such phenomenally different types of learning can be understood in terms of the same principles.

*Paired-Associate Motor Learning.* It was noted previously that certain types of discrimination tasks may be considered as paired-associate motor tasks. Numerous other tasks that have been studied with children seem to qualify as paired-associate motor tasks. Among them are the familiar coding or substitution tasks of mental tests, such as the Wechsler (1944) Digit Symbol Test; clerical tasks such as typing and telegraphy; and perhaps even the formboard tasks often given younger preschool children (e.g., Skeels, 1933). In each of these tests, the subject is required to associate a different motor response with each stimulus. Most studies of children's performance on such tasks have been concerned with obtaining normative data rather than with the study of variables that affect the learning of the tasks.

The task used in Kirkwood's (1926) study of children's learning also belongs to this class. She had preschool children associate blocks to picture stimuli, where the block and picture of each pair had a slight resemblance to each other. The experimenter showed the child a picture and asked him to select the block that went with it. The response measure was the number of correct associations the child gave each time through the 20 pairs. Kirkwood's task has the advantage that the strength of associations between stimuli and responses can be manipulated by varying the degree of within-pair similarity, a convenient means of varying task difficulty.

Spiker and Holton (1958) developed a paired-associate motor task analogous to paired-associate verbal learning with the anticipation method. The apparatus permits the presentation, one at a time, of six stimulus lights differing in hue. To each light, the subject is required to push a different one of nine pushbuttons, arranged in a semicircle. Beside each button is a small pilot lamp. The subjects were given two seconds to select the correct button (the anticipation interval). At the end of this interval, the pilot lamp beside the correct button was turned on and, with the stimulus light, remained on for two seconds (the joint-presentation interval). At the end of the joint-presentation interval, both the stimulus light and the information light were turned off for two seconds (the interstimulus interval). In a similar procedure Norcross (1958) used automatically presented pictures as stimuli.

The motor paired-associate task has several advantages over its verbal counterpart. First, it is easy to equate the difficulty of the stimulus-response connections, since given stimuli do not tend to elicit particular button selections. In some experiments it is desirable to equate two halves of a task so that the same subject may perform under both experimental and control conditions. To equate or control the initial differences in the associative strengths of the stimulus-response pairs of verbal tasks requires elaborate experimental and/or statistical procedures. Experimental control requires preliminary research to select pairs with equal associative strengths. Statistical control necessitates the preparation of several word lists, which must then be used in a counterbalancing design. The statistical procedure often results in an equivocal interaction between lists and experimental conditions. Comparable control in the motor task can be achieved with fewer sets of stimulus-response pairings ("lists") and with less likelihood of an ambiguous interaction. Second, pushing a button is a clear-cut discrete response, which makes observation and recording easy. Third, the response provides a mechanical energy, which permits convenient measurement of response times. The use of the voice key to accomplish the same purpose in verbal learning is complicated by stammering and stuttering. Finally, since the buttons are available to the subject at the beginning of the task, the learning that occurs reflects the acquisition of specific stimulus-response associations and is uncomplicated by the subject's learning which responses are appropriate to make in the situation. In the usual verbal paired-associate procedure the subject must first learn which words he can use as response words and then associate them with the appropriate stimuli. The degree to which this list learning affects performance is not yet known.

One of the major limitations of the motor paired-associate task is the restricted number of response possibilities. If one wished to give a series of tasks, with different stimuli and different responses in each task, the foregoing task would be inappropriate. A task like that of Kirkwood (1926) would be better for this type of problem, since a number of variations in the characteristics of the blocks could be manipulated.

*Maze Learning.* The maze learning of children has been extensively studied. These studies include children's performance on the ball-rolling maze (Mattson, 1933), the finger-maze (Wieg, 1932), the slot- or stylus-maze (McGinnis, 1929), and the body-maze (Wenger, 1933). These mazes usually consist of several choice points, with either two or three choices available at each point. Selection of the correct path at each point results in arrival at the goal or at the end of the maze.

The use of the maze, either the small hand-maze or the body-maze, permits the study of important variables. The effect of different types of incentive on maze performance was studied systematically by Abel (1936). Jones (1945) compared the effectiveness of different events to signal correct responses. Holodnak (1943) studied the effects of signaling correct responses as opposed to signaling incorrect responses. Melcher (1943) compared visual and manual guidance in learning the maze. McGinnis (1929) and Jones and Yoshioka (1938) have studied transfer of training from one maze pattern to another. It would also be possible to vary the number and type of cue the subject receives at the choice point. With a slot-maze, in which the blind alleys are hidden beneath the surface of the maze, it would be possible to vary the visual cues at each choice point, increasing or decreasing the distinctiveness of the choice points.

The usual maze for the study of children's learning can be viewed as a sequence of spatial discrimination problems, with the choice at each point determined by previous choices. As such, it will be recognized as considerably more complex than the corresponding paired-associate problem, in which each pair may be learned relatively independently of the other pairs. It is probably this complexity of the maze task that has caused it to lose favor among recent investigators of simpler types of learning.

*Motor Serial Learning.* The experimental study of motor tasks analogous to the verbal serial learning tasks described previously has not yet been reported in the literature. Superficially, it might appear that the maze parallels the verbal serial task. It will be noted, however, that only two or three different responses are involved in maze performance. By contrast, many different responses are used in the typical verbal serial task. A motor task more nearly analogous to the verbal task would involve, for example, ten response-buttons. The subject would have to learn a sequence of ten button-pushing responses, utilizing each button only once. It would be interesting to discover whether the phenomena commonly observed in verbal serial learning (e.g., the serial position effect, remote associations, and savings on derived lists) also appear in the motor analogue.

*Complex Motor Skills.* In all the tasks considered thus far it has been assumed that the responses involved are already in the repertoire of the subject. In such tasks what is learned, then, is to make the appropriate response to each stimulus. The present section considers motor tasks in which the responses must be to some degree developed, either completely or by the integration of elemental responses already existing in the subject's repertoire. The literature on children's learning contains numerous studies of the learning of motor skills, although few of the skills have been studied systematically. For example, the effects of practice have been investigated with such tasks as drawing, writing, climbing, cube manipulation, scissor cutting, ring tossing, throwing at targets, performance with mirror reversals, and so on (Munn, 1954, pp. 387–407). In most cases the experimenter's major interest appears to have been whether or not children's performances on his particular task were subject to improvement with practice. Typically, the variables studied were individual difference variables (age, sex, intelligence, school grade, etc.) rather than variables subject to experimental manipulation (e.g., type of instruction, type, amount, and frequency of reward, and type, amount and distribution of practice). Consequently, although some normative and developmental data are available for performance on these types of task, relatively little is known about the experimental variables that affect the learning of them. In connection with the older studies, it would seem that the primary criterion for selection of the type of motor task studied was its relatively frequent occurrence in everyday life and/or its social significance. Although the psychologist may often make experimental use of these "natural situations," it is probably more frequently the case that his hypotheses require less complex, better-controlled situations.

The student of children's learning who is interested in motor skills would do well to examine some of the motor tasks conventionally used with adults. For example, Langhorne (1933) studied performance on the Renshaw-Weiss pursuitmeter as a function of age with subjects as young as 7 years. More recently, Ammons, Alprin, and Ammons (1955) investigated performance on the rotary pursuit apparatus with third-grade children. Similar adaptations could be made for the Star Discrimeter (Duncan, 1953), the two-hand coordinator (Shephard and Lewis, 1950), and the modified Mashburn apparatus (Lewis and Shephard, 1950). Children normally find such tasks interesting and challenging, and comparison of their performances on these devices with those of adults would provide a significant addition to our knowledge of human learning.

## Concept Formation

It is difficult to identify the common features of all experiments that have been referred to as concept formation studies. As Vinacke (1951) implies in his thorough review of methods and results of concept formation experiments, there are some profound differences within this group of studies that make questionable the practice of referring to all of them by the same name. Most such studies, however, can be characterized by the fact that the subject learns to make the same response (motor and/or verbal) to each member of a set of stimuli and learns not to make this response to stimuli not belonging to the set. In most studies the subject is given several sets of stimuli concurrently and is required to learn a different response to each set. In addition, a concept is said to be attained only when the subject makes the appropriate response to stimuli he has not previously observed in the experiment. Thus the members of a set of stimuli must have some feature in common— color, form, texture, size, function, name, material, etc.—and the members of different sets must be discriminable in some respect. The latter requirement excludes tasks in which the subject learns the same name for each member of a set of stimuli arbitrarily and randomly assembled by the experimenter, since the subject could not be expected to make the response to a new stimulus without having previously learned to do so.

Although some students appear to restrict concept formation to situations involving verbal responses of human subjects, others (e.g., Vinacke, 1951; Long, 1940) would include the nonverbal responses of preverbal children. In terms of available data, there is no good reason to exclude infrahuman subjects if preverbal human subjects are to be included. If these considerations are accepted, the formation of concepts in animals has already been demonstrated in transposition experiments. Thus, when chimpanzees are trained to select the smaller of two particular stimuli and subsequently choose the smaller of a new pair of stimuli, they have met the criterion of concept attainment.

## TYPES OF CONCEPT FORMATION

When the two-year-old child is told on successive occasions that his wagon, his mother's dress, the catsup, the stop light, certain of his blocks, etc., are "red," he is presumably learning the concept "red." When he points to the first fire-truck he has ever seen and says "red," he is demonstrating some learning of the concept. If he consistently responds to other red things with "red" and does not use the term for non-red things, he demonstrates an understanding of the concept. When reference is to this type of original learning, the term *concept learning* is used.

Now consider a set of cards consisting of several instances of triangles, circles, and squares, with several instances of each form colored red, green, or blue. If an adult is asked to sort a deck of such cards, he may do it in terms of color, form, or combinations of both color and form. If the experimenter consistently rewards him when he sorts on the basis of color, the subject will eventually sort the entire deck consistently on this basis. The subject discovers, through experimenter prompting, the concept the experimenter considers relevant. The learning that takes place in this type of situation is called *concept discovery*. In concept discovery the subject learns to attend to dimensions or features of the stimuli, *for which he has already learned names*, in order to solve the problem the experimenter has devised for him.

Although something is learned in both concept learning and concept discovery, there are obvious differences in what is learned in the two situations. The child learns, in effect, that objects having "that property" are called "red." The adult learns that the experimenter wishes him to call the red objects "meef" or to push the left button when red stimuli are presented. It would be surprising, indeed, if exactly the same laws governed learning in the two situations.

Clear-cut studies of concept learning are rare in the literature, and the systematic study of it has scarcely begun. The excellent study of children's concept learning by Long (1940) is still a proto-type that has not been subsequently utilized. Experiments by Welch (1938) and Welch and Long (1940a,b) also provide examples of the study of concept learning. Most concept formation experiments with children, however, have not been concerned with the teaching of concepts. They have been concerned with testing to determine the concepts children have already acquired at different ages (e.g., Hicks and Stewart, 1930; Thrum, 1935). In this respect, they resemble the concept discovery experiments conducted with adults (e.g., Heidbreder, 1946, 1947; Buss, 1950). The early experiment by Hull (1920) is one of the few systematic investigations of concept learning in adults. The referents of Hull's concepts were Chinese characters, unfamiliar to his subjects, imbedded in complex stimulus patterns. Thus his subjects were required to learn new concepts.

## METHODS FOR STUDYING CONCEPT FORMATION

*The Paired-Associate Method.* The procedure used by Hull was subsequently modified and improved by Heidbreder in a series of experiments with exemplary methodology (Heidbreder, 1946, 1947; Heidbreder, Bensley, and Ivy, 1948; Heidbreder and Overstreet, 1948). The procedure is similar to that of paired-associate learning by the anticipation method. Several series of stimuli are prepared, each of which contains a different member (instance) of each of several classes of stimuli (concepts). The subject is given the first series of these stimuli and is required to learn a different nonsense syllable to each stimulus in the series. When the first series has been learned, the subject is given the second; when the second series has been learned, he is given the third; and so on. The subject learns the same nonsense syllable to each instance of a given concept. Thus, to the circular stimulus in each series, he learns the syllable "Fard," to the stimulus in each series having exactly two identical components, he learns "Ling," and so on. The primary measure of the speed of concept attainment is the number of the series on which the subject begins to anticipate consistently the correct nonsense syllable for a given concept. This method is appropriate for the study of either concept discovery or concept learning.

*The Stimulus-Sorting Method.* Heidbreder (1949) also utilized a card-sorting procedure. In this case the stimuli were placed on cards, and the subject was asked to sort the deck of cards into a specified number of classes. Since Heidbreder was primarily interested in the order in which different types of concepts would be discovered, she permitted the subjects to classify the complete deck without prompting by the experimenter. The basic measure of the primacy of the concept was the number of subjects who correctly sorted each concept. It would also have been possible to prompt the subject after each card was classified, with the number of deck-sortings required to classify correctly as the measure of the speed of concept attainment.

*Simple Discrimination-Learning Method.* Long (1940) developed a nonverbal method for the study of concept learning in children with relatively low verbal facility. It is essentially a simultaneous discrimination-learning procedure that is equally appropriate for infrahuman subjects. Long used two compartments with glass windows on the front. In one of the compartments he placed a rubber ball and in the other a three-dimensional cube. To obtain a reward, the subject learned to press the window of the compartment containing the ball, regardless of the compartment it occupied. After the subject had reached a high performance criterion on this problem, other stimuli were placed in the compartments. If the subject continued to respond to an orange, a golf ball, a circle, the more circular of two ovals, etc., he had learned the concept of roundness. The necessary adaptations to extend this method to infrahuman subjects are obvious.

A procedure resembling the successive discrimination method has been used with adults by Buss (1950). Three-dimensional stimuli differing in height, width, and color were presented one at a time. The subject was rewarded for pushing one response key to the tall stimuli and a different one to the short stimuli. Since his subjects were college undergraduates, Buss's study deals with concept discovery rather than concept learning.

*Interview-Questionnaire Method.* This method is exemplified in its simplest form by Welch (1940), although it has been used extensively by Piaget (e.g., 1930). Welch's subjects were asked questions that contained the concepts under investigation. For example, a child might be asked, "What kind of food do you like best?" If the child's answer referred to a specific food, the answer indicated that the child understood, at least to some degree, the concept "food." The method is better adapted to the study of the concepts available to the subject than it is to the teaching of new concepts.

A related procedure was used by Welch and Long (1940a, 1940b). In these experiments the subjects were given instructions that contained concepts previously taught to the subjects. The instructions required the children to perform certain acts with the relevant stimuli. If the children followed the instructions, it was accepted as evidence of concept attainment.

## General Considerations

A review of the literature on research methods in children's learning indicates that a wide variety of techniques is presently available for the study of simpler types of learning. Practical methods have been developed for the study of classical and instrumental conditioning, discrimination learning, rote verbal and motor learning, and concept formation. Moreover, many procedures utilized in the study of infrahuman and adult human learning appear to be readily adaptable for use with children. Inadequate apparatus and procedures are no longer a serious obstacle to the intensive and extensive study of children's learning, although future research will undoubtedly result in the refinement of all methods.

Although the student of children's learning may be encouraged by the variety of serviceable methods and procedures, the sparsity of application of these methods provides no cause for complacency. The systematic study of a given area of children's learning is still rare. The majority of experiments are single-shot investigations rather than series of thorough studies of particular problems. It is to be hoped that the future will bring the systematic research with children that can already be observed in the study of the rat in the T-maze, the infrahuman primate in discrimination problems, the adult in eyelid conditioning, and the college sophomore in verbal learning tasks. There is a serious need to analyze the learning performance of children in the relatively complex rote learning and concept formation situations in an attempt to apply the principles obtained from the simpler conditioning and discrimination-learning situations. Systematic investigations of children's learning in these areas would do a great deal to enhance our understanding of principles of general psychology.

Many of the procedures that have been discussed in the preceding pages appear to be appropriate for applied research as well as for the basic research for which they were developed. The recent research program of Skinner (1958) and his associates provides an excellent illustration. These investigators are bringing laboratory methods to the teaching of academic content. They have devised apparatus—teaching machines—that permits the administration of carefully prepared teaching programs to the learner. These machines enable the experimenter to control and manipulate with laboratory precision such psychologically potent factors as amount of practice, immediacy of reinforcement, stimulus presentation methods, and problem sequence, in order to maximize the transfer of previous learning to new situations. This approach promises to place the findings of basic research in learning at the disposal of those whose task it is to cause children to learn. How successful this attempt will be depends to a very great degree on the availability of knowledge obtained from basic research on children's learning.

## REFERENCES

Abel, L. B. 1936. The effects of shift in motivation upon the learning of a sensorimotor task. *Arch. Psychol.*, 29, No. 205.

Alberts, E., and D. Ehrenfreund. 1951. Transposition in children as a function of age. *J. exp. Psychol.*, 41, 30–38.

Ammons, R. B., S. I. Alprin, and Carol H. Ammons. 1955. Rotary pursuit performance as related to sex and age of pre-adult subjects. *J. exp. Psychol.*, 49, 127–133.

Amsel, A., and J. Roussel. 1952. Motivational properties of frustration: I. Effect on a running response of the addition of frustration to the motivational complex. *J. exp. Psychol.*, 43, 363–368.

Andrews, T. G., S. Shapiro, and C. N. Cofer. 1954. Transfer and generalization of the inhibitory potential developed in rote serial learning. *Amer. J. Psychol.*, 67, 453–463.

Baker, K. E., and R. C. Wylie. 1950. Transfer of verbal training to a motor task. *J. exp. Psychol.*, 40, 632–638.

Bass, M. J., and C. L. Hull. 1934. The irradiation of a tactile conditioned reflex in man. *J. comp. Psychol.*, 17, 47–65.

Bayley, Nancy. 1926. Performance tests for three, four and five year old children. *Pedag. Sem.*, 33, 435–454.

Bijou, S. W. 1955. A systematic approach to an experimental analysis of young children. *Child Develpm.*, 26, 161–168.

———. 1957a. Methodology for an experimental analysis of child behavior. *Psychol. Rep.*, 3, 243–250.

———. 1957b. Patterns of reinforcement and resistance to extinction in young children. *Child Develpm.*, 28, 47–54.

———. 1958. A child study laboratory on wheels. *Child Develpm.*, 29, 425–427.

Brogden, W. J. 1951. Animal studies of learning. In S. S. Stevens (Ed.), *Handbook of experimental psychology*. New York: Wiley. Pp. 568–612.

Buss, A. H. 1950. A study of concept formation as a function of reinforcement and stimulus generalization. *J. exp. Psychol.*, 40, 494–503.

Cantor, G. N. 1955. Effects of three types of pretraining on discrimination learning in preschool children. *J. exp. Psychol.*, 49, 339–342.

Dernowa-Yarmolenko, A. A. 1942. The fundamentals of a method of investigating the function of the nervous system as revealed in overt behavior. *J. genet. Psychol.*, **42**, 319–338.

Duncan, C. 1953. Transfer in motor learning as a function of degree of first-task learning and inter-task similarity. *J. exp. Psychol.*, **45**, 1–11.

Ebbinghaus, H. *Über das Gedächtnis: Untersuchungen zur experimentellen Psychologie.* Leipzig: Duncker and Humblot, 1885. (Trans., H. A. Ruger and C. E. Bussenius. *Memory: A contribution to experimental psychology*, Columbia Univer. Coll. Educ. Reprints, No. 3 New York: Teach. Coll., Columbia Univer., 1913.)

Gerjuoy, I. R. 1953. Discrimination learning as a function of the similarity of the stimulus names. Unpublished doctoral dissertation, State Univer. Iowa.

Gewirtz, J. L. and D. M. Baer. 1958a. The effect of brief social deprivation on behaviors for a social reinforcer. *J. abnorm. soc. Psychol.*, **56**, 49–56.

———. 1958b. Deprivation and satiation of social reinforcers as drive conditions. *J. abnorm. soc. Psychol.*, **57**, 165–172.

Guttman, N., and H. I. Kalish. 1956. Discriminability and stimulus generalization. *J. exp. Psychol.*, **51**, 79–88.

Haner, C. F., and P. A. Brown. 1955. Clarification of the instigation to action concept in the frustration-aggression hypothesis. *J. abnorm. soc. Psychol.*, **51**, 204–206.

Harlow, H. F. 1949. The formation of learning sets. *Psychol. Rev.*, **56**, 51–65.

Heidbreder, E. 1946. The attainment of concepts: II. The problem. *J. genet. Psychol.*, **35**, 191–223.

———. 1947. The attainment of concepts: III. The process. *J. Psychol.*, **24**, 93–138.

———. 1949. The attainment of concepts: VII. Conceptual achievements during card-sorting. *J. Psychol.*, **27**, 3–39.

———, M. L. Bensley, and M. Ivy. 1948. The attainment of concepts: IV. Regularities and levels. *J. Psychol.*, **25**, 299–329.

Heidbreder, E., and P. Overstreet. 1948. The attainment of concepts: V. Critical features and contexts. *J. Psychol.*, **26**, 45–69.

Hicks, J. A., and F. D. Stewart. 1930. The learning of abstract concepts of size. *Child Develpm.*, **1**, 195–203.

Hilgard, E. R. 1951. Methods and procedures in the study of learning. In Stevens, S. S. (Ed.), *Handbook of experimental psychology*. New York: Wiley. Pp. 517–567.

———, and A. A. Campbell. 1936. The course of acquisition and retention of conditioned eyelid responses in man. *J. exp. Psychol.*, **19**, 227–247.

Hilgard, E. R., and D. G. Marquis. 1940. *Conditioning and learning*. New York: Appleton-Century.

Holodnak, H. B. 1943. The effect of positive and negative guidance upon maze learning in children. *J. educ. Psychol.*, **34**, 341–354.

Holton, R. B. Variables affecting the change in instrumental response magnitude after reward cessation. Unpublished doctoral dissertation, State Univer. Iowa.

Hovland, C. I. 1937a. The generalization of conditioned responses: I. The sensory generalization of conditioned responses with varying frequencies of tone. *J. Gen. Psychol.*, **17**, 125–148.

———. 1937b. The generalization of conditioned responses: II. The sensory generalization of conditioned responses with varying intensities of tone. *J. genet. Psychol.*, **51**, 279–291.

———. 1937c. The generalization of conditioned responses. III. Extinction, spontaneous recovery, and disinhibition of conditioned and of generalized responses. *J. exp. Psychol.*, **21**, 47–62.

———. 1951. Human learning and retention. In S. S. Stevens (Ed.), *Handbook of experimental psychology*. New York: Wiley. Pp. 613–689.

Hull, C. L. 1920. Quantitative aspects of the evolution of concepts. *Psychol. Monog.*, No. 123.

———. 1943. *Principles of behavior.* New York: Appleton-Century-Crofts.

Hurlock, E. B., and E. D. Newmark. 1931. The memory span of preschool children. *J. genet. Psychol.*, **39**, 157–173.

Irwin, O. C. 1947. Infant speech: Consonantal sounds according to place of articulation. *J. Speech Dis.*, **12**, 397–401.

Ivanov-Smolensky, A. G. 1927. On the methods of examining the conditioned food reflexes in children and in mental disorders. *Brain*, 50, 138–141.

Jeffrey, W. E. 1958. Simultaneous and successive presentation of stimuli in discrimination learning with children. *Amer. Psychol.*, 13, 333.

Jersild, A. T. 1932. Training and growth in the development of children: A study of the relative influence of learning and maturation. *Child Develpm. Monogr.*, 10, 73.

Jones, H. E. 1930. The retention of conditioned emotional reactions in infancy. *J. genet. Psychol.*, 37, 485–498.

——. 1931. The conditioning of overt emotional responses. *J. educ. Psychol.*, 22, 127–130.

——. 1945. Trial and error learning with differential cues. *J. exp. Psychol.*, 35, 31–45.

——, and J. G. Yoshioka. 1938. Differential errors in children's learning on a stylus maze. *J. comp. Psychol.*, 25, 463–480.

Kantrow, R. W. 1937. An investigation of conditioned feeding responses and concomitant adaptive behavior in young infants. *Univer. Iowa Stud. Child Welf.*, 13, No. 3.

Kasatkin, N. I., and A. M. Levikova. 1935a. The formation of visual conditioned reflexes and their differentiation in infants. *J. genet. Psychol.*, 12, 416–435.

——. 1935b. On the development of early conditioned reflexes and differentiations of auditory stimuli in infants. *J. exp. Psychol.*, 18, 1–19.

Kirkwood, J. A. 1926. The learning process in young children: an experimental study in association. *Univer. Iowa Stud. Child Welf.*, 3, No. 6.

Krasnogorski, N. I. 1925. The conditioned reflex and children's neuroses. *Amer. J. Dis. Child.*, 30, 753–768.

Kuenne, M. R. 1946. Experimental investigation of the relation of language to transposition behavior in young children. *J. exp. Psychol.*, 36, 471–490.

Lahey, Sister M. F. L. 1937. Retroactive inhibition as a function of age, intelligence, and the duration of the interpolated activity. *J. exp. Educ.*, 6, 61–67.

Lambert, W. M., E. C. Lambert, and P. D. Watson. 1953. Acquisition and extinction of an instrumental response sequence to the token-reward situation. *J. exp. Psychol.*, 45, 321–326.

Langhorne, M. C. 1933. Age and sex differences in the acquisition of one type of skilled movement. *J. exp. Educ.*, 2, 101–108.

Lepley, W. M. 1934. Serial reactions considered as conditioned reactions. *Psychol. Monog.*, 46, No. 205.

Lewin, K. 1954. Behavior and development as a function of the total situation. In Carmichael, L. (Ed.), *Manual of child psychology*. New York: Wiley. Pp. 918–983.

Lewis, D., and A. H. Shephard. 1950. Devices for studying associative interference in psychomotor performance. I. The modified Mashburn apparatus. *J. Psychol.*, 29, 35–46.

Lipsitt, L. P., and A. Castaneda. 1958. Effects of delayed reward on choice behavior and response speeds in children. *J. comp. physiol. Psychol.*, 51, 65–67.

Logan, F. A. 1952. The role of delay of reinforcement in determining reaction potential. *J. exp. Psychol.*, 43, 393–399.

Long, L. 1940. Conceptual relationships in children. The concept of roundness. *J. genet. Psychol.*, 57, 289–315.

Longstreth, L. E. 1957. Classical conditioning of goal responses as a determinant of locomotion speeds in young children. Unpublished doctoral dissertation, State Univer. Iowa.

Lund, F. H. 1927. The role of practice in speed of association. *J. exp. Psychol.*, 10, 424–433.

Marquis, D. P. 1931. Can conditioned reflexes be established in the newborn infant? *J. genet. Psychol.*, 39, 479–492.

Mattson, M. L. 1933. The relation between the complexity of the habit to be acquired and the form of the learning curve in young children. *Genet. Psychol. Monogr.*, 13, 299–398.

McAllister, W. R. 1953. Eyelid conditioning as a function of the CS-US interval. *J. exp. Psychol.*, 45, 417–422.

McGeoch, J. A. 1928. The influence of sex and age upon the ability to report. *Amer. J. Psychol.*, 40, 458–466.

——, and A. L. Irion. 1952. *The psychology of human learning*. New York: Longmans-Green.

McGinnis, E. 1929. The acquisition and interference of motor-habits in young children. *Genet. Psychol. Monogr.*, 6, 209–311.

Mednick, S. A., and L. E. Lehtinen. 1957. Stimulus generalization as a function of age in children. *J. exp. Psychol.*, 53, 180–183.

Melcher, R. T. 1934. Children's motor learning with and without vision. *Child Develpm.*, 5, 315–350.

Metzger, R. 1958. A comparison between rote learning and concept formation. *J. exp. Psychol.*, 56, 226–231.

Moon, L. E., and H. F. Harlow. 1955. Analysis of oddity learning by rhesus monkeys. *J. comp. physiol. Psychol.*, 48, 188–194.

Morgan, J. J. B., and Morgan, S. S. 1944. Infant learning as a developmental index. *J. genet. Psychol.*, 65, 281–289.

Mowrer, O. H. 1947. On the dual nature of learning—a re-interpretation of "conditioning" and "problem-solving." *Harvard Educ. Rev.*, 17, 102–148.

Munn, N. L. 1954. Learning in children. In Carmichael, L. (Ed.), *Manual of child psychology.* New York: Wiley. Pp. 374–458.

Norcross, K. J. 1958. Effects on discrimination performance of similarity of previously acquired stimulus names. *J. exp. Psychol.*, 56, 305–309.

———, and C. C. Spiker. 1957. The effects of type of stimulus pretraining on discrimination performance in preschool children. *Child Develpm.*, 28, 79–84.

———. 1958. Effects of mediated associations on transfer in paired-associate learning. *J. exp. Psychol.*, 55, 129–134.

Pavlov, I. P. 1927. *Conditioned reflexes.* (Trans. by G. V. Anrep.) London: Oxford Univer. Press.

———. 1928. *Lectures on conditioned reflexes.* (Trans. by W. H. Gantt.) New York: International.

Perkins, M. J., H. P. Banks, and A. D. Calvin. 1954. The effect of delay on simultaneous and successive discrimination in children. *J. exp. Psychol.*, 48, 416–418.

Piaget, J. 1930. *The child's conception of physical causality.* New York: Harcourt, Brace.

Postman, L., and G. Murphy. 1943. The factor of attitude in associative memory. *J. exp. Psychol.*, 33, 228–238.

Razran, G. H. S. 1935. Conditioned responses: An experimental study and a theoretical analysis. *Arch. Psychol.*, No. 191.

Reese, H. 1958. Motor paired-associate learning as a function of level of stimulus pretraining and similarity of stimulus names. Unpublished doctoral dissertation, State Univer. Iowa.

Rheingold, H. L., and J. L. Gewirtz. 1957. The conditioning of vocalizations in infants using an adult's social response as reinforcer. *Amer. Psychol.*, 12, 392.

Roussel, J. 1952. Frustration effect as a function of repeated nonreinforcements and as a function of the consistency of reinforcement prior to the introduction of nonreinforcement. Unpublished master's thesis, Tulane Univer.

Schaeffer, M. S., and I. R. Gerjuoy. 1955. The effect of stimulus naming on the discrimination learning of kindergarten children. *Child Develpm.*, 26, 231–240.

Schlosberg, H. 1937. The relationship between success and the laws of conditioning. *Psychol. Rev.*, 44, 379–394.

Screven, C. G. 1954. The effects of interference on response strength. *J. comp. physiol. Psychol.*, 47, 140–144.

———, and T. E. Nunis. 1954. Response strength as a function of reduction in rate of subgoal reinforcement. *J. comp. physiol. Psychol.*, 47, 323–325.

Shepard, W. O. 1954. Effects of verbal pretraining on discrimination learning in preschool children. Unpublished doctoral dissertation, State Univer. Iowa.

———. 1956. The effect of verbal training on initial generalization tendencies. *Child Develpm.*, 27, 311–316.

———. 1957. Learning set in preschool children. *J. comp. physiol. Psychol.*, 50, 15–17.

Shepherd, A. H., and D. Lewis. 1950. Devices for studying associative interference in psychomotor performance. II. The modified two-hand coordinator. *J. Psychol.*, 29, 53–66.

Siegel, P. S., and J. G. Foshee. 1953. The law of primary reinforcement in children. *J. exp. Psychol.*, 45, 12–14.

Skeels, H. M. 1933. A study of some factors in form board accomplishments of preschool children. *Univer. Iowa Stud. Child Welf.*, 7, No. 2, 9–148.

Skinner, B. F. 1938. *The behavior of organisms.* New York: Appleton-Century-Crofts.

———. 1958. Teaching Machines. *Science*, 128, No. 3330, 969–977.

Smith, S. L., and A. E. Goss. 1955. The role of the acquired distinctiveness of cues in the acquisition of a motor skill in children. *J. genet. Psychol.*, 87, 11–24.

Spence, K. W. 1952. The nature of the response in discrimination learning. *Psychol. Rev.*, 59, 89–93.

———. 1953. Learning and performance in eyelid conditioning as a function of intensity of the UCS. *J. exp. Psychol.*, 45, 57–63.

———. 1956. *Behavior theory and conditioning.* New Haven: Yale Univer. Press.

Spiker, C. C. 1956a. The effects of number of reinforcements on the strength of a generalized instrumental response. *Child Develpm.*, 27, 37–44.

———. 1956b. The stimulus generalization gradient as a function of the intensity of stimulus lights. *Child Develpm.*, 27, 85–98.

———. 1960. Associative transfer in verbal paired-associate learning. *Child Develpm.*, 31, 73–87.

———, I. R. Gerjuoy, and W. O. Shepard. 1956. Children's concept of middle-sizedness and performance on the intermediate size problem. *J. comp. physiol. Psychol.*, 49, 416–419.

Spiker, C. C., and R. B. Holton. 1958. Associative transfer in motor paired-associate learning as a function of amount of first-task practice. *J. exp. Psychol.*, 56, 123–132.

Spiker, C. C., and S. H. White. 1959. The effect of work on the differential instrumental conditioning of preschool children. *Child Develpm.*, 28, 1–7.

Stevenson, H. W., and E. F. Zigler. 1958. Probability learning in children. *J. exp. Psychol.*, 56, 185–192.

Terrell, G., Jr., and W. A. Kennedy. 1957. Discrimination learning and transposition in children as a function of the nature of the reward. *J. exp. Psychol.*, 53, 257–260.

Thrum, M. E. 1935. The development of concepts of magnitude. *Child Develpm.*, 6, 120–140.

Vinacke, W. E. 1951. The investigation of concept formation. *Psychol. Bull.*, 48, 1–31.

Warren, A. B., and R. H. Brown. Conditioned operant response phenomena in children. *J. genet. Psychol.*, 28, 181–207.

Watson, J. B., and R. Rayner. 1920. Conditioned emotional reactions. *J. exp. Psychol.*, 3, 1–14.

Wechsler, D. 1944. *The measurement of adult intelligence.* (3rd ed.) Baltimore: Williams and Wilkins.

Weise, P., and M. E. Bitterman. 1951. Response selection in discrimination learning. *Psychol. Rev.*, 58, 185–195.

Weiss, G. 1954. Discrimination learning in preschool children under three levels of instruction. Unpublished master's thesis, State Univer. Iowa.

Welch, L. 1938. A preliminary study of the interaction of conflicting concepts of children between the ages of 3 and 5 years. *Psychol. Rev.*, 2, 439–459.

———. 1940. The genetic development of the associational structures of abstract thinking. *J. genet. Psychol.*, 56, 175–206.

———, and L. Long. 1940a. The higher structural phases of concept formation of children. *J. Psychol.*, 9, 59–95.

———. 1940b. A further investigation of the higher structural phases of concept formation. *J. Psychol.*, 10, 211–220.

Wenger, M. A. 1933. Path-selection behavior of young children in body-mazes. *J. exp. Educ.*, 2, 197–236.

———. 1936. An investigation of conditioned responses in human infants. *Univer. Iowa Stud. Child Welf.*, 12, No. 1, 7–90.

White, S. H. 1958. Generalization of an instrumental response with variation in two attributes of the CS. *J. exp. Psychol.*, 56, 339–343.

Wickens, D. D. 1938. The transference of conditioned excitation and conditioned inhibition from one muscle group to the antagonistic muscle group. *J. exp. Psychol.*, 22, 101–123.

———. 1939. A study of voluntary and intion during response generalization. *J. exp. Psychol.*, 25, 127–140.

Wickens, D. D. 1943. Studies of response generalization in conditioning. I. Stimulus generalization during response generalization. *J. exp. Psychol.*, 33, 221–227.

———, and C. Wickens. 1940. A study of conditioning in the neonate. *J. exp. Psychol.*, 26, 94–102.

Wieg, E. L. 1932. Bi-lateral transfer in the motor learning of young children and adults. *Child Develpm.*, 3, 247–268.

chapter 10

# The Study
# of Problem
# Solving
# and
# Thinking

Bärbel Inhelder
Benjamin Matalon
*University of Geneva*

The child's solution of cognitive problems depends on the one hand on the
nature of the particular problem and on
the other hand on his own intellectual
equipment. Whereas most psychological
studies of problem solving have been
concerned with the outcome of these
intellectual processes, others have studied the nature of the processes by which
the child attempts to adapt himself to
new situations. We have selected for review those methods designed for the
study of the processes rather than of
their results.

We are grateful to Miss Eleanor Duckworth
for the translation of this chapter and to Dr.
G. N. Seagrim and Dr. D. E. Berlyne for
their advisory assistance.

These processes can be studied fruitfully by comparing them with animal
behavior on the one hand and with
adult thought on the other. But although
the techniques used are closely related
to those used in animal studies, with an
increasing use of language as the phenomena under study approach adult
thought, they cannot be modeled too
closely on them. Techniques used in
studies of animals and adults have been
found to be fruitful to the extent that
they have been harmonized with the
characteristics of the infantile processes
themselves.

We must recognize that the methods applied to the study of problem
solving in the child cannot be reduced
to the study either of external behavior
(as in the case of animals) or of language taken alone (as is frequently the
case in the study of adult thought) but
must equally take note of intellectual
operations. These operations are considered to proceed from actions (the
behavioral aspect) but to be structured
later in systems that, though based on
language, involve coordinations more
general than the mere linguistic connections.

We have classed the methods into
three groups, according to the phenomena to be studied:

1. *The sensori-motor processes.* It is
in this domain that the methods derived from animal psychology have
been most employed. Whether they are
accompanied by verbal elements or
not, the role of language is reduced to
a minimum, and it plays only an accessory part here.

2. *Thinking proper.* The methods
used to study the particular characteristics of children's thinking—including

the discovery of a logical principle, the acquisition of an experimental method, and the interpretation of phenomena of the physical world—must be adapted to different levels of child thought if they are to avoid the dangers of adultomorphism.

3. *Concept formation*. Although it is artificial to separate the formation of concepts, which are the fundamental instruments of thought, from thought elaboration itself, it seemed to us preferable to devote a special section to it because of the importance of the problem and the specificity of the methods employed. These methods are closely bound up with the way in which different authors envisage the concept-formation processes, some attributing fundamental importance to the cultural verbal models, others to the structuring activity of the subject in the elaboration of the concepts.

Since we have been asked to write from our own experience as experimenters, the methods that are most familiar to us have necessarily received more than their share of emphasis in the discussion that follows.

### Sensori-motor Processes

#### LEARNING VERSUS INSIGHT

With infants, and sometimes even older children, problem solving and learning have rarely been formally distinguished, at least from the point of view of the experimental design. It is striking that in Carmichael's *Manual of Child Psychology* problem solving or puzzle solving is discussed only by Munn (1954) in the chapter devoted to learning. Munn justifies this by the following:

Every learning situation presents a problem of one sort or another. Escaping from maze, buttoning a coat . . . are problems when confronted initially (p. 423).

Similarly, every problem, even the most abstract, presents an aspect of "learning" from perceived data, trial and error, etc., which makes the distinction difficult from the outset. Still, one can say, by and large, that one speaks of a "problem" when the situation permits of a solution by logic or "insight," whereas one would more readily class as "learning" an experience in which the correct behavior can be attained only gradually by successive trials. However, terminology is likely to vary considerably from one author to another.

This apparent confusion between two things which seem at first sight very different, is justified by the difficulty of distinguishing them in practice; the distinction is often made after the conclusion of the experiments and concerns the behavior of the subject more than the problem. As we will see later, this is especially the case with all experiments bearing on insight.

Moreover, with very young children as with animals, one can only set the task and convey what is expected of the subjects through a process of training. Even with older subjects verbal elements are to be avoided, since they present a problem in interpretation, both for the subjects trying to understand the instructions and for the experimenter attempting to interpret their verbal responses. These experiments are thus conducted as if they were learning experiments, in which the subject is led to grasp the problem as a result of his first successes or failures. The study of sensori-motor or practical intelligence obviously forms an excellent field for such methods, for at this elementary level sensori-motor behavior, thinking, and learning are closely associated. A great part of the research on these problems originated in Köhler's work on the intelligence of apes. After his publication, several workers tried to find out whether the types of behavior he observed (i.e., success through trial and error or insight) are also found in children. Most of the problems presented to young children in this connection involve a detour or an intermediary (for the construction of tools that can be considered a kind of detour).

## USE OF AN INTERMEDIARY

One kind of problem frequently studied involves placing within the child's sight, but beyond his immediate reach, a lure consisting of a piece of candy, a toy, or some other attractive object. To obtain this reward, he must either draw the lure towards him, move towards it, or do away with the obstacle.

Alpert (1928) studied very nearly the same situations as Köhler. In one of his experiments, for example, the reward was suspended from the ceiling in such a way that it could be reached only by moving over a nearby block of wood, and climbing onto it.

Richardson (1932) placed a toy in the sight of the subject (28 to 52 weeks old) but too far away to be reached directly. In front of the child were several strings, only one of which was attached to the object. The arrangement of these strings varied from one situation to another: some of them ended near the toy without being attached to it; others went in different directions, and some of the correct strings made a detour just before reaching the toy. Like Alpert, Richardson noted the various attempts made by the child, any remarks he might make, and the time he took to reach the goal. He also took into account, as a criterion of insight, the facial expression and the suddenness of the response. No words were spoken; the experimenter merely attracted attention to the toy by showing or shaking it.

The lever is another intermediary and requires a movement in the opposite direction to the one that would be normal in order to bring the reward to the subject. This problem has been studied especially by Richardson (1934) and Moriya (1937).

Finally, there is the detour proper, with locomotion towards a goal. In McGraw's (1935) experiment the child had to step over a transparent partition in order to reach the object placed behind it. Lewin (1936) and Fajans (1933) simply used a barrier, which the subject had to walk around, so that for a moment he had to lose sight of the goal. Kendler and Kendler (1956) used a logical rather than motor intermediary to study what they call "inferential behavior." The child was placed in front of a box with two apertures out of which came two strings, $X$ and $A$. The experimenter had him pull one of these strings, $X$, and he was made to see that by so doing he pulled out a little object, $Y$. Then by pulling $A$, he obtained another little object $B$. Finally, he observed in the same way that by pulling the object $Y$ he could bring out of the box a little car, much more attractive than $B$ or $Y$. Each observation was repeated two or three times. In the test phase of the experiment all objects were put back into the box; the child was then asked to make the car come out again. The subject had to understand that he must first obtain $Y$ and therefore must pull $X$. Different groups of subjects made the three observations in all possible orders. Other control groups made some of the observations but not all.

Problems relating to practical intelligence in older children (3 to 7) have been studied by Rey (1935). One of the problems involving the use of a tool and a detour is the following. The apparatus consists of a crate, three sides of which are transparent. One of these sides has an opening in it. On the bottom of the crate in the center is a sort of drawer, which is open on one side; it can pivot on an axle and thus take various positions. The apparatus is placed on a table. A 5-centimeter cube is placed in the crate, in the center of the drawer; two sticks are available, and the subject is to use them to take the cube out of the crate. The experimenter explains that the cube contains a piece of candy. He simply indicates with his hand the sticks that are necessary to obtain it.

Bussmann (1946) examined problems of "transfer" from the same point of view. She presented to the child problems for which the necessary tool had to be constructed by combining certain elements provided by the experimenter. When the subject had succeeded, spontaneously or with hints, a similar problem was set him, but one in which the dimensions of the material made it necessary to combine greater numbers of elements. For example, a small token with a loop had to be taken out of a high narrow receptacle without turning the receptacle over. The child was given hooks, each of which was too short to reach the loop. The only solution was to fit the two hooks together. In the transfer situation the jar was deeper and five hooks were needed to reach the token. Finally, Bussman studied the generalization of the solution to a slightly different situation: this time, instead of hooks, small sticks had to be fitted together to form a long rod.

Most of these experiments and others following the same pattern were modeled exactly on animal psychology. The role of language was reduced to a minimum, and the method of analysis was the same, since the aim was to compare the behavior of children and animals. The experimenters tried to see if they could find in the child the behavior that was recorded in animal experiments, such as trial and error or insight. Hence the experimental settings were as similar as possible, with the important exception of the motivational factors.

It is clear that an animal must be hungry at the time of the experiment, if food is the reward, whereas a child can understand without an immediate need the few words of the experimenter, which explain what is to be done. The attractiveness of the reward maintains the interest but does not serve as a "release" as it does for the animal.

## TEMPORAL RELATIONS

Another kind of problem requires the subject to introduce temporal elements into his responses and thus a more complete internalization.

This is the case, for instance in the double-alternation problem, in which the subject has to give one of the possible responses twice in succession, then the other twice in succession, and so on. The problem demands a more thoroughgoing internalization, since the subject has to behave differently in the same situation, according to the temporal position of the trial.

Experiments on double alternation fall into two categories. First, the temporal maze consists of a chamber divided into two parts, each closed by a door that can be controlled silently by the experimenter. The right-hand door is opened for two consecutive trials, then the left-hand door twice in succession, and so on. This device, first used by Hunter (1913), has been widely used with animals, especially rats and monkeys.

Gellermann (1931) took up the same device with human beings, both children and adults. Each trial consisted of eight successive responses, separated by intervals of approximately fifteen seconds. In the discussion of the results, particularly in comparing animals and human beings, Gellermann emphasizes the fact that differences in experimental procedures for humans and animals are related to differences in motivation. Whereas the animals were strongly mo-tivated (by hunger or fear of electric shock), human subjects did not anticipate any reward and were merely stimulated, if necessary, by the experimenter's instruction to "keep going." Because of this fundamental difference in motivation, the number of trials per session was varied: with human beings, it was possible to continue training until the task was learned during the course of a single session; with animals, their motivation being short-lived, it was necessary to employ several short sessions.

The temporal maze takes up considerable space. Gellermann (1931), with monkeys, and Hunter and Bartlett (1948), with children, adopted a second, less cumbersome method. The subject is placed in front of two boxes. One of them contains a reward, namely, the right-hand one twice running and then the left-hand one twice running. These boxes are placed in front of a screen that hides the experimenter and his movements. First the experimenter lets the subject familiarize himself with the apparatus by manipulating it freely, opening the boxes, etc. He then tells him that he is going to put a piece of candy in one of the boxes. The subject opens one of them, and if the candy is not in it he looks in the other.

The authors, in conducting experiments of this kind, noted that it is important that the subject see as little as possible of the experimenter, since he will tend to be distracted by searching for irrelevant cues other than the successive positions of the reward.

Another means of studying temporal relations is by delayed responses. From among several alternatives, the right choice is indicated by a signal that disappears a certain time before the subject is allowed to react. As in the case of double alternation, the delayed response situation has been widely used in comparative psychology, since it can be applied with rats, monkeys, etc., as well as children. The principal variables studied have been the interval between the disappearance of the signal and the response, the number of possibilities, and the nature of the different possible cues that the subject has to discriminate.

In the first research of this type (Hunter, 1913) the subject had to choose one of three boxes, the correct one being indicated by a lamp, which was lighted a certain time before the subject had to make his choice. Later, the same author simply hid a toy in one of the boxes within view of the child. Miller (1934) considered the problem of the cues discriminated by the child, and he made use of the delayed reaction as a means of isolating certain factors, such as position and color. The experimenter put a toy in one of the boxes and hid them behind a screen, which he withdrew after a fixed time to allow the child to make his choice. The experiment started with a series of trials intended to explain the situation to the child and during which the toy remained in the box in which the experimenter had placed it. Then, in the crucial trials, the boxes were changed, and each one now contained a toy. The cue that determined the choice (color or position) was noted. It is clear that this method goes beyond the simple study of memory, which is all it may seem to involve at first glance, and that it constitutes an instrument of wider scope applicable to the study of the more general problem of discrimination.

## SENSORI-MOTOR INTELLIGENCE

Ever since the work of Preyer (1882) on the beginning of mental activity in the child, the psychology of early infancy has constantly been enriched by collections of observations. Three methods have been used:

1. The monograph, which contains information concerning the outstanding facts about one child.

2. The inventory or atlas, which records the presence of a behavior pattern at a given stage of the development in a sampling of children.

3. The longitudinal study, which observes the same child at regular intervals in characteristic situations whose symptomatic value has previously been shown by the first two methods, especially the second.

Although these methods have greatly contributed to our knowledge of the development of motor and emotional functions or of the over-all course of mental development, they give us little information about the formation of cognitive functions or, in particular, about the acts of intelligence involved in problem solving.

It is true that several scales of mental development include problem-solving items for the preverbal period. The "baby tests" of Bühler-Hetzer (1932/1935), among others, make use of tests such as K. Bühler's (1918) string problem. This test consists of placing a toy with a string outside the child's immediate reach but in such a way that the end of the string is accessible to him. It has been shown that at first infants do not know what to do with the string, whereas 75 per cent of babies 11 months or older are able to make use of it to obtain the toy. These methods give us information only about the presence or absence of problem-solving behavior, not about its formation. The important question that arises is this: did this behavior appear abruptly without antecedent, or did it develop progressively out of a more elementary pattern of behavior—grasping an object, for instance?

This "genetic" approach to problem solving is characteristic of Piaget's investigations and of his method, which we will call "developmental." In fact, Piaget has studied the question—whose bearing is as much epistemological as psychological—of the formation of one of the first invariants in the child's knowledge of the external world: the schema of the permanent object. In his two monographs (1936/1953, 1937/1955) devoted to the development of the first acts of intelligence in his three children he made use of a mixture of observation and experiment, a sort of functional exploration in which experiments are suggested by previous observations.

For instance, Piaget was intrigued by a curious observation: a 13-month-old child was playing with a ball, which first rolled under an armchair where he could easily find it, then under a couch where he could not reach it. After a short unsuccessful search under the couch, the child went back to look for his ball under the armchair. This observation led Piaget to create experimental situations in which he could observe systematically the behavior of children towards objects disappearing from the visual field or moving about within it:

1. An object of interest (in this case a watch) is taken away from the child while he is handling it and is placed within his sight, a slight distance away.

2. The object is hidden under a pillow.

3. It is hidden under pillow A, to the left of the child, then brought out again within his sight and hidden under pillow B, to his right.

4. The same procedure as in 3, but with the difference that when it is moved from A to B the object is wrapped in a cloth so that the displacement is visible but not the object itself.

Between 6 and 18 months, the three children who were observed succeeded in solving progressively, in order of increasing complexity, all the items of the experiment, although they had failed them all at first. Their behavior toward the missing object changed completely. Although they were already capable of coordinating the movements of their eyes and hands to grasp objects, nevertheless they made no effort at first to find an object when it disappeared from their visual field, and behaved as if it were no longer available. A few months later, they were able to locate an object whose position had been changed in any of the ways described above.

This experiment was followed by one involving the rotation of an object: at feeding time, the experimenter turned the baby's bottle 180 degrees and presented it the wrong way round. If the child did not spontaneously try to turn the bottle around, or show other signs of recognition, the bottle was presented in such a way that the nipple was still visible. The infants who at first refused the bottle the wrong way round, or who even tried to suck at the opposite end, were able a few weeks later to turn it around, in whatever position it was presented. In addition, the experiment with the watch was repeated with the bottle, with the same results.

It is evident that in these experiments certain rules must be observed: the object must be familiar and sufficiently interesting to the child. The experiments should not be done too frequently in order to keep the child interested in the relatively novel situation and to elicit in him genuine discoveries. The different types of behavior are recorded by means of protocols, which note movements, gestures, facial expressions, cries, and phonemes of the child and which take into account the functional context of the experimental situation.

The originality of Piaget's "developmental" method consists not so much in observational and experimental procedures but, on the one hand, in the search for affiliations (developmental transitions) between different levels of behavior; and, on the other hand, in the demonstration of a whole network of related behaviors, which can be regarded as the elementary structures of sensori-motor intelligence.

These affiliations seem to be ensured by so-called schemata, which, for Piaget, constitute the unities of behavior. A schema is a mode of action elaborated by the subject, a mode of action capable of conservation, of transformation by generalization, and of coordination with other schemata. The functional aspects of these schemata appear as "patterns of behavior." From this perspective, it is possible to note a continuous series of schemata, from the grasping reflex to the recognition of permanent objects and their changes of position in space. This series, continuous from the point of view of functional activity (which does not necessarily imply continuity in the underlying neuromuscular maturation), culminates in a profound transformation of behavior. Whereas at the beginning of cognitive development objects have no meaning except in the functioning of the infant's own subjective activity (e.g., being touched, fed, or looked at), they progressively acquire an objective and independent meaning and form the first invariants of his physical and spatial world—that is, permanent objects that continue to exist even when they are not seen, and can be recognized no matter what their position.

The observations concerning this particular genetic affiliation, based on such a limited number of cases, would certainly be lacking in substance if they did not fit into a whole network of cognitive behavior described by Piaget. Thus, for example, he has been able to show that the schema of the permanent object is bound up with behavior related to its displacements (changes of position in space). Being able to order the positions of objects in space will later allow the child to order his own displacements in space; for instance, to make detours or to return to a starting point. Completing this progressive coordination of schemata of activity, the child will be able to achieve a certain reversibility in his own displacements, as well as in those of objects, canceling a movement in one direction with one in the opposite direction. This reversibility of sensori-motor and mental activity, which Piaget sees as the essential characteristic of intelligence, seems to be the culmination of a true process of development whose final structure is somewhat isomorphic with Poincaré's "mathematical group of displacements." It has likewise been found in investigations of the formation of the first intellectual instruments, namely intermediaries and tools.

Like all monographs, these are limited by their non-normative character. But they are, nevertheless, an ensemble of original facts, which have enabled Piaget to show that the invariants of logical thought are based on such sensori-motor invariants.

## CONCLUSIONS

The field of sensori-motor intelligence is above all one of comparative psychology. Indeed, nearly all the problems we have discussed can be set both for children and for animals. Moreover, it should be noted that the principal notions that play a part in the analysis of behavior in this kind of situation were first introduced for the description of animal behavior.

Trial and error and insight were concepts of animal psychology, and much of the research during the years 1925–1935 was aimed solely at verifying their value for human and especially for child psychology.

Quite apart from the fact that in children and in animals similar types of laws of organization are assumed, the comparison is made even more necessary by the similarity of experimental requirements.

In both cases language is excluded and a part of the experiment must be devoted to the "communication" of the task. This part usually resembles learning experiments, since the subject, child or animal, has to learn by trial and error to give a certain response. Only then is it possible to go on to the critical part of the experiment, the "test" phase, i.e., the part which involves the variables that are being studied.

In contrast to these fundamental similarities in experiments on children and on animals, an important motivational difference should be noted: it is easy enough to induce a child, even a very young one, to persist in his directed efforts, whereas in animals the activity tends to cease with the satisfaction of the induced need. It is almost always possible to wave an object in front of a child and to make him try to reach it, and it is also possible to repeat the experiment several times in succession. This is evidently difficult with animals, and a fair number of studies aimed at comparing species have had to use differing techniques because of these limitations, for instance, in the temporal interval between trials. The same problems arise in the next section.

### Thought Processes

The distinction we have chosen to make between the elementary sensori-motor processes and the higher processes involved in "thinking" is, of course, difficult to maintain in all cases, especially since many of the authors to whom we have referred do not observe it. In certain cases the distinction cannot but be arbitrary. For example, among the studies of sensori-motor processes we mentioned experiments on double-alternation, keeping in mind the fact that research workers who made use of this technique were primarily interested in relations of elementary temporal order. Recently, Matalon (1959) made a further study of the double-alternation problem by modifying the usual method of presentation in order to reveal the activity of higher thought processes. The main modification was in the method by which subjects were informed of the correctness or incorrectness of their responses at each trial. One group of 8-year-old children only saw whether the side chosen was correct or incorrect. For the second group, when they made an incorrect choice they saw the reward on the opposite side. In addition, the trials were given in a continuous sequence until the subject gave 12 successive correct responses and not, as was the case in Gellermann's study (1931), in isolated blocks of trials.

The group which, after an incorrect choice, had to infer what the correct choice would have been took many more trials to find the principle, thus showing that even in such a simple problem inferential activity seems to play a role.

The processes involved are probably similar to those necessary for the discovery of more complex principles, which we shall now consider.

## THE DISCOVERY OF A PRINCIPLE

The general scheme is the following: for each trial of the experiment the subject must choose between two, or sometimes several, elements shown to him. During his successive trials, he is able, by noting his successes and failures, to discover the rule that would enable him to succeed on every trial.

Heidbreder (1927, 1928) presented her subjects with two boxes, in one of which was a doll. The experiment consisted of three parts, each one involving a different principle. In the first the doll was always in the box on the right, whether near or far. In the second the correct box bore the picture of a flower, whereas the other one bore only a simple figure. The third principle was more complicated: some of the boxes had labels with red dots, others did not. If the boxes had dots on them, the nearer one was correct. The instruction was simply to find the doll; there was thus no mention of a principle that might lead to a solution. In order to obtain information on the mechanisms brought into action, the experimenter asked the reason for each choice; after a wrong choice, the subject was allowed to open the other box to verify that the doll was there. Once again, as in the sensorimotor problems, it is evident that the behavior in such an experiment can be regarded as a learning process. Moreover, the technique is similar to the one used in the study of discrimination learning in animals.

In this experiment, the principle to be discovered was quite arbitrary. But other experiments deal with empirical or logical laws. A method similar to Heidbreder's has been used by Wohlwill (1959) in a study of the role of perceptual factors in the formation of number. The subject was placed before a screen with three windows, which he could open and on which the experimenter could hang cards bearing a certain number (4, 5, 6) of points, regularly arranged. It was explained to the subject that a token was hidden behind one of these windows and that on each trial he would be given a card indicating which window it was behind. Each sample card bore a number of dots, corresponding to the number of dots on one of the windows but arranged differently. The token was behind the window bearing the same number of dots as the card given to the subject. In another part of the test the sample card was replaced by small buttons. They were at first arranged in the same way as the dots on one of the windows; then the experimenter disordered them and removed or added one within sight of the child. The correct window was indicated by the final number of buttons. The subject's task was to find the token, that is, to open the window that bore the number of dots equal to that on the model.

Petersen's experiment with a scale balance (1932) is one example of a situation in which the principle to be discovered is an empirical law. After indicating to the subject that all the problems he was going to set him involved the same general principle, the experimenter presented one of them, gave the solution, and showed experimentally that it was correct. Then he set another which the subject had to solve by himself and continued to alternate in this way a problem whose solution was given by the experimenter with one that the subject had to solve. At the conclusion of the experiment, the subject was asked to state the principle. A correlation was computed between the number of correct responses given by a subject and his IQ.

The same problem of balancing a pair of scales was studied in a quite different way by Inhelder and Piaget (1955/1958). The child was placed in front of a scale balance and a series of weights which he could manipulate freely. He was asked to balance the scales while the experimenter interviewed him to find out how he went about it and noted how his trials proceeded. The experimenter did not intervene actively, except to motivate the subject or to suggest a new situation when the subject had achieved equilibrium in one situation without seeking to go any further. In analyzing the results, the emphasis was placed above all on the method of seeking the law, the systematic nature of the trials, and the technique of proof rather than on the results actually obtained in each single case.

## VERBAL PROBLEMS

With this last example, we come to a type of research that tries to grasp the subject's thought through his verbal behavior; in the preceding examples verbal intervention was avoided as much as possible on the part of the experimenter as well as on the part of the subject.

The more developed the processes under study, the more difficult it is not to call upon spoken language. In fact, it is difficult to grasp logical reasoning in any other way, since formalized logic is more a matter of discourse than one of action.

Wertheimer (1945) made an important contribution without using a real experimental method. He departs from simple observation only insofar as it is necessary for the posing of the problem (such as the celebrated one of calculating the area of a parallelogram) and then, without intervening, observes the successive attempts at its solution.

Apart from these few studies, little work has been done in the field of logical thinking in the child, and what has been done has not involved strict experimental methods. On the other hand, there is abundant data on the behavior of children of different ages confronted with tests of logical ability. Good examples of such tests are to be found in Burt (1919–1920). It goes beyond the limits of this chapter to study these numerous school tests. Although they are useful for diagnosis, they furnish little information about the mechanisms that are brought into play or about the methods used in the solutions.

This very problem already had occupied the school of Graz, Duncker, and Claparède (1934). They tried to deal with it by asking the subject to report verbally on his attempts and reflections. Apart from the theoretical criticisms to which this technique gives rise (lack of

objectivity and accuracy in the reports, the introspective aspect, etc.), it is obviously next to impossible to apply it to children. John and Miller (1957) tried to fulfill the requirements of objectivity by using an electronic apparatus that records the subject's different attempts. Even though they used it only with adults and the problems set were too complicated for children, it would seem possible to extend its application without difficulty to the logic of the child. We shall return later to a discussion of the way in which the authors analyzed the data they gathered with this method.

## THOUGHT CONTENTS OF THE CHILD

The long-standing interest in the beliefs and explanations of children had received renewed impetus from the field of anthropology in the study of the so-called primitive mentality of certain societies, characterized by collective animism, realism, and magic. In addition, the exploration of the unconscious in civilized adults had revealed a system of projective mechanisms, which foster, among other things, a belief in causality through participation. The question then arose whether such beliefs and explanations, which are also found in children, were due to social and emotional factors alone or whether cognitive factors were involved as well, the conceptions in this case being the authentic expression of a general, though transitory, stage in human thinking.

This was the state of the problem when Piaget (1926/1929, 1927/1930) undertook to study systematically the development of the different ways in which children represent and explain, in situations not involving conflict, a number of everyday phenomena.

His investigations dealt with the workings of simple machines, such as the bicycle, as well as with more complex notions derived from physical and psychological experience, such as the origins of names and their relation to the objects they name, the movements of stars and clouds, and the attribution of consciousness and life to living beings or to objects. It is of much less importance to know what significance the child attributes to one specific event than to know the common characteristics of his conceptions of the world. The psychological study of the development of children's beliefs has an epistemological bearing; it sheds light on the relations between the subject and the object. Thus the exploration of the successive types of explanation offered by children brought out new data to support the hypothesis that the traditional distinction between the two poles of knowledge—the subject with his thoughts, desires, and intentions and the object obeying physical laws—far from being primitive, is, on the contrary, the result of a long process of development, based on experimentation and socialization. In elementary forms of thought the two appear undifferentiated, thus giving rise to confusions comparable to the adualism of the ego and the nonego postulated by Baldwin.

This research, which was carried out quite some time ago, inspired a number of similar studies and raised a series of criticisms regarding the method and the validity of its results. Perhaps it is worthwhile to specify the characteristics of the "clinical" method used by Piaget in exploring the beliefs of children. However, let us point out that the procedures used in his more recent (and more analytical) studies bear a closer resemblance to experimental methods.

It is important to keep in mind the aims of the method: (*a*) to establish an inventory of children's beliefs and explanations; (*b*) to evaluate their authenticity; (*c*) to distinguish the trends followed by changes in children's conceptions of the world in the course of their development.

The plan for each of the investigations originated in spontaneous remarks of children. In the case of the relation between a name and its object, for instance, the point of departure was a conversation between two 6.6-year-olds as they were playing at building, a conversation that seemed to reveal a tendency toward nominal realism.

X:  And when there weren't any names...
Y:  If there weren't any names you'd be in trouble. You couldn't make anything. How would you make things (if there weren't any names)?

Certain authors, for example, Isaacs (1930), have confined themselves to pure observation. Certainly, this method has the advantage that the reflections remain in their natural context, and it avoids the risk of influencing them unnaturally by questions that do not always correspond to the thoughts with which the child is concerned at the moment. However, pure observation does not enable us to form an exhaustive picture of all the possible ways of solving a particular problem. Children do not generally express their beliefs because they think that everyone believes as they do, because they are afraid of making mistakes or, finally, because the ideas are not sufficiently systematized to be formulated.

The clinical approach seeks not only to record beliefs that are already formulated but also to make explicit those that direct the child's reasoning more or less implicitly. It provokes reflection with a set of questions that complete and supplement one another. The interrogation on nominal realism, for instance, is built around the following questions:

1. What is a name?
2. How did names start?
3. How did we know the sun's name?
4. Where is the sun's name?
5. Do things know their names?
6. Did the sun always have its name, or was it there without a name at first and got its name afterward?
7. Why do we call the sun "the sun"?
8. Your name is X and your friend's name is Y. Could we have called the sun "moon" and the moon "sun"?

Several experimenters took up Piaget's research into the mentality of the child, particularly in reference to animism and magic, but using a set of standard questions based on Piaget's, and without permitting themselves to follow up the answers in an exploratory fashion. This procedure makes it easier for the results to be scaled and for several judges to evaluate them; it also neutralizes the individual differences be-

tween interviewers. However, although it introduced important controls in areas that had already been explored, this technique proved to be inadequate for exploring new ground with as many unknowns as the domain of children's beliefs. In the rigid application of a pre-established schema, we run the risk of imposing on the child an orientation that is not his own. Moreover, without a knowledge of their context, the raw results are often unintelligible, and there is no way of estimating the amount of confabulation, a frequent factor at that age.

Piaget, aware of the disadvantages of pure observation on the one hand and standardized tests on the other, adopted an intermediate method inspired by the one used by psychiatrists. It consists in conducting a free conversation with the child, and directing it toward the nonexplicit regions of his thought. By exploring the context of each of the child's reflections, and asking control questions, the interviewer tries to verify their authenticity. If a child believes that the names of things are part of the things themselves and that, for example, it is sufficient to stare hard at the moon in order to find its name, one can only ask how is it that a child speaking another language would use another word. The art of the "clinical" or, better, "critical" method consists in letting the child talk and at the same time checking the working hypotheses during the discussion itself and not only afterward. Clearly, the successful use of this delicate method requires both aptitude on the part of the diagnostician and a long period of training.

In Piaget's exploratory researches the

results are evaluated qualitatively: first, they are classified according to the type of belief they reveal. Here, for example, are a few typical categories of replies that show the progressive elimination of nominal realism:

1. Names have always been a part of things; things know their names.

2. Names have always been a part of things; things do not know their names.

3. Names were given to things by men; it is sufficient to look at things to know their names. It is not possible to change the names of things.

4. It is not sufficient to look at things to know their names; one invents or learns names. One can change them if everyone agrees, for example, when one goes to another country.

Then these ideas are ordered as they gradually appear and disappear with age. Finding this order constant for each of the beliefs studied, Piaget was able to establish "stages" in the conception of the world and of causality. The term "stage" has often aroused dispute, since it suggests the erroneous idea of discontinuity in development. In actual fact the transitions between the successive types of conceptions of the world are gradual and continuous and reveal a trend in thought from nondifferentiation to differentiation of subject and object. (Names that are first located in things and are part of their essence are gradually understood to be of human invention and arbitrarily attached.)

Of the many attempts at standardization, we may mention the ones that Russell and Dennis (1939) devoted to animism. The technique of interrogation with alternative questions mentions 20 standard objects. Three independent judges, classifying the results, were in agreement 87 per cent of the time, and the test-retest correlation was 0.81. The authors were also concerned with sampling, a factor neglected in Piaget's original work, which centered on general developmental mechanisms rather than on diversifying environmental factors. Russell (1940a) was able to show the generality of primitive forms of animism and their gradual decline, regardless of sex and place of residence (urban, suburban, or rural). Russell, Dennis, and Ash (1940b) found the same beliefs in feeble-minded children, and these results were confirmed by Werner and Carrison (1944) in their study on brain-injured children; Dennis and Mallinger (1949) found a greater percentage of these "infantile" beliefs in a group of senile adults, as compared with other adults and older children. Carrying out this research on Zuñi and Hopi children (Dennis, 1943) they obtained results similar to those obtained in Switzerland. Their work, which thus confirms and extends the original investigations, nevertheless puts us on guard against hasty generalization about the age limits of the stages. The ages seem the more likely to fluctuate the more the tests involve verbal-thought content because it is here rather than in the reasoning structures themselves that the forms of adult thought are reflected. Moreover, the latter, far from being a homogeneous whole, always contains traces of the thought of the child.

Interesting studies such as those of

Huang and Lee (1943, 1945) on Chinese children and of Mead (1932) on the young Manus indicate, on the other hand, a low degree of animism. Since, however, their investigatory procedures differed from those of the other writers, it is somewhat difficult to decide how much of the difference is due to the method and how much to cultural influence. We can see how valuable it would be to pursue comparative research into the structures as well as the content of children's thought by using methods that are comparable but adjusted to different cultural contexts.

## CONCLUSIONS

Under the rather vague term of "thinking," we have grouped a series of studies with two goals: the first is to determine the mechanisms of the child's thinking, the intellectual instruments he possesses, insofar as they can be distinguished (at least in analysis) from an immediate action, in contrast to sensori-motor processes. Such a study might be limited to observing the differences of behavior or efficiency in children of different ages faced with a given task; or it might center on the developmental process itself, in an attempt to understand how the higher levels of behavior are constructed from the lower ones, by studying their filiation. These two approaches assume different theoretical backgrounds and, of course, different experimental methods. If the difference between the thought of two children of different ages is considered solely as quantitative and of the same nature as the difference between two subjects of the same age, the experimenter will devote his interest

above all to performances; the test will have to be strictly standardized and presented as far as possible in the same way at all ages. On the other hand, if the center of interest lies in the evolution of thinking and the differences between successive stages of development, the method must be more supple, capable of distinguishing qualitative changes from one stage to the next.

The second goal would be a study of the contents of the child's thinking: his beliefs, his interpretations of what he observes. One important variable to be taken into consideration is his socio-cultural environment and particularly the current beliefs. The manner in which the child assimilates these beliefs to his own cognitive structures could then be the object of a specific study.

## Concept Formation

The study of concept formation and of the acquisition of word meanings embraces a vast field that can be analyzed from two points of view. On the one hand, the development of concepts is closely tied from the start both to the acquisition of the symbolic function (which consists in relating significants to signified and which appears equally in play, in drawing, etc.) and to the development of the child's judgments. On the other hand, since concept formation is a product of both social and intellectual factors, we must study the respective roles of language (which is acquired by social transmission) and of the elaboration of mental operations (which are derived from sensori-motor actions).

## THE STUDY OF WORD MEANING

To study the significance that the young child attributes to the first words of his vocabulary, the method of integral observation is recommended. It consists in recording the spontaneous vocabulary in its natural context and relating it to the child's activities as a whole.

Thanks to the systematic findings of C. and W. Stern (1927) and to the judicious observations of Bühler (1918) and Piaget (1945/1951), we have reliable data on the (developmental) filiation characterizing the formation of concepts. The first verbal expressions such as "Mama" are still closely tied to desires and actions and cannot be understood independently of them. The naming function, which generally appears during the second year, is contemporaneous with the beginnings of symbolic activity. In fact, it is precisely when the child attributes various symbolic significances, first to his own gestures and then to any object whatever, that one can observe his increasing interest in the names of things. However, these first names are not yet concepts in the sense of logical classes. They are preconcepts, whose significance is rather elastic, like the symbols that children use in imaginative play. The onomatopoeia "wow-wow," for instance, can refer sometimes to one dog in particular or sometimes to any number of different objects. What is missing in these preconcepts is the comprehension of the genus-species relationship and the differentiation of the logical quantifiers "one," "some," "all." One child of 2.6 years, out for a walk, came across two different snails, and each time her comment was "There is *the* snail." Even when she went back to see the first, she could not decide if they were two members of the class snail or the same member. In another case the reaction of a 3.6-year-old shows an astonished interest in the significance of the "all" concept. She had just been told that all birds lay eggs, and for every bird she saw she asked, "That one too? That one too?" A child of 6.7 years, sorting different species of mushrooms, asked, "Is 'mushrooms' the name of all of them?", thus showing the beginnings of an understanding of genus-species relationships.

Questions like "Bob is a boy; are boys people?" appear about the same time. One 5-year-old established spontaneously the distinction between the concepts "all" and "some" in the following remark, "I'm not going to give you all my flowers, just some of them"; but the distinction is full of difficulties when it is presented in connection with a system of class-inclusion, as the following test shows (Inhelder and Piaget, 1959): The child is asked: "A boy gave me all his roses. I gave the bunch back to him and then I asked him, 'Give me some of your flowers.' He gave me the same bunch again. Was that right?" The solution of the problem assumes the understanding that all of $a$ form some of $b$ if $a$ is included in $b$.

These few examples show that even if it is true that only spontaneous remarks can reveal the appearance and the significance of concepts, which change according to the context, nonetheless a systematic interrogation is necessary each time we want to determine when and how the concepts become stabilized as veritable instruments of logical thought.

After having noted the place of observation in the study of spontaneous vocabulary, let us refer once again to methods designed to analyze the child's understanding of adult language. There are two procedures capable of shedding light on this understanding, which becomes more and more adequate as the child grows older. One involves definition of words, and the other involves inference from cues given by the verbal context of the sentence.

The definition tests introduced by Binet (1903, 1908) in his mental development scales are presented in the following way: "You have seen a chair; tell me what a chair is." They have revealed that young children tend to define by use ("it is for . . .") before they can construct conceptual definitions. Since conceptual definitions are often formally taught, it is sometimes very difficult to dissociate the part played by schooling from the need the children themselves feel to define in terms of concepts. By means of a more clinical analysis, Piaget (1924/1926, 1951) was able to reveal some typical difficulties encountered by young children, not only in the matter of definition, but also in understanding concepts expressing reciprocal relations such as "brother" or "foreigner." The intellectual egocentrism of young children, sometimes reinforced by emotional factors, creates an obstacle to the comprehension that they can themselves be brothers or foreigners from the point of view of other people.

Werner and Kaplan (1950) conceived and judiciously analyzed a test for children of 8.6 to 13.6 years, a test whose goal is to study experimentally the processes underlying the acquisition of word meaning through verbal contexts. An artificial word, "soldeve," whose meaning is to be guessed ("wither" or "fade"), is used in six different sentences.

1. The dinner was good, but the fruit was soldeve.
2. When we were driving in the evening, we did not feel safe because things on the road seemed to soldeve.
3. The older you get, the sooner you will begin to soldeve.
4. People like a blossoming plant better than one that is soldeve.
5. Putting the dress on the sunny lawn made the color of the cloth soldeve.
6. Because the windshield was frozen, things looked soldeve.

The whole experiment is composed of 12 series of sentences, and the meanings of the words range from concrete to abstract. The authors warn against an interpretation of the levels of conceptualization as static; they are, on the contrary, dynamic and fluctuating. A level of abstract conceptualization is attained only insofar as the underlying intellectual processes themselves have acquired a stability that resists the natural tendency to regress toward levels of concrete symbolization whenever the task becomes more difficult.

Remarks of the same order could be made about the much-discussed tests of syllogisms (Burt, 1919–1920, 1923) and absurd sentences (Binet and Simon, 1908). The following is an example from Burt:

Where the climate is hot, aloes and rubber will grow; heather and grass will grow only where it is cold. Heather and rubber require plenty of moisture; grass and aloes will grow only in fairly dry regions. Near the river Amazon it is very hot and very damp. Which of the above grows there?

These tests, although destined to examine the capacity of children and adolescents to reason from hypotheses, are used in their classical form, without sufficient analysis, and they run the risk of measuring not so much the level of conceptualization as the degree of familiarity that a child has with a certain kind of new problem.

Word associations have almost never been used as a means of investigating the mechanisms of children's thinking, except for a few studies done some time ago by authors who accepted without question the pure associationist theory.

Certain authors undertook an empirical study of children's associations with the idea of creating an instrument of intellectual diagnosis.

Kent and Rosanoff's (1910) important statistical document served as the point of departure for a series of researches into variations in the frequency of certain types of association or of certain responses (for given stimuli) in children and for comparisons of these frequency distributions between children and adults (Woodrow and Lowell, 1916).

However, for the study of the development of thinking, the value of these findings is very limited. The classifications on which they are based are always the reflection of an implicit hypothesis as to the role that associations

play in thinking, unless they are derived from external distinctions such as grammatical word categories; moreover, the statistics concerning variations in frequency (common or original responses) are strongly influenced by the choice of stimuli.

One of the very first experimental studies of word associations in children is perhaps the most interesting from the point of view of the theory of thinking. Ziehen (1899/1900) limited his study to the notions brought into play by word associations, particularly the ones evoked by the stimuli; he distinguishes two types of notion: (a) those that reflect individual, concrete contents and (b) those that reflect judgments. He observed that there is a clear predominance of the first type in children, whereas the second appears only toward adulthood. The author considers that all the peculiarities of children's associations are due to their responses in terms of individual contents.

In a recent study Morf (1954) tries to relate adult associations to reactions found in very young children (4 to 5 years old), the latter being characterized by the fact that their explicit, and virtually their only, function is the interpretation of the stimulus. In the first place, he shows that the meanings attributed to the stimulus, and involved in the association itself, develop according to the developmental level toward a progressive conceptualization, and the numerous adult associations, which are to all appearances "associations of ideas" in the classical sense, are in reality concealed interpretative reactions. In the second place, he analyzes the nature of the associative connections, relating them to the level of interpretation of the stimuli, and concludes that, in general, these connections are experimental artifacts and not the product of pre-existing associations, as claimed by the experimenters of the associationist school and by those who used associations, such as Jung (1915), in psychoanalytic investigation.

We have seen the diversity of methods, based on an analysis of the child's language, that are applied to the study of concept formation. But if these methods throw light on one particular aspect of concept formation, one must nevertheless recognize that concept formation goes beyond the progressive acquisition of the mother tongue or of the correct use of an already formed language. The formation of concepts involves in addition the relating of names to things and, more particularly, a logical activity that appears in the guise of the process of classification.

## LANGUAGE IN ASSOCIATION WITH CONCRETE CONTENTS

One group of experimental studies on concept formation has its basis in the method, made famous by Hull (1920), of associating verbal stimuli with concrete situations. From the behaviorist point of view, a concept can be defined as the common response to a class of phenomena whose members have certain common characteristics. Although there are many differences of opinion as to the nature of a "common characteristic" (for Hull they are identical elements, for Smoke (1932), dynamic wholes), and, although these differences of opinion are reflected in the choice of experimental material, the methods

recognize, nevertheless, one and the same principle: that concepts are based on objective resemblances. Thus the technique involves varying the objective data so that the resemblance between the various elements becomes less and less marked.

In contrast to research in the field of classification (which we shall consider later), where the child discovers by himself the various possible conceptual criteria, in this case he learns ready-made concepts by association. Names, which, in adult speech, are attributed to specific objects or classes of objects, are replaced by nonsense syllables. Each experiment starts with the learning of associative relations, either one-one or many-one, between verbal signs and objects or pictures presented to the child. Heidbreder (1949) contributed a great deal to the development of such tests of concept formation in the adult, but Welch and Long (1940a,b) are mainly responsible for having studied this learning mechanism in children of different ages. For illustration, we shall single out their studies on what they term vertical and horizontal generalizations in a conceptual system.

One experiment, dealing with a vertical hierarchy of concepts, is composed of four main items, and variations of them:

1. Prelearning, associating nonsense syllables with blocks of different forms.
2. A first-degree hierarchy: the child learns to designate two different triangles by MEF and TOV and their union by VIC; similarly, two rectangles by YOP and ZIL and their union by DAX.
3. A second-degree hierarchy: he learns to designate the union of triangles and rectangles by XIP.

4. By means of instructions like, "Put TOV on DAX," or, "Take back the VIC's," it is possible to test in this way how successfully a hierarchy is learned.

One hundred and three subjects, 42 to 83 months old (3.6 to 7 years), were thus examined. It was found that it is easier to learn to identify the objects than to learn first-degree hierarchies. Instructions referring to the second-degree hierarchy seem to present the greatest difficulties.

A second experiment deals with horizontal generalizations, in which a given object may have different names as it is encountered in different situations. Two stimuli, a cube and a cylinder, are presented in three different contexts: in a bowling alley situation they become missiles, in a drum situation, the tips of drumsticks, and in a scale situation, weights.

The objects and the contexts are once again associated with nonsense syllables, and the child can manipulate the object each time the corresponding verbal signal is pronounced.

With 54 children, 67 to 89 months old, it was found that "learning a different name for the same object in three different situations (a horizontal generalization) is confusing but not as difficult as learning the position of an object in a second hierarchic structure (a vertical relation)."

Such a method is highly interesting if we make the assumption that for a child the objects around it have always been recognized as separate, stable entities. But evidently the method loses some of its significance when we consider that the formation of concepts depends on active operations, i.e., on a structuring on the part of the subject leading to the construction of objects in the outer world, and not only on the properties of objects already given.

The approach of the Soviet school, which attributes a fundamental importance to language as a second signal system, is comparable to this method and, at the same time, different from it. It is comparable in that concepts are assumed to be acquired by conditioned-reflex mechanisms and different in that they study the demands of socialization, which give birth to language, and the influence of language on the progress of thought itself. A typical example is provided by Luria and Yudovich (1956/1959), Luria being known for his work in the field of aphasia. They studied a pair of identical twins whose language development was still considerably retarded at 5 years of age, a phenomenon frequently observed among twins. This language retardation was accompanied by more general difficulties in processes of abstraction, in play situations, in carrying out precise instructions, and above all in classifying. Once separated, the twins felt the need to communicate with others in a more elaborate language, and a genuine linguistic learning took place, which was accompanied by improvement in their cognitive activity.

These methods are capable of revealing the role of certain activities of the subject, in this particular case the linguistic activity in the acquisition of concepts. But it is probable that logical operations have a more fundamental basis than in language, in that they are based on the coordinations of actions. This hypothesis gives rise to two sorts of methods: one group, influenced by the Gestalt theory, seeks to reveal the general types of structuring that are common to perception, action in general, and classification in particular; the other looks for the source of classifications in reversible[1] operations, qualitatively distinct from perceptual structures.

## THE MECHANISMS OF CLASSIFICATION

No concept is formed in isolation; each one is bound up with a whole system of classificatory operations. It is possible to distinguish two points of departure in research devoted to the study of elementary classificatory behavior. One starts from the diagnosis of neuropsychiatric syndromes in adults and then brings its findings to bear on the special difficulties that children have in conceptualizing; the other is oriented toward the study of the formation of logical classes and attempts to analyze the mechanisms of conceptualization in their development.

Typical of the first approach are the sorting tests originated by Goldstein and Scheerer (1941), with the collaboration of Gelb and Weigl, for the diagnosis of symptoms of mental deterioration caused by cerebral injury. In these tests, which inspired a number of investigations on children's thought at the preconceptual level, two types of material are used: on one hand, everyday objects, both of natural size and in miniature and, on the other, geometrical material comprising tri-

[1] Reversible refers to the possibility of canceling one thought operation by its inverse (or negative) operation

angles, squares, and circles in four different colors. There are essentially three aspects to the investigation. The first deals with the formation of a class; the experimenter, designating a single object, asks, "Which of all the remaining objects belong with it?" The second is concerned with discovering the criterion that determined a class that already exists, "Why do all these belong together?" The third deals with the possibility of shifting from one criterion to another.

It is important to note the different forms of classificatory behavior and their characteristics, for example, rigidity or flexibility, narrowness or overgeneralization, concreteness or abstractness. Reichard, Schneider, and Rapaport (1944), applying such sorting tests to children, found that they remained attached to the concrete and functional aspects of the concepts. Classification, they found, precedes the discovery of the principle or definition of the class, but this active classification never becomes so elaborate as the definition, which has a more conventional character.

It is well known how Goldstein's ideas inspired Wallon's (1945) notion of a "precategorial" level in the thought of a child. In this connection, one of his collaborators (Ascoli, 1950) undertook research on children's classification, asking children to classify geometrical shapes according to two or three criteria, which they had to discover. Oleron (1951) and Vincent (1957), too, took up a special aspect of the problem, that of the relations between classification and language in deaf-mutes. Finally, the problem has been studied by means of a technique particularly well adapted for young children. Slama-Cazacu (1957) has developed a "cupboard game" in which the child can find a hidden toy only if he opens a compartment marked by pictures of different species of one genus (for example, a dog, a horse, a cat, a giraffe, for the genus "animal"). The author observes that in preschool children the notions of genus are unstable as far as their denotation and content are concerned, but she also notes a process of generalization, based on abstraction.

Typical of the second approach are the investigations of Vigotsky (1931) who, by using a classification test devised by Ach, showed that the evolution of concept formation in children follows differentiated stages, beginning with pseudoconceptual and so-called complexual forms. (Instead of grouping objects according to criteria defining a class, children merely put them together in a complex heap.) Hanfmann and Kasanin (1937) started from these genetic studies when they developed their tests for adults, which make it possible, in Rapaport's (1946) phrase, "to diagnose the encroachment of maladjustment upon conscious thinking."

The particular problem taken up by Inhelder and Piaget (1959) was that of understanding why the organization of classificatory behavior takes the forms it does and why these successive forms tend toward logical structures. The following three methods have been combined in this study, but any one by itself is not sufficient: (1) spontaneous classifications of natural and geometrical objects; (2) the shifting from one criterion to another and the anticipation of visual classifications (for instance, the child is asked what would be the minimum number of envelopes needed to class geometrical figures, differing in form, size, and color, and presented to him in a random order); (3) the formation of the operational mechanisms themselves. Techniques were designed to bear on the problem of how the structure of inclusion is formed. This structure is certainly not present from the beginning, either hereditarily or as a Gestalt, and its development is much too laborious to permit of an explanation simply in terms of verbal learning.

One experiment already carried out (Piaget and Szeminska, 1941/1952), and standardized later but yet to be published, revealed the difficulty experienced by children of less than 6.6 years of age in understanding that there are more elements in the whole class $B$ than in the sub-class $A$ included in it (if $B = A + A'$). In this technique the child is presented with an open box containing a dozen beads, which he can easily see are made of wood. Most of the beads (ten) are brown, and two are white. He is asked, "Are there more wooden beads or more brown beads in this box? Could we make a longer necklace with all the wooden beads or with all the brown beads?" (He is made to understand that after making the necklace of wooden beads he can take it apart again to make the one of the brown beads.) Finally he is asked, "If I take all the wooden beads out of the box, will there be any beads left? If I take out all the brown beads, will there be any beads left?" Because of the immobility of his thought, the child younger than 6 years of age cannot conceive of the same beads as forming part of two collections.

He answers that there are more brown than wooden beads, "because there are only two wooden ones." Once the brown ones are included in one class, he cannot at the same time include them in a second class. He can compare subclass $A$ (the brown beads) only to subclass $A'$ (the white beads) and not to the total class $B$ (all the beads).

It was discovered that the problem of inclusion, even when it was solved with material consisting of a collection of countable objects, continued to offer difficulties when applied to a hierarchy of concepts such as the system of classes of animals. Without entering into the details of the technique, let us remark that it involved organizing pictures of familiar animals into a hierarchy of three classes and that the concept of the hierarchy was concretized by means of transparent boxes that could fit one inside the other. In this particular case, the correct solution consisted in putting the ducks into the smallest box, $A$; the class of birds, composed of $A$ and its complement $A'$ (birds that are not ducks) into the second box, $B$; and the animals, $A + B + B'$ ($B'$ being animals that are not birds) into the largest box, $C$. Once this hierarchy is concretely established by the child, he is asked questions of the same kind as those regarding the beads. Here, as in all the research on classification, it was seen that the logical mechanisms do not operate as completely developed structures, which are applied to any content, but that they are gradually developed in relation to the different contents to be conceptualized. The divergence among authors as to the age at which the first conceptual systems appear would seem, then, to be partly the result of observations that too often have been sporadic or of experimentation limited to a single context.

Another question deserving of analysis in the field of genetic psychology and necessitating specialized methods is that of the relations between perceptual configurations and operational mechanisms, and their variations with age. This question arose with some urgency in connection with the matrix tests adapted for children (Raven, 1938), in which the subject is to find among several pictures the one that fulfills two or three criteria at once. These criteria have to be abstracted from other pictures arranged in matrix form. The test is supposed to reveal the mechanism of logical multiplication, but the spatial arrangement of the elements can facilitate certain of the solutions to such a degree that it is difficult to distinguish the respective parts played by perceptual and operational mechanisms. In order to distinguish them, we must analyze the procedures used by children of different ages by systematically varying the factors involved. Not only the number of criteria but also the number of possible choices must be varied. [It was found that with perceptual configurations certain three-criterion matrices are more easily solved by very young children than by older ones, but only as long as there are very few choices (Inhelder and Piaget, 1959).]

In addition, we must do more than record the first choice; we must also offer other possibilities, since the degree of certainty or uncertainty is revealing. Finally, we must try to get the child to give the reasons for his choices, since the agreement or lack of agreement between actions and motivations is another significant index of his level of conceptualization. This method (used by Inhelder and Piaget, 1959), which is subtler than the usual test procedure, yet standardized and compatible with a statistical evaluation of the results, reveals, in fact, a progressive decline of configurational factors in favor of operational factors.

## GENETIC ANALYSIS
## OF INTELLECTUAL OPERATIONS

Among the concepts that are formed during childhood, those that serve as a point of departure for scientific thought deserve special interest on the part of psychologists. Piaget and his colleagues have studied the formation of the notions of number, space, speed-time, and probabilistic causality from an original point of view. Having first analyzed the operations that are fundamental to these concepts once they are acquired, they asked whether the concepts resulted only from socially transmitted learning or whether the individual had some active contribution to make in their formation. The following experiments were designed essentially to examine this intervention of the child's activity.

We can follow step by step this development in the child, from its origin in his sensori-motor activities, through the period when it is enriched by mental representations, and finally to its accomplishment in a genuine system of operations.

We can outline here only a few of the techniques used:

1. The principle of numerical invariance (Piaget and Szeminska, 1941/1952). This technique was designed to study the manner in which children from 4 to 6 come to establish two equivalent collections of objects and to discover that this equivalence is preserved no matter how the elements may be arranged. In one form of the technique the children were first asked to take from a small basket as many eggs as there were eggcups in a row before them. The experimenter noted, in particular, the way in which the children established the correspondence between the two collections. (The youngest children, not yet having discovered one-to-one correspondence, tended to construct two rows of equal length, regardless of the number of objects.) Once the one-to-one correspondence was established, the experimenter increased the spacing of one of the rows. Then, to find out if the child still accepted the equivalence of the collections, he put a series of questions in the following vein: "Are there the same number of eggs as eggcups?" "Are there more or less eggs than eggcups?" "Can we put each egg in an eggcup without there being any empty eggcups or any eggs left over?" In all the experiments of this kind they took care that neither the intonation of the voice nor the order of the questions was suggestive. The analysis of the children's

behavior and replies revealed that under the conditions described here, and in this particular cultural environment, numerical conservation is absent in most 4-year-olds and that it is acquired gradually between the ages of 4 and 6, until most 6-year-olds assert it with a feeling of logical evidence. This process of acquisition, which can, of course, be accelerated by training, corresponds to a general progress toward an "operational" quality in the thought of the child. The qualitative analysis of the reasoning seems to show that little by little the transformations imposed on collections of objects come to be conceived operationally; that is, each transformation can be mentally canceled by its inverse. This can be formulated by the child in the following way: "I only have to put the eggs back opposite the egg cups and I know there is always the same number."

2. The principle of conservation of quantity. The formation of invariant concepts has been followed systematically in different domains of the child's thought. Once attained, each of the concepts is based on a nucleus of operations comparable to mathematical group structures (but more limited than they are), which Piaget has named a semigroup or "grouping" of concrete thought.

To study the physical invariants of matter, weight, and volume, as the ideas develop between the ages of 4 and 11, one method involved two balls of plasticene, identical in shape, size, and weight. (Piaget and Inhelder, 1941.) One of the balls was stretched into the shape of a sausage, broken into little bits, etc., and

questions of the following sort were asked:

Is there the same amount of plasticene in the sausage as in the ball?

Is there more in one than in the other?

How do you know that there is always the same amount? How do you know that there is more? (Or how do you know there is less?)

Will the ball and the sausage weigh the same on the scale?

A similar experiment concerns the conservation of the weight of sugar when it is dissolved in water.

3. Spontaneous measurement (Piaget, Inhelder, and Szeminska, 1948). Of a number of experiments in the realm of spatial concepts, we shall single out the one dealing with spontaneous measurement. How do 4-year-olds discover on their own the conditions necessary for measurement, such as the use of a common measure involving transitivity, the constancy of the measuring instrument when its position is changed, and the construction or breaking down of the instruments into units. The authors started with a situation familiar to the child: building a tower with wooden blocks. They asked the child to build the tower just as high as a model tower, made of a single piece of wood and standing on a table at a different height from the one on which the child was to build. Every measurement involves a transportation of the measuring instrument, and in this experiment it was possible to classify the different types which tend to follow one another as the child develops. The earliest are direct visual or manual comparisons of height from the floor. They do not

make use of a common measure. Next come various attempts to use part of the body or a gesture as the common measure, neglecting the conservation of the "transported" dimensions or distances. Finally, the child discovers the need for a common measure with stable dimensions. At first, this has to be the same size as the model; but it is replaced by measures that are first bigger, then smaller, and finally by repeatable units of any size. After this general experiment, a series of more specific studies was designed, with a view to examining one by one the conditions necessary for measurement in Euclidean space, and the application of measure to areas and volumes.

4. Speed (Piaget, 1946). The study of the complex of speed-time-space concepts has shown that the notion of "passing," as a change in order, is both fundamental and relatively primitive. However, its development follows certain stages, which one can discern with the help of the following material: (a) two cars on two straight, parallel tracks, moving for equal periods of time at different speeds; (b) two cars, again moving for equal periods of time at different speeds but on two circular, concentric tracks. Although the starts and finishes are simultaneous, the distances traveled are unequal. The phenomena included in the experiment are passing, catching up, gaining ground, and crossing. Each of the children is asked to say, after witnessing the phenomena, if the two cars moved at the same speed. The factors that the children take into account in comparing the speeds vary with their ages. Between the ages of 5 and 9, the following reactions are observed: first, they take account only of the passing of one car by another, then only of relative positions at the finish; gradually, they take account of the starting points, as well, and finally of the set of rectilinear and circular paths traversed. At the end of this development, they discover the elementary operations of the concept of speed and the establishment of correspondences between displacements of objects in a given time.

5. Chance and probability (Piaget and Inhelder, 1951). The formation of these concepts has been studied with the help of a number of games of chance of the roulette or progressive mixing type. The accidental character of chance as an interference between independent causal series is discovered by the child only through a system of logical or mathematical operations. For example, in the case of the progressive mixture of balls, the child first comes to understand the fortuitous character of the mixture as the interference of independent movements. Later, after he has dissociated in this way the certain from the possible, he is gradually able to quantify the latter and to make probability judgments. In terms of our example, he is now able to refer to a theoretical system of permutations to conceive of the quantitative aspect of the progressive mixing.

In contrast with the studies of Piaget and Inhelder, which are limited to the concept of objective probabilities in children 5 to 14 years of age, Cohen and Hansel (1955) have explored the realm of subjective probability and its use in predictions with preadolescents and adolescents; for instance, for the study of the prediction of a binary event on the basis of previous outcomes they utilized a display board with 16 pairs of lights. One light of each of the first ten pairs was successively illuminated, nine on one side and one on the other. The position of the single lights varied (in random order) from position 1 to position 10 in different trials. After seeing the lights, one to ten, illuminated in rapid succession, the subject had to guess on which side the eleventh light would appear.

## THE EXPLORATIVE APPROACH TO THE STUDY OF INTELLECTUAL OPERATIONS

The essential characteristics of the methods adopted by Piaget and his colleagues seem to be the following:

The experiments are designed to study one specific but fundamental aspect of the formation of the concepts, viz., the construction of the underlying intellectual operations. They enable us to establish the total inventory of operations that are active in children's thinking as well as the obstacles that hinder their formation. The different experimental situations reveal their real significance only when their results are compared, since they offer a system of mutual cross-checks and points of comparison.

In all the experiments the children are confronted with changes in the physical world. In contrast to the techniques inspired by the associationists or Gestalt psychologists, who studied reactions to isolated elements or to configurations, the so-called "operational" techniques present the children with processes of transformation and study the way in which they are progressively interpreted in terms of actual mental operations.

The approach is essentially developmental. For each particular problem situation, they study the changes that come with age in children's reasoning and active behavior. In this way, they attempt to distinguish the stages of intellectual elaboration and its implicit hierarchy in order to grasp the formative processes underlying this elaboration.

The method aims at an analysis of the different qualitative forms of this intellectual elaboration. It attempts to list them and to evaluate their internal consistency. It is somewhat analogous to the experimental method used in studies of problem solving in that it uses apparatus and to the interview method in that it involves discussion with the subject. This aspect, the discussion, plays an important role in that it enables the experimenter to grasp the type of reasoning that underlies the child's conduct.

Among the objections made to this kind of investigation, let us mention the two main ones, one referring to the flexible nature of the questioning procedure and the other to the lack of a statistical analysis of the results. For the sake of comparative studies, research is now being carried out in Geneva that will lead to a standardization of procedure and a statistical evaluation of the frequencies of different types of solution. But let us insist upon the fact that the flexible, exploratory investigation is the only way of revealing all the frequently unsuspected peculiarities of concept formation in the child. The standardization, which necessarily involves a certain schematization, is fruitful only after the whole range of possible qualitative solutions has been established. One further difficulty involved in this method is the amount of training required of the experimenter: he must not only record but also provoke the problem-solving behavior; at the same time he must neither project his own interpretive scheme to the child nor lose sight of the information he is seeking.

## Use of Theoretical Models

### LOGICAL MODELS

When the presentation of problems is essentially verbal, it is generally tempting to analyze the different stages of the solution in terms of formal logic and to describe the observed behavior in terms of logical operations. This has the advantage of reducing the qualitatively different performances found at different stages to a common language, thus enabling one to identify the operations of which children are capable at various ages.

Logical errors have been studied frequently enough in the adult. The numerous studies on the syllogism, particularly on "atmosphere effects," emotional factors, etc., are well known (Woodworth and Snell, 1935). In each of these cases the assumption is that the subject (a normal adult) possesses the necessary logical instruments, and the

aim of the research is to study the factors that prevent these instruments from functioning and which thus result in false reasoning.

In the child the logical analysis of behavior can take on a more profound significance: here we are actually trying to find out what logical tools a given subject possesses. The disturbing emotional variables, interesting as they are in the case of adults, must then be reduced as far as possible so that the child can give his maximum.

This is the kind of analysis that Piaget has undertaken. On the one hand he has tried to establish a formalized model of natural thought and its development (1949) and on the other to study this development concretely, using the logical model to describe it. [Inhelder and Piaget (1955/1958).] Their subjects (aged 5 to 16) are presented with apparatuses that exemplify simple physical laws (for instance, the equilibrium of a scale balance, the inclined plane, nonelastic reflection, and communicating jars), which they must discover by experimenting freely with the material. The level of organization of the experimentation, the conclusions that the subject draws from each new item of information, and the generalizations made are analyzed in terms of the classical logic of propositions. In their latest work (1959) in which they analyze classification and seriation they make use of the logic of classes and relations for their description. The essential point of interest is that in both these cases the logical analysis treats the actions and not only the verbal behavior of the subject.

Apart from the work of Piaget and

his school, no other attempts seem to have been made to examine the thought of the child from the point of view of mathematical logic.

Nevertheless, we may ask which type of logic can accomplish this study most satisfactorily. Piaget uses classical logic, with the qualification that his classes are serially inclusive, since this is the type of classification that seems to him especially adapted to natural thought. But perhaps it would be possible to take a weaker model, such as intuitionist logic, which rejects the principle of the excluded middle. Certain relationships that are erratic from the point of view of classical logic can be described in this form, and it would be interesting to see if thought could be considered consistent in terms of this weaker framework.

Instead of using a logical model to describe behavior and to compare it to a norm, several authors have constructed problems in which different logical constants come into play. With subjects 7 to 12 years of age, Morf (1956) presented verbal problems that require disjunction, conjunction, implication, etc. This approach was also suggested in a project by Moore and Anderson (1954), although they had in mind its application to adult thought only. In similar fashion, John and Miller (1957) constructed their problems on the basis of Boolean algebra. The application of this type of problem to children seems to present certain difficulties, since most of them necessitate hypothetico-deductive reasoning, too difficult for children before 11-13. This is no doubt why applications to children are almost nonexistent.

## STATISTICAL MODELS

Unlike logical models, statistical models are not well suited to describing the processes involved during the solution of a problem.

It is for this reason that statistical analysis of problem solving has been limited for so long to the study of performances, quantified more or less arbitrarily with a view to comparing different distributions (in different conditions or at different ages) or to calculating the correlations of these performances with other variables.

Peterson (1932), for example, in the research already mentioned on the comprehension of the equilibrium of a scale balance, correlates the performance of each subject with his intelligence quotient.

This is the technique used in work based on a factorial conception of intelligence. Quite aside from the fact that this procedure provides no information whatever about the process that led the subject to his solution, we must note a serious insufficiency: the difficulty of finding criteria of quantification. Since each subject must receive a "score" for his performance, it is first necessary to find a scale of measurement on the basis of which a specific "score" can be attributed to each distinguishable type of behavior. In particular, we must avoid the situation in which the same score is attributed to two subjects simply because they have made the same number of mistakes, although the items on which the mistakes were made may be entirely different. This approach may be perfectly justified in applied psychology, in which an external validation is sufficient, but it is of little value in a study of the thought mechanisms involved.

One fruitful approach to these problems, which partially escapes these criticisms, consists of the application in the realm of thought, particularly from the developmental point of view, of the techniques used by social psychologists in the study of attitudes (see Stouffer et al. 1950). A series of items on an opinion questionnaire is said to be scalable if a positive reply to item ($n$) implies that a positive reply was given to item ($n-1$) and thus to the ($n-1$) previous items. That is possible if the questionnaire has been constructed so that the questions imply one another and if the subject is consistent. Although these conditions are difficult to obtain for attitudes, they are probably fundamental in cognitive development. In fact, it is probably not too strong a hypothesis to suppose that certain conducts that appear in the course of development are scalable in this sense.

We would thus have a series of problems of increasing complexity, such that any subject who solved the $n$th problem would also have solved the $n-1$th problem. Specifically, we could apply this technique in describing the development of integrated stages, that is, of a series of stages, each of which integrates the achievements of the preceding ones.

It is naturally difficult to find problems that are strictly scalable, since other factors, notably the content, can prevent a subject from solving a problem that is in reality easier than others he had solved. We are more likely to be able to find "semiscales." Vinh Bang (1959) and Nassefat (1960), among others, have undertaken to describe cognitive development in this way. Starting from Piaget's investigations employing the "clinical" method, they standardized the procedure by substituting for free-interrogation a series of predetermined questions and problems. The subjects were still required, however, to justify the reply they gave. The replies given were classified according to the degree of correctness of the answer and the justifications given by the subject. They verified as stringently as possible the hypotheses that (1) the responses to a given problem showed a progressive and constant change with age, and, (2) that a group of these problems formed a Guttman-scale.

Of course, this successive integration is not the only aspect of intellectual development. It is also possible simply to order the various reactions of subjects of different ages to a given problem in terms of a criterion such as "correctness" without introducing "integration."

At the present time it would appear that only a longitudinal study could reveal whether a succession found in this way is constant or if the order can vary from one individual to another. Nonetheless, it is to a certain extent possible to verify it by finding the correlation between ages and the hierarchy of conducts arranged according to a given criterion (a logical criterion above all). Nassefat does just that in the work mentioned above. He arranges the observed responses according to the number of elements that the subjects take into account and then establishes the significance of the correlation between this order and age. Theoretically, it would be possible to avoid such an a priori order simply by taking the one that is best correlated with age development. Unfortunately, this procedure requires endless calculations, and it scarcely seems possible without improved computers.

## Conclusions

A first factor brought to light in the preceding analysis is the considerable diversity of methods for each of the points that we have examined. This diversity might be disquieting if the psychological problems were reducible to one single type. But the problems themselves remain extremely varied, in view of the fundamental fact that the psychology of thinking seems to be just at the junction of biology (behavior), sociology (language, education), and logic and mathematics (since the thought of the child is itself the source of logicomathematical structures). This variety of problems explains, and at the same time justifies, the variety of methods used.

Thus our second conclusion is that one method is no better or worse than another: their values are essentially relative to the particular problem to be solved. This assertion is perhaps not so trite as it seems. It sometimes happens that a method is chosen and used without sufficient awareness of the problems. The first condition of an adequate method is a sufficiently thorough pre-liminary analysis of the problem that one is called upon to solve.

## REFERENCES

Alpert, A. 1928. The solving of the problem-situation by preschool children. *Teach. Coll. Cent. Educ.*, **22**, 11–69.

Ascoli, G. 1950. Comment l'enfant sait classer les objets. *Enfance*, **3**, 411–433.

Binet, A. 1903. *L'Étude expérimentale de l'intelligence*. Paris: Schleicher Frères.

———, and Th. Simon. 1908. La Mesure du développement de l'intelligence chez les enfants. *Année psychol.*, **14**, 1–94.

Bühler, Ch. and H. Hetzer. 1932. *Kleinkindertest*. Leipzig: Barth. Trans., 1935. *Testing children's development from birth to school*. New York: Rinehart.

Bühler, K. 1918. *Die geistige Entwicklung des Kindes*. Iena: G. Fischer.

Burt, C. 1919-1920. The development of reasoning in school children. *J. exp. Pedag.*, **5**, 68–77, 121–129.

———. 1923. *Handbook of tests for use in schools*. London: Staples.

Bussmann, E. 1946. *Le Transfert dans l'intelligence pratique chez l'enfant*. Neuchâtel, Paris: Delachaux et Niestlé.

Claparède, E. 1934. La Genèse de l'hypothèse *Arch. Psychol.*, **24**, 1–154.

Cohen, J., and C. Hansel. 1955. The idea of distribution, *Brit. J. Psychol.*, **46**, 111–121.

———. 1955. The idea of independence. *Brit. J. Psychol.*, **46**, 178–190.

Dennis, W. 1943. Animism and related tendencies in Hopi children, *J. abnorm. soc. Psychol.*, **38**, 21–36.

———, and B. Mallinger, 1949. Animism and related tendencies in senescence *J. Geront.*, **4**, 218–221.

Dennis, W., and R. W. Russel. 1940. Piaget's questions applied to Zùni children, *Child Develpm.*, **11**, 181–187.

Fajans, L. 1933. Die Bedeutung der Entfernung für die Stärke eines Aufforderungscharakters beim Säugling und Kleinkind, *Psychol. Forsch.*, **17**, 215–267.

Gellermann, L. 1931. The double alternation problem, II, *J. genet. Psychol.*, **39**, 197–226.

Goldstein, K., and M. Scheerer. 1941. Abstract and concrete behavior and experimental study with special tests," *Psychol. Monogr.*, 53, 151 pp.

Hanfmann, E., and J. Kasanin. 1937. A method for the study of concept formation," *J. Psychol.*, 3, 521–540.

Heidbreder, E. F. 1927. Reasons used in solving problems. *J. exp. Psychol.*, 10, 397–414.

———. 1928. Problem-solving in children and adults, *J. genet. Psychol.*, 35, 522–545.

———. 1949. The attainment of concepts (VII): Conceptional achievements during card sorting. *J. Psychol.*, 27, 3–39.

Hull, C. L. 1920. Quantitative aspects of the evolution of concepts. *Psychol. Monogr.*, 28, No. 123.

Huang, I., and H. W. Lee. 1943. Experimental analysis of child animism, *J. genet. Psychol.*, 63, 71–121.

———. 1945. Experimental analysis of child animism, *J. genet. Psychol.*, 66, 69–74.

Hunter, W. H. 1913. Delayed reactions in animals and children," *Behav. Monogr.*, 2, No. 6.

———, and S. C. Bartlett. 1948. Double alternation behavior in young children. *J. exp. Psychol.*, 38, 588.

Inhelder, Bärbel, and J. Piaget. 1955. *De la Logique de l'enfant à la logique de l'adolescent.* Paris: P.U.F. Trans. 1958. *The growth of logical thinking.* New York: Basic Books.

———. 1959. *La Genèse des structures logiques élémentaires.* Neuchâtel, Paris: Delachaux et Niestlé.

Issacs, S. 1930. *The intellectual growth in young children.* London: Routledge and Kegan Paul.

John, E. R., and G. A. Miller. 1957. The acquisition and application of information in the problem-solving process. *Behav. Sci.*, 2, 291–299.

Jung, C. G. 1915. *Diagnostische Assoziationsstudien. Beiträge zur experimentellen Psychopathologie.* Leipzig: Barth. Vol. I.

Kendler, M. M., and J. S. Kendler. 1956. Inferential behavior in preschool children, *J. exp. Psychol.*, 57, 311–314.

Kent, G. M., and A. S. Rosanoff. 1910. A study of associations in insanity. *Amer. J. Insan.*, 1910, 67, 37–96, 317–390.

Lewin, K. 1936. *Principles of topological psychology.* New York: McGraw-Hill.

Luria, A. R. 1947. *Traumatic aphasia.* Moscow. (See also in B. Simon (Ed.), 1956. *Psychology in the Soviet Union.* London.

———, and F. Yudovich. 1956. Trans. 1959. *Speech and the development of mental processes in the child.* London: Staples.

McGraw, M. B. 1935. *Growth: The study of Johnny and Jimmy.* New York: Appleton-Century.

Matalon, B. 1959. Apprentissages en situations aléatoires et systématiques," *Étud. d'épistém. génét.*, X. Paris: P.U.F.

Mead, M. 1932. An investigation of the thought of primitive children with special reference to animism. *J. R. anthrop. Inst.*, 62, 173–190.

Miller, N. E. 1934. The perception of children, *J. genet. Psychol.*, 44, 321–339.

Moore, O. K., and S. B. Anderson. 1954. Modern logic and tasks for experiments and problem-solving behavior. *J. Psychol.*, 38, 151–160.

Morf, A. 1954. Les Associations de mots chez l'enfant. Études génétiques et fonctionnelles. Unpublished dissertation. Geneva.

———. 1956. Les Relations entre la logique et le langage lors du passage du raisonnement concret au raisonnement formel, *Étud. d'épistém. génét.*, III, Paris: P.U.F.

Moriya, M. 1937. An observation of problem-solving behavior in preschool children, *J. exp. Psychol.* (Japan), 4, 63–81, 147–160.

Munn, N. L. Learning in children. 1954. In L. Carmichael (Ed.), *Manual of Child Psychology.* (2nd ed.) New York: Wiley. Pp. 374–458.

Nassefat, M. 1960. Comparaison entre les opérations concrètes et formelles. Unpublished dissertation, Univer. Geneva.

Oléron, P. 1951. Pensée conceptuelle et langage. *Année psychol.*, 51, 89–120.

Peterson, G. M. 1932. An empirical study of the ability to generalize, *J. gen. Psychol.*, 6, 90–114.

Piaget, J. 1924. *Le Jugement et le raisonnement chez l'enfant.* Neuchâtel, Paris: Delachaux et Niestlé. Trans. 1926. *Judgment and reasoning in the child.* New York: Harcourt, Brace.

———. 1926. *La Représentation du monde*

chez l'enfant. Paris: Alcan. Trans., 1929. *The conception of the world.* New York: Harcourt, Brace.

Piaget, J. 1927. *La Causalité physique chez l'enfant.* Paris: Alcan. Trans., 1930. *The child's conception of physical causality,* New York: Harcourt, Brace.

———. 1936. *La Naissance de l'intelligence chez l'enfant.* Neuchâtel, Paris: Delachaux et Niestlé. Trans., 1952 and 1953. *The origin of intelligence in children.* New York: International Univer. Press.

———. 1937. *La Construction du réel chez l'enfant.* Neuchâtel, Paris: Delachaux et Niestlé. Trans., 1954. *The construction of reality in the child.* New York: Basic Books.

———. 1945. *La Formation du symbole chez l'enfant.* Neuchâtel, Paris: Delachaux et Niestlé. Trans., 1951. *Play, dream and imitation in childhood.* New York: Norton.

———. 1946. *Les Notions de mouvement et de vitesse chez l'enfant.* Paris: P.U.F.

———. 1949. Traité de logique. Paris: A. Collin.

———, and B. Inhelder. 1941. *Le Développement des quantités chez l'enfant.* Neuchâtel, Paris: Delachaux et Niestlé.

———. 1951. *La Genèse de l'idée de hasard chez l'enfant.* Paris: P.U.F.

———, and A. Szeminska. 1948. *La Géométrie spontanée chez l'enfant.* Paris: P.U.F. Trans., 1959. London: Routledge and Kegan Paul.

Piaget, J. and A. Szeminska. 1941. *La Genèse du nombre chez l'enfant.* Neuchâtel, Paris: Delachaux et Niestlé. Trans., 1952. *The child's conception of number.* London: Routledge and Kegan Paul.

Piaget, J., and A. M. Weil. 1951. Le Développement chez l'enfant de l'idée de patrie et des relations avec l'étranger, *Bull. intern. Sciences soc.* Unesco, 3, 605–622.

Preyer, W. 1882. *Die Seele des Kindes.* Leipzig. Trans., 1888–1889. *The mind of the child.* New York: Appleton.

Rapaport, D. 1946. *Diagnostic psychological Testing.* Chicago: The Year Book Publishers (5th ed.), p. 389.

Raven, I. C. 1938. *Progressive matrices.* London: Lewis.

Reichard, S., M. Schneider, and D. Rapaport.

1944. The development of concept formation in children. *Amer. J. Orthopsychiat.,* 14, 156–162.

Rey, A. 1935. L'Intelligence pratique chez l'enfant. Paris: Alcan.

Richardson, H. M. 1932. The growth of adaptive behavior in infants. *Genet. Psychol. Monogr.,* 12, 230.

———. 1934. The adaptive behavior of infants in the utilization of the lever as a tool. *J. genet. Psychol.,* 44, 352–377.

———, and W. Dennis. 1939. Studies of animism I.A. Standardised procedure for the investigation of animism. *J. genet. Psychol.,* 55, 389–400.

Russell, R. W. 1940a. Studies in Animism II. *J. genet. Psychol.,* 56, 353–366, 57, 83–91.

———, and F. E. Asp, 1940b. Studies in Animism III. Animism in feeble-minded subjects. *J. genet. Psychol.,* 57, 57–63.

Slama-Cazaccu, T. 1957. Relatii dintre giudire si limbaj in ontogeneza. (Les Rapports entre la pensée et le langage dans l'ontogenèse) *Acad. Rep. Popul., Romina,* Bucàrest, 508 pp.

Smoke, K. K. 1932. An objective study of concept formation. *Psychol. Monogr.,* 42, No. 4.

Stern, C. and W. 1927. *Die Kindersprache.* Leipzig: Barth.

Stouffer, S. A., et al. 1950. *The American Soldier.* Vol. iv: *Measurement and Prediction.* Princeton: Princeton Univer. Press.

Vigotsky, L. 1931. Thought in Schizophrenia. Trans. *Arch. Neurol. Psychiat.,* 31, 1063–1077.

Vincent, M. 1957. Sur le Rôle du langage à un niveau élémentaire de pensée abstraite. *Enfance,* 10, 443–463.

Vinh-Bang. 1959. Evolution des conduites et apprentissage. *Etudes d'Epistem. genet.,* ix, Paris: P.U.F.

Wallon, H. 1945. *Les Origines de la pensée chez l'enfant.* Paris: P.U.F.

Welch, and Long. 1940a. A further investigation of the higher structural phases of concept formation. *J. Psychol.,* 10, 211–220.

———. 1940b. The higher structural phases of concept formation of children. *J. Psychol.,* 9, 59–95.

Werner, H., and E. Kaplan. 1950. The acquisition of word meanings. A developmental study. *Child Develpm. Pub. Monogr.,* 15, No. 51, No. 1.

———, and D. Carrison. 1944. Animistic thinking in brain-injured children. *J. abnorm. soc. Psychol.,* 39, 43–62.

Wertheimer, M. 1945. *Productive thinking.* New York: Harper.

Woodworth, R. S., and S. B. Snell. 1935. An atmosphere effect in formal syllogistic reasoning. *J. exp. Psychol.,* 18, 451.

chapter 11

# Standardized Ability Testing

Anne Anastasi
*Graduate School, Fordham University*

What are the major methodological and interpretative problems encountered by the research worker who uses tests with children? What types of instruments are available to him, and what considerations should guide his choice of specific tests? In this chapter, questions such as these are considered with special reference to the use of standardized tests for the measurement of cognitive traits or abilities, as distinguished from the assessment of emotional, social, motivational, and attitudinal characteristics commonly designated as "personality" and treated elsewhere in this book. It should be noted, however, that the distinction between ability and personality tests—though customary—is neither sharp nor basic. By altering instructions to subjects and other concomitant circumstances, the same type of test content can be adapted to the measurement of both cognitive and personality traits. Such a situation is under-standable when we realize that in taking any test, as in all his behavior, the individual is influenced by his abilities and by his emotional, motivational, interest, and other nonintellectual traits. A differentiating feature of ability tests is that they undertake to discover the individual's maximum performance in a given area (Cronbach, 1960, pp. 29–34). In administering such tests every effort is made to establish optimal conditions and to ensure that the individual is motivated to "do his best" on the test.

Although the principal types of available ability tests for children are summarized and illustrated in this chapter, no attempt will be made to survey or evaluate specific tests. For this kind of information, the investigator is directed to a number of published sources, the principal one being the series of *Mental Measurements Yearbooks* edited by Buros (1959). These yearbooks cover nearly all commercially available psychological, educational, and vocational tests published in English-speaking countries; they are especially complete for paper-and-pencil tests. Each yearbook includes tests published during a specified period, thus supplementing rather than supplanting the preceding yearbooks. The *Fifth Mental Measurements Yearbook*, published in 1959, covers the period from 1952 to 1958. In addition to such routine data as publisher, price, forms, age levels, and the like, each yearbook provides critical reviews of most of the tests, prepared by one or more test experts. A nearly complete list of names and addresses of test publishers is also given.

Other sources that can readily be consulted for information on recently published tests include the *Psychological Abstracts*, which contains a special section on new tests, and such journals as *Educational and Psychological Measurement* and the *Journal of Consulting Psychology*, which list and review new tests. Descriptions of the principal tests in each area, as well as fuller expositions of some of the testing principles discussed in this chapter, can be found in any recent textbook on psychological or educational testing (e.g., Anastasi, 1954; Cronbach, 1960; Lindquist, 1951; Nunnally, 1959; Thorndike and Hagen, 1955). A standard guide for the evaluation of psychological tests is the *Technical Recommendations for Psychological Tests and Diagnostic Techniques*, published by the American Psychological Association (1954). A similar guide has been prepared with special reference to achievement tests (1955).

## TYPES OF ABILITY TESTS

The investigator who plans to utilize standardized ability tests in research with children has a wide choice of instruments for measuring his subjects from cradle to college. Tests applicable prior to school entrance are generally subdivided into *infant tests*, designed for the first 18 months of life, and *preschool tests*, covering the ages of 18 to 60 months (Anastasi, 1954, Ch. 11). With regard to test administration, the infant must be tested while lying down or supported on a person's lap. Speech is of little or no use in giving test instructions. Most of the tests at this level are actually controlled observations of sen-sori-motor development, as illustrated by the infant's ability to lift his head, turn over, reach for and grasp objects, and follow a moving object with his eyes. At the preschool level, on the other hand, the subject can walk, sit at a table, use his hands in manipulating test objects, and communicate by language. At these ages the child is also much more responsive to the examiner as a person, whereas for the infant the examiner serves chiefly as a means of providing stimulus objects. Preschool testing is a more highly interpersonal process—a feature that increases both the difficulties and the opportunities presented by the test situation.

Some available scales, such as the Yale Developmental Examination (Gesell and Amatruda, 1947), span both the infant and preschool periods. Others are restricted to one or the other level, as in the case of the California First-Year Mental Scale and the Minnesota Preschool Scale. Of special interest for longitudinal studies is the Cattell Infant Intelligence Scale, which was developed as a downward extension of the Stanford-Binet, thus providing a uniform score scale from the age of 2 months to the adult level.

In the development of some infant scales, such as the Northwestern Intelligence Tests (ages 13 to 36 weeks), a special effort was made to utilize items measuring the child's adaptation to the physical and social environment rather than physical growth or maturation. Examples of such items from the Northwestern scale include responsiveness to the sudden disappearance of the examiner's face, retrieving a toy hidden under a towel, pulling a string to obtain a toy, and looking for a toy that has been removed. In the previously mentioned Cattell scale there are also items involving rudimentary instrumentation, such as pulling a string or using a stick to attain a toy that is out of reach. Vocalization and linguistic responses are likewise found in several parts of the scale. There are indications, moreover, that infant and preschool tests of the future will make increasing use of items involving learning and linguistic development and may as a result prove to be somewhat better predictors of the child's subsequent intellectual progress.

Following school entrance, there is a rapid increase in the variety of test content, as well as testing techniques, which may be utilized. An important distinction is that between *individual and group tests*. Individual tests must be administered singly to each subject and usually require a highly trained examiner. Although more time-consuming, such tests frequently permit better control of testing conditions and provide additional opportunities for the observation of work methods, social and emotional reactions, and other qualitative aspects of the child's behavior. Group tests, on the other hand, are particularly designed for mass testing. They not only enable one examiner to test a large group but are also relatively easy to administer and score.

Infant and preschool scales are typically individual tests, although some group tests constructed for the primary grades can be administered to kindergarten children in small groups. At the elementary- and high-school ages, individual tests such as the Stanford-Binet and the Wechsler Intelligence Scale for Children (WISC) are used principally as clinical instruments for intensive study of special cases, whereas group tests serve for most other testing purposes. The latter are very numerous and can be illustrated by the various levels of the Pintner General Ability Tests: Verbal Series and of the Lorge-Thorndike Intelligence Tests (Anastasi, 1954, Ch. 9; Cronbach, 1960, Ch. 8).

Tests may also be classified with regard to *testing medium and content*. The commonest type employed from the fourth grade through the adult level is the paper-and-pencil verbal test. To take such a test, the subject must have an adequate understanding of English and must be able to read and write. Although the content is predominantly verbal, arithmetic problems and other numerical items are often included. Group tests for the primary grades have sometimes been described as "nonverbal," since the items usually consist of printed pictures and diagrams, which the child marks in accordance with oral instructions by the examiner. In Fig. 11-1 are four illustrative items from the Pintner-Cunningham Primary Test, with the corresponding oral instructions. Such tests obviously call for an understanding of spoken language. Some of their subtests, moreover, are designed specifically to test linguistic comprehension.

Nonlanguage tests, on the other hand, require neither spoken nor written language, having been specially planned for use with foreign-speaking, illiterate, or deaf groups. Familiar examples include the Army Beta and the Pintner Non-Language Test (Anastasi, 1954, Ch. 10). Sample items from the six

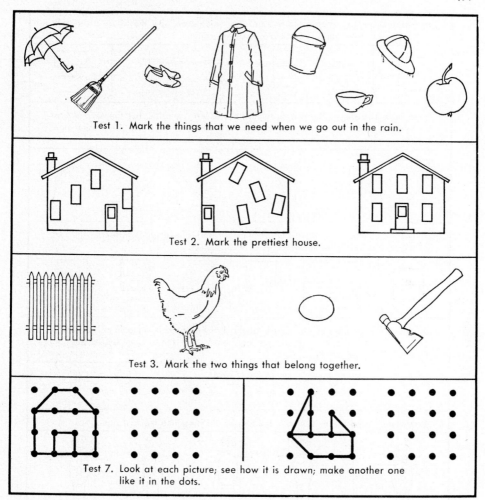

Test 1. Mark the things that we need when we go out in the rain.

Test 2. Mark the prettiest house.

Test 3. Mark the two things that belong together.

Test 7. Look at each picture; see how it is drawn; make another one like it in the dots.

Fig. 11-1. Illustrative items from the Pintner-Cunningham Primary Test. (Copyright by World Book Company.)

subtests of the latter are reproduced in Fig. 11-2. Performance tests, such as the Arthur Performance Scale and the performance section of the WISC, utilize such materials as form boards, picture puzzles, blocks, and the like, instead of paper and pencil. Some performance tests can be given both with and without oral instructions. The latter procedure utilizes pantomime, gesture, and demonstration. Examples of performance tests can be seen in Figs. 11–3, 11–4, and 11–5. It should be noted parenthetically that a number of non-language and performance tests have been specially developed or adapted for use with physically handicapped persons, such as the blind, deaf, and ortho-

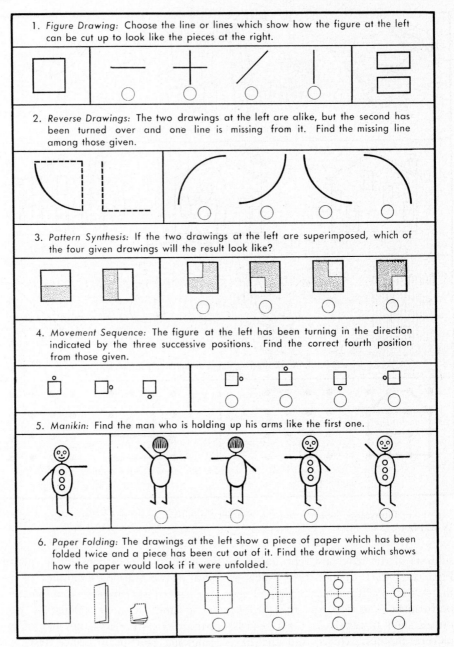

1. *Figure Drawing:* Choose the line or lines which show how the figure at the left can be cut up to look like the pieces at the right.

2. *Reverse Drawings:* The two drawings at the left are alike, but the second has been turned over and one line is missing from it. Find the missing line among those given.

3. *Pattern Synthesis:* If the two drawings at the left are superimposed, which of the four given drawings will the result look like?

4. *Movement Sequence:* The figure at the left has been turning in the direction indicated by the three successive positions. Find the correct fourth position from those given.

5. *Manikin:* Find the man who is holding up his arms like the first one.

6. *Paper Folding:* The drawings at the left show a piece of paper which has been folded twice and a piece has been cut out of it. Find the drawing which shows how the paper would look if it were unfolded.

Fig. 11-2. Sample items from the Pintner Non-Language Test. (Copyright by World Book Company.)

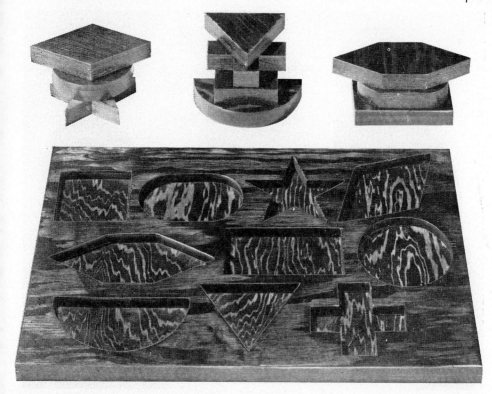

Fig. 11-3. Seguin Form Board, from Arthur Point Scale of Performance Tests, Revised Form II. The task is to insert the blocks in the appropriate recesses as quickly as possible. (Courtesy The Psychological Corporation.)

pedically handicapped (Anastasi, 1954, pp. 268–272).

Still another basis for differentiating among tests is the extent to which *power and speed* influence scores. In a pure power test items are steeply graded in difficulty (i.e., of progressively greater difficulty) and time limits are long enough to allow all subjects to try every item. Pure speed tests, on the other hand, present relatively easy items of uniform difficulty and employ short time limits. Individual differences in score on the latter tests thus reflect only variability in speed of work. Most tests fall between these two extremes, involving varying combinations of power and speed. It should be borne in mind, however, that the relative contribution of power and speed to a given test may vary with the age, ability level, and other characteristics of the subjects.

Finally, ability tests have been traditionally classified into those designed to measure intelligence, special aptitudes, and achievement, respectively. *Intelligence tests* characteristically provide a global score, such as an IQ, purported to gauge the individual's "general intellectual level." A wide

Fig. 11-4. Arthur Stencil Design Test I, from Arthur Point Scale of Performance Tests, Revised Form II. The sample design in the center is to be reproduced by superimposing cut-out stencils in different colors upon a solid card. (Courtesy The Psychological Corporation.)

variety of tasks is included on the assumption that through "the sinking of shafts at critical points" (Terman and Merrill, 1937, p. 4) all important intellectual functions will be sampled. In actual practice, intelligence tests are overweighted with certain functions, usually verbal ability, and may completely omit others. Moreover, since they have usually been developed within an academic framework, intelligence tests are primarily measures of scholastic aptitude. At the same time, different intelligence tests, such as the previously mentioned verbal and per-

formance types, may cover a different combination of functions. An IQ is thus of little meaning unless referred to the particular test from which it was derived.

Shortly after the first intelligence tests came into general use, their limited coverage became apparent and efforts were made to construct *special aptitude tests* to fill the gaps. Since intelligence tests concentrate chiefly upon relatively "abstract" verbal and numerical functions, a particular need was felt for tests to cover the more "concrete" and "practical" areas. Accordingly, me-

Fig. 11-5. Object Assembly Test of the Wechsler Intelligence Scale for Children (WISC). When properly assembled, the cut-out pieces form an animal. (Courtesy The Psychological Corporation.)

chanical aptitude was among the first special areas for which tests were devised. Tests of musical and artistic aptitudes followed, as well as some having a more directly vocational orientation, such as clerical aptitude tests (Anastasi, 1954, Chs. 15 and 16; Cronbach, 1960, Chs. 10 and 11).

A large number of standardized tests have likewise been constructed for measuring various aspects of vision, hearing, and motor dexterity (Anastasi, 1954, pp. 388–408). Certain rapid screening tests of visual and auditory functions are now routinely administered to school children in order to identify cases of mild sensory deficiencies. More precise instruments, which yield a multiplicity of scores, are available for intensive individual measurement (Anastasi, 1954, pp. 390–402). Certain vision tests, for example, provide measures of near and far acuity, depth perception, lateral and vertical phorias (muscular balance), and color discrimination. Of special interest in connection with research on children are the Oseretsky Tests of Motor Proficiency (Doll, 1946), which yield a "motor age" analogous to the mental age found on intelligence tests. More detailed discussion of sensory and motor tests may be found in Chapters 7 and 8, respectively.

A word of explanation should be added regarding the concept of "special aptitudes." The term originated at a time when the major emphasis in testing was placed on "general intelligence." Mechanical, musical, and other special aptitudes were thus regarded as supplementary to the IQ in the description of the individual. Following the application of refined statistical procedures and the accumulation of research data on trait organization, however, the picture has changed considerably. It is now recognized that "intelligence" itself comprises a number of relatively independent "special aptitudes," such as verbal comprehension, numerical reasoning, numerical computation, spatial visualization, associative memory, and the like (Anastasi, 1958a, Chs. 10 and 11). In the more recently developed multiple-aptitude batteries the various aptitudes covered by conventional intelligence tests (e.g., verbal comprehension, numerical reasoning, computation) are combined with several of those traditionally measured by special aptitude tests (e.g., perceptual speed and accuracy, mechanical comprehension, spatial visualization). Such batteries are discussed in a later section of the present chapter concerned with the differentiation of abilities.

The principal object of *achievement tests* is to appraise the effects of a course of instruction or training (Anastasi, 1954, Chs. 17 and 18; Cronbach, 1960, Ch. 13; Nunnally, 1959, Ch. 12). Although not restricted to school work, such tests have found their principal application in education. At the ele-

mentary-school level there are available a number of comprehensive batteries, such as the Sequential Tests of Educational Progress (STEP) and the Stanford Achievement Test. Similar batteries have been developed for the high-school student, although with increasing curricular specialization at the upper levels more use is made of achievement tests in special areas. Of particular interest in psychological research with children are the many tests designed to gauge readiness for, or to identify special disabilities in, reading and arithmetic.

Achievement tests have generally been contrasted with aptitude tests, the latter including both intelligence and special aptitude tests. From one angle, the difference between achievement and aptitude testing stems from the degree of uniformity of relevant antecedent learning. Achievement tests measure the effects of relatively standardized sets of experiences, such as a course in fourth grade arithmetic or American history. By contrast, aptitude-test performance reflects the cumulative influence of a multiplicity of experiences of daily life. Thus achievement tests may be said to measure the effects of learning under partially known and controlled conditions, whereas aptitude tests measure the effects of learning under relatively uncontrolled and unknown conditions. In this connection we should guard against the erroneous assumption that achievement tests are concerned with the effects of learning, whereas aptitude tests tap "innate capacities" independently of learning. Although this misconception was prevalent in the early days of testing, it is now recognized that all tests measure current developed abilities, which inevitably reflect the influence of prior learning.

A second distinction between aptitude and achievement tests pertains to their use. Although aptitude tests serve to predict subsequent performance, achievement tests generally provide a terminal evaluation upon the completion of training. Even this distinction, however, is one of degree. Any achievement test, for example, could be used as a predictor of future learning and thus serve the purpose of an aptitude test. Thus the progress that a pupil has made in arithmetic, as revealed by his present achievement-test score, may be employed to predict his subsequent success in algebra. The fact that a test score has a "past" does not preclude its having a "future." It should also be added that a number of recent achievement tests cover relatively broad and unstandardized educational experiences and thus fall midway between traditional aptitude and achievement tests. As examples may be cited tests of creative thinking, critical ability, reasoning, and scientific aptitude (Anastasi, 1954, pp. 489–492, 514–516). Such tests stress the application of previously acquired knowledge to novel situations, as illustrated by the evaluation of conclusions from given facts or the derivation of scientific principles from imaginary data.

## PROBLEMS OF TEST ADMINISTRATION

Each type of test and each age level present their own characteristic problems of test administration. Individual tests, such as the Stanford-Binet, as well as infant and preschool tests, require a special course of training before they can be properly applied. Practical suggestions regarding general testing procedure at the infant and preschool level can be found in Goodenough (1949, Ch. 20) and Watson (1951, Ch. 12). Terman and Merrill (1960, pp. 46–58) discuss problems in the individual testing of older children. Helpful hints regarding group testing are given by Thorndike (1949, pp. 261–265) and Ligon (1942). A more detailed analysis of desirable group testing practices, with supporting data, is provided by Traxler (in Lindquist, 1951, Ch. 10). Some of the major recommendations regarding test administration will be considered in the paragraphs which follow. But the reader interested in testing at a particular level is urged to consult the original sources cited for fuller discussions.

A fundamental requirement of all good test administration is advance preparation. In testing there can be no emergencies. Special efforts must therefore be made to foresee and forestall emergencies. The type of necessary preparation may range from the memorization of oral instructions, through the checking of materials and the choice of an adequate testing room, to conferences and "dry runs" with proctors and assistants.

Test scores can have little meaning unless they are obtained under *uniform testing conditions*. Failure on the part of inadequately trained examiners to realize the susceptibility of test scores to even slight variations in conditions is one of the chief causes of inaccurate test results. The need for uniformity applies not only to such obvious factors as time limits and wording of directions but also to more subtle conditions. In certain tests, for example, performance may be appreciably affected by the rate at which the examiner speaks, where he places emphasis and when he pauses in his presentation, his facial expression while pronouncing key words that might give away the correct answer, and the position of materials to be employed by the subject. There is evidence that the use of desks rather than chairs with desk arms may significantly improve scores on tests given with a separate answer sheet (Lindquist, 1951, p. 360). Any unusual condition of the subject, such as illness, fatigue, or excessive worry, is, of course, likely to affect test scores adversely. Even the nature of the subject's activities immediately preceding a test must be taken into account. Thus two studies employing the Goodenough Draw-a-Man Test with school children showed that mean scores tended to be higher after an emotionally gratifying experience than after a neutral or depressing activity (McCarthy, 1944; Reichenberg-Hackett, 1953).

Underlying the use of all ability tests is the assumption that the subject is "doing his best." Consequently, if conditions are to be kept uniform in this regard, every subject should be motivated to put forth his maximum efforts on the test. Among the motivational and emotional conditions that have been found to affect test scores may be mentioned praise, reproof, ridicule, knowledge of results, presence of observers, competition and rivalry, and various conditions evoking feelings of frustration, failure, and discouragement (Anastasi, 1954, pp. 47–50; Cronbach, 1960, Ch. 3). When a group of children were examined with the Stanford-Binet upon entering kindergarten and retested with a parallel form two months later, a significant mean rise in IQ was found (McHugh, 1943). This gain was attributed largely to the effect of the kindergarten experience in reducing shyness, fear of strangers, and other attitudes inhibiting oral speech. Support for such a hypothesis was found in the fact that the mean test-retest improvement was only 4.7 per cent in manipulatory tasks, as contrasted to 11.2 per cent in the oral items. In another study (Hutt, 1947), the Stanford-Binet was administered by a modified procedure in which each task failed was followed by an easier item. In the standard administration of this scale failures are often followed by more difficult items, the test continuing until all items within a single year level are failed. The hypothesis under investigation was that such a procedure may produce a mounting awareness of failure, which prevents the child from doing as well as he might on the later tasks. The results showed that poorly adjusted children tended to score higher when tested by the adapted than by the standard procedure, whereas well-adjusted children did equally well by both methods.

It is likely that motivational factors in general play a more prominent role in the test performance of certain types of subjects. Most middle-class American school children today are not only fairly test-wise, but they are also as a rule motivated to succeed in test situations. Special motivational problems are encountered, however, in testing such groups as emotionally maladjusted individuals, preschool children, ethnic minorities, and members of low socioeconomic classes. Juvenile delinquents and others tested in institutional settings are likely to manifest unfavorable attitudes, such as suspiciousness, insecurity, fear, or cynical indifference. Specific factors in the past experiences of such individuals are also likely to influence their test performance adversely (Sears, 1943). Such children may, for example, have developed feelings of hostility and inferiority toward any academic material as a result of early failures and frustrations experienced in school work.

Experimental findings regarding the effects of motivation upon test scores have a number of important implications for testing procedure. First, such results highlight the necessity for adhering to the prescribed motivating conditions in test administration as long as the individual's performance is to be evaluated in terms of standard norms. A second implication is that in the interpretation of scores any unusual motivating conditions must be taken into account. This is especially true in the case of subjects whose experiential background is unlike that of the standardization sample. Finally, it is apparent that the establishment of rapport prior to the administration of a test is an important part of the testing procedure. Insofar as the situation permits, the examiner should make certain that the subject is ready to do his best before the test begins.

The specific techniques for establishing *rapport* vary with the age level and other characteristics of the subjects. In testing preschool children, special factors to be considered include s. with strangers, distractibility, negativism. A friendly, cheerful, relaxed manner on the part of the examiner helps to reassure the child. The shy, timid child may need more preliminary time to become familiar with his surroundings. For this reason, it is better for the examiner not to be too demonstrative at the outset but rather to wait until the child is ready to make the first contact. Test periods should be brief, and the tasks should be varied and intrinsically interesting to the child. The testing should be presented to the child as a game, and his curiosity should be aroused before each new task is introduced. A certain flexibility of procedure is necessary at this age level because of possible refusals, loss of interest, and other instances of negativism.

Children in the first two or three grades of elementary school present many of the same problems encountered in testing the preschool child. The "game" appeal is still the most effective way of arousing their interest in the test. The older school child, on the other hand, can usually be motivated by an appeal to his competitive spirit and his desire to do well on a test. It should be borne in mind, however, that every test presents an implied threat to the individual's prestige. Some reassurance should therefore be given at the outset. It is helpful to explain, for example, that no one is expected to finish or to get all items correct. It is also desirable to eliminate the element of surprise from the test situation insofar as possible. For this purpose, many group tests provide a preliminary explanatory statement, which is read to the group, or even a practice booklet administered in advance of the testing session.

That test scores may be appreciably raised by special *practice and coaching* has been repeatedly demonstrated (Anastasi, 1958a, pp. 190–194). The effects vary markedly, however, with the nature of the test and with the age, ability, and previous experience of the subjects. In the case of certain tests repetition of the identical form within a few weeks may make the retest score meaningless because of recall of responses, change in work methods, and other disturbing factors. Even retesting with alternate forms generally leads to some improvement when time intervals are short. In such cases some adjustment in score should be made to allow for practice effect. General test sophistication must also be considered in interpreting test performance. In general, the child who has had considerable test-taking experience tends to score higher than the one who is taking his first test.

In evaluating the effect of practice and coaching upon test scores, a fundamental question to consider is the breadth of such influences (Anastasi, 1950a). Is the improvement limited to the specific test items, or does it extend to the broader area of behavior that the test is designed to predict? The answer to this question represents the difference between coaching and education. Rote memorization of the correct responses to a list of vocabulary test items will markedly raise a child's score on that particular test without appreciably improving his over-all apprecia-

tion of word meanings. This would be coaching in the narrow sense and would reduce the predictive value of the test for that child. On the other hand, a year of carefully selected reading, accompanied by discussion of word meanings, would improve *both* the child's vocabulary test score and his general verbal comprehension, thereby leaving unaltered the test's validity.

Test scores may also be invalidated through deliberate *cheating* on the part of subjects. Cheating on ability tests may take various forms: copying from a neighbor in group examinations; illicit use of outside sources such as books or notes; "jumping the gun," or premature starting before the signal to begin, as well as continuing after the instruction to stop; and obtaining prior information regarding specific test items. Improper and unscrupulous coaching would also fall under the last-named category. General precautionary measures include safeguarding the security of test materials and providing adequate proctoring and proper seating arrangements in group testing. The use of tests with several alternate forms also helps to minimize cheating. Premature starting and failure to stop on signal can be partially controlled by the design of test booklets in such a way that a page must be turned at the beginning of each separately timed part. In scheduling test sessions, attention should also be given to reducing the opportunity for communication among subjects tested at different times. If copying or collusion with another examinee is suspected, certain statistical checks based on number of identical errors may be applied to detect cheating (Anikeeff,

1954; Dickenson, 1945). In the use of tests with older children for research purposes only, preserving the subject's anonymity is often an effective way to reduce the motivation to cheat. Reassurance that the tests are to be utilized for research only usually has somewhat the same effect. It should be noted, however, that these motivating conditions are not comparable to those prevailing during the operational use of tests, and results may vary from one situation to the other.

## NORMS AND THE INTERPRETATION OF TEST SCORES

A major step in test standardization is the establishment of norms. The "raw score," such as the number of items correct or the time required to complete a task, is meaningless until compared with the norm or average performance. Psychological tests have no pre-established standards of passing or failing. In the process of developing a new test, it must be administered to a large, representative sample of the population for which it is designed. The scores obtained by this group provide the test norms. Test manuals should always include such norms, together with information on the size and nature of the normative sample. The test user will thus be in a position to evaluate the adequacy of the published norms as well as the comparability of the normative sample to the type of subjects he plans to test. Owing to differences in the characteristics of samples upon which different tests have been standardized, the same individual may appear to score much higher on

one test than on another. This is one of the reasons why test scores should always carry the name of the test with which they were obtained.

An individual's position in relation to the norms may be expressed in a number of specific ways. Basically, however, all such derived scores in current use can be subsumed under three types (Anastasi, 1954, Ch. 4; Cronbach, 1960, Ch. 4). The first is the traditional *ratio IQ*, found by dividing mental age by chronological age. Theoretically, mental age represents the age of normal children whose test performance the subject equals. Thus if a child does as well on the test as the average 10-year-old, his mental age is 10, regardless of his chronological age. A second major type of score is the *percentile rank*, which indicates the percentage of cases in the normative sample falling at or below the subject's score. Percentiles are not to be confused with the ordinary percentage score representing the percentage of *items* correctly completed.

Despite their wide popular appeal, both ratio IQ's and percentiles have serious limitations and are not in general suitable for research purposes. Ratio IQ's can be properly applied only to age scales that have been specifically designed to yield comparable IQ's at all ages. When indiscriminately employed, ratio IQ's may vary widely in meaning at different age levels. On the Merrill-Palmer Scale, for example, an IQ of 114 at one age level indicates the same degree of superiority as an IQ of 141 at another age (Stutsman, 1931). As for percentile scores, their chief weakness stems from the marked variation in size of unit. Owing to the greater clustering of cases at the center of the range and the decrease in frequency as the extremes are approached, percentile units near the center (i.e., 50) cover a much smaller distance than those near the ends of the scale (i.e., 0 and 100).

The most precise measure is provided by *standard scores* and their various derivatives. In all such scores the individual's distance from the mean is expressed in standard deviation units (SD). Thus, if the normative sample has a mean of 38 and an SD of 4, a raw score of 34 would correspond to a standard score of $-1.00$. Such simple standard scores, based directly on the SD units, are often called $z$ scores. Several available variants of standard scores provide more convenient scales, which avoid the use of negative values and decimals. An example is the $T$ score, representing standard scores in a normal distribution with a mean of 50 and an SD of 10. A $z$ score of $-1.00$ would thus correspond to a $T$ score of 40. Another type of standard score is the stanine, which utilizes a single-digit scale ranging from 1 to 9 and having a mean of 5 and an SD of 2.

Of particular interest is the deviation IQ, currently employed in the WISC and Stanford-Binet, as well as in several recently developed group tests. WISC deviation IQ's are actually standard scores with a mean of 100 and an SD of 15. Thus a child with a deviation IQ of 100 falls exactly at the mean of his age group. Deviation IQ's of 115 and 85 correspond to one SD above and one SD below the mean, respectively; a deviation IQ of 130 represents two SD's above the mean, and so forth. In a similar fashion, the 1960 Stanford-Binet uses a deviation IQ with a mean of 100 and an SD of 16. The relation of the various forms of standard scores to one another and to percentiles is given in Fig. 11–6.

## TEST RELIABILITY

One of the questions that needs to be asked in evaluating any psychological test concerns its reliability. In general, test reliability refers to the consistency of scores obtained by the same individuals on different occasions. Random fluctuations in test scores may result from a number of chance errors affecting test administration, scoring, condition of subject, or selection of items constituting a particular form of a test. Different methods of computing test reliability are influenced by one or more of these various types of chance errors of measurement. Consequently, not all reliability coefficients have the same meaning. To interpret a reliability coefficient, it is necessary to know by what procedure it was found.

The principal types of test reliability in current use include retest, equivalent-form, split-half, and Kuder-Richardson reliability (Anastasi, 1954, Ch. 5; Cronbach, 1960, Ch. 6). All express reliability in the form of a correlation coefficient between independently secured measures. *Retest reliability* is the correlation between scores on the identical test administered at different times. The interval may vary from a few days to several months. Obviously, such a correlation indicates temporal stability from one test session to another. When parallel forms of the test are administered on the two occasions,

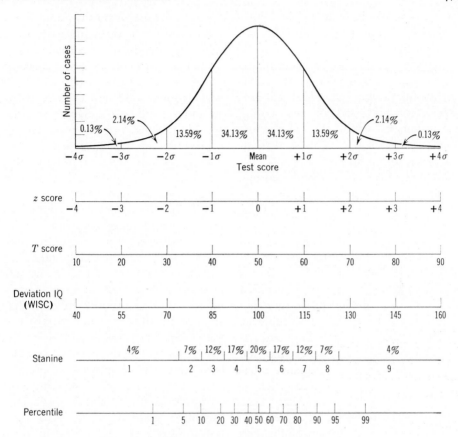

Fig. 11-6. Types of test norms.

the correlation between them represents *equivalent-form reliability*. Such a measure is influenced both by temporal fluctuations and by the extent of individual variability from one comparable set of test items to another.

The latter characteristic alone is measured by *split-half reliability*. The commonest way of computing split-half reliability is to find each person's score on the odd items and on the even items. From these two scores the reliability of the whole test can be determined in several ways (Anastasi,

1954, 108–109; Cronbach, 1951; Thorndike, 1949, Ch. 4). Like split-half reliability, *Kuder-Richardson reliability* is derived from a single test session. Being ultimately based on interitem consistency, however, it is also influenced by homogeneity of test content. For example, in a test consisting of 50 verbal analogies and 50 number-series completions, the Kuder-Richardson reliability would be lower than in one composed of 100 items of either type alone. Any discrepancy between subjects' performance on the verbal and on the numerical items would be reflected in a lowered Kuder-Richardson reliability in the former test.

Mention should also be made of *examiner* and *scorer reliability*. Most tests provide such highly standardized procedures for administration and scoring that variations attributable to the examiner are negligible. This is particularly true of group tests designed for mass examining and machine scoring. In most infant and preschool tests, however, as well as in other individual tests, such as the Stanford-Binet, testing procedure leaves more room for the skill and judgment of the examiner to operate. Under such conditions, it has been found that even properly qualified examiners may obtain appreciably different results from the same subjects. Various techniques, including correlation and analysis of variance, may be employed to check on examiner reliability. Certain types of tests, such as the Goodenough Draw-a-Man Test, present special problems of scorer reliability. In one investigation of this test interscorer discrepancies amounting to as much as a year of mental age were found for about 25 per cent of the drawings (McCarthy, 1944). In any research project utilizing tests whose scoring has qualitative features at least a sample of papers should be independently rescored by another examiner and the degree of agreement determined.

In interpreting the reliability coefficients reported in test manuals, certain cautions should be observed. First, single-trial methods, such as the split-half and Kuder-Richardson techniques, are inapplicable to *speed tests*. In a pure speed test, for example, subjects will make no errors (or possibly a negligible number of errors through carelessness). Thus an individual with a total score of 20 would have odd and even scores of 10 and 10, respectively, one scoring 28 would obtain odd and even scores of 14 and 14, and so on. Such a situation would obviously result in perfect or nearly perfect reliability. But this reliability would have no reference to speed of work, which is the essential determinant of scores on such a test. Insofar as speed plays an appreciable part in determining test scores, reliability coefficients computed by these methods are correspondingly inflated.

A second caution concerns the subjects upon whom reliability was established. All correlation coefficients are affected by the *range of scores* within the group. The greater the variability, the higher will be the correlation. Since tests are usually employed to discriminate among individuals within single age or grade levels, reliability coefficients should be reported separately for these levels. Such a procedure also makes it possible to determine whether the test is equally reliable for all ages. A single reliability coefficient found on a highly heterogeneous standardization sample, on the other hand, may be misleadingly high. Finally, it should be noted that reliability is directly related to *test length*. Thus an abbreviated form of a test can be expected to show some loss in reliability. Similarly, subtests or parts of a test will have lower reliability than the complete test. If subtest scores are to be separately analyzed, as in an aptitude profile, reliability coefficients should be determined for each subtest.

With school-age children, most well-constructed ability tests yield reliability coefficients clustering around .90. In the case of *infant and preschool tests*, however, reliabilities tend to run lower (Anastasi, 1954, Ch. 11). Among the conditions contributing to such low reliability may be mentioned distractibility, shyness, negativism, and other factors interfering with rapport and test administration. Reliability may be further lowered by scoring irregularities, since many test responses of the young child consist of fleeting movements that leave no permanent record. Despite these difficulties, some of the more carefully developed infant tests, such as the Cattell Infant Intelligence Scale and the California First-Year Mental Scale, have yielded promising results, their split-half reliabilities falling between .70 and .95 after the first 3 months of age (Anastasi, 1954, p. 288). Even during the first three months, there is evidence that when a larger number of items is employed and purely motor tasks are excluded, as in the Northwestern Infant Intelligence Tests, split-half reliabilities in the .80's and .90's are obtained (Anastasi, 1954, p. 288).

## TEST VALIDITY

The most important property of a test is undoubtedly its validity. The concept of validity concerns the "external relations" of a test to other data about the individual. Such relations enable us to state *what* the test measures and *how well* it does so. It is meaningless to say that a test is "valid" or has "high validity," without indicating the purpose or criterion for which it possesses the specified validity. For the selection of appropriate tests, as well as for the proper interpretation of test scores, full information is required regarding the procedures followed in estimating test validity.

In accordance with current usage, the various kinds of validity may be classified into four categories, namely, predictive, concurrent, content, and construct validity (American Psychological Association, 1954, pp. 13–28; Anastasi, 1954, Ch. 6; Cronbach, 1960, Ch. 5). To measure *predictive validity*, test scores are checked against performance in a specified area at some future time. For example, scores on a reading-readiness test administered upon school entrance may be correlated with actual reading achievement at the end of the first grade. *Concurrent validity* utilizes essentially the same procedure, except that no time lag is involved. The administration of an intelligence test to school children and to children of the same ages in an institution for mental defectives would illustrate this type of validation. If the mental defectives score significantly poorer than the normal children, the test discriminates in the expected direction and can in that sense be said to be measuring "intelligence."

*Content validity* is most often used in the case of achievement tests. Also designated as "intrinsic" and "logical" validity, this type of validity concerns primarily the adequacy with which the test items sample the content area to be measured. The test may thus be checked against relevant course syllabi, textbooks, and the judgment of subject-matter experts. Coverage of essential topics, in the correct proportions, is the major consideration. It is also desirable to secure, if possible, objective data on the extent to which irrelevant abilities, such as reading comprehension in a mathematics test, may affect scores. Gulliksen (1950) has suggested a number of objective procedures for improving content validation.

*Construct validity* is a very broad concept, covering a variety of validation procedures. It is concerned primarily with an experimental verification of hypotheses regarding the psychological traits or "theoretical constructs" that account for performance on the test (Cronbach and Meehl, 1955). The commonest application of this validation procedure to ability tests is found in factorial validity. Thus, if a factor of spatial visualization has been established by factor analysis, the correlation of a test with this factor is its factorial validity. Essentially, such a correlation indicates the extent to which the test measures an ability common to a group of similar tests which sample a relatively unified area of performance. Almost any experimental evidence regarding the behavior of test scores would contribute to construct validity. If, for instance, it is hypothesized that a given ability is not susceptible to practice effect, a comparison of test scores obtained before and after practice would provide information relevant to construct validation. Another example is provided by a study of the role of reading comprehension in tests designed to measure such traits as numerical or spatial aptitudes. As a part of the

validation of such tests, it should be established that low scores do not commonly result from inability to understand complicated wording of questions or instructions.

Most aptitude and intelligence tests have been validated in terms of predictive or concurrent validity. These two types of validity, which have sometimes been jointly designated as "empirical validity" (Anastasi, 1954, Ch. 6; Guilford, 1946), consist basically in the correlation or other statistical comparison of test scores with a criterion. The *criterion* is an independent index of those behavioral characteristics that the test is designed to measure. Special aptitude tests and multiple-factor batteries have frequently been validated against performance in different types of courses, such as English, mathematics, shop work, mechanical drawing, art, and music. Intelligence tests have utilized many criteria, although the commonest center around general academic achievement. Preschool and infant tests have generally been validated in terms of age differentiation. In other words, individual items, as well as the test as a whole, are checked against chronological age to determine whether performance shows a progressive improvement with advancing age.

Ratings of intelligence by teachers, nursery-school workers, and other observers have provided criterion data for validating certain intelligence tests. Contrasted groups have likewise been employed, as when intelligence test scores of children in institutions for mental defectives are compared with those of unselected public school pupils of the same ages. Actually, such a criterion is based upon the cumulative and uncontrolled selective influences operating in daily life that determine the individual's membership in one or the other of the contrasted groups. Internal consistency is sometimes reported as evidence of validity. In this case either test items or subtests are correlated with total test score as a criterion. Although indicative of test homogeneity and unidimensionality, which are themselves desirable properties, this type of measure should not be regarded as a substitute for validity. It might be added that some psychologists would classify age differentiation, contrasted groups, and internal consistency under construct validity (Cronbach and Meehl, 1955). The distinction cannot be very sharply drawn in terms of current usage.

Partly because of the multiplicity of possible criteria, different intelligence tests may vary widely in the nature of abilities measured. This is especially true of tests designed for different age levels or types of subjects. In fact, even a single test, such as the Stanford-Binet, may tap a different combination of functions at different ages. A consideration of such variations in coverage among "intelligence" tests is particularly important in planning and interpreting longitudinal studies (Anastasi, 1958a, pp. 225-226). For example, a factorial analysis of intelligence-test scores obtained over an eighteen-year period by the subjects of the Berkeley Growth Study suggested that the functions measured during the first 2 years could be characterized largely as

"sensori-motor alertness"; those covered between 2 and 4 years, as "persistence"; and those tested after the age of 4, as "manipulation of symbols" (Bayley, 1955; Hofstaetter, 1954).

## LONG-RANGE PREDICTION

In the evaluation of infant and preschool tests the results of long-range follow-up studies have often been cited in connection with both reliability and validity. When the time interval is of several years' duration, however, it does not seem appropriate to regard a retest correlation as a reliability coefficient. Changes occurring over such periods are likely to be cumulative and progressive for each individual, rather than random. Moreover, they usually characterize a relatively broad area of behavior rather than being restricted to the test items. Nor can such retest correlations be properly considered as validity coefficients. Whether the same or a different test is used as the "criterion," it is likely that somewhat different functions are sampled when testing is repeated at widely separated age levels. Furthermore, intervening experiences may substantially alter the child's intellectual status, producing changes that should be detected by a sensitive test. Although affected by both the reliability and validity of the measuring instrument, long-range correlations reflect primarily the regularity of behavior development and the intercorrelations among functions measured on the different occasions. It should be added that at the infant and preschool levels development occurs so rapidly that retests over as short a period as three months may be influenced by broad behavioral changes and should therefore be classified with long-range follow-ups.

The traditional problem of the "constancy of the IQ" is concerned with long-range predictability of intellectual functioning and should be differentiated from considerations of test reliability and validity (Anastasi, 1954, pp. 290–291, 302–304; Anastasi, 1958a, pp. 231–238). On the basis of the Berkeley Growth Study data, Bayley (1955) concluded that tests given at 4 years of age may permit grade-school predictions within wide classifications; tests given between 2 and 4 years of age will predict 8- and 9-year-old performance with some success; but scores obtained before 18 months are completely useless in the prediction of abilities during school ages, the correlations being zero or negative. Similar results have been obtained by other investigators (Bradway, 1944; Goodenough and Maurer, 1942; Honzik, Macfarlane, and Allen, 1948). Shorter follow-ups within the preschool period yield higher correlations. Thus correlations of .56, .67, and .71 were found between Stanford-Binet IQ's at the age of 3 years and Cattell Infant Intelligence Scale administered at the ages of 12, 18, and 24 months, respectively (Cattell, 1947). During the school years retest correlations with both individual and group intelligence tests are sufficiently high to make predictions over five to ten years practicable.

The magnitude of retest correlation depends upon a number of factors. *Length of interval* over which predic-

tions are made is obviously a major condition. Among school-age children, for example, correlations drop from .90 for immediate retests to about .70 after a five-year lapse (Thorndike, 1933, 1940). *Nature of intervening experiences* influences the amount and direction of change in individual children. It has been repeatedly demonstrated that even in later childhood large shifts in IQ may occur. Such changes are often associated with the cultural milieu and emotional climate of the child's environment (Bayley, 1955; Bradway, 1945; Honzik, Macfarlane, and Allen, 1948; Sontag, Baker, and Nelson, 1958). In general, children reared in underprivileged environments tend to lose with age, and those reared in superior environments to gain, in relation to test norms. Large changes in IQ have also been found to be associated with certain personality characteristics of the child, such as emotional independence and achievement motivation (Sontag, Baker, and Nelson, 1958).

The comparison of results obtained with preschool and elementary-school children has already suggested that *age* at the time of the initial test is an important determiner of retest correlations. When length of interval is constant, predictions from infant and preschool tests are much less certain than those made from school-age tests. There are several reasons for this increasing "constancy of the IQ" with age. The generally lower reliability and the less satisfactory procedures of test construction, administration, and scoring, which characterize available preschool and infant tests, are undoubtedly contributing factors. Nature of test content may likewise account for part of the difference. An item analysis of the Minnesota Preschool Scale suggested that tests of sensori-motor coordination and those calling for specific items of information have less predictive value than those emphasizing perception of spatial relations, controlled attention, memory, and logical relations (Maurer, 1947). A third possible factor concerns school entrance itself. Unlike the school child, the infant and preschool child have not been exposed to the relatively standardized series of experiences represented by the school curriculum. Hence in the latter cases the test constructor lacks the large pool of common experiential material from which test items can be drawn. Under these conditions, the development of effective testing instruments is much more difficult.

A final explanation is provided by Anderson's "overlap hypothesis" (Anderson, 1940). Anderson writes, "Since the growing individual does not lose what he already has, the constancy of the IQ is in large measure a matter of the part-whole or overlap relation" (Anderson, 1940, p. 394). Even if annual increments in intellectual development bore no relation to one another, the intellectual level would exhibit growing constancy with age because earlier acquisitions constitute an ever-increasing proportion of the child's total intellectual fund. Anderson demonstrated that test-retest correlations obtained in published longitudinal studies agree closely with the correlations theoretically expected on the basis of this overlap hypothesis.

## DIFFERENTIATION OF ABILITIES

One of the major distinguishing features of current psychological testing is its emphasis upon the differential measurement of ability. More and more, aptitude profiles, which provide a set of scores in different abilities, are being substituted for such global measures as the IQ. An example of a profile is given in Fig. 11-7. From many angles, psychologists have become increasingly aware of intra-individual differences in intellectual development. The application of factor analysis to the study of trait organization has provided the theoretical basis to such a differential approach.

Elementary introductions to the logic and mathematical techniques of factor analysis can be found in Adcock (1954), Anastasi (1958a, Chs. 10 and 11), Fruchter (1954), and Guilford (1954, Ch. 16). For the present purpose, it suffices to note that factor analysis identifies traits by an investigation of the intercorrelations among a wide variety of tests. In his pioneer work on the nature of intelligence Spearman (1927) reported a single common factor through all intellectual functions, which he called a *general factor* (*g*). Subsequent research has revealed a number of *group factors*, each common to a more limited area of activity (Anastasi, 1958a, Ch. 10).

The principal effect of factorial research upon test construction has been the development of *multiple-aptitude batteries*, which yield a set of scores in relatively independent abilities. Following their investigations on college students and school children, the Thur-

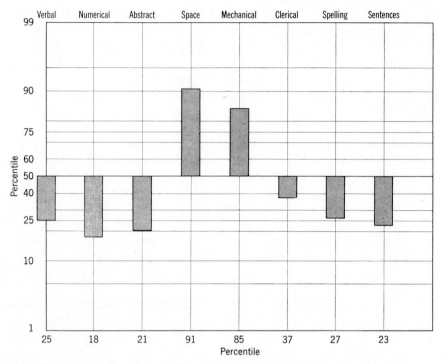

Fig. 11-7. Aptitude profile of an eighth-grade boy on the Differential Aptitude Tests. The heights of the vertical bars show how far above or below the norm the subject scores in each aptitude. (Copyright by The Psychological Corporation.)

stones (1938, 1941) prepared the tests of Primary Mental Abilities. In their later abbreviated versions these tests are available for three age levels. At the youngest level, suitable for ages 5 to 7, separate scores are provided for verbal-meaning, quantitative, space, perceptual-speed, and motor factors. An illustrative item from each of the tests used to measure these factors is shown in Fig. 11-8. The 7-to-11-year level includes verbal-meaning, number, reasoning, space, and perceptual-speed factors. The number and reasoning factors represent further differentiation of the rudimentary quantitative factor appearing at the younger level. The highest level,

designed for ages 11 to 17, comprises verbal-meaning, word-fluency, number, reasoning, and space factors. Thus there are two verbal factors represented at this stage, viz., verbal-meaning and word-fluency. An associative memory factor, included in the earlier, longer version of these tests, has been omitted from the later forms. Several other multiple-aptitude batteries are now available, but they are directed primarily to the high-school level (Anastasi, 1954, Ch. 14, 1958a, Ch. 11; Cronbach, 1960, Ch. 10).

Factorial analyses conducted at different ages suggest that intelligence may be relatively undifferentiated in early childhood, becoming increasingly specialized with age. Spearman's g factor would thus be more prominent at the younger ages, whereas group factors would predominate at the older ages. Garrett (1946) formulated such a developmental theory on the basis of factorial results obtained with different age groups. Corroborative data were likewise provided by both cross-sectional and longitudinal investigations specifically designed to test the age differentiation hypothesis. Since a number of subsequent studies have yielded inconsistent data, no conclusive statement regarding age changes in trait organization can be made at this time. Nevertheless, Burt (1954), who proposed a similar age-differentiation hypothesis as early as 1919, has recently reaffirmed this position following an examination of later published work. The contradictory findings of other studies he attributes to methodological limitations. Although Burt offers a maturational interpretation of the differentiation of abilities, there is some evidence to indicate that educational experiences may lead to the development of group factors (Anastasi, 1958a, pp. 360–361).

## CULTURAL FACTORS IN TEST SCORES

The literature on cultural differences in test performance has attained vast proportions (Anastasi, 1960). Even within a single nation, large significant mean differences in test scores are found among socioeconomic classes, urban and rural populations, and various ethnic minority groups, such as American Negroes and American Indians. On tests like the Stanford-Binet and the WISC, for example, the IQ's of children whose fathers are in the professions average about 20 points higher than those of children of unskilled laborers (McNemar, 1942; Seashore, Wesman, and Doppelt, 1950).

Any group comparison in "intelligence," however, must be qualified by the fact that the relative performance of groups varies with the *nature of the test*. For instance, children from higher socioeconomic levels tend to excel more in verbal than in spatial and mechanical aptitude tests (Eells et al., 1951; Havighurst and Breese, 1947; Havighurst and Janke, 1944; Janke and Havighurst, 1945). Similarly, the fund of common knowledge from which many intelligence-test items are drawn differs among cultures or subcultures. In a pioneer study on this question Shimberg (1929) constructed two forms of a general information test, one on urban and one on rural children. When both forms were administered to new samples of city and country children, the former excelled on the urban version, the latter on the rural. Suggestive results along the same lines have likewise been obtained with tests developed in other cultures, such as a Draw-a-Horse Test standardized on American Indian boys (DuBois, 1929) and a footprint-matching test constructed by Porteus (1931, p. 401) for Australian aborigines.

A growing trend in the psychological study of group differences is the shift from a description of the *status quo* to an analysis of *change*. Several large-scale surveys of the intelligence test performance of comparable populations

VERBAL-MEANING is measured by Vocabulary, Sentence Comprehension, Sentence Completion, Paragraph Comprehension, and Auditory Discrimination items. In each type of item, the subject marks the picture which best fits the examiner's oral statement, as shown below.

*Vocabulary:* Mark the Dog.

*Sentence Comprehension:* Mark the picture which answers this question. In which one does mother carry her money when she goes shopping?

*Sentence Completion:* If you want to keep something cold you keep it in the . . . . . . . . . . Mark it.

*Paragraph Comprehension:* Mark the picture that goes with this story. Betty is hanging the doll's dress on the clothesline.

*Auditory Discrimination:* Mark Pear.

Fig. 11-8. Illustrative items from SRA Primary Mental Abilities Tests for ages 5 to 7. (Copyright by Science Research Associates.)

PERCEPTUAL-SPEED.
Mark the kite in the little box. Then mark the other kite
that is just like the one in the little box.

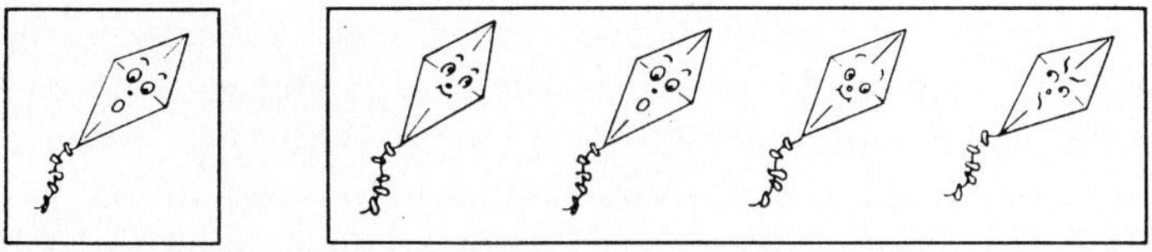

QUANTITATIVE.
Three policemen were standing on a corner. One
went home. How many policemen were there then?
Mark them.

Mark the largest doll and the smallest doll.

MOTOR.
Draw lines connecting top and bottom dots as quickly as
possible. Four samples have already been filled in.

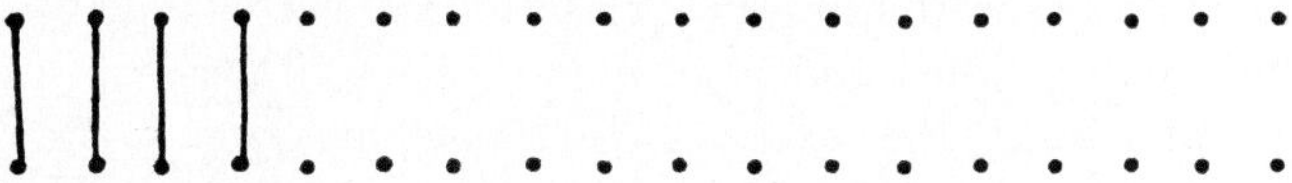

SPACE.
Mark the two parts which can be fitted together to
make a square.

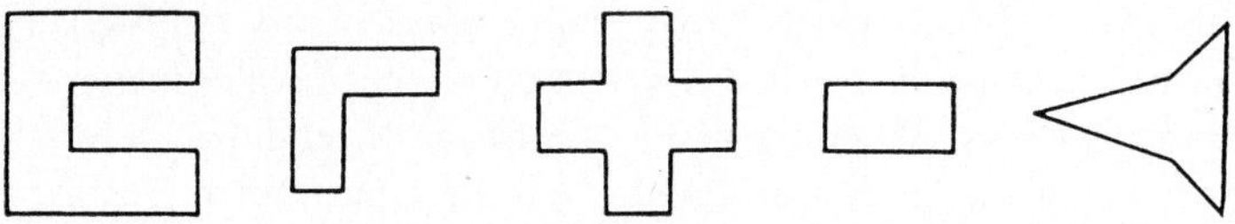

Fig. 11-8. (*Continued*)

have revealed significant rises in mean scores that paralleled improvements in socioeconomic and educational conditions. Such findings are illustrated by the Scottish surveys of nearly complete samples of 11-year-old children tested in 1932 and in 1947 (Scottish Council, 1949), by Finch's (1946) study of American high-school students over a twenty-year period, and by Wheeler's (1942) 10-year retests in a rural Tennessee community that had made unusual progress in social and educational conditions during the interval. There is also evidence of a progressive diminution of the gap between urban and rural groups (Anastasi, 1958a, Ch. 15).

One of the major sources of variation among cultural groups is to be found in the amount and kind of their formal *schooling*. Educational differences are especially conspicuous in the case of social classes and ethnic minority groups. Until recently, urban-rural differences in this regard also were large. Such group differences stem in part from economic factors and outside pressures on the child's time and in part from more subtle motivational and attitudinal conditions. That the extent and nature of schooling that the child receives will in turn affect his intelligence-test performance is now generally recognized by psychologists. Evidence in support of this conclusion may be found in the previously cited cross-sectional investigations of comparable populations as well as in longitudinal studies conducted in America (Lorge, 1945; Owens, 1953) and in Sweden (Husén, 1951).

The testing of children reared in different cultures or subcultures presents many technical difficulties. In the case of groups speaking different languages most available intelligence tests are inapplicable. Linguistic deficiency may also seriously handicap the performance of bilingual children on verbal-type tests. Although under certain conditions the acquisition of a second language will enrich verbal comprehension and stimulate intellectual development, *bilingualism* as it occurs among children of immigrants or other minority groups often serves to reduce proficiency in both languages and retard school progress (Anastasi, 1958a, Ch. 16; Arsenian, 1945; Darcy, 1953). On verbal intelligence tests such children average consistently lower than monoglots from the same groups. When nonlanguage or performance tests are substituted, their scores reach or excel those of monoglots. It cannot be assumed, however, that all such intelligence tests measure the same abilities. Most nonlanguage and performance tests draw heavily upon spatial visualization and perceptual functions, in contrast to the predominantly verbal and numerical aptitudes covered by the commoner intelligence tests.

Moreover, persons from certain cultures or subcultures will be handicapped even on nonlanguage tests because of the specific information, skills, and work habits required. Each culture fosters the development of a different pattern of abilities. Tests constructed within a particular culture reflect such an ability pattern and thus tend to favor individuals reared in that culture. To meet these additional difficulties, a number of so-called *culture-free tests* have been prepared (Anastasi, 1954, pp. 255–

268). Current examples include the Leiter International Performance Scale, the Cattell Culture-Free Test of Intelligence, the Raven Progressive Matrices, and the Goodenough Draw-a-Man Test (for references, cf. Anastasi, 1954, Ch. 10). Sample items from two of these scales are shown in Figs. 11–9 and 11–10. A test specifically designed to eliminate "social class bias" from test content is the Davis-Eells Games (Anastasi, 1954, pp. 266–268).

Although no test can be truly *free* from cultural influences, it is theoretically possible to construct a test that presupposes only the experiences that are *common* to different cultures. This is what available culture-free tests have tried to accomplish. In actual practice, however, such tests fall short of their objective. No existing test is entirely unrestricted in its cultural reference, the difference between "culture-free" and other tests being one of degree. The mere use of paper and pencil or the presentation of abstract tasks that have no immediate practical significance will favor some cultural groups. Other relevant factors that differ among cultures or subcultures include extent of familiarity with pictorial or diagrammatic representation, rapport with the examiner (especially if he belongs to a different race from the testees), test-taking motivation, drive to excel, and previously developed problem-solving

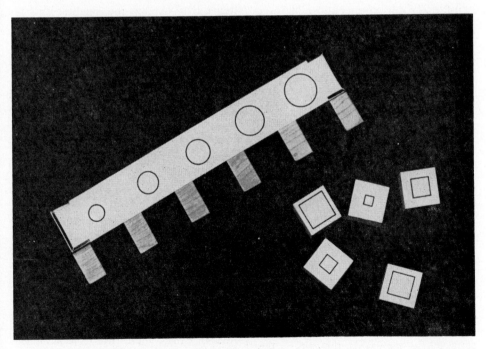

Fig. 11-9. Typical materials for use in the Leiter International Performance Scale. The test illustrated is the Analogies Progression Test from the six-year level. Each block must be inserted in the proper recess. (Courtesy R. G. Leiter.)

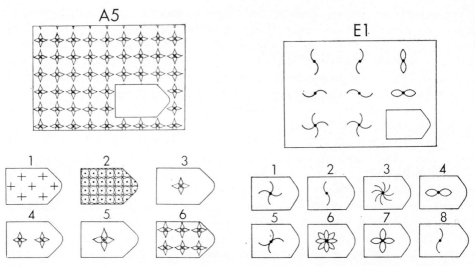

Fig. 11-10. Two items from the Progressive Matrices. The subject must choose the missing part of each design from the six or eight alternatives provided. (Courtesy J. C. Raven.)

attitudes. In this connection it is interesting to note that in a review of over twenty years of research with the Draw-a-Man Test, Goodenough and Harris (1950, p. 399) concluded that "the search for a culture-free test, whether of intelligence, artistic ability, personal-social characteristics, or any other measurable trait is illusory."

Finally, it should be recognized that the reduction of cultural differentials or the elimination of cultural bias in a test may reduce its validity for the prediction of many important criteria (Anastasi, 1950a). Cultural factors influence behavior development at many levels (Anastasi, 1958b). Not only test performance but also broader aspects of the child's intellectual development may be fundamentally affected by the cultural conditions under which he is reared. In other words, the criteria that the tests are designed to assess may themselves be culturally loaded. Test

items that exhibit the smallest differences between cultural groups are likely to measure the more trivial and socially less important intellectual functions. It should be obvious that the contribution of cultural factors to individual development cannot be ruled out by eliminating cultural differentials from test scores.

## REFERENCES

Adcock, C. J. 1954. *Factorial analysis for non-mathematicians*. Carlton, N. 3, Victoria: Melbourne Univer. Press. New York: Cambridge Univer. Press.

American Psychological Association. 1954. *Technical recommendations for psychological tests and diagnostic techniques*. Washington, D. C.: American Psychological Association.

Anastasi, Anne. 1950a. The concept of validity in the interpretation of test scores. *Educ. psychol. Measmt.*, 10, 67–78.

———. 1950b. Some implications of cultural

factors for test construction. *Proc., 1949 Invit. Conf. Test. Probl., Educ. Test. Serv.,* 13–17.

——. 1954. *Psychological testing.* New York: Macmillan.

——. 1958a. *Differential psychology.* (3rd ed.) New York: Macmillan.

——. 1958b. Heredity, environment, and the question "How?" *Psychol. Rev.,* 65, 197–208.

——. 1960. Cultural differences. *Encycl. educ. Res.* (3rd ed.), 350–358.

Anderson, J. E. 1940. The prediction of terminal intelligence from infant and preschool tests. *Yearb. nat. Soc. Stud. Educ.,* 39, Part I., 385–403.

Anikeeff, A. M. 1954. Index of collaboration for test administrators. *J. appl. Psychol.,* 38, 174–177.

Arsenian, S. 1945. Bilingualism in the postwar world. *Psychol. Bull.,* 42, 65–86.

Bayley, Nancy. 1955. On the growth of intelligence. *Amer. Psychologist,* 10, 805–818.

Bradway, K. P. 1944. IQ constancy on the revised Stanford-Binet from the preschool to the junior high school level. *J. genet. Psychol.,* 65, 197–217.

——. 1945. An experimental study of factors associated with Stanford-Binet IQ changes from the preschool to the junior high school. *J. genet. Psychol.,* 66, 107–128.

Buros, O. K. (Ed.) 1959. *The fifth mental measurements yearbook.* Highland Park, N. J.: Gryphon.

Burt, C. 1954. The differentiation of intellectual ability. *Brit. J. educ. Psychol.,* 24, 76–90.

Cattell, Psyche. 1947. *The measurement of intelligence of infants and young children.* New York: The Psychological Corporation.

Committees on Test Standards, AERA and NCMUE. 1955. *Technical recommendations for achievement tests.* Washington, D. C.: Amer. educ. Res. Ass.

Cronbach, L. J. 1951. Coefficient alpha and the internal structure of tests. *Psychometrika,* 16, 297–334.

——. 1960. *Essentials of psychological testing.* (2nd ed.) New York: Harper.

——, and P. E. Meehl. 1955. Construct validity in psychological tests. *Psychol. Bull.,* 52, 281–302.

Darcy, Natalie T. 1953. A review of the literature on the effects of bilingualism upon the measurement of intelligence. *J. genet. Psychol.,* 82, 21–57.

Dickenson, H. F. 1945. Identical errors and deception. *J. educ. Res.,* 38, 534–542.

Doll, E. A. (Ed.) 1946. *The Oseretsky Tests of Motor Proficiency.* Minneapolis: Educ. Test. Bur.

DuBois, P. H. 1939. A test standardized on Pueblo Indian children. *Psychol. Bull.,* 1939, 36, 523.

Eells, K., et al. 1951. *Intelligence and cultural differences.* Chicago: Univer. Chicago Press.

Finch, F. H. 1946. Enrollment increases and changes in the mental level. *Appl. Psychol. Monogr.,* No. 10.

Fruchter, B. 1954. *Introduction to factor analysis.* New York: Van Nostrand.

Garrett, H. E. 1946. A developmental theory of intelligence. *Amer. Psychologist,* 1, 372–378.

Gesell, A., and Catherine S. Amatruda. 1947. *Developmental diagnosis.* (2nd ed.) New York: Hoeber.

Goodenough, Florence L. 1949. *Mental testing.* New York: Rinehart.

——, and D. B. Harris. 1950. Studies in the psychology of children's drawings: II. *Psychol. Bull.,* 47, 369–433.

Goodenough, Florence L., and Katherine M. Maurer. 1942. *The mental growth of children from two to fourteen years.* Minneapolis: Univer. Minnesota Press.

Guilford, J. P. 1946. New standards for test evaluation. *Educ. psychol. Measmt.,* 6, 427–438.

——. 1954. *Psychometric methods.* (Rev. ed.) New York: McGraw-Hill.

Gulliksen, H. 1950. Intrinsic validity. *Amer. Psychologist,* 5, 511–517.

Havighurst, R. J., and F. H. Breese. 1947. Relation between ability and social status in a midwestern community: III. Primary mental abilities. *J. educ. Psychol.,* 38, 241–247.

Havighurst, R. J., and L. L. Janke. 1944. Relation between ability and social status in a midwestern community: I. Ten-year-old children. *J. educ. Psychol.,* 35, 357–368.

Hofstaetter, P. R. 1954. The changing composition of "intelligence": A study of T technique. *J. genet. Psychol.,* 85, 159–164.

Honzik, Marjorie P., Jean W. Macfarlane, and Lucile Allen. 1948. The stability of mental test performance between two and eighteen years. *J. exp. Educ.*, **17**, 309–324.

Husén, T. 1951. The influence of schooling upon IQ. *Theoria*, **17**, 61–88.

Hutt, M. L. 1947. "Consecutive" and "adaptive" testing with the revised Stanford-Binet. *J. consult. Psychol.*, **11**, 93–103.

Janke, L. L., and R. J. Havighurst. 1945. Relation between ability and social status in a midwestern community: II. Sixteen-year-old boys and girls. *J. educ. Psychol.*, **36**, 499–509.

Ligon, E. M. 1942. The administration of group tests. *Educ. psychol. Measmt.*, **2**, 387–399.

Lindquist, E. F. (Ed.) 1951. *Educational measurement.* Washington, D. C.: Amer. Coun. Educ.

Lorge, I. 1945. Schooling makes a difference. *Teach. Coll. Rec.*, **46**, 483–492.

Maurer, Katherine M. 1946. *Intellectual status at maturity as a criterion for selecting items in preschool tests.* Minneapolis: Univer. Minnesota Press.

McCarthy, Dorothea. 1944. A study of the reliability of the Goodenough drawing test of intelligence. *J. Psychol.*, **18**, 201–216.

McHugh, G. 1943. Changes in IQ at the public school kindergarten level. *Psychol. Monogr.*, **55**, No. 2.

McNemar, Q. 1942. *The revision of the Stanford-Binet Scale: an analysis of the standardization data.* Boston: Houghton Mifflin.

Nunnally, J. C. 1959. *Tests and measurements: assessment and prediction.* New York: McGraw-Hill.

Owens, W. A., Jr. 1953. Age and mental abilities: A longitudinal study. *Genet. Psychol. Monogr.*, **48**, 3–54.

Porteus, S. D. 1931. *The psychology of a primitive people.* New York: Longmans, Green.

Reichenberg-Hackett, Wally. 1953. Changes in Goodenough drawings after a gratifying experience. *Amer. J. Orthopsychiat.*, **23**, 501–517.

Scottish Council for Research in Education. 1949. *The trend of Scottish intelligence.* London: Univer. London Press.

Sears, R. 1943. Motivational factors in aptitude testing. *Amer. J. Orthopsychiat.*, **13**, 468–493.

Seashore, H., A. Wesman, and J. Doppelt. 1950. The standardization of the Wechsler Intelligence Scale for Children. *J. consult. Psychol.*, **14**, 99–110.

Shimberg, Myra E. 1929. An investigation into the validity of norms with special reference to urban and rural groups. *Arch. Psychol.*, No. 104.

Sontag, L. W., C. T. Baker, and Virginia L. Nelson. 1958. Mental growth and personality development: A longitudinal study. *Monogr. soc. Res. Child Develpm.*, **23**, No. 2 (Serial No. 68).

Spearman, C. 1927. *The abilities of man.* New York: Macmillan.

Stutsman, Rachel. 1931. *Mental measurement of preschool children with a guide for the administration of the Merrill-Palmer Scale of Mental Tests.* Yonkers, N. Y.: World Book.

Terman, L. M., and Maud A. Merrill. 1937. *Measuring intelligence.* Boston: Houghton Mifflin.

———. 1960. *Stanford-Binet Intelligence Scale: Manual for the third revision, Form L-M.* Boston: Houghton Mifflin.

Thorndike, R. L. 1933. The effect of interval between test and retest on the constancy of the IQ. *J. educ. Psychol.*, **24**, 543–549.

———. 1940. "Constancy" of the IQ. *Psychol. Bull.*, **37**, 167–186.

———. 1949. *Personnel selection: test and measurement techniques.* New York: Wiley.

———, and Elizabeth Hagen. 1955. *Measurement and evaluation in psychology and education.* New York: Wiley.

Thurstone, L. L. 1938. Primary mental abilities. *Psychometr. Monogr.*, No. 1.

———, and Thelma G. Thurstone. 1941. Factorial studies of intelligence. *Psychometr. Monogr.*, No. 2.

Watson, R. I. 1951. *The clinical method in psychology.* New York: Harper.

Wheeler, L. R. 1942. A comparative study of the intelligence of East Tennessee mountain children. *J. educ. Psychol.*, **33**, 321–334.

chapter 12

# Language
# and
# Communication

Orvis C. Irwin

*Institute of Logopedics*
*Wichita, Kansas*

During the last thirty or forty years there has been an increasing awareness among educators, clinicians, psychologists, speech therapists, and people interested in child development of the existence in the population of a considerable number of individuals with various degrees of speech handicaps. Surveys on the incidence of speech disorders in the general population, however, are not in agreement. Milisen (1957) attempted a summary statement that gives only approximate estimates.

From kindergarten through fourth grade, roughly 12 to 15 percent of the children have seriously defective speech. In the next four grades between 4 and 5 percent are seriously defective. General estimates above the eighth grade are based on highly selected samples and therefore the best guess as to the incidence of speech disorders in persons over 14 years of age would be about the same as for the upper elementary grades—4 to 5 percent (p. 250).

Milisen's estimates are for the incidence of serious speech handicaps among school children. His figures do not include those cases in which speech difficulties are less serious. Moreover, the incidence of speech problems among handicapped persons, such as the mentally retarded, the cerebral palsied, and the aphasics, is known to be very much higher than among the general run of school children.

The recognition of the striking incidence of language disturbances in the population has forced professional attention to these problems. Accordingly, strenuous efforts are being made to improve the training of speech therapists as well as of research workers. The development of enriched therapy programs and of methods for the evaluation of abnormalities of articulation, voice, rhythm, and of symbolization are seriously needed.

All this points to the importance of the area of language and communication as a discipline in its own right. The materials presented in this chapter aim to provide a summary of the more commonly used research methods that have been applied to children in this field of investigation.

The problem of selecting a comprehensive set of categories for classifying the numerous methods of research on children's speech and language is not a simple one. A number of classifications may be feasible. The method of straight observation may be compared with one in which calibrated instruments are employed. A second dimension might be in terms of the longitudinal-cross-sectional approach. A third organization might involve control groups as contrasted with a method that does not avail itself of this device. Another might be the single variable versus the multiple variable type of study. Obviously, any one of these may serve as the main category, the others being subsumed under it. There is no logical reason for such an arrangement, except perhaps personal preference. No matter what approach is used, there would still be several research techniques that could not be subsumed under the scheme. Among them would be the manner in which the data are recorded, the problem of establishing the reliability of the observer, and the verbal test method.

In the absence of any comprehensive principle for organizing the methodology in the speech and language area, a simple listing of methods found in the literature will be followed. The manner of presenting the materials is to explain various methods and to describe several of the important researches that illustrate each method and to supplement them with briefer mention of other studies. This treatment is applied in turn to the several areas of language development, such as infant vocalization, vocabulary measurement, the mastery of sentence structure, thought unit analysis, speech errors, functions of language, and diagnosis and assessment of deviant speech.

Much of what is known about infant speech actually is based on research with adults. For example, our knowledge of the placement of the tongue in articulation and a great deal of our knowledge of speech errors and difficulties that comes from work with adults has been applied to children. The approach here is concerned with recent methods that have been used in researches on the speech of children.

In the literature of infant vocalization there are many scattered reports by parents and relatives on the speech of single cases. Instances are those by Lobischi (1851), Taine (1877), Humphreys (1880), Schultze (1880), Stern and Stern (1907), Nice (1915), Hoyer and Hoyer (1924). Other examples are by Darwin (1877) and Preyer (1889). Perhaps the most famous report of this type is that by Shinn (1900). Most of this work was done in a very casual and unsystematic manner. It is spotty, meager, unscientific, and almost entirely unconcerned with standardized recording techniques. Its value is largely prescientific. Occasionally it throws light on where significant problems of early speech lie and shows flashes of insight, but it reveals little in the way of careful methodology. Exceptions to these strictures must be made to the work of Leopold (1939) and of Lewis (1951).

## THE INTERNATIONAL PHONETIC ALPHABET

One of the important requisites for the accurate recording of speech sound data is the use of a scientific alphabet. The International Phonetic Alphabet was invented for this purpose. The ordinary alphabet is too limited in the number of its symbols. It has too many discrepancies between its symbols and pronunciation that make it unreliable for precision work. The international alphabet is a set of symbols, each of which represents one and only one elemental speech sound. In a broad transcription there are about 40 symbols; in a narrow transcription others are added to represent finer shadings of sound. Fairbanks' (1940) arrangement of a broad transcription with a few modifications has proved to be a useful instrument for work with American infants and children and may be employed in analyzing the speech of children of other nationalities.

Phonemes are elemental speech sounds that are classified as vowels and consonants. A vowel is a sound that is uttered with little or no stoppage of the emitted breath stream. A consonant is a sound uttered when the breath stream is interrupted in some manner. Vowels are classified as front, middle, and back. The basis for this classification in the main is the position of the arch or hump of the tongue. In the process of uttering vowels the tongue arches or humps up. In the case of front vowels the hump is in the front part of the tongue. The vowel [i], as in feet, is articulated by the front part of the tongue and mouth. Back vowels are uttered when the hump is located in the posterior part of the tongue. The sound [u], as in food, is uttered with a raised hump in the back of the tongue. Likewise, a middle vowel such as [ɝ], as in bird, is articulated with the hump in the middle of the tongue. Diphthongs are the rapid blending of two vowel sounds, the first stressed and the second unstressed, so that together they seem to be a different single sound. There are in broad transcription two classes of diphthongs, [u] and [i]. The basis of classification usually is the second unstressed vowel of the pair. An example of the [u] diphthong occurs in the word toe. The two-vowel sounds in the word sail illustrate the [i] diphthong.

Consonants are categorized in several ways. One classification is in terms of voiced and voiceless sounds. A voiced sound is caused by the air stream setting the vocal cords into vibration. In a voiceless sound the cords are not vibrated. For instance [b], as in ebb, is voiced, whereas [p], as in step, is voiceless. Another set of consonantal categories depends on the place or the parts of the mouth involved in the articulation. The categories are labials (the two lips articulating together), labio-dentals (upper teeth on lower lip), lingua-dentals (tongue tip touching gum ridge), post dentals (tongue tip pointing toward but not touching the gums and teeth), velars (back of tongue touching the soft palate), and glottals (sudden opening of the glottis). A third classification is based on the manner of articulation, depending on how the breath stream is acted upon. The categories are nasals (resonance in nasal passages), plosives (sudden release of air pressure in the air tract), semivowels (a sound partaking of the nature of both vowel and consonant quality), fricatives (air stream forced through a narrow opening), and glides (transition from one sound to another). There is a large array of consonant blends. They are classed as double consonant blends, such as [pl] in place, and as triple consonant blends, such as [spl] in splash.

Both the vowels and the consonants in their various subdivisions appear in the table which follows. A word should be said for inclusion of the voiceless stopplosive [ʔ]. It is a glottal stop. In the German language this sound is added in the initial position of open-vowel words. It is rarely used in adult English speech, but it is almost universally found among the sounds of infants. It is for this reason that it is included here. Presented is a broad transcription of the International Phonetic Alphabet (IPA), with key words adapted from Fairbanks (1940).

## INTERNATIONAL PHONETIC ALPHABET

### Vowel Symbols

| Front | | Middle | | Back | |
|-------|------|--------|-------|------|------|
| [i] | seat | [a] | ask | [a] | calm |
| [ɪ] | sit | [ʌ] | hut | [ɒ] | hot |
| [e] | bait | [ə] | above | [ɔ] | tall |
| [ɛ] | bet | [ɜ] | bird | [o] | coke |
| [æ] | bat | | | [ʊ] | full |
| | | | | [u] | tool |

### Diphthongs

| U Diphthongs | | I Diphthongs | |
|--------------|------|--------------|------|
| [oʊ] | oak | [eɪ] | hail |
| [aʊ] | cow | [aɪ] | eye |
| | | [ɔɪ] | soil |

Among the workers who have employed the International Alphabet to transcribe infant speech are Wellman, Case, Mengert, and Bradbury (1931), Gregoire (1937), Krehbiel (1941),

Irwin and Curry (1941), Irwin (1941), Chen (1942), Lewis (1951), Fisichelli (1950), Spiker (1951), and Catalano and McCarthy (1954). Lynip (1951) is critical of the International Phonetical Alphabet on the grounds that it is too dependent upon the vagaries of the human ear. He holds that the use of this alphabet by an observer is too subjective a procedure and that it is difficult to obtain reliable data with it.

## OBSERVER RELIABILITY

The problem of the reliability of the individual who observes and records the speech of infants is of paramount importance because an investigation stands or falls on the ability of the observer to transcribe sounds accurately. Establishing the reliability of the human recorder is analogous to the calibration of an instrument. Frequently the transcription must be recorded live, that is, with paper and pencil, depending on where the subjects are found and on their ages. The presence of a tape recorder or any mechanical apparatus frequently inhibits speech production in young children. At other times a record can be made on tape with an electrical recorder. In either

### Consonant Articulation

| | Nasal | Stop-plosive | | Semivowel | Fricative | | Glide | |
|---|-------|--------------|------|-----------|-----------|------|-------|------|
| | Voiced | Voiceless | Voiced | Voiced | Voiceless | Voiced | Voiceless | Voiced |
| Labial | [m] | [p] | [b] | | | | [ʍ] | [w] |
| Labio-dental | | | | | [f] | [v] | | |
| Lingua-dental | | | | | [θ] | [ð] | | |
| Post-dental | [n] | [t] | [d] | [r] | [s] | [z] | | [j] |
| | | | | [ɻ] | [ʃ] | [ʒ] | | |
| Velar | [ŋ] | [k] | [g] | | [χ] | [ç] | | |
| Glottal | | [ʔ] | | | [h] | | | |

case the reliability is measured by the percentage of agreement between two or more trained listeners, each of whom records the child's vocalizations simultaneously and independently. A similar procedure is followed for establishing observer reliability when tape recorded sounds are listened to and transcribed.

A number of studies on observer reliability in which live transcriptions were used have been reported by Irwin and his associates. Among them are Irwin and Curry (1941), Irwin and Chen (1941), Krehbiel (1941), Irwin (1945), Spiker (1951), McCurry and Irwin (1953). Among studies establishing reliability in hearing sounds from a tape record are those by Fisichelli (1950), by Flores and Irwin (1955), by Irwin (1959). In general, the percentages of agreement between two observers in these studies vary from about 70 to 100 and average about 90. This means that when this method is used the error amounts to about 10 per cent.

The employment of electric recorders assures a permanent record and enables the observer to read and check the tape record repeatedly and thus to safeguard the observations. In the field of infant work the leaders in its use were Fisichelli (1950) and Catalano and McCarthy (1954). Irwin (1956a,b,c, 1957b,c) has made extensive use of tape recording to establish observer reliability.

## CROSS-SECTIONAL AND LONGITUDINAL METHODS

Essentially, the cross-sectional and longitudinal methods consist of an analysis of age trends. The distinctive feature of the cross-sectional method is that a different sample of subjects is used at each of several age levels. In contrast, the longitudinal approach uses the same sample of subjects at several age levels.

The advantage of the cross-sectional method is the relative economy in securing data. For instance, the researcher who wishes to study the speech errors of children in grades one through six can test the available children in each of the grades. The administration of tests can be completed in shorter time than if the subjects in grade one were followed year by year until they had reached the sixth grade. On the other hand, something may be lost because of the lack of continuity of the subjects. Extraneous factors, such as variation from classroom to classroom, different teaching methods, and different school neighborhoods, may affect the results and might be better controlled by following through with the same sample of subjects and teachers. However, individual trends cannot be followed with the cross-sectional methods. This, on the other hand, is the great advantage of the longitudinal approach, but the time factor is a practical difficulty in its use. The time needed to complete a longitudinal study is ordinarily almost prohibitive.

A careful research that illustrates the cross-sectional method of studying the phonetic development of infants is Fisichelli's (1950). The subjects were 100 orphanage infants, 20 in each of five age groups, 6, 9, 12, and 15 months. A microphone was suspended over the child's crib or play pen and a warm-up period of twenty minutes was given to allow the subject to become accustomed to the situation. The recorder was then turned on for a half hour. A minimum of 30 phonemes during the half hour was recorded on the tape. Other nonverbal behavior was noted in half-minute intervals during the period. The data were transcribed from the tape by two phoneticians in the International Phonetic Alphabet. Observer reliability was determined, the values ranging from 86 to 95 per cent agreement, most of which exceeded 90 per cent. The reliability of the data was also determined by correlating the odd versus the even sounds in the record. These correlations varied from .82 to .99 for the five age groups. There was regular progression of scores with increasing age.

The cross-sectional method is also illustrated in the classical work of Smith (1926), a study of the vocabulary and sentence structure of children 8 months to 6 years old. Her main interest was in the growth of these two language skills with increasing age. She did not use the International Phonetic Alphabet but devised a shorthand of her own. The cross-sectional method was also employed by Wellman, Case, Mengert, and Bradbury (1931) in a study of phonetic development of children 2 to 6 years old. These workers transcribed the data live in the International Phonetic Alphabet. The children's vocalizations were elicited by the presentation of toys and pictures and by questions. The sounds, 133 in all, 66 consonants, 48 consonant blends, 15 vowels, and 4 diphthongs were tested. The subjects were children in the preschool laboratories of the Iowa Child Welfare Research Station, and the average IQ was 115.9 ± 15.4. Test reliability was determined by the split-half method on 123 sounds by 57 children. The correlation was .96 ± .01. The range of item difficulty for consonants calculated by the number of children passing the items was 40.3 to 98.5 per cent. For the blends, it was 27.4 to 82.7, for vowels, 78.2 to 95.9, and for diphthongs it was 80.8 to 84.4 per cent. The validity of the test was not reported.

Williams and McFarland (1937) and his students revised the Wellman test by reducing the number of items from 133 to 98. He selected the most frequently used sounds in the International Kindergarten Union Test and the first 2500 words of the Thorndike list. His test was then given in two parts, Form I and Form II. The responses were obtained by means of pictures and by having the subjects repeat the words after the experimenter. Using 65 children of the university and hospital staff at the University of Michigan, Poole (1934) studied their phonetic responses to pictures, objects, and questions. Her purpose was to determine the order of difficulty of consonants. She reported that the first sounds were labials, a result that later work has not substantiated (Winitz and Irwin, 1958).

An example of the use of the longitudinal approach to speech development is a study by Chen (1946). Its purpose was to determine the course of mastery of the elemental speech sounds during the first year of life. The measures used were the number of phonemes, designated phoneme types, and the number of repeated sounds, called phoneme frequency. The subjects were 47 boys and 48 girls, children of laborers, skilled workers, clerks, businessmen, lawyers, physicians, and college teachers. About half of them were classified in the category of professional families, according to the Minnesota Occupational Scale. The infants were visited in their homes twice a month, at which time a sample of spontaneously produced sounds was recorded live. The broad transcription of the International Phonetic Alphabet according to Fairbanks (1940) was used.

The behavorial unit method was used by Chen to observe the sounds. This was an innovation by Irwin and Curry (1941). With this device, the unit of observation is the single respiration of the infant, instead of a time unit. Sounds uttered on the exhalation phase of a breath are noted and recorded by the observer. The advantage of the method is that the number of sounds vocalized by the infant on a single breath lies within the ordinary attention span of the observer.

The sounds carried on 30 breaths constituted the sample at each visit. Observer reliability varied from 72 to 91 per cent. The reliability of the data was determined by correlating the odd versus the even sounds in the record. For the period of one to twelve months, the correlation was .97 for vowels and .90 for consonants. A further check was made by comparing the sounds carried on the first 30 respirations with those on the second 30. Fifty-seven per cent of the correlations exceeded .70. A special problem for the observer arose when the infant vocalized rapidly on consecutive breaths. The method of solving this problem was as follows.

Two observers recorded live the sounds of a group of infants on the consecutive, alternate, and fourth exhalations when the subjects were producing sounds rapidly. The distribution of phoneme frequencies was similar for the three samples. Therefore, if the observer occasionally failed to record sounds on the consecutive breath and took the sounds on a subsequent breath, the difference would not be great enough to distort the result. Irwin and Chen (1946) and Irwin (1947b,c), using the same procedures, have extended the investigation to cover the age range from the first to the thirtieth month and have reported the findings in terms of phoneme type and phoneme frequency.

Other studies that utilize the longitudinal method are by Krehbiel (1941) and Anderson (1942). Shirley (1933) jotted down the vocalizations of 25 babies during the first two years of life. A phonetic alphabet was not used to record the sounds, the earliest of which were described as coos and grunts. She also recorded comprehensible words in terms of length, that is, one-, two-, and three-syllable words.

## THE CONTROL GROUP OR COMPARATIVE METHOD

A technique for studying a variety of developmental processes is the comparative method. The control may be a specially selected group, or it may be constituted by data from another research. The matching may be by groups, or it may be by individuals on the basis of external criteria, such as age, mental status, economic background, or education. The method may be used to provide a basis of comparison of the speech of the sexes, of age groups, of normal and of various types of speech-deviate children. Carrow (1957) has studied the linguistic functioning of bilingual and monolingual children. The two groups were similar in regard to age, grade, socioeconomic status, and intelligence. Several tests of language skills were administered, namely, silent reading (vocabulary and comprehension), oral reading (accuracy, comprehension, and rate), hearing vocabulary, spelling, and arithmetic reasoning. Comparison between the two groups was made with regard to articulation, number of words used, length of clause, degree of subordination, complexity of sentence structure, and the number and type of grammatical errors.

A careful and valuable study, comparing four psychological scaling methods of articulation defectiveness, was done by Sherman and Moodie (1957). The scaling methods were equal-appearing intervals, successive intervals, paired comparisons, and the method of constant sums. The materials used for the four methods of scaling articulation defectiveness consisted of five-second excerpts from the continuous speech of children 5 to 10 years old. The excerpts ranged from normal to severely defective speech. Records of the samples were played back to 350 listeners who judged the quality of articulation in terms of the four scaling methods. The method of equal-appearing intervals seems to be the most useful for scaling defective articulation.

An interesting and suggestive variant of the comparative method is Templin's (1957) terminal status technique. She presents terminal status measures for each of four major language areas: articulation of speech sounds, speech-sound discrimination, sentence structure, and vocabulary. Separate scores are presented by age levels for boys and girls and for children in the upper and lower status groups. For each of the four language areas, the mean score of the 8-year-old group was taken as the terminal status measure. The percentage of the value of this mean score for each younger age level was calculated. Thus, with the mean score of the 8-year-old subjects as the terminal status measure, comparisons were made of the development of articulation, sentence structure, sound discrimination, and vocabulary. Chen's (1946) differential percentage index is a similar device, which uses adult speech status as a basis of comparison for the speech of infants.

A careful investigation was conducted by Fisichelli (1950) who compared the speech-sound status of 100 orphanage babies with that of a group of Chen's (1946) subjects as controls. These orphanage children showed a paucity of speech-sound mastery in comparison to children living in their own homes. Brodbeck and Irwin (1946), in a similar job with 95 orphanage babies under 6 months of age, compared their phonetic output with that of infants of the same age range living in their own homes. Curves of speech sounds of the orphanage children were significantly lower than those of the control group. Carr (1953) published an investigation of the speech-sound status of fifty 5-year-old deaf-born children, with that of hearing infants as controls. The former were greatly inferior to the controls.

An instance of the combination of the comparative and longitudinal methods is a study by Irwin (1958a,b,c). In order to increase the amount of speech-sound stimulation in the homes of working-class people, the mothers of a group of children 13 to 30 months of age were instructed to read to them daily for a period of fifteen minutes from illustrated baby books. The mothers pointed out objects in the pictures, named them, made up stories about them, and talked frequently to the children. A second group of infants of comparable ages in working-class homes in which no systematic stimulation occurred served as the control. The differences in amount of phoneme frequency between the two groups after the eighteenth month were significantly in favor of the experimental group. The study is an illustration of the combination of the control or comparative method with the longitudinal approach. It also illustrates two limitations of the longitudinal method. Five years were required to collect the data, and during that time a number of subjects dropped out because their families moved to other communities.

The use of the comparative approach to speech behavior in children has been productive of a large body of new information about the speech of both normals and deviants. With proper instrumentation and appropriate statistical controls, the comparative method undoubtedly is the most reliable and precise of all the methods discussed in this chapter. Instances of the compara-

tive method with the use of instruments are those by Travis (1937) employing the brain-wave technique to compare stutterers and nonstutterers. Perlstein, Gibbs, and Gibbs (1953) have done an exhaustive research on the electroencephalogram in 1500 cases of infantile cerebral palsy. Williams (1953) used electromyography to study the action currents in the masseter muscles of stutterers and nonstutterers.

An especially effective comparative method uses the same subjects as controls. A test measuring some aspect of speech defectiveness is administered to a group of subjects before a course of treatment is applied, a set of instructions given, or a remedial program is undertaken. Following the treatment, the test is again administered. Octoby (Branscom et al., 1956) measured the effect of instructions to stutterers to prevent, modify, or replace their customary patterns of reaction to expectancy of stuttering. With stutterers a method of measurement is to count the number of stuttered words in a selected passage read by the subject. In this study the subject was required to read a 200-word passage aloud five times in succession. Jones (1956) investigated the effect of clinical instruction for periods varying from two weeks to two years. He used five 250-word factual reading passages. Another test was administered after an interval during which spontaneous recovery of stuttering had occurred.

In the area of verbal learning in children a comparative method now being used with the same subjects is based on the principle of mediated generalization. It is applicable to the phenomenon of associative transfer in paired-associate learning. In the paired-associate method the child is presented with a series of pairs of words, the first word of each pair being the stimulus and the second, the response. The child is instructed to associate each response with its stimulus so that when he sees the first word he can say the second. For instance, if the pair is "cake" and "boat," he would say boat when he sees the word cake. Usually, in an experiment, a list of pairs, perhaps 6 or as many as 15, are presented. On the first run through the list the child observes the pairs and tries to associate each response with its stimulus. On the second trial the stimulus is presented first, and the response word is presented following an interval of several seconds. This is called the anticipation interval. The subject is required to call out the response during this period. If he succeeds, it is recorded as correct, but if the response word is presented before he is able to say it an error or omission is recorded. The pairs are presented in a different order on each trial. It is necessary to use two or more lists of word pairs to study transfer effect.

In this connection, it is necessary also to define the concept of generalization. When a stimulus A comes to evoke response B, stimuli similar to A, such as $A_1$, $A_2$, likewise tend to elicit B. This is stimulus generalization. When stimulus A is able to evoke response B, it will likewise elicit similar responses, $B_1$, $B_2$, etc. This is response generalization. A third form of generalization is known as the phenomenon of associative transfer and is used in verbal paired-associate learning with children. The principle involved is that a response to a stimulus in turn becomes a stimulus to another response. The design calls for two preliminary lists of paired words and a third test list administered in an A–B, B–C, A–C sequence. That is, B is the response to A, C is the response to B, and C in the test list is the response to A. It will be noted that B is in the intermediate position and serves a mediating function in the transfer from A to C. The degree of associative transfer is tested by administering the A–C list. A further variant of the design may be made by giving a D–C list of words to serve as a control. The D list is a new list.

The lists are presented visually by means of a card master, which consists of two parts. One part is a metal box containing a bin in which a stack of cards with paired words is placed and a conveyer system that delivers the cards one at a time to an aperture. Here the card is exposed for a given period, the anticipation interval. The second part of the apparatus is a system of electric timers that controls the rate of presenting the cards at the aperture as well as the exposure time. A more detailed description of the apparatus and the results of experiments with children may be found in the chapter on Research Methods on Children's Learning by Dr. Spiker (see Chapter 9). Here only the general principles of paired-associate learning have been explained. Two carefully designed studies in this field, with children as subjects, are those of Norcross and Spiker (1958) and Spiker (1958).

The particular advantage of using the same subjects in a test-retest situation is that the method not only provides information about the progress in rehabilitation made by the group as a whole, but it reveals specific information about each individual composing the group. In statistical language, it provides a within-group analysis. Accordingly, the method is of value to the speech therapist working with a single child. It assumes, of course, the availability of a reliable and valid measuring instrument.

## INSTRUMENTAL METHODS

A number of mechanical and electrical devices has been used to analyze various aspects of speech, although not all have found extensive use with children. An attempt will be made to describe them as nontechnically as possible. For the technical details of their construction and operation, the reader is referred to a comprehensive treatment with numerous diagrams and pictures in *Handbook of Speech Pathology* edited by Travis (1957).

A widely used device for recording speech sounds is the magnetic tape recorder. The entire unit consists of a microphone, a coil, an amplifier, and a loud-speaker. A tape treated with magnetic oxide of iron upon which a pattern is impressed is passed through the coil. The passage through the coil produces a series of electrical impulses, which, upon amplification, are converted by a loud-speaker into sounds. Thus, by means of the recorder, sound is translated into electricity and then converted back into sound. Its advantages are ease and fidelity of recording and permanence of the record. The

unit is somewhat heavy and cumbersome for transportation, although lightweight recorders are being manufactured.

For the purpose of detecting structural abnormalities of the lips, teeth, palate, pharynx, larynx, and nasal passages, several instruments are available. These include tongue blades, mirrors, or laryngoscopes, which combine a mirror and a light source, and the nasal speculum, a device for distending the nostrils. There are several devices for measuring speech-sound intensity. The deflections of the pointer on an oscillograph may be photographed on film on which decibel lines are traced. The fundamental frequency of the human voice has been investigated with the phonophonelescope. This consists of a motor-driven turntable film-drum, a phonograph recording and pick-up heads, an amplifying unit, and an optical system. Fairbanks (1940) investigated pitch of children's voices with the phonophonelescope.

The Bell Telephone Laboratories have developed the sound spectrograph for use in recording and analyzing speech sounds. It has had considerable use with adult subjects, but work with infants and children is in an early stage. It provides a highly promising technique for the acoustic analysis of the phonetic equipment of young subjects. The instrument is a device for converting auditory into visible records. A technical description of recent refinements of the sound spectrograph is given by Prestigriacomo (1957). The measurements are in terms of the frequency, intensity, and duration characteristics of sound. It is important, however, to recognize that the instrument yields acoustic rather than phonetic or linguistic measures. A necessary procedure for the interpretation of these measures is the identification by trained listeners of the sounds uttered by the subjects.

Essentially, the apparatus consists of a means of recording magnetically a sample of speech sounds to be analyzed. The analysis of sound samples is made by a heterodyne wave analyzer. The resulting data are plotted with frequency on the vertical axis and time on the abscissa. The intensity of the sound is indicated by the darkness of the marking. Another plot, often referred to as a cross-sectional picture, has amplitude in decibels on the ordinate and frequency on the abscissa. This plot appears as a series of harmonics and inharmonics, and the peaks or points of energy concentration in the spectrum are known as formants. They are usually numbered according to their order in a frequency scale, from low to high as formant one, formant two, etc.

It has been suggested that it is important to distinguish auditory and acoustic phenomena and that the final interpretation of the physical properties of sounds depends upon their auditory identification by skilled listeners. This is but an illustration of the fact that all scientific findings by means of an apparatus, no matter how precise or refined it may be, in the last analysis must be checked and identified in terms of the sense data of an observer. Likewise, the formants, for their valid interpretation, must be correlated and identified with the phonemes they are supposed to represent acoustically. This

is the procedure followed by workers in this area of investigation. Koch (1952) plotted formant one versus formant two of the same vowel sounds uttered by a man, a woman, and a child. He found that the frequencies for similar vowels produced by the three individuals were not alike but that nevertheless the speech was intelligible. G. E. Peterson obtained the same result. A study by Peterson and Barney (1952) is pertinent to this discussion. They used 33 men, 28 women, and 15 children to correlate acoustic measurements and auditory identifications of ten vowel sounds. The average correct recognition of the ten vowels amounted to 79 per cent. Thus the identification of sounds uttered by vocal cavities of different sizes and shapes is not an impossible task. Liberman, Harris, Hoffman, and Griffith (1957) have demonstrated that listeners will identify a given phoneme, for example [b], although the spectrogram exhibited several acoustically different patterns. The listeners perceived and divided a stimulus continuum including [b], [d], and [g] into three sharply bounded phonemic categories. For a study on some of the factors in vowel identification, see Tiffany (1953). The matter of reduction to the sense data of an observer has been stressed because of its importance in interpreting spectrographic work with infants and children.

Two studies, one by Lynip (1951) and the other by Winitz (1958) have used the spectrograph to study the acoustic characteristics of sounds uttered by infants. Lynip criticized previous work on the speech development of infants on the grounds that the gathering of speech data must be devoid of such handicaps as the fallibilities of the human ear and also of the use of phonetic systems and that the data must be analyzed in an objective manner. He worked with one infant from birth to 56 weeks. Lynip's view is that the resonance pattern of the infant's vowel sounds is different from that of adult vowels. That there are differences between the acoustic patterns of infants and adults is not in itself the least unusual, as indicated in Peterson and Barney's (1952) study in which differences among 33 men, 28 women, and 15 children speaking various dialects were reported. Thus there is some question about Lynip's interpretation of his data. Winitz (1958) repeated Lynip's experiment, using 31 vowel sounds agreed upon by seven judges, with results similar to those reported by Koch (1952).

## METHODS OF STUDYING SPEECH SOUND ERRORS

It is obvious that the focus of the therapist's attention should be upon the errors made by a child, for here the burden of remedial effort will be directed. It follows then that methods of studying speech-sound errors occupy a major role in the diagnosis of the child's speech status.

A number of studies have been concerned with noting the errors in children's speech. Four types of error are usually reported: substitutions, omissions, distortions, and additions. A substitution error is the use of one consonant for another, such as [w] for [r] or [s] for [z]. An omission means that a sound is lacking in its proper place in a word. A distortion is usually defined as a modification that only approximates the standard sound, such as a hissing or whistling [s]. Frequently the [s] sounds take on the quality of a lateral, [ʃ], in which case it becomes a substitution. An addition may be illustrated by the pattern "puhlease" for please.

The methods of collecting data on speech-sound errors vary. Simple observation with live recording (paper and pencil) is frequently used in the studies. Sometimes the spontaneous sounds are recorded in play situations. In other studies test items are assembled to elicit responses to objects, pictures, and questions (Branscom, Hughes, and Octoby, 1956). In some of the work selected words are read to the subject, who is instructed to repeat them.

Bryngelson and Glaspey (1951) have developed picture articulation tests for commonly missed consonant sounds for rapid testing of young children. This type of test does not, however, provide a complete phonetic inventory. Halstead and Wepman (1949) developed a test for aphasics, and Eisenson (1954) published a graded test for the examination of aphasics. In tests of stuttering the subjects are requested to read selected passages, and stuttered words are counted. In the sound discrimination test pairs of similar sounding words with but one different phoneme are presented to the child either verbally or pictorially.

Wellman, Case, Mengert, and Bradbury (1931) tested 204 nursery-school children to produce the sounds of the English language by recording live in the International Phonetic Alphabet verbal responses obtained by questions and the presentation of pictures and toys. The relative difficulties of consonant elements, consonant blends, vowels, and diphthongs were studied. Williams and McFarland (1937) followed this research with a study on the nature of the commonest errors of preschool children and concerned himself mainly with the most frequent substitutions in 104 speech sounds in consonant elements, consonant blends, triple blends, vowels, and diphthongs. Melreaux (1950) used 116 children of average or above intelligence in a guidance center. There were seven ages: 18, 24, 30, 36, 42, 48, and 54 months. The responses of each child were recorded in the international alphabet. Correct production, substitutions, and omissions of sounds in the initial, medial, and final positions in words were noted.

Roe and Milisen (1942) published an extensive survey on consonant substitution and omission errors in the speech of 1989 normal children in grades one to six. They found that substitution errors were more frequent than omissions. Sayler (1949) continued the Roe and Milisen work upward through grades seven to twelve with the same result. Bangs (1942) selected a homogeneous group of primary aments from an institution and studied the substitutions, omissions, and additions in their speech by using 65 picture cards as stimuli. He reports that retarded children committed fewer substitution errors than omissions. Irwin (1959) devised a short test consisting of the ten most difficult consonants reported in the literature

and administered it to a group of retarded children with IQ's ranging from 25 to 49 and to another group with IQ's ranging from 50 to 90. The first group made more omission than substitution errors, but the reverse situation was found for the second. Omission errors in the final position accounted for the bulk of errors made by the low IQ group. Irwin (1956b) found that omissions are more frequent than substitutions in the speech of cerebral palsied children. Johnson and Leutenegger (1956) have edited a number of studies on stuttering, and Johnson, Brown, Curtis, Edney, and Keaster (1948) have discussed the speech problems of handicapped school children.

Irwin (1956c, 1957c,f, 1958a,b) has constructed a series of short tests for use with cerebral palsied children. Since these children fatigue quickly and their attention span often is limited, each of the tests was limited to about 15 or 20 words, in which speech elements were placed in various positions. A further aim of the project was to secure a nationwide sample, so that it is representative of the entire population of the country. The observer reliability in reading the tape recordings averages about 90 per cent. Thus the error in this work amounts to about 10 per cent. The reliability of the test, using the Hoyt (1951) formula based on an analysis of variance, is .91 ± .01. The criterion of age progression of the scores in terms of phoneme type and phoneme frequency is not always met with these children. The ranges of difficulty of the items vary from about 20 to 90 per cent. The correlations of items with the score of the total test is high, whereas the intercorrelations of items generally is low. Thus the discriminating power and the uniqueness of the items are both statistically satisfactory. The validity of these tests was determined by the method of extreme groups (Adkins, 1947). Irwin (1957c) has also presented good evidence of its validity.

Westlake (1951) has built a test for examining the oral muscular functions of cerebral palsied children. The test consists of four parts, organized as follows:

A. Tongue
   1. Move tip below lower lip
   2. Move tip above upper lip
   3. Move tip from corner to corner
   4. Move tip against lower teeth
   5. Move tip against upper teeth

B. Lips
   1. Extend corners of lips backward from forward rounded position (teeth together)
   2. Open and close lips (teeth together)

C. Mandible
   1. Open and close mouth (jaw and lips move together)

D. Respiration
   1. Sustain even phonation of the sound for 10 seconds
   2. Sustain even silent exhalation for 10 seconds

The number of times in one minute each of the oral movements occurs successfully constitutes the score. Their sum is the total score. The number of seconds the respiratory responses are sustained yields another score. Irwin (1957c) has determined the reliability of this test in terms of correct scores recorded by each of two observers. The mean of one observer was 62.4, of the other, 62.5. The ranges were identical. Irwin has correlated the scores on Westlake's oral test and a short consonant test with 226 cerebral palsied children $3\frac{1}{2}$ to 19 years old. The $r$ is .534 ± .049. The $r$ for correct speech scores and respiration was .296 ± .063. It would seem that oral movement is somewhat better as a predictor than respiration of consonantal articulation.

The speech-sound discrimination test offers a method that is both objective and easy to score. Speech-sound discrimination is usually defined as the ability to recognize auditory distinctions among different phonemes. It represents a perceptual factor in speech and language ability. The test is constituted by a series of words paired in such a way that only one sound in each pair differs. A simple illustration would involve the ability of a child to recognize and discriminate the difference between the initial consonant in *h*at and *f*at or in the pair "horn-corn." The subjects may be presented with paired words, spoken orally by the experimenter, or with paired pictures and asked to tell whether they are the same or different.

An early speech-sound discrimination test was constructed by Travis and Rasmus (1931). It has served as the prototype of subsequent tests. They compared functional articulation defectives with good freshman speakers at a university and at the elementary-school level. At every age compared the cases with disorders made significantly more errors than the normal speakers.

Mansur (1950) built a sound discrimination test, which was later modified by Pronovost and Dumbleton (1953). It consists of 36 pairs of discrimination words presented in 72 picture items.

Templin (1957), influenced by this work, has reported two speech-sound discrimination tests, one designed for use with children 3 to 5 years old and one with children 6 to 8. The first test includes 59 picture items or pairs. Pairs of pictures of familiar objects whose names are words similar in pronunciation except for single sounds were pasted on a card and shown to the child. An example is "box" and "blocks." The examiner pronounced the name of one of the two objects, and the child was required to point to it. This is called the stimulus word method. It is a useful device, but a difficulty may arise because of the child's limited vocabulary. By carefully selecting words used in preschool word and story books, in childrens' conversations, and in the vocabulary sections of preschool intelligence tests, this difficulty in large part may be obviated. The discrimination test for the 6-to-8-year-old children was composed of 50 pairs of words which were read to the children.

Schiefelbusch and Lindsey (1958) have constructed a new test of sound discrimination. Eleven consonant sounds were selected for the initial and final positions in words selected for the study. They are [s], [ʔ], [r], [ʃ], [θ], [v], [t], [g], [k], and [tʃ]. The words with their picture representations were arranged on cards. On each card were three pictures, two alike in regard to rhyming, initial, or final sounds and a third that contained a sound fre-quently substituted for the one employed in the other two pictures. There was a total of 90 pictures. This test was used to determine three discrimination abilities, one as the children hear the items spoken by others, another as they produce them themselves, and a third part in which they evaluate the items silently. The picture cards were presented in three ways:

1. The therapist named the three pictures on each card and asked the subject to select the two that sounded alike.

2. The child was instructed to name the three pictures and to determine the two that were alike.

3. The child was instructed to look silently at three pictures and select the two that contained the similar elements.

The pictures were presented to matched groups of children with defective articulation and children with normal speech. Significant differences were found between the speech-defective and the normal speaking groups in ability to discriminate sounds. The method of presentation did not show any conclusive results that would indicate that speech-defective children have greater difficulty when instructed to look silently at the three pictures and to select the two that contained the similar element.

## VOCABULARY MEASUREMENT

Before proceeding with the evaluation of vocabulary tests, something should be said about the studies that report the appearance in infant speech of the first word. There is a number of reports in the literature on this matter. Bühler (1930), Leopold (1939), and Lewis (1951) have summarized these observations. In the main, the results were obtained by casual observation without careful controls or recording apparatus.

There is a special problem in identifying and defining the earliest words of infants, for many of them are mutilations or approximations to standard words. McCurry and Irwin (1953) have given the following definitions:

A standard word is defined in terms of its phonetic listing in Kenyon and Knott's Pronouncing Dictionary of American English (p. 133).

A word approximation is defined as a phonetic pattern in which one or more of the phonetic elements of the standard word, either vowel or consonantal elements, are present. This means that some elements of the standard pattern are omitted and other elements are substituted or added (p. 133).

The relevance of these definitions to problems of methodology is that the reports in the literature on the appearance of the first word usually fail to make the distinction between the standard word and the approximation to the standard word. This failure sometimes renders inconclusive the results of the method of observing the first words.

A widely used research method in the area of speech development is the vocabulary test. Wechsler (1949) has included a vocabulary test as a separate unit in his intelligence scale for children. Reliabilities for this unit are reported in the manual describing the scale as ranging from .77 to the .90's. The verbal part of Wechsler's scale correlates well with the Revised Stanford-Binet Test.

Vocabulary tests for use with normal children are presented by Smith (1926), Van Alstyne (1929), Williams and McFarland (1937), Seashore and Eckerson (1940), whose test was used by Smith (1941). Other tests are those by Ammons and Ammons (1948) and Templin (1957) and a series of short tests for use with cerebral palsied children by Irwin (1956a,c, 1957b,c,d,e).

Since some of these tests do not measure up to the criteria for the standardization of a testing instrument, at this point it might be pertinent to indicate briefly what these requirements are. There is a number of techniques for the selection of items in a testing instrument. Some are based on scaling methods, and factor analysis is also used. Usually a statement of the reliability and validity of a test is considered sufficient to establish its usefulness, but such statements are not always given. Moreover, there are other valuable criteria for estimating the usefulness of a test, such as age progression in the scores of normal children, the range of difficulty of the items, the discriminating power of the items, and their uniqueness. The following definitions are given of these criteria in order that they may be applied to a number of tests to be considered.

One of the first requirements of a test is its internal consistency or reliability, which may be determined in several ways. Among the most acceptable is the Kuder-Richardson Formula (1937) or Hoyt's (1941) method based on an analysis of variance. The range of difficulty of an item is determined by the percentage of testees passing. If a large percentage passes an item, it is rated easy. If only a small percentage passes it, it is considered difficult. The range of difficulty of the items of a test should ordinarily be 10 or 15 per cent to 85 or 90 per cent. The problem of age progression, or the increasing size of scores with age, may frequently be determined by inspection. It is important in a standardized test that its items discriminate the individuals taking the test. If all the testees, irrespective of their ability, make the same scores on an item, that item lacks the power to discriminate them. This criterion is calculated by the correlation of the item scores with the scores on the whole test. High correlations indicate satisfactory discriminating power. Item uniqueness means that two items do not to any great degree test the same function. It may be determined by the intercorrelations among the items. A small $r$ between two items indicates their uniqueness. These values should be lower than the $r$'s for discriminating power.

The most important criterion of a test is its validity. An acceptable method for establishing the validity of a testing instrument is to give it together with a previously standardized test to the same sample of individuals. A high correlation is taken as evidence of the validity of the new test. Ammons and Ammons (1948) validated their picture vocabulary test against Wechsler's (1949) intelligence scale for children. The $r = .82$. If an external criterion, such as another test, is not available, another technique for establishing validity is the Adkins (1947) method of extreme groups. For instance, if the difference between the means of the articulation

scores of two extreme groups, say mildly involved and severely involved cerebral palsied children, is significant statistically, it may be taken as evidence of the validity of the data. The physician's rating of the degree of involvement constitutes the external criterion and thus meets the requirement for establishing validity. Age progression of test scores may also be taken as evidence for the validity of a test.

One of the earliest vocabulary tests was published by Smith (1926). Two hundred and forty-four children, varying in age from 8 months to 6 years, were observed. One hundred children were recruited from the Baby Examining Laboratory, 95 from the Preschool Laboratories of the Iowa Child Welfare Research Station and the Primary Group of the University Elementary School, 30 from the Day Nursery, and 19 from the Home of the Friendless in Cedar Rapids, Iowa. Thus there were more children at the upper and lower ends of the mental scale than would be found in a normal distribution. Test items taken from the Thorndike (1921) Word Book numbered 203. An object or a picture was presented to the child and appropriate questions were asked. The order of difficulty of the words was determined in terms of the frequency of their knowledge by 61 children. The reliability of the test was secured by administering two halves of it to 53 children varying in age from 4 to 6 years. The product moment correlation was $.95 \pm .02$. The correlation with scores on the Terman (1916) Vocabulary List was $.84 \pm .03$. The criterion of age progression, that is, the increase in correct scores from the youngest to the oldest age, was met in this study. Nothing, however, is indicated about the discriminating power or the uniqueness of the items. This test was widely used and has had a pronounced influence on the development of other tests.

Williams and McFarland (1937) produced a revision of the Smith Vocabulary Test. The number of items was reduced and cast into two lists, Form I and Form II, each containing 42 words. The test was given to 252 children, 27 to 74 months of age, who were attending the preschool laboratories of the Iowa Child Welfare Research Station and a second group of 64 orphanage children, 28 to 73 months of age. Here, again, one group included almost exclusively children of superior status and above average mentality, the other, children of low socioeconomic status and below average intelligence. In neither the Smith test nor the revision by Williams and McFarland was the distribution of cases typical of the population. The reliability of the test, determined by the correlation between scores on Forms I and II, was .96 ± .003 for 359 children. The order of difficulty of the items was determined for both lists. The range is 0 to 99.6 per cent. There is progression in the scores with both chronological and mental age. Since age is an external criterion, age progression in scores may be taken as a form of validity. Validity, in the sense of correlation with another vocabulary test, is not reported. No statements are made concerning the discriminating power or the uniqueness of the items of this test.

Van Alstyne (1929) built a picture vocabulary test for use with 3-year-olds but which could be used with children whose mental ages are between 2 and 5 years. The multiple-choice method was used to test the children. The child was presented with a card with four pictures and asked, "Show me the _____," for nouns, and "What is _____ing?" for verbs. There are 45 cards in all, and the test words include 31 nouns and 14 verbs. Norms are based on the scores of 80 children from 33 to 39 months of age. Two criteria of test construction are reported. The reliability correlation of the test was 0.87, and there is almost perfect correlation with the Kuhlman Mental Test. Other criteria are not reported.

Ammons and Ammons (1948) developed a full-range picture-vocabulary test for the purpose of securing quick estimates of verbal ability of children. It can also be used to test the intelligence of the physically handicapped and the retarded child. Van Alstyne's multiple-choice recognition picture approach, involving the procedure of the child pointing to the appropriate picture named, was adopted. The materials are 64 ink line drawings arranged in groups of four, so that there are altogether 16 plates. The words, organized by plates, are in order of difficulty. There are 253 words and phrases in the list. The subjects were 51 white children all from the same school, two boys and two girls from each grade level from kindergarten through the twelfth grade. The average IQ was 115. Test reliability, using the odd-even method, was .95 ± .01. Instead of reporting a range of difficulty of the items of the test, an attempt was made to determine the 50 per cent level of difficulty by throwing out items that were not passed by 50 per cent of the testees. The validity of the test, measured by the correlation between the total picture-vocabulary test and scores on the Binet vocabulary test, was .96 ± .01. Templin (1957) found that there is age progression in scores of her subjects when tested with the Ammons Full-Range Picture-Vocabulary Test. Seashore and Eckerson (1940) issued a vocabulary test available for use with children from grades 1 to 12. Smith (1941) established norms for it on 867 children. The odd-even reliability for this test was about .90 for grades 5 to 9.

A very significant vocabulary study was done by Mildred Templin (1957). She emphasized the method of discriminating between the vocabulary of use and the vocabulary of recognition or understanding and studying the two separately. The vocabulary of use includes those words that are actually produced in oral or written speech. The vocabulary of understanding consists of words that are recognized or understood when read or heard. She also introduced the method of comparing results obtained with children of upper socioeconomic status with those of lower socioeconomic status. The vocabulary of recognition was measured by the Ammons Full-Range Picture-Vocabulary Test and the Seashore-Eckerson English Recognition Vocabulary Test. The subjects were 30 boys and 30 girls aged 3, 3.5, 4, 4.5, and 5 years. There was a steady increase with age in mean scores of 60 children on the Ammons test. When the data

were combined into whole year intervals, the scores tended to be quite similar to those reported by Ammons and Holmes (1949). In administering the Seashore-Eckerson Test, Smith (1941) first asked each child to define a word; then, if he was unable to do so, he was given four possible meanings from which to choose the correct one. Templin followed the manual of directions prepared by Smith for administering the test. In studying the vocabulary for use, 50 remarks were secured from her subjects. There was a steady increase in the number of different words used from one age to another.

Gesell's (1928) scale includes items for indicating language development. It is limited to the period below 30 months of age. In her standardized scales of the mental development of babies from 1 to 24 months Griffiths (1954) included a section with items on speech and hearing. The items are largely premeaning sounds.

## METHODS OF STUDYING SENTENCE STRUCTURE

The babbling speech of the young baby is chaotic, meaningless, and completely devoid of conventional form and content. In no sense is it a language. Quite literally, it is only the raw materials from which a language, any language, may be formed. It is one of the supreme accomplishments of the human being that from these meaningless speech sounds the infant eventually molds and constructs such a complicated structure as a compound or complex sentence, not to say a fullblown meaningful language, and that he does it for the most part quite early in life. It is important then that the development of language should be carefully studied and information gathered as to how the child manages to achieve the skill of combining words into sentences.

There is a problem of defining the sentence. It is sometimes designated as a verbalization. Templin (1957) defines the term verbalization as a thought unit, something "in which the child has something to express. A unit might be as brief and incomplete as a single word; it might be a grammatically complete and accurate sentence; or it might be several clauses uttered one after another as a loosely integrated sentence" (p. 74). Williams and McFarland (1937) preferred to use the term "expression unit" rather than the sentence. This is a unit "in which the child has something to express to someone else." "This might be as brief and incomplete as a single word, or might extend over several highly connected clauses given together as a more or less integrated unit" (p. 10). Williams goes on to treat the expression unit in several ways: (1) correctness and completeness of word usage, (2) mean length of the expression unit, (3) sentence completeness in terms of subject-predicate-object relationship, and (4) complexity of organization of the unit in terms of the grammatical classification of simple, compound, and complex. For the measurement of the expression unit, arbitrary weights of 0, 1, 2, and 3 were assigned to unintelligible, simple, complex, and compound-complex units.

Templin (1957) has devoted an appendix to rules defining sentences. They are adapted from the lists of McCarthy (1930) and Davis (1937). The appendix is quoted in full:

### Rules Followed for Classification of Words and Sentences

#### A. Rules for Counting Number of Words

1. Contractions of subject and predicate like "it's" and "we're" are counted as two words.
2. Contractions of the verb and the negative such as "can't" are counted as one word.
3. Each part of a verbal combination is counted as a separate word: thus "have been playing" is counted as three words.
4. Hyphenated and compound nouns are one word.
5. Expressions which function as a unit in the child's understanding were counted as one word, thus "oh boy," "all right," etc., were counted as one word, while "Christmas tree" was counted as two words.

#### B. Classification of Sentence Structure

I. Complete sentences.
  A. Functionally complete but structurally incomplete. This includes naming; answers in which omitted words are implied because they were expressed in the question; expletives; and other remarks, incomplete in themselves, which are clearly a continuation of the preceding remark.
  B. Simple sentence without phrase.
  C. Simple sentence containing (1) phrase used as adjective or adverb in opposition, (2) compound subject or predicate, (3) compound predicate.
  D. Complex sentence (one main clause, one subordinate clause) with (1) noun clause used (a) as subject, (b) as object, (c) in apposition, (d) as predicate nominative, (e) as objective complement; (2) adjective clause (a) restrictive, (b) non-re-

strictive; (3) adverbial clauses of (a) time, (b) place, (c) manner, (d) comparison, (e) condition, (f) concession, (g) cause, (h) purpose, (i) result; (4) infinitive.

E. Compound sentence (two independent clauses).

F. Elaborated sentence: (1) simple sentence with two or more phrases, or compound subject, or predicate and phrase; (2) complex sentence with more than one subordinate clause, or with a phrase or phrases; (3) compound sentence with more than two independent clauses, or with a subordinate clause or phrases.

II. Incomplete sentences.

A. Fragmentary or incomprehensible. Example: "Well—not this, but—."

B. (1) Verb omitted completely, (2) auxiliary omitted, verb or participle expressed, (3) verb or participle omitted, auxiliary expressed.

C. Subject omitted, either from main or subordinate clause.

D. Introductory "there" omitted.

E. Pronoun other than subject of verb omitted.

F. Preposition (usually needed sign of infinitive) omitted.

G. Verb and subject omitted.

H. Main clause incomplete, subordinate clause or second clause of compound sentence complete.

I. Main clause complete, subordinate or second clause incomplete. Example: "I know why."

J. Omission from both main and subordinate clauses.

K. Essential words present, but sentence loosely constructed because of (1) omission of conjunction, (2) insertion of parenthetical clause, (3) changes in form halfway in sentence. Example: "We have—my brother has a motorcycle."

L. (1) Definite, (2) indefinite article omitted.

M. Object omitted from either main clause or prepositional phrase.

N. Sentence left dangling.

McCarthy's (1930) careful study on language development in the preschool child introduced a method that has been followed extensively by subsequent workers. She secured 50 verbalizations by 140 children ranging in age from 18 months to 54 months. The verbalizations were elicited by means of toys and books. The responses were analyzed in terms of their length, their grammatical form, and the parts of speech used. A similar pattern was used in a study of twins 2 to 5 years old by Day (1932) and by Davis (1937), whose samples consisted of only children, children with siblings, and twins 5.5 to 9.5 years of age. Other reports on this problem are by Shire (1945), Little and Williams (1937), and Templin (1957).

The length of response in terms of number of words is considered to be the most easily determined and objective method of studying the sentence. It has been widely used. Examples are the studies by Smith (1926), McCarthy (1930), Day (1932), Fisher (1932), Davis (1937), Shire (1945), and Templin (1957). LaBrant (1933) used the mean length of the clause in her work and suggested that the counting of predicates is an objective method for the study of the sentence.

Templin (1957) classified the remarks of 60 children 3 to 8 years old into six major categories: (1) functionally complete but structurally incomplete; (2) simple without phrase; (3) simple with phrase; (4) compound and complex; (5) elaborated; and (6) incomplete. She has employed several other methods of categorizing the children's sentences. One is the conventional grouping of sentences into declarative, interrogative, imperative, and exclamatory. Another makes use of noun, adjectival, and adverbial clauses. Her treatment of the use of parts of speech by children 3 to 8 years old involves a sample of 128,000 words. The parts of speech listed are noun, verb, adjective, adverb, pronoun, conjunction, preposition, article, and interjection. Templin's work undoubtedly presents the most comprehensive treatment found in the literature of the methodological problem of sentence structure of children.

## FUNCTIONS OF LANGUAGE

Piaget's (1926) volume on the language and thought of the child precipitated a controversy on the amount of egocentric speech indulged in by children. Methodology in this area on the side of research design is meager. It is concerned rather with how the data are to be analyzed. Piaget made records on the verbal behavior during free play of two 6-year-old children at La Maison des Petites. Two observers followed each child for about a month at the morning class, taking down in minute detail and in its context everything that was said by the child. The data consisted of about 1500 remarks.

Egocentric speech is defined by Piaget as (1) repetition, vocalization in which the child repeats words and syllables for the pleasure of talking; (2) monologue, in which the child talks to himself as though he were thinking aloud; (3) collective monologue, in which another child is present but his point of view is never taken into account. Socialized speech is defined as (1) adapted information, when the child really exchanges his thoughts with others; (2) criticism, which includes remarks about the work or behavior of others; (3) commands, requests, and threats; (4) questions; (5) answers.

Piaget estimated that 38 per cent of the child's remarks were egocentric and 62 per cent were socialized.

McCarthy (1930) repeated Piaget's work meticulously, using his definitions of egocentric and socialized verbal behavior. In order to stimulate the child's speech, she used pictures of animals, illustrated Mother Goose rhymes, and toys consisting of an auto, a cat, a telephone, a mouse, a music box, and a small ball. There were 140 children in the investigation, ranging in age from 18 to 54 months and selected so as to be representative of the population. Fifty remarks from each of the subjects constituted the data. McCarthy reports that only 3.6 per cent of the vocalizations of children are egocentric in nature. Day (1932) and Davis (1937) used the McCarthy method in their studies. These investigations also failed to confirm Piaget's findings, but a study by Fisher (1932) supported his results. Her subjects were 72 children, 37 girls and 35 boys whose ages ranged from 22 to 60 months. The mean IQ of the group was the unusually high value of 136. The data were obtained from stenographic records. On three different days, when his language was being recorded, each child was followed by a trained stenographer from the moment he arrived in the morning until he had finished his lunch and was ready to enter the sleeping room for his after-noon nap. The length of time of ob-servation for each subject was nine to twelve hours.

The controversial aspects of these studies arises not so much in the methods used to collect the data as in the manner of categorizing them. McCarthy (1954) has commented that the studies that have repeated Piaget's work, using his categories, have literally failed to substantiate him, whereas those which have attempted new definitions, usually in terms of the subject of the sentence, agree with his findings.

In connection with Piaget's concepts of the functions of language a word should be said about other views. This is also a somewhat controversial matter, for there are two extremely different schools of thought. One, exemplified by Wundt (1912) holds that the func-tion of language is to express psychic processes, such as ideas, feelings, and emotions. On the other hand, for DeLaguna (1927) it is a form of be-havior. She writes:

Speech is the great medium through which human cooperation is brought about. It is the means by which diverse activities of men are coordinated and cor-related with each other for the attainment of common and reciprocal ends. Men do not speak simply to relieve their feelings or to air their views, but to awaken a re-sponse in their fellows and to influence their attitudes and acts (p. 19).

An intermediate or eclectic notion of the function of language is that of Lewis (1951). Language for him has three functions: (1) expressive of the emo-tions; (2) representative, taking the place of things and pointing them out;

and (3) evocative or social, in the sense that it arouses a response in the listener. The foregoing discussion of other views was introduced in order to emphasize the fact that there are other dimensions of language besides Piaget's rather limited treatment.

## RELATIONSHIPS
## OF THE MEASURES
## OF LANGUAGE DEVELOPMENT

Something should be said about the problem of the interrelations of lan-guage skills. This is an area in which the problem of methodology in the design of a language study does not play a major role. After a number of test results have been secured, their in-terrelationships may be determined by a statistical treatment. Williams and McFarland (1937) administered tests to 38 preschool children and secured measures of speech sounds, word usage, length of expression unit, completeness and complexity of sentences, the Van Alstyne vocabulary, and the Williams vocabulary. He then calculated zero-order correlations and partial correla-tions holding chronological and mental age constant. Templin (1957) has in-tercorrelated measures of articulation, length of response, complexity of re-sponse, sound discrimination, vocabu-lary, and number of different words. A feature of this study is an attempt to use a terminal status measure as a base for estimating the interrelations of the various language skills. The percentage of terminal status scores attained on each of the major language measures is the method employed. Other studies concerned with the problem are by

Harris (1948), Gerwitz (1948), Yedinack (1949), Spiker (1951), and Schneiderman (1955).

## THE PROBLEM OF EVALUATION OF METHODS

The problem of evaluating methods in speech and language research is neither easy nor simple. The advantages and disadvantages of particular methods have been indicated in the chapter, and no comprehensive attempt is made here. The adoption of a method, and in turn a judgment of it, depends in large measure on the purpose the experimenter has in mind. The efficiency of a method is determined by the nature of the hypothesis he wishes to test, the degree of precision to be attained, the nature of information wanted, and the costs of conducting the research. If one wishes to compare the uncontrolled method of observation used by Shinn (1900) or by Piaget (1926) with the carefully controlled methods employed by Spiker (1958) or by Peterson and Barney (1952), the extreme contrast is readily apparent. But how can a differential evaluation be made of the work of Fisichelli (1950), who used a cross-sectional method, and the comparative study of Sherman and Moodie (1957), who were concerned with the relative merits of psychophysical methods. Both used careful controls. The difficulty of comparing the advantages of a test of sound discrimination, such as that of Schiefelbusch and Lindsey (1958), with, for instance, a test in another area, such as Williams and McFarland (1937) revision of the Smith Vocabulary Test, is apparent.

The cost of conducting an experiment is an important factor in its design. There is a vast difference between the expense involved in doing a job with a small centralized group or with a state or nationwide sample. Both may be meticulously controlled, one with precision instruments, the other with non-instrumental comparative methods. Yet both methods contribute valuable information. Each method, when buttressed by proper controls for the safeguarding of the data so as to yield the information wanted, has a legitimate place in the armory of the research worker.

The directions that the improvement of research techniques in the field of speech and language seem to be taking at present are twofold: (1) the further development and refinement of tests such as those used not only with normal children but also with retarded children, those with cleft palates, cerebral palsy, aphasia, etc.; (2) the invention of precision instruments of both mechanical and electrical nature.

Hall in Travis' *Handbook of Speech Pathology* indicates one area in which progress is needed. She states:

It is to be hoped that further investigation will be made along the line of objectifying and measuring articulation. A valid, reliable, standardized quantitative index of articulation would be extremely valuable, both for research purposes—so that articulation data could be handled statistically and have meaning throughout the country—and for clinical progress with speech therapy (p. 777).

Efforts in this direction are being made. The work of Sherman (1957) and her colleagues on the relative merits of several psychophysical methods for investigating defective articulation illustrates Hall's statement. Bangs (1942) has worked with retarded children. Dale O. Irwin (1959) has devised a short articulation test for the purpose of discriminating the speech of children of various mental levels. Templin (1957) has devised several tests for use with normal children, and Spriestersbach, Darley, and Rouse (1956) have used them with cleft-palate children.

A special problem is encountered with handicapped children that in the future must be taken into consideration, especially with those with cerebral palsy. It is a well-known fact that these children fatigue very easily and that their attention span is quite brief. The problem presented to the test constructor as well as to the therapist is to secure optimal results during the brief period in which testing can be done without fatigue. With this type of child, short tests that do not place too great a burden on them should be used. With this purpose in mind, Irwin (1958a,b, 1957e, 1956c) has devised a series of tests, each of which requires about five to ten minutes for administration. Further, he has attempted to standardize these tests on a nationwide sample of cerebral palsied children, so that they would have meaning throughout the country.

Further refinement of tests will undoubtedly result from more careful standardization techniques. In standardizing future tests, it should be insisted that the reliability, and wherever possible the validity, of the test be reported. In the past such statements have often been omitted, with the result that

no accurate judgment concerning dependability can be made by others who wish to use the test. As indicated above, other test criteria that might be met and reported are the difficulties, the discriminating power, and the uniqueness of its items. Moreover, whenever a test is composed of subtests, it is good practice to report the intercorrelations.

A brief word must be said about trends in the use of precision instruments. A casual reading of Steer and Hanley's (1957) chapter on "Instruments of Diagnosis, Therapy and Research" in Travis' handbook will reveal the tremendous progress that has been made in the invention and application of apparatus to problems of speech in the last few years. At present, nowhere else in the literature is there gathered in one place the amount of valuable descriptive and illustrative materials as here. Future trends will probably be concerned not so much with the invention of new instruments as with the refinement of the present supply of instruments and applications to new speech problems as they arise. There is an increasing trend toward the wider use of these instruments not only in the speech laboratory but in connection with clinical diagnosis and the processes of therapy. The chapter in the handbook is highly recommended to the research man, the clinician, and the therapist.

## REFERENCES

Adkins, Dorothy. 1947. Construction and analysis of achievement tests. Washington, D. C.: U. S. Government Printing Office.
Ammons, R. B. and H. S. Ammons. 1948. The

full-range picture vocabulary test. New Orleans. Authors.

Ammons, R. B., and J. C. Holmes. 1949. The full-range picture vocabulary test: III. Results for a pre-school age population. *Child Develpm.* 20, 5–14.

Anderson, Frances Julia. 1942. Speech sounds of infants: the 16th, 17th and 18th months. Unpublished master's thesis. Iowa City: State Univer. Iowa.

Bangs, J. L. 1942. A clinical analysis of the articulatory defects of the feebleminded. *J. Speech Dis.*, 7, 343–356.

Branscom, Margaret E., Jeanette Hughes, and Eloise Tupper Octoby. 1956. In W. Johnson and R. R. Leutenegger, *Stuttering in children and adults.* Minneapolis: Univer. Minnesota Press.

Brodbeck, A. J. and O. C. Irwin, 1946. The speech behavior of infants without families. *Child Develpm.*, 17, 145–156.

Bühler, C. 1930. *The first year of life.* New York: Day.

Carr, Josephine. 1953. An investigation of the spontaneous speech sounds of five-year-old deaf born children. *J. Speech Dis.*, 18, 22–29.

Carrow, Sister Mary Arthur. 1957. Linguistic functioning of bilingual and monolingual children. *J. Speech Dis.*, 22, 371–380.

Catalano, F., and Dorothea McCarthy. 1954. Infant speech as a possible predictor of intelligence. *J. Psychol.*, 38, 203–209.

Chen, H. P. 1946. Speech development during the first year of life: A quantitative study. Unpublished doctoral dissertation. Iowa City: State Univer. Iowa.

———. 1942. Speech sounds of infants: Newborn period. Unpublished master's thesis. Iowa City: State Univer. Iowa.

Crabtree, Margaret, 1958. The Houston Test for Language Development. Houston, Texas.

Darwin, Charles. 1877. A bibliographical sketch of an infant. *Mind*, 2, 285–294.

Davis, E. A. 1937. The development of linguistic skill in twins, singletons with siblings, and only children from age five to ten years. *Inst. Child Welf. Monogr. No. 14.* Minneapolis: Minnesota Press.

Day, E. J. 1932. The development of language in twins: I. A comparison of twins and single children. *Child Develpm.*, 3, 179–199.

DeLaguna, G. A. 1927. *Speech: Its function and development.* New Haven: Yale Univer. Press.

Eisenson, J. 1954. *Examining for aphasia.* New York: Psychological Corporation.

Desoendres, Alice. 1921. Le Developpement de l'enfant de deux á sept ans. Paris: Delachaux et Niestlé.

Fairbanks, G. 1940. Voice and articulation drillbook. New York: Harper.

Fisichelli, Regina Molloy. 1950. An experimental study of the prelinguistic speech development of institutionalized infants. Unpublished dissertation. New York: Fordham Univer.

Fisher, M. S. 1932. Language patterns of preschool children. *J. Exp. Educ.*, 1, 70–85.

Flores, Pura M. 1955. An analysis of the correct status of five consonants in the speech of cerebral palsy children. Doctoral dissertation, Iowa City: State Univer. Iowa.

———, and Orvis C. Irwin. 1956. Status of five consonants in the speech of cerebral palsy children. *J. Speech Dis.*, 21, 238–244.

Gerwitz, J. L. 1948. Studies in word fluency: I. Its relation to vocabulary and mental age in young children. *J. genet. Psychol.*, 72, 165–176.

Gesell, Arnold. 1928. *Infancy and human growth.* New York: Macmillan.

Gegoire, A. 1937. L'Apprentissage du langage des deaux première années. Paris: Droz.

Griffiths, Ruth. 1954. *The abilities of babies: A study in mental measurement.* London: Univer. London Press.

Guilford, J. P. 1950. *Fundamental statistics in psychology and education.* New York: McGraw-Hill.

Halstead, W. C., and J. Wepman. 1949. The Halstead-Wepman aphasia screening test. *J. Speech Dis.*, 14, 9–15.

Harris, C. W. 1948. An exploration of language skill patterns. *J. educ. Psychol.*, 39, 321–336.

Hoyer, A., and I. Hoyer. 1924. Über die Lallsprache eines Kindes. *Z. angew. Psychol.*, 24, 363–384.

Hoyt, Cyril. 1941. Test reliability obtained by analysis of variance. *Psychometrika*, 6, 153–160.

Humphreys, W. 1880. A contribution to infantile linguistics. *Trans. Amer. phil. Soc.*, 5–17.

Irwin, Dale O. 1959. An investigation of the ability of retarded children to articulate difficult consonantal speech sounds. Unpublished study. Iowa City: State Univer. Iowa.

Irwin, O. C. 1941. The profile as a visual device for indicating tendencies in speech data. *Child Develpm.*, 12, 111–120.

———. 1942. The developmental status of speech sounds of ten feebleminded children. *Child Develpm.*, 13, 29–39.

———. 1945. Reliability of infant speech sound data. *J. Speech. Dis.*, 10, 227–235.

———. 1947a. Infant speech: Consonant sounds according to the manner of articulation. *J. Speech Dis.*, 12, 397–401.

———. 1947b. Development of speech during infancy; Curve of phonemic frequencies. *J. exp. Psychol.*, 37, 187–193.

———. 1947c. Infant speech: Consonant sounds according to place of articulation. *J. Speech Dis.*, 12, 397–401.

———. 1948a. Infant speech: The effect of family occupational status and of age in sound frequency. *J. Speech Dis.*, 12, 224–226.

———. 1948b. Infant speech: Development of vowel sounds. *J. Speech. Dis.*, 13, 31–34.

———. 1953. Phonetic speech development in cerebral palsied children. *Proc. Amer. Acad. Cerebral Palsy*, 53–62.

———. 1955. Phonetic speech development in cerebral palsy children. *Amer. J. phys. Med.*, 34, 325–334.

———. 1956a. A second study on substitution and omission errors in the speech of children with cerebral palsy. *Cerebral Palsy Rev.*, 17, No. 3.

———. 1956b. Substitution and omission errors in the speech of children who have cerebral palsy. *Cerebral Palsy Rev.*, 17, No. 3.

———. 1956c. Short test for use with cerebral palsy children. *J. Speech Dis.*, 21, 446–449.

———. 1957a. Phonetical description of speech development in childhood. In Kaiser's *Manual of Phonetics*. Amsterdam: North Holland. Ch. 26.

———. 1957b. Word equipment of spastic and athetoid children. *Cerebral Palsy Rev.*, 17, No. 1.

Irwin, O. C. 1957c. Validation of short consonant articulation tests for use with children who have cerebral palsy. *Cerebral Palsy Rev.*, 18, No. 2.

———. 1957d. Correct status of a set of six consonants in the speech of children with cerebral palsy. *Cerebral Palsy Rev.*, 18, No. 3.

———. 1957e. A second short test for use with children with cerebral palsy. *Cerebral Palsy Rev.*, 17, No. 4.

———. 1958a. A fourth short consonant test for use with children with cerebral palsy. *Cerebral Palsy Rev.*, 19, No. 2.

———. 1958b. A third short consonant test for use with children with cerebral palsy. *Cerebral Palsy Rev.*, 19, No. 1.

———. 1958c. The effect on speech sound frequency of systematic reading of stories to infants. Unpublished study, *Iowa Child Welf. Res. Sta.*

———, and Han Piao Chen. 1941. A reliability study of speech sounds observed in the crying of new-born infants. *Child Develpm.*, 12, 351–368.

———. 1946. Development of speech during infancy: Curve of phonemic types. *J. exp. Psychol.*, 36, 431–436.

Irwin, O. C., and T. Curry. 1941. Vowel elements in the crying vocalization of infants under ten days of age. *Child Develpm.*, 12, 99–109.

Johnson, W., and R. R. Leutenegger. 1956. Stuttering in children and adults. Minneapolis: Univer. Minnesota Press.

Johnson, W., S. F. Brown, J. F. Curtis, C. W. Edney, and Jacqueline Keaster. 1948. Speech Handicapped school children. New York: Harper.

Jones, E. Leroi. 1956. Explorations of experimental extinction and spontaneous recovery in stuttering. In W. Johnson and R. R. Leutenegger, *Stuttering in Children and Adults*. Minneapolis: Univer. Minnesota Press. Pp. 226–231.

Koch, W. E. 1952. The problem of selective voice control. *J. acoust. Soc. Amer.*, 24, 625–628.

Krehbiel, Thelma E. 1941. Speech sounds of infants: The fourth, fifth, and sixth months.

Unpublished master's thesis. Iowa City: State Univer. Iowa.

Kuder, G. F. and M. W. Richardson. 1937. The theory of the estimation of test reliability. *Psychometrika*, 2, 111–116.

La Brant, L. L. 1933. A study of certain language developments of children in grades four to twelve inclusive. *Genet. Psychol. Monogr.*, 14, 387–491.

Leopold, W. F. 1939. Speech development of a bilingual child: A linguist's record. Vol. I. Vocabulary growth in the first two years. Northwestern Univer. Stud. Human., 6, p. 188.

Lewis, M. M. 1951. Infant Speech: A study of the beginnings of language. New York: Humanities Press.

Liberman, A. M. 1957. Katherine S. Harris, H. S. Hoffman, and B. C. Griffiths. The discrimination of speech sounds within and across phoneme boundaries. *J. exp. Psychol.*, 54, 358–368.

Lobischi, E. I. 1851. *Die Seele des Kindes.* Wien.

Lynip, A. W. 1951. The use of magnetic devices in the collection and analysis of the preverbal utterances of an infant. *Genet. Psychol. Monogr.*, 44, 221–262.

Mansur, W. 1950. The construction of a picture test for speech sound discrimination. Unpublished master's thesis. Boston: Boston Univer.

McCarthy, Dorothea. 1930. Language development of the preschool child. Inst. Child Welf. Monogr. Series No. 4. Minneapolis: Univer. Minnesota Press.

———. 1954. Language development in children. In L. Carmichael (Ed.), *Manual of Child Psychology.* (2nd ed.) New York: Wiley. Pp. 492–630.

McCurry, W. H., and O. C. Irwin. 1953. A study of word approximations in the spontaneous speech of infants. *J. Speech Dis.*, 18, 133–139.

Milisen, R. 1957. The incidence of speech disorders. In L. E. Travis, *Handbook of speech pathology.* New York: Appleton-Century-Crofts. Pp. 267–309.

Nice, M. M. 1915. The development of a child's vocabulary in relation to environment. *Pedag. Sem.* 22, 35–64.

Norcross, Kathryn J. and C. Spiker. 1958. The effects of mediated associations on transfer in paired-associate learning. *J. Exp. Psychol.*, 55, 129–134.

Perlstein, M. A., Erna L. Gibbs, and F. A. Gibbs. 1953. The electroencephalogram in infantile cerebral palsy. *Proc. Amer. Acad. Cerebral Palsy.* 63–82.

Peterson, G. E., and H. L. Barney. 1952. Control methods used in the study of vowels. *J. acoust. Soc. Amer.*, 24, 175–184.

Piaget, J. 1926. The language and thought of the child. New York: Harcourt, Brace.

Poole, I. 1934. Genetic development of articulation of consonant sounds in speech. Elem. Engl. Rev., 11, 158–161.

Prestigriacomo, A. J. 1957. Plastic-tape sound spectrograph. *J. Speech Dis.*, 22, 321–327.

Preyer, W. 1889. The mind of the child. Part II: The development of the intellect. New York: Appleton.

Pronovost, W., and C. Dumbleton. 1953. A picture-type speech sound discrimination test. *J. Speech Dis.*, 18, 253–266.

Roe, V., and R. Milisen. 1942. The effect of maturation upon defective articulations in elementary grades. *J. Speech Dis.*, 5, 37–50.

Sayler, H. K. 1949. The effect of maturation upon defective articulation in grades seven to twelve. *J. Speech Dis.*, 14, 202–207.

Schiefelbusch, R. L., and Mary Jeanne Lindsey. 1958. A new test of sound discrimination. *J. Speech Dis.*, 23, 153–159.

Schneiderman, Norma. 1955. A study of the relationship between articulation ability and language ability. *J. Speech Dis.*, 20, 259–264.

Schultze, F. 1880. *Die Sprache des Kindes.* Leipzig.

Seashore, R. H. and L. D. Eckerson. 1940. The measurement of individual differences in several English vocabularies. *J. educ. Psychol.*, 31, 14–38.

Sherman, Dorothy, and Catherine E. Moodie. 1957. Four psychological scaling methods applied to articulation defectiveness. *J. Speech Dis.*, 22, 698–706.

Shinn, M. W. 1900. The biography of a baby. Cambridge: Houghton Mifflin.

Shire, Sister Mary Louise. 1945. The relation of certain linguistic factors to reading achievement in first grade children. Unpublished doctoral dissertation, New York: Fordham Univer.

Shirley, Mary M. 1933. The first two years: A study of twenty-five babies. Minneapolis: Univer. Minnesota Press. Vol. II.

Smith, Madora Elizabeth. 1926. An investigation of the development of the sentence and extent of vocabulary in young children. *Univer. Iowa Stud. Child Welf.*, No. 5. Vol. III., p. 92.

Smith, Mary K. 1941. Measurement of the size of general English vocabulary through the elementary grades and high school. *Genet. Psychol. Monogr.*, 24, 311–345.

Spiker, C. C. 1958. Associative transfer in verbal paired-associate learning. Unpublished study, Iowa City: Iowa Child Welf. Res. Sta.

———. 1951. An empirical study of factors associated with certain indices of the speech sounds of young children. Unpublished doctoral thesis. Iowa City: State Univer. Iowa.

Spriestersbach, D. C., F. L. Darley, and Verna Rouse. 1956. Articulation of a group of children with cleft lips and palates. *J. Speech Dis.*, 21, 436–445.

Steer, M. D., and T. D. Hanley. 1957. Instruments of Diagnosis, therapy and research. In L. E. Travis *Handbook of speech pathology*, New York: Appleton-Century-Crofts. Ch. 6.

Stern, C., and W. Stern. 1907. Monographien über die seelische Entwicklung des Kindes. Vol. I: Die Kindersprache: eine psychologische und sprachtheoretische Untersuchung. (3rd ed) Leipzig; Barth.

Taine, M. 1877. The acquisition of language by children. *Mind*. 2, 212–252.

Templin, Mildred C. 1957. Certain language skills in children. Minneapolis: Univer. Minnesota Press.

Terman, L. M. 1916. The measurement of intelligence. Boston: Houghton Mifflin.

Thorndike, E. T. 1921. The teacher's word book. New York: Bureau of Publications, Teach. Coll. Columbia Univer.

Tiffany, W. R. 1953. Vowel recognition as a function of duration, frequency, modulation, and phonetic contest. *J. Speech Dis.*, 8, 289–301.

Travis, L. E. 1937. Bilaterally recorded brain potentials from normal speakers and stutterers. *J. Speech Dis.*, 2, 239–241.

Travis, L. E. 1957. *Handbook of speech pathology.* New York: Appleton-Century-Crofts.

———, and Bessie J. Rasmus. 1931. The speech sound discrimination ability of cases with functional disorders of articulation. *Quart. J. Speech*, 17, 217–226.

Van Alstyne, D. 1929. The environment of three-year old children: Factors related to intelligence and vocabulary tests. *Teach. Coll. Contr. Educ.* No. 366.

Wechsler, D. 1949. Wechsler intelligence scale for children. (Manual.) New York: The Psychological Corporation.

Wellman, Beth L., Ida M. Case, Ida G. Mengert, and Dorothy E. Bradbury. 1931. Speech sounds of young children. Iowa City: *Univer. Iowa Stud. Child Welf.* No. 2.

Werner, H., and Edith Kaplan. 1952. The acquisition of word meanings: A developmental study. *Monogr. Soc. Res. Child Develpm.*, 15, No. 1. 1–120.

Westlake, H. 1951. Muscle training for cerebral palsy speech cases. *J. Speech Dis.*, 16, 103–109.

Williams, D. 1953. An evaluation of masseter muscle action potentials in stuttered and nonstuttered speech. *Speech Monogr.* 29, 190–191.

Williams, H. M. 1932. Some problems of sampling in vocabulary tests. *J. Exp. Educ.* 1, 131–133.

———, and Mary L. McFarland. 1937. A revision of the Smith Vocabulary test for preschool children in development of language and vocabulary in young children. Iowa City: *Univer. Iowa Stud. Child Welf.* No. 2, Vol. XIII.

Winitz, H. 1958. A spectrographic study of infant speech. Unpublished study. State Univer. Iowa.

———, and Orvis C. Irwin. 1958. Syllabic and phonetic structure of infants' early words. *J. Speech Dis.*, 1, 250–256.

Wundt, W. M. 1912. *Völkerpsychologie.* Leipzig: Ernst Wieghadt. Vol. 1.

Yedinack, J. G. 1949. A study of the linguistic functioning of children with articulation and reading disabilities. *J. genet. Psychol.* 74, 23–59.

# chapter 13

# Psycholinguistic Research Methods

Jean Berko
Roger Brown
*Massachusetts Institute of Technology*

Descriptive linguistics is the branch of anthropology concerned with the structure of language. Until very recently the psychologist studying child language has been innocent of the findings of linguistics. Our evaluation of language in the abstract has been conventionally exalted: language is, presumably, the characteristic human behavior, the behavior separating man from the animals. At the same time, much research and theory concerning the child's acquisition of speech has reduced this behavior to something that might reasonably be expected of many animals. Partly, no doubt, this is because we have wanted to see in language only as much as we felt ready to explain. Partly it is because many aspects of language are visible only from the linguist's vantage point; when the full range of variation in human speech has been grasped, one begins to see how profound is the effect of each language in shaping the minds of those who speak it. To the psychologist who has studied linguistics, the child's acquisition of speech seems a more interesting topic than it has ever seemed before. For the study of this topic, we need a new set of methods informed with both linguistic and psychological knowledge. With characteristic optimism, the name for these methods was coined in advance of their invention. They were to be called "psycholinguistic." Today some of them have actually been worked out and tried; others we can envision only in a general way.

Every natural language is a system. From knowledge of one part, it is possible to anticipate many other parts correctly. The linguistic scientist studies some finite set of utterances (his linguistic "corpus") in search of the recurrent elementary units and patterns of combination that will generate the infinite set of utterances belonging to the language. Every child, in learning his first language, does much the same thing. He is not, in his first few years, exposed to all possible utterances belonging to the community language but only to that small sample brought to him by his family and their friends. Exposure to the sample, however, teaches him to understand and to produce utterances not actually experienced but implied by what has been experienced. The child may begin as a parrot imitating what others say, but he will end as a poet able to say things that have not been said before but that will be grammatical and meaningful in his community. This is the terminal achievement that a theory of language acquisition must explain.

Every natural language is constructed from a small number of distinctive elements—vowels and consonants, levels of pitch, pauses, and stresses—the "phonemes" of a language. It is conceivable that the linguist might work out a set of rules of phoneme combination that would generate all the acceptable sentences in the language, but any such set of rules would be far too complex to be useful. Descriptions that can be grasped are achieved by working at several "levels." On the first, the phonological level of description, the phonemes of a language and also the permitted patterns for their combination are enumerated. These never include all conceivable patterns. In English, for instance, we do not begin syllables with *nk* or *kn* or *sr* or with any of a number of other logically possible consonant clusters.

On the grammatical level of description the morphemes of a language, and also the rules for their combination, are enumerated. The morphemes are the smallest individually meaningful elements in the utterances of a language; a much larger set than the phonemes but still a finite set. Free morphemes are meaningful forms that can stand alone, such as *dog* and *cat*. Bound morphemes are forms that never stand alone but that retain some consistent meaning in the various combinations into which they enter; e.g., the possessive *'s* of *dog's* and *cat's*.

Grammatical description is often subdivided into the morphological and syntactic levels. Morphological rules describe the construction of words from free and bound morphemes, whereas syntactic rules describe the construction of utterances from words. In fact, to obtain a usefully simple set of rules, syntactic description has to work with classes of functionally equivalent words. It may be that descriptive grammar will eventually do without the word as a unit of analysis and also, therefore, without any distinction between morphology and syntax. The postulates of grammatical description are by no means so clear and objective today as are those of phonological description. For the present, morphology and syntax are usually distinguished and are so here. This chapter undertakes to describe those few researches that have approached language as a system, dividing the report into procedures for the study of the phonological system, procedures for work on the morphological system, and procedures for work on the syntactic system.

Various morphemes and combinations of morphemes are associated with identifiable nonlinguistic circumstances. *Bunker Hill Monument* goes with a certain artifact; *singing a hymn* is the name of a human performance; *Mr.*, as a term of address, is associated with certain characteristics of the addressee and of the relation between addressee and speaker. In fact, language makes reference. The linguistic scientist is little interested in what we will call the reference system. He has tried to purge his analytic methods of any reliance on the determination of particular meanings and reluctantly retains in his postulates judgments of the presence or absence of meaning and of identity and difference in meaning. However, the psychologist studying language acquisition will not wish to exclude reference from which linguistic meaning develops. The study of linguistic meaning in that full sense which includes the many varieties of connotation is identical with the study of verbal behavior, and this, of course, includes the larger part of social science—attitude scaling, all sorts of paper and pencil tests, interviewing, etc. We see this clearly in the fact that the Semantic Differential (Osgood, Suci, and Tannenbaum, 1957), a paper-and-pencil method for studying connotative meaning, is used for everything from the evaluation of psychotherapy to research on consumer motivation. In order to keep this chapter focused on methods that are psycholinguistic in a narrow sense, we restrict our discussion of meaning to the reference system.

We call reference a system because, like the three strictly linguistic systems, it has its regularities. With reference, as with phonology, morphology, and syntax, the child must and does extrapolate beyond the information he is given. Linguistic forms do not name unique space-time points; they name categories or concepts. Having heard a certain man called *Uncle Fred* on several occasions, the child correctly identifies this referent when it turns up in an unaccustomed quarter of town wearing a new suit. Having been taught the difference between "Go into that room" and "Do not go into that room," the child may understand at once the difference between "Come over here" and "Do not come over here." Though he has not heard the sentence *The keeper kicked the ostrich*, he may know the direction of the action from

his understanding of the general association between word order and subject-object relations. We extend our coverage, therefore, to include some of the methods used to study the reference system.

In an important sense, the rules written down by the linguist for phonology, morphology, and syntax and by the lexicographer for reference are what naïve adult speakers of the language already know and what children born into the community will learn. There is also a sense in which these rules are not known either to the child or to the naïve adult. They are *not* known explicitly; they are not formulated by the naïve speaker. They *are* known in that they are obeyed. For example, most adult speakers of English, if asked how they usually form the past tense of a verb, will say that they add *-ed*. This is a notion derived from the written form of the language, which does not accurately summarize all the details of speech practice. To regular verbs ending in voiced consonants, such as *grab* or *sag*, or ending in vowels, such as *sow* or *die*, the speaker of English adds /d/ for the past. However, for regular verbs ending in voiceless consonants, such as *kick* or *sip*, the appended consonant is, /t/, as you will notice if you listen to yourself. When a verb already ends in a /d/ or a /t/, as with *bat* or *pad*, the past is formed by appending /əd/. All of us who speak English follow these rules, but few of us would have said in advance that the form of the regular inflection for past tense is contingent on the character of the preceding vowel or consonant; after voiced consonants or vowels /d/ is appended, after voiceless consonants /t/, and with verbs ending in /d/ or /t/ one adds /əd/. As an explicit rule, this set of contingencies is "news" to the ordinary naïve speaker, but, in another sense, it is not "news," since he regularly follows these contingencies, and indeed they were abstracted as rules from his unwitting practice.

The speaking of utterances that follow rules really does not compel us to credit the speaker with "implicit" knowledge of the rules. He may simply be repeating what he has heard in total innocence of any regularities in the things he says. It is only when the child says something new or applies an utterance to a new referent so as to conform to linguistic rules that we are forced to credit him with more than a repertoire of rehearsed sayings. The difficulty with this requirement is that the psychologist usually cannot know exactly what sample of speech has been fed into a subject and so cannot ordinarily tell whether a correct utterance results from the extension of an implicit rule or simply from exposure to that utterance.

When a child is under continual surveillance, and that usually means he is in one's home, it is possible to have some idea of the speech sample to which he has been exposed. A 3-year-old boy, whom one of us has watched acquire English, heard for the first time the expression *another one* in connection with two books. "This is a book and that is another one" is the sentence he heard. Shortly thereafter he heard, "This is one of my shoes," and he supplied together with the correct referent the continuation, "And here is the other one." This could be recognized as an impressive abstraction of a rule of reference for the reason that the observer could be reasonably sure that his subject had not heard *another one* in connection with shoes. For this reason, parents can make valuable observations as to the acquisition of language rules and the various diaries of language development (Leopold, 1947; Lewis, 1936; Stern and Stern, 1928) provide the data for nonexperimental psycholinguistic research.

When the child's past experience of the language is not known to us, the clearest evidence of implicit rules derives, ironically, from his systematic errors. If he says *sheeps* or *I bringed*, he says something he probably has not heard from others, and what he says is a projection of a general rule. Because English is not so simply regular, the child makes an error, and the error reveals his knowledge of regularities. Most of the time this knowledge will lead him to say what is correct, and so it is hard to be sure that he is not repeating what he has heard. But when he oversimplifies the language, the generalizing process is made evident.

For the detailed study of language acquisition, one cannot wait for the production of errors. It is possible to study the child's knowledge of the language system by asking him to invent new forms or to interpret linguistic inventions of the psychologist or to name referents he cannot have seen before. He can, for instance, be asked to make up words to see whether his creations follow the phonological rules of the language. He might, on the morphological level, be shown a picture of a

using the tests for free variation, a set of results opposite to those defining free variation identifies phonemically distinct phones. It is important to note that all of these linguistic procedures are adaptable to children and can be used to work out the phonemic system of a child's speech.

Articulatory and acoustic variations that serve to differentiate phonemes in one language may differentiate allophones or free variants in another language. In English, as we have mentioned, most of our consonants can be paired as voiced and voiceless phonemes. Pittman (1948) reports that in the Oto language (Oklahoma) some of these consonant pairs are in free variation, i.e., one member of the pair is an acceptable substitute for the other, as if *din* and *tin* were the same word. In English today we produce vowels of relatively long duration before voiced consonants and shorter vowels before voiceless consonants. (Contrast *mode-mote, tied-tight, news-noose.*) These longer and shorter vowel pairs are allophones of a single phoneme, since they occur in complementary distribution (the one before voiced consonants and the other before voiceless). In English of the past and in many languages today this difference is phonemic, i.e., a change of vowel length ordinarily signals a change of meaning. In Navaho, for instance, the long and short [o] are two different vowels as surely as /o/ and /i/ are different to us. For the psychology of language acquisition, it is of great importance to know that acoustical and articulatory variations may function distinctively in one language and not in another. All languages

do not recognize the same distinctions; phonemes are not marked off by acoustic features that are prepotent for the whole human species. Speakers of a given language have to learn what range of variations is treated as invariant by their community and what variations are treated as distinctive. In short, there are perceptual problems of phoneme constancy and acquired distinctiveness of cues.

The "distinctive features" of an individual phoneme would be those aspects of the process of articulation and their acoustic consequences that serve to contrast one phoneme with others. In English speech the phoneme /b/ is always a stop (i.e., it is produced by an abrupt explosion of air), and in this respect it contrasts with a phoneme such as /v/, which is a fricative (i.e., it is produced by means of a constricted, continuous stream of air). The /b/ phoneme is also voiced, and, in this respect, it contrasts with /p/. Jakobson, Fant, and Halle (1952) have proposed that any phoneme may be described as a bundle of concurrent distinctive features. They have given us a list of these features (about a dozen) that is presumably adequate for the specification of the phonemes of all languages. Each feature is characterized in both articulatory and acoustic terms, and, perhaps because the authors are impressed with the binary computer as an analogue to human nervous processes, each is conceived as operating on a two-alternative basis. This distinctive feature analysis, which is completely general, makes it possible to compare the phonemic system of one language with the systems of other languages. It is also extremely economical. It is not yet clear how adequate the description is to the facts of speech in many languages, but distinctive feature analysis has already proved very fruitful for a number of studies (e.g., Miller and Nicely, 1955; Brown and Hildum, 1956).

The various phonemes of a language do not occur with anything like the same frequencies nor do they succeed one another with the same frequencies. There are always many conceivable phoneme combinations that do not occur at all. These frequency characteristics of the language are eventually absorbed by a person who learns the language and function as important determinants of his perception of speech. Numerous studies (Miller, Bruner, and Postman, 1954; Brown and Hildum, 1956) have shown that the likelihood of correct perceptual identification of phonemes is a function of the probabilities of occurrence of the phonemes in the given contexts. This is, perhaps, more obvious with handwriting than with speech. Handwritten letters of the alphabet are more likely to be erroneously identified by a typist when they occur in unusual proper names than when the same letters occur in familiar words in which they are predictable from context. The same sort of thing is true for the phonemic identification of individual phones in speech. Acoustic cues combine with probabilities generated by context to determine phoneme identifications. Methods in use for studying the role of probability in adult speech perception could easily be adapted to work with children, but this work has hardly begun.

For a general introduction to pho-nemic procedures, we recommend the treatment by Gleason (1955) for both clarity and accuracy. Work in acoustic phonetics is very ably evaluated in Hockett (1955). Connections between the mathematical theory of communication and phonology are described by Miller (1951) and by Cherry (1956). Brown (1958) provides an extended psychological discussion of phonology.

Most phonological learning occurs in the first three years of life, and, therefore, it is probably most likely to be studied by parents in their own children. To conduct such studies, a parent will need training in phonetic transcription. The difficult part of this training is the auditory discrimination, not the memorization of a set of symbols. In addition, the parent will need to study closely the linguistic procedures for discovering the phonemes of a language from adult speakers. The methods to be used with children are essentially modifications of these procedures, which allow for the limited understanding of very young children. We describe the general character of these procedures and also several linguistic studies that put them to use. In general, however, linguists who have worked on this problem do not give as many details of procedure as the psychologist is accustomed to and do not include all of the controls we should like. So the psychologist with some linguistic training who tackles this problem will have some methodological problems to solve on his own. It is certain, however, that psychologists as well as linguists have important contributions to make in this work. They will see how to place phonological learning within the general context of intellectual development, will see its relevance to learning theory and cognitive theory, and will think of empirical problems not likely to occur to the linguist. Now, we offer a rough guide to procedure.

There is today much valuable information (Irwin, 1947a,b,c; Irwin and Chen, 1946) on the frequencies with which various phones occur in the vocalization of children at different ages. In these studies the investigator makes a phonetic transcription of the sounds children produce and constructs frequency polygons listing the phones along the ordinate. With advancing age, these polygons change toward an ever-improving approximation of similar polygons plotted for adult speech, and the results provide a dramatic representation of one aspect of phonological development. However, they are not directly relevant to the study of the child's phonemic systems.

The mere occurrence in child vocalization of a phone, which the adult observer would classify as belonging to a certain phoneme in the adult language, does not demonstrate that the phoneme exists as a cognitive construct for the child; neither does any particular frequency of such a phone provide this evidence. Suppose, for example, that a child employs in his vocalization both [s] as in *sin* and [S] as in *fish*. We should place these two sounds in distinct English phonemes, but we cannot tell whether or not the child does so from the single fact that he speaks both.

How might we go about discovering whether the two sibilants function as distinct phonemes for the child? We could use procedures essentially the same as those the linguist would use if he were dealing with a naïve adult speaker of an unfamiliar preliterate language. We are, in the first place, interested only in sounds used in meaningful forms, forms used selectively to signal needs or to identify referents. The forms need not be the conventional words used by adults, but they must be meaningful to the child. Phonemic conclusions cannot be based on babbling or echoic speech. Indeed, many linguists (Jakobson, 1941; Velten, 1943) believe that phonemic structure begins to develop only after the babbling period has ended and that there is usually a term of silence separating the two processes and occurring near the end of the first year.

If, in a child's meaningful forms, the two sibilants [s] and [S] occur in complementary distribution, then probably they function for him as allophones of one phoneme. If these two consonants occur in some of the same phonetic environments, e.g., *sill* and *shill*, then they may be either free variants of a single phoneme or members of distinct phonemes. When the two forms *sill* and *shill* have clearly different semantic rules, whether of reference or expression, then the probability is that [s] and [S] belong to different phonemes for this child.

The conclusion suggested by the distribution of [s] and [S] in the child's meaningful forms can be checked by asking the questions used by the linguist with adult informants. These questions will also distinguish between receptive and productive control of phonemic differences and, in this way, refine the conclusions suggested by distribution alone. For example, hearing the child say *shill*, we might ask him to repeat it several times, to say the word again and again. If he sometimes says *shill* and sometimes *sill*, evidently he does not have productive control of the distinction between [s] and [S]; on the productive side they are functioning as free variants of a single phoneme. With an adult informant, this productive free variation would ordinarily imply receptive free variation, but in the child these two kinds of control of a phonemic distinction may not be at the same level of development. To test receptive control, we might offer *sill* as our repetition of his *shill*, and, if he accepts it, then the two sibilants are free variants on the receptive as well as the productive side. It often happens, however, that such "repetitions" will be rejected in the speech of another, even though they are unwittingly produced in the child's own speech. The questioning technique for learning about the child's receptive and productive control might be supplemented with an experimental test described on p. 532 in reporting a study by Brown and Horowitz.

Jakobson (1941) has been far in advance of all others, both linguists and psychologists, in distinguishing the learning of phonemic contrasts from simple babbling. This author believes that phonological development, viewed as the progressive differentiation of the phonemes of the community language, reveals universal human regularities. In his 1941 work he describes the sequence in which phonemic contrasts seem to emerge in any language, and in 1956 with Halle he sets forth such a sequence in terms of their "distinctive feature"

analysis of the phoneme. Jakobson and Halle (1956) believe that the child begins in a "labial stage" in which his only utterance is /pa/. This involves the consonant-vowel contrast.

From the articulatory point of view the two constituents of this utterance represent polar configurations of the vocal tract; in /p/ the tract is closed at its very end, while in /a/ it is opened as widely as possible at the front and narrowed toward the back, thus assuming the horn-shape of a megaphone. This combination of two extremes is also apparent on the acoustical level: the labial stop presents a momentary burst of sound without any great concentration of energy in a particular frequency band, whereas in the vowel /a/, there is no strict limitation of time, and the energy is concentrated in a relatively narrow region of maximum aural sensitivity (p. 37).

This, according to the authors, is the primal syllable, contrasting an ideal consonant with an ideal vowel. The next stage, they report, is likely to involve a nasal-oral opposition, a distinction between /n/ and /p/. Alternatively, it may involve a grave-acute distinction between /p/ and /t/. The first vowel division is said to occur on the compact-diffuse axis and the next division on the grave-acute so that the child has /a/, /u/, and /i/. The discussion goes on to outline a complete sequence, conforming to the general notion that the greatest possible phonemic distinctions are made first, with smaller differentiations following later. Jakobson and Halle are familiar with the international literature on speech acquisition and, presumably, derive their conclusions from this literature. However, the Jakobson and Halle report does not set down the detailed empirical support for the various generalizations that are made and does not give any explicit attention to methodological considerations. Necessarily, therefore, we must regard their generalizations as hypotheses rather than facts that have been established to the satisfaction of the reader.

There are two published studies reporting deliberate, fully competent inquiries into the learning of phonemic systems. Leopold (1947) kept a very detailed record of the speech of his daughter Hildegarde from her eighth week until her seventh year. The resulting four-volume publication is the ideal model for the descriptive diary of a child's language development. Leopold is trained as a phonetician and so was able to transcribe Hildegarde's speech with phonetic symbols. The vital importance of such training for the potential diarist is apparent if one listens to the untrained American parent imitating the speech of a very young child. The sounds heard from the child are often those that do not occur in adult American English, but the imitating parent regularly assimilates them to his own standard versions of English phonemes and, not uncommonly, transforms what he hears into familiar words. The untrained adult cannot even approximate an accurate phonetic record.

Leopold's method was to scribble notes on bits of paper whenever Hildegarde spoke and later, at his leisure, to enter them into a chronological record. This is an enormously difficult thing to do and requires considerable practice. It is difficult to stay in the role of participant-auditor in one's own home.

Since one cannot always be with a child, nor always recording when present, a diary cannot be a complete record of the child's speech. It is, however, possible during the first few years of life to exhaust the child's finite speech repertoire in sample observation periods.

Leopold's record is informed throughout with a linguistic and psychological sophistication that is unique among diaries of child speech. He makes careful definition of all his linguistic units, telling us, for example, the behavioral criteria for a "word." Psychologist-observers have almost never done this, and so it is impossible to make meaningful comparisons between the "vocabulary" reported for one child and that reported for another. Leopold summarizes his chronological record by describing the development of each of the major speech systems and, in addition, compares these results for Hildegarde with the speech development of his second daughter Karla and with what can be gleaned from earlier published records. In general, this work should be studied by the psychologist who is planning a diary record. However, as an example of procedures that can be used in working out child phonology, it is complicated by the fact that Hildegarde developed as a bilingual child (learning both English and German), and so we turn to a much shorter report by Velten for an account of his method.

Using a phonetic transcription, Velten recorded (in order of appearance) all of the meaningful speech forms used by his daughter Joan from her eleventh month until her thirty-sixth month.

Meaningful forms are, in general, those used with some consistency of reference. From this linguistic corpus, Joan's phonemic system is abstracted according to the following rules. When two meaningful forms differ with regard to a single phone, e.g., [ba] and [da], it is possible that the two phones ([b] and [d]) belong to the same phoneme for the child or that they belong to distinct phonemes. If [ba] has the same meaning as [da], if the one form is offered as a repetition of the other, then the two consonants are free variants. If, however, [ba] has a different meaning than [da], then [b] and [d] must belong to distinct phonemes. In Velten's actual materials, as it happened, [ba] seemed to mean *bottle* whereas [da] seemed to mean *down*. There was also [za] for *that*, and Velten concludes that these three consonants were organized by his daughter as distinct phonemes. Joan's words also made use of the consonants [p], [s], and [t], which are the unvoiced mates of [b], [z], and [d], respectively. It was clear from her words [ap], [as], and [at] that the three unvoiced consonants were phonemically distinct from one another, but one must also ask whether each voiced consonant was distinguished from its unvoiced mate: ([b] from [p], [d] from [t], [z] from [s]). In Joan's vocabulary the voiced consonant was always in initial position and the voiceless consonant, in terminal position; i.e., the consonants were in complementary distribution and, therefore, to be regarded as allophones (voiced and voiceless versions) of single phonemes. There were, for instance, the words [ba] and

[ap] but neither [pa] nor [ab]. Joan did not have two words of different meaning in which the only phonetic distinction marking the difference of meaning was the contrast between voiced and unvoiced. This feature, which is "distinctive" for the adult speaker of English, was not yet distinctive for Joan.

The psychologist who studies child phonology thinks at once of a number of questions concerning the learning of phonology that have not been answered by linguistic research but that are open to study by the experimentally inclined parent. Velten might, for instance, have undertaken deliberately to teach Joan to distinguish the voiced-voiceless feature. This could have been done by methods of discrimination training long familiar in both animal and human psychology. Velten might have taken a simple contrasting pair of forms like *bo\** and *po\** and used them as names for two very unlike toys. He could have played a game with Joan in which she was required to bring to him the toy he named. If he then presented *bo\** and *po\** in random alternation and Joan was able consistently to fetch the indicated toy, there would have been evidence that she had acquired some receptive control of the voiced-voiceless feature for a particular pair of consonants in a particular pair of words. How widely would this learning have generalized? Would Joan promptly have shown control of the distinction in *go\** from *ko,\* do\** from *to,\** and *zo\** from *so\**? Would she perhaps have distinguished the first two pairs, but not the third, for the reason that /g/, /k/,

/d/, and /t/ are all stop consonants as are /b/ and /p/ but as /z/ and /s/ are not?

By means of questions and informal experimentation, as we have indicated above, a distinction can be made between the child's receptive and productive control of phonemic contrasts. One of us, for instance, spoke to a child who called his inflated plastic fish a *fis*. In imitation of the child's pronunciation, the observer said, "That is your *fis*?" "No," said the child, "my *fis*." He continued to reject the adult's imitation until he was told, "That is your *fish*." "Yes," he said, "my *fis*." The /s/ and /S/ were not perceived as equivalent in the speech of an adult, but the child, in his own speech, used only the [s]. This sort of observation has often been made (Leopold, 1947), and it is the view of most linguists that in the development of the phonological system, as in the development of other linguistic systems, receptive control precedes productive control.

What is the larger importance of phonemes? The set of phonemes used to distinguish one meaningful form from another in a language can be learned from a very small speech sample, and such learning seems usually to be completed in the first few years of life. All of the thousands of meaningful forms learned thereafter are compounded of these same few phonemes. As long as an utterance is phonemically invariant, it is likely to be the "same" utterance with the same meaning, but if the phoneme sequence is disturbed a new form and a new meaning are created. The special importance of learning the phoneme structure of a language is surely the fact that invariance here is ordinarily a sign of some kind of invariance in the nonlinguistic world. One person after another may say of one animal after another, "See the dog," and though their pronunciations will vary in many dimensions there is phonemic invariance and also an invariance of reference that is essential dogginess. When the sentence changes to "See the cat," there is a new phoneme sequence and also a new reference. Phonemes are the terms in which the community tells the child when things or events are to be regarded as equivalent and when they are to be regarded as different.

## The Reference System

A morpheme is a segment of an utterance that recurs in various utterances with approximately the same meaning. In addition, morphemes are the smallest individually meaningful segments, and so any meaningful segment that can be further subdivided into consistently meaningful parts does not itself qualify as a single morpheme. The word *older*, for instance, is made of two morphemes because the suffix *-er* consistently means the comparative degree in such forms as *younger*, *faster*, etc. The identification of morphemes involves "recurrence" of a segment, and "recurrence" means not absolute identity of pronunciation but the same phonemes in the same sequence (phonemic invariance). However, a phonemically invariant sequence does not always analyze as a single morpheme. The same phonemic segment occurs and is meaningful in the forms *older* and *runner*, but these suffixes must be analyzed as two different morphemes because of the distinction of meaning between the comparative *-er* appended to adjectives and the operative *-er* appended to verbs.

Linguistic forms that make reference are always one morpheme or more. Distinctive features and phonemes signal changes of meaning but do not themselves have meaning; e.g., the phoneme /b/ does not "stand for" anything outside of speech. When we think of reference, we are likely to think of a full deliberate procedure of the kind an adult may use in teaching a child the meaning of some word. Although some privileged children in an affluent and leisurely society do receive quite a bit of deliberate tuition in reference, many more do not but somehow pick up the meanings of utterances from speech overheard at home and in the streets. We may think of reference quite generally as a correlation between the use of linguistic forms and various nonlinguistic recurrences without requiring the full deliberate pointing-and-naming operation. Of course, the referent is not invariably present when the form is used. *Ford* is often said in the absence of such a car. The referent is there only when the linguistic form occurs in certain constructions, such as "Here is your Ford," "Get a load of that Ford," etc. The referent that is physically present when the form appears in these contexts is conceived of only when the form appears in such sentences as, "Did you see a Ford out in front?"

## SIGNALING A CHANGE OF REFERENCE

We have said that the general benefit a child derives from learning to perceive speech phonemically is that he knows how to identify utterances as invariant or as variant. Reference begins with the recognition that a linguistic form has recurred and that there is probably a recurrence of referent or that a linguistic form has changed and that, therefore, there must be a change of referent. Brown and Horowitz (Brown, 1957) have conducted a small experiment that demonstrates this essential matter.

Farnsworth has developed, with the Munsell Color Company, a series of 85 color chips equally spaced around the hue dimension; saturation and brightness are constant. For the Brown and Horowitz experiment, eight alternate chips were drawn from the red-blue region of the series. There was the same very small perceptual gap between each adjacent pair of the series. The subject was shown this series of chips and told that the experimenter had a way of classifying them. It was the subject's job to discover this classification. The experimenter moved the series behind a screen and then exposed them one at a time (in random order), naming each chip with a nonsense syllable. The subject simply watched this process until all eight had been named. He was then asked to group the chips as the experimenter had grouped them with his verbal behavior.

As Fig. 13-1 shows, there were four groups of two chips each. The groups

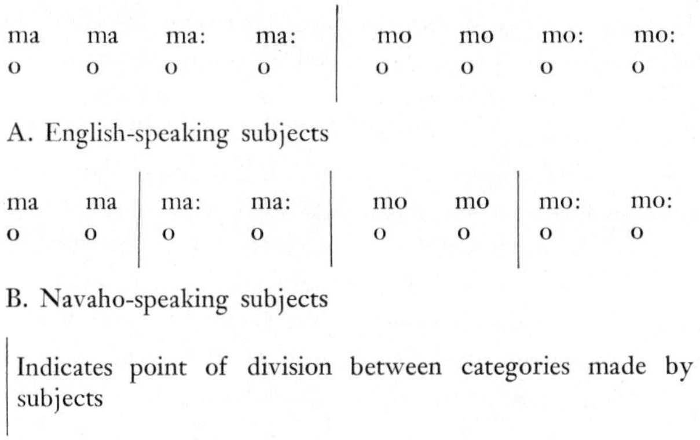

| ma | ma | ma: | ma: | mo | mo | mo: | mo: |
|----|----|-----|-----|----|----|-----|-----|
| o  | o  | o   | o   | o  | o  | o   | o   |

A. English-speaking subjects

| ma | ma | ma: | ma: | mo | mo | mo: | mo: |
|----|----|-----|-----|----|----|-----|-----|
| o  | o  | o   | o   | o  | o  | o   | o   |

B. Navaho-speaking subjects

| Indicates point of division between categories made by subjects

Fig. 13-1. Categorizations of eight color stimuli in terms of nonsense names varying in phonetic characteristics.

were named [ma], [ma:], [mo], [mo:]. The colon in [mo:] and [ma:] is a phonetic marking used to indicate that the vowel is prolonged. The difference between [a] and [o] is phonemic in English, but the difference between the long and short forms of each vowel is not. To produce the proper length, the experimenter thought of a voiceless consonant to follow the short form and a voiced consonant to follow the long form. Thus he pronounced [mo] by thinking *mote* and [mo:] by thinking *mode*.

Fifteen Harvard students, whose native language is English, after hearing one series generally divided the colors into two groups of four chips each, as in Fig. 13-1. The line of division corresponds to the line of phonemic change. They did not make a line of division when the vowel changed in length. With four repetitions, the subjects persisted in their two-group classification.

In the Navaho language vowel length is always a distinctive feature. Each

vowel has a long and short form, and these are different phonemes. Fifteen monolingual Navahos, given the same problem of concept attainment, generally divided the colors correctly into four classes of two colors each, as in Fig. 13-1, and persisted in this division through four repetitions.

It is clear that English-speaking subjects were able to distinguish the prolonged vowel from the short vowel, for when the experimenter rejected the two-group classification as erroneous subjects discovered vowel length and the proper grouping of colors. Many then remarked that they had from the first noticed some variations in the vowels but had assumed they were accidental. There could be no better statement of the cognitive status of non-phonemic variations. They are, like the variations of brightness and legibility among coins of a given denomination, thought of as unintentional and of no significance. Navaho subjects did not assume that the variations in vowel length were accidental, since in their language variations of this kind function to distinguish meanings. Once the English subjects learned that the vowel-length feature was significant, they made no errors in identification.

The groupings produced by both English and Navaho subjects were isomorphic with the groupings they heard in the experimenter's speech. Having different sets of distinctive attributes (phonemes) for speech, they came up with different groupings. When the English-speaking subjects were corrected, they re-examined the experimenter's speech and discovered the attribute to which he gave significance. This is a method that tests for perceptual or receptive control of phonemic contrasts (see p. 528) and which demonstrates the fact that phonemic change causes subjects to look for a change of reference.

REFERENCE
REQUIRING IDENTIFICATION
OF NEW INSTANCES

A very nice report of deliberate instruction in reference is provided by Dr. Jean-Marc-Gaspard Itard (American edition, 1932), who, in eighteenth-century France, undertook the education of the feral boy called Victor of Aveyron. Victor was a boy of 11 or 12 found running naked in the Caune Woods in 1797 and believed to have lived in the forest outside all human society from about the age of 7. When captured, Victor had no speech and no understanding of speech. Dr. Itard had recently been appointed physician to a

new institute for deaf-mutes in Paris, and he obtained permission to take Victor there to try to civilize and educate him. Dr. Itard's methods for teaching the rudiments of language and for testing Victor's understanding of words are essentially the same as experimental methods used today.

In order to teach Victor the referents of certain words, Itard arranged several objects, such as a pen, a key, a box, and a book, on a shelf in the library. Each thing rested on a card on which its name was written, and Victor had already learned to identify the names. Itard next disarranged the objects and cards and indicated to Victor that he was to match them up again. After a little practice, the boy did this very well. Itard then removed all the objects to a corner of the room. He showed Victor one name and gave him to understand that he was to fetch the object named. Victor also learned this very quickly.

The next test went badly at first. Itard locked away in a cupboard all of the particular objects with which Victor had practiced but made sure that there were in his study other objects of the same kinds—other pens, keys, boxes, and books. He then showed Victor a word, e.g., *livre*, and indicated that the boy was to bring the referent. Victor went to the cupboard for the familiar book and finding the cupboard locked had to give up the task. He showed no interest in any other book. The same failure occurred with the other words. Victor had understood each word to name some particular thing rather than a category of things.

Itard then spread out a variety of books, turning their pages to show what they had in common. He indicated that the word *livre* could go with any of them. After this lesson, when shown the word *livre*, Victor was able to fetch a book other than the specific book of his training. However, he did not correctly constitute the book category at once, for he brought a handful of paper at one time and a pamphlet and magazine at another. As his errors were corrected, however, he learned to distinguish books from other sorts of publications and also to recognize such categories as *key*, *pen*, and *box*. The crucial test for understanding of the referent category was always Victor's ability to identify new instances, and this is still the best experimental test.

Itard next approached the difficult problem of conveying an understanding of words that name qualities and relations rather than objects that have size, shape, and weight. He took out two books, one large and one small, and Victor promptly labeled each with the word *livre*. Itard then took Victor's hand and spread it flat on the front of the large volume, showing how it failed to cover the full surface. The same hand spread out on the smaller book did cover that surface. Victor seemed puzzled, as if wondering why one word should name these two different objects. Itard gave him new cards labeled *grand livre* and *petit livre* and matched them with the appropriate books. Now came the test to see whether Victor had learned specific habits or had abstracted a general relationship. Itard produced two nails, one large and one

small, and asked that the cards *grand* and *petit* be correctly assigned. Victor learned this relationship and others besides.

Itard had another good idea for verbs that name actions. He took a familiar thing, e.g., a book, and made it the object of some action—pounding it or dropping it or opening it or kissing it. In each case he gave the boy the appropriate verb in the infinitive form. The test was for the boy to label such actions when their object was changed, e.g., to a key or a pen. This, too, Victor learned.

As long as Victor could do no more than match some particular referent with its name, his performance could be the result of rote learning. Evidence of the abstraction of general rules of reference derives from the boy's ability to identify new instances of a referent category (not the particular book of his training trials but any book). This is possible only if the essential attributes of books (pages and a cover) are separated from such accidental attributes as a particular title and color of cover and if the essential attributes can be identified when they appear in conjunction with different sets of accidental attributes. It is in this respect that reference is a system, for we deal with the ability of a subject to go beyond the information he has been given.

Itard's test is of course the same as the general experimental criterion for concept attainment used by Hull (1920), Heidbreder (1948), Smoke (1932), Bruner, Goodnow, and Austin (1956), and many others. All of the studies in which subjects are required to abstract the concept named by a nonsense syllable are, of course, studies of the process of linguistic reference. Identification of new instances has also been used experimentally to explore a child's understanding of a meaningful utterance in the native language. Perhaps one example from the work of Piaget (1952) will serve to illustrate.

To Piaget's mind the study to be described is concerned with the child's conception of quantity. We would add only that the conception is inferred from the child's referential use of words like *more*, *less*, and *equal*, and so it is at least as accurate to say that the study is concerned with the child's understanding of the vocabulary of quantity. Piaget is inclined to see through words as though they were not there and to imagine that he directly studies the child mind. In fact, he is often concerned with the comprehension of utterances.

In the present case the experimenter ranged side by side two tumblers filled with water to exactly the same height and asked his young subjects whether the tumblers contained equal amounts, or, if not, which one contained more. Then, while the child watched, Piaget poured the water from one tumbler into a container of different shape, narrower and taller. In this new container the water rose to a greater height than the water in the remaining tumbler. The child was asked whether the amounts of water were still equal. The younger children usually answered that they were not. Some thought there was more water in the new container. Piaget decided that such children were judging quantity by the size of the container,

without reference to the height of the liquid in the container. Older children and adults judge liquid quantity by taking account of both container size and the degree to which the container is filled. The vocabulary of liquid quantity has reference for us to a relationship between these two variables. Very young children attend to one or the other of the two but not to both. It is possible to interpret these results as evidence of inevitable stages in the development of the child's mind, and it may be correct to do so. (In our section on the morphological system other examples are reported of a progression from simple uncontingent rules to more adequate contingent rules.) However, if we think of Piaget's findings as relevant to the acquisition of word meanings, we shall see that the sequence Piaget discovered might be the result of particular vocabulary training for which adults are responsible rather than an indication of what can be comprehended by the child mind at various ages. The vocabulary of quantity is likely to be introduced with simplified comparisons in which one of the variables is constant. With a set of glasses all the same size, *more*, *less*, and *equal* are directly tied to the height of the contained fluid. With a set of canisters varying in size but all filled to the top, quantity varies with the volume of the container. Moving outside these simplified situations, the child, at first, makes an inappropriate extension of his semantic rule and has to learn to take account of two variables at once. He can also solve the problem, of course, by grasping the reversibility of the pouring process. Having seen water poured from one container to another, we should know that the quantity had not changed because the process could be reversed to restore the original situation. For the very young child, pouring seems to be an irreversible process that alters the quantity of the fluid.

## REFERENCE
## REQUIRING A DEFINITION

Correct identification of new instances is one sort of evidence for the possession of a general rule of reference. In addition, of course, one can ask the subject to formulate the rule governing his application of a linguistic form. This test will often be failed when the identification-of-instances test can be passed. Victor could identify books but could not define them, and Piaget's child subjects would certainly have been unable to define the various terms in their vocabulary of quantity. It is tempting, therefore, to think of definition as a test of the understanding of a reference that is less sensitive to lower levels of understanding than the identification test very much as recall is a less sensitive test of retention than recognition. In fact, however, this would not be correct, for adequate performance on the definition test (the less sensitive) does not by any means guarantee successful performance on the identification test (the more sensitive) in the way that correct recall generally implies correct recognition. Any definition is an utterance, and any utterance can be rote-learned. A child might define an *orange* as *a round edible citrus fruit of orange color* and yet be quite unable to identify oranges as

distinct from apples and pears or anything else.

For the purpose of studying the types of definition provided by children, many experimenters have used the problems of the Stanford-Binet. Feifel and Lorge (1950), for instance, used these problems for hundreds of children 6 to 14 years of age, classified the definitions into five qualitative categories, and described age trends for types of definitions provided by children. Synonyms (orange is a fruit) and explanations (skill is being able to do something well) increased in frequency as children grew older, whereas definition by use (ball is to be thrown) decreased. The methodological complexities in research of this sort arise in the classifying of the definitions, which is a variety of content analysis and calls for the calculation of reliability coefficients for independent judges. The experimenter must supply definitions of the categories in his classification to other judges to see whether they can sort the children's responses as he has done. Verbal definitions often do not suffice to produce reliability of judgment. Even verbal definitions with examples may not do it. In his study of the causal explanations of children Piaget (1930) offered no reliability coefficient and so no guarantee that his system of classifying explanations could be used by others. J. M. Deutsche (1943) undertook to check the Piaget stages in the development of the notion of causality with a large sample of American children. To do this she had to be able to sort new causal statements into Piaget's 17 classes. Deutsche abstracted the best definition of each class given by Piaget and combined it with examples from the original work. After studying these materials, Deutsche and two colleagues independently classified a collection of new statements. There was much disagreement among the three judges; only 21.76 per cent of the items were classified in the same way by all three of them. What Piaget had written about his classes of explanation did not convey the ability to identify new instances in a reliable fashion. With content-analysis, building reliability is an important part of the procedure, and a high coefficient is an essential guarantee that the categories of the analysis can be shared.

It is very important to remember that the child's definitions can be rote-learned as well as independently constructed. Because of this fact, changes in definition-type with age do not necessarily reflect age changes in the child's style of cognitive function. They might result from the fact that parents and teachers consider different types of definition to be appropriate to children at different ages and so change what they say to children. This in turn would change what children say to experimenters.

## SEMANTICS WITH THE CONDITIONED RESPONSE

Studies of verbal conditioning were made first by Russian investigators in several laboratories in the USSR and then by American psychologists (Razran, 1939). Riess (1946) is one of the few to do the verbal conditioning experiment with children, and his pro-

cedure provides a model. As unconditioned stimulus, he used a loud buzzer to produce an unconditioned electrodermal response (EDR). This harmless stimulus is a great improvement for research with children over the electric shock that has often been used with adults. The conditioned stimuli are printed words (with children old enough to read), and classical conditioning is effected when the words that have been accompanied by the buzzer elicit the EDR.

In one study Riess was concerned with measuring the generalization of a conditioned response from the training word to a homophone, to a synonym, and to an antonym for the training word. Accordingly, his stimulus words came in sets of four (training, homophone, synonym, antonym), and he elected to use five such sets, or 20 critical words in all. The first step in the procedure was to determine the unconditioned EDR to each word as a kind of baseline from which to determine the conditioned response. Subjects were told to try to memorize the words they saw. In the next stage the training words were presented in a series with neutral words, and the conditioned response was established by reinforcing the training word with the buzzer. Conditioning was judged to be established when the conditioned stimulus elicited an EDR at least three times the base value for that word on three successive trials in the absence of reinforcement. Finally, generalization was tested by presenting the homophones, synonyms, and antonyms and measuring the EDR elicited on five trials for each word.

Riess performed this experiment with

children in four age groups; children in their eighth year, their eleventh year, their fourteenth year, and their nineteenth year. Riess advises varying the size of the letters of the exposed words to suit the age group. He gave warning of the buzzers and explained the electrodes as necessary to determine the subjects' sweat reaction to the temperature of the closed and windowless room.

We mention only one result that is of peculiar interest in connection with the acquisition of linguistic reference. For the youngest group, the conditioned response generalized most strongly to the homophones (words of different reference but identical phonemic sequence, e.g., *pale-pail, ate-eight*). For the oldest group, the greatest generalization was to synonyms (*pale-light, ate-fed*). Homophones are alike in sound; synonyms do not resemble one another as phoneme sequences but do resemble one another in their referents or, more broadly, in their meanings. For the younger children, the important dimension of similarity seems to have been the sound and appearance of the words themselves, but with advancing age and experience words apparently become transparent and are seen through to their meanings, which provide a new basis of resemblance. Here is evidence that responses trained to one word will be extended to others linked with it by the reference system.

Russian psychologists have recently been very much interested in the role of language (for which they use the Pavlovian term "the second signal system") in facilitating the formation of nonlinguistic conditioned responses.

Liublinskaya (1957), for instance, reports the following study with preschool children. A conditioned response was produced to the color (in another case to the size) of a paper cup, under which the children found a sweet as a reinforcement. With the experimental group, the successful solution was accompanied by verbal designation of the distinguishing feature (*red* color, *small* size); with the control group, the differentiating feature was not named. There were many differences in the performances of the two groups. The experimental group formed the conditioned response much more quickly; for this group, the response lasted over a longer period than for the control group; the experimental group showed a quick, even immediate, generalization of the response to such new stimuli as a red cup or a red box, but the control group did not. Of course, all of these effects were more pronounced for older children than for younger, since the older would be more likely to have a well-developed understanding of the references for *red* and *small*. The Russians are systematically exploring the role of the reference-making linguistic form as a signal, making possible rapid abstraction and generalization in the formation of new conditioned responses.

## The Morphological System

The grammar of a language consists of its morphology and syntax, categories that often overlap and are difficult to describe independently of one another. As we have said, a morpheme is a minimal unit of meaning in a language. A phoneme does not in itself mean anything, although it is used to signal differences in meaning. In English the /p/ phoneme distinguishes the word *pig* from similar words *fig* or *big;* but there is nothing about /p/ by itself that conveys the idea of pigginess. Nor can we find any common denominator of meaning in *pull, porch, pig, pleasure,* and the other words beginning with this phoneme. But if we look at a series of words such as *hats, ships, cats, elephants,* we note that the final *-s* does convey a common meaning: that of plurality. In a series such as *unhappy, unaware, untied* the *un-* seems to mean *not,* and in both of these instances we are dealing with morphemes. A single morpheme may be many phonemes long and capable of standing by itself, like *elephant,* or it may be only one phoneme long and bound to other morphemes, like the *-s* in *elephants.* The *-s* of *elephants* is called one allomorph of the plural. Although the plural is pronounced /s/ in this case, it is only one of several phonological shapes that in English signal this meaning. An allomorph is one variant of a morpheme that occurs in certain environments. The plural allomorph /-s/ occurs after all voiceless sounds, except after /s/, as in *kiss,* /S/, as in *hash,* /č/, as in *latch.* The other regular allomorphs of the plural in English are /-əz/ after the /s/, /S/, and /č/ already mentioned, and also after the voiced counterparts of these phonemes, /z/, /Z/, as in *azure,* /ǰ/, as in *judge,* and /-z/, which is the commonest allomorph and occurs after all other sounds. That is, it occurs after all voiced sounds, except those that call for /əz/. Thus we

have regular plurals, such as *rags* /-z/, *racks* /-s/, and *rashes* /-əz/. They are called regular because they are used in the great majority of English plural formations. The particular allomorph that will be used in forming a plural can be predicted from the form of the final phoneme of the singular form. These allomorphs, like allophones, are variations in form conditioned by the phonetic environment. These forms are also called the productive forms of the plural. They are productive in the sense that English continues to form new plurals from new words, according to this basic rule.

When we say that English continues to do something, nothing mystical is implied. This means, of course, that the speakers of English do something, and what adult speakers of English do with new words added to the language indicates the way in which they have structured the language system, even as what children do with new words added to their vocabularies indicates the way in which they have structured what they know of the language. If a new word comes into English, we quite automatically know what its plural should be. There is no question in our minds that the plural of *bazooka* is *bazookas,* with a /-z/, despite the fact that there is nothing in English phonology to prevent us from adding /-s/ after a vowel to form [bəzuwkəs]. In adding /-z/, we show that we know something more than a phonological rule that tells us what sound combinations can occur: we know a morphological rule for the formation of the plural. We also know other kinds of plurals in English, words such as *oxen, men, data, alumnae,* and *sheep,* but no general rule seems to cover these instances, and we do not make new plurals according to these models. Despite the fact that some words for animals, such as *sheep* and *deer,* take no ending in the plural, we are not tempted to make the plural of a new word for an animal by adding nothing. To say *one wug\** and *two wug\** sounds vaguely Chinese to us.

It may be noted here that the criterion of phonetic similarity, which guides the identification of allophones, is not essential for the identification of the allomorphs of a morpheme. Before we can say that the aspirate [p'] of *pot* and the [p] of *spot* are allophones of the phoneme /p/, we have noted that [p'] and [p] resemble one another. Quite obviously, the /-s/ of *books* and the /-ǝn/ of *oxen* are not phonetically similar. They are classed as allomorphs of the same morpheme because they both serve the same function, that of indicating that the noun to which they are appended is to be regarded as a plural form.

Morphology, of course, deals with very much more than the expression of the plural. What has gone before has been by way of example. The native speaker's knowledge of morphology often enables him to guess the meanings of words he has never seen before and, upon occasion, to make up new words. If a child in reading comes across the word *unkindness,* his knowledge of the meanings of the separate morphemes, *un-, kind,* and *-ness,* might enable him to guess the meaning of the word even though he had never seen it before. When new words come into the

language they are rarely made of entirely new elements; more often they are made of morphemes that are already familiar. A suffix like *-ness* stands ready to transform adjectives and adverbs into nouns, should the need arise, as witness the recently coined *togetherness.*

For the most part, the free morphemes of the language comprise its lexicon. The bound morphemes are used to derive new words and to express certain grammatical categories. Not all languages express the same grammatical categories, and each language is unique in its choice of morphological and syntactical means of expression. Often grammatical meanings can be expressed in two or more ways in the same language; one of these ways can involve morphology and the other, syntax; in English, for example, genitive relations can be shown either by special endings (morphology), as in *the horse's hoof,* or by juxtaposition of words and special function words (syntax), as in *the hoof of the horse.* It is thus impossible to describe grammar without considering both morphology and syntax.

Word order in English is very important. "The girl loves the farmer" and "The farmer loves the girl" mean quite different things; and actor and object are indicated only by the position of the words. In Latin both *Puellam amat agricola* and *Agricola amat puellam* mean "The farmer loves the girl." Word order is not important here, and actor and object are expressed by the case endings on the nouns. English thus uses syntax and Latin uses morphology to express this kind of relationship, and to speak of English nouns as being in the "nominative" or "objective" case is a fiction, since there is no difference in the form of words like *girl* and *farmer*, whether they are actor or acted upon in any given construction.

As the child acquires his native tongue, he must learn to use those patterns of morphology and syntax that are required for the production of grammatical utterances in that language. Language learning thus involves much more than the acquisition of a finite number of sounds or words. It involves learning great numbers of intricate patterns for the formation of words from morphemes and the formation of sentences from words.

For a general introduction to the problems of morphology, and an outline of English morphology, we recommend the works of Gleason (1955), Hockett (1958), and Bloch and Trager (1942). In addition to the works already cited, numerous detailed accounts based on the observation of actual child language have appeared. A picture of morphological development in diverse languages is provided by Lewis (1936) on English, Stern (1928) on German, Guillaume (1927) on French, and Gheorgov (1908) on Bulgarian.

## NONEXPERIMENTAL OBSERVATION OF CHILD GRAMMAR

The works of Lewis, Stern, and Gheorgov are, again, parents' detailed accounts of their children's language development, based on informal observation and set down in notes and diaries. Guillaume's findings are based on observations he made at a French nursery school. His subjects were children between 2 and 5 years old; after these children became used to his presence as an observer, they ignored him, and he wrote down their conversations. All of these observers report that small children produce new forms by analogy with words they already know and that the direction of the new forms is toward eliminating the irregularities and inconsistencies of the language—the equivalent of saying *I ringed* and *two mouses*. Guillaume found that French children often regularized common irregular forms, but irregular forms, even the commonest, never served as patterns for analogical formations.

Observant parents have thus contributed much of what we know about the grammar as well as the phonology of child language. Aside from possessing a trained ear and a consistent system of notation, the observer must know enough about language as a system to recognize new developments when he hears them. Any diary should also include pertinent information about the diarist and his subject. The writer should identify himself and his relationship to the child; he should indicate what other people are in contact with the child, including older or younger siblings, what languages are spoken to the child, and what dialects. Since we are dealing with verbal behavior, we should also expect a record of what was said to the child just before and just after his utterance. These adult comments to the child should also be recorded with great care, since they comprise the text the child is studying. Without this information, certain questions can never be answered. Reduplication (words like *da da* and *boo boo*) and the use of *-ie* suffixes (as in *doggie*), for example, seem to be features of English child language. One might ask if the child says these things because he is taught them as explicit words or because they are his own invented simplifications. If a child who had never heard adult baby talk produced a reduplicated word or called a horse a *horsie*, we would have the beginning of an answer to these questions. Diarists are in a position to supply us with this information.

Since it is possible that any correct utterance of a child may be something he has previously heard, the investigation of the learning of morphology relies heavily, as we have mentioned, upon observations of children's errors in speaking. These errors are indicative of the child's productive system. The work in Russian of K. Chukovskij (1956) has employed this method. Chukovskij's approach is largely anecdotal and springs from a summer of informal observation and conversation spent at the seaside some forty years ago. Since that time, Chukovskij has attempted in an examination of children's language to explore and set forth the "strange regularities" of child thought as a whole. His newspaper articles have attracted attention in the Soviet Union, and schoolteachers and parents have sent to him many hundreds of letters containing children's compositions and citing words and expressions coined by Russian-speaking children. His many examples also demonstrate the extraordinary vigor of the Russian morphological system and the readiness

with which children learning this language invent new forms and distort Russian forms of foreign origin in order to make morphological "sense." A 3-year-old child, for example, was sent to get some *vaseline*, which is a borrowing into Russian in the form *vazelin*. A few minutes later she appeared, looking for the *mazelin*,* as she called it. This transformation was by no means an articulatory error. *Maz'* in Russian means *liniment* or *oil*, and *mazat'* means *to grease*. *Mazelin** is therefore a very likely word for a kind of oil, since it contains a morpheme referring to oil. In the course of her wanderings from room to room, this small child regularized a foreign form and placed it within a constellation of Russian words that have morphological reference to oil.

The dexterity with which Russian children handle derivational prefixes and suffixes is shown by numerous examples: one child, wishing to express the fact that her grandmother loved her very much, referred to her grandmother as her *lyubovnitsa*. Since *lyubov'* means love, and *-nitsa* is a feminine ending meaning agent (like the *-er* of English), the combined morphemes should mean *a feminine person who loves*. Indeed it does, but the Russian word *lyubovnitsa* means, more precisely, *paramour*. It seems unlikely that this child had ever heard the word *paramour* before, let alone applied to her grandmother, so that it is safe to assume that she had created a new word out of productive elements of Russian morphology. What strikes us most in Chukovskij's work is that Russian child language is characterized by very great activity in the formation of folk etymologies and new words from derivational morphemes. This is in contradistinction to English child language, in which we find that the inflexional morphemes are learned before the derivational ones and in which new words tend to be compounded of free morphemes rather than derived. These differences in child language reflect the differing linguistic structures of English and Russian and may well be indicative of future developments in these languages.

A method similar to Chukovskij's, but dealing with several languages, has been employed by Kahane, Kahane, and Saporta (1958) in their study of the development of categories of the verb in child language. Here they have relied solely upon the written reports of others, but these reports have been the work of such astute observers as Leopold (1947) and Grégoire (1937–1947). The advantage here is that these are very careful studies, often covering a number of years and including samples of the child's language in a great variety of natural situations. The limitations of this method spring from the same source as the advantages: from so few cases it is difficult to tell what is common to all child speakers and what reflects the particular idiolect of the often bilingual child of the linguist. Since the speech occurred in such a variety of situations, it is impossible to duplicate these conditions for the purpose of comparing results with other children. In addition, too great a burden is placed upon the parent and linguist's subjective feelings about what the child is saying or what he *really* means, regardless of what he is

saying. This point will be elaborated presently.

The object of this study was to describe the evolution of verbal categories in English, French, and German child language. The authors concerned themselves only with those categories that are formally marked in the verbs of the adult speakers of each of these languages. For instance, in the sentences *John is loved* and *Mary is loved* one could say that *loved* has both a masculine and feminine meaning. Since it is never possible in English to tell from the form of the participle itself whether it is masculine or feminine, we cannot say that the category *gender* is expressed in English verb forms. In French, however, one says *Le livre est ouvert*. (*The book* (masculine) *is open*) but *La porte est ouverte* (*The door* (feminine) *is open*) and the contrasting forms [uver] and [uvert] provide a basis for saying that there exists a marked category of gender in French participles.

The Kahane and Saporta study notes with examples two stages in the evolution of verbal categories. In the first the child means a certain category, but does not mark it in his speech, and the second occurs when the meaning contrast is accompanied by a contrast in form. In the first stage the child might say "Bear eat mama up" to mean *The bear will eat mama up* and also to mean *The bear is eating mama up*. In the second stage futurity is marked by the contrasting form *will*. It is, however, very difficult to decide what the child means in the earliest stages of language. The French child's saying "tume" at one point is interpreted to be a shortening of the form *costume* (suit), and this brief syllable is considered to mean *I've put on my Sunday suit*, a postulation that requires some imagination on the part of the observer. In considering several languages, these authors have demonstrated a general feature of child language and have shown how in each of these languages children progress toward using the forms employed by adult speakers.

## AN EXPERIMENTAL APPROACH TO ENGLISH MORPHOLOGY

As we have noted earlier, one of the difficulties in observing actual speech is that we cannot tell if the form the child uses represents the workings of a productive system or if it is something he has heard and is repeating. If a child says "feet," for instance, we have no guarantee that he knows the form *foot*, and he may say "shoes" and "climbed" without being able to make the plural of new nouns or the past tense of new verbs. When he says "two mouses," we begin to suspect that he has some sort of morphological system that he employs in the creation of new forms.

An experimental investigation of the child's morphological system for English was made by Berko (1958). In this experiment preschool and first-grade children were presented with pictures labeled with nonsense words and asked to supply English inflexions, derivations, and compounds of those words. The areas under consideration were the plural, possessive, verbal, and adjectival inflexions and several derivational forms,

such as the adjectival *-y*, as in *meaty*, and the agentive *-er*, as in *teacher*. As a typical example, the experimenter would show the child a picture of a small animal and say "This is a *wug.\**" Two such animals were then shown, and the experimenter would continue, "Now there are two of them. There are two _____?" At this point the child would usually supply the plural form *wugs.\**

In designing this study, the first and most general question had been: do children possess morphological rules? A preliminary study of 1000 words appearing most frequently in the first grader's vocabulary, based on Rinsland's (1945) listing, showed that first graders use real words involving all of the basic English morphological processes. Asking questions about real words might, however, be tapping a process no more abstract than rote memory. We can be sure that the nonsense words were new words to the child, and that if he supplied the right morphological item he knew more than the individual words in his vocabulary; he must possess general rules enabling him to deal with new words. If knowledge of English consisted of no more than the storing up of many memorized words, the child might be expected to refuse to answer on the grounds that he had never before heard of a *wug\** and could not possibly give the plural, since no one had ever told him what it was. This was decidedly not the case. The children answered the questions. The answers were not always identical with those of an adult comparison group, but they were consistent and orderly answers, and they demonstrated that children in this age range unquestionably operate with clearly delimited morphological rules. No differences between the sexes appeared, and although first graders were considerably better on some items than preschoolers the over-all character of the answers of both groups was much the same.

When asked to supply the regular plural allomorphs /-s~-z~əz/ to new words, these children did best with the /-z/ form, which is the commonest of the three allomorphs. They could also usually supply /-s/. They did not, however, use the rule for the addition of /-əz/ to new words. If a word ended in a sibilant, they regarded it as already in the plural: they said *one tass** and *two tass.** At the same time, it was demonstrated that over 90 per cent of them could produce the real form *glasses,* which showed that although they did not yet generalize this rule they had a model for generalization.

The possessive of the noun and the third person singular of the verb, as in *horse's* or *he passes,* are phonologically identical with the plural, and children operated with the simplified rules described above. There was, however, one major difference: they scored higher on these forms than on the noun plurals. They were asked to produce three nearly identical forms: a man who *nazzes,** *two nizzes,** and a *niz's** hat. On the verb they were 48 per cent right; on the possessive they were 49 per cent right, and on the noun they were only 28 per cent right. This was an example of items that were phonetically identical but learned at dif-

ferent times because they function differently.

On the verbs the children performed best with the progressive -*ing* form; 90 per cent said that a man who knew how to *zib** was *zibbing.** This is an important form, and it may be noted that although other verbal morphemes have several allomorphs there is only one form of the progressive and the rules for its application are completely regular. The allomorphs of the past are /-t~-d~əd/, and the children's rules are again simplified by comparison with adult speech. Although it was shown that they knew real forms such as *melted,* they were unable to extend the comparatively rare /-əd/ to new words. They said that a man who *bods** every day, *bod** yesterday. They did best when asked to supply the commonest form, /-d/.

The picture that emerged was one of high consistency among the children and of over-regularity from the point of view of adult language. The children did not treat new words according to idiosyncratic patterns. They did not model new words on patterns that appear infrequently. When they provided inflexional endings, their best performance was with those forms that are the most regular and have the fewest variants. With morphemes that have several allomorphs, they could supply the commonest forms long before they could deal with allomorphs that appear in a limited distribution range. And, unlike the Russian children, they did not use suffixes in deriving words. Instead, they tended to put two free morphemes together to form compounds of the *blackboard* variety. Adults said a very little *wug** might be called a *wuglet**; children called it a *baby wug.** Adults said that a man who *zibs** is a *zibber**; children called him a *zibman.**

## MORPHOLOGY
## IN NONLINGUISTIC LEARNING

Until now in this section we have talked about children's morphological productions, but it is also evident that before children are able to use certain forms they understand them (i.e., receptive control precedes productive). In the following section we discuss ways in which the form of a new word and its position in a sentence influence our expectation about what it might mean. Here we report one experiment in the understanding of morphology and its relationship to learning. In an experiment with preschool children Sack (1957) tested the effect of the comparative *-er* ending on children's ability to learn a principle of comparison.

Eight Munsell color chips, shading from green toward blue, were used. Each chip was three just noticeable differences (jnd's) bluer than the one before it. The children were divided into two groups. Half of the children in each group were told that some of the chips were called *kef.** Children in the other half of each group were told that some of the chips were *kefer,** and they had to learn to recognize the chips that were *kef** or *kefer.**

The first group had before it a task of absolute learning. For them, the four bluest chips were always *kef** or *kefer.** On being presented with a pair of chips, they had to recognize if both, none, or one was *kef** or *kefer.** The second group had before it a task of relational learning. On being presented with two chips, they had always to choose the bluer as *kef** or *kefer,** and a chip that was *kef** or *kefer** in relation to one chip might not be in comparison with another. Since this was a problem in relational training, one of the questions was: would the *-er* ending facilitate learning a principle of comparison and hamper the acquisition of an absolute category? Among the children who had been given the word *kef** the absolute discrimination was made more easily than the relational one. For the groups using the word *kefer,** the relational discrimination was easier. Young children thus utilized the morphological signal *-er* in the performance of a learning task.

Experimentation with English-speaking children has indicated that they have a productive morphological system and that there is very little variation from child to child in the nature of the system. It has been suggested elsewhere that there is perhaps a regular order in which children learn the phonemes of their language. Here we have seen that the child's morphological system evolves according to a very definite pattern: the productive system is based on the largest general cases and it contains no irregularities. Further experimentation should indicate when and how the child's very regular system becomes the adult's somewhat irregular system and it should provide information on the acquisition of other morphological and syntactic patterns. Probably this kind of complete picture can be obtained only by the use of an experimental method that covers the whole range of a linguistic system with a large number of children. Experiments based on the major morphological and syntactic patterns and administered to children of varying ages should yield scales of language acquisition and patterns of cognitive organization.

## The Syntactic System

The postulates of syntactic description are, at the present time, both too complicated and too unsettled to be presented here. We must be content to sketch one aspect of syntax that has inspired several psychological experiments with children. This is the fact that forms in any language can be grouped into classes of functional equivalents. Morphemes, words, and phrases fall into "form classes," the members of which have similar privileges of occurrence in building larger constructions.

If we were to examine a very large sample of English speech, we should find a certain number of nearly identical utterances. We might, for instance, find *That street is clean; That house is clean;* and *That face is clean.* The forms *street, house,* and *face* have identical privileges of occurrence, and we begin to think of them as belonging to one form class. If we found next the sentences *This is his street* and *This is his house,* we probably would expect sooner or later to find *This is his face.* If a child heard others produce the first five sentences, he might very well create the sixth on

his own. The sentence could be original with him, though both the constituent forms and the pattern have been learned from others. As it happens, he would in this case have produced a grammatically acceptable English sentence.

As adult speakers of English, we organize the meaningful elements of our language into form classes. This is evident if we make a kind of phenomenological report on the grouping of constituents in a pair of sentences; e.g., *She bought a new hat; He likes the old man.* We probably feel an affinity here between *He* and *She* and another affinity between *bought a new hat* and *likes the old man.* The first two are subjects and the second two are predicates. Within the subject class the two members can be interchanged, and this is also true within the predicate class: *She likes the old man; He bought a new hat.* A Gestalt theorist might say that the members of the subject form-class are organized by "common fate," i.e., similar privileges of occurrence in larger constructions, and the members of the predicate form-class, by a different common fate. The linguist would say that the division of these sentences into subject and predicate is a first-level analysis into their immediate constituents (Hockett, 1958), which belong to different form classes.

In English subject and predicate are very large form classes, each of which embraces an immense variety of morphemes, words, and phrases. The parts of speech, the noun, verb, adjective, and adverb, are also very large form classes. Smaller form classes having familiar names include animate nouns, mass nouns, particular nouns, proper nouns, transitive verbs, and intransitive verbs. In general, form classes grow smaller as the membership requirements grow more stringent. Transitive verbs are nearer having completely identical privileges of occurrence than are verbs in general.

One part of the linguistic description of syntax is the assignment of forms to form classes on various levels of generality. There can be no doubt that with syntax, as with phonology and morphology, each of us in learning the language does unconsciously what the linguist does deliberately. In the case of syntax, the importance of the system is most evident. Suppose we were to hear the sentence: *The iggle\* squigs\* trazed\* wombly\* in the harlish\* goop.\** Though we do not know the meanings of any of the major words, we are able to assign them to form classes on the basis of their order and of certain inflections and marking words. As a result, we are prepared to form a vast number of utterances that we expect to be grammatically acceptable (though they might turn out to be peculiar from a semantic point of view). "Squigs\* are iggle,\* they say, and squigs\* know how to traze,\* though in a wombly\* fashion. As for goop,\* it is harlish.\* It may be that I also am harlish.\* I might even be a squig,\* whether iggle\* or no, etc., etc." When a new form is introduced in such a way as to place it in one or more form classes, a population of utterances involving the form is placed in readiness and a larger population is ruled out.

The description of syntax, which has been given less than cursory treatment here, is set forth in detail in the works of Harris (1951), Hockett (1958), and Gleason (1955). A new and very promising approach in terms of rules of transformation is outlined by Chomsky (1957). The adult speaker who can say "The boy hit the ball" can also transform this sentence into "The ball was hit by the boy." The investigation of the child's syntactic system should indicate when and how children learn to make such transformations.

## FORM CLASSES AND WORD ASSOCIATION

As long as child speech is nothing more than the production of practiced utterances, we should expect any isolated word to suggest to a child the word that most commonly follows it. We should, in short, expect word association to follow primarily sequential paths. As meaningful forms become organized into classes of functional equivalents, we should expect an isolated word to suggest another word from the same form class, although that other word may never directly follow the stimulus word in any utterance. Word-association tests with children ought to show that with increasing age vocabulary is bundled together in terms of general functional equivalence rather than in terms of particular sequences. Ervin (1957), for one, has found such evidence.

A list of common words belonging to various form classes was presented to children in kindergarten and in the first, third, and sixth grades. The responses were classified according to form class. The two youngest groups of children gave 48 per cent noun responses to *hand*, whereas the sixth graders gave 79 per cent noun responses to this stimulus word. Comparable increases occurred with verbs and prepositions, and there was a reduction in frequency of words from classes that generally follow the stimulus word. Similar results were obtained with words representing a variety of form classes: *him, these, there, always, walking, sorry, sick, either.* The younger children tended to give more phrase responses; e.g., to such verbs as *build* and *give* they responded with articles plus nouns more often than with verbs. With the older children, generally, there was an increase in paradigmatic responses—words that are functionally equivalent. This learning of form classes founded on the principle of substitutability is what makes possible the creation of new sentences.

Members of a form class may be marked with some phonetic common denominator, may be identified by some reliable concomitant form (as *the* helps to identify nouns in English), and may have more or less consistent semantic correlates in addition to the shared privileges of occurrence that define the class. Languages differ in the means used to mark various classes. We would expect the age at which classes are learned to be a direct function of the clarity with which class membership is marked.

## IDENTIFICATION
## OF FORM-CLASS MEMBERS

An approach to form-class recognition was made by Porter (1955) in an investigation of the concept of the verb. Using adult subjects and children between the ages of 7 and 13, he at-

tempted to discover by what cues we identify verbs and if there are differences between adults' and children's ideas of the verb. Since the verb may be identified by its position in the sentence, by special function words, by affixes, or by its lexical meaning, he attempted to manipulate each of these variables.

The subjects were presented with a sentence typed on a 3 x 5 card and asked to identify the verb. Children in the third, fourth, fifth, sixth, and seventh grades were interviewed individually for this experiment. A sample sentence with the verb underlined, *The cow* JUMPED *the fence*, was shown them, and they were told they were playing a guessing game. Their instructions were: "See if you can guess the word I am thinking of. It will be one like this, JUMPED." They were then given a practice sentence, *A chicken lays eggs,* and after they correctly chose the verb the test was administered. Adults were simply shown the sample sentence and told to pick words like *jumped.* A variety of cards was presented, and the available cues for the identification of the verb were controlled. Children were asked on every fifth card, "Why did you choose that word?" Children were presented with three parallel sets of sentences, each containing 26 sentences. The first ten in each set were English sentences of increasing complexity. Sentences 11 to 15 were nonsense sentences containing varying cues. Some were as cue-laden as *A cudof\* biced\* the sitev,\** others as abstruse as *Posiv\* niret\* malug\* fohik\* gujol.\** Sentences 16 to 20 were English sentences with less obvious cues, and

21 to 26 were nonsense sentences of a different paradigm. Adult subjects saw all but the first ten sentences in each series.

In identifying the verb, the cue that proved most effective was position and the least, lexical meaning. The main difference between adult and child responses was a tendency for the children to choose on the basis of position, disregarding other cues. This was true only on the five-word sentences, however. There, adults chose the third word, whereas children chose the second, which was the position of the verb in most of the English sentences. In the sentence *Docib* *hegof* *gufed* *rupan* *tesor* the children erred in the direction of choosing *hegof* rather than *gufed* as the verb. In the children's verbalizations it was often obvious that they had chosen—and correctly—without being able to make conscious their principle of selection. One child, when asked why he chose the word *saw* in *Bill saw a distant house*, said, "Bill *saw* a distant house—it sounded right when I said it loudly." Many of these subjects were thus able to identify new instances of the form-class verb without being able to supply a definition of that class.

## THE SEMANTICS OF ENGLISH PARTS OF SPEECH

One of the aims of psycholinguistic research is to investigate the influence of language on cognition and perception. The determining influence of the vocabulary of a language is quite clear, yet anthropologists like Whorf (1956) have felt that grammatical features of the language affect the speaker's cognition and that speakers of structurally different languages have different world views. The studies described in this section undertake to show how one kind of grammatical practice, the allocation of words to one or another part of speech, affects cognition.

The studies described above have shown that as speakers grow older they tend more and more to group together members of the same form classes. In their free associations they come to respond with members of like classes, and they recognize new instances of these classes. These studies have indicated that groupings are made on the basis of certain formal and structural equivalences and in the absence of any common meaning. We have all been told in school that a noun is "the name of a person, place, or thing," but it is obvious that *truth* is neither a person nor a place, and if it is a thing the meaning of *thing* must be very ambiguous. It is impossible to demonstrate that a consistent semantic underlies each of the English parts of speech, that verbs always refer to actions, nouns to things, adjectives to qualities, and so on. Yet it is just these semantic implications that we would expect to affect cognition.

In an examination of children's vocabularies Brown (1957) investigated the possibility that in child language the parts of speech are more clearly definable in semantic terms. He found this to be so. In a comparison of adults' and children's most frequent nouns and verbs he found that most of the children's nouns referred to picturable objects, such as *truck* or *barn*, whereas fewer of the adults' nouns named categories having a characteristic visual contour. Similarly, in a comparison of verbs he found that the children's verbs characteristically name movements and that a much smaller percentage of adults' verbs refer to actions. These studies confirmed the impression that the nouns and verbs used by children have more consistent semantic implications than those used by adults.

New words are generally introduced to children in a way that makes their part-of-speech membership clear. The child is told "Look at the *dog*" or "See him *running*." If a part of speech has reliable semantic implications, it could call attention to the kind of attribute likely to belong to the meaning of the word. A child who had absorbed the semantics of the noun and verb would know the first time he heard *the dog* that it was likely to refer to an object having some characteristic size and shape, whereas *running* would be likely to name some type of movement. The part-of-speech membership of a new word could act as a filter, selecting for attention probably relevant features of the nonlinguistic world. In an experiment with preschool children Brown (1957) attempted to determine whether children experience any filtering of attributes by introducing newly invented words assigned to one or another part of speech and then inquiring about the meanings the words appeared to have.

The parts of speech under consideration were a verb ending in *ing*, a noun, and a subclass of the noun known as a mass noun. Mass nouns in English

are nouns like *milk* and *rice;* when *some* is used with a particular noun like *barn*, the noun is made plural—*some barns*, whereas a mass noun would be in the singular—*some rice*. Mass nouns usually name extended substances having no characteristic size or shape.

Brown's experiment involved presenting three sets of four pictures to individual preschool children. A typical set consisted of the following: the first picture showed a pair of hands performing a kneading motion with a mass of red confettilike material, which was piled into and overflowing a striped container. The important features were the kneading motion, the material in the container, and the container. Each of the remaining three pictures reproduced one of the three salient features of the first picture. In order to represent the motion a second time, it was also necessary to show a mass and a container, but these were of different colors. The other two sets of pictures involved different content but always a motion, a mass substance, and a particular object. The children were shown the first picture in conjunction with a new word identifiable either as a mass noun, a particular noun, or a verb; they were then shown the other three pictures and asked to point out again what had been named in the first picture. The stem words used were *niss,** *sib,** and *latt.** If the word was to function as a mass noun, the experimenter would ask the child, "Have you ever seen any *sib*?" He would then show the first picture and say, "In this picture you can see some *sib.**" He then showed the other three pictures and asked the child to find another one that showed some *sib*,* and the child was expected to point to the other picture containing a mass. For the verb, the child was told the picture showed *sibbing*,* and for the particular noun he was told it showed a *sib*.* He was accordingly expected to select the other pictures showing the motion or the container.

The results showed unambiguously that the children chose the container when the word was presented as a particular noun, the mass substance when it was given as a mass noun, and the action when the nonsense word took the form of a verb. This study suggests that the part-of-speech membership of a word indicates its general meaning, whether action, object, or substance, and that with very young children learning English the semantic implications of the verb, the mass noun, and the particular noun are discovered and utilized.

## FORM-CLASS SEMANTICS IN NONLINGUISTIC SORTING

An experiment concerning the Navaho language was conducted by Carroll and Casagrande (1958) in an attempt to see if Navaho object class would affect children's form or color preferences. In the Navaho language it is obligatory when using verbs of *handling* to employ different verbal forms, depending on the shape or other physical attributes of the object being talked about. The nouns themselves carry no class marker, but all speakers know the verb stem appropriate for any given noun. Because of this classificatory system, the experimenters hypothesized that Navaho children would discriminate form earlier than English-speaking children.

One hundred and thirty-five children on the Navaho reservation were subjects in this experiment. On the basis of a bilingualism test, they were divided into balanced bilinguals, English-dominant, and Navaho-dominant groups. The tests were conducted in English or Navaho, depending on the child's dominant language, with the aid of an interpreter when necessary. Testing was done in the hogans and in the presence of family members and other observers. In the experiment 3-to-ten-year-old children were presented with pairs of objects—sticks, ropes, blocks, etc. The members of the pairs differed from one another in two respects—size and shape, shape and verb-form class, color and size, color and shape. For each pair, the child was shown a third object similar to each member of the pair in only one of two relevant characteristics and asked which of the pair went best with the third object. The child might be shown a pair consisting of a yellow stick and a blue rope and then be asked which of them went best with a yellow rope. If he chose the stick, it was on the basis of color; if he chose the rope, it was on the basis of the Navaho verb form classification. Children whose dominant language was Navaho tended to choose on the basis of similarity of shape or verb-form classification rather than on the basis of size or color. English-dominant Navaho children were, on the contrary, more attracted to size and color. The performances of Navaho children were also compared with results from a group of upper middle-class American children from the Boston area. The youngest Navaho-dominant children showed more form preference than their American age-mates, but at older levels the Navaho-dominant and American children were about the same. English-dominant Navaho children showed much less form preference than either the Navaho-dominant or American children.

The authors postulate that the tendency of a child to match on the basis of form rather than color increases with age. This discrimination may be facilitated by a society (like the American) that gives its children elaborate toys that require form discrimination; or it may be influenced by the child's speaking a language like Navaho, where obligatory verbal categories direct his attention to the forms of the objects surrounding him.

The organization of linguistic forms into functional classes represents the development of a flexible grammatical system, which makes language an infinitely adaptable instrument rather than a finite set of rehearsed sequences. It is clear that children are able to assign forms to the proper form class on the basis of syntactic and phonetic cues. In addition, however, they are aware of rough semantic correlates and use the form-class membership of a new word in guessing the sort of reference the word is likely to make. It is, in addition, possible that continuing attention to these semantic dimensions for the purposes of first-language learning causes a generally heightened sensitivity to them that affects perception and cognition even when language is not explicitly involved.

There is some amusement to be had from the invention of language games for young children, but the scientist who is not wantonly eccentric will profess an aim beyond his own entertainment. What are the large questions that the psycholinguist dreams of answering with his phonemics and morphemics, with his *wugs,** *zazzes,** and *zibs*?*

Linguistic science itself aims to find a set of procedures and a set of analytic units of complete generality, free of bias from any particular language and adequate to the description of all languages. This aim has been accomplished for phonology, is near accomplishment for morphology, and is well begun on syntax. As languages are described in the abstract terms of phonemics, morphemics, and grammar, they become comparable one with another. The Hawaiian language has fewer segmental phonemes than the Chippewayan, but (and indeed, one could say "therefore") Hawaiian morphemes are generally longer phonemic strings than are Chippewayan morphemes (Hockett, 1958). Russian has greater morphological complexity than Chinese, but (and again, perhaps, "therefore") Chinese has the greater syntactical complexity. The student of child language will hope to see his work follow close behind descriptive linguistics, turning up laws about the relative advantages, difficulties, and delays attendant on learning languages that have varied structural characteristics.

The psycholinguist is also likely to have in mind the far-reaching propositions concerning linguistic relativity and linguistic determinism, which have been championed by Whorf (1956) and by many others. Whorf holds that persons speaking very different native languages (e.g., English and Hopi) will have very different cognitive psychologies. This is the linguistic-relativity thesis, which maintains that cognitive style and language structure covary. Whorf holds, in addition, that the native language is a major determinant of cognitive style. The language offered the child is held to be a kind of mold, giving shape to his mind. Study of the relativity thesis involves cross-cultural investigations of language and of adult nonlinguistic behavior. However, to establish language as a formative influence on perception and thought, it is necessary to study the acquisition process in children belonging to different language communities. Several of the studies described in this chapter have had this determinism thesis in mind; they include the work of Brown (1957) and of Carroll and Casagrande (1958). Whorf's realization that language is more than a perceptual-motor skill, that it is a prime agent of cognitive socialization, has given the study of language acquisition a new interest for psychology.

It may seem strange that we psychologists should need to have language described for us by a special linguistic science. Since language is everywhere about us and within us, we have only to look to see what it is. Still it is a fact that the descriptions of language behavior written by psychologists have usually been far too simple and rigid; we have been prone to falsify the nature of language to make it fit a few principles discovered in animal learning. The linguistic emphasis on system should make this kind of thing impossible for the future. Man is not a simple sort of monster gorged with words and phrases that are shaken out of him like pennies from a piggy bank. We experience a sample of language function when we are young and are thereby structurally altered so that we spin out the implications of that experience the rest of our lives. That makes us a complicated sort of monster.

## REFERENCES

Berko, Jean. 1958. The child's learning of english morphology. *Word*, 14, 150–177.

Bloch, B. and G. L. Trager. 1942. *Outline of linguistic analysis*, Baltimore: Waverly.

Brown, R. W. 1956. Language and categories. Appendix to J. S. Bruner, Jacqueline J. Goodnow, and G. A. Austin, *A study of thinking*. New York: Wiley. Pp. 247–312.

———. 1957. Linguistic determinism and the part of speech. *J. abnorm. soc. Psychol.*, 55, 1–5.

———. 1958. *Words and things*, Glencoe, Ill. Free Press.

———, and D. C. Hildum. 1956. Expectancy and the perception of syllables. *Language*, 32, 411–419.

Bruner, J. S., Jacqueline J. Goodnow, and G. A. Austin. 1956. *A study of thinking*. New York: Wiley.

Carroll, J. B. and J. B. Casagrande. 1958. The function of language classifications in behavior. In Eleanor E. Maccoby, T. M. Newcomb and E. L. Hartley (Eds.), *Readings in social psychology*. (3rd ed.) New York: Holt. Pp. 18–31.

Cherry, C. 1956. *On human communication*. New York: Wiley.

Chomsky, N. 1957. *Syntactic structures*. The Hague: Mouton.

Chukovskij, K. 1956. *Ot Dvuch do Pyati.*

Moskva, Gosudarstvennoe Izdat-el'stvo, Dom Detskoj Knigi.

Deutsche, J. M. 1943. The development of children's concepts of causal relations. In R. G. Barker, J. S. Kounin, and H. F. Wright (Eds.), *Child behavior and development*. New York: McGraw-Hill. Pp. 129–145.

Ervin, Susan M. 1957. *Grammar and classification*. Paper read at the meetings of the American Psychological Association.

Feifel, H. and I. Lorge. 1950. Qualitative differences in the vocabulary responses of children. *J. educ. Psychol.* 41, 1–18.

Gleason, H. A. 1955. *An introduction to descriptive linguistics*, New York: Holt.

Gheorgov, I. A. 1908. Ein Beitrag zur grammatischen Entwicklung der Kindersprache. *Arch. ges. Psychol.*, II, 242–432.

Grégoire, A. 1930. L'Apprentissage de la parole pendant les deux premières années de l'enfance. *J. Psychol.*, 30, 375–389.

——. 1937–1947. *L'Apprentissage du langage*, Liège-Paris: Droz. 2 vols.

Guillaume, P. 1927. Le Développement des elements formels dans le langage de l'enfant. *J. Psychol. norm. path.*, 24, 203–229.

Harris, Z. S. 1951. *Methods in structural linguistics*, Chicago: Univer. Chicago Press.

Heidbreder, E. 1948. The attainment of concepts: VI. Exploratory experiments on conceptualization at perceptual levels. *J. Psych.*, 26, 193–216.

Hockett, C. F. 1955. *A manual of phonology. Indiana Univer. Publ. Anthr. Ling.*, 11.

——. 1958. *A course in modern linguistics*. New York: Macmillan.

Hull, C. L. 1920. Quantitative aspects of the evolution of concepts. *Psychol. Monogr.* 38, No. 123.

Irwin, O. C. 1947a. Infant speech: Consonantal sounds according to place of articulation. *J Speech Dis.*, 12, 397–401.

——. 1947b. Infant speech: Consonantal sounds according to manner of articulation, *J. Speech Dis.*, 12, 402–404.

——. 1948. Infant speech: Development of vowel sounds. *J. Speech Hearing Dis.*, 13, 31–34.

——, and H. P. Chen. 1946. Infant speech: Vowel and consonant frequency. *J. Speech Dis.*, 11, 123–125.

Itard, J. M. G. 1932. *The Wild Boy of Aveyron*. (Trans. by G. and M. Humphrey.) New York: Century.

Jakobson, R. 1941. *Kindersprache, Aphasie und allgemeine Lautgesetze*. Uppsala: Almgvist and Wiksell.

Jakobson, R., C. G. M. Fant, and M. Halle. 1952. *Preliminaries to speech analysis*. Cambridge: Acous. Lab., Mass. Inst. Techn., tech. rep. No. 13.

——, and M. Halle. 1956. *Fundamentals of language*, The Hague: Mouton.

Kahane, M., R. Kahane, and S. Saporta. 1958. *Development of verbal categories in child language*, Bloomington, Ind.: Indiana Univer. Res. Ctr. Anthrop., Folklore, Ling.

Leopold, W. F. 1947. *Speech development of a bilingual child*. Evanston: Northwestern Univer. 4 vols.

Lewis, M. M. 1936. *Infant speech*, London: Kegan Paul.

Liublinskaya, A. A. 1957. The Development of children's speech and thought. In B. Simon (Ed.), *Psychology in the Soviet Union*. Stanford: Stanford Univer. Press.

Miller, G. A. 1951. *Language and communication*. New York: McGraw-Hill.

——, J. S. Bruner, and L. Postman. 1954. Familiarity of letter sequences and tachistoscopic identification. *J. genet. Psychol.*, 50, 129–139.

Miller, G. A. and P. E. Nicely. 1955. An analysis of perceptual confusions among some English consonants. *J. acous. Soc. Amer.* 27, 338–352.

Osgood, C. E., G. J. Suci, and P. H. Tannenbaum. 1957. *The measurement of meaning*. Urbana: Univer. Illinois Press.

Piaget, J. 1930. *The child's conception of physical causality*. New York: Harcourt, Brace.

——. 1952. *The child's conception of number*. London: Routledge.

Pittman, D. 1948. *Practical linguistics*, Cleveland: Mid-Missions (314 Superior Avenue).

Porter, D. 1955. *Preliminary analysis of the grammatical concept "verb."* Unpublished paper, Harvard Graduate School of Education.

Razran, G. H. S. 1939. Studies in configural conditioning: I. Historical and preliminary experimentation. *J. gen. Psychol.*, **21**, 307–330.

Riess, B. F. 1946. Genetic changes in semantic conditioning. *J. exp. Psychol.*, **36**, 143–152.

Rinsland, H. D. 1945. *A basic vocabulary of elementary school children*. New York: Macmillan.

Sack, Sallyann. 1957. *Absolute versus relational learning in young children: Some effects of the English language structure on learning*. Unpublished honors thesis. Cambridge: Radcliffe College.

Smoke, K. L. 1932. An objective study of concept formation. *Psychol. Monogr.*, **42**, No. 191.

Stern, Clara, and W. Stern. 1928. *Die Kindersprache*. Leipzig: Barth.

Velten, H. V. 1943. The growth of phonemic and lexical patterns in infant language. *Language*, **19**, 281–292.

Whorf, B. L. 1956. *Language, thought, and reality*. Cambridge: Technology Press.

# part IV

# The
# Study
# of
# Personality
# Development

chapter 14

# Interviewing
# Children

Leon J. Yarrow
*Family and Child Services*
*Washington, D. C.*

Many research problems in child development are concerned with the impact of environmental events on the child's development and functioning. Such events can be defined in terms of an "objective" analysis of the stimulus conditions or they can be defined subjectively in terms of the experiencing person in the situation. The interview is a technique particularly well adapted to uncovering subjective definitions of experiences, to assessing a child's perceptions of the significant people and events in his environment, and to studying how he conceptualizes his life experiences.

The interview has a variety of applications in developmental research. It may be the principal instrument for data collection, as in studies on concept development and research on attitudes

I wish to express my appreciation for constructive suggestions to my colleagues Hadassah Davis, Marion Goodwin, and Lovisa Tatnall.

and values. Interviewing may be used in pilot studies for developing hypotheses to be tested subsequently with other techniques; in pretesting personality questionnaires and attitude scales the interview may be useful in uncovering ambiguous or unclear items. More recently, interviewing has been utilized in a significant way in experimental studies. In learning or frustration experiments the child may be interviewed after the experimental procedure to explore his perception of the experimental situation, thus helping to clarify the impact of varied experimental procedures. A similar application of the interview, the "focused interview" (Merton and Kendall, 1946), has been made with adults in an attempt to pinpoint specific elements of a larger situation, such as a film or radio broadcast, which have been significant in influencing attitudes. Concurrent with the growing interest among psychologists in the development of ego-functions, the interview situation is being used increasingly to observe the child's manner of coping with varied aspects of a defined social situation, e.g., attempts at mastery, persistence, dependency, and passivity.

The major share of literature on interviewing has been clinically oriented, although recently several excellent articles and books have given detailed consideration to the use of the interview in social research (Hyman, 1954; Kahn and Cannell, 1957; Maccoby and Maccoby, 1954). There is, however, little available literature on methods of interviewing children for research. This chapter focuses on those aspects of the interview technique that are particularly relevant to research on children.

The interview is distinguished from

other research approaches commonly used with children by its dependence on an interpersonal relationship. This is a source of strength as well as difficulty in its use as a research instrument. The commonest justification offered for the choice of the interview over more impersonal techniques, such as the personality inventory or attitude questionnaire, is the presumed facilitating effect of the personal relationship in the communication process. It is likely that in many research situations the interpersonal relationship will contribute substantially to the validity of the data. The direct relationship in the interview reduces misunderstandings by providing the opportunity to clarify the meaning of unclear questions. Furthermore, very inhibited children may need the reassurance of the interviewer's permissive attitude before they are able to express negative attitudes or reveal emotionally charged feelings or experiences. We cannot, however, assume uncritically the greater value of the interview for all kinds of problems. For example, a child may be freer in expressing criticism of some aspect of school policy on a written questionnaire than in a direct interview with a strange adult. Similarly, an adolescent may be less able to express verbally in direct interview the details of his sex information than in writing. The fact that the nature of the child's relationship with the adult in the interview situation exerts a significant influence on the content of his responses provides a source of variance difficult to control.

Numerous problems in interviewing children are determined primarily by age-level characteristics. A major problem derives from the child's limitations in language facility and comprehension of language. Other problems have their origins in the conventional role relationships between children and adults in our culture. Thus we may have overdependent behavior at one developmental stage and extreme negativism at another period. In establishing comparability of meaning between one interview situation and another there may be special difficulties because of differing stages of language maturity in children of approximately the same age. Other difficulties in interviewing, although not uniquely characteristic of its use with children, do require special considerations, e.g., developing adequate rapport with the child while keeping the relationship within nontherapeutic bounds and avoiding communication of the interviewer's biases.

In planning the research use of the interview, therefore, a major concern is the establishment and control of the relationship between the child and the interviewer. In addition to the broad question of rapport, there are many aspects of the relationship to be considered, such as the meaning of the interview relationship to the child and the role relationships established. In this chapter we have attempted to formulate some general principles relating to the varied aspects of the interpersonal relationship and to consider the major issues in the construction of interview schedules. Although it is not possible to present "cookbook" directions for interviewing, specific attention is given to such issues as the choice of language in the formulation of questions and the degree of directiveness and structure in the interview as a whole. From the general principles developed and the examples of specific techniques, it should be possible to derive creative adaptations to particular research goals and specific research situations.

## USE OF THE INTERVIEW AT DIFFERENT AGE LEVELS

Developmental factors enter into consideration of interview procedures at several points. These factors—comprehension of language, language facility, affective and role relationships between children and adults, and normative motivations (motivational characteristics of different age levels, e.g., negativism, independence strivings)—must be considered in evaluating the use of the interview with children and in suggesting the adaptations required in interview procedures at different developmental levels.

Our first concern is how far down the developmental scale we can go in applying interview procedures. Because of its dependence on language, the conventional interview is not applicable at a preverbal stage of development or during a period when the child is still concerned with mastery of the mechanics of language; similarly, it is inapplicable to children having auditory or language handicaps and emotionally disturbed children with severe language inhibitions. There has been a general reluctance to use the interview with children under 6 years of age because of the assumption that the preschool child's language comprehension, his language facility, and his lack of motivation to communicate preclude effective

use of the interview. The research bearing on this question is very meager. Radke (1946) in a study of parental attitudes used a direct interview productively with intellectually superior children just under 4 years of age in assessing their perceptions of parental roles and control techniques. She was impressed with "the clarity and coherence of the individual reports of the children and . . . the degree of correspondence between reports of the child and reports of the parents on the same issues."

Ammons (1950) used a verbal interview in conjunction with doll play to study awareness of racial differences in 2-, 3-, 4-, and 5-year-old children. In terms of the cooperativeness of the children, his findings are positive in regard to applicability of the interview to children more than 2 years of age. Among the 2-year-olds there was a high percentage of refusals to respond (56 per cent of the children) and a sharply decreasing number of refusals at other age levels, diminishing to a negligible number (10 per cent) of 5-year-olds.

Despite these positive evaluations of the effectiveness of the interview in the preschool period, considerable reluctance to use a direct verbal technique at these ages exists. This reluctance derives partly from the data on language characteristics of preschool children, i.e., data on vocabulary, articulation, and the functional use of language. Vocabulary at 2 years of age is limited; the total vocabulary is estimated at 200 words (McCarthy, 1954). Although there is a very great increase in vocabulary between 2 and 3 years of age, the child's language is still very self-conscious. One might draw a parallel between the child's use of language during this period and his earlier awkwardness and uncertainty in locomotion, when his concern with the mechanics of the process transcends its functional value. Children between 2 and 3 years of age use words in a very limited way for exchanging information, ideas, or concepts; speech may be a form of play, or language may be used in an instrumental way to express the child's needs and, to some extent, to control the behavior of others in accordance with his needs. There may be some difficulty at this age in understanding the child's language because of poor articulation. According to available research on comprehensibility of children's speech, about 30 per cent of responses of 2-year-old children are incomprehensible. By 3½, even though articulation may not be perfect, only a negligible percentage of language responses cannot be understood (McCarthy, 1930; Metraux, 1950).

By 4, children's speech is not only more easily understood but there is a great change in the function of language. Between 4 and 5, children become much more interested in exchanging information, in describing events in their experiences, and, in a very conscious way, in directing activities of others. Even after children have acquired a large vocabulary, they remain limited in the complexity and subtlety of ideas they are able to express directly in words. Very complex and subtle concepts are often expressed in highly symbolic language, a fact that offers difficulties to the adult in interpreting children's interviews. Lois Murphy (1956), in discussing obstacles to communication between children and adults, notes,

Children under five may not be able to express their feelings in words; their language may be full of phrases expressing their wants, and descriptions like "Garage man fixes broken bumper," which may reflect some concern about body damage; but such directly expressed remarks as, "I was very angry at my mother for not giving me two ice creams" are not within the range of many preschool children. At best, a grumbling "stinky old mommy" attempts to convey the feeling (page X).

Similarly, Vigotsky (1939) has pointed out that the egocentric language of early childhood is based on a grammar of thought and syntax of word meaning that differ markedly from the conventional socialized speech of adults.

The meaning of the child's words is derived from the whole complex of subjective experience which it arouses in him, and one word in his egocentric speech may be saturated with sense to such an extent that it would require many words in socialized speech to explain it (Hartley et al., 1952, p. 7).

These observations point up some of the hazards and suggest the lower limits in terms of age for the use of the interview. On the whole, research evidence suggests that the direct interview can be used effectively with 4-year-olds. Under this age, interviewing can be carried on productively with special adaptations to children's linguistic and motivational characteristics. We can take advantage of the fact that passive vocabulary develops much earlier than active vocabulary by using techniques requiring only the comprehension of language. A valuable adaptation of the conventional interview for children under 4 years of age is the picture-choice technique, in which the problem is defined verbally and the only response required of the child is a choice among a series of pictures (Horowitz, 1943). Creative use of this technique provides the possibility of studying rather complex and subtle feelings and attitudes without making great demands on the child's verbal ability. It is a technique that continues to be interesting to children into adolescence. Another adaptation of the standard interview is the doll-play interview, in which the child acts out with the dolls his response to a verbal question and a scene set up by the experimenter. The doll-play interview is more limited in the age range for which it is effective; its greatest usefulness is between 3 and 5 years of age. Although it retains interest value for girls well into middle childhood, with boys it begins to lose its usefulness after 5.

A number of factors other than linguistic ones inhibit adequate communication between the preschool child and the adult and affect the validity of the interview. During this period, when there is persistent testing out of adults, the child may simply refuse to respond to the interviewer's verbal approach or he may use this opportunity to engage in playful teasing behavior that might be expressed in deliberate distortion of his responses. These are sources of difficulty that can be handled to some extent by skillful manipulation of the situation and establishment of a relationship that would make such behavior unlikely and inappropriate. If the interviewer is casually permissive and avoids communicating any anxiety of his own

about the child's responding, he is less likely to arouse teasing negativism. Testing-out behavior may be decreased if the interviewer is not a complete stranger to the child; in interviewing done in a nursery school setting the interviewer may become familiar to the children as an observer in the nursery school some time before the first interview. Playing a game with the child or showing him a trick gadget before the interview may help establish rapport.

Although the young child may be negativistic, he may at the same time be highly suggestible, and special care must be exercised by the interviewer to avoid influencing the child to give the response he thinks will win adult approval. Careful wording of questions to suggest that any one of several alternative responses is acceptable may be helpful, e.g., "some children think that. . . . Others think that. . . . Maybe you have some different ideas about it. . . . We like to know all the different ideas that 6-year-old boys have about this. . . ." Sometimes systematic use of countersuggestion may be effective, e.g., presenting the same question in several forms, slanting the response first in one direction and then in the opposite direction. (See p. 582 for further discussion of these techniques.)

During the middle childhood or latency period, the child makes important strides in language ability and in his whole conceptual development. Children of this age are capable of thinking about ideas that are removed from their immediate concrete experiences. They have well-developed language skills and their concepts of time are becoming clarified; time is measured in terms of life history events (Stone and Church, 1957). In contrast to the early preschool child's feeling-oriented speech, language at this age is socially directed and utilitarian. Biber and her associates (1952), in describing a group of superior 7-year-olds, note, "Social exchanges through the medium of language in this group are on what appears to be practically an adult level as far as understanding and purpose are concerned." They feel that language is used very little at this age as a means of expressing feeling. It tends to be used almost exclusively in the service of communication of ideas.

Although language facility may be no bar to communication in the middle childhood period, clinicians have noted among children at this age an intensified resistance to revealing their feelings, concerns, and attitudes to adults. There is a tendency for children in middle childhood to exclude adults actively from their private world. Unlike the preschoolers who often think out loud, in the middle childhood period children are more likely to keep their feelings and thoughts to themselves. This behavior has been considered a normal developmental phenomenon, which is part of the process of the child's establishing control of his developing ego. In the latency period, according to psychoanalytic interpretation, the child has achieved a calm based on a temporary abeyance of the conflict between biological impulses and social demands. The defensiveness against revealing significant feelings to adults is considered adaptive behavior motivated by fear of upsetting this unstable equilibrium.

The latency period is a time of intense interest in exploring and mastering the environment. We can capitalize on these normative characteristics to enhance rapport and facilitate verbal expression, e.g., giving the child materials to handle or build with during the interview or playing a game prior to the interview. This is an age when competitive games have special appeal. A game that is moderately involving, but more dependent on chance than on skill (e.g., Parchesi), is desirable to avoid inducing a failure experience and to avoid fostering a competitive relationship between the child and adult. The use of a game *during* the interview procedure is appropriate only for certain kinds of interview content. It may be quite inappropriate for an interview focused on personal relationships involving rivalry feelings or feelings of personal or intellectual adequacy. There are difficulties, too, in controlling failure experiences in a game during the interview. Any manipulation by the interviewer to assure the child's success may be perceived by the sensitive child and result in a deterioration in the relationship.

Throughout the literature on interviewing, there are casual statements suggesting that the sex of the interviewer may influence significantly the responses of boys and girls, particularly during the middle childhood and adolescent periods. In the latency period, boys' social code requires overt rejection of girls and women. There is no clear parallel among girls. Although girls may show distain for boys, this disdain does not generalize to adult men. There are no systematic research findings on the influence of the sex of the interviewer on the responses of boys and girls. Studies of adults have pointed up the biasing influence of the interviewer's sex on responses to certain kinds of ego-involving material. However, there are no firm conclusions that the sex of the interviewer introduces systematic bias in all kinds of interview situations. In the clinical literature on therapy with children there are contradictory suggestions as to the significance of the sex of the therapist. In child therapy women analysts have worked with apparent success with boys during the latency period. On the other hand, Fleming and Snyder (1947), who studied this problem specifically in relation to nondirective therapy with boys, found that 10-year-old boys did not respond so well to a female as to a male therapist. Although it may be generally characteristic of this developmental period in our society that boys have difficulty in relating to a woman in an interview situation, it is by no means a universal phenomenon and undoubtedly is modified by the specific experiences of the child. The personal characteristics of the interviewer may play an equally significant role in terms of associations with familiar figures in the child's environment. The influence of the interviewer's sex may also vary with class or other social-background factors. In the research interview in which contact may be limited to one session, it is important to be aware of the possible inhibiting influences of the sex or personality of the interviewer.

The adolescent's resistance to adult attempts to probe his private world is a characteristic that has been discussed so much that it has acquired the status of a stereotype. It is a real factor that must be considered in research with adolescents. We must be aware, too, that there are significant differences between different periods of adolescence. Whereas the late adolescent period is comparable to adulthood insofar as interview methods are concerned, the early adolescent, roughly between 12 and 14, tends to be closer in psychological orientation to the late latency child. Here we find a rejection of parental identification with a replacement by a peer group identification. At this age it is likely that the adult whose attitudes express an acceptance of the child on an equal-status basis will be better able to establish rapport than the adult who represents the parents or adult-authority figures. However, despite the emotional resistance at this age, there are other characteristics, such as intense intellectual curiosity and idealism that might well be used to motivate cooperation in research. In the next period, middle adolescence, roughly 14 to 16, there tends to be heightened preoccupation with self and a greater withdrawal within the self. The child at this period is also striving to find a satisfactory ego-ideal; these strivings may result in a heightened awareness of attitudes and opinions of others and a tendency to accept and incorporate the opinions of acceptable adults. This tendency necessitates greater vigilance on the part of the interviewer not to reveal his own attitudes and not to suggest any response. It is important, too, during this stage that the interviewer does not threaten the child through overfriendliness.

Geelerd (1957) suggests in relation to psychotherapy with adolescents that "the ego of the adolescent is already so threatened by the increased id drives that a very little overeagerness on the analyst's part may be too overwhelming."

The sex of the interviewer is likely to have a significant effect on rapport at this age. We might anticipate that boys will be inhibited by women interviewers and girls will feel less free with men interviewers during adolescence than in the latency period. It is even more likely that an interactive influence will exist between the interview content and the sex of the interviewer.

The motivations that will be effective in involving the child in the interview and in stimulating free response also vary somewhat for children of different ages. With the young child it is not possible to capitalize on any abstract motivations relating to research. For him the gratifications must be immediate; he is not capable of conceptualizing the interview as a step toward a deferred goal. On the other hand, the adolescent, like the adult, may be motivated to express his feelings and attitudes about a particular topic, or he may see the interview as an opportunity to influence a desired change, e.g., bring about changes in school policies. Although the indirect association between the research findings and some desired outcome can sometimes be stressed meaningfully, ethical considerations would prevent the interviewer from deliberately misleading the child to anticipate any direct results.

The most effective motivations to communicate with the adult are developed during the course of the interview. The interview experience itself can be a gratifying one to children of all ages; their feelings of status are enhanced by receiving the full attention of an interested adult. After the child has been in the interview situation and has had an opportunity to air his thoughts and feelings to a permissive adult, the positive feelings developed may be sufficient to sustain the interview and to motivate the child to respond to difficult questions requiring real effort.

It is convenient to discuss the characteristics of children that offer difficulties in interviewing in terms of developmental stage phenomena. However, we know that motivational characteristics cannot be too closely defined by a given chronological age; there may be considerable overlap between developmental periods. Also, it must be recognized that individual characteristics may transcend age-level characteristics.

## INTERPERSONAL RELATIONSHIP AND INTERVIEW SETTING

A research interview has characteristics that make it uniquely different from other familiar social situations in the child's life. In this setting the child has the full attention of an adult who is interested in him and in his ideas. This person is nonjudgmental and accepts the child's attitudes and feelings without criticism or threat. He accepts information or answers to questions without judging them right or wrong. In another sense, the interview relationship is unique. Unlike normal social intercourse, the interviewer submerges or mutes his own personality and identity, and, while maintaining anonymity, he remains an empathic and responsive person.

Some of the basic orientations to interpersonal relationships growing out of therapeutic interviewing might well be adapted to the research interview. The interviewer must convey to the child his genuine interest in him and in his feelings and ideas. Children's sensitivity to the genuineness or lack of sincerity on the adult's part has been repeatedly pointed out by clinicians, teachers, caseworkers, and others working directly with children. To be able to convey to the child genuine liking and acceptance, and at the same time to maintain a sense of neutrality and objectivity, demands of the interviewer very fine skills in social relations. He cannot be a completely neutral object, but he needs to elicit quickly a positive response from the child in order to secure cooperation. The level of the relationship in terms of empathy and responsiveness must be carefully controlled and will vary from one type of interview to another. An interview that probes feelings, attitudes, and deeply personal orientations requires a deeper level of relationship in terms of warmth, sensitivity, and responsiveness than one concerned primarily with obtaining factual data.

Although the therapeutic approach has much to offer in the way of an orientation to research interviewing, the basic difference in goals between the therapeutic and research interviews creates fundamental differences in the relationship. The respondent in the research interview is helping the interviewer by his cooperation, instead of being the recipient of help, as in the therapeutic interview. Another important difference necessitating modifications in technique is in the duration of the relationship. The research interview often involves a single contact with the child, as distinguished from the therapy situation in which there are often-repeated contacts over a period of months or even years. There is need, therefore, for a different approach to develop more rapidly the character of the relationship desired for the research interview. However, in some research situations, such as longitudinal research, the contacts between interviewer and child continue over a period of years, but are less frequent and less intensive than in the therapeutic relationship. In this setting there may be advantages in proceeding more slowly in establishing the desired relationship. In some treatment interviews the transference relationship is consciously fostered in the service of the therapeutic goals. In the research interview there are ethical as well as methodological reasons for avoiding the development of a relationship that could not be adequately handled by the interviewer in his limited time with the child. Certainly, negative transference could seriously impair the adequacy of communication between the child and the interviewer. On the other hand, there is the danger of developing a too strongly positive relationship. Overidentification with the interviewer might distort the responses; the child might attempt to give responses he thinks the interviewer wants, or that would be acceptable to him, and to inhibit responses he thinks the interviewer would find unacceptable. Unless the research objectives require that the child be able to project onto the interviewer feelings that he has toward parental figures or other significant adults in his environment, it is necessary that the interviewer clarify his identity early and do it in a way to differentiate clearly his role from that of the parent or teacher.

Because of its very uniqueness and ambiguity, the interview relationship may initially be anxiety provoking. To avoid the development of anxiety, it is important that the interviewer be very explicit in defining the nature of the situation. It may be done verbally as well as nonverbally. The definition of the situation involves clarifying for the child the purpose of the interview, the interviewer's expectations of him and the interviewer's role.[1]

When a child is brought to a strange setting for an interview, some time must be planned for him to become familiar with the environment and with the interviewer. At the beginning the interviewer may assume a relatively neutral role while the child is given freedom to explore the environment. However, the interviewer should be available and supportive without forcing himself on the child. Play materials may help put the child at ease because of their familiarity

and pleasant associations. By focusing attention on the toys, the child's self-consciousness may be diminished and he may be stimulated to offer spontaneous comments about similarity or lack of similarity to his playthings at home. The play materials should be simple and challenging but not too difficult for the child to master and not so absorbing that they detract from the relationship with the interviewer. The materials should have a limited time-involvement so that the child can quickly satisfy his curiosity about them or successfully master them before the formal interview procedure is started. With older children, toys become less effective, and the interviewer is more dependent on his skills in interpersonal relationships to convey to the child quickly his warmth and genuine acceptance of him. Some "trick" gadgets are often useful to break the ice and to help put the child at ease by shifting the focus of attention away from himself to the object or game. In helping the child discover the possibilities of the game, the interviewer can communicate warmth and permissiveness, setting the tone for the interview relationship. In some kinds of research, such as in studies on aggression, it may be methodologically important to standardize the preinterview experience to control for possible effects of antecedent failure, frustration, or fear (Yarrow, 1948).

A useful procedure in establishing rapport and stimulating the child to talk is to have the child or parent bring to the interview some creative products, such as pictures the child has drawn or painted. This situation en-

---

[1] H. S. Sullivan (1954), in discussing the psychiatric interview, emphasizes the importance of the definition of the situation: "Social or cultural definition is very important indeed in the earlier stages of an interpersonal relation; in fact, it is finally important if one of the people concerned overlooks it, since this means that the relationship will not be developed in any meaningful sense" (p. 29).

ables the interviewer to express his appreciation of the child's productions and places the child in the role of the "expert" with this particular material. He is the only one able to tell the interviewer all about it, thus facilitating spontaneous conversation and giving him confidence that what he has to say is important. The interviewer can then divert the conversation to the desired area.

Some consideration needs to be given to the physical setting in which the interview is conducted. In general, we think of the ideal setting as one that reduces anxiety and maximizes rapport. A quiet room that fosters a feeling of privacy, one free from "convenient" distractions, will facilitate the interview process. On the other hand, for some kinds of emotionally involving material, an interview on the spot in the situation may yield significant data (Redl, 1959). (See p. 591 for discussion of this technique.) For some research problems, a setting may be created to facilitate or stimulate deliberately the expression of attitudes or feelings of aggression, anxiety, or sympathy. Many obvious practical considerations govern the appropriateness of any given physical setting for an interview; an interview about the child's attitudes toward his teacher might not be most freely conducted in an alcove off the principal's office. Other aspects of the physical situation will also affect rapport, such as seating arrangements. A different atmosphere with different expectations in the child is created when the interviewer and child are separated by a desk than when they are seated at the same level side by side. Often a child's

concentration of attention is improved when the physical arrangements impose limits, such as being seated at a table with paper and crayons. Sometimes children in a strange situation will feel more comfortable if they are partly "protected" by a table or desk than if they are "exposed" in the middle of a large room.

In addition to the nonverbal definition of the situation, communicated by the physical setting and by the interviewer's initial approach to the child, it is usually desirable that there be a clear verbal definition. The interviewer should be explicit about the purposes of the interview as well as such factors as the length of time involved and the confidentiality of the content.

With the preschool child, it has been traditional to define the interview as a play situation. If this orientation is given, then it is important to make the interview situation a genuinely pleasurable one. The child may, with good reason, become resistant if he has been given the expectation of having fun and the situation becomes a serious one or one without clear purpose to him. With preschool children, the use of props during the interview (e.g., talking through the medium of dolls or carrying on a conversation via toy telephone) is often more effective than a straightforward question-answer approach. Giving the child an opportunity to use crayons or clay while talking during the interview may also help to decrease self-consciousness. However, these accessory materials must not be so interesting that they will offer a convenient escape from the interview or become so absorbing that the child will see the interview questions as an annoying distraction from his play.

During the middle childhood period, after school entrance, when the child has some background of experience in serious discussion with adults, it is usually less desirable to structure an interview as play unless it is really carried out as a free-play interview. During this age period the interviewer must rely more on the child's willingness to accept adult authority and on the inherent interest of the content of the interview questions. An explicit verbal definition of the purpose of the interview is especially important at this age. A simple statement, such as, "We are interested in finding out what boys your age think about different kinds of TV programs so that we can plan programs that boys like," may be an adequate definition of the interview purpose.

An important aspect of the definition of the interview situation is the clarification of role relationships. Research on interviewing adults has emphasized the importance of status roles, of the in-group or out-group identification of the interviewer, and of his degree of expertness in the topic under consideration. Although there is no relevant research, it is likely that different role considerations are important with children. The significant roles may be those that relate to the child's daily experiences—teacher, father, mother, coach—roles that have meaning in terms of authority, discipline, and trust. The research interviewer, as a permissive person who encourages the child to express his thoughts or feelings with impunity, does not easily fit any of these conventional roles. It may be difficult for the child to conceptualize the interviewer's role, and role ambiguity may be a source of anxiety. The interviewer should be as explicit as possible about his role early in the interview. He defines his role verbally as well as by his behavior. If he is aware of the various possible roles in which he might be perceived by the child, he can encourage the role perception that will facilitate the purposes of the interview. For the preschool child, the interviewer seen as parent-surrogate will probably arouse the least anxiety. With children known to have very disturbed parental relationships, it is important to convey quickly to the child the attitude of the "good parent." Similarly, during adolescence, with resistance to parental probing already strongly established, one might assume that the parental role would hinder communication. A neutral adult who is able to accept the adolescent on an equal-status basis in terms of the adequacy of his ideas and knowledge, yet who maintains some degree of adult authority, is probably the ideal role. The degree of authority, the degree of equality, and the degree of neutrality will vary somewhat with the purpose of the interview.

Although it is important that the interviewer's behavior be carefully controlled to provide comparability from case to case, preoccupation with standardization of behavior may detract from spontaneity and result in "stiff" behavior. It is unrealistic to assume that a rigid behavior pattern can be defined

interviewee's responses to keep them within the desired structure. At the other extreme, with the nondirective approach, the interviewer may simply open up an area of discussion and follow completely the child's leads in the direction of the topic, keeping the interview moving by reflecting content or feelings expressed (Rogers, 1945; 1951; Axline, 1947).

In reality, neither extreme in directiveness is well adapted to research interviewing. The more directive approach is usually adequate for obtaining factual information about topics of minimal ego-involvement, e.g., favorite games. The directive, highly structured interview is comparable to the written questionnaire, and there probably is not much gain in validity over the questionnaire for obtaining factual information, except with children who have not yet mastered reading skills.

Increasing recognition has been given to the value of the nondirective approach in interviewing adults, particularly in personality assessment and in research on attitudes and feelings that are not fully conscious. Its major value is that it gives the respondent an opportunity to select content that is particularly significant to him and to present it in a context that may offer further clues to its meaning to him. The nondirective interview also has value with children to the extent that it is differentiated from the formal question and answer approach, an approach that may be unfamiliar to the young child and one that is associated by older children with testing procedures in school.

**Degree of Structure of Interview**

*Questions.* The degree of directiveness and the degree of structure in interviewing are often not clearly distinguished. Directiveness, as we have used it, refers to the behavior of the interviewer, the degree of control he exercises over the movement of the interview and the interviewee's responses. Structure refers to the characteristics of the questions, the degree of specificity of content. High directiveness and a high degree of structure usually go together, but it is possible for a nondirective interviewer to use a highly structured stimulus-situation to focus on specific content and allow the interview to proceed nondirectively.

Possible variations in question structure range from a highly structured question in which both the stimulus and response frameworks are structured to the unstructured question in which both the stimulus and response aspects are relatively ambiguous. The possible variations are schematized below with an example based on a doll-play interview with 4- and 5-year-old children in regard to mother-child relationships (Winstell, 1951).

The questions with highly structured stimulus-situations are best adapted to problems in which we wish to focus on a very specific topic, such as the child's feelings about specific aspects of parental control techniques, e.g., his reaction to being frustrated in play by the mother. If we are interested in a broader characterization of the mother-child relationship, then the less structured approach is desirable because it gives the child freedom to select the most salient framework for characterizing his relationship to his mother.

## POSSIBLE VARIATIONS IN STRUCTURE
## OF INTERVIEW QUESTIONS

| Stimulus Framework | Response Framework |
|---|---|
| Structured | Open |
| *Example:* "This little boy is busy playing and his mother stops him and says it's time to go to bed." | "What does he say?" |
| Structured | Structured |
| *Example:* "If this little boy is busy playing and his mother stops him and says it's time to go to bed." | "Does he get mad or does he say, 'All right, mother?'" |
| Open | Open |
| *Example:* "This little boy is playing and his mother comes in." | "Let's make up a story about what she says to him and what he says to her." |
| Open | Structured |
| *Example:* "This little boy is busy playing and his mother comes in." | "Does the boy ask his mother to play with him or does he just go on playing as if his mother was not there?" |

There are obvious dangers in interview questions with highly structured response possibilities because of young children's high suggestibility. This approach may be useful when we wish to facilitate the expression of culturally inappropriate attitudes. When alternative response possibilities are given, the form of the question can suggest that both are socially acceptable, e.g., "Some boys think this way, others think that way."

***Direct, Indirect, and Projective Questions.*** In terms of directness, we can distinguish three major types of in-terview question: direct, indirect, and projective. The direct and indirect questions are differentiated in terms of the extent to which the purpose of the question is made explicit; the projective question is distinguished from the other two in regard to the referent of the actor, i.e., the actor is a hypothetical child rather than the interview subject. Questions may vary along a continuum of directness.

The straightforward direct question is most commonly used for obtaining factual information and in simple attitude studies, e.g., "Can you tell me the names of all the books you have read in the past month?" Indirect questions are used to explore feelings or attitudes when resistance to a direct approach is anticipated because of cultural taboos or unconscious inhibitions or when the cultural standards might prompt invalid responses. In the indirect question the child is asked to state what he would do or how he feels about a topic, but the purpose of the question is disguised. For example, instead of asking the child which parent he prefers, the question might be, "If you were shipwrecked on an island and could have either your mother or your father with you, which one would you take?" In the projective question the purpose is further disguised in that the child is asked to interpret the feelings or predict the actions of a hypothetical child. Frequently dolls or pictures are presented with the question. For example, "Mother is feeding the baby. This little boy comes in and sees them. What does he do? What does he think about it?"

The foregoing example illustrates another significant difference between the projective and the direct question. Typically, the direct and the projective questions differ on the dimension of situational specificity as well as in the identification of the actor. The projective question often uses a specific situation in an attempt to explore a generalized attitude, e.g., sibling rivalry. The direct question characteristically uses a less structured stimulus-situation, e.g., "What do you think about the new baby in your house?" Thus the questions differ not only in whether the child is asked directly about *his* feelings but in the generality of the attitude. In the projective approach a series of questions involving a number of different situations might be necessary to establish generalized attitudes toward the sibling, as distinguished from a reaction to a specific situation, e.g., being displaced by the sibling in the feeding situation.

In the use of the projective question we are operating on the assumption that the child, in telling what another child will do, is expressing his own motives. This may often be a valid assumption (Getzels, 1951), but it cannot be uncritically accepted for all kinds of questions and in all sorts of interview situations. In some situations the child may give the response that represents the cultural norm of his group rather than his unique personal feelings or attitudes. Sometimes a child's response to a projective question may represent a blend of fantasy with reality. For example, in response to a projective question involving a hypothetical parent's reaction to the misbehavior of a hypothetical child, children often attribute to the parent a stronger reaction and harsher discipline than is characteristic of the reality situation. This obviously poses problems in interpretation. There are, however, many kinds of questions that cannot be asked directly, when the child is not consciously aware of his true feelings or when he cannot express them because the cultural inhibitions are too strong. In such cases projective questions are the best available approach. Insofar as we recognize that responses to projective questions may reflect unconscious feelings or may represent symbolic or disguised expressions of culturally inappropriate sentiments, we will not analyze them at their face value but will try to utilize principles of interpretation derived from our knowledge of psychodynamics.

*Choice of Interview Approach.* One's theoretical assumptions about human behavior will partly influence the kind of interview approach chosen, e.g., with a psychodynamic orientation, one would favor the use of projective questions. The kind of research problem being investigated also influences the approach used. If we are studying attitudes with strongly defined cultural taboos, indirect or projective questions are generally preferable. However, if our interest is in the extent to which the child has internalized the cultural patterns of thinking and behavior with regard to these taboos, direct questions would be more meaningful.

In the study of personality characteristics or interpersonal relationships an important aspect of the analysis may be in terms of the way in which the child structures his responses, the particular content selected, and the sequence of his associations. The nondirective approach with the less structured question is best adapted to this kind of analysis.

We have pointed out earlier some advantages of the open interview with children in creating a freer, more natural atmosphere. This conclusion does not apply equally to the structure of questions. On the whole, questions that are completely unstructured in terms of the situational components are not likely to be useful at the youngest age levels. With his limited associational ability, the young child may have difficulty with an unstructured approach; he needs some framework within which he can focus and direct his thinking and language. Unstructured questions in a nondirective interview with children over the age of 6 years may be valuable in determining the significant dimensions of the child's psychological environment, the areas of gratification and anxiety and the clarities and distortions in his perceptions of the significant people in his environment. In short, for assessing conscious and near-conscious personality trends and their significant environmental supports, the nondirective open interview may be a very useful method. Of the many limitations and difficulties inherent in the free and unstructured interview as a research instrument, the major ones are the danger of lack of comparability from case to case in the kinds of data obtained, the consequent difficulty in quantitative pooling of data, and the decreased control of interviewer bias.

Interviews need not be rigidly limited to one kind of approach. The techniques and form of question may be varied at different points in the interview. The interview may begin with an open question and then proceed nondirectively. After an appropriate time interval, the interviewer may introduce increasingly more structured questions and may assume a more directive role. There are some dangers, however, in radical shifts in interview approach. Rapport in an interview grows out of the respondent's increasing familiarity with the interviewer's approach and in knowing what to expect of the interview situation. Therefore, an abrupt shift in technique from a nondirective to a directive approach is not desirable and may be disruptive of rapport.

## CONSTRUCTION OF INTERVIEW SCHEDULES:

*Pretesting.* In the development of a questionnaire or interview schedule, pretesting is useful in helping to eliminate unclear, inappropriate, or anxiety-arousing questions and to identify the most effective motivational techniques. The pretesting should be done on a population chosen for its comparability to the experimental population in characteristics relevant to the research problem. Considerable pretesting of the kind Piaget (1951) has used may be necessary to develop an interview schedule for children of the preschool years. One form of "pretesting" suggested by Piaget's work involves detailed recording of the spontaneous conversation of children in situations designed to elicit verbal comments on the topic under study. Questions can then be formulated with the words and concepts that are part of the active vocabulary of children of the research sample. Following formulation of the questions, there is still need for the more conventional kind of pretesting, in which the actual interview schedule planned for the research is used. The results of the pretest must then be evaluated. Each question requires careful consideration in terms of its ease of comprehension, its effect on rapport, and its effectiveness in eliciting a response relevant to the research objectives. Necessary revisions can then be made in the light of these evaluations. Although pretesting may add considerably to the time and expense of a research project, it is usually well worth the effort in terms of the ultimate returns.

**Formulation of Questions.** The basic considerations in the formulation of questions are (1) that the question be readily understood by the child being interviewed, (2) that the meaning or interpretation of the question not vary significantly from one child to another, and (3) that the form of the question not "lead" the child to a given response.

One way to insure the child's comprehension in the interview would be to limit language used to the equivalent of a child's basic English. There is a considerable body of knowledge of children's language and concept development (Baldwin, 1955; Jersild and Ritzman, 1938; McCarthy, 1954; Piaget, 1951; M. K. Smith, 1941) available to guide us in constructing questionnaires and interview schedules. Before the pretest or first trial of a standardized interview, it would be desirable to check the words with one of the standard lists commonly used with preschool or school-age children (International Kindergarten Union List, 1928; a Combined Word List, Buckingham and Dolch, 1936).

In addition to the specific language used, other characteristics of the question may affect comprehension and motivation in the interview. Ammons' (1950) study of racial attitudes in preschool children, although not designed as a methodological study and based on a limited sample of cases and questions, offers some interesting suggestions regarding form of interview questions. He found few refusals at all ages to questions with simple response alternatives, such as "yes" or "no," or to questions involving a choice between concrete alternatives, e.g., "white" or "colored." The highest rate of refusals was to open-ended questions. Children at all ages were more likely to respond to questions about their *actions* than to questions about what they would *say*. Although children may respond easily to questions with simple response alternatives, the validity of such responses is sometimes questionable. There is a real possibility that young children who do not completely understand a question may choose a response on a purely chance basis simply in an attempt to please the examiner.

A number of specific techniques, which have grown out of clinical and research experience in interviewing adults, may be helpful in formulating questions for interviews with children. These are discussed in several books and articles (Cantril, 1940; Jahoda, Deutsch, and Cook, 1951; Kahn and Cannell, 1957; Maccoby and Maccoby, 1954; Payne, 1949; Parten, 1950). We have limited discussion here to suggestions for formulating questions to facilitate the expression of responses that the child might consider culturally unacceptable.

1. Suggest in the question that other children might feel the same way. The question may sanction a specific attitude or a general feeling. For example, "Some boys think they shouldn't have to take their little brothers along with them when they go out to play. How do you feel about it?" "All of us get mad sometimes when something happens that we don't like. What sorts of things make you feel mad?"

2. Present two alternatives, both of which might be considered acceptable. Example: "If your little brother pulls out all the books from the shelves, do you punish him so that he won't do it again or do you see that your mother finds out about it?"

3. Choose words that will soften an undesirable response or present the response in a context that might make it more desirable. For example, in the preceding example, instead of saying, "would you tell your mother on him?" the use of the phrase, "see that your mother finds out about it" places the response in a more acceptable context.

4. Avoid placing the child in a position in which he has to deny some undesirable behavior by wording the question to assume that he has engaged in this behavior. "What sorts of things do you and your brother fight about most?" This technique must be used sensitively and with awareness of limits to avoid arousing guilt feelings that cannot be adequately handled.

5. Give the child an opportunity to express a positive response before presenting a question that will require negative or critical evaluations. "What things do you like best about school? . . . What things aren't so good?"

Questions combining these different approaches may be used: "There are some things most boys like about school and other things they don't like at all. . . . What are some of the things you like best . . . and what are some of the things that aren't so good about school?"

*Question Sequence.* The sequence of questions may significantly influence rapport as well as the validity of the responses. The organization of topics should be guided by consideration of what is most meaningful to the child, as illustrated in Piaget's interviews in which the sequence is adapted to the child's concepts and comprehension level. The opening questions in an interview with a child are especially important to help set the tone of the relationship and to define what is expected of him. It is important that he be able to respond to the opening questions without difficulty or embarrassment to give him the assurance that he can successfully play the required role. The more difficult questions and those that may involve some threat to the child, e.g., the expression of hostile feelings, are best introduced late in the interview, after maximum rapport has been established. With young children whose attention span is limited, the sequence of the interview may be utilized to control interest. Sequential variations in kinds of questions or content areas may help to reduce fatigue and boredom.

A common sequence, the funnel sequence, begins with the most general and follows with more differentiated and specific questions. This sequence enables the child to state his frame of reference and to respond in terms of categories salient for him without being influenced by the specific questions that define the interviewer's frame of reference. For some kinds of research problems with children, a reversal of the conventional funnel sequence may be desirable; that is, the interview begins with specific questions, which are followed by the introduction of general questions toward the end of the interview. This sequence may be desirable with very young children who might have difficulty structuring an area from general questions. By starting with questions to which they are able to respond, they may be encouraged to attempt a response to a more difficult general question.

In a free interview the interviewer can often take the cue from the child when a given topic has been exhausted and he is ready for the introduction of a new area. Often it is desirable to use some kind of transition statement to indicate that a new topic is going to be opened up. For example, "You've given me lots of good ideas about the kinds of games girls like to play; now I'd like to get some of your ideas about the kinds of books 8-year-old girls like to read." This device may prevent the child from carrying over the frame of reference from the previous topic to the new one.

In young children there are tendencies to perseverate on a given idea or frame of reference. Thus a child's response to successive questions in a series may not be a true reaction to the content of the question but may be a perseveration from a previous question. There are no data on the conditions under which perseveration occurs. It may be partly a developmental phenomenon, but it seems likely that it is more frequent when the child is anxious or fatigued or when he is unclear about a question or what is expected of him. The establishment of good rapport may decrease the likelihood of perseverative responses. The sequence of questions and appropriate transitional statements may also be used to minimize perseverative tendencies.

*Length of Interview.* In the development of interview schedules for use with children it is particularly important to plan the total length of the interview within a time period appropriate for the child's attention span. The validity of an interview may be seriously impaired by a child's response when he is fatigued or satiated. Frequently, under such conditions, the child throws off an easy response in an attempt to end the interview quickly and escape from the situation. The length of an interview cannot, of course, be absolutely prescribed because the child's attention span will certainly vary with the content of the material as well as with the manner of presentation and other rapport-relevant factors in the situation. In recognition of the limited attention span of young children the range of ideas and concepts covered in a single interview should be limited. If it is necessary to cover a variety of concepts and themes, it is sometimes better to plan a second interview. The gain in validity through this procedure needs to be weighed against the added cost.

*Probing.* Often in an interview there is need to clarify or elaborate on a response to a question. The technique of probing is used to stimulate additional responses. To avoid creating defensiveness in the child, probes should be natural and without pressure. At most ages, if the child senses too great anxiety on the part of the adult to extract information, he is likely to react with negativism. The nondirective follow-up question is usually the most successful approach. A nondirective probe, in the form of a restatement of expressed content or feelings, ending in a questioning tone, may stimulate the child to elaborate his response (Rogers, 1945, 1951). The danger is that the interviewer's biases may be communicated in his probes, thus affecting the validity of the interview. In a free interview without standardized probes the interviewer's biases may influence the choice of points at which probes are introduced as well as the content of the probe. The interviewer who understands his own biases and maintains an awareness of them is less likely to transmit them than the interviewer who lacks such awareness.

*Handling Suggestibility.* The suggestibility of young children may seriously affect the validity of their responses. Several approaches are useful in counteracting suggestibility. The question can be phrased in a way that avoids giving the child any indication that one response is more acceptable than another. It is equally important that the examiner's manner and tone of voice be controlled when presenting a topic so as not to reveal his biases. Countersuggestion, in which several questions on the same topic are systematically slanted in different directions, is sometimes effective. For example, in studying the degree of parental control over choice of playmates the following series of questions might be introduced at different points in the interview:

1. "Do your mother and father let you play with anybody you want to play with?"

2. "Do your mother and father often tell you which children you can bring home to play with?"

3. "When a new boy comes to live in the neighborhood do you always ask your mother if you can play with him?"

If countersuggestion is not used sensitively and subtly, there is danger of some uncontrolled effects. If the child has committed himself to a position on a question early in the interview, this position may be maintained whether or not it is a valid representation of his point of view. Also, the use of countersuggestion may strain rapport. The child may refuse to respond if he recognizes a question as essentially similar to one he has already answered.

*Handling Anxiety.* For ethical reasons, as well as from the standpoint of effective motivation, the interviewer should avoid placing the child in a position requiring responses that are completely unacceptable in the child's culture or responses that may arouse guilt feelings. Sometimes one can free a child to admit to knowledge or discuss feelings on which there are cultural taboos and yet avoid or minimize guilt feelings by the form of the question. Matter-of-fact acceptance by the interviewer of everything the child says is the most effective means of avoiding the development of anxiety. If the interview has been essentially nondirective and has not pushed the child to express unacceptable feelings, it is likely that what he has expressed will not be too disturbing. If taboo areas have been discussed, some provision should be made, either during or following the interview, to reassure the child and to handle any guilt feelings. Assurance of confidentiality can be given if it seems appropriate, and the child can be given an opportunity to express acceptable attitudes on a variety of related topics. Even though the interview is not therapeutically oriented, it may be necessary to help a child achieve some closure on an anxiety-evoking topic that has been opened up in the interview. There is a sensitive line between stirring up more anxiety by probing and subtly leading the child to an acceptable resolution.

## SPECIAL ADAPTATIONS
## OF INTERVIEW TECHNIQUES

There are many variations on the conventional interview method that have been developed specifically for use with children. These variations have grown out of attempts to adapt the interview to the language, interests, and motivations of children. We have selected a few interviewing techniques that have proved their value with children and a few other creative approaches to interviewing that seem to show promise. These specific techniques might be viewed not so much as models but as points of departure in the development of a method for a particular problem.

*Piaget's Méthode Clinique.* Piaget's work (1928, 1929, 1951) has served as a model for the combined interview-experimental approach to the study of concept development. This *méthode clinique* represents a creative approach to interviewing children and to the formulation of questions appropriate to the child's level of comprehension. The first step in this method involves observation of children in natural situations with verbatim recording of spontaneous conversation. The spontaneous concepts and language of children in these natural settings are used as the basis for formulating questions, although standard questions are not used. In the interview proper the interviewer introduces the subject in a casual conversational tone and allows the child to talk, "noticing the manner in which his thoughts unfold." There is considerable stress on empathy with the child's way of thinking. The interviewer must be attuned to the child's thought processes and reflect this understanding in his questions as well as in his probes. Probes in the form of direct questions are introduced in the same casual conversational manner, following up on leads given by the child. Claparède in the introduction to *Language and Thought of the Child* (Piaget, 1951) characterizes the method as follows:

This clinical method, therefore, which is also an art, the art of questioning, does not confine itself to superficial observations, but aims at capturing what is hidden behind the immediate appearance of things. It analyzes down to its ultimate constituents the least little remark made by the young subjects. It does not give up the struggle when the child gives incomprehensible or contradictory answers, but only follows closer in chase of the ever receding thought, drives it from cover, pursues and tracks it down until it can seize it, dissect it and lay bare the secret of its composition (p. xiv).

The lack of standardization of questions in this method has been subjected to severe criticism on the grounds that variations in wording of questions will have different meanings. Some support for this criticism comes from Nass's (1956) research on children's concepts of physical causality, in which he obtained data on the effects of variation in the form of the question. He concluded that questions worded to suggest the possible operation of animistic, supernatural, or dynamic forces yielded more such non-naturalistic types of responses than questions less suggestively worded.

*Use of Dolls in the Verbal Interview.* The use of dolls in conjunction with the direct verbal interview is a technique that has demonstrated its value in research on a variety of problems.[1] Doll play was introduced in therapy as an adaptation of the conventional psychoanalytic procedure for children. The earliest use of this technique in research was made by David Levy (1933, 1936) in studies of sibling rivalry. Levy's basic

[1] The distinction between "projective" doll play and the doll-play interview is not a sharp one. In this chapter the discussion of doll play is limited to its use in conjunction with a verbal interview.

technique involves stimulating the child to talk through the medium of situations set up with dolls. The experimenter probes the child's reactions to a series of problem situations created by manipulating the dolls and by verbal definition. In studying sibling rivalry the examiner sets a scene of a mother feeding the baby, with the baby doll in the nursing position, and a child doll of the same sex as the subject observing the feeding. The problem is then presented verbally. "The sister comes and sees a new baby at the mother's breast. She sees it for the first time. Now what does she do? Do whatever you think." There are several variations on this basic situation. The situation may simply be presented to the child without any suggestions as to the direction of the child's activity, or there may be direct stimulation for the child to express negative feelings. For example, in Levy's study, after the general question, the experimenter encouraged the expression of rivalry feelings by verbal suggestion. "When the sister saw the baby, she thought 'the nerve, at my mother's breast!'" There are also variations in the degree of directness of identification of the dolls. Sometimes the baby doll in Levy's study is explicitly identified as the child's sibling and the other doll is identified as the child subject.

Conn (1938) has used a similar technique in the clinical exploration of a variety of problems, such as children's sexual knowledge, awareness of sex differences, and the dynamics of car sickness. Conn and Kanner's (1947) research on children's knowledge of the origin of babies illustrates a number of variations in the doll-play interview. A scene is set up with a baby doll lying in a toy crib and several larger dolls to represent siblings standing nearby. The interviewer points to one doll and asks, "What does he want to know about the baby?" If no spontaneous curiosity is expressed about the origin of babies, he then introduces a more structured probe. "Which one of them wants to know where babies come from?" In the next step the experimenter points to various dolls in succession, asking, "What is he saying?" In this manner the child is encouraged to carry on a dialogue between the dolls. Although the basic approach involves encouraging the child to talk through the medium of the dolls, one variation Conn has employed is the use of a direct question, "What do you think?" An interesting variation, used to overcome the child's inhibitions to expressing unacceptable impulses, is the "tough boy technique." A doll identified as a "tough boy" is introduced. This "tough boy," it is explained, is one who does not need to be nice and can say things that nice boys cannot say.

Bender (1953) employed an even more directive approach in a study of the dynamics of aggression and hostility in disturbed children ranging in age from 3 to 15 years. In this technique the examiner stimulated the child's expression of aggression by several different approaches. In the doll test the examiner pushed over a small doll, repeating this procedure three times with the question, "What has happened to it?" If the child made no attempt to imitate the examiner, she offered mild encouragement, saying, "Would you like to play with it?" She then offered stronger encouragement, "Knock it down." The children's behavior with the dolls and their verbalizations were recorded. Bender used several other situations to probe attitudes toward aggression. In the cowboy-soldier test the examiner set up a scene with a cowboy and an Indian placed between two soldiers and asked, "What are they doing?" If the child answered, "Fighting," the examiner then probed, "Why are they doing it?" She then probed further, "Is it right to do it?" In the automobile test the examiner placed a lead soldier between three toy automobiles, which were pointed toward the soldier. The examiner asked, "What is this? What will happen? Do you want to play with this?"

These adaptations of a clinical therapeutic method have in common the use of a highly structured approach in focusing on a specific content area and in encouraging the discussion of behavior not sanctioned by cultural norms. Although the stimulus is highly structured, there is considerable latitude given to the child in terms of the kind of response and level and degree of elaboration of the response.

In a study of awareness of racial differences among 2-to-5-year-old children Ammons (1950) used a more controlled "doll-play interview." In the setting of a miniature playground he placed a Negro and white doll and then interviewed the subjects with direct questions about their experiences as well as with indirect questions, using "framed situations." The dolls were introduced as follows: "Here are two little boys who would like to play on the playground. Do they look the same? How are they different?" Later in the interview contrived situations are introduced, e.g., "This (white) boy's mother comes along and sees the boys playing. What does she say?" "This little boy (white) throws sand at this one (colored). What does this boy (colored) do?"

A variation of a doll-play interview and multiple-choice technique was used by Radke and Trager (1950) in a study of perceptions of social role in 5-to-8-year-old children. They presented a series of plywood formboards with cutout figures of white and Negro adults. The children were given various possibilities of costumes representing "dress-up," "work," and "shabby" clothes. The examiner introduced the materials, posing questions as follows: "What would a man be doing if he were wearing these clothes?" (pointing to one at a time). After the child has identified what each costume means to him, he is asked which he likes best and why. The dolls are then presented: "Now let's look at these dolls. We have two men. What do you think? Are they just alike or are they different?" If the child answers "Different," he is asked how they are different. Then the examiner says: "This is a colored man and this is a white man. Now let's dress these men. You put on their clothes. Any one will fit; they're all the same size." After the child has dressed both dolls, he is asked, "What would this man be doing wearing these clothes? Can you tell me a story about this man?", pointing to the white doll and then to the Negro doll. Following the repetition of the procedure of dressing

the dolls, the examiner presents cutouts of two kinds of houses, a "good house" and a "poor house." The following instructions are given: "Here are some houses. Which do you like best? In which house does the colored man live? Why do you think so? In which house does the white man live? Why do you think so? Do you think these two men are friends? Which house is like your house?" The child is given the opportunity to assign both dolls to the same kind of house or one to a good house and one to a poor house.

Among the real advantages of the doll-play interview, especially for young children, is its interest value. By shifting the focus from the strangeness of the unaccustomed adult-child interaction to the dolls, inhibiting shyness will be lessened. Frequently, too, a complex situation can be conveyed more adequately in a setting or scene than by a purely verbal approach. A basic assumption in the use of this technique is that the child is freer to express socially unacceptable feelings through the medium of the dolls than if he were asked directly. There is a convincing amount of clinical experience to substantiate this assumption, but the meaning and basic validity of verbal responses given under these circumstances needs some clear-cut methodological investigation. One possible consequence of having the expression of unacceptable actions or ideas facilitated in this way may be that the attitudes or feelings that are expressed under these circumstances are an exaggerated reflection of the intensity of the child's feelings. This is particularly likely to be the case where there is strong pressure to express feelings, as in Bender's study (1953) previously described. Although it may not be a serious drawback for therapeutic work, it has obvious limitations for diagnostic and research purposes. Unless we can develop a "conversion index," which permits the simple translation of intensity of response in this situation to intensity of feeling, there is a real possibility of seriously biased findings.

***Story and Sentence Completion.*** The story completion and sentence completion techniques are usually more acceptable than doll play to children beyond the preschool age. Both techniques have been used extensively as variations on the written questionnaire. Their use as an adjunct in interviewing has been limited.

The story-completion method may vary from a completely verbal approach to one combining verbalization and the use of dolls. In a study of father relations of war-born children, aged 4 to 8, Faust, in collaboration with Stolz (1954), presented a series of incomplete stories verbally and accompanied the verbal presentation with appropriate doll action. The themes selected were, for the most part, quite direct and structured to be relevant to a specific hypothesis. For example, one story designed to test the hypothesis that the war-separated child would not feel so free as a nonseparated child to admit his misdeeds to his father had the following content: "A child is playing in his room with his daddy's watch, although he knows that he is not to play with his daddy's things. The child drops the watch and it breaks. His parents do not hear the watch drop and

the child wonders what he should do."

Faust found the use of dolls effective in obtaining story completions from preschool-age children but discovered that the dolls hindered rapport with the older boys. They responded better when the incomplete stories were read from an illustrated book, with instructions to complete the story verbally.

Basically similar to the story-completion technique is the sentence-completion approach. This technique has been used fairly extensively in recent years with young school-age children and adolescents (Sanford, 1943; Stein, 1947; Rohde, 1946; Rotter, 1951; Graham et al., 1951; Kates, 1951). There have been many adaptations on the sentence-completion technique as a variation on direct interviewing. Most frequently, this technique is used as a written test rather than an interview. Often the questions are very direct; e.g., "When I do or think something which I know is wrong, I. . . ." Indirect statements referring to the actions of hypothetical persons are also used.

The story- and sentence-completion techniques can capitalize on young children's inherent interest in stories. The situation of an adult reading a story approximates a familiar life-situation with pleasant associations for most children. Older children may be challenged by the creative possibilities in the task of completing a story. As in structured doll play, these approaches allow some freedom of response while permitting a relatively high degree of focus on a specific theme.

***Pictures as an Adjunct to the Interview.*** Another variation on a structured technique is the use of pictures to portray a very specific situation. There are several variations in method. On the simplest level the child is asked to make a choice among alternative pictures. He may be asked specific questions relating to the pictures, or he may be given the task of completing the story defined by the picture and verbally interpreted by the interviewer. These techniques have been used very effectively in studying peer relations and in getting at a child's perception of parents, teachers, and members of other racial and religious groups.

Fauls and Smith (1956) studied sex-role learning in 5-year-old boys by use of a multiple-choice picture technique. There were six pictures, three portraying female appropriate activities, and three showing male appropriate activities. One picture showed a boy about to play baseball; in another the boy was engaging in doll play. The interviewer introduced the pictures with a verbal interpretation: "This boy is going to play baseball. His mother and father are watching as he goes to play. There he is in this picture holding a doll in his arms and looking at it. Which of these do you do? Which do you like best? Which does his mother want the boy to do? Which does his daddy want the boy to do?"

In studying the complex problem of self-identification in young children Horowitz (1943) developed a picture-choice technique for preschool children. She used several series of pictures, three for racial identification, three for identification with reference to familial position, and one each for age, size, sex, and eating habits. The children were asked to make a choice among several pictures, each of which was defined by a standard verbal description. For example, to study age identification, four pictures of children of different ages were presented: infant, nursery school child, elementary school child and adolescent. The children were asked, "Which one is you? Which one is (name of subject)?" Horowitz suggests with regard to methodology that it is important that "the materials be simple and as nearly unequivocal as possible, and the choices given be really parallel and mutually exclusive, so that if the subject makes one choice, he is excluding the other possibilities presented."

Biber and Lewis (1949) used a picture-interview technique to study children's feelings and their functioning in different kinds of classroom atmospheres. The child was presented with a series of pictures, each depicting a different kind of problem situation occurring in the classroom. The interviewer told what was happening in the picture and asked the child to elaborate or tell what would happen next. For example, in studying reactions to trouble situations, they used a picture of a sick boy, and presented it with the following explanation: "This little boy is not feeling well. He is coming up to the teacher and telling her he has a stomach-ache. What do you think the teacher is saying to him?"

The authors point up a number of methodological implications in this kind of approach. One must be aware of the possibility that the responses may reflect either the real practices in the classroom or the feelings that are displaced from the child's broader life experience. Thus in their responses the children may be projecting onto the teacher-figure expectations derived from their out-of-school activities with adults. In using any kind of semiprojective technique, one must be aware of potential distortion and attempt to utilize pictures and question forms that will minimize this possibility. Biber and Lewis also point out the difficulties in developing situations and questions that are equivalent for exploring a given area of feeling. For example, they found the intensity of response quite different toward two trouble pictures they had considered essentially equivalent. A situation depicting a lost bracelet aroused much more intense feeling than one portraying illness in a child. This observation emphasizes the necessity for careful pretesting of questions and situations.

Another variation of the picture technique is that used by Radke, Trager, and Davis (1949) in a study of children's perceptions of the social roles of Negroes and whites. The children were asked to interpret pictures portraying white and Negro children in a variety of social situations. Some pictures were ambiguous and others were highly structured. The pictures presented varied alternatives regarding interracial relations. For example, one picture showed white and Negro children on a playground clearly playing together. Another showed a Negro child on a fringe of a group of white children on the playground. The interview opened with the general question, "Tell me about this picture." The subsequent questions became increasingly specific, e.g., "What is this little boy doing?

Why? This little boy isn't playing with the others. Why?" The authors emphasize that a child's response to any single picture is not in itself a sufficient basis for interpreting his attitudes; rather, the constellation of responses to a series of pictures must be used.

E. Hartley and associates (1948) used a combined interview-picture method in research on children's perceptions of overlapping social roles. A series of pictures of the same person in different roles, accompanied by verbal definitions, was presented to the child. For example, one series consisted of four pictures: (1) a father, mother and a child, (2) a mailman, (3) a mailman at work, and (4) the same man as a father with his child. The interviewer's comments and questions relating to each picture were as follows:

(1) "This is Jimmy with his father and mother."

(2) "Who is this? This is the mailman, isn't it?"

(3) "What is he doing? Is he still a father when he is a mailman?"

(4) "Who is this? Is he still a mailman when he is a father at home?"

In this technique, beginning with a simple concept familiar to the child, the complex concept of overlapping roles is developed by a step-by-step procedure. This approach would seem to be promising for the study of complex attitudes, feelings, and concepts in young children. For example, children's understanding of multiple motivations and feelings underlying parental discipline might be explored by presenting pictures of the scolding mother and the loving mother. Similarly, concepts of overlapping motivations determining children's aggressive behavior might be studied by some adaptation of this technique.

A combination of interview and pictures has been employed successfully in studies of children's perceptions of their peers and others in their environment. It has been used largely with school-age and adolescent children. Harris (1946) adapted this technique in studying the social perceptions of children in a kindergarten. In an interview setting she showed the young child a series of sketches, depicting a child in a variety of activities, e.g., helpful or aggressive. The situation was defined as a guessing game. Each picture was presented with the instructions: "This is a picture of someone at school. Who do you think it is?" If the child named a member of the kindergarten group, he was asked with reference to the picture: "What is . . . doing?" The picture choices were followed by a free interview about each child in the group, e.g., "John goes to your school, doesn't he? Tell me something about him." If the child did not respond, the experimenter asked, "You know John, don't you? Tell me what he does at school." The child was given crayons and paper or beads to string and told he could play while he talked with the experimenter.

A variation on this technique involves presenting the child with a series of personality or trait descriptions and requesting him to select the picture of the child who best typifies a particular trait (Campbell, Yarrow, and Yarrow, 1958). Further exploration of specific attitudes can be made with follow-up questions. This technique has been used with school-age and early adolescent children.

Pictures, like dolls, are a useful prop for the interviewer in involving the child and in maintaining interest. By the use of such techniques, it is possible to focus more specifically on a given topic and to give it a concreteness not readily attained by purely verbal means. As in the doll-play interview, there is no sharp line between the use of pictures to stimulate fantasy in a projective technique and the use of pictures as an adjunct to a focused interview. In an enthusiasm for projective techniques, schematic or ambiguous pictures are sometimes used when they are inappropriate for the research problem. Such unstructured material in stimulating fantasy is likely to produce responses not directly relevant to the limited research questions being studied. If our objective, in using pictures, is to facilitate the child's verbalization on a well-defined topic, then structured pictures may be more useful than ambiguous ones in helping the child to focus on specific content. We can also limit the range of response to a picture by verbally reinforcing the content area illustrated in the picture, e.g., "This boy is trying to get the wagon away from the girl." These suggestions are applicable if we are not interested in eliciting projective responses or unconscious material but are specifically directing our efforts toward obtaining data on conscious attitudes and concepts. (The use of pictures in projective techniques is discussed in Chapter 15 in this book.)

*Group Interviews.* For certain kinds of problems, such as the study of modal values or attitudes of a given age group, an interview conducted in a group setting has real value. For latency-period children and those in early adolescence, the group atmosphere might have a facilitating effect.

L. Murphy (1956) describes an interesting integration of doll play and group interview. Three or four children are brought to the experimental room and given an opportunity to play house, each child selecting his own role. The fantasy is focused around the handling of two baby dolls. Questions are thrown out to the group naturally at appropriate points in relation to the ongoing play: open questions about parental roles, such as, "What do mommies do? What do daddies do?"; more specific questions about feelings, such as, "Everybody gets mad sometimes. What makes you mad?" The experimenter enters into the situation by assuming one of the roles not taken by the children. Murphy feels that the group not only has a facilitating effect on the production of fantasy but the group situation decreases the amount of anxiety that might otherwise be aroused by this kind of direct questioning.

A group interview with puppets has been developed by R. Hartley (1952) in eliciting children's feelings and attitudes about a variety of common adjustment situations: the arrival of a new baby, peer aggression, and resentment about separation from a parent. Puppet plays were presented to groups of five or six children, using a family of dolls—a mother, a father, a boy, a girl, a baby, a monkey, and an unidentified character adaptable to any special role required. After the basic situation was presented by manipulation of the puppets, with appropriate verbalization (scripts were developed for each of the problems), the identification character expressed his feelings about the situation, e.g., harsh treatment by a parent. The children were then encouraged to verbalize their feelings and asked to indicate how the situation should be handled. Hartley points out the necessity for using this technique sensitively to avoid arousing in the children disturbing emotions with which the interviewer cannot cope. When using this technique, careful consideration should be given to the content of the plays as well as to the composition of the groups, e.g., anxious or timid children might be overwhelmed by aggressive themes or vigorous expression of hostility by other members of the group.

*The Life Space Interview.* A creative variation on the standard interview approach has been introduced by Redl (1959) in research and therapy on disturbed delinquent children. This approach, the "life-space interview," attempts to assess the child's reactions and feelings about a given situation, not retrospectively after some time lapse, but immediately after the occurrence of the incident and preferably in the physical setting in which it has occurred. In this concrete setting the child's perception of the event and his feelings about it are explored. Clearly, the degree of affective involvement is much greater in this situation than in the aseptic office environment in which interviewing is ordinarily carried out. Presumably, the depth of feeling the child will express under these circumstances will differ significantly from that expressed in the ordinary interview environment.

There are many possible adaptations of this interview technique in research with young children. One would be to try to "catch" a child's reaction immediately after an event has occurred, e.g., his first sight of a new sibling, his first day in school, after an aggressive encounter with another child. Another variation would be to create or re-create experimentally a situation involving frustration or parental discipline and then to interview the child in the experimental setting. Although these suggested adaptations of the life-space interview are especially appropriate for use with the preschool child because of his limitations in time perspective, it has relevance for the entire age span, particularly when it is desired to obtain the child's feelings about a previous experience. There are, of course, some kinds of research problems in which maximum recall is not desired; for example, when we are primarily interested in the child's selective perceptions and distortions about a past event.

## NONVERBAL COMMUNICATION IN THE INTERVIEW

Observation of behavior can be used meaningfully to supplement the verbal data obtained during the interview. Children are less likely than adults to attempt consciously to control or disguise their behavior, and they have not internalized so completely as adults the techniques that are often used unconsciously to cover up significant feelings, attitudes, and motivations. Observation of the child's behavior during the or-

dinary interview may be used in several ways. The child's reactions to a specific question may be helpful in interpreting the significance of the question to him or in evaluating the validity of his response. On another level, the child's reactions to the variety of stimuli impinging on him during the conventional interview may offer clues to motivational and personality characteristics, e.g., ways of handling stress, patterns of dominance and submission in interpersonal relationships, and characteristic defenses. The validity of these clues will depend on the adequacy of the behavior sample, the sensitivity of the interviewer in making relevant observations, and his skill in drawing inferences from raw behavior about motivational and personality functions.

The interview may be used as a standardized setting for observing specific aspects of behavior. For example, in a controlled interview there may be systematic observation of the child's capacity to relate to a stranger, or the observation may focus on dependency in relating to the interviewer in a problem-solving situation. Interview settings have been creatively utilized as experimental or semiexperimental situations in which the subject may be systematically subjected to special stimulus-conditions relevant to the research, e.g., stress.

Although lip service has traditionally been given to the value of behavioral observation during the interview, there have been few systematic attempts to develop reliable behavioral indices. Recently a number of efforts at systematizing diagnostic clues has been based on expressive behavior in the communication process (Birdwhistell, 1952a,b; Wolff, 1946; Smith, 1956). Despite these attempts at systematization, the use of nonverbal cues in the interview to assess personality characteristics or to judge the validity of verbal responses remains essentially an intuitive art.

Nonverbal cues characteristically used in assessing behavior can be summarized under the following major categories:

1. Physical—posture, e.g., freedom-constraint; gestures, facial expression, e.g., somber–gay; speed of movement; vigor of movement; energy output; motor coordination; area of free movement, e.g., whether the child is expansive or restricted in his use of space.

2. Physiological—vasomotor instability, e.g., blushing, perspiring; muscular tension.

3. Formal characteristics of language —e.g., loquacity, fluency, tempo, speed of verbal output.

4. Interactional behavior—ways of relating to the interviewer, e.g., attempts to control the situation, resistance, compliance, dominance, passivity, dependency, withdrawal.

5. Personality style—e.g., spontaneous, inhibited, compulsive, loosely organized, focused, scattered.

All of these nonverbal cues are dependent on subjective judgments, and adequate criteria of validity are difficult to establish, particularly for the categories interactional behavior and personality style, which are on a more complex level, are further removed from direct observation, and require high-order inferences from behavior.

Objectivity of observations can be increased by introducing some standardization in the observation procedures by the use of observation guides or standardized observational or rating techniques. These techniques will increase the likelihood that the same aspects of behavior will be noted by different interviewers and from one interview situation to another. Obviously, all of the relevant cues cannot be included in a guide or rating scale, and in some kinds of research problems there can be latitude for free observation. Observer reliability can be determined by standard procedures, e.g., having a second observer make simultaneous observations behind a one-way screen. For some kinds of research, the use of an observer to record interview content may be a standard part of the research design. (See detailed discussion of observational techniques in Chapter 3.)

## RECORDING INTERVIEW RESPONSES

An adequate transcript of the interview content is a basic requirement for valid analysis of the data. Our major concern is to record the interview content and the respondent's behavior accurately in such a way that the recording procedure will not interfere with the interview relationship. The main questions center around the timing and the content of the recording, i.e., whether it should be done during or after the interview and whether it should be verbatim or selective or in terms of a pre-established code.

All the available methodological data emphasize the loss in accuracy when the recording of an interview is based on recall of content after completion of the interview (Symonds and Dietrich, 1941; Payne, 1949). It is important, therefore, that it be done at the time of the interview. Children's reactions to the examiner's writing during the interview will vary somewhat at different age levels and with different kinds of interview material. Children of preschool age tend to adapt rather quickly, and the interviewer's writing does not, in general, seem to inhibit their communication. During preadolescence and adolescence it is more likely to have an inhibiting effect. It may be reassuring to the child if the interviewer is himself comfortable about writing and can do it unobtrusively. At all ages children's questions about the writing must be answered casually and without evasiveness. Some variation on the simple statement, "I am writing down some of your ideas so I won't forget them," is applicable to most interview situations. With older children, assurance of the confidentiality of the material might be in order. On the whole, if the relationship is a good one, the content not too threatening, and the recording mechanics not too obtrusive, children tend to accept the examiner's writing rather easily.

The amount of detail recorded will depend on its ultimate use. In studying children's vocabularies or language development, or in some kinds of studies of concept development, verbatim recording may be essential. In dynamically oriented research on personality development, verbatim recording may be important to the extent that the idiosyncratic choice of words is significant or the sequence of ideas may have meaning in the analysis. For studies in which the focus is on very specific limited content, brief recording on an interview guide or direct recording on a rating or code sheet may be the most efficient procedure.

When a detailed account of the interview is desired, a common procedure is to jot down key words and phrases or summary notes in the appropriate sequence and fill in the details immediately after the interview. This is not nearly so satisfactory as full recording during the interview by mechanical means or by an observer-recorder present in the interview room or behind a one-way screen. The use of a mechanical recording device is probably the most satisfactory solution to verbatim recording. This approach has proved especially useful in the free, unstructured interview. However, some concern has been voiced among research workers as to the effects of the electronic recording procedure on rapport in the interview situation. There is a feeling among many clinically oriented interviewers that use of a recording machine may be inhibiting to the respondent. Although this problem has not been systematically studied, the impression has been growing among researchers who have used electronic recording with adults, as well as with children, that there is fairly quick adaptation if the recording device is not too intrusive. In fact, it is thought that the interview may proceed more smoothly when the interviewer is free to devote his full attention to the content of the responses and to observation of the respondent's behavior. When a recording device is used with children, their questions about the technique should be answered in a way to satisfy their curiosity quickly so that they will not be distracted by the machine. Frequently children are eager to hear their own voices, and the promise of a playback at the end of the interview may serve as added motivation for cooperation. There are limitations in the use of electronic equipment in recording children's interviews. Even the most sensitive recording equipment sometimes fails to give a comprehensible record of speech that is full of articulatory distortions and in which there is much variation in loudness. A stenographic record by a stenographer trained to understand children's speech may be more reliable. Before deciding on the use of electronic equipment, it is best to pretest the recording under conditions simulating the actual interview.

## ANALYSIS OF INTERVIEW DATA

Data collection and data analysis are not completely independent processes. Ideally, collection procedures are planned within a research design in which the analysis problems and techniques have been anticipated. The form in which the data are collected and recorded will determine the kinds of analyses that will be possible. Although the interview is particularly well adapted to the study of the unique aspects of a child's world, its use is not limited to individual case study. It is possible to pool data that give insight into the unique worlds of individual children and to build up meaningful norms for a developmental stage or derive generalizations significant for broader theoretical issues.

Analysis of interview data recorded in terms of simple categories, such as "approve, disapprove," presents no unique problems; it is basically similar to analysis of any directly quantifiable data. We can tally the frequencies with which a given response occurs for an age or sex group or for experimental or control groups and then apply the statistical procedures appropriate for the research problem, e.g., correlational analysis or analysis of the significance of differences between control and experimental groups. On the other hand, qualitative data of the sort obtained in open-ended interviews require special techniques for translating the data to a form amenable to statistical treatment. The coding procedures may be quite complex, involving a number of steps in the transformation of qualitative data to quantitative form. Methods of analysis of qualitative material obtained from adults have been described in a number of articles (Berelson, 1954; Cartwright, 1953; Guetzkow, 1950; Schutz, 1950; Spiegelman et al., 1953; White, 1951). These procedures of qualitative analysis are adaptable to analysis of children's interviews. It is important, however, when coding children's interview responses to be especially sensitive to possible differences between children and adults in concepts and frames of reference. There is danger that the categories chosen by the adult coder may not adequately represent the child's frame of reference, thus decreasing the validity of the coding. Appropriate definition of the codes and careful selection and training of coders will help minimize such distortions. Knowledge of language and concepts characteristic of the age level being studied is a desirable qualification of the coders.

In this chapter we can sketch only the main steps in coding qualitative data. For detailed discussion of coding procedures, the references cited above should be consulted.

Before developing a coding outline, it is necessary to have a tentative design for analysis based on the major questions of the study. In the development of the coding scheme a first step is to list the variables relevant to the problems or hypotheses of the study. The variables may evolve out of a systematic theoretical framework, or they may be empirically derived from careful inspection of the data. Empirically derived variables are likely to be more limited than variables derived from theoretical considerations. A theoretically based set of variables often helps alert the coder to covert meanings in the data that might be overlooked in a purely empirical approach.

A major step in coding is the translation of the research variables into appropriate categories for analysis. There are many systems of categorization, ranging from the use of simple dichotomous categories to those on a complex continuum. The most appropriate categorization system will depend somewhat on the problem and on the form of the available data. The simplest type of coding system uses dichotomous categories, in which the data are analyzed simply in terms of the presence or absence of a given characteristic,

e.g., anxiety about separation from the mother or no anxiety. On a somewhat more complex level the responses are rated or ranked in terms of intensity, usually on a three-to-five-point scale: very high anxiety, moderately high anxiety, etc.

In many kinds of analyses the categories are qualitatively different rather than on a simple continuum. For example, if we are interviewing children about their first reactions to entering nursery school, the interview data might be analyzed with reference to different foci of anxiety: anxiety about separation from the mother, anxiety about being displaced by a younger sibling, or anxiety about own abilities in relation to peers.

In the actual coding procedure the selection of meaningful units of analysis is a major methodological consideration. We need to set up criteria for choice of psychologically meaningful response units in the interview. In dealing with interview responses, the problems are basically similar to those involved in choice of meaningful behavior units in observational studies (Barker and Wright, 1954; Wright and Barker, 1950). For some categories, a response to a single question may be the appropriate unit of analysis; for more complex categories, responses to several questions may be taken as the unit of analysis. Cartwright (1953) makes a useful distinction between the unit of analysis and the context unit—the frame of reference within which a single analysis unit is interpreted. The context unit may be much larger than the analysis unit. The interpretation of a response will differ when our frame of reference is a single question and when it is analyzed in the context of the total interview.

Frequently it is possible to use the same unit of analysis in several different codes, especially responses in open-ended interviews. A response such as the following to a single open-ended question about school could be analyzed in terms of several categories: "Well, it's hard because the other kids are studying all the time trying to get high marks and I don't like to have to study so much." We can use this response to code separately the child's attitude toward school, his feelings about his peers, and his achievement orientation.

In assigning a given unit of analysis to the appropriate category, clear-cut definitions of the categories are essential. Conceptual as well as concrete definitions of the categories are desirable. When fine differentiations are required between dimensions of a category, illustrations are useful to define its limits. Definitions should be broad enough to encompass the psychological meaning of the category, yet sufficiently definitive to avoid overlapping with other categories. Responses may be coded in terms of manifest content, or the coding may require complex inferences about attitudes, feelings, or personality characteristics. For example, in a study of perception of peers, the child's response to a question about another child may be, "I like him; he's always making me laugh; he's lots of fun, always cheers you up." On one level this might be coded simply as a positive response to the other child. On a manifest level, in terms of perception of valued characteristics in chil-

dren, this response might be coded as indicating attribution of high value to having a sense of humor or being cheerful. On another level, this response could be coded in terms of valuing others in relation to their need-gratification potential, i.e., the ability to gratify one's own needs.

The reliability of the coding can be established by the standard procedures for rater reliability—by having two or more raters independently code the same sample of data and then determining the degree of correspondence among their ratings The validity of a code is much more difficult to establish. Ideally, validation requires comparison of the coded data with completely independent data about the child, e.g., data based on direct observation or parental reports about the child. In many circumstances it is not possible to obtain completely independent data to use as criteria of validity. Moreover, in order to use such criteria to establish coding validity, we must first assume the validity of the interview. Practically, the best way to assure coding validity is to choose competent coders and provide them with adequate training and well-defined codes. Discussion among coders after some experience with the coding outline will help clarify difficult categories and improve reliability and validity. This procedure permits informal determination of the reliability of the categories as well as of the coders. Categories on which there are consistent disagreements among the coders may require redefinition or may have to be discarded.

Although it might be assumed that

coders' knowledge of the research hypotheses would improve the validity of the coding, there are some conditions under which it may be important that the coders be unfamiliar with the hypotheses being tested. It may also be necessary to conceal from the coders the identity of the subjects, i.e., whether they are in the experimental or control group. There is some question whether coding should be done by the person who has collected the data because of the possibility of his judgments being influenced by factors outside the recorded material, i.e., subjective impressions obtained during the interview. If his impressions represent valid recall of significant nonverbal cues in the interview, the validity of the coding might be increased; however, such impressions may also tend to bias the coding because of distortions in recall or "halo effects." Furthermore, the determination of reliability is made more difficult by the introduction of bases for judgment that are not part of the recorded data. The relative advantages and disadvantages of using coders with outside knowledge of the data need to be evaluated for a specific research problem.

## ADVANTAGES AND LIMITATIONS OF THE INTERVIEW

The choice of a research technique for use with children, whether an observational approach, a questionnaire, or an interview, depends on the kind of problem and the level of data needed to answer the research questions. Some of the values of the interview, as well as its limitations, have been suggested.

A comparison of the interview with other techniques frequently used in studying similar problems with children may help point up some values of the technique.

Compared with the observational approach, which has been used with much greater frequency in child development research, the interview has some clear-cut advantages. It permits study of subjective phenomena not amenable to direct observation, such as aspirations, wishes, dreams, and anxieties. The interview also enables meaningful study of a wider time span in the child's life than is possible with any cross-sectional observational technique. In comparison with the observational approach, the interview is much less vulnerable to time-sampling errors and is probably less sensitive to fluctuations in mood or to the impact of recent experiences.

In comparing the interview with the written questionnaire, a number of advantages are apparent. In the interview situation it is possible for the interviewer to be aware of the child's lack of comprehension or misunderstanding of a question and to be in a position to clarify the question. Better control of the influence of question sequence and the context of questions is possible in the interview than in the questionnaire. In the questionnaire the respondent may read all of the questions before responding. Thus his response to any one question may be influenced by the content of later questions. In regard to the depth of data obtainable, there are contradictory opinions, based on limited findings, on the relative advantages of the interview and the questionnaire. For questions that might arouse emotional resistance, it has been generally assumed that the direct person-to-person relationship in the interview will reduce resistance and facilitate the child's responses, although some findings with adults suggest that some kinds of ego-relevant data are given more freely in the anonymous questionnaire (Ellis, 1947). Certainly, further research is needed in which the character of the relationship with the interviewer is carefully controlled. To the extent that the interview permits meaningful probing on leads given by the respondent, it is likely to yield data at a deeper level than most written questionnaires. [See Ellis (1946) for an evaluation of the uses and limitations of the written questionnaire.]

A cogent consideration in the choice of an interview over other techniques is whether the problem is one requiring an interpersonal relationship for obtaining the desired data or one in which the relationship may contribute substantially to the validity of the findings. The ultimate value of the interview as a research tool is dependent on the interviewer's knowledge of developmental psychology and his ability to apply this knowledge sensitively in relating to children.

## REFERENCES

Ammons, Carol H., and R. B. Ammons. 1952. Research and clinical applications of the doll-play interview. *J. Psychol.* **21**, 85–90.

Ammons, R. B. 1950. Reactions in a projective doll-play interview of white males two to six years of age to differences in skin color and facial features. *J. genet. Psychol.*, **76**, 323–341.

Axline, Virginia. 1947. *Play therapy*. Boston: Houghton Mifflin.

Baldwin, A. L. 1955. *Behavior and development in childhood*, New York: Dryden.

Barker, R. G., and H. F. Wright. 1954. *Midwest and its children*. Evanston, Ill.: Row, Peterson.

Bender, Lauretta. 1953. *Aggression, hostility, and anxiety in children*. Springfield, Ill.: Thomas.

Berelson, B. 1954. Content analysis. In G. Lindzey (Ed.), *Handbook of social psychology*. Cambridge: Addison-Wesley. **1**, 488–522.

Biber, Barbara and Claudia Lewis. 1949. An experimental study of what young school children expect from their teachers. *Genet. Psychol. Monogr.*, **40**, 3–97.

Biber, Barbara, Lois Murphy, Louise Woodcock, and Irma Black. 1952. *Life and ways of the seven to eight year old*. New York: Basic Books.

Bingham, W. V., and B. V. Moore. 1941. *How to interview*. (Rev. ed.). New York: Harper.

Birdwhistell, R. N. 1952a. Body motion research and interviewing. *Hum. Organiz.*, **11**, 37–38.

———. 1952b. *Introduction to kinesics (An annotation system for analysis of body motion and gesture)*. Washington, D. C.: Foreign Service Institute.

Buckingham, B. R., and E. W. Dolch. 1936. *A combined word list*. Boston: Ginn.

Campbell, J., L. Yarrow, and Marian Radke Yarrow. 1958. A study of adaptation to a new social situation. *J. soc. Issues*, **14**, 3–7.

Cantril, H. 1940. Experiments in the wording of questions. *Public Opinion Quarterly*, **4**, 330–332.

Cannell, C. F., and R. L. Kahn. 1953. The collection of data by interviewing. In L. Festinger and D. Katz (Eds.), *Research methods in the behavioral sciences*, New York: Dryden. Pp. 327–380.

Cartwright, D. 1953. Analysis of qualitative material. In L. Festinger and D. Katz (Eds.), *Research methods in the behavioral sciences*, New York: Dryden. Pp. 421–470.

Conn, J. H. 1938. The child speaks to the psychiatrist; An introduction to the method of the play-interview. *Occup. Ther.* **17**, 231–244.

Conn, J. H., and L. Kanner. 1947. Children's awareness of sex differences, *J. Child Psychiat.*, 1, 3–57.

Crutchfield, R., and D. H. Gordon. 1947. Variations in respondents' interpretations of an opinion-poll question. *Int. J. Opin. Attitude Res.*, 1, 1–12.

Dennis, W. 1942. Piaget's questions applied to a child of known environment. *J. genet. Psychol.*, 60, 307–320.

Despert, J. Louise. 1940. A method for the study of personality reactions in preschool children by means of analysis of their play. *J. Psychol.*, 19, 17–29.

Ellis, A., 1946. The validity of personality questionnaires. *Psychol. Bull.*, 43, 385–440.

———. 1947. A comparison of the use of direct and indirect phrasing in personality questionnaires. *Psychol. Monogr.*, 61, No. 2, (Whole No. 284).

———. 1953. Recent research with personality inventories, *J. consult. Psychol.*, 17, 45–49.

Fauls, L. B., and W. D. Smith. 1956. Sex-role learning in five year olds. *J. genet. Psychol.*, 89, 105–119.

Faust, Margaret S. 1951. A study of father-child relations using a story-completion technique. Unpublished master's thesis, Stanford Univer.

Fleming L., and W. U. Synder. 1947. Social and personal changes following non-directive group play therapy. *Amer. J. Orthopsychiat.*, 17, 101–116.

Geelerd, E. R. 1957. Some aspects of psychoanalytic technique in adolescence. In R. Eissler et al. (Eds.), *Psychoanalytic study of the child*. New York: International Univer. Press, 12, 263–283.

Getzels, J. W. 1951. The assessment of personality and prejudice by the method of paired direct and projective questions. Unpublished doctoral thesis, Harvard Univer.

———. 1958. The method of paired direct and projective questionnaires in the study of attitude structure and socialization. *Psychol. Monogr.*, 72, 1, 30.

Grace, H. A., and J. Lohmann. 1952. Children's reactions to stories depicting parent-child conflict situations. *Child Develpm*, 23, 61–74.

Graham, F. K., W. A. Charwat, A. S. Honig, and Paula C. Weltz. 1951. Aggression as a function of the attack and the attacker. *J. abnorm. soc. Psychol.*, 46, 512–520.

Guetzkow, H. 1950. Unitizing and categorizing problems in coding qualitative material. *J. clin. Psychol.*, 6, 47–58.

Hammond, K. R. 1948. Measuring attitudes by error-choice, and indirect method. *J. abnorm. soc. Psychol.*, 43, 38–48.

Harris, Esther K. 1946. The responsiveness of kindergarten children to the behavior of their fellows. *Monogr. Soc. Res. Child Develpm.*, 11, No. 2.

Hartley, E. L., M. Rosenbaum, and S. Schwartz. 1948. Children's perceptions of ethnic group membership. *J. Psychol.*, 26, 387–398.

Hartley, E. L., and S. Schwartz. 1951. A pictorial doll-play approach for the study of children's intergroup attitudes. *Int. J. Opinion Attitude Res.*, 5, No. 2.

Hartley, Ruth E. 1959. Development of concepts of women's social roles. Unpublished manuscript. New York: City College of New York.

———. 1952. *Understanding children's play*. New York: Columbia Univer. Press.

———, L. K. Frank, and R. M. Goldenson. 1952. *New play experiences for children*. New York: Columbia Univer. Press.

Horowitz, Ruth. 1943. A pictorial method for study of self identification in preschool children. *J. genet. Psychol.*, 62, 135–148.

Hyman, H. 1954. *Interviewing in social research*. Chicago: Univer. Chicago Press.

International Kindergarten Union. 1928. *A study of the vocabulary of children before entering the first grade*. Baltimore: Williams and Wilkins.

Jahoda, Marie, M. Deutsch, and S. W. Cook. 1951. *Research methods in social relations*. New York: Dryden.

Jersild, A. T., and R. Ritzman. 1938. Aspects of language development, the growth of loquacity and vocabulary. *Child Develpm.*, 9, 243–259.

Kahn, R. B., and C. G. Cannell. 1957. *The dynamics of interviewing*. New York: Wiley.

Kates, S. L. 1951. Suggestibility, sensitiveness to parents and peers, and extrapunitiveness, intropunitiveness, and impunitiveness in children. *J. Psychol.*, 31, 233–241.

Levy, D. M. 1933. Use of play technique as experimental procedure. *Amer. J. Orthopsychiat.*, 3, 266–277.

——. 1936. Hostility patterns in sibling rivalry experiments. *Amer. J. Orthopsychiat.*, 6, 183–257.

——. 1937. Studies in sibling rivalry. *Res. Monogr. Amer. Orthopsychiat. Ass.*, No. 2.

McCarthy, Dorothea. 1930. The language development of the preschool child, *Inst. Child Welf. Monogr.*, No. 4. Minneapolis: Univer. Minnesota Press.

——. 1954. Language development in children. In L. Carmichael (Ed.), *Manual of Child Psychology.* (2nd ed.) New York: Wiley. Pp. 492–630.

Maccoby, Eleanor E., and N. Maccoby. 1954. The interview: A tool of social science. In G. Lindzey (Ed.), *Handbook of Social Psychology.* Cambridge; Addison-Wesley. 1, 449–487.

Merton, R. K., and P. L. Kendall. 1946. The focused interview, *Amer. J. Sociol.*, 51, 541–557.

M. Fiske, and P. L. Kendall. 1956. *The focused interview.* Glencoe, Ill.: Free Press.

Metraux, Rhoda W. 1950. Speech profiles of the preschool child, 18-54 months, *J. Speech Dis.*, 15, 37–53.

Miller, F. M. 1952. The participant observer and over-rapport. *Amer. sociol. Rev.*, 17, 97–99.

Moustakas, C., and H. D. Schalock. 1955. An analysis of therapist-child interaction in play therapy. *Child Develpm.*, 143–157.

Murphy, Lois B. 1956. *Methods for the study of personality in young children.* New York: Basic Books, Vol. I.

Nass, M. L. 1956. The effects of three variables on children's concepts of causality. *J. abnorm. soc. Psychol.*, 53, 191–196.

Parten, Mildred B. 1950. *Surveys, polls, and samples,* New York: Harper.

Payne, S. L. 1949. Interviewer memory faults. *Publ. Opin. Quart.*, 13, 684–685.

Piaget, J. 1928. *Judgment and reasoning in the child.* New York: Harcourt, Brace.

——. 1951. *The language and thought of the child.* New York: Humanities Press.

——. 1929. *Introduction to the child's conception of the world.* New York: Harcourt, Brace.

Radke, Marian J. 1946. The relation of parental authority to children's behavior and attitudes. *Inst. Child Welf. Monogr.*, No. 22. Minneapolis: Univer. Minnesota Press.

——, and Helen G. Trager. 1950. Children's perceptions of the social roles of Negroes and Whites. *J. Psychol.*, 29, 3–33.

——, Helen G. Trager and Hadassah Davis. 1949. Social perceptions and attitudes of children. *Genet. Psychol. Monogr.*, 40, 372–447.

Redl, F. 1959. Strategy and techniques of the life space interview. *Amer. J. Orthopsychiat.*, 29, 1–18.

Rogers, C. R. 1945. The non-directive method as a technique for social research. *Amer. J. Sociol.* 50, 279–283.

——. 1951. *Client-centered therapy.* Boston: Houghton Mifflin.

Rohde, A. R. 1946. Explorations in personality by the sentence-completion method. *J. appl. Psychol.*, 30, 169–181.

Rotter, J. B. 1951. Word association and sentence-completion methods. In H. H. and Gladys L. Anderson (Eds.), *An introduction to projective techniques.* New York: Prentice-Hall. Pp. 279–311.

Sanford, R. N., et al. 1943. Physique, personality and scholarship. *Monograph Soc. Res. Child Develpm.*, 8, No. 1.

Schutz, W. 1950. Theory and methodology of content analysis. Unpublished doctoral dissertation, UCLA.

Sears, R. 1947. Influence of methodological factors on doll play performance. *Child Develpm.*, 18, 190–197.

Seaton, J. K. 1940. A projective experiment using incomplete stories with multiple-choice endings. *Genet. Psychol. Monogr.*, 41, 149–218.

Sheatsley, P. B. 1951. The art of interviewing and a guide to interviewer selection and training. In Marie Jahoda et al. (Eds.), *Research methods in social relations.* New York: Dryden. 2, 463–492.

Smith, H. L. 1956. *Linguistic science and the teaching of English.* Cambridge: Harvard Univer. Press.

Smith, Mary K. 1941. Measurement of the size of general English vocabulary through the elementary grades and high school. *Genet. Psychol. Monogr.*, 24, 311–345.

Spiegelman, M., C. Terwilliger and F. Fearing. 1953. The realiability of agreement in content analysis. *J. soc. Psychol.*, 37, 175–187.

Stein, M. I. 1947. The use of a sentence-completion test for the diagnosis of personality. *J. clin. Psychol.*, 42, 320–329.

Stolz, Lois M., et al. 1954. *Father relations of war-born children*. Stanford: Stanford University. Press.

Stone, L. J., and J. Church. 1957. *Childhood and adolescence: A psychology of the growing person*. New York: Random House.

Sullivan, H. S. 1954. *The psychiatric interview*. New York: W. W. Norton.

Symonds, P. M., and D. H. Dietrich. 1941. The effects of variations in the time interval between an interview and its recording. *J. abnorm. soc. Psychol.*, 36, 593–598.

Vigotsky, L. S. 1939. Thought and speech, *Psychiatry*, 2, No. 1, 29–51.

White, R. K. 1951. Value-analysis: The nature and use of the method. *Soc. Psychol. Study soc. Issues*.

Winstell, B. 1951. The use of a controlled play situation in determining certain effects of maternal attitudes on children. *Child Develpm.*, 22, 299–311.

Wolff, W. 1946. *Personality of the preschool child: The child's search for his self*. New York: Grune and Stratton.

Wright, H. R., and R. G. Barker. 1950. *Methods in psychological ecology*. Lawrence: Dep. Psychol. Univer. Kansas.

Yarrow, L. J. 1948. The effects of antecedent frustration on projective play. *Psychol. Mongr.*, 62, No. 6.

chapter 15

# Projective Techniques

William E. Henry
*The University of Chicago*

A large number of projective techniques may be used for research in child development. Certain of these were designed with children specifically in mind. Others, though originally developed for adults, may still be profitably used with children.

The techniques may be grouped in a variety of ways so as to highlight their similarities and differences. Frank (1939) has made one categorization based upon the nature of the response required of the subject. He proposed the terms *constitutive, interpretative, cathartic,* and *constructive.* The *constitutive* techniques are those that require the subject to assign a form or structure to a stimulus relatively unstructured. Thus in the Rorschach he must name an object, that is assign a specific form, to a stimulus essentially ambiguous in nature. Similarly, in the use of finger paints, he must create a picture or a design. An *interpretative* technique relies more upon the subject telling what a stimulus means to him.

In the Thematic Apperception Test he must give a meaning to a picture, as he does also in the Szondi when he indicates whether or not he likes certain photographs of persons. In the *cathartic* techniques the stress is upon the expression of feeling and affect, as when the child plays with dolls or toys. The *constructive* methods require the child to create an order and organization by the manipulation of, for example, blocks, as when he is asked to build a specific unit, his own home, out of blocks and toys.

Other persons have suggested somewhat different ways of categorizing these instruments. Each system throws additional light upon various aspects of them. For more detailed material on these various classifications, the reader is referred to Helen Sargent (1945), to Campbell (1950, 1957), and to Cattell (1951). For our purposes here, another set of categories based upon the response process of the subject is used. This is the system proposed by Gardner Lindzey (1960). The categories are *associative, construction, completion, ordering,* and *expressive.*

The *associative* techniques are those in which the subject responds to a stimulus—a word, a picture, a sound—with the first word, image, or thought that occurs to him. In the Word Association Test, used more commonly with adults than with children, the subject is presented with a list of words, to each of which he is to respond with the first word that comes to mind. In some cases he may be asked to give several words, a chain of associations to each stimulus word. The *Rorschach* is probably the best known of the methods utilizing this associative form of response. Useful with subjects from nursery-school age and on, the Rorschach is a set of ten inkblots, irregular and variegated in shape and color, to which the subject again responds with the first things that come to mind, as in the Word Association Test. In the Rorschach, however, the subject may give many responses to each of the ten cards, and in each case he identifies as best he can the area of the card about which he is talking as well as the characteristics of the section of the card that made him think of that particular response.

The *Cloud Pictures* of Struve (1932) and William Stern (1938) are also associative in form. They are a series of pictures of clouds on which the subject is to outline objects that he perceives and identify them with some label or name. Also associative, but based upon vague sounds heard rather than upon words or pictures seen, are two forms of auditory projective tests. The *Verbal Summator* of Skinner (1936) presents vowel sounds on a record. The subject is asked to identify these sounds as though they were actual words heard somewhat indistinctly. Another form of this idea is the *Tautophone*, devised primarily for adult psychiatric settings by Shakow and Rosenzweig (1940). Davids and Murray (1955) have developed a more elaborate and more promising form, based upon patterns of sounds that are not merely formally meaningless but are also related to certain personal dispositions, such as optimism, distrust, anxiety, trust, egocentricity, and so forth.

The *construction* techniques are those that call upon the subject to construct a product, typically a story, out of a picture stimulus. There is no particular demand here for the first idea that occurs to the subject. Rather the stress is upon the development of some sort of plot. This will have associative qualities but will also involve the cognitive task of organizing ideas in some sort of a sequence to constitute a story. The *Thematic Apperception Test* of Murray (1943) is probably the best known of this kind of method. This instrument consists of a set of 30 cards of varying content and degrees of ambiguity. One card is blank. The subject is shown each card individually and asked to create a story that describes what is going on in the picture, what led up to it, what the people are thinking and feeling, and how it will all come out. Certain of the cards are to be used for all subjects, regardless of age and sex, and certain are specifically intended for boys, girls, or adult males or females.

The *Make-A-Picture-Story Test* (MAPS) of Shneidman (1948, 1949, 1952) is a close relative of the TAT but adds one special feature. In it the subject is provided with background scenes and a large number of human and animal figures from which he may select. Once he has chosen the figures he wishes to use, he then constructs a story, as in the TAT. Van Lennep's *Four Picture Test* consists of four colored scenes, which are presented simultaneously, rather than sequentially, to the subject. He must then arrange these four scenes in any order he chooses and incorporate them into a single story. (Lennep, 1948, 1951)

A number of modifications of the

TAT has been devised for such special purposes or subjects as children, Negroes, adolescents, interacting groups, the family, and persons in other cultures. Modifications have also been made to facilitate the study of such specific variables as achievement, affiliation, anxiety, aggression, with one set, the *Blacky Pictures* (Blum, 1950) formulated on the base of a series of psychoanalytic variables related to stages of psychosexual development. Some attention is also given to the analysis of *dreams* under this rubric. Although dreams are not usually considered a projective technique, they meet most of the basic criteria of such techniques, except for the obvious fact that the stimulus to the resulting product is not under the control of the examiner.

The *completion* techniques present the subject with some incomplete situation, which he is to complete in any manner he chooses consistent with the instructions. The *Sentence Completion Test* is the basic and best-known test in this form. It consists of a series of incompleted sentence stems, which the subject may complete with any words he chooses to make a sentence. The particular sentence stems vary widely and may be made up readily by an investigator to study one or more variables.

The *Rosenzweig Picture Frustration Test* (Rosenzweig, 1949) is also in this completion form and presents a series of cartoons all dealing with situations of some potential frustrating circumstance. In these cartoons the subject is to complete the cartoon by giving the response of the person portrayed as frustrated. There are 24 such scenes, each dealing with some element of frustration.

The Sargent (1955) *Test of Insight into Human Motives* is closely related to both of these instruments. This test, adopted for children by Engle (1958), consists of a series of armatures, or incomplete stories, and the subject is asked to tell what the central character does, and why, and how he feels.

In the *ordering* or choice techniques the subject looks at a series of picture stimuli provided by the examiner and ranks or orders them according to some principle set by the examiner. The *Szondi* (Deri, 1949) is the best known of this type. It presents a series of 48 photographs of individuals taken from eight psychiatric diagnostic categories. The subject is presented with these photographs in six sets of eight pictures. In each set he is to view all eight photographs and to select the two he likes the best and two he likes the least. He is then again asked to indicate his most liked and least liked from those previously selected by him as liked or disliked.

The *Picture Arrangement Test* of Tompkins and Miner (1957) provides both ordering and completion features, although the primary work to date has gone into the ordering elements. The test consists of 25 cards showing cartoonlike figures, each involved in three different but related activities. The subject orders these three in the sequence in which he feels the activities took place. In addition, he is to give a sentence for each picture descriptive of what is going on in it.

The *expressive* techniques differ from those in the previous categories in several ways. In some of these techniques the subject provides data by the manipulation of various objects or equipment. Although this process frequently results in an end product (a painting, a drawing, a block construction), which can be analyzed subsequent to its creation by the subject, it is also characteristic of these methods that the actual process of manipulating the materials—whether or not they are recorded in some way for future examination—is seen as relevant data. Thus with some forms of *play techniques* the subject may make several play constructions during an hour's time—rearranging, breaking them up, making new ones, verbalizing about them. This process is seen as crucial data about various areas of the subject's life, even though only a movie camera and a sound recorder would provide a full record for subsequent examination. Similarly, the various forms of *psychodrama* and *role playing* involve a process of acting out, often with other actors and an audience, some particular role or plot selected by the examiner. The relevant data are again principally the process of acting out these roles, and no end product is normally available. In the case of *drawings* or *paintings*, there is normally an end product that may be analyzed to provide various assessments of the personality. Even here, however, there is considerable information to be derived from observing the process of creating this end product.

In the expressive techniques possibilities also exist of some direct expression of attitudes and viewpoints, an expressive process that is often felt to be not merely diagnostic but in some way therapeutic. The use of play materials in child therapy is well known. Here, as often in the psychodrama, the central interest has been in the therapeutic effects of the expression or acting-out elements rather than in the diagnostic use of either that process or any possible end product.

Various modifications of these three processes—drawing, playing, acting out —have been made with a view to maximizing the diagnostic and personality-evaluation elements. In this chapter we concern ourselves principally with three later modifications in such forms of the drawing process as Machover's (1948) system of the analysis of drawings of the human figure and Buck's (1948a) form in which the person is to draw a house, a tree, and a person. Each of these provides the subject with standard equipment and a system for the analysis of the end product. Napoli (1951) has made important contributions to the earlier work of Ruth Shaw (1934) in developing drawing and, in particular, finger painting as a projective technique.

Lois B. Murphy (1956) has made a notable contribution to the research use of projective techniques in her development of various "projective situations." These share some of the characteristics of the playing and the role taking in, for example, the various *Group Play Techniques*. These are planned and semistructured experimental situations in which certain attributes of persons are explored. They include the *Potential Leadership Game*, the

*Imposed Leadership Game*, and *Family Play*. It should be noted that each of these, as in role playing, has to some extent an axis of social interaction. Designed to explore less interactive and more impulse-dominated elements are such methods as the *Balloons Test*, related to the performance of aggression, the *Cold Cream and Dough Situations*, related to sensory and impulse concerns. The *Blocking Techniques*, used by Murphy and developed earlier by Lerner (see Murphy, 1956) relate to frustration. Murphy also has developed a set of *Miniature Life Toys* which, similar to the *World Test* of Buhler and Kelly (1941) and Bolgar and Fischer (1947) are a standard set of toys used for both diagnostic and therapeutic purposes.

This system does not subdivide all projective techniques useful with children into completely independent categories. It serves, however, to call attention to the range and variety of these methods and to suggest certain general principles of procedure involved in them. In the sections that follow certain broader previews related to the development, definition, and research use of these methods are discussed, and each of the methods briefly mentioned here is dealt with in greater detail.

## Conceptual Background of Projective Techniques

The projective techniques of personality study have entered into psychological and social sciences research and appear destined to remain there as integral parts of the body of techniques and concepts now characteristic of the field. Undoubtedly a wide variety of influences has been responsible for the rapid growth of the use of these techniques in the last twenty or more years. The greatest single influence perhaps has been the development and spread of psychoanalytic theory among persons concerned both with research and direct clinical work. Even though many persons dealing with research related to children have not adopted all aspects of psychoanalytic theory, the great vigor and apparent relevance of psychoanalytic theses have influenced to some degree almost all elements of personality theory. The projective techniques have seemed particularly relevant to an analytically oriented personality theory, in part because of their purported relevance to the delineation of those elements of the person of which he was consciously unaware. The investigator who was prepared to accept a logic of unconscious motivations found himself drawn to techniques that seem to have an affinity to just these motivations. The data of the projective instrument also bear considerable similarity to the dreams, associations, and clinical interviews within the framework of which psychoanalysis itself developed.

A second determinant of the increased concern with projective techniques has been the emphasis upon the concepts of *holism*. The holistic emphasis has been upon study of the full context of behavior and on viewing the actions of individuals in terms of their essential unity and interrelatedness. The investigator who has accepted some elements of this viewpoint, and who feels the need to relate each item of behavior to other items, finds it increasingly difficult to limit himself to the traditional objective instruments for personality measurement. The projective techniques provide the investigator with a rationale for implementing an interest in holistic theories. They also adapted themselves to the description and study of a wide variety of personality characteristics and avoid the necessity of studying, in relative isolation, a small number of specific predetermined dimensions.

A general growth of interest in instrumentation, stemming from the rise of logical positivism, with its attendant stress upon operationalism, has also encouraged the development of techniques in all spheres, including the projective.

As researchers, as well as society at large, became aware of and receptive to the idea that human behavior is complexly determined, a wide range of new problem areas, or new approaches to old problems, came into being. Among these have been studies of the relation of the personality to the social environment, of personality communalities in persons holding membership in similar social groups, in the process of socialization, in the relation of infant and child behavior to subsequent adult behavior, in the study of persons as consumers, and in the study of the personality correlates of social attitudes, perception, learning, occupational choices. In each of these areas, and in others, the projective methods have increasingly been used.

## The Nature of a Projective Instrument

It has already been suggested that a projective instrument is one whose users find it adaptable to a particular theoretical viewpoint. This viewpoint is one which, on the theoretical side, contains substantial portions of psychodynamic concepts—even if not always specifically psychoanalytic—and utilizes a holistic approach to the study of behavior. On the methodological side, the projective techniques have appealed to persons who choose to implement their psychodynamic and holistic interests by attention to problems of instrumentation and the operations of data collection. We can define the projective instruments, however, somewhat more specifically than by this reference to their conceptual context. The term projective technique first appeared in a publication of Ruth Horowitz and Lois B. Murphy (1938). Here they give credit for the origination of the term to Lawrence K. Frank, whose article on these methods appearing in 1939, gave great impetus and definition to the field. In this article, Frank described his view of these techniques:

. . . we may approach the personality and induce the individual to reveal his way of organizing experience by giving him a field (objects, materials, experiences) with relatively little structure and cultural patterning so that the personality can project upon that plastic field his way of seeing life, his meanings, significances, patterns, and especially his feelings. Thus we elicit a projection of the individual personality's *private world* because he has to organize the field, interpret the material and react affectively to it. More specifically, a projective method for the study of personality involves the presentation of a stimulus-situation designed or chosen because it will mean to the subject, not what the experimenter has arbitrarily decided it should mean (as in most psychological experiments using standardized stimuli in order to be "objective"), but rather he imposes upon it, his private, idiosyncratic meaning and organization. The subject then will respond to *his* meaning of the presented stimulus-situation by some form of action and feeling that is expressive of his personality (1939, pp. 402–403).

Subsequent to this initial definition, other writers have defined the projective instruments—always with overlapping emphasis but sometimes choosing to stress one point more than another or noting additional characteristics in no way contradictory to Frank's statement. Following Gardner Lindzey's excellent summary and analysis (Lindzey, 1960) of these various definitions, we may point to several more crucial characteristics of this class of instrument. These features may lie in the characteristics of responses elicited from the subject, in the nature of the material presented to him for response, or in the attitude taken by the experimenter in his subsequent treatment of those responses.

*With respect to the characteristics of response by the subject,* the projective instruments are notable for several features.

*Sensitivity to unconscious or latent aspects of personality.* This refers, of course, to that realm of covert, latent, unconscious components of personality that Frank identifies as his "private world." This would appear to be the central purpose of the projective instruments, regardless of the particular material presented to the subject or the mode of overt response called for from him.

*Multiplicity of response permitted the subject.* In contrast to instruments requiring specific and limited responses from the subject (the questionnaire "yes," "no," or "?" or a simple choice from a list of four or five possible responses), the subject in the projective experiment is permitted and encouraged to respond with a wide range of ideas and/or actions. It is of further importance that this wide variety of response also stems from the subject's own imagination and ideas, in terms appropriate to his own "private, idiosyncratic meaning and organization."

*The lack of awareness of the subject of the purpose of the test.* Although the subject may be quite aware of the very general interest of the investigator—that his "personality is being studied," "his imagination tested"—in none of the projective techniques as ordinarily used is he directly aware of the details of this goal. Specifically, he is not informed of any expectation of the investigator of any particular mode of response, and, most importantly, he is not aware of the variables subsequently to be used in the analysis of his responses. This is in contrast to the majority of objective scales and questionnaires in which the dimension at issue is either clearly stated or may be easily guessed by the subject and in which, by the exercise of a little imagination, the subject may ,direct his response to influence subsequent interpretation.

*The amount of response is substantial in quantity and complex in quality.* In contrast to the objective techniques, the response of the subject is usually voluminous, rich, varied.

*The response is of a fantasy character and structured by no formal rules of "right or wrong" set by the examiner.* Most projective techniques call for a response stemming entirely from the subject—without a "guessing" framework as to the "real" answer, presumably known by the examiner. The subject is, of course, given some instruction: "Tell a story," "Make up an ending," "Tell me what you see," and so forth, but emphasis is laid on the response being "just whatever occurs" to the subject.

*With respect to the analysis of the responses,* there are several elements of importance.

*Multiplicity of concepts of analysis.* The very richness and elaborateness of responses to most projective techniques, and the fact that so few guidelines are provided to the subject in responding, tend to result in a kind of data to which a wide range of personality concepts may be applied. Thus the projective data may generally be analyzed in terms of many concepts applied to them subsequent to securing the response. A TAT story may be analyzed with respect to the degree of cognitive organization and structure, with respect to the images of adult figures presented, or with respect to the degree of

achievement and ambition displayed. A single Rorschach response, containing, for example, both color and form determinants, may reflect upon the extrovertive aspects of the person, upon the degree of his organizing qualities, as well as upon the degree of commonness or uniqueness of his thought processes.

*Holistic analysis.* As suggested earlier, investigators preferring a more holistic view of man have been prominent among those utilizing the projective instruments. The attraction for them of these techniques lies, of course, in the very fact that the completeness of data and the multiplicity of concepts that can be applied to them permit and encourage the investigator to examine the complexities of the individual and to see the various interrelations of one element of the personality to others.

*With respect to the physical characters of the test-stimulus presented to the subject,* the projective techniques differ from many other techniques.

The various forms of the projective instruments are portrayed in a subsequent section. Here it is indicated merely that they range widely over the realm of "objects, materials, experiences" to which Frank referred. Among the objects and materials, mention may be made of such diverse stimuli as ink blots, jars of cold cream, incomplete sentences, miniature toys representative of people, places, and things, photographs of persons from various nosological categories, cartoons representing various frustrating circumstances, collections of paints, paper, and coloring pencils, and so on. Among the "experiences" mentioned by Frank might be included such things as the instruction to act out certain roles, as in the psychodrama, and the presentation of two toy trains with the comment by the examiner that they are on the same track and cannot pass, "What will happen?" Perhaps the balloon-situation described by Stone in Murphy (1956), in which it is possibly the license to "pop" them as much as the balloons themselves that constitutes the stimulus to projection, should also be included.

Usually, the projective instrument is seen as one, as Frank comments, of "relatively little structure and cultural patterning." This is indeed true of many of the projective stimuli and perhaps is truer of them generally than of the objective personality instruments. This characteristic of "ambiguity" or "lack of structure," however appropriate it may be when comparing the projective instruments with other personality methods, does not lie so much in the stimuli themselves as in the context and setting in which they are used. Many of the stimuli used in various forms of miniature toys are in themselves perfectly well structured and even culturally patterned—the toys are familiar enough to most children; dogs are recognizable as such. Even the houses are culturally patterned, at least for American children, in that they are clearly not Swiss chalets nor Navaho hogans. The automobiles are not necessarily recognizable as Fords, Chevrolets, etc., but they are familiar and are again clearly not Simcas, Volvos, or Fiats. Although the Rorschach ink blots are not culturally patterned in the sense that they represent reality-objects in common use, they are perfectly identi-

fiable as what they are—ink blots. The Szondi pictures are certainly "strange" in that they appear "old-fashioned." They are as stimuli hardly unstructured and ambiguous—they are old photographs.

It is true that some of the Rorschach cards, even though recognizable as ink blots, are more complex than others and harder to deal with and some of the Thematic Apperception Technique pictures are similarly stranger, more complicated, and harder to identify than others.

It is when the subject attempts to implement the *instructions* given with the projective stimuli that the issue of ambiguity becomes most relevant. An ink blot is still an ink blot and remains perfectly unambiguous until the subject accepts the condition, "Imagine what else it might be"; the boy with the violin in the TAT is perfectly straightforward and quite highly structured until the subject concedes he will try to "tell a story" about it; even a pile of paints, paper, and crayons is unambiguous until the subject applies his efforts to creating an imaginary situation, as he does when he paints a picture, tells a story, or "sees" a dancing bear. The ambiguity lies in the fact that there are no, or very few, guidelines provided for him when he proceeds to create this imaginary situation or product. Ambiguity may be only a relative term and not sufficiently descriptive of the projective stimuli per se, but it is a most appropriate characteristic when we consider that the response made stems from the total context of the technique itself and the task set for the subject.

## Psychological Theory and Projective Techniques

It has already been suggested that one of the notable characteristics of the projective techniques is the wide range and variety of concepts to which they have relevance. In the next section, which deals with a number of specific techniques, attention is called to the concepts customarily used in connection with each instrument. As a general background, however, it may be useful to discuss briefly some ways in which psychological theory relates to the projective techniques.

The central question is, "In what ways do the projective techniques relate to general psychological theory?" Here one is concerned with the ways in which general personality theories, or general theories of behavior, serve as explanatory systems for the behavior of the individual during the process of utilizing the stimuli of the technique and for the resultant responses. This concern reflects the fact that the projective techniques and their interpretive systems appear to have been developed with only minimal explicit relation to theories aimed at accounting for realms of behavior broader than, but presumably including, the projective situation. This neglect stems not from the view that this area of theory is unimportant but rather from the fact that the efforts in this direction are few in number and only in their embryonic stage.

It may be recalled that the projective techniques were developed within a clinic-oriented setting and by persons influenced, if not entirely absorbed, by psychoanalytic theory. The Rorschach, in particular, was presented initially by Herman Rorschach (1942), himself greatly interested in psychoanalytic theory. His monograph makes occasional reference to this body of theory. His posthumous publication of a single case psychoanalyzed by Oberholzer (Rorschach and Oberholzer, 1942) deals more explicitly with the relation of this theory to the Rorschach. In more recent years, Schafer has concerned himself with an explicit concern for psychoanalytic theory in one book (1954a) and one article (1954b). Similarly Rapaport (1950, 1952) has dealt with this topic in several influential publications. The reader may also be referred to Holt (1954) for a general discussion of the relation of personality theory to the Rorschach and to Klopfer (1954) for a similar consideration of its relation to Jungian psychoanalytic psychology. An excellent discussion and review of attempts to relate various psychological theories, including the psychoanalytic, to projective testing may also be found in Lindzey (1960).

Lindzey's summary statement presents the present state of affairs in this area.

In general, it appears that projective techniques and psychoanalytic theory possess many congruent elements. A considerable number of psychoanalytic concepts display real utility in accounting for, or making rational, practices found among projective users. This, of course, is scarcely remarkable in view of the extent to which these practices have been established by individuals influenced by psychoanalytic theory. Less encouraging are the steps that have been taken toward a careful and precise specification of the detailed relationship between psychoanalytic theory and projective techniques. Several interesting and encouraging attempts have been made to demonstrate the utility of some portion of psychoanalytic theory in the understanding or interpretation of some segment of projective techniques. However, it seems clear that a rational and carefully specified bridge from psychoanalytic theory to projective techniques remains a hope for the future—it is definitely not an accomplishment of the past (1960, p. 22).

Although the psychoanalytic body of concepts would appear, as a single theoretical stance, to have the most relevance for the projective techniques at present, at least two other bodies of theory have interested various investigators. These are perception theory and stimulus-response theory. In the instance of perception theory, the connecting links have been the obvious fact that the response to the projective instrument involves some elements of perception and that body of research relating perception to personality and motivational variables. The effort here has been similar to that in the psychoanalytic area—to explore the extent to which projective data can be explained in perception theory terms and, via that mechanism, be related to the broad body of general psychological theory in a more integral way. Abt (1950) has made an effort in this direction, including attention to holistic theories but relying heavily upon perception. Eriksen (1951, 1954) and Eriksen and Lazarus (1952) have undertaken investigations aimed at demonstrating the pertinence of perception theory to the projectives. Bruner (1948) sees in per-

ception theory a possible mechanism of overcoming the primarily empirically based development of the Rorschach. All of these authors point to the relevance of various aspects of perception theory to projective interpretation and to a possible pathway for demonstrating the continuity of these instruments with general theory.

Similar efforts have been made to integrate projective instruments with stimulus-response theory. Auld (1954) has, with the TAT, shown certain correspondence between some concepts of stimulus-response theory and projective data. Goss and Brownell (1957) have applied S-R concepts to elements of the projective stimuli and the interpretive process. Certain elements of the work of McClelland, Atkinson, Clark, and Lowell (1953) stem from S-R theory.

In each of these efforts to relate the projective field to one or another general theory—psychoanalytic, perception, stimulus-response—the major contribution might be said to be to the theory itself rather than to the field of projective testing. Individual experimenters with the projective must still rely upon some other branch of theory in the direct task of classifying or interpreting responses. However, by showing that certain concepts of these theories have relevance for the projective stimuli or data, they do throw new light upon these phenomena. In so doing, they extend our knowledge of the meaning of the stimulus situation and of the elements of response in relation to their interpretation in some broader terms. Some of these efforts have provided direct guides to the interpretation of projective response. More have been limited to demonstrating that the projectives may be seen as a subclass of behavior explainable in part by the theory in question. Although all of these are admittedly tentative first efforts, they show promise and serve as important steps to the end of exploring the relation of projective test behavior to broader concepts and theories.

It is also possible to relate certain specific scores or interpretive concepts used in projectives to personality concepts, if not to such broad realms of theory as suggested above. These studies of smaller issues have an immediacy and direct relevance to the use researchers may make of the instruments. The majority of these studies have had the Rorschach as their focus. This may stem in part from the Rorschach's longer history. In part it may stem from the fact that, more than most projectives, the Rorschach has been developed with a limited range of specific response scores, each of which, alone or in specified combinations, has a stated meaning in personality terms. It becomes therefore considerably more manageable to inquire into the correlates of these scoring categories and to examine the meaning given to them by a priori statement in clinical judgment.

Examples of these efforts are found predominantly in the examination of the Rorschach movement response. This has been a logical choice in that most experts in this field agree on the centrality of this category of response to the Rorschach interpretive system. The initial statement of Rorschach (1942) about the $M$ response dealt with personality and behavioral correlates. Various workers in the Rorschach have extended or modified these notions, but few have attempted a theoretical rationale for such relationships as empirical clinical notations seem to indicate. Schachtel (1950) has paid considerable attention to this issue, in the $M$ and other responses, seeing the $M$'s as representing a direct projection of kinesthetic sensations that are intimately connected with the deepest layers of personality. Piotrowski (1957) noted a greater direct relation between the $M$ and certain overt tendencies. Thus he comments that the $M$ response reflects ". . . a steering mechanism which directs the individual to play certain definite roles in those interhuman relationships that are vital to him." The $M$ responses for Piotrowski are "accessible to direct observation in the external motor behavior of the subject . . ." Both Schachtel and Piotrowski have a great deal more to say about such responses, but for our purpose here they are notable in their effort to provide a theoretical rationale as well as empirical correlates. Rapaport (1950, 1952) and Werner (1945) have also made specific statements of the theoretical meaning of these responses, and Singer and his associates (Singer and Spohn, 1954; Singer, Meltzoff, and Goldman, 1952; Meltzoff, Singer, and Korchin, 1953) have reported experiments based upon various theoretical formulations.

In the case of the TAT, studies in this area have been largely in the general relation of fantasy to overt expression, in part a concern with issues of interpretation and in part an effort to explain the relation of TAT responses to other personality concepts. Sanford, et al. (Sanford, Adkins, Miller, and Cobb, 1943), have reported low positive correlation between aggression as seen in TAT responses and measures of overt aggression. Mussen and Naylor (1954) have also studied this relationship, adding a more specific attention to the social-class background of subjects and to the anticipation of punishment for aggressive acts to be expected in this social-class group. Kagan (1956) continued this trend of thought, introducing the issue of anxiety and subdividing aggression into types. Other persons have approached this issue in different ways, in each instance, however, attempting to introduce experimental variables related theoretically to the proposed explanation of various relations between fantasy and overt expression.

In including these brief statements of ways in which theory and projective data have been related, the object has been only to call attention to the fact that the relation of the projective techniques to systematic behavior theory is indeed a tenuous one. This does not diminish the very substantial research on the projectives in which various empirical relations have been observed, but it does emphasize the continuing need to undertake investigations that stem from a theoretical position. Such studies will serve the objective of strengthening the knowledge of the meaning of projective data as well as the goal of lending a more substantial rationale to observed empirical relations.

## Specific Projective Techniques

### ASSOCIATIVE TECHNIQUES

The associative techniques present a stimulus to the subject and require him to respond with the first thought that comes to mind. The principal technique here is the Rorschach, in which plates of inkblots are presented and the subject is asked to report what he sees in them. Other forms present words to which associations are requested.

The *Rorschach Test* consists of ten plates or cards upon which are reproduced symmetrical ink blots. These are such that might be produced by folding a piece of paper over a drop of ink. Five are gray and black on a white background, two others have some colored portions, and the remaining three are almost entirely colored. They are presented to all subjects in the same order, with instructions to report what they see in the blots. Emphasis is usually laid upon the suggestion that there are no expected right answers, but that whatever the subject sees is what is wanted. The examiner intervenes in this process to a minimal degree, merely recording the responses verbatim and passing the subject each succeeding card as he appears to be finished with the preceding. The elapsed time between the initial presentation of each card and the subject's first response is also recorded. Once the subject has given as many responses to each of the ten cards, which may range from about 15 responses for the total set of cards in younger children (and subjects in the 70's) to 25 to 40 for adolescents and adults, the subject is to re-examine each of his responses and to tell the examiner more about the factors contributing to his response. In this phase, usually called the inquiry, the examiner's role becomes somewhat more elaborate. Here he must secure from the subject information permitting a scoring on *location, determinant,* and *content.* Location is scored in terms of the area of the blot used by the subject when he identifies what he sees. Commonly, a response is scored for location in terms of its reference to the whole blot ($W$) or a detail of it. The detail responses may be usual details ($D$), small details ($Dd$), or rare or unusual details ($Dr$). Use of the white spaces is scored separately ($S$). The *location* scoring is seen as answering the question, What part of the total stimulus did the subject use in his response? The *determinant* scoring is designed to answer the question, What element in the stimulus prompted the response? Here a common pattern is to score $F$ if the subject indicates it was primarily the form or shape of the particular blot area; $M$ for movement if seen in human figures, $FM$ for movement in animal figures, and $m$ for inanimate figures. Responses may also be determined by shading or texture in the grayish blot areas or by the use of color. Certain combinations of determinants are also common. Thus a response that appears to be based both on form and color may be scored $FC$ if the form appears to come first or $CF$ if the color predominates. *Content* is normally scored for its originality ($O$) or popularity ($P$) among responses and for some further breakdown of content

such as the categories human ($H$), human detail ($Hd$), animal ($A$), animal detail ($Ad$), nature ($N$), and so on. The total responses ($R$) and the reaction times to cards also figure in the scoring.

This statement of scores is only a general one indicative of many of the basic issues thought relevant to the categorization of responses. Different specialists elaborate this system in various ways, which they consider to reflect most appropriately the psychological processes influential in producing the responses in question. We may add to this scoring statement various ratios of responses—the proportion of $M$ to $C$, the percentage of $F$, the ratio of human to animal response, etc. These scores and ratios are then summated into a psychogram that serves as a device for bringing the total pattern of scores together for review in graphic presentation.

Once the scores are summated in this fashion, the interpretive task begins. This is based upon certain assumptions and empirical findings regarding the relation of the scoring patterns to personality variables. The publications of specialists, which are suggested below, must be studied for a full picture of the quite complex process of interpretation. A very rough review may be given here, however, of the general order of concepts used in this process. As summarized by Beck (1951), the three central areas of personality dealt with by the Rorschach are intellectual activity, the externalized emotions, and the inner emotional life. In the area of the intellective activity the perception of form ($F$) is seen as a crucial indication. The perception of certain amounts of good form is seen as a measure of clearness of perception. At the same time, extreme amounts of form responses in, for example, depressive states are representative of rigid, obsessive caution, whereas very low form suggests unstable emotional conditions and clouded perception. In the area of the location scores ($W$, $D$, $Dd$, etc.) also lie indicators of the intellectual life, particularly in the perception of $W$ responses, in the order and sequence of $W$ and detail responses, and in the degrees of organization, which Beck calls $Z$. The originality versus the commoness of response is also relevant, as estimates of the originality of thought processes. Animal responses, very easily seen in the cards, suggest a lack of richness of mental process.

In the area of the externalized emotional life, the use of color and of shading in response is seen as crucial. Color represents a mechanism for projecting the exciting, usually positive, externalized feeling. Within the varieties of color responses, the purer responses— those involving minimal form—suggest the more egocentric and self-gratifying orientations. Color well mixed with form—the $FC$—suggests the socially tempered person able to interpret his own desires with those of other persons. The shading responses, in which the light and darkness elements of the blot are used, suggest more painful emotion, anxiety, depressed feelings, the sense of inadequacy. Use of the white space appears to relate to stubbornness, hostility.

The inner life itself appears most centrally reflected in the movement responses seen as portrayals of strongly felt wish references. The $M$ is thus the internalized element of emotion as the $C$ is the externalized.

Studies of the stability and validity of the Rorschach have resulted in encouraging if not definitive findings. The approaches to these problems have been varied. They may be divided, following Rabin (1951a), into molar, molecular, and experimental studies. The molar approach is essentially the one in which the complete interpretation of the individual record is compared with some comparable independent data, the psychiatrist's report, therapy records, and life history. These studies show positive correlation, suggesting that, in the hands of skilled interpreters, diagnostic validity can indeed be demonstrated. They normally utilize forms of comparable global criteria, such as psychiatric diagnosis, which are themselves open to question. It seems unquestionable that the Rorschach is a *useful* tool in clinical diagnosis, even though its validity regarding the prediction of personality structuring and dynamics is less clearly demonstrated.

Molecular studies attempt to investigate the validity of specific Rorschach variables, or combinations of them, normally against some hypothetically related behavior in another domain. Thus color response has been shown to correlate with the use of color in drawings.

Experimental studies attempt to create a situation of some specified effect upon the subject in terms of which particular Rorschach responses would be expected to change. Thus hypnotically induced mood changes produce certain patterns of scores hypothesized in relation to those moods. Sodium amytal, normally producing cooperativeness and friendliness, does seem to reduce the amount of card rejections. Other forms of experimental studies alter the stimulus itself—achromatic cards—or change the method of administration—reversed order of presentation. Correlates of Rorschach patterns in somatic and psychological spheres have also been undertaken. All of these experimental studies add considerably to knowledge of the validity of responses and interpretive possibilities. In total, however, they are by no means definitive. They suggest that much work is yet to be done to establish the general usefulness of the instrument and, more importantly, perhaps, to determine the extent to which specific scores and indices are indeed reflective of the psychological processes proposed by various investigators.

The Rorschach has been used principally with disturbed adults, and it is to this setting that the majority of the comments above apply. The use with children has been less extensive but still follows the same basic principles. The age of 3 seems frequently referred to as the lower age limit, though use has been made profitably with younger children of advanced intellectual development. The central issue regarding age appears to be the question of the stage of intellectual development or, more centrally, the development of perception. The use of the instrument with adolescents and adults assumes fully developed intellectual and perceptual equipment. It is upon this premise that the meaning of scores is based.

If, however, children have less well-developed perceptual processes, as seems clear, then to what extent may we assume the same interpretive principles? This dilemma is accentuated by the fact that it is often difficult to secure from children full inquiry information vital to the assigning of scores in the usual fashion. It is for these two reasons—limited inquiry and incomplete development—that Rorschachs of children below school age should be interpreted with caution and their administration undertaken with special attention to the communicativeness of the instructions. A central problem of scoring, and subsequent interpretation, stems from the inadequacy of inquiry information, particularly in children under 4. The issue is, should one score exclusively on the basis of information received or should one guess? The "guess" is, of course, based on the usual determinants of comparable responses when given by older subjects. Beyond a general adaptation of the language of the examiner to the age of the child, examiners differ somewhat as to how much variation there should be in the method of administration used with older subjects. A common method seems to be to modify the procedure only with an eye to the establishment of adequate rapport—appropriate, of course, for all subjects—and to assume that reduced inquiry specificity represents not a failure of administration but the true state of the mental processes being studied.

These issues are excellently reviewed by Klopfer (1956) in the second volume of *Developments in the Rorschach*

*Technique*. In particular, the reader should examine Chapter 1 on problems of administration, scoring, and method by Klopfer, Fox, and Troup; Chapter 2 on interpretation by Klopfer, Spiegelman, and Fox; Chapter 4 on the significance of age patterns by Fox; and Chapter 5 on the study, with Rorschach and other methods, of the development of perception in children by Meili-Dworetzki. Additional references on these topics will be found following each of these chapters. A new report of norms for children 6 through 11 will be found in Ledwith (1959).

The child's reaction to the Rorschach situation is discussed and illustrated by Anna Hartoch (1956). In her discussion particular stress is laid upon the interaction of tester and child during the process of securing the record and upon the utilization of this full range of data in the interpretation of the resulting record.

Since the use of the Rorschach with children is a special case of the use of this test, the reader should also examine the more general Rorschach literature. The original report on this instrument is that of Herman Rorschach's *Psychodiagnostics: A Diagnostic Text Based on Perception* (1942). Beck's three volumes (1944, 1945, 1952); Klopfer and Kelley (1942), and Klopfer, Ainsworth, Klopfer, and Holt (1954) describe the central principles and practices. Rabin's chapter (1951a) in Anderson and Anderson's *Introduction to Projective Techniques* provides a statement and additional references on the issue of validity. A review of other uses of the Rorschach less related to children—

alternative forms used to study specific variables and special indices for limited purposes—may be found in Gardner Lindzey (1960).

## OTHER ASSOCIATIVE TECHNIQUES

The most useful of the associative techniques, and the one in this group about which the greatest information can be found in research and accumulated experience, is indeed the Rorschach. Nonetheless, the basic model for the associative methods is perhaps the *Word Association Test*. In this test a list of stimulus words is presented, usually verbally and one at a time, to which the subject is asked to respond with the first word that occurs to him. The time elapsing between hearing the stimulus word and the response is normally recorded. In some uses the subject may also be asked to give other words that occur to him, a chain of associations initiated by the original stimulus word. Various lists of standard words exist, particularly the early list of 100 words of Kent and Rosanoff (1910) and the more recent list of 60 by Rapaport, Gill, and Schafer (1946). In Rapaport et al. a statement of the principles of analysis and interpretation of these responses and an important new statement of a theoretical rationale for the instrument will also be found.

In general, the assumption of analysis is based upon the logic that particular patterns of response-words and either very long or slow reaction times are indicative of psychological disturbance. The variable of neurotic disturbance is the principle one investigated, although the choice of a different set of words would permit study of other, and less general, concepts. The development of a special set of words—appropriate to the vocabulary and life circumstance of children—would probably be necessary for its use with other than adult groups. It would be necessary, even with such a new list, to administer this list to substantial groups of children of various characteristics to gain a background of expected responses and to experiment with administration appropriate to the verbal skills of children. Such a list would have to be composed to investigate some specific predetermined variables for maximal usefulness. In nearly all forms, however, the instrument would provide only the judgment of "disturbed or not-disturbed," or perhaps "usual or not-usual," with respect to the variables reflected in the stimulus words. Such a limitation is a very considerable one and places this technique very low on the list of projective instruments useful with children.

Woodrow and Lowell (1916) did combine a set of norms based upon 1000 children, 9 to 12 years of age, using the Kent-Rosanoff list, less ten words. Other studies with children include one by McGehee (1944) on age norms, one by McDowell (1928) on stutterers, and one by Mitchell, Rosanoff, and Rosanoff (1919). The study by Sanford (1936) on school-age children illustrates the use of this technique not for general clinical analysis but for the investigation of a specific variable. Anthony (1943) has used the instrument on 11- and 12-year-old children with a modified method of administra-tion. Useful treatment of the method will also be found in Bell (1948) and Rotter (1951).

Another associative technique of some interest but of very limited use has been the *Cloud Pictures* of Struve (1932) and Stern (1938). This instrument consists of a set of three pictures of clouds, suggested by the game of seeing things in passing clouds. The objective was to design a set of indistinct, visual stimuli appropriate for the study of normal children. Following some elements of the Rorschach procedures, the subject is to outline each object he sees and to name it. Stern also proposed a suggestive phase—roughly analogous to the "testing the limits" of the Rorschach. In spite of a certain superficial appropriateness to ordinary childhood activities, this method has appealed very little to psychologists and, in the presence of techniques of much greater scope and power, seems unlikely to do so in the future.

The same general conclusion might apply to associative techniques based upon auditory stimuli. The *Verbal Summator* of Skinner (1936) and a modification by Shakow and Rosenzweig (1940) present various indistinct sounds to which subjects are asked to give meaning. Although certain positive results are found when comparing groups, there is always a very limited value in it for studies with children or for studies of individual dynamics. More material on this approach may be found in Bell (1948) and Lindzey (1960). One modification, by Davids and Murray (1955), shows somewhat greater promise, though work on it has been limited to the initial report. Its advantage appears to lie in the fact that the sounds used are organized according to eight different dispositions: pessimism, distrust, anxiety, resentment, and so on. The subject is asked to identify the ideas he heard and to say which were major and which minor ideas. Although no work with children is reported, independent clinical judgments and other data on adults appear to relate meaningfully to ratings derived from the test.

## CONSTRUCTION TECHNIQUES

The construction techniques involve the subject in the development of some form of an organized plot, told in response to pictorial stimuli of varying degrees of structured content. These methods require a more elaborate and integrated verbal response than the associations required in the associative techniques.

*Thematic Apperception Techniques.* The TAT is the principal and most widely used construction technique. It is the model upon which other related techniques are based. The instrument was devised by Morgan and Murray (1935). As presented in its first published form by Murray (1943), the test consists of 30 pictures of varying content and degrees of ambiguity. One of these is a blank card. These 30 cards consist of ten so-called neutral cards, which are administered to males and females, ten for females alone, and ten for males alone. Of the ten cards for male subjects, certain are intended for both adults and children, and some are for only one or the other. The same

applies to the female cards. Thus a given subject will be given the ten neutral cards plus the ten cards appropriate to his age and sex.

There are various sets of specific instructions for the administration of this test. They will be found in the several general manuals indicated below. All are modifications of the basic and still commonly used instructions of Murray. In essence, the subject is presented each card individually and asked to tell a story about it. He is to tell what is going on in the scene, what the people are thinking and feeling, what led up to the scene, and how it will come out. Murray (1943) prefers that the set of 20 be administered in two separate sessions, followed by an inquiry into the origin of the stories and some association to certain elements. Rapaport, Gill, and Schafer (1946) suggest an inquiry, either after each card or the entire series, into any elements of unclarity—of a perceptual, verbal, or meaning sort. Rotter (1946) and Henry (1956) prefer delaying inquiries until all stories are completed. Regardless of the particular location of the inquiry, most examiners use only a few general questions of no set character, aiming principally at clearing up points that appear ambiguous in the story as told or about points that appear to be of unusual interest.

The analysis of the resulting record is by no means standardized at present. Murray's initial proposal first identified the hero, the central figure of each story, and then described the motives of the other characters and the pressures upon the hero as they were portrayed in the story. These were described in terms of the set of needs and pressures earlier presented by Murray and others in *Explorations in Personality* (1938). Although this approach is frequently used by many investigators, various other methods have been suggested [Aron (1949), Tomkins (1947), Bellak (1947), Fry (1953), Fine (1955), Stein (1955), Henry (1956)]. A number of these systems may be examined as they are compared in application to a single case in Shneidman (1951). Many of the basic principles of interpretation have been summarized by Lindzey (1952).

The central assumption of the TAT method, as well as most of its modifications, is that the subject reveals basic elements of his personality in constructing his stories. These elements may be seen in the particular *content* of the stories he tells as well as in the *form* in which he tells them. Most of the comprehensive systems of interpretation are based upon these two elements of stories. The *form* elements of stories, partially independent of the content, include such variables as length of stories, degree of organization, responses to details of cards, inclusive whole responses, preponderance of attention to past, present, or future references, and variability in such factors as these from one story to another. *Content* variables include such molar units as the thema or central elements of plot in each story or somewhat less comprehensive elements as the kinds of action attributed to various figures— male, female, old, young—the outcomes of stories—happy, sad, hostile, affiliative —in relation to particular people in stories or to kinds of thema, the sequences of action, and the kinds of

people or issues introduced for which there are no direct representatives in the picture stimulus. In addition, most interpreters utilize the concept of symbolic content, in reference to some form elements of cards seen as having special symbolic implications, or total story situations reflective of various crucial life crises—oedipal drama, authority resentment, sexual anxiety, and so forth.

Plans of analysis also normally involve interpretive inference as a basic element. Such schemes differ in the stress upon the amount of inference required and in the attention that they call to describable elements of the responses themselves used as documentation of their inferences. In comparison with the Rorschach, it is often said that the TAT provides data relevant to the content of the personality rather than its structure. There is a certain justification for this notion in the fact that the TAT stories provide an obvious richness of content related to specific attitudes, viewpoints, role relationships, conflicts, and personal dispositions. However, both instruments have been used to develop inferences in both structural and content areas. The distinction stems more from the fact that the customary focus of analysis of the Rorschach has been upon form variables, whereas that of the TAT has been upon content variables.

The elements of personality with which the TAT deals have been excellently stated by Lindzey:

The richness of the response data elicited provides a relatively satisfactory basis for a wide variety of different kinds of analysis. The thematic material contained in the stories permits the interpreter to make inferences concerning many different dispositions and conflicts and, in addition, a great deal can be learned concerning the subject's psychological world and his relation with others, as well as with his physical world. Furthermore, the widespread use of this technique, in addition to the special forms that have been developed, make clear that a good deal is known about its operation in a number of special settings. The test appears to be sensitive to depth or unconscious factors but at the same time clearly reflects conscious factors and situational determinants so that under appropriate circumstances it can be used to assess any of these kinds of variables. The test activity is a relatively natural one for almost all subjects and thus it is usually easy to explain to subjects and to elicit cooperation. The absence of a single widely accepted objective scoring system has led to a healthy approach to the instrument in which the method of analysis employed is not accepted as God-given and beyond criticism and furthermore is usually constructed in such a manner as to maximize the interests of the particular investigator.

On the other hand the data collected by the instrument are ponderous and difficult to subject to analysis. Furthermore, the absence of a single objective scoring system means that the individual employing the instrument often spends dozens of hours in analysis for every hour spent in the collection of data. The fact that the instrument is responsive to dispositional, situational and fleeting personal determinants means that it is difficult for the interpreter to be certain whether a given test characteristic reflects an enduring personal characteristic or a transient state. The entire test procedure rests upon complex linguistic skills so that for subjects who because of education or intelligence find it difficult to manipulate verbal symbols the test is relatively inappropriate. Furthermore, when individuals from a different culture are studied it is difficult to interpret their stories with confidence because of the differences in the language which they employ (1960).

The TAT has been shown to be useful with nursery-school children by Schafer and Leitch (1948), for somewhat older children by Sanford (1943), and for psychotic children by Leitch and Schafer (1947). Rautman and Brower (1945) have shown that stories written by third-to-sixth-grade children provide useful data. There is a variety of modifications of the principle of the TAT with specific reference to children. Horowitz and Murphy (1938) describe several of these. These modifications generally involve the selection of a new set of pictures and aim either at the general description of personality or the investigation of some specific facet of it. Balken and Vander Veer (1942, 1944) utilized a special set in the study of neurotic children. Their set consisted of 12 pictures chosen from a number of sources, including magazine illustrations, children's scrapbooks, and the TAT. Henry (1947) has reported a study of Hopi and Navaho children based on a special set of line drawings intended to reflect certain issues contained in the TAT.

*The Children's Apperception Test* (Bellak, 1954) consists of ten pictures, each consisting of animal figures only. The authors propose that children can identify themselves more easily with animals than persons. The scenes reflect common problems of childhood—feeding conflicts, sibling rivalry, toilet training, Oedipal problems. Published experience with this instrument has not been extensive to date. Profitable use has been made of the instrument in clinical settings, though at least two researches (Biersdorf and Marcuse, 1953; Light, 1953) suggest that the productivity is not greater in comparison with the TAT. An unpublished research of Budoff (1955) developed a set of pictures of humans paralleling each of the CAT pictures. In a study with normal children the human set produced more and more psychologically relevant material. Those children who were by other means judged less well adjusted appeared to be among those with whom the animal pictures of the CAT were more productive.

*The Michigan Picture Test* was developed by Hartwell, Hutt, Andrew and Walton (1951) and consists of 20 pictures, only one set of 12 having been published to date. They are aimed at grade-school children and are scenes, largely school-dominated, of events common to children of these ages.

The instrument is aimed principally at distinguishing well-adjusted from poorly adjusted children in school situations. Preliminary well-documented work by the authors suggests it is successful at that task. Subsequent work in process may demonstrate its usefulness beyond this area.

Other techniques closely related to the TAT are now available, although the work on them has been too limited to evaluate their usefulness with children.

*The Make-A-Picture-Story Test* of Shneidman (1948, 1949, 1952) has certain properties that might make adaptation of it very useful with children. The test consists of a number of background scenes presented individually to the subject along with a large number of movable human and animal figures from which the subject selects to put on the picture and about which

he then tells a story. The opportunity to select, reject, and manipulate the figures, and the attendant opportunity for process observation and interview, suggests the potential appropriateness to children.

van Lennep's *Four Picture Test* (1948, 1951) contains four-colored pictures representing two persons interacting, a group setting, and two pictures of a single person. The subject is to put these four in any order he chooses and tell a story incorporating them. Only one story is available, although the order of choice of pictures is an added variable.

*The Object Relations Test* of Phillipson (1955) consists of three series of four pictures and a blank card. The pictures represent a one-person, two-person, three-person, and a group situation. The series differ in respect to the reality content and context, each, however, being vague and ambiguous as to age and sex of persons. Details of the figures, in particular the faces, are omitted or are very indefinite. The set is administered in a fixed order, the blank card being given last. Phillipson stresses the development of a positive subject-examiner relation prior to administering—somewhat more than many examiners do. Beyond this precaution, the instructions of administration are highly similar to those proposed for the TAT. Phillipson's cards present an impression rather of the order of the shading portions of the Rorschach. Although they contain representations of human figures, they are, nonetheless, vague and abstract. Series A and B are in light and darker charcoal shading, respectively, whereas Series C is somewhat more lifelike, though still ambiguous. In C some color is introduced.

The logic of this set is bound to the psychology of object relations developed by various British psychoanalysts, notably Melanie Klein (1948) and W. R. D. Fairbairn (1952). The intention in the three series is to parallel an hypothesized development of object relations. Series A is designed "to stimulate primitive dependent needs and the consequent anxieties while the indefiniteness of the situation and the absence of other reality content will help to emphasize the subject's way of dealing with these early tension systems." Series B, somewhat more definite, in darker shading, is intended to stress fantasy about threatening and uncompromising objects. The darkness is seen as evoking expression of anxieties about the control of forces inside the self and in the outer world. Series C, still more lifelike, is seen as presenting a rich and varied environment. The lighter level of reality representation and the color is to intensify the threats and supports of the stimulus in terms of emotional involvement. The blank card is seen as a point of "maximal tension" and as an opportunity for the "dominant unconscious fantasy" to be expressed and the transference relation to the tester to be seen.

Although it remains to be seen how successful Phillipson has been in his intentions, it is apparent that the design of the cards parallels the British object-relations theory and that a basic definition of the latent implications of the stimuli are in these terms. The resulting stories, being plots as in most TAT stories, lend themselves to interpreta-tion in most any system, however. Phillipson's interpretation is, of course, along the lines of examining the variety and character of the object relations.

The test has been used fairly widely by Phillipson and his associates in clinical and other settings, but sufficient material has not yet been published to evaluate its use, especially with preadolescent subjects. However, the test is important, if only because of its systematic relationship to a specific theory of some elements of personality. The Blacky Pictures, it will be seen below, have been developed in the same spirit; they hold a similar relationship to classical psychosexual stage development as Phillipson's instrument to object relations theory.

Sets of pictures have also been successfully used, not as an alternative TAT, but with respect to some special interest. Horowitz (1939) used a set of children of different races to investigate racial attitudes. Amen (1941) used a special set of 15 pictures, with certain movable cut-out figures, in an investigation of the development of perceptual responses. Vernon (1940a,b) and Grotjahn (1941) have also studied perceptual processes in the reaction of children to pictures and the relation of these elements to personality.

A single card representing a group of four persons, a younger couple and an older couple, has been used by Neugarten and Gutmann (1958) to study age and sex grading in adults. This approach, bearing similarity to Horowitz's earlier study of social attitudes, has considerable promise for work with younger subjects. Hess (1959), using a modified TAT set and an administration procedure proposed by Henry and Guetzkow (1951) for studying interacting groups, has investigated the emotional climate and organization of family groups with adolescent children.

A somewhat more specific use of new pictures or a modified use of the TAT set has been used to investigate specific variables. These include study of achievement (McClelland, Atkinson, Clark, and Lowell, 1953), affiliation (Atkinson, Heyns, and Veroff, 1954), dominance (Veroff, 1957), group cohesiveness (Libo, 1953). Although used more with adults than children, this approach holds promise for the study of children.

*The Blacky Pictures* (Blum, 1949, 1950; Blum and Hunt, 1952) combine several of the principles of modification of the TAT principles suggested earlier. It is a set of 12 pictures. The pictures are of animals in cartoon style and purport to be various scenes in the life of a dog called Blacky. These scenes also deal with Mama, Papa, and Tippy, a sibling. The sex of both Blacky and Tippy is unspecified, permitting subjects to attribute either maleness or femaleness to either or both dogs. This cast of characters recurs throughout but in differing circumstances. Although the scenes are designed in part to reflect various childhood problems, more importance is to be placed in their design around certain psychological variables stemming from psychoanalytic theory of sexual development. This instrument thus combines the advantages of being designed to investigate certain specific variables while also providing data appropriate to broader,

more holistic interpretation. Moreover, its childlike facade appears not to limit its usefulness to that age group.

Each card is presented with a brief identification, e.g., "Here is Blacky with Mama," and the subject is asked to tell a story in the regular TAT style. A planned and often multiple-choice inquiry follows. Then choices of best- and least-liked cards are elicited. Analysis is in terms of the 11 psychoanalytic variables around which the test was designed. These include such variables as oral eroticism, Oedipal intensity, masturbation guilt, castration anxiety (penis envy), and positive identification. An additional modification (Blum, 1956) secures information on the tendency of subjects to employ various of the analytically defined mechanisms of defense.

*Dreams* are not generally considered a projective technique, presumably because they are entirely spontaneous products of a subject, are seldom under any control by an experimenter, and involve no specific stimulus materials. However, the end product, the dream, partakes of the most crucial of the qualities of a projective response, the reflection in an outward form of the inner preoccupations of the subject. The analysis of this end product has seldom been undertaken in a systematic way, though the problem presented differs little from that of analyzing a TAT or other forms of verbal productions, including thematic elements.

The biggest drawback to any planned use of dreams as a projective instrument is, of course, that the experimenter must wait for the subject to report his dreams rather than stimulate that production under circumstances convenient to the examiner. The subject can also readily alter or censor his dream in the reporting of it, though a comparable degree of censoring probably applies to most other projective performances. Dreams have been produced experimentally under hypnosis by several investigators (Fahrer and Fisher, 1943; Klein, 1930; Sweetland and Quay, 1952), but there is some question of the relation of such dreams to the dreams of regular sleep (Brenman, 1949; Kanzer, 1953) and of the applicability of this procedure to children. Unfortunately, not all persons dream, or at least many report that they do not.

Dreams have been considered most sensitive to the deepest and most intensely personal aspects of personality. As productions, they are entirely the product of the dreamer, uninfluenced, except in the reporting, by any set or preferences or suggestion of an examiner. Although certain transformations undoubtedly occur in reporting, such distortions at least stem principally from the dreamer himself. The background of the dream, and, in part, the mechanisms of transformation, may be studied by the traditional psychoanalytic technique of securing free associations to the dream. Some standardization of the conditions of reporting the dream may be arranged (Hall, 1956).

The intimate relation of the dream to the inner world of the subject recommends further study of the dream, and especially sequences of dreams, in spite of the various difficulties involved in systematizing the collection of them. The basic procedures of analysis might readily start from procedures now in use with other projective instruments. The resemblance of certain projective instruments to dreams has frequently been pointed out (Holt, 1951). The most extensive use of the dream has been in therapeutic settings, often through the technique of free association. The aim here has been related to some element of the therapy process. The basic logic for this process should lend itself to analysis in more diagnostic circumstances. This logic stems largely from Freud's *The Interpretation of Dreams* (1953). Relevant books on dream language by Guthiel (1939) and by Fromm (1951) would be useful. Hall's works (1953, 1956) relate dreams to more traditional psychological and research concerns.

## COMPLETION TECHNIQUES

The completion techniques require the subject to examine some situation devised by the experimenter and to respond to some stated question regarding the outcome or completion of that situation. The situation may be short, as with incomplete sentences, or it may be more elaborate, as with the cartoons of the Picture-Frustration Test and the semiplots of the Insight Test. In comparison with the construction techniques, the cues provided by the stimuli usually form a more integral part of the subject's response and thus limit to some extent the nature of the reply. In comparison with the association techniques, the stimulus is usually more defined and, excluding possibly the Rorschach, more complex.

*The Sentence-Completion Method.*
The sentence-completion technique is based upon the concept of the word association test. It differs importantly, however, in that the stimulus is normally longer and more complex, and the response required must result in a full sentence. A typical form of this test may contain 25 to 100 stems, and they may be very short (I . . . My mother . . .) or more elaborate and aimed at some more specifically defined situation (When the boss bawled him out, he . . .). The usual instruction asks for the completion of the stem in any way the subject chooses. Speed is not a crucial element, though subjects are usually requested to report fairly quickly whatever occurs to them without too much thought. Items may be phrased in the first person or the third person. Hanfmann and Getzels (1953) have demonstrated that the first-person format tends to encourage responses more related to conscious and manifest aspects of person, whereas the third person form taps less overt material.

Some forms of this instrument take on the character of a more standardized test to estimate some single variable. The Rotter Incomplete Sentences Blank (Rotter and Rafferty, 1950; Rotter and Willerman, 1947) is designed to top the variable of personal adjustment. The test includes 40 items and a fairly objective scoring system that demonstrates satisfactory scorer reliability and correlation with independent measures of the same variable. Other forms are designed to test an array of personal variables—attitude towards heterosexual relations, friends, superiors, school, fears, guilt feelings, abilities, and goals.

The Sacks Sentence Completion Test (Sacks and Levy, 1950) is of this order.

In general, this instrument is seen as providing information on attitudes, motives, and conflicts at a more conscious level rather than on the structure and organization of personality. One advantage of this fact is that a sentence-completion instrument may be designed by each investigator to study attitudes in a wide variety of contexts. One disadvantage of this very flexibility is, of course, that normative data tends to be limited, and each study must rely upon logics of internal consistency or the face validity of the items. It can readily be used with any subjects able to read and write, thought it can also be read to subjects and their verbal responses recorded.

Productive use of special groups of incomplete sentences has been made in a number of researches. Cameron (1938a,b) has studied both children and adults. His interest was not personality but rather the nature of language and thinking processes. Sanford et al. (1943), designed an instrument of 30 items, with the Murray need-press system as a guide in the design of stems, and used it with third- through eighth-grade school children. Rohde (1946) used the need-press system not for the original design of stems but for categorization of responses in a study of high-school children. She found the test valuable for personality analysis in these ages. The test has also had extensive use in a variety of clinical situations with adults (Rotter, 1951). Its application in the study of attitude structure and socialization has been shown by Getzels and Walsh (1958).

Summaries of work with this instrument are provided in chapters by Rotter (1951) and Bell (1948) and in a recent comprehensive book by Rhode (1957).

**Storytelling and Completion Methods.** Storytelling and completions represent a useful variation of the TAT and sentence-completion methods. Despert and Potter (1936) and Despert (1940) have used a story-telling method. They report on the retelling of such stories as The Big Bad Wolf and Goldilocks by children 4 to 14. In addition, they asked these children to make up stories on topics given by the experimenter. Wright (1941, 1945) in a more formal circumstance used stories and other methods to evaluate the effect of moral conflict upon children. She also used toys and at one stage asked the children to make up stories about the toys. Another variant of the story method is seen in the work of Haggard (1942). This form was based on comic-strip characters. Children chose their favorite characters, told what was happening in the newspaper version of these comic strips, and then created their own plot around these characters.

Various other efforts in this direction utilize the completion aspect more centrally. The Story Elaboration Test of Murray (1937, 1938), used with college students, consists of 32 different dramatic situations. Each is to be developed by the subject into a full plot. Zucker (1943) studied the emotional attachment of children to their parents by the use of a story-completion method. He presented stories essentially complete, except for the ending, and asked his subject to state the outcome. A multiple-choice format has also been developed by Kelly and Bishop (1942) and by Roody (1943).

Sargent's *Insight Test* (1944, 1955) and its adaptation for children by Engel, the *Children's Insight Test* (1958) represent a very useful combination of the advantages of the paper-and-pencil-test format and some principles of the projective tests. The two tests present a series of armatures describing in skeletal form several plot situations to which the subject is to respond by answering the questions: 1. What did the person described in the armature do? 2. How did he feel? The following is a typical armature from the Children's Insight Test: A boy came home from school and found his dog had run away. What did he do? How did he feel? Other armatures deal with the child's mode of problem solving in relation to his parents, unrelated adults, other children, school failure, loss of love object, distance, time, and illness. A boy's and a girl's form, of 13 items each, are available. The test is appropriate for children between 6 and 10.

A system of scoring and analysis has been worked out, which focuses upon various elements of the expression of affect, defensiveness against affect, and thought processes indicative of maladjustment.

*The Picture-Frustration Study* of Rosenzweig (1945) provides a series of cartoon situations, each dealing with some kind of frustrating circumstance. The subject is asked to provide a verbal response for the person who has been frustrated. The cue to the frustrating circumstance is contained in a statement made by one of the persons and is illustrated by the cartoon. A children's form (Rosenzweig, Fleming, and Rosenzweig, 1948), as well as an adult form, is available, as is a modification aimed at attitudes toward minority group members (Brown, 1947; Sommer, 1954).

The focus in analysis is upon the direction of the verbal response—extrapunitive, intrapunitive, impunitive—and upon the mode of response—obstacle dominant, ego defensive, need persistent. Combinations of scores indicate the tendency of the subject to employ various of these manners of response. They are also an indication of how common this response pattern is. Scoring is aided by sample responses and by various norms (Rosenzweig et al., 1948; Rosenzweig, Fleming, and Clark, 1947).

The P-F Study has been used fairly widely in research and in clinical situations (Lindzey and Goldwyn, 1954; Mirmow, 1952). The data of the P-F are limited to the specific variables used by Rosenzweig and would appear to reflect more generally the manifest and overt levels of behavior than they do deeper levels. At the same time these variables are clearly defined and well measured by this instrument. The theoretical conception of frustration used is stated in Rosenzweig's volume *Psychodiagnosis* (Rosenzweig, 1949).

## EXPRESSIVE TECHNIQUES

The expressive techniques are those that tend to combine diagnostic and therapeutic features. Although not all of the expressive techniques dealt with here need be utilized therapeutically, most of them are so employed by some

investigators. They present to the subject a flexible, plastic material or situation to which he is to respond by incorporating the stimuli into some kind of personal, novel production. Unlike the construction techniques, the production is often not exclusively verbal, and the process of producing the end result is frequently as important as the final production. When the process is of central importance and the investigator places stress upon it, the technique has a greater tendency to be used therapeutically.

***Play Techniques.*** The contemporary uses of various forms of play techniques for personality research are the derivative of some of their uses in the therapeutic realm. Freud's report of Little Hans (Freud, 1925) and the child analysis through play reported by Hug-Hellmuth (1921) represent the beginnings in this area. Since those days, the work of Anna Freud (1928) and of Melanie Klein (1932) has considerably extended this therapeutic use. Reviews of the therapeutic work with play may be found in Kanner (1940), Rogerson (1939), Bell (1948), and Solomon (1951). The use of play in therapy with modifications of technique and a different theoretical background are represented in the work of Taft (1933), Allen (1942), and Lowenfeld (1935, 1938). A bridge to the investigation of specific personality elements occurs in such normative studies as those of Bonham and Sargent (1928), Horne and Philleo (1942), in the use of play to study social adjustment of children, as in Anderson (1937), Issacs (1933), and Wright (1942). Erikson, in addition to his classic monographs (1937, 1940) on the interpretation of play constructions has extended this descriptive and normative concern in his studies of the Sioux (1939) and the Yurok (1938), as has Roheim (1941, 1943) in his explorations of the Normanby Islanders and Henry and Henry (1944) in their study in Pilaga.

These studies and others make it amply clear that the play methods have great usefulness in the diagnosis and measurement of personality attributes. The work of Levy (1933, 1936, 1937) has been instrumental in showing the potentialities of play in a relatively standardized way for the study of specific elements of personality—hostility and sibling rivalry. The work of Sears and his associates (Phillips, 1945; Pintler, 1945; Sears, 1947; Sears, Whiting, Nowlis, and Sears, 1953) has advanced the uses of this instrument by study of various issues of technique and the experimental study of such variables as aggression and dependency.

The materials of the play techniques vary with the investigator but normally include an array of objects that the subject is to use, play with as he chooses, or arrange in accordance with some instructions. In some instances, the objects are quite varied and numerous. The *Miniature Life Toys* of Lois Murphy (1956), for example, include the following:

. . . dolls, which might be representative of family members, furniture for the main areas of home activity; planes, trains, cars, boots, animals, and soldiers for activity outside of home; farm animals and a fence; wild animals; cowboys, Indians, soldiers; and Lincoln blocks and larger blocks, which can be adapted for any purpose. The material is of different colors. There are some broken pieces, some obviously old, some new in each box.

The instructions and testing circumstances are very unstructured and emphasize the child's freedom to play with the toys in any manner he chooses. The examiner records verbalization and play sequences, interfering very little beyond maintaining some involvement by following conversational cues provided by the child.

The *World Test* is not dissimilar in nature and use. Developed initially by Lowenfeld (1939), its use and diagnostic relevance are described by Buhler and Kelly (1941) and by Bolgar and Fischer (1947).

More structured forms, generally including fewer toys related directly to more limited objectives, are those of Sears and Levy referred to above and others made by Lynn (Lynn, 1955, 1957; Lynn and Lynn, 1959). Despert (1937), in a more clinical setting, has also introduced a specific element of structure in a different way. Entrusting a child with a sharp knife and the instruction to scrape cardboard, Despert notes a useful method of encouraging latent aggression trends. The shavings were then mixed with glue and various forms were modeled. Although Despert's method has a strong therapeutic intent, it illustrates an early approach to the use of play circumstances for the study of specific psychological elements.

A related series of play situations with more limited goals than those of the Miniature Life Toys or the World Test include tests developed for research use by Murphy, Lerner, Stone, and others (Murphy, 1956). These cover a wide range of test situations related to the study of various personality attributes. Some are aimed at the expression of latent feelings and are comparatively limited in nature. These are the *Sensory Toys* and the *Dough* and *Cold Cream Situations*, involving exploration of sensory and tactile modalities. Various active play methods involve the presentation of specific situations aimed at the study of aggression and frustration. Group techniques are an interesting modification, since they are used with small groups of children and partake of psychodrama elements. They include semistructured situations in which children participate under adult guidance in a *Potential Leadership Game*, an *Imposed Leadership Game*, and a *Family Game*. Each of these methods is presented in fuller detail in Murphy (1956). Bell (1948) and Woltman (1952) also provide general discussions of these methods and of work with them.

## DRAWING AND PAINTING

Drawing and painting are two modes of securing projective data that lend themselves readily to the study of children. Developments in this field might be said to have had three general sources. One is undoubtedly the interpretation of the free drawings and other art products in the psychiatric study of disturbed children. The reports of Bender (1937), Bender and Rapaport (1944), Bender and Woltmann (1937), and Despert (1938) illustrate the use of drawing in the clinical setting. Montague (1951) presents a discussion of the use of such drawings in the

psychoanalytic study of schizophrenic children. The second approach is that normally called the study of expressive movement and includes drawing among a variety of other expressive personal movements. Here the work of Wolff and Precker (1951) and of Harms (1946) is noteworthy. The well-illustrated volumes of Alschuler and Hattwick (1947) provide excellent documentation of the nature and variety of children's drawings and paintings. The third approach to drawing has stemmed from its early use as a measure of intelligence. The work of Goodenough (1926) called attention to drawing as an indicator of cognitive development in children as well as to the various features of these drawings that appeared to relate more to personality variables than to cognition.

Out of these combined beginnings has come several contemporary uses of both drawing and painting as projective devices. One of the best known is the technique described by Machover (1948, 1951). In her usage, the subject is asked to draw a person and, after this has been drawn, to draw a person of the opposite sex. Standard equipment is used each time, and any verbal comments or unusual approaches to the task are recorded. A closely related form is that of Buck (1948a,b, 1949), who asks for a drawing of a house, a tree, and a person. Buck has proposed a series of hypotheses related to the areas of personality sampled by his method. These include intelligence, interpersonal relations, family relations, major personality needs, affect state, and psychosexual stage. Although many of these require experimentation, the procedure has been thoughtfully developed and holds promise.

Painting is highly similar to drawing and was brought to public attention in the form of finger painting by Ruth Shaw (1934). Elkisch (1945) and particularly Napoli (1946, 1947, 1951) have developed this procedure as a projective technique.

In both the Machover draw-a-person approach and the Napoli development of fingerpainting the interpretive rules stem from attributing various meanings in personality terms to the end product and to the behavior of the subject during the process. In the Machover format such elements as the following are seen as crucial: thickness and thinness of line, location of drawing on the page, size of drawing, symmetry, and content. In addition, various sectors of the figures are seen as conveying data regarding particular personality areas. Thus the head and facial features are seen as expressive of social needs and responsiveness as well as a reflection of intellectual ambitions and the extent of drive for a rational control of impulse. Within these head features further subdivision also occurs. The hair, for example, is seen as having sexual symbolic meaning, as has the nose. The interpretive process involves the application of general clinical logic to the various modes of response and the gradual building up of a personality portrait.

In the finger-painting format particular attention is given to the process of creating the final product. Thus the administrator must be sensitive to such factors as the way in which the hands are used, the kinds of motions—smear-ing, scrubbing, patting, scribbling—rhythm, order, and other related elements. More than one painting is generally desired, and interrelations within a series are important. Interpretation is made within the three basic areas of data, the performance observation, the painting itself, and the verbalizations. Principles of analysis are not dissimilar to those of Machover, though they are aided by various empirical studies. A distinctive feature of finger painting is color, which is given special significance beyond its role in the analysis of other parts of the total production. Thus blue is found to be a color dominantly used by males and is thought to reflect masculinity, security, drive, sincerity. Extreme amounts suggest sadism, violence. Black with blue in a male indicates despondency. Green indicates a controlled but highly developed emotionality and reflects a creative potential.

An extensive summary of these empirical rules and their personality correlates is provided in Bell (1948). Anastasi and Foley (1940, 1941a,b,c) have summarized a great deal of the literature on art production in the abnormal. Swensen (1957) provides a summary of experiments designed to test certain of the interpretive procedures of the drawings of the human figure.

## PSYCHODRAMA AND ROLE PLAYING

The psychodrama is the unique contribution of J. L. Moreno to what Haas and Moreno (1951) call the "action" approach to the study of human interrelations. Some of the basic ideas of the psychodrama are presented in Moreno (1946).

The psychodrama requires the individual to act out, by himself or with others, some kind of human drama or personality relevant situation. It has been used in various forms in industrial-training situations, in survey research, in studies of military adjustment, and in the study and treatment of a wide variety of personal maladjustments. These have included studies of the behavior disorders of children (Greenhill, 1945; Horwitz, 1945; Shoobs, 1944; Sullivan, 1945) and a proposal regarding its use in the social psychological study of the family by Foote and Cottrell (1955). Del Torto and Cornyetz (1944) have developed a series of nine psychodramatic test situations, which they see as a projective instrument to provide data on the subject's social interactions.

Although this method has been used less frequently in the study of personality attributes, it appears to hold considerable potentiality if brought into context of more limited personality variables. The Activity and Situation Tests and Leadership Games of Murphy (1956) have elements closely related to psychodrama methods, adapted to the study of more specific attributes in children.

## EXPRESSIVE MOVEMENTS

The realm of phenomena usually called expressive movements is closely intertwined with the study of personality and the projective techniques. This area is, however, more a field of study of certain elements of behavior and their unconscious correlates than a projective technique. Certain expressive movements are, of course, involved in some projective techniques. In this sense, certain of the procedures for analysis of play and painting, of the sensory toys of Murphy, and of the movements of acting out in psychodrama concern themselves with expressive movements. One area of expressive movement, handwriting, may in some senses be considered a projective technique.

The distinction made by Bellak (1944) and utilized by Wolff and Precker (1951) calls attention to three aspects of behavior. There is that behavior that is *adaptive* and involves centrally realistic adjustment or response to tasks demanded of us. Although certain responses may be inappropriate, hence maladaptive, the focus is still upon the effort to make a realistic adjustment to some external world stimulus. Certain behavior is *projective* and concerns behavior in which one ascribes or reveals one's own wishes and needs without necessary conscious awareness of doing so. This is, of course, one of the crucial features of the behavior elicited by a projective technique. Certain behavior is *expressive* and involves one's style of response. The emphasis in the expressive element of behavior is upon the individual manner of approaching a task and may apply to behavior that is also adaptive and/or projective. Thus the field of finger painting involves certain body movements, ways of making line and figures, and a similar style of making the resulting painting. In this sense, expressive behavior is not the centrally projective element, but study of those aspects of the total painting process will aid in the analysis of that projective medium.

Studies of expressive movement include such areas as motor behavior—characteristic movements or bodily postures—handwriting, facial expressions, proportion and sizes involved in drawings and doodles, voice qualities, speech attributes, and various others. Many of these movement attributes are assumed to have some characteristic individual consistency, hence to bear upon the study of personality. As such, they bear more relevance to those projective behaviors that include bodily gestures or movement than upon those that emphasize verbal response or some resulting finished product.

Additional material on studies of expressive movements and the ways in which they may be utilized in the analysis of certain projective techniques may be found in Wolff and Precker (1951), in Wolff (1946), and in Bell (1948). Material dealing directly with handwriting analysis may be found in a chapter by Wolfson (1951) and in Bell (1948).

## Choice or Ordering Techniques

The choice techniques present the subject with a set of stimuli, which he is asked to place in a certain order or among which he is to indicate preference. In the two methods briefly discussed here, the Szondi and the Picture Arrangement Test, the stimuli are pictures.

## THE SZONDI TEST

The Szondi test presents 48 photographs of adult psychiatric patients drawn from eight diagnostic groupings. The pictures are shown to the subject in sets of eight, each set containing a picture from each of the diagnostic groups. In each set the subject is to select the two he likes the best and the two he likes the least. Upon reviewing all sets in this fashion, he is asked to select again from those he indicated as "liked" the four he likes the most and similarly the least liked. Susan Deri (1949) reports that the results are not meaningful unless the test is administered in this fashion at least six different times.

The pattern of choices is then arrayed by each of the diagnostic factors represented by the pictures, indicating the number of likes and dislikes for each factor. Interpretation is based upon the logic that the choices, positive or negative, for a given factor reflect the psychic state of the subject with respect to the factor. The factors reflect the diagnostic groups and include a sexual-vector, reflecting homosexual and sadistic factors, a paroxysmal-vector, reflecting epileptic and hysterical factors, a contact-vector, reflecting depressive and manic factors, and a self-vector, including catatonic and paranoid factors.

In introducing this text, Dr. Szondi, a Hungarian psychiatrist, also presented a fairly elaborate background theory regarding the effect of recessive genes upon behavior. This theory has never been taken seriously in this country.

In any event, it is not crucial to the interpretation of the instrument. Interpretation is also largely restricted to the Szondi factors; hence it has limited utility beyond this frame of reference.

Because of its limited use with children, further information is not given here. The test, however, has been used quite often with adult clinical groups and should not be underestimated in that circumstance. Further material may be found in Deri's book (1949), in a chapter by Rabin (1951b), and in a review of the Szondi literature by Borstelman and Klopfer (1953) and by David (1954). These references include the uses with children and adolescents reported up to 1954. In addition Deri reports on the use with delinquents (Deri, 1954) and Fancher and Weinstein (1956), on the responses of 7-year-olds.

## THE PICTURE-ARRANGEMENT TEST

This instrument consists of 25 cartoonlike pictures depicting the same figure in three different but related activities. The subject is to indicate the order in which these activities took place and to describe what is going on in each picture with a sentence. The sentence may be interpreted clinically, though comparatively little work has been reported on this part of the response data. The central effort has gone into development of objective methods of describing the arrangement of the pictures chosen by the subjects. A representative normal sample of 1500 provides the base for describing the frequency of occurrence of various arrangements. Each of the patterns of arrangements found may be seen potentially as an indication of some specific personality issue. Easy to administer and to score, this instrument combines projective and objective features and holds promise for future development with children. In the major presentation of this work by Tomkins and Miner (1957) norms, as well as rationale and interpretive suggestions, are provided, which include some limited normative material on children.

## Summary

The projective techniques have been used principally within the framework of interest in the study of individuality. Whether case by case in a clinical setting or by larger numbers of cases representing some group of special interest, the utility of the projective method has been its sensitivity to idiosyncratic features of personality.

At the same time, other uses of the data of the projective instruments have arisen, which concern themselves with the exploration of specific variables of personality. Here the stress is not upon the full range of inferences derivable by skilled clinical study of the projective protocol. It is, rather, upon the contribution that limited and previously defined elements of the projective response can make to the study of a specific variable.

Work with the projective instruments in the future will undoubtedly follow both of these productive routes. In the first instance, the framework of individuality, the problems will continue to be those of the systematization of interpretative procedures, the study of the constructs in terms of which interpretations are made, and the analysis of the circumstances of use and interpretation under which the validity of inferences may be maximized. In the second instance, the framework of specific variables, the central problem, in addition to those above that the two approaches share, stems from the isolation of the variables studied from their context of other personality variables.

Considerable inventiveness has been exercised, and is still possible, in the development of new projective instruments or in novel ways of employing more familiar ones. The more successful ventures, with such new instruments or novel methods of analysis, appear to be those wherein the choice of instrument and of its mode of analysis has been closely considered in terms of the personality variables it was desired to study. This implies, in part, that the choice of a presently available instrument should be made by prior study of its potentialities of revealing the desired data under the circumstances of subject and setting proposed. The various approaches to the examination of specific variables also suggest that we need not presume that the concepts of analysis originally attributed to the instrument are necessarily the only terms in which it can be properly analyzed. New terms of analysis, however, more easily applied to some techniques than to others, require the same scrutiny being given increasingly to the more traditional systems of analysis. Entirely new methods, regardless of the objectives of their

analysis, should be devised principally with regard to their relevance to some body of theory or some personality constructs possible of definition and study. This does not mean that new techniques should not be devised. It implies only that their value in the field will lie less in the inventiveness of their stimulus qualities than in their demonstrable usefulness in the study of personality concepts.

# REFERENCES

Abt, L. E. 1950. A theory of projective psychology. In L. E. Abt and L. Bellak (Eds.), *Projective psychology: clinical approaches to the total personality*. New York: Knopf. Pp. 33–68.

Allen, F. H. 1942. *Psychotherapy with children*. New York: Norton.

Alschuler, R. H., and L. W. Hattwick. 1947. *Painting and personality, a study of young children*. Chicago: Univer. Chicago Press. 2 vols.

Amen, E. W. 1941. Individual differences in apperceptive reaction: a study of response of pre-school children to pictures. *Genet. Psychol. Monogr.*, 23, 319–385.

Anastasi, Anne, and J. P. Foley, Jr. 1940. A survey of the literature on artistic behavior in the abnormal. III. Spontaneous production. *Psychol. Monogr.*, 52, 71.

———. 1941a. A survey of the literature on artistic production in the abnormal. II. Approaches and interrelationships. *Ann. N. Y. Acad. Sci.*, 42, 166.

———. 1941b. A survey of the literature on artistic behavior in the abnormal. I. Historical and theoretical background. *J. gen. Psychol.*, 25, 111–132.

———. 1941c. A survey of the literature on artistic behavior in the abnormal. IV. Experimental investigation. *J. gen. Psychol.*, 25, 187–237.

Anderson, H. H. 1937. Domination and integration in the social behavior of young children. *Genet. Psychol. Monogr.*, 19, 342–408.

Anthony, S. 1943. Study of personality and adjustment as diagnosed by a test of word association. *Charact. & Pers.*, 12, 15–31.

Aron, Betty. 1949. *A manual for analysis of the thematic apperception test.* Berkeley: Berg.

Atkinson, J. W., R. W. Heyns, and J. Veroff. 1954. The effect of experimental arousal of the affiliation motive on thematic apperception. *J. abnorm. soc. Psychol.*, 49, 405–410.

Auld, F. 1954. Contributions of behavior theory to projective techniques. *J. proj. Tech.*, 18, 421–426.

Balken, Eva R., and A. H. Vander Veer. 1942. The clinical application of a test of imagination to neurotic children. *Amer. J. Orthopsychiat.*, 12, 68–80.

———. 1944. Clinical application of the thematic apperception test to neurotic children. *Amer. J. Orthopsychiat.*, 14, 421–40.

Beck, S. J. 1944. *Rorschach's test.* Vol. I. Basic Processes. New York: Grune & Stratton.

———. 1945. *Rorschach's test.* Vol. II. A variety of personality pictures. New York: Grune & Stratton.

———. 1951. The Rorschach test: a multi-dimensional test of personality. In H. H. and Gladys L. Anderson (Eds.), *An Introduction to projective techniques.* New York: Prentice-Hall. Pp. 101–122.

———. 1952. *Rorschach's test.* Vol. III. Advances in interpretation. New York: Grune & Stratton.

Bell, J. E. 1948. *Projective techniques.* New York: Longmans, Green.

Bellak, L. 1944. The concept of projection. *Psychiat.*, 7, 353–370.

———. 1947. *A guide to the interpretation of the thematic apperception test.* New York: The Psychological Corporation.

———. 1954. *The thematic apperception test and the children's apperception test in clinical use.* New York: Grune & Stratton.

Bender, L. 1937. Art and therapy on the mental disturbances of children. *J. nerv. ment. Dis.*, 86, 249–263.

———, and J. Rapaport. 1944. Animal drawings of children. *Amer. J. Orthopsychiat.*, 14, 521–527.

Bender, L., and A. G. Woltmann. 1937. The use of plastic material as a psychiatric approach to the emotional problems of children. *Amer. J. Orthopsychiat.*, 7, 283–300.

Biersdorf, K. R., and F. L. Marcuse. 1953. Responses of children to human and animal pictures. *J. proj. Tech.*, 17, 455–459.

Blum, G. S. 1949. A study of the psychoanalytic theory of psychosexual development. *Genet. Psychol. Monogr.*, 39, 3–99.

———. 1950. *The Blacky pictures: Manual of instructions.* New York: The Psychological Corporation.

———. 1956. Defense preferences in four countries. *J. proj. Tech.*, 20, 33–41.

———, and H. F. Hunt. 1952. The validity of the Blacky Pictures. *Psychol. Bull.*, 49, 238–250.

Bolgar, Hedda, and L. K. Fischer. 1947. Personality projection in the world test. *Amer. J. Orthopsychiat.*, 17, 117–128.

Bonham, M. A., and M. K. Sargent. 1928. The behavior of human infants twenty-four and thirty months of age. Master's thesis. Washington, D. C.: Library of the Catholic Univ. Amer.

Borstelmann, L. J., and W. G. Klopfer. 1953. The Szondi test: A review and critical evaluation. *Psychol. Bull.*, 50, 112–132.

Brenman, Margaret. 1949. Dreams and Hypnosis. *Psychoanal. Quart.*, 18, 455–465.

Brown, J. F. 1947. A modification of the Rosenzweig picture frustration test to study hostile interracial attitudes. *J. Psychol.*, 24, 247–272.

Bruner, J. S. 1948. IV. Perceptual theory with the Rorschach test. *J. Pers.*, 17, 157–168.

Buck, J. N. 1948a. The H-T-P test. *J. clin. Psychol.*, 4, 151–159.

———. 1948b. The H-T-P technique: a qualitative and quantitative scoring manual. Part I. *J. clin. Psychol.*, 4, 151–159.

———. 1949. The H-T-P technique: a qualitative and quantitative scoring manual. Part II. *J. clin. Psychol.*, 5, 37–76.

Budoff, M. 1955. An investigation of the relative usefulness of animals and persons in a picture-story test for children. Unpublished Master's thesis, Committee on Human Development, Univer. Chicago.

Buhler, Charlotte, and G. Kelly. 1941. *The world test: A measurement of emotional disturbances.* New York: The Psychological Corporation.

Cameron, N. 1938a. A study of thinking in senile deterioration and schizophrenic disorganization. *Amer. J. Psychol.,* **51,** 650–664.

———. 1938b. Reasoning, regression, and communication in schizophrenia. *Psychol. Monogr.,* **50,** 1–34.

Campbell, D. T. 1950. The indirect assessment of social attitudes. *Psychol. Bull.,* **47,** 15–38.

———. 1957. A typology of tests, projective and otherwise. *J. consult. Psychol.,* **21,** 207–210.

Cattell, R. B. 1951. Principles of design in projective or misperception tests of personality. In H. H. and Gladys L. Anderson (Eds.), *An introduction to projective techniques.* New York: Prentice-Hall. Pp. 55–100.

David, H. P. 1954. A Szondi test bibliography, 1939–1953. *J. proj. Tech.,* **18,** 17–32.

Davids, A., and H. A. Murray. 1955. Preliminary appraisal of an auditory projective technique for studying personality and cognition. *Amer. J. Orthopsychiat.,* **25,** 543–554.

Del Torto, J., and P. Cornyetz. 1944. Psychodrama as expressive and projective technique. *Sociometry,* **7,** 356–75.

Deri, Susan. 1949. *Introduction to the Szondi test: Theory and practice.* New York: Grune & Stratton.

———. 1954. Differential diagnosis of delinquents with Szondi tests. *J. proj. Tech.,* **18,** 33–41.

Despert, J. L. 1937. Technical approaches used in the study and treatment of emotional problems in children. Part II. Using a knife under certain definite conditions. *Psychiat. Quart.,* **11,** 111–30.

———. 1938. *Emotional problems in children.* New York: N. Y. State Hospital Press.

———. 1940. A comparative study of thinking in schizophrenic children and in children of pre-school age. *Amer. J. Psychiat.,* **97,** 189–213.

———, and H. W. Potter. 1936. Technical approaches used in the study and treatment of emotional problems in children. I. The story, a form of directed phantasy. *Psychiat. Quart.,* **10,** 619–638.

Elkisch, Paula. 1945. Children's drawings in a projective technique. *Psychol. Monogr.,* **58,** No. 1.

Engel, Mary. 1958. The development and applications of the children's insight test. *J. proj. Tech.,* **22,** No. 1.

Eriksen, C. W. 1951. Some implications of TAT interpretation arising from need and perception experiments. *J. Pers.,* **19,** 282–288.

———. 1954. Needs in perception and projective techniques. *J. proj. Tech.,* **18,** 435–440.

———, and R. S. Lazarus. 1952. Perceptual defense and projective tests. *J. abnorm. soc. Psychol.,* **47,** 302–308.

Erikson, E. H. 1937. Configuration in play. Clinical notes. *Psychoanal. Quart.,* **6,** 135–214.

———. 1938. Observations on the Yurok: World map and childhood tradition. *Univer. Calif. Amer. Archeol. Anthrop.,* **35,** No. 10.

———. 1939. Observations in Sioux education. *J. Psychol.,* **7,** 101–156.

———. 1940. Studies in the interpretation of play. Clinical observations of play disruption in young children. *Genet. Psychol. Monogr.,* **22,** 557–671.

Fahrer, L. H., and C. Fisher. 1943. An experimental approach to dream psychology through the use of hypnosis. *Psychoanal. Quart.,* **12.**

Fairbairn, W. R. D. 1952. *Psycho-analytic studies of personality.* London: Tavistock Publications.

Fancher, E. C., and M. A. Weinstein. 1956. A Szondi study of developmental and cultural factors in personality: The 7-year old. *J. Genet. Psychol.,* **88,** 81–88.

Fine, R. 1955. A scoring scheme and manual for the TAT and other verbal projective techniques. *J. proj. Tech.,* **19,** 306–316.

Foote, N. N., and L. S. Cottrell. 1955. *Identity and interpersonal competence.* Chicago: Univer. Chicago Press.

Frank, L. K. 1939. Projective methods for the study of personality. *J. Psychol.,* **8,** 389–413.

Freud, Anna. 1928. Introduction to the technic of child analysis. *Nerv. ment. Dis. Monogr.* No. 48.

———. 1925. *Collected papers.* London: Hogarth Press. Vol. III, 194–195.

———. 1953. The interpretation of dreams.

In S. Freud, *The standard edition of the complete psychological works.* London: Hogarth, (Oxford pub. 1900). Vols. IV and V.

Fromm, E. 1951. *The forgotten language.* New York: Rinehart.

Fry, F. D. 1953. Manual for scoring the thematic apperception test. *J. Psychol.,* **35,** 181–195.

Getzels, J. W., and J. J. Walsh. 1958. The methods of paired direct and projective questionnaires in the study of attitude structure and socialization. *Psychol. Monogr.,* **72,** 1–34.

Goodenough, Florence L. 1926. *Measurement of intelligence by drawings.* Yonkers: World Book.

Goss, A. E., and Marjorie H. Brownell. 1957. Stimulus-response concepts and principles applied to projective test behavior. *J. Pers.,* **25,** 505–523.

Greenhill, M. 1925. Psycho-dramatic play therapy in disorders of children. *Proc. Inst. Child Res. Clin. Woods Schs.,* **12,** 107–122.

Grotjahn, M. 1941. A child talks about pictures: Observations about the integration of fantasy with the process of thinking. *Psychoanal. quart.,* **10,** 385–394.

Guthiel, E. A. 1939. *The language of the dream.* New York: Macmillan.

Haas, R. B., J. L. Moreno. 1951. Psychodrama as a projective technique. In H. H. and Gladys L. Anderson (Eds.), *An introduction to projective techniques.* New York: Prentice-Hall. Pp. 662–675.

Haggard, E. A. 1942. A projective technique using comic strip characters. *Charact. & Pers.,* **10,** 289–295.

Hall, C. S. 1953. *The meaning of dreams.* New York: Harper.

———. 1956. Current trends in research on dreams. In D. Brower and L. E. Abt (Eds.), *Progress in clinical psychology,* Vol. II. New York: Grune & Stratton. Pp. 239–257.

Hanfmann, Eugenia, and J. W. Getzels. 1953. Studies of the sentence completion test. *J. proj. Tech.,* **17,** 280–294.

Harms, E. 1946. The psychology of formal creativeness. I. Six fundamental types of formal expression. *J. genet. Psychol.,* **69,** 97–120.

Hartoch, Anna. 1956. The child's reaction to the Rorschach situation. In Lois B. Murphy, *Personality in young children.* I. Methods for the study of personality in young children. New York: Basic Books. Pp. 153–180.

Hartwell, S. W., M. L. Hutt, G. Andrew, and R. E. Walton. 1951. The Michigan picture test. Diagnostic and therapeutic possibilities of a new projective test for children. *Amer. J. Orthopsychiat.,* **21,** 124–137.

Henry, Jules, and Zunia Henry. 1944. The doll play of Pilaga Indian children. *Amer. J. Orthopsychiat. Res. Monogr.* No. 4.

Henry, W. E. 1947. The thematic apperception technique in the study of culture-personality relations. *Genet. Psychol. Monogr.,* **35,** 3–135.

———. 1956. *The analysis of fantasy.* New York: Wiley.

———, and H. Guetzkow. 1951. Group projective sketches for the study of small groups. *J. soc. Psychol.,* **33,** 77–102.

Hess, R. D., and G. Handel. 1959. *Family worlds.* Chicago: Univer. Chicago Press.

Holt, R. R. 1951. The thematic apperception test. In H. H. and Gladys L. Anderson (Eds.), *An introduction to projective techniques.* New York: Prentice-Hall. Pp. 181–229.

———. 1954. Implications of some contemporary personality theories of Rorschach rationale. In B. Klopfer, M. D. Ainsworth, W. G. Klopfer, and R. R. Holt, *Developments in the Rorschach technique.* Vol. I. Technique and theory. Yonkers: World Book. Pp. 501–560.

Horne, B. M., and C. C. Philleo. 1942. A normative study of the spontaneous play activities of normal and mentally defective children. *J. genet. Psychol.,* **61,** 33–46.

Horowitz, Ruth E. 1939. Racial aspects of self-identification in nursery school children. *J. Psychol.,* **7,** 91–99.

———, and Lois B. Murphy. 1938. Projective methods in the psychological study of children. *J. exp. Educ.,* **7,** 133–140.

Horwitz, S. 1945. The spontaneous drama as a technic in group therapy. *Nerv. Child.,* **4,** 252–273.

Hug-Hellmuth, H. von. 1921. On the techniques of child analysis. *Int. J. Psycho-Anal.,* **2,** 294–295.

Issacs, S. 1933. *Social development in young children*. London: Routledge.

Kagan, J. 1956. The measurement of overt aggression from fantasy. *J. abnorm. soc. Psychol.*, 52, 390–393.

Kanner, L. 1940. Play investigation and play treatment of children's behavior disorders. *J. Pediat.*, 17, 533–546.

Kanzer, M. 1953. The metapsychology of the hypnotic dream. *Int. J. Psycho-Anal.*, 34, 228–231.

Kelly, G. A., and F. Bishop. 1942. A projective method of personality investigation. *Psychol. Bull.*, 39, 599. (abstract)

Kent, Grace, and A. J. Rosanoff. 1910. A study in association in insanity. *Amer. J. Insan.*, 67, 37–96.

Klein, D. B. 1930. Experimental production of dreams during hypnosis. *Univer. Texas Bull.* No. 3009.

Klein, Melanie. 1932. *The psychoanalysis of children*. London: Hogarth.

———. 1948. *Contributions to psycho-analysis, 1921–1945*. London: Hogarth.

Klopfer, B. 1954. Rorschach hypotheses and ego psychology. In B. Klopfer, M. D. Ainsworth, W. G. Klopfer, and R. R. Holt, *Developments in the Rorschach technique.* Vol. I. Technique and theory. Yonkers: World Book. Pp. 561–598.

———. 1956. *Developments in the Rorschach technique.* Vol. II. Fields of application. Yonkers, N. Y.: World Book.

———, and D. M. Kelley. 1942. *The Rorschach technique.* Yonkers, N. Y.: World Book.

Klopfer, B., Mary D. Ainsworth, W. G. Klopfer, and R. R. Holt. 1954. *Developments in the Rorschach Technique.* Vol. I. Technique and theory. Yonkers, N. Y.: World Book.

Ledwith, Nettie. 1959. *Rorschach responses of elementary school children.* Pittsburgh: Univer. Pittsburgh Press.

Leitch, Mary, and Sarah Schafer. 1947. A study of the thematic apperception tests of psychotic children. *Amer. J. Orthopsychiat.*, 17, 337–342.

Lennep, D. J. van. 1948. *Four-pictures test.* The Hague: Martinus Nijhoff.

———. 1951. The four-picture test. In H. H. and Gladys L. Anderson (Eds.), *An introduction to projective techniques.* New York: Prentice-Hall. Pp. 149–180.

Levy, D. M. 1933. Use of play technique as experimental procedure. *Amer. J. Orthopsychiat.*, 3, 266–277.

———. 1936. Hostility patterns in sibling rivalry experiments. *Amer. J. Orthopsychiat.*, 6, 183–257.

———. 1937. Studies in sibling rivalry. *Res. Memo. Amer. Orthopsychiat. Ass.* No. 2.

Libo, L. M. 1953. Measuring group cohesiveness. Ann Arbor: Inst. Soc. Res., Univer. Michigan.

Light, B. 1953. A comparison of the CAT and TAT pictures. Paper delivered at Midwestern Psychological Association Meeting, Chicago.

Lindzey, G. 1952. Thematic apperception test: Interpretative assumptions and related empirical evidence. *Psychol. Bull.*, 49, 1–25.

———. 1960. Projective techniques and their application in cross-cultural research. To be published by Appleton-Century-Crofts.

———, and R. M. Goldwyn. 1954. Validity of the Rosenzweig picture-frustration study. *J. Pers.*, 22, 519–547.

Lowenfeld, Margaret. 1938. The theory and use of play in the psychotherapy of childhood. *J. ment. Sci.*, 84, 1057–1058.

———. 1935. *Play in Childhood.* London: Gollancz.

———. 1939. The world pictures of children. *Brit. J. med. Psychol.*, 18, 65–101.

Lynn, D. B. 1955. Development and validation of a structural doll play test for children. *Quart. Bull. Indiana Univer. Med. Ctr.*, January.

———. 1957. Structured Doll play test manual. Unpublished manuscript, Indiana Univer. Med. Sch. Library.

———, and Rosalie Lynn. 1959. The structured doll play test as a projective technique. *J. proj. Tech.*

McClelland, D. C., J. W. Atkinson, R. A. Clark, and E. L. Lowell. 1953. *The achievement motive.* New York: Appleton-Century-Crofts.

McDowell, E. D. 1928. *Educational and emotional adjustments of stuttering children.* New York: Columbia Univer. Press.

McGehee, W. 1944. The free word associations of school children. II. Verbal responses. *J. genet. Psychol.*, 31, 119–24.

Meltzoff, J., J. L. Singer, and S. J. Korchin. 1953. Motor inhibition and Rorschach movement responses: A test of the sensory-tonic theory. *J. Pers.*, 21, 400–410.

Machover, Karen. 1948. *Personality projection in the drawing of the human figure.* Springfield, Ill.: Thomas.

———. 1951. Drawing of the human figure; a method of personality investigation. In H. H. Gladys L. Anderson (Eds.), *An introduction to projective techniques.* New York: Prentice-Hall. Pp. 341–369.

Mirmow, Esther. 1952. The Rosenzweig picture frustration study. In D. Brower and L. E. Abt (Eds.), *Progress in clinical psychology.* New York: Prentice-Hall. Vol. I.

Mitchell, I., I. R. Rosanoff, and A. J. Rosanoff. 1919. A study of association in Negro children. *Psychol. Rev.*, 26, 354–355.

Montague, J. A. 1951. Spontaneous drawings of the human form in childhood schizophrenia. In H. H. and Gladys L. Anderson (Eds.), *An introduction to projective techniques.* New York: Prentice-Hall. Pp. 370–385.

Moreno, J. L. 1946. *Psychodrama.* New York: Beacon House. Vol. I.

Morgan, C. D., and H. A. Murray. 1935. A method for investigating phantasies; the thematic apperception test. *Arch. Neurol. Psychiat., Chicago*, 34, 289–306.

Murphy, Lois B. 1956. *Personality in young children.* New York: Basic Books. 2 vols.

Murray. H. A. 1937. Techniques for a systematic investigation of fantasy. *J. Psychol.*, 8, 115–143.

———. 1938. *Explorations in personality.* New York: Oxford Univer. Press.

———. 1943. *Thematic apperception test.* Cambridge: Harvard Univer. Press.

Mussen, P. H. and H. K. Naylor. 1954. The relationship between overt and fantasy aggression. *J. abnorm. soc. Psychol.*, 49, 235–240.

Napoli, P. J. 1946. Finger painting and personality diagnosis. *Genet. Psychol. Monogr.*, 34, 129–231.

———. 1947. Interpretative aspects of finger painting. *J. Psychol.*, 23, 93–132.

———. 1951. Finger painting. In H. H. and Gladys L. Anderson (Eds.), *An introduction to projective techniques.* New York: Prentice-Hall. Pp. 386–415.

Neugarten, Bernice L., and D. Gutmann. 1958. Age-sex roles and personality in middle age: A thematic apperception study. *Psychol. Monogr.*, 72, 1–33.

Phillips, R. 1945. Doll play as a function of the realism of the materials and length of the experimental sessions. *Child Develpm.*, 16, 123–143.

Phillipson, H. 1955. *The object relation techniques.* Glencoe, Ill.: Free Press.

Pintler, Margaret H. 1945. Doll play as a function of experimenter-child interaction and initial organization of materials. *Child Develpm.*, 16, 145–166.

Piotrowski, Z. A. 1957. *Perceptanalysis: A fundamentally reworked, expanded and systematized Rorschach method.* New York: Macmillan.

Rabin, A. I. 1951a. Validating and experimental studies with the Rorschach method. In H. H. and Gladys L. Anderson (Eds.), *An introduction to projective techniques.* New York: Prentice-Hall. Pp. 123–148.

———. 1951b. The Szondi test. In H. H. and Gladys L. Anderson (Eds.), *An introduction to projective techniques.* New York: Prentice-Hall. Pp. 498–512.

Rapaport, D. 1950. The theoretical implications of diagnostic testing procedures. *Int. Cong. Psychiat. Rapports*, 2, 241–271.

———. 1952. Projective techniques and the theory of thinking. *J. proj. Tech.*, 16, 269–275.

———, M. Gill, and R. Schafer. 1946. *Diagnostic psychological testing: The theory, statistical evaluation, and diagnostic application of a battery of tests.* Chicago: Year Book Publ. Vol. 2.

Rautman, A. L., and E. Brower. 1945. War themes in children's stories. *J. Psychol.*, 19, 191–202.

Rogerson, C. H. 1939. *Play therapy in childhood.* New York: Oxford Univer. Press.

Rohde, Amanda R. 1946. Explorations in personality by the sentence completion method. *J. appl. Psychol.*, 30, 169–181.

———. 1957. *The sentence completion method.* New York: Ronald.

Roheim, G. 1943. Children's games and rhymes in Duan (Normanby Island). *Amer. Anthrop.*, **45**, 99–119.

———. 1944. Play analysis with Normanby Island children. *Amer. J. Orthopsychiat.*, **11**, 524–530.

Roody, S. I. 1943. The plot completion test. *J. exper. Educ.*, **12**, 45–47.

Rorschach, H. 1942. *Psychodiagnostics: A diagnostic test based on perception*. (4th ed.) New York: Grune & Stratton (orig. pub. 1923).

———, and E. Oberholzer. 1942. The application of the form interpretative test. In H. Rorschach *Psychodiagnostics*. (4th ed.) New York: Grune & Stratton (orig. pub. 1923). Pp. 184–216.

Rosenzweig, S. 1945. The picture-association method and its application in a study of reactions to frustration. *J. Pers.*, **14**, 3–23.

———. 1949. *Psychodiagnoses*. New York: Grune & Stratton.

———, E. E. Fleming, and H. J. Clark. 1947. Revised scoring manual for the Rosenzweig picture-frustration study. *J. Psychol.*, **24**, 165–208.

Rosenzweig, S., E. E. Fleming, and L. Rosenzweig. 1948. The children's form of the Rosenzweig picture-frustration study. *J. Psychol.*, **26**, 141–191.

Rotter, J. B. 1946. Thematic apperception test: Suggestions for administration and interpretation. *J. Pers.*, **15**, 70–92.

———. 1951. Word association and completion methods. In H. H. and Gladys L. Anderson (Eds.), *An introduction to projective techniques*. New York: Prentice-Hall. Pp. 279–311.

———, and Janet E. Rafferty. 1950. *Rotter incomplete sentences blank*. New York: The Psychological Corporation.

Rotter, J. B., and B. Willerman. 1947. The incomplete sentences test. *J. consult. Psychol.*, **11**, 43–48.

Sacks, J. M. and S. Levy. 1950. The sentence completion test. In L. E. Abt and L. Bellak (Eds.), *Projective Psychology*. New York: Knopf. Pp. 357–402.

Sanford, R. N. 1936. The effects of abstinence from food upon imaginal processes: a preliminary experiment. *J. Psychol.*, **2**, 129–136.

Sanford, R. N. 1943. Personality patterns in school children. In R. G. Barker, J. S. Kounin, and H. F. Wright. *Child behavior and development*. New York: McGraw-Hill.

———, M. H. Adkins, R. B. Miller, and E. A. Cobb. 1943. Physique, personality and scholarship. *Monogr. soc. res. Child Develpm.*, **8**, No. 34.

Sargent, Helen D. 1944. An experimental application of projective principles to a paper and pencil personality test. *Psychol. Monogr.*, **57**, No. 5. P. 57.

———. 1945. Projective methods: Their origin, theory and application in personality research. *Psychol. Bull.*, **42**, 257–293.

———. 1955. *The insight test*. New York: Grune & Stratton.

Schachtel, E. G. 1950. Projection and its relation to character attitudes and creativity in the kinesthetic responses. *Psychiat.*, **13**, 69–100.

Schafer, R. 1954a. *Psychoanalytic interpretation in Rorschach testing theory and application*. New York: Grune & Stratton.

———. 1954b. Some applications of contemporary psychoanalytic theory to projective testing. *J. proj. Tech.*, **18**, 441–448.

Schafer, Sarah, and Mary Leitch. 1948. An exploratory study of the usefulness of a battery of psychological tests with nursery school children. *Amer. J. Psychiat.*, **104**, 647–652.

Sears, R. R. 1947. Influence of methodological factors in doll play. *Child Develpm.*, **18**, 190–197.

———, J. W. M. Whiting, V. Nowlis, and Pauline S. Sears. 1953. Some child-rearing antecedents of aggression and dependence, in young children. *Genet. Psychol. Monogr.*, **47**, 135–236.

Shakow, D. and S. Rosenzweig, 1940. The use of the Tautophone (Verbal Summator) as auditory apperceptive test of the study of personality. *Charact. & Pers.*, **8**, 216–226.

Shaw, Ruth F. 1934. *Finger painting*. Boston: Little, Brown.

Shneidman, E. S. 1948. Schizophrenia and the MAPS test. *Genet. Psychol. Monogr.*, **38**, 145–224.

———. 1949. *They make a picture story test*.

New York: The Psychological Corporation.

Shneidman, E. S. 1951. *Thematic test analysis.* New York: Grune & Stratton.

———. 1952. Manual for the MAPS test. *Proj. tech. Monogr.*, 1, No. 2, 1–92.

Shoobs, N. E. 1944. Psychodrama in the schools. *Sociometry,* 7, 152–168.

Singer, J. L., J. Meltzoff, and G. D. Goldman. 1952. Rorschach movement responses following motor inhibition and hyperactivity. *J. consult. Psychol.*, 16, 359–364.

Singer, J. L., and H. E. Spohn. 1954. Some behavioral correlates of Rorschach's experience type. *J. consult. Psychol.*, 18, 1–9.

Skinner, B. F. 1936. The verbal summator and a method for the study of latent speech, *J. Psychol.*, 2, 71–107.

Solomon, J. C. 1951. Therapeutic use of play. In H. H. and Gladys L. Anderson (Eds.), *An introduction to projective techniques.* New York: Prentice-Hall. Pp. 639–661.

Sommer, R. 1954. On the Brown adaptation of the Rosenzweig P-F for assessing social attitudes. *J. abnorm. soc. Psychol.*, 49, 215–218.

Stein, M. I. 1955. *The thematic apperception test: An introductory manual for its clinical use with adults.* (Rev. ed.) Cambridge: Addison-Wesley.

Stern, W. 1938. Cloud pictures: A new method for testing imagination. *Charact. & Pers.*, 6, 132–146.

Struve, K. 1932. Typische Ablaufsformen des Deutens bei 14–15 jährigen Schulkindern. *Z. angew. Psychol.*, 37, 204–234.

Sullivan, L. A. 1945. Psychodrama in the child guidance clinic. *Sociometry,* 8, 296–305.

Sweetland, A., and H. Quay. 1952. An experimental investigation of the hypnotic dream. *J. abnorm. soc. Psychol.*, 47, 678–682.

Swensen, C. H. Jr. 1957. Empirical evaluations of human figure drawings. *Psychol. Bull.*, 54, 431–466.

Taft, Jessie. 1933. *Dynamics of therapy in a controlled relationship.* New York: Macmillan.

Tomkins, S. S. 1947. *The thematic appercep-*

*tion test.* New York: Grune & Stratton.

Tomkins, S. S., and J. B. Miner. 1957. *The Tomkins-Horn pictures arrangement test.* New York: Springer.

Veroff, J. 1957. Development and validation of a projective measure of power motivation. *J. abnorm. soc. Psychol.*, 54, 1–8.

Vernon, M. D. 1940a. The relation of cognition and phantasy. Vol. I. *Brit. J. Psychol.*, 30, 273–94.

———. 1940b. The relation of cognition and phantasy. Vol. II. *Brit. J. Psychol.*, 31, 1–21.

Werner, H. 1945. Motion and motion perception: A study on vicarious functioning. *J. Psychol.*, 19, 317–327.

Wolff, W. 1946. *The personality of the preschool child.* New York: Grune & Stratton.

———, and J. A. Precker. 1951. Expressive movement and the methods of experimental depth psychology. In H. H. and Gladys L. Anderson (Eds.), *An introduction to projective techniques.* New York: Prentice-Hall. Pp. 457–497.

Wolfson, Rose. 1951. Graphology. In H. H. and Gladys L. Anderson (Eds.), *An introduction to projective techniques.* New York: Prentice-Hall. Pp. 416–456.

Woltmann, A. G. 1952. Play and related techniques. In D. Brower and L. E. Abt (Eds.), *Progress in clinical psychology.* New York: Grune & Stratton. Vol. I. Pp. 278–289.

Woodrow, H., and F. Lowell. 1916. Children's association frequency tables. *Psychol. Monogr.*, 22, No. 5, 110.

Wright, B. A. 1941. An experimentally created conflict expressed in a projective technique. *Psychol. Bull.*, 38, 718.

———. 1945. An experimentally created conflict expressed by means of a projective technique. *J. soc. Psychol.*, 21, 229–245.

Wright, M. E. 1942. Constructiveness in play as affected by group organization and frustration. *Charact. & Pers.*, 11, 40–49.

Zucker, H. 1943. The emotional attachment of children to their parents as related to standards of behavior and delinquency. *J. Psychol.*, 15, 31–40.

# chapter 16

# The Measurement of Children's Attitudes and Values

Marian Radke Yarrow

*National Institute of Mental Health*

The 12-year-old Democrat or Republican is often quite as fervent and sure in his attitudes as the politician. An 8-year-old defending his religion or his father shows no doubts. As he feeds the stray puppy, houses the fallen bird, or protects the caterpillar on the sidewalk from careless steps, the 6-year-old's humane values are apparent. A child's guilty feelings over telling a lie attest to his sense of wrongdoing.

The pro's and anti's, should's and should not's of children are often very strong and unyielding. Side by side with these attitudes are surprising areas of amorality, undisturbed unawarenesses of adult prohibitions, values, and affects.

There are, also, vague, uncrystallized attitudes, and there are uneasy and unsettled values as the child struggles with incompatible pressures and rewards in a social environment of mixed values.

The formation and inculcation of attitudes and values constitute a critical dimension of child development and one closely linked with many other aspects of development—personality, intellectual and physical development, social behavior, etc. Neither theories nor data nor methods of investigation have succeeded fully in giving understanding of this field, although it is rich in thoughtful and fruitful research.

Attitudes and values appear under many names and in varied contexts in research. Norms, sanctions, and mores of communities and cultures are investigated in anthropological and sociological research. In the psychoanalytic framework values may be dealt with in terms of superego functioning. Learning theorists may absorb attitude into behavior theory as afferent-habit strength, efferent-habit strength, drive strength, etc. The educator (secular or religious) is concerned with character education or conscience or human relations. The particular framework in which one views the concepts of attitudes and values influences to some degree the research questions one designs to answer as well as the methodological paths one chooses for investigation. There is great variety in techniques, representing fundamentally different approaches and allowing the investigator to exercise preference for "precision" or "depth," statistical or clinical, or cultural or individual approaches.

## PLAN OF CHAPTER

The methodological issues and the literature on attitudes and values are very extensive and specialized. In attempting to bring methodological knowledge into service of research on children, we have tried to avoid skimming widely and duplicating in dilute form the existing treatises on measurement methods. We have selected representative techniques in this field, evaluating them as to their particular applicability or disadvantages in work with children. When detailed discussions of given techniques exist in the literature or in other chapters of this book, reference is made to these sources.

First, however, we wish to see research techniques in some perspective by considering the following:

1. What are the concepts of attitudes and values with which we are dealing?
2. What are the potential contributions of research on children's attitudes and values to basic developmental theory and to an empirical descriptive science of childhood?
3. What are the ethical requirements in this research field? This is often an afterthought, a last paragraph of research design. That it deserves more than postscriptive recognition arises from the fact that one cannot divorce research approaches to children from fundamental assumptions about children, and, therefore, one cannot divorce research design from conscious or unconscious research ethics.

The power of various measurement techniques is then discussed in relation to the requirements of the research problem and research subject. We have dealt with characteristics or dimensions of measurement (such as verbal or behavioral indices and disguised or undisguised approaches) with illustration from specific techniques embodying these characteristics.

## ATTITUDES AND VALUES— CONCEPTS

Some working concepts of attitudes and values are necessary if we are to discuss their measurement. Both are hypothetical constructs. In most general terms, they are concepts concerning the individual's orientation toward aspects of his personal and impersonal environment and toward himself. In many writings attitudes and values are used interchangeably; in many other writings they are dealt with as distinct concepts. The concept of attitude is most frequently formulated in terms of a "state of readiness for motive arousal," or a "readiness to act" in a given consistent manner toward a specified class of stimuli. Attitudes are further elaborated as having cognitive, affective and conative components. Krech and Crutchfield (1948, p. 152) define attitude as "an enduring organization of motivational, emotional, perceptual and cognitive processes with respect to some aspect of the individual's world." A great many discussions and reviews of this concept have appeared in the literature (see, for example, Allport, 1935; Campbell, 1950; Green, 1954).

The concept of values has been less discussed in psychology, but in its formulation there is reasonable convergence from psychological, psychoanalytic, and sociological points of view. Lewin (1944, p. 14) speaks of values as influencing and guiding behavior, determining which types of behavior have a positive or a negative valence, but not having the character of a goal. Similarly, psychoanalytic theory speaks of values as internalized parents. From the sociological point of view, Williams (1958) describes a value as "any aspect of a situation, event, or object that is invested with a preferential interest as being 'good,' 'bad,' 'desirable,' " and the like. "Values are not concrete goals of action, but rather the criteria by which goals are chosen."

Perhaps it is useful to maintain a distinction between the concepts of attitude and value, with value involving a dimension of acceptability or unacceptability, of should or should not, in the subject's or society's frames of reference. Like attitudes, values must be inferred from a consistency of responses to a given class of object or events. The assumption of consistency in the definition of attitudes and values is in itself a complicated assumption. There may be manifestly different responses that represent a single consistent orientation toward a class of objects. There may be consistently similar responses to manifestly different objects or events that become unified by virtue of the attitude or value. As an example of the first kind of consistency, a child's attitudes toward pets may be inferred from a variety of responses—the amount of time he spends caring for his pet, his choice of playmates who own pets, the route he follows in walking home from school, the books he reads, etc.; each represents an approach re-

sponse to a class of objects. As an example of the second kind of consistency, a child's attitudes regarding his family's social status may lead him consistently to refuse gestures of friendship or help in many different circumstances from many different children, all of whom he has classified as "outsiders."

The core characteristics of attitudes and values are then an involvement in the object (or principle or event), a consistency in orientation toward the object, and a potential effect on behavior relating to that object. Within these definitions there is considerable latitude for differential conceptualization and differential emphasis in measurement.

The conscientious investigator of children's attitudes and values may not be satisfied with this brief discussion of concepts. He will want to know where and how these concepts fit into general psychological theory, how different theoretical positions (such as learning theory and cognitive and field theory) deal with attitudes and values, and what contributions have been made within these different frameworks. For instance, a treatment of attitude from a field theoretical point of view is to be found in Krech and Crutchfield (1948, p. 152). Doob (1947) puts forth a behavior theorist's view in which he predicts and hopes for the early demise of the concept of attitudes. He takes the position that "attitude" can be incorporated into general behavior theory, "any 'principles' pertaining to attitude are only special cases of psychological theory" (p. 155). Green (1954), in reviewing quantitative attitude measurement, takes basically a statistical point of view. Attitude is defined as "a latent variable whose meaning is derived from the covariance of a set of responses."

## CONTRIBUTIONS OF STUDIES OF ATTITUDES AND VALUES

To enable the reader to judge for himself the significance of attitude and value studies in child development, it may be helpful to delineate types of scientific objectives in the study of children and to localize questions of attitudes and values within them. Grossly these objectives are three: (1) descriptive knowledge of children, (2) understanding of change that is developmental in the life cycle, and (3) prediction of response from knowledge of given stimulus conditions and conditions of the organism. Descriptive research produces profiles of abstractions—what children of a given age, sex, or cultural group are like with respect to one characteristic or another. More truly developmental research is concerned with the detailed study of the processes of change in given functions, such as the development of a love response in the child, of cognitive processes, or of causal thinking. Research on prediction is concerned with the prediction of responses under current specified stimulus conditions or prediction of antecedent-consequent relations in a longitudinal, developmental sense, such as conditions in early childhood in relation to adolescent personality.

Where do questions of attitudes and values enter into these objectives?

Clearly, attitudes and values are part of the first objective, the normative and descriptive data on children's orientations toward their human and physical environments and toward themselves. Here the cognitive side of attitudes (especially for young children) becomes very important. To what extent is the child aware of various qualities of experience, and what kind of cognitive structure exists for him to which he responds affectively?

The weight of evidence points to the child as a very sensitive perceiver and at a very early age. These early sensitivities and beginnings of crystallized attitudes and values have been documented most impressively in studies of young children's awareness of social group mores and social prejudices. Goodman's (1952) study of kindergarteners' awareness of racial differences and their preferences associated with these differences demonstrates this point systematically, as do similar findings in other studies, such as Clark and Clark (1939), Horowitz (1936), and Radke, Trager, and Davis (1949).

Attitude studies of children have flourished in this area of social awareness with considerable experimentation in techniques of measurement. In other areas of the child's life similar data on attitudes and values are not so likely to be found. We know much less about children's attitudes toward their parents' authority and affection, toward socially defined children's roles, and about children's value systems with regard to morality, justice, altruism, etc.

The descriptive and normative investigations of children's attitudes and values, when simple enumerations of age changes, may be relatively drab and contribute little to a theory of development or behavior. On the other hand, such descriptions in the company of a theory or such descriptive data as the raw materials for the development of concepts and theory are essential data. Some investigators have taken the position that the concept of developmental stages in perceptual, cognitive, and motivational aspects of behavior is relatively useless, that experiential factors account for most of the variance. Failures to replicate Piaget's findings on developmental changes in thought characteristics have been cited as supportive evidence (Sears, 1958). Present information leaves us without a full answer, and it is well worth investigating how far in the life cycle the maturational level is significant in accounting for variance in attitudes and values.

Research on antecedent-consequent relations may involve the study of attitudes and values as responses and as intervening states. They are dealt with as responses in the following kinds of questions: Variations in attitudes and values are resultants of what kinds of experience and what kinds of personality structure? What are the conditions under which a particular attitude is acquired? How does it change under varied training conditions? In deliberate cultivation of an attitude or value, how does one proceed? Still regarding attitude as a response, one may be interested in questions about the "environment" of the attitude within the individual. In what kind of dynamic relation to other attitudes and variables does a given attitude exist? What is the degree of situationality versus gener-

ality or consistency of the attitude, of stability versus changeability? What is necessary to sustain the attitude or value? How close to behavior is the attitude and value? Many of the goals of child rearing and education are directed toward developing desired attitudes about authority, altruism, science, morality, etc.

Attitudes and values enter research problems also as intervening states. The child is exposed to given experiences, let us say, to certain specified rearing practices of the parent; certain behavioral characteristics of the child are observed. These outcomes are not uniform, however, from child to child. Couplings of parent practices and behavioral outcomes are only in the vicinity of +.25 to +.35 correlations. Attention to intervening conditions, among them the child's attitudes and values, may refine these relationships. What is experienced by the child? What is the nature of the cognitive framework in which he interprets the parent's actions, the nature of the attitudes and values brought into play by the parent's behavior?

How may the intervening states modify and complicate the antecedent-consequent couplings? For example, internalized peer group values regarding defiance of adult authority may affect the adolescent's response to his mother's efforts at cultivating dependent behavior in him. Children's reactions to new persons and conditions can be predicted only in part from knowledge of the new stimulus situation. The set of values regarding personality, status, etc., which the child brings into the new situation, can be strongly influential in determining his response. Generally, "warm, democratic" adult leadership tends to be coupled with confident and secure relationships between child and adult. However, children whose cultural training devalues democratic procedures, disdaining such signs of adult "weakness," are likely to respond quite differently to democratic adults. Thus predictions or explanations of children's behavior without regard to intervening attitudinal or value states suffer many errors. Incorporating attitudes and behavior into explanatory schemes would seem to be a needed elaboration in research design and theory, even though resulting formulations will be less tidy.

By having identified some of the problems and objectives of research in which attitude and value measurement has a role, the breadth of measurement problems may perhaps have become more apparent and the issues of measurement more multisided than at first quick glance. With the goals of research partly codified, our next step is to consider the actual conduct of attitude and value research with children, as it affects children.

## RESEARCH WISDOM
## AND RESEARCH ETHICS

Children are now much more in the "public" domain of researchers of many training backgrounds and interests than was the case in the first half of the century, when research on children came almost exclusively from departments of child welfare and education. Also, children are now involved in a much greater volume of research. The need and obligation of investigators to acquire some understanding of children before using them as research subjects assume, therefore, rather considerable importance. The child cannot be used naïvely as a substitute for the college sophomore or for the rat, for reasons methodological as well as ethical. The reasons we wish to discuss here are those that concern the cognitive and affective sides of the child's research participation, the involvements most directly affected in research on attitudes and values.

Usually a close relation exists between research wisdom and research ethics in studying human behavior. This is nowhere more evident than in work with children. The essence of research ethics is consideration for the research participant. Maintaining confidentiality of data and exercising precautions to prevent harmful effects of data gathering and reporting are the essential elements. Beyond this core of agreement, opinions and ethical practices vary.

By definition, attitudes and values are affect-laden, and to them may be attached rewards and punishments of "conscience" and society. They are part of the "private" world of the individual, to reveal or conceal as he sees fit; therefore, by probing into them in research, one is immediately confronted with something of an ethical dilemma. However, on many issues subjects of our research-wise culture are not hesitant about laying bare their attitudes.

The subject's permission is usually recognized as his to give or withhold before research is done. With children, this permission-giving power is usually vested in the parent or parent-surrogate, leaving to the child a much smaller

margin of power, that of being cooperative or not, once he is in the research. One can readily feel a legitimacy
in this procedure while at the same
time also feeling that the adult's right
to decide must not be the sole guide in
deciding a child's participation. The
obligation remains of granting some
degree of self-determination on the
part of the child. His developmental
level and the problem under investigation may be guides in weighing research
hazards to the subject and deciding research policy in this regard.

The child's willingness to participate
and his understanding of what he is
asked to participate in should be looked
at together in considering ethics and
procedures. Concealment of research
purpose—by stating a different research
objective from the real one, by partly
disguising the objective, by giving no
explanation, by completely concealing
the fact that research is going on—has
become very nearly conventional in experimental approaches, testing, interviewing, and observations. The primary defense for this practice is, of
course, that without camouflage many
problems could not be subjected to
systematic scrutiny. For example, the
subject's self-conscious awareness of the
research purpose would seriously affect
studies of "influence" factors in attitude change, studies of "negative" attitudes and values, studies of attitudes
toward power figures, and so on. With
older children, our explanations of objectives (true or camouflaged) approximate those used with adults. In one
sense or another, the subjects are informed that it is research. In many instances they accept the fact that they

do not know the specific purpose, but
they are willing to "go along" or to
wait until after it is over to be told its
significance. With younger children,
we have been quite uniform in disguising research as "play."

When the older child and adult are
taken into confidence to the degree
that "this is research on such and such,"
they have, most likely, some concept
of research. Its prestige and its stereo-
types will vary. Whether the research
worker is believed to be "psychoana-
lyzing us," is referred to somewhat ap-
prehensively, somewhat hostilely as a
"head-shrinker," or is regarded as a
"scientist" is probably of some importance in the subject's response. These
several meanings of research filter down
the age scale, so that it is not surprising
to have a 10-year-old observe: "You're
doing research on us. I know because
back at school a man came around
getting us to tell stories about some
pictures he had. Do you know what
research he was doing? What is your
research about?" Often simple, frank,
and satisfying explanations can be
given. Thus in a study of children's
attitudes and behavior in an interracial
camp this 10-year-old was told: "We
are interested in learning more about
children's camps, what children do together that they like or don't like, how
they learn to know other children, and
so on."

But below some age or intellectual
level there is no concept of "research."
Here one should consider most carefully the child's reactions to the research. One should ask oneself whether
the content of the research task is congruent with a "play" explanation. When

interview questions or projective play devices tap attitudes regarding ego-involving, possibly painful experiences, the child expecting to play with the investigator may feel "sold" or tricked.

The child's "seduction" into participation in research may take something of the following pattern. An adult, often a stranger, arrives at the nursery school. The teacher may invite the child to leave his play to join the adult for "more" games. The two leave the room and go to a room where they are alone. A brief "rapport" period follows in which the adult may converse with the child in a friendly way or may give him toys with which to play. Then, sometime later, other gadgets (the research toys, pictures, dolls) are brought out, and the child is requested to shift to them. Through the toys or purely in verbal terms, the investigator portrays various human relationships and interactions, to which the child is asked to respond. (For example, a picture or story may depict a child being disciplined by a teacher, a parent giving his child a present, several children fighting.) Just how the child feels about the revelations he is asked to make or what meanings their communication has for him often go unnoticed by the researcher interested in some specific variable of response.

A responsibility for knowing the impact of the research experience on the child should be part of any investigator's task. Although we know that this is not fully possible, it is possible to build into one's procedures some provisions for evaluating the impact. Planned alertness to the spontaneous comments, gestures, and postures of the child can furnish information. Such cues are illustrated in a kindergartener's reactions to telling stories about ambiguously structured pictures. She drew a deep breath at the presentation of a picture of white and Negro children together on a playground, and commented gravely. "This is getting serious." From another child came a question after some story telling, "How did Jeanie do on this test?" And from another, "Did I do it right?" (An explanation of "play" in this instance had not changed the expectation of "test.")

Despite the limitations of the "play" approach, it must also be said that "it works" in many situations. Its congruence with task is perhaps the best guide to the reasonableness of its use. There are other alternatives that can better be used when content is not playlike. An investigator's explanation to children that he is writing a book on what children think about such and such or that he is studying how children solve problems are examples of plausible purposes in line with the research objectives, yet do not necessarily interfere with the process under study. The feasibility and value of taking child subjects into full confidence should not be completely overlooked. This was done in a study in which preadolescent children were seen in small friendship groups by group workers in a neighborhood house. The children were invited to come together to talk about intergroup problems, as they experienced them in their school and neighborhood, to help the worker who was interested in studying these problems and writing about them in a book on children.

Hand in hand with the meanings that the researcher tries explicitly to give to the child are the subjective meanings to the child. We know that the investigator of attitudes and values may bring the child uncomfortably close to distressing areas of his life (conflicts with authority figures, guilts, painful problems of self awareness). The investigator often faces the hard reality that to some degree and for some children his research may contribute to a child's problems. This may come about as a result of having brought latent feelings to the surface through the research by direct questions or by indirect techniques. (The possibility exists, too, that the child's verbalization and playing out of feelings in the research may have a therapeutic effect.) Also, research may create conflicts where none existed before. For example, when investigating values regarding honesty, the researcher may devise situations in which the child is motivated to receive certain rewards or to avoid failures. In order to do so, dishonest behavior may be involved. The investigator may have a hard time deciding how seriously the child will regard his own transgressions. Are the experimental techniques justified? Should there be some built-in "repair" procedures as part of the research to handle possible traumata?

The child's welfare sometimes enters research in another form. The investigator may suddenly find himself with a personal responsibility, which comes from privileged knowledge of the child or adolescent. Through the child's revelations in the research, clinically and socially serious attitudes are revealed. To divulge them to the parent, teacher, or therapist, from whom help can come, is to violate the confidentiality promised the child. Not to reveal them may leave remediable conditions unremedied. When data are gathered in childhood and adolescence for follow-up study in later years of childhood or adulthood, the carry-over of the child's expressed attitudes into the future may have consequences for the individual in cases in which the attitude has particular social or personal relevance.

These methodological-ethical issues pose difficult questions. To what extent should the researcher restrict himself to the use of methods that keep to a minimum disturbing responses in children, in spite of the fact that other methods might be more effective and productive? To what extent is the investigator morally responsible for helping a child to restore equilibrium after eliciting from him emotional reactions associated with some of his attitudes and values? The specific instrument used, the context in which the research is done, the investigator characteristics, and the child characteristics together determine the impact of a given procedure and help to determine answers to these questions. No research is justifiably undertaken on children's attitudes and values without consideration of its effects. In part, the answer to what is ethical in research lies in what the investigator is equipped to understand about children and what he is equipped to do by way of "treatment" in the event that some is necessary.

Having stressed the problematic aspects of attitude research with children, one should not be frightened away from it. The moral is not to blunder into children's feelings and conflicts and private worlds. Knowledge of children, although it appears self-evident, is critically important in designing and conducting research. Research errors of misinterpretation and misjudgment of the child often arise because of a lack of this knowledge, thereby rendering research less efficient and mildly or seriously trampling on the rights of the child. Errors tend to be of two sorts—either making the same assumptions for the child as for the adult or far underestimating the child's sensitivities and capabilities. Areas of error involve the relationship of investigator to child, the thought processes and verbal facilities of children, and the research-induced motivations used for children. We return to these issues in the discussion of research techniques.

## THE CHOICE
## OF MEASUREMENT TECHNIQUES

How does one decide on a technique for a given problem of attitude measurement with children? How does one adapt or develop a technique for particular research subjects? At least part of the answer is suggested in the questions. Choice must be in terms of the specific problems and research subjects. Techniques cannot be rank-ordered for effectiveness or validity in vacuo. What is a very good approach in one problem may be a blundering approach in another. We shall see some examples later on. To bring research problems and techniques into happy union, we must know what the problem asks or requires of measurement and what the techniques can yield: what assumptions are made in a given technique, what modifying or limiting factors are introduced by the particular child subjects and the particular research content.

Both attitudes and values involve the idea of a continuum, from positive to negative, right to wrong, or valued to devalued. Measurement in terms of a quantitative scale along such a continuum is, therefore, a reasonable expectation. But this information is not always possible or sufficient. Often, measures sensitive to the "process" and "organization" of attitudes and values are desired, as opposed to the net product of affect or to a point on a continuum. Therefore, many of the procedures for studying attitudes and values are not measurement in the strict quantitative sense of the word.

A bird's-eye view of the varieties of approaches can be achieved by organizing stimulus and response characteristics of measurement procedures into a conventional classificatory scheme, such as that in Table 16-1. In selecting or developing a technique, the investigator will choose between verbal or behavioral indices, undisguised or disguised approaches, single or multiple indices, manifest or latent meaning analyses, contrived or natural situations, and clinical or statistical approaches. These procedural properties are obviously not exclusive to attitude measurement, and many of the pros and cons for their use with children, which have been discussed in other chapters (Chapters 14 and 15), apply to attitudes and values as well.

**TABLE 16-1. APPROACHES TO THE MEASUREMENT OF ATTITUDES AND VALUES**

| Variations in Stimulus Situations | Variations in Response Situations |
|---|---|

Verbal Stimuli

Undisguised purpose or disguised purpose questions
What do you like about school?
Would you describe a typical school day?

Open ended or structured-alternative questions
If a teacher finds that a pupil has stolen money from her desk, what should she do with the pupil?
If a teacher . . . , which of the following do you think she should do? Talk to him and find out why he did it? Scold him in front of the class? Send him home with a note to his parents?

Single questions, series of questions, attitude tests, attitude scales or interviews

Written forms or oral forms

Personal terms or impersonal terms
What do you think you should do?
What should a child do?

Standardized questions or clinically, individually oriented questions

Hypothetical or story situations or real-life situations
Which of the following would you be willing to share with a Russian child . . . a German child . . . etc.? Your home, your playground, your school room, etc.?
Which of the children in your class do you like the very best? Which next best? Next best? Which least of all?

Incomplete stimulus situations—sentences or stories
A mother is a person who . . .

Responses may be oral or written. Alternative responses are presented; subject indicates his choice. Subject responds freely in his own terms. Free responses may be guided along given lines to elicit certain aspects of attitude or value, such as emphasizing subject's feelings, the cognitive content of his attitudes, or his mode of resolving conflicting value alternatives.

**TABLE 16-1.** *Continued*

| Variations in Stimulus Situations | Variations in Response Situations |
| --- | --- |
| Verbal Stimuli Plus "Props" | |
| Pictorial material accompanied by question probes | Verbal responses as above. Behavioral responses may require manipulation of pictorial and play materials. Behavioral responses may be confined to alternative choice or may be freely interpretive. |
| What are the boys doing in this picture? | |
| Doll material accompanied by question probes | |
| What is this mommy doll going to do? | |
| Behavioral Settings | |
| Contrived social situations and problem-solving situations | |
| Mother and children brought to experimental playroom to wait for "detained" experimenter | Subject may be permitted to behave only in structured alternative terms. Subject behaves "naturally" in the situations. Subject is asked to report retrospectively on his behavior. |
| Children's honesty tested in classroom situations in which cheating is possible | |

## VERBAL INDICES IN ATTITUDE AND VALUE MEASUREMENT

Most research indices of attitudes and values are verbal. The verbal expression of one's attitudes (and values) calls for introspection on the part of the subject, requiring him to call up within himself a cognitive organization of a given object or class of objects or set of events and to express some preference, inclination, or interpretation with regard to it. A comparison of objects (ranking, expressing degrees of affective intensity, etc.) may be involved. How well able the child is to do this will depend upon his age, mental level, and experience, the nature of the task required, and the nature of the testing situation. Cognitive limitations, limitations in verbal comprehension and facility, and characteristics of thought in early childhood set the lower limits, developmentally, at which one can expect the awareness and the power of generalization necessary for attitudes or values. Characteristics that most directly affect the study of attitudes and values in young children are these:

1. The young child has a narrow experience range. Often the very common content about which we want to study attitudes may not be a part of the child's experienced world or may have very idiosyncratic meaning for him. Although he may oblige a friendly investigator by responding about things that are largely unknowns to him, it would be in error to ascribe attitudes to him.

2. His ties to the concrete and the immediate in his experience and his difficulty in dealing with the abstract and remote confine the child, too, in handling verbal-test situations. Further difficulties derive from his inability to handle adequately part-whole relations, inclusiveness of membership in a class of objects or events, and self-other comparisons. Such abstractions, however, are often part of attitude measurement.

3. We ordinarily assume a clear differentiation in the adult between the real and the fantasied. In the young child's thinking, these boundaries are less distinct; the real, the imagined, the wished for, the wished away may not always be distinguishable. In measurement this fact is often lost sight of. In fact, in many of our indirect question approaches, hypothetical situations, or doll-play techniques, we toy with the irreal, interpreting it now as fantasy, now as real. That our intention may not always coincide with the plane on which the child is responding injects a source of difficulty into verbal measurements.

4. Language skills, the child's understanding, and his ability to express himself are critical in attitude research. Language barriers as well as experience barriers may confound the child when the experimenter asks him for a choice, an interpretation, or an expression of feeling. It is not always easy to distinguish which it is. Errors or peculiarities in the meaning of words for young children have contributed often delightful, sometimes pathetic little dramas in child-adult interactions and misunderstandings. In verbal interactions for research purposes, unless one is tuned to recognizing these errors or peculiarities, one can be led to erroneous conclusions. For example, in a study of kindergarteners' attitudes toward different religious groups (Radke et al., 1949), some children, though familiar with the labels, Catholic and Jewish, had not attached religious connotations to them but rather specific meanings growing out of specific contacts and experiences. (Catholic meant another school in the neighborhood at which children got spanked if they were bad. Jewish meant pickles.) Clearly, the feelings expressed by these children toward the verbal labels have not the same meaning as feelings expressed by children for whom "Catholic" represents a more abstract class of membership and belief. Whether early feelings attached to these labels will generalize as the labels come to stand for groups of people is a question needing further study. Research concerned with the life history of attitudes or values needs to be concerned with beginnings such as these, with the way in which early fragments of association affect subsequent incoming experiences and the ways in which they become organized into attitudes.

Although language skills of young children are severely limiting for research, the child's ability to communicate feelings through the limited language he possesses is also notable. Without logical and coherent replies to research stimuli, the preschool child is often well able, with a few choice words, to convey the emotional significance of the stimulus situation. Also, when the content or context of the research is in the familiar world of the child, he may be remarkably perceptive in the variables being studied.

The characteristics of language and thought that have been noted affect research most when one attempts attitude studies with children of ages below 6 or 7, but careful assessment of similar problems in later years of childhood is not to be overlooked. There is a tendency to sigh with relief once early childhood is past and to assume that now the child can think and express himself essentially like an adult. This may be true; but cognitive and thought processes of school-age children have not received the same careful scrutiny (except for a study by Inhelder and Piaget, 1958) that has been given to the preschool child.

A study by Meltzer (1926) demonstrates nicely how far from the understanding of many children (10 years and older) are many social concepts (democracy, capitalism, etc.). How careful then must the investigator be when his investigations are concerned with abstractions!

We know that thought and communication are closely bound up with all aspects of development and experience, and what we elicit as attitudes or values at any age should be interpreted always in the light of what is known about intellectual and motivational characteristics or preoccupations at given childhood periods and of children of given backgrounds. Several examples illustrate this point. Ideas about and use of rules change over the childhood years. This can have a bearing on attitude studies. An absolutist of 8, when absolutisms tend to be frequent and widespread, is to be judged quite dif-

ferently from the 15- or 16-year-old with similar absolutist attitudes. The diagnostic personality significance of such attitudes is probably much less at 8 years of age than in later adolescence.

In the changing nature of make-believe, imagination, and ideals through childhood we have another example of the influence of developmental features on research. Children of different ages may interpret the same research task within very different frameworks. Make-believe themes play a prominent and public role in the language and play of the preschool age; later, fantasies and wishes are more likely to be covert and private and more separated from reality. Lewin (1935) observes that ideologies may be extremely forceful during adolescence and not readily distinguishable from what is "real." These differences inject another shading into attitude research with children at different ages. Since inferences regarding attitudes are frequently drawn from the child's responses to questions couched in "what if," "make believe" terms, the stimulus value of "what if" is of considerable importance.

## DIMENSIONS OF VARIATION IN VERBAL ATTITUDE TECHNIQUES

A very long and hopelessly specific account of instruments of measurement would be required to cover all the variations of techniques that have been employed with children. Such an approach is impractical as well as unlikely to come up with general principles that can be applied in further research.

Techniques can be sorted, however, on a number of dimensions—degree of disguise or openness, degree of structuring given, whether the task framework is hypothetical or real, and whether it is personalized or impersonalized. By evaluating some of the virtues and hazards in child research along dimensions such as these, an investigator is in a better position to appraise a given technique for a given research problem.

## DISGUISED
## OR UNDISGUISED APPROACHES

Direct undisguised questions in daily interaction provide most of us with a sizable portion of our information about the attitudes and values of persons around us. The predictions we make from the responses we receive turn out quite well, and we learn to count on them in determining our behavior. There are some areas of attitudes and values about which we would never think of asking a direct question of our daily associates, yet we make inferences, too, about them. Surprisingly, these frequently appear to be valid, particularly when we are drawing on a large and varied sample of the behavior of the individual in question. In research our sample of the individual is usually a very limited one and our relationship very specialized. Within these severe limits, how well do various approaches succeed? What are the relative merits of disguised and undisguised approaches?

One of the constants in research with children, which enters into the evaluation of disguised and undisguised methods, is the authority role of the adult.

The kind of authority varies, it is true, but cultural prescriptions regarding the child's role with respect to the adult (even the child's defiance of the adult) are significant ingredients of all research situations.

The decision to use an undisguised approach relies on the child's readiness to reveal his attitudes to an adult. It assumes that he will not be inhibited in expression by an authority figure, and, also, that he will not be motivated to respond according to his conceptions of adult norms. For many attitudes, these assumptions are reasonably met, especially if the research task is set up so as not to be a matter of giving "correct" responses and if the adult stands in no unique role with respect to the content in question (such as court officer interviewing a delinquent). Attitudes and values concerning foods, friends, competition, parental disciplinary techniques, politics, religion, etc., may be revealed freely by the child under good testing circumstances. He may welcome a permissive situation in which to voice attitudes troubling him or significant to him.

On the other hand, the child's keen cue seeking regarding the adult's expectation, his greater suggestibility and, at times, his possessive privacy can introduce difficulties with direct questions. An illustration from the behavior of a 5-year-old in a play interview illustrates difficulty with his suggestibility. The child built an enclosure out of large blocks. The examiner asked, "Would you like to be in this all by yourself?" "Yes," replied the child. "Would you like your daddy with you?" "Yes." "Would you like your mommy in there with you?" "Yes." "Would you like to be in this all alone?" "Yes," this time with emphatic agreement.

Directness and disguise with children are matters of degree and cannot really be discussed as two opposite alternatives. The most open approach might be illustrated by: "How do you feel about the kinds of punishments your parents use with you?" "Do you like to play with Negro children?" Here both the investigator's objective and the question form are direct. This approach is characteristic of many attitude tests and questionnaires. The objective may be somewhat more concealed, though the questions may be direct and apparently undisguised. Thus, having knowledge of the parent's actual disciplinary practices, the investigator may ask: "Here are different kinds of punishments that parents use. Which do you think is the fairest?" "Which next?" And so on. Or, in studying sex preferences the investigator may ask each member of a classroom of boys and girls: "Which children do you want as your friends? Which children do you not want as friends?"

There are many studies in which the topic of the research (attitudes toward teachers, toward sex, toward ethnic groups) is not really concealed but is left "unspoken." The respondent may only gradually acquire insight into the area being investigated, as his own responses make it increasingly explicit. An example is a study by Biber and Lewis (1949), in which they investigated first- and second-grade children's expectations of their teachers. Familiar schoolroom situations are presented in pictures. Each picture is explained by the interviewer, and questions are asked the child.

Oh look at this little girl. She's crying —see her tears? She's telling the teacher that she has lost the new bracelet she got for her birthday. What do you think the teacher is saying to her?

The children are told this is a "game of looking at pictures." There are 13 such presentations, each involving relationships with the teacher and life in school. Studies of attitudes of young children toward ethnic groups have a similar pattern. Thus a series of photographs or pictured interactions or both may be presented. Skin-color differences appear as part of each pictured stimulus and sometimes in the investigators' questions. (Horowitz, 1936; Clark and Clark, 1939; Goodman, 1952; Radke, Trager, and Davis, 1949; Ammons, 1950.)

It seems likely that the respondent acquires some level of insight into the purposes of these "games," "stories," etc., as they touch repeatedly on given themes. The investigators, of course, do not necessarily assume complete or lasting disguise. This procedure may be used quite consciously as a step-by-step procedure for gaining access to certain areas of attitudes, less accessible through direct questioning. Whether the child, after recognizing the investigator's purposes, goes along undisturbed or becomes upset or angry depends on many other characteristics of the testing situation (see pp. 668–670) especially on the relationship or rapport between child and investigator. If complete disguise is an important objective, techniques of real subtlety are required. Probably only careful try-outs with children can establish the completeness of disguise. Situations relying on behavioral indices are sometimes more successful than verbal techniques in achieving thorough concealment, for example, in using participant observational techniques (see pp. 678–682).

Whether open and direct techniques can be used more successfully with children than with adults cannot be answered categorically. Suggestibility and orientation to adult standards are on the debit side, but fewer defenses and rationalizations in many areas are on the credit side. With adults, any probes into their fantasies, wishes, and dreams are likely to be regarded suspiciously. Children who have not learned of the latent significance in these responses are less reluctant to reveal them on direct request.

## STRUCTURED AND UNSTRUCTURED TECHNIQUES

Degree of structure and degree of disguise in a technique often vary inversely, the more highly structured, the less disguised. All combinations of these dimensions are possible, however. The highly structured technique presents an organized stimulus, one "complete" insofar as conveying a common meaning to subjects. The unstructured stimulus situation, in contrast, intentionally leaves much of the process of organization, of giving of meaning, to the subject. It is "ambiguous," vague, or incomplete. The response that is called for in either stimulus situation may be highly structured, a choice of given alternatives, or relatively unstructured, a "free" response to the stimulus. The tasks presented by these variations make quite different demands on the child. Both can capitalize on certain psychological characteristics of children, and both can err by the same token. Before discussing the possibilities in these alternative approaches, we shall look at some of the concrete variations that have been employed with children.

Illustrative of a highly structured technique is a study by Eberhart (1942) of children's values regarding property rights. Pairs of statements are presented, and the child is asked to indicate which is the more serious of the two. ("To borrow your brother's baseball without asking or to swipe flowers from a park?") Boys from grades 1 to 12 were tested. With children through grade 3, the offenses were pictured and the test administered individually.

Any number of examples from questionnaire and interview items illustrate this highly structured technique, which requires on the part of the child a yes-no response or an indication of degree of agreement or a choice of multiple alternatives.

How do you feel about parents knowing what teenagers talk about? (Check one.)
  a. I think parents have every right to know.
  b. I think parents should feel included sometimes but not expect to be in on all the secrets.
  c. I think that what teenagers talk about should be their own business, if they want to keep it private.

In another variation of the structured approach the child is given a list of words (cousin, roommate, neighbor, etc.) heading columns opposite a list of races and nationalities. The child is instructed to write "yes" or "no" to show his willingness or unwillingness to have the relationship indicated with a member of the groups listed (Zeligs, 1948).

A picture technique may be equally highly structured. Temple and Amen (1944) presented a series of pictures with a central child figure in each. The child is shown in circumstances such as eating alone and watching his father playing with a younger child. The child is given two paper faces, a happy one and a sad one, and asked to choose one to put on the central child in the picture. Following his choice, the child is asked his reasons. This combination of structured stimulus with unstructured response occurs frequently in studies of children, in interviews, in questionnaires, and in picture and doll-play techniques. Further illustrations of this method follow: in interviews with children (10 to 15 years of age) on attitudes toward different cultures (Frenkel-Brunswik and Havel, 1953) questions such as "What is an American?" and "Why don't people like Mexicans?" were used. The questions are direct, undisguised, structured. The child is expected to organize the response. In other cases an episode of behavior is described in specific detail (verbally or pictorially), such as a child being scolded by his mother because he has failed in school. The child is called upon to give his reactions, usually aided by probes: "How does he feel about the punishment, etc.?" "This little boy isn't feeling well. He's coming up to the teacher and telling her he has a stomachache. What do you think the teacher is saying to him?"

From the highly structured stimulus, one can move gradually toward less and less structure, toward requiring the subject to impose more and more of his own organization and meaning upon the stimulus. Instead of a picture of mother spanking child, mother and child's intentions may be suggested only by facial expressions or gestures. Even fewer clear cues may appear in the picture; the child's face may now be turned away and the mother's expression may tell unclearly of anger or worry or fear. The interpretation is up to the child.

Many studies with children use approaches somewhere in the middle range on this continuum. Pictures used by Trager and Yarrow (1952) in studying attitudes of 5-to-8-year-old children portray children at play, with one child possibly seen as being on the sidelines. Racial differences are suggested in the drawings. The child is first asked an open-ended question, "Tell me about the picture." Increasingly focused questions follow, "Tell me about this little boy (child on sidelines). . . . He's not playing. Why isn't he playing?" And so on.

The free-association test used by Meltzer (1943) with children 9 years and older to get at their attitudes toward parents falls in this intermediate group. He introduces his procedure as a game in "loud thinking." He presents a word and the child is asked to "shout out" the first ten things he thinks of. Names of people like Washington and Lincoln are given, followed by "your mother" and "your father."

With children in the upper grades, written tasks of this semistructured variety have been developed. One of the most revealing in the study of children's values (Kalhorn, 1944) is a simple procedure in which the child is asked,

What could a child be doing at home that is a fine thing to do and someone is praising him? What could a child be doing at home that he should not do, and someone is scolding him?

This is repeated with the addition of "a very fine thing and someone is praising him very much" and, similarly, "something he should never do and someone is scolding him very hard." Each time he is asked who is praising or scolding. With fourth to eighth graders this approach brought out value differences and differences in the sources of values between Mennonite children and non-Mennonite children.

The incomplete sentence technique, which can be graded from the semistructured ("I feel like cheating when . . .") to the most incomplete provocation for response ("Most girls . . ." "My mother . . ."), also appears in attitude studies (Harris and Tseng, 1957). This form of the technique and certain applications of doll play, in which the manipulation of the materials and the child's verbalizations are relatively undirected, represent minimally structured approaches to attitudes and values. They are less likely to be used in investigations of attitudes and values than in studies of personality and motivation, since a very large sampling of responses would be required to elicit data relevant to the specific attitude or value.

The virtues and failings of structured and unstructured approaches are discussed in the literature from varying points of view (Campbell, 1950; Deri et al., 1948; see also chapters in this book on interviewing and projective techniques). There are certain issues particularly pertinent to research with children. Attention to developmental characteristics of limitations in language and thought processes is particularly important in certain structured techniques. Some make minimal demands on the expressive verbal facility of the child and in this sense they are highly suitable for work with children. These are techniques requiring the choice of alternative responses, agree to disagree, like to dislike, yes or no, and similar categories. In reality, these techniques require, on the part of the children, very attentive responses and a sifting of associations and inclinations in order to reach a resolution in the form of one of the presented alternatives. This is a complex process for an easy-answer product. It should be remembered that the process as well as the product must be applicable to the child subject. When using such techniques, in which a simple model of response is given, namely, choosing one of a standard set of alternatives, one must be extremely careful to keep the child's attention on the stimulus. It must be sufficiently simple and motivating if the child is not to slip into a routine and meaningless pattern of choices. The young child's tendency to perseverate may manifest itself most readily in these techniques. A lack of comprehension of the questions, or a lack of motivation or actual resistance from children of any age, can be masked quite easily in apparently co-operative selections of alternative choices. To guard against this kind of "misuse" by the subject, the investigator can employ various "checks." Thus, by repeating questions in varied forms at several points in the measuring process, as a check on the consistency of reactions, he can arrive at a safer estimate of the meaningfulness of data. By following the structured responses with open-ended probes, such as, "Could you tell me why you feel that way?" or "What are your reasons for choosing X?", he may gain assurance or discouragement about his technique.

Structured alternative responses in attitude and value areas run several other risks with children. They may produce too-neat representations of what may be very unclear and uncertain processes. The structured response cannot readily differentiate between the child who values altruism or honesty very highly and the child who has barely formulated principles. Research techniques of multiple-choice responses can force or create the form of the attitude by the items and alternatives presented and can impose a framework which, though not incorrect, is partly out of step with the child's reality. Both points need illustration. Suppose we are interested in children's attitudes toward mentally ill behavior; we describe an episode of paranoid behavior and then ask whether the person acting this way does so because he is (1) "bad," (2) "sick," or (3) "unhappy about something." The adult framework is automatically stamped on the child. The child may not have thought of any of these ex-planations; he may not indeed have seen the "paranoid" behavior.

To illustrate the "miss" of reality in another way, suppose one is investigating children's attitudes toward parent's behavior or characteristics that have social connotations (being alcoholic, adhering to "foreign" customs or language, being in a given occupation, etc.). Expression of like or dislike, pride or shame, might be obtained with structured questions and limited alternative responses, which would very reasonably assess attitudes. On the other hand, more significant dimensions might be missed. We will suppose in this case that the child lacks a general framework with regard to each of the specific parent characteristics. Instead his feelings about his parent's adherence to particular customs or forms of speech might be situationally determined. ("I like them when we are alone in the family. I'm ashamed of them in front of my teacher.") Feelings about the father's occupation, although negative in two children, may have very different qualities. ("It makes me want to cry." "I wish I could run away." "I hate my father.")

The limitations and risks of a structured technique by no means rule it out as useful and appropriate for many attitude problems. An awareness of limitations should, however, influence instrument construction and most certainly the interpretation of findings from a given instrument.

The strengths of structured response techniques are apparent from a number of standpoints. When attitude areas disturbing to the individual (attitudes toward self, sex, parents, etc.) are investigated, an approach that takes away from the child the burden of verbalizing the painful thoughts has advantages. With highly specific, pointed questions and with carefully differentiated alternative responses, the structured approach also has the advantage of being able to explore systematically the subareas of attitudes and values and to sample widely along dimensions deemed important. By this means the extent to which a generalized response tendency does exist and the limits or boundaries of the attitude may be assessed. Structured techniques however, do not always sample either widely or well but rely on a few questions chosen rather arbitrarily to index the attitude. Adequacy of item sampling depends upon an explicit theory underlying item selection.

By using relatively unstructured stimuli and free responses it is assumed that artificialities of structured techniques are avoided and that the "natural" form of the attitude is obtained. To discover the structure of attitudes, freedom from adult-imposed organization is needed; to obtain the cognitive and motivational aspects, the child must be able to contribute freely and uniquely in the testing situation.

The question of relative validity and reliability of the two approaches has not been resolved in all-or-none fashion (again, see discussions in the literature cited above). This is certainly true for work with children; the specific technique and application determine the answer. The unstructured approaches have the potentiality but not the assurance of greater depth. In ferreting out test unreliabilities from attitude changes that have occurred in the child between measurement times, the open-ended responses (if they are sufficiently descriptive) have some advantage. Thus an attitude that appears changed on a score of negative-to-positive affect may contain unchanged cognitive and motivational factors. On the other hand, an attitude score may be the same on two testing circumstances, yet considerable cognitive reorganization may have taken place. These test-retest trends are more readily discernible in clinical type data than in the entirely prestructured response categories. If the research problem is one concerned with development and change in attitudes, the investigator will do well to choose his technique knowing its possibilities and limitations with respect to the amount of information he desires about the attitude change.

## THE HYPOTHETICAL AND IMAGINED VERSUS THE REAL

Attitudes can be approached obliquely or frontally in another respect; namely, by putting the issue in hypothetical or imagined terms or in real terms. Consider the following alternative forms that might be used in studying attitudes toward given social characteristics of peers:

1. "Suppose you were going to choose three boys to go with you on a camping trip. Which would you choose?" (A series of descriptions of hypothetical companions is given the subject from which he will make his selection.)

2. "We are teaming up next week

for field trips in botany. Which classmates would you prefer to have with
you on your trip? Name three."

An investigation of children's attitudes toward the father's authority role
in the family could proceed with questions of either of the following forms:

1. "Suppose you were dropped from
the high-school team because of poor
grades and when your father heard
about it he stopped your allowance.
How would you feel about that?"
2. "Think of the last time your father
punished you. Why was the punishment given? What did your father do?
How did you feel about that?"

Investigators have been somewhat
cavalier about choosing one or the
other of these techniques, when perhaps it is important to be more concerned about the inferences that are
made from responses to each kind of
question. Does the child subject perceive and respond to the hypothetical
and real differently? On what planes
of reality and generality are the responses to each approach? In the example on attitudes toward the father's
discipline, are the child's reactions a
reflection of his image of his own
father, a digest of fathers he has observed, a highlighted experience with
his own father, a stereotype of what
fathers are like, a fantasied hoped-for
father? Is one or another of these possibilities encouraged more by "hypothetical" or "real" approaches? The
familiar picture of the unbearably cruel
teacher and punitive mother portrayed
by children "playing school" or "playing house" raises similar questions as to

the plane on which the child is responding.

We have raised these questions of
data interpretation but have not found
methodological research that goes far
in sorting out answers. However, the
questions raised may leave the investigator somewhat more reserved and
modest in his conclusions and generalizations from attitude studies than he
might otherwise have been.

PERSONALIZED
OR IMPERSONALIZED
TECHNIQUES

In one approach to attitude measurements, the child is asked to react in
terms of his own attitudes. In an alternative approach, his attention is directed
away from himself to qualities of the
stimulus situation (how does the child
in the picture feel?). In the latter
the child's reponses, manifestly, are not
about himself, but it is assumed that his
handling of the materials is determined
by attributes within him. This "projective" approach is popular in attitude
research, for it avoids the direct approach to sensitive areas, and, with
some techniques, it avoids verbal responses. As a research method with
children it has a particular appeal, since
play materials and situations can be
readily transformed into projective devices (doll play, dramatic play, story
telling, etc.).

The theory and technology of projective methods is the topic of Chapter 14 and is not discussed here. Uses
of projective instruments for the measurement of attitudes and values involve
no special assumptions or problems

other than those that apply in the use of projective methods in the study of child personality. However, because attitude studies are often quite specific as to content, i.e., attitudes toward parental authority, siblings, sex identity, or illness are investigated, projective techniques tend to be somewhat more focused in research on attitudes than in personality research. For example, when using doll play to study attitudes, the investigator is likely to identify the dolls as representing given persons or roles (parent, sibling, teacher, or social-group member) or even to set up quite specific situations or interactions for eliciting the attitudes. Thus in a study of young children's attitudes toward sex differences Conn and Kanner (1947) supply a variety of dolls, to represent a new baby and the child's siblings. Questions are asked in such a way that the child answers for the dolls. Pointing to the doll, the interviewer asks, "What would he want to know about the baby?" "Which one of them wants to know where babies come from?" Attitudes of 4-year-old hospitalized children toward nurse, doctor, and medical procedures are approached similarly through doll play by Erickson (1958), again with the investigator carefully identifying each object for the subject.

Play media of many kinds are used, dolls and doll equipment more often than any other. Dolls, interestingly, are adaptable to ages beyond the doll-playing years if carefully staged. In the context of drama, for example, older children can be made interested (Chein and Evans, 1948). Puppets similarly are suitable for older children. (Older boys, however, may not always go along wholeheartedly.)

Pictures are used widely and are adaptable to many contents and to a wide age range. They have been applied fruitfully in studying attitudes in many different areas, attitudes toward parents (Grace and Lohmann, 1952), toward teachers (Biber and Lewis, 1949), toward self (Horowitz, 1943). The model in this kind of study is usually a pictured interaction, varying in ambiguity, presented with a series of interview questions. General questions of the "tell-me-what-is-happening" variety begin the series and are followed by more specific and directed questions, such as "What does he expect the doctor to do?" This picture approach is fine for the preschool-age child, and it is equally adaptable to the adolescent.

Not all uses of pictures in the study of attitudes or values are "projective." Pictures often serve as important interview props, but questions are directed toward the respondent: "Here is a picture of a boy getting a prize in school. Has this ever happened to you? What did your mother say when it happened? How do you feel about school?" An example of this approach is found in a study by Morgan and Gaier (1957) of child and parent reactions to punishment situations.

Incomplete stories and sentences are still other projective devices to which children respond reasonably well, depending on the appeal and provocative quality of the story or sentence (Harris and Tseng, 1957; Seaton, 1949). Verbal facility becomes an important factor here.

Although it is not difficult to devise

play approaches to which children will respond with interest, it is difficult to design projective tests of attitudes or values in such a way as to be certain that one has sampled the attitude process adequately. Have essential and enduring aspects been sampled in the particular limited doll play or story by the child? How far can one safely generalize about a child's "conscience" or social values from his play with dolls in a given structured circumstance or from his completions or interpretations of given story stimuli? At present, research is at the stage of quite arbitrary selection of projective situations, with not enough concern about problems of generalization. What is needed is more careful consideration on the part of the research worker of the specific assumptions he is making in devising a particular form of projective stimulus and in using the response to it as representative of a generalized attitude or value system.

In the preceding pages we have looked at major dimensions in which attitude techniques differ, whether the technique uses interview, test, scale, or behavior. We turn now to "techniques" in the specific sense. In coming to representative methods, it should be pointed out that the following paragraphs are not complete in themselves as analyses of each technique, but they bring up additional special points, unique to the given approach, which have not been discussed.

## INTERVIEW
## AND QUESTIONNAIRE METHODS

The interview, in one or another of its various forms, is the most frequently chosen approach to children's attitudes and values. Its adaptability to developmental differences of interviewees and to psychological requirements of various contents and problems makes the interview an extremely valuable research tool. Nonetheless, as in most research techniques, its efficiency depends on understanding the conditions that are created for the respondent by the technique, per se, and the conditions that are optimal for given research objectives. Some of the conditions of interviewer-child relationships and of question form, of particular relevance in the measurement of attitudes and values, are discussed here. Interviewing is treated more fully in Chapter 14.

One of the most critical factors in using the interview in the study of attitudes is the symbolic value of the interviewer for the child and its influence upon the research process. In experiments in learning and conditioning, characteristics of the examiner have been found to influence the course of learning, though the task is objective and often simple and the investigator is assumed to be "neutral." The interviewer's influence on the respondent in an investigation of attitudes and values is probably many times greater and more direct. One such influence, as pointed out earlier, stems from the interviewer's relationship to the child as a particular kind of authority. In his authority role, the investigator may be respected, rebelled against, distrusted, or admired by the child. His role may be very specific, such as teacher, doctor, law officer, or parent. Whatever the child's image of this authority and the codes governing his relation to the authority, it is likely that these factors will influence his response to the research task. We know that authority in general as well as specific authority roles carry different meanings for children depending on their age, social and cultural background, and specific experiences. Systematic biases can, therefore, become part of attitude findings by virtue of the interviewer-child relationship. When the interview is used to compare attitudes and values of children of different ages or of different social and cultural groups, the findings may include a spurious age-linked or social group-linked relationship that derives from the interviewer-child relationship. A hypothetical study illustrates this point. We wish to study values of honesty and altruism in children from two cultural groups. In one of these cultural groups parental control and dominance are strong and demanding; in the other, parent-child status differences are less marked and relationships are more informal. The interview questions explore circumstances and considerations under which selfish and unselfish motives, honest and dishonest behavior are accepted by the child. Our findings show considerably greater adherence to moral principles by children in the first than in the second group; but, before we conclude cultural differences and theorize as to inculcation processes in each, we shall want to consider a possible research error deriving from the relation between interviewer and child. How free do the children of the two backgrounds feel to express their own motives when these motives conflict with the pre-

sumed adult sanctions? In this instance, children governed by the more controlling parents may not feel free to express selfish motives to the adult or to compromise on honesty for fear of adult disapproval. Children brought up with the more informal relationship with parental authority, on the other hand, may be freer to reveal their own feelings. Is it these differences or is it differences in values that are reflected in the research findings? An adequate research design must take these several possibilities into account.

In addition to the interviewer's authority roles, there are other symbolic properties that may affect attitude measurements. The interviewer may symbolize a group, an ideology, or a convention with a direct bearing on the content of the interview. Thus one might expect a systematic biasing influence from the race of the interviewer in studies of racial attitudes, the sex of the interviewer in interviews about attitudes toward physical characteristics or sex, the age of interviewer in adolescents' discussions of dating patterns, of parent practices, etc. The more subtle personality characteristics of the interviewer are probably also significant. In a careful research design many sources of bias can be avoided; if they cannot, an attempt should be made to measure the nature of bias that exists.

These liabilities in the interviewer do not minimize the over-all importance of a personal relationship in obtaining valid data from the child subject. It is only when a supportive relationship has been established between interviewer and child that the delicate and ego-involving contents common in attitude and value studies can be studied with maximum effectiveness and with some understanding of the defenses, rebellion, reluctance, puzzlement, fears, etc., that are evoked by the research. We know from research experience that children do become distressed in investigations of attitudes (Clark, 1939; Goodman, 1953; Radke et al., 1949) that touch on highly emotional areas in their personal lives. Ethical considerations, therefore, place importance on the personal responsibility of the investigator for understanding and handling the distresses occasioned by him.

In contrast to the interview, with its personal relationship, is the written questionnaire. The two approaches create very different subjective settings for the child, although identical questions may appear in both instruments. A questionnaire distributed to groups of children at a time involves a minimal personal relationship between subject and investigator. Therefore, motivations for doing the task, cushions for possible traumata occurring as a result of the content, guards against idiosyncratic interpretations of the task, and handling of reverberations that continue within the child afterward—these factors must either be ignored or built into written instructions and group administrative procedures. The latter is not possible except in a general way.

Some investigators have proposed that anonymity, which is possible on a questionnaire, is an advantage in the study of affect-laden areas; they argue that the child will be freest under these circumstances, freer perhaps than with an interviewer, and will be less traumatized by revealing personal attitudes. There is some validity in this argument, but it is limited by another factor; namely, anonymity is feasible primarily in written, group-administered questionnaires with structured, check-list responses. As soon as free responses are called for, the subject's fear of revealing his identity and the children's difficulties in writing elaborate responses arise. Therefore, any advantages from anonymity are restricted by the limits of a highly structured measuring technique.

If one may hazard a formula for deciding between a written group questionnaire and a personal interview for investigating the attitudes of children, it might be as follows: faith in a written questionnaire for children should vary inversely with emotional content, expectation of resistance, likelihood of culturally stereotyped responses, and degree of deviance in the child group. Whenever it is used, the attitude questionnaire should be tested as an interview, to establish a "feel" for children's reactions to it, before applying it in the field.

Interviews and questionnaires are the research creations of professional persons who, as a class, have the "peculiarity" of being very verbal. It is well to remind oneself of this fact in devising questions for children. Many children, especially children whose home and community cultures do not foster verbalizing one's feelings and values and ideas, may find intensive questioning difficult and foreign to their ways.

The technique of asking questions,

which at first blush is a simple, common-sense procedure, is not such if it is to be used fruitfully with children. It requires a combination of various kinds of knowledge and skills.

1. A theoretical sophistication is necessary in the selection of questions. Specific questions only sample a general attitude or value. How adequate is the sample chosen in a given interview? What assumptions are made about the specific questions in relation to the attitude? These are questions of validity (see pp. 682–684); they are questions, too, that, if considered even speculatively, will help to avoid the more carelessly chosen stimulus items.

2. A technical knowledge of the influences of question form on response is important. The form of the question must not itself bias the response. Problems of "leading" questions, ambiguity, double-barreledness, and similar problems of item construction, which have been explored in the adult testing field, are applicable downward in the age scale, with added attention to the child's tendencies toward suggestibility and perserveration, discussed earlier.

3. Knowledge of the psychology of the respondent is a necessary guide in formulating questions. In research with children this is knowledge of developmental and social environmental factors (see earlier discussion, pp. 656–658, 669). In formulating questions for children, the adult's frame of reference inevitably enters in, variously sensing, variously distorting the child's perspective. On occasion, the child and adult may not be "speaking the same language" at all. An example of this is found in a study by Landreth and Johnson (1953) on the meaning of skin-color differences to preschool-age children. Social interactions were pictured. One face was omitted, and the child was asked to fill in the appropriate face by choosing from insets differing in "skin" color. Even though the children responded thoughtfully to the research task, the judgments of a portion of the subjects were made out of considerations quite foreign to the purposes of the investigators. White upper-class children in the sample perceived the task as a perceptual color-matching problem, whereas the other children, as ascertained by their remarks, perceived it as a racial question. The investigators were alert to this fact.

"Questions" in attitude interviews with children quite often are only part of the testing stimulus. Props of pictures, dolls, and story settings are used liberally as "provocations," for research experience has demonstrated the value of concretizing the child's task in these ways. The attitude questions can be phrased in terms of tangible objects or events furnished by the props. Not only are the ideas and concepts made easier by the tangible referents, but the child can respond in the language of actions and deeds, which is easier for him than summaries of his feelings, motives, or ideology. Although he cannot readily verbalize his ideologies regarding fairness, altruism, or morality, he can express specific acts or decisions indicative of his ideology. For example, when presented with the story of the two children who have broken their mothers' dishes, one who has broken ten dishes accidentally and the other who has broken one dish intentionally, children from preschool to high school are able to deal with this stimulus productively at their various levels of sophistication.

Another method of increasing the concreteness of questioning in exploring the attitudes of children is that of exposing them to a given limited experience (seeing a movie on warfare, playing or working with children of other national origin, or having the teacher carry out specified authority patterns) and questioning them after the experience. A funneling of specific to general questions (the reverse of the usual procedure) might be suited to this technique, i.e., starting with concrete events in the experience and moving toward generalizations beyond these specifics.

A suggestion by Merton et al. (1956), in a discussion of the focused interview with adults, seems very appropriate for children. When studying attitudes about events in the past or about complex relationships in the present, the investigator might stimulate the child to bring to mind the details of the critical events by describing them, "reliving" them. After this concretizing has occurred, questions of attitude are asked. This would mean a procedure something like the following: the investigator exploring attitudes toward siblings or toward illness would ask the child to describe what he and his brother had done together the preceding day or week or to describe when he has last been sick or when someone in his family had been sick. This would serve to focus the child's attention and to leave less doubt concerning his referents in responding to attitude questions.

## SPECIAL INTERVIEW OR QUESTIONNAIRE APPROACHES

*Sociometric Techniques.* An interview and questionnaire technique that has proved highly useful in attitude research is the sociometric technique (see Chapter 19 for a more general discussion of sociometric techniques). It has many variations, but its most typical form is to have each member of a group respond about every other group member in terms of some specified reaction or interaction. One may attempt to tap very general attitude sets or preferences with questions such as, "Who are the children that you like most? Least?" One may also focus on more narrowly specified dimensions, "Whose manners, appearance, ideas, etc., do you like best?" Or interactions, "Whom would you like to sit with, eat with, have at your birthday party?" (There are many discussions of this methodology; see Lindzey and Borgatta, 1954.)

As a technique for children, this has the advantage of asking simple questions. When a child is asked to choose the children he likes best, the ones he wants for friends, or does not like, one is not setting up a particularly difficult task, at least, not one entirely outside his usual experience. He has been making these decisions in the course of his everyday associations. Whether he is 4 or 14, the choice in some sense involves similar processes. Hence the technique can be useful for studies related to age changes, in which the equivalence of verbal stimuli at successive ages is often a difficult question.

The emphasis in sociometric attitude studies may be on individual children in the stimulus group, in terms of the attitudes expressed toward them by the respondents, or on the attitudes of the respondents as they are revealed in choices and rejections of stimulus children. For example, the stimulus children may be subgrouped by the investigator (into boys and girls, whites and Negroes, preadolescents and adolescents, upper class and lower class, etc.). Choices on sociometric questions are interpreted in terms of these subgroups. Thus, what are the respondents' attitudes regarding sex, maturity, class, etc.? Overchoosing or underchoosing of members of a given subgroup beyond a chance expectancy is taken as an indication of a positive or negative attitude. (See Lindzey and Borgatta, 1954, for statistical methods.)

Several assumptions are made in studies of this kind: (1) the subgroupings in the mind of the investigator are also in the awareness of the children, and (2) when a selective bias appears, the subgroup characteristics, and not some other unknown correlated factor, are the basis of choice. Let us suppose that we found children's choices on a playground predominantly within their own sex group. We might conclude that attitudes of preference for own sex are very strong. However, when we decide to investigate further, we find that these children have been at-tending sex-segregated schools. Thus prior acquaintance enters as a factor to be reckoned with. The problem of correlated variables, known and unknown, complicate interpretations of sociometric data. Whatever the specific purpose of using sociometric techniques (to assess group cleavage, personal preference, etc.), an assumption is always being made that the variable that is real to the investigator is real to the subject and is not confounded by other correlated variables.

The adaptability of the sociometric technique, in form and purpose, has added to its popularity as an approach with children. With it one may elicit and compare the wished for, the expected, the accustomed, the sanctioned. ["With whom would you like to be friends? Who will choose you as a friend? With whom have you played most? Whom should you (not) choose as a friend?"]. Questions may be directed to affect ("Who is liked or disliked?"), to intentions regarding behavior ("Whom will you choose as a partner?"), or to cognitive elements in perception and choice. In the guess-who technique, an example of this approach, the child is asked to look among his associates and to tell, "Who likes to boss others around," "Who is someone that everybody likes," "Who is afraid," etc.

The sociometric method may be directed with equal ease to the child's attitudes concerning his face-to-face groups (such as his class or club) or to attitudes concerning hypothetical groups that can be defined simply verbally or pictorially. A favored approach with children is to present pictures, individual photographs, such as the Horowitz "Faces" test (1938), or group scenes in which readily identifiable characteristics are represented (age, sex, race, etc.). The subject is asked to indicate which of the pictured persons he would choose as fulfilling given descriptions. Sometimes the child's immediate interaction group is pictured, in this way making certain that each group member is brought to the attention of the respondent. Yarrow et al. (1958) followed this procedure in studying the formation of interpersonal preferences and perceptions in children's groups in the early stages of getting acquainted. By placing before the respondent the pictures of all the children in the group, difficulties of not remembering names and the possibility of overlooking certain children were bypassed, and comparisons and contrasts among children were probably made easier.

Sociometric adaptations blend into other assessment procedures that require the child to sort individuals along prescribed dimensions. Thus rank orderings, social distance tests, and certain projective tests are akin to sociometric methods. Of the social distance test, a bit more should be said, for it could be used, more than it has been, for assessing the social or personal "distances" that the child feels. In its original form (Bogardus, 1925), this test, of course, dealt with the willingness of the individual to admit members of different national groups into various social relationships (entrance to country, residence in neighborhood, acceptability as a marriage partner). The relationships were roughly "scaled" in terms of the distance or intimacy of the relationship. One need not dwell on the inappropriateness of these particular items for children (below adolescence), but it should be apparent that items more critical in the child's life space might be devised and presented in this form. The form of the test is appealingly simple and can be made meaningful to the child.

Not only in studying social attitudes toward different groups of people but as a technique for exploring attitudes of "personal distance," this approach appears to have potentialities that have not been used with children. For example, the "distance" between the child and various significant adult figures, between child and different family members, or between child and other children might be explored in this manner.

The common characteristic in the techniques discussed in this section is that of obtaining the child's placement of persons relative to one another on a variety of yardsticks. The data furnish meaningful "summary" judgments or decisions of the respondents, but there are limitations in such decisions in attitude assessment. Sociometric choice cannot be automatically equated with attitudes, for situational and personality factors (e.g., unfamiliarity with stimulus persons or conscious distortion) can enter into choice. Sociometric and related techniques are best used, therefore, in the company of other approaches. It is important to measure in this way the correspondence between sociometric data and independent criteria of attitudes as estimates of validity, but it is equally important to use several techniques planfully, with the objective of obtaining data from them on different qualities or aspects of the attitude, thus to arrive at a better understanding of the nature of the attitude.

*Attitude Scales.* If groups of individuals are to be compared or if the effects of particular experiences are to be measured in "before" and "after" assessments, an attitude "score" may be desired. This requires the development of a scale. With adults, the scaling of attitudes and opinions is a highly developed field and constitutes a large body of literature in psychology and sociology. The standard techniques of scale construction are amply reported (see Thurston and Chave, 1929; Likert, 1932; Stouffer et al., 1950; Green, 1954, as well as many textbook discussions). Here we are concerned not with the technicalities of scale construction but with the question of how well the capacities of children make them suitable subjects for the use of scales.

The construction of an attitude scale requires the selection of a set of items to which the individual can respond (indicating his agreement, preference, approval, and the like) and from which he can be assigned a score on a quantitative continuum. The response model for most scales is a simple one: a yes-no type of decision or a graded yes-no. The items follow one upon the other, calling for rapid shifts of problem and focus by the respondent. In some scales the items are manifestly quite distinct. In other scales the items may vary only slightly on the same theme. The subjects' comprehension, concentration, and openness are essential for valid scale responses.

The main considerations when using scales with children are the following:

1. One cannot use scales with children unless one has evidence that the children have reasonably organized or crystallized attitudes on the issue studied (see earlier discussions of developmental and experiential factors in language and thought of the child and problems of meaningless and perseverative responses on structured questions).

2. The requirements of responding to a battery of questions would not seem to be especially trying to school-age children accustomed to tests at school. However, length and difficulty level of a scale should be considered in terms of the age and other characteristics of the children being studied.

3. One cannot assume that because questions are consistently and meaningfully ordered for adults they will be similarly ordered for children. It is necessary to test scalability on children of the particular developmental age one is studying. Just as scales do not readily transfer from one culture to another, so, too, they cannot be assumed to transfer from adult to child culture. For example, attitudes regarding property, components of prejudice, attitudes toward illness, age, and sex could be expected to differ for children and adults. Children must themselves be used in scale construction, much as the taste panel for flavored drugs consists of a group of children. Comparisons of adult

and child scale-criterion groups may indeed be interesting developmental data in themselves.

In general, scales are useful in the measurement of children's attitudes when it makes sense to deal with a single dimension; too often investigators attempt to force multidimensional problems into the Procrustean bed of one dimension because scales seem "scientific." It may be well to look at some of the kinds of research problems on attitudes and values that do not lend themselves to scale measurement. If an investigator is interested in the formation of attitudes or values, in the *processes* of change over time or as the result of identifiable experiences, in the constellation of forces maintaining an attitude, or resisting or creating change in an attitude, more "qualitative" measures would seem necessary.

Through a detailed report of data on a preschool child's values regarding the use of aggression, we can perhaps see more concretely what one could and could not measure with a scale approach. Murphy, Murphy, and Newcomb (1937, pp. 407–409) cite a study by Fite of children's values regarding aggression. The following is part of the description of one child just under 4 years of age.

When Nancy was asked what she would do if another child hit her, she said she would tell the teacher. Would she hit him back? "No, because I want to be good because my mother and father say I should, so I'm trying my best." And later she generalizes still further; "You have to tell the parents. You must tell everything to the parents 'cause they're bigger. The child asks the parents what to do and then they help the child." . . . In a repetition of the

situation two weeks later with the second series of pictures, her strongly filial attitudes held up pretty well. No, she would not hit back, and if her aggressor kept at her, she would call her mother to make him stop. "Mother would say, 'This boy hurts, and 'cause it's not nice and would he please take his hands off 'cause it's not nice.'" The experimenter tried to make it harder: "But suppose you were at school, and you called the teacher, and the teacher didn't hear you." Nancy admitted in that case that she'd have to "push his hand off." Then for a moment her feelings slipped through: "Then I would show him how it feels." But as if in contrition over that admission, she replied to the next question, "Would you hit him?" with, "I would be nice and good. I would give him a lollypop."

Several months later, at the beginning, when the experimenter asked if she should make her own doll hit Nancy's, Nancy responded, "Yes," rather casually. But at the actual hitting, her face grew serious, and at the suggestion that she make her doll hit the experimenter's, she drew her doll back from the experimenter's and, with a very anxious expression said, "No, I don't want to." She seemed quite near the point of tears, and to each question about hitting replied vehemently that hitting was not all right: "I know because my father and mother say so, I know it." Both the experimenter and the assisting research worker were struck by the unhappiness of her tone and expression, and the vehemence with which she pulled her doll back when asked to make it hit. Might there be a reason to suspect that in some way her confidence in what her parents said was being undermined, and that the degree of emotionality shown was a sign of some conflict?

Six months later, she replied with complete casualness that she didn't think it right to hit people. " 'Cause it hurts. 'Cause I felt it one time." (Note that "it hurts" seems to be the first true "reason" to develop.) "I think it's not so good— neither does my mother."

This time, when asked, "If some other child hits you first, then what's the thing to do?" Nancy's immediate response is, "Hit them back." Moreover, she's not above romancing a little to back this up: " 'Cause that's what my mother tells me every night before I go to bed." (The pure fiction of this statement was checked with the parents.) Also, another reason was mentioned: " 'Cause that's what sometimes other children do to me." Now it seems that in fantasy she has loaded her parents on her side and in actuality she has her social experience to back her up, and thus perfect accord is made.

A scale score could register this child's resistance to the use of aggression, but it could not reflect the emotion with which the child responded nor her competing impulses. It might not have marked the change at the sixth-month questioning, when the child still thought it "not right" to hit people, but had resolved much of the conflict that she had portrayed in her earlier responses.

Before leaving the topic of scaling attitudes, it should be noted that it is possible to make use of the principles of scaling, yet not obtain data through a scale composed of structured questions with fixed answer categories. Children may be asked questions about their attitudes toward aggression or adult supervision and may be allowed to give free responses. The investigator can assign responses to scale categories. Kohn and Carroll (1960) used this procedure in an interview study with 10-year-olds concerning their social relationships with peers and parents. For example, a number of questions in the interview schedule pertain to the child's attitudes toward his relationships with his father. Responses to these items were assigned categories by the interviewer. A Guttman-type scale was constructed for these items.

Behavioral measures of attitudes and values might be handled similarly for some research purposes. Data obtained in observational records of behavior in experimental or natural situations could be coded and scaled (see pp. 679–682). Investigators working with children have not generally made use of these procedures, but they would appear to be useful and worth exploring.

## PERSONAL DOCUMENTS AND SELF-RATINGS

This approach has serious limitations for systematic study of attitudes and values with children as with adults (Allport, 1942). The occasional productive use that has been made of children's themes, artistic products, diaries, and the like, deserves passing reference. The casual and often accidental accumulation of such materials is an important limiting factor in their usefulness in research. In general, these documents can be revealing as data used with more systematically gathered data. In achieving clinical understanding of a given child, they may also contribute substantially.

Paintings and drawings, especially, have interested investigators working with children at all ages (Wolff, 1943), though more often in the interests of personality diagnosis than in attitude measurement. Pupils' themes have been put into service in various studies as sources of data on attitudes and values, although the extraneous and uncontrollable factors that enter into such productions (such as literary ability and secondary motivations as in a classroom theme) raise major reservations. They may, however, be sufficiently diagnostic to reflect group differences or to serve as relatively gross screening techniques.

In the company of a more "solid" technique the child's day-to-day products can act as catalysts for verbal expression of attitudes. Yarrow (see Chapter 14, p. 570) reports a highly successful technique for getting at certain personal data on 5- and 6-year-olds. The child brings his scrapbook of recent experiences and collections to the interview. Semistandard questions are explored in the context of these materials, with the child's involvement greatly enhanced. As a technique for approaching attitudes toward self, this approach appears to have interesting possibilities.

Self-ratings by the child have rarely been tried. However, sociometric questions are sometimes turned on the child himself, i.e., asking him by whom would he be chosen or for which of a series of guess-who items would he pick himself? From his choices, inferences are possible about his self regard. More direct self-ratings by children would probably suffer from the same kinds of distortions and biases found in their use with adult subjects.

## BEHAVIORAL INDICES OF ATTITUDES AND VALUES

Thus far only verbal indices of attitudes and values have been discussed, although behavior may also serve as the basis for inference. Observations of behavior can be made and coded in terms of attitudes and values. Behavioral studies have several strong appeals: they avoid verbal barriers, they can (but may not always) circumvent self-conscious and possibly threatening revelations, and identical behavioral indices can be used for children of a wide range of age levels and cultural backgrounds. They can also be supplemented by verbal responses, either by including verbal data in the observational records or by following observational records with verbal tests or interviews. Behavioral measures are suited to experimental as well as naturalistic approaches.

There are drawbacks, too. First, the behavior that one would like to observe in order to assess attitudes or values may not be easily induced. The critical behaviors may be very infrequent in occurrence, and thus a very large volume of irrelevant data may have to be recorded and analyzed in order to achieve a reasonable sample of the relevant data. Then, too, behavior (as well as verbal responses) may be embroidered or faked. To be certain that comparable behavioral circumstances are being observed for different subjects and at different times and that there are no important determinants of the behavior other than the attitudes or values in which one is interested, very careful prescriptions must be laid down for behavioral measures. This applies equally to contrived and natural situations. Here an explicit theory or set of hypotheses linking behavior with attitude or value is of help to the investigator in guiding his sampling of behavior and his analysis of behavior,

Let us consider an example of the possible use of behavior in a study of attitudes. Suppose the investigator's purpose is to study attitudes of children toward physical handicaps in their peers, and he decides to use classroom observations of behavior as his data source. In each classroom there are several children with visible physical handicaps. He will do well to specify in advance exactly what information concerning attitudes he will attempt to obtain and in what behaviors he assumes the attitude will be manifested. Thus he may be interested solely in general affective qualities of attitudes, which he may define behaviorally as approach and avoidance behavior of the nonhandicapped toward handicapped children. Approach and avoidance may be defined concretely in terms of choice of peers for desired classroom functions, as partners, etc. He may be interested in the more differentiated cognitive aspects of attitudes. He will then want behavioral data on a wider spectrum of personal interactions, coded in terms such as subordinate-dominant relations, nurturant-succorant interactions, aggressive-affiliative reactions, etc. He may be interested in attitudes in relation to specific situations. In this case, he will need to specify situational factors carefully.

Since behavior in school may be governed by an institutional ideology of democratic relations, the investigator might also want to obtain behavior that is more "private," reasoning that under such circumstances the more personal and genuine attitudes would be displayed. For this purpose, his design may include contrived (though to the child, natural) situations to get at the child's behavior when he is not aware that he is being identified or observed.

None of these suggested behavioral indices is a "pure" measure of attitudes. For each, the investigator must be concerned with the things that influence behavior but are neither attitudes nor values. For example, the immediate environment may influence the opportunities for certain behaviors to occur. Classroom seating arrangements or ability groupings may thus influence peer choices. Personality differences contribute another important, nonattitudinal influence.

The use of behavioral data requires observational techniques for data gathering. For discussions of basic issues of observational techniques—sampling, observational schemes, recording devices, and analysis schemes—the reader is referred to Chapter 3 and to comprehensive treatments of the topic, such as that of Heyns and Lippitt (1954). Variations of behavioral designs that have been used successfully in the investigation of children's attitudes and values are reviewed there.

Many studies of children make use of behavior "once removed" from the child's own behavior by asking him to use test materials in certain ways. The subject is asked to choose dolls or pictures to represent his responses (Clark and Clark, 1939) or to manipulate dolls or other play materials to convey his ideas and feelings. In this nonverbal approach, complex stimuli can be used and children can respond meaningfully who could not manage the same problems verbally. For instance, several groups of investigators have succeeded in studying awareness and values of young children, in regard to social class and social roles, by introducing class and role symbols into backgrounds in doll play (housing and street scenes of differing economic levels, costume differences, etc.). (Hartley and Schwartz, 1951; Trager and Yarrow, 1952). In these studies interview questions supplement performance data.

Dolls are used by Chein and Evans (1948) in studying social attitudes in ways acceptable to older children. Subjects, 7 to 14 years of age, are supplied with miniature "movie sets" and asked to provide action and dialogue for standardized story situations. Role playing may be used similarly. The investigator may pose a problem, take the role of one of the significant actors, and have the child assume the other role. The investigator may take the role of the child and ask the child subject to assume the role of doctor or mother. This approach is highly revealing in individual cases in which considerable rapport and comfort have been established. It has been more of a clinical than a research technique. However, the possibility of its development for systematic research purposes appears feasible. Stanton et al. (1956) describe this type of technique as they have used it for survey research with adults, on problems of parent-child relations, housing, and marital adjustment. The approach seemed to work very well. It should be noted, however, that there was usually some special entry into the households; it was not simply a polling type of contact. This technique seems worth more study with children.

Experimental situations that do not rely on the child's representation of behavior with actors, but which obtain behavior from the child in his own right, have an important place in research on children's values. Most of these experimental situations set up choice or decision situations. In level of aspiration or problem-solving designs, in which achievement values or attitudes of self regard are the object of research, the situation is likely to be set up with a testlike quality (Lewin et al., 1944). More often, however, the investigator is interested in contriving a "natural" choice situation for the display of values, one in which the child is not aware of the fact that he is being tested.

An extensive series of ingenious behavioral tests of values with this "real" quality about them were devised by Hartshorne and May, a long time ago (1928). The "tests," in which opportunities to cheat in school work and at games, to steal, to give false answers about themselves, to choose between personal or group rewards, between keeping or sharing with a needy person, and so on, were devised, were given to 11,000 school-age children. No study of children's values has since been carried out on such an impressive scale, both qualitatively and quantitatively.

A few studies following this model have been reported. One by Wright (1942) used an experimental laboratory technique successfully for studying selfishness and generosity in children,

5 to 8 years old. She used simple but child-motivating situations in which the child retained or shared toys with other children variously described to him by the experimenter. Selfish or generous behavior was studied in relation to the perceived traits of the other children (such as their degree of need).

It would seem most fruitful to review and replicate the Hartshorne and May studies (1928, 1929) with the benefits of modern developments in observational techniques and within a systematic theoretical framework in which the antecedents and personality correlates of differences in value orientations are considered. This approach combines the advantages of experimental control with genuineness of the situation and ego-involvement by the subjects. In devising experimental studies, the desires for experimental cleanness and for the intactness of the value or attitude process are often in conflict. Except in rather rare designs, one or the other tends to suffer. Sacrifice of experimental controls means a loss in the explanatory power of the data. Reduction of the attitude or value to a simple standard decision in an activity that is not ego-involving may leave only a tortured inference that the processes being measured are attitudes or values. Undoubtedly, one of the most difficult steps in designing experimental studies is the devising of reasonable and effective motivating conditions for children in which behavior indicative of attitudes or values can be elicited. Of utmost importance is the experimenter's sensitivity to what constitutes reasonable and effective motivating conditions for chil-

dren; reasonable in the sense that ethical principles are not compromised; effective in that children can comprehend and can be emotionally involved in the situation. Unfortunately, the nature of values and attitudes is such that the contrived tests are potentially disturbing to the child. Consider, for example, the anxiety and guilt that may follow the "undetected" and rewarded dishonesty that the child exhibits in the experimental situation or the severe conflicts occasioned by tempting the child in areas of moral prohibitions. Any investigation in this field will do well to have built into it a measure of the impact of the research upon the child; this can be done by planned observations or interviews during and after the procedure. The research design should also include criteria for a decision to terminate a procedure with a given child, should the procedure cause marked disturbance in him.

To avoid the necessity of inducing value issues experimentally and to be able to study powerful value issues, research has turned to field studies of behavior in its natural settings. In field designs several procedural choices are open. The completely untampering approach is that of the participant observer. His approach may be that of the anthropologist. Studies of the value systems of primitive cultures and the inculcation of values in their young have been made with this method. It relies heavily upon the synthesizing capabilities of a trained observer living for a time in the culture and having wide access to its "inner workings." (Mead, 1928; Whiting, 1941). Such studies yield what may be regarded as a case study of the attitudes and values of a group, and like individual case studies can run the gamut from unsystematized description to an observational account fashioned by a specific theoretical position.

To go beyond case studies of individual children or groups of children, it is clearly necessary to introduce the familiar requirements of systematic research procedures: specified criteria for sampling behavior, for categorizing behavior, and for recording behavior. Only in this way has the investigator the bases for comparing or drawing conclusions about values and attitudes expressed by different children, at different times, in unlike circumstances. (See Chapter 3 for analysis of methodological problems of field studies.)

By investing the participant observer with the philosophy and tools of the experimenter, field studies and experimental studies are brought somewhat closer together in techniques. Researchers in roles such as teacher or counselor or nurse can study the children's attitudes and values in natural settings. However, studies of this kind are few in comparison with the investigations in which verbal responses of children are used.

The observer in a field study can proceed very much as he would in laboratory group studies. Time sampling, event sampling, running accounts, and precoded rating categories are techniques transferable from the laboratory to the field.

Unless a natural situation presents itself, in which the values or attitudes of interest to the investigator have a high likelihood of manifesting themselves, the naturalistic approach may be somewhat sterile. If, on the other hand, one is able to find the "right" circumstances, extremely powerful and ego-involving attitudes and values, which could not be duplicated in the laboratory, can be studied. One might, for example, do studies of children's behavior, expressive of attitudes or values in situations of illness or disaster, in first days at school, in separations from family or friends, or in serious competitive activities.

## VALIDITY AND RELIABILITY

Problem formulation and data-gathering in research on children's attitudes and values have been the emphases in this chapter. Problems of analysis have generally been slighted in the belief that characteristics of children necessitate research adaptations mainly in the problem formulation and data-gathering phases. Sometimes, however, methods of analysis are also involved. When properties of data from children differ from "parallel" data from adults, identical analysis procedures in the scoring or ordering of responses or in the interpretation of findings may not be justified. Such examples have been noted, as in attitude scaling, in which scalability for adults may not mean scalability for children (p. 675), and in the personality interpretations of rigidity in attitudes of children and adults (p. 658). The importance of designing studies of attitudes or values, with data analysis as much in mind as data collection, is underscored; the fuzzy nature of indices of attitudes and values only makes the demands on analysis more stringent. For the specific and detailed discussions of data analysis, the reader is referred to manuals and papers dealing with analytic procedures in social and psychological research, such as Berelson (1956); Festinger and Katz (1953); Jahoda et al. (1951).

Questions of validity and reliability of attitude measures are issues at all stages of a research project, and some attention is due them in regard to the techniques that have been discussed for children. Investigators in this field often ignore these issues. The difficulties in validating inferred processes such as attitudes and values are obvious major deterrents. However, some examination of attitude and value assessments is usually possible in terms of what they predict, how they relate to other independent measures of presumably the same processes, or how they conform to an accepted theory or validated relationship.

Because data on attitudes and values vary greatly from items that are "self-evident" in meaning ("Which classmates do you like best?") to items requiring complex inferences ("What will the boys in this picture do if the teacher asks them to stop what they are doing?"), the questions of validity are varied too. Face validity is more readily accepted for items of the first illustration, in which the response has a common meaning for all, than for data of the second kind. The reliance on face validity has in its support the argument that we are, after all, interested in the subjective orientation of the child, his reality, and his evaluation of a situation presented to him in the testing. This position is defensible only if the investigator is content to restrict his conclusions very carefully. However, he is in a stronger position by comparing results based on his verbal instrument or behavioral test against theoretically reasonable external criteria. Although not a test of "validity" in the strictest sense (since the criteria are not direct measures of the inferred variables), such checks add to the known character and meaning of the attitudinal data obtained.

The reliability of children's responses is also very puzzling to the investigator. To characterize a process in the individual child, to compare individuals or groups, or to predict to other processes, a consistency or stability in the attitude measurement is necessary. It is well documented that several factors tend to contribute instability to children's responses. The tendency for children's reactions to be situationally determined to a very considerable extent has often been observed. This applies more to younger than older children. Consistency in retest responses may, therefore, be low, even though at the time of the test the child may truly be expressing his feelings of the moment. This suggests the necessity for a wide sampling of an attitude within the child subject before one assumes "a generalized response tendency" or a stable measure. Also, it calls for closer attention to situational influences in the measurement circumstances themselves, which may contribute to stability or instability. Among these influences, the relationship of investigator to child is an exceedingly influential situational variable (see pp. 668–669).

Changes over time as a function of

maturational and experiential factors may be anticipated in such fluid and formative processes as children's attitudes and values. There may be more dramatic changes, and changes that occur within shorter time intervals, for the child than the adult. Teasing out the various sources of change may be exceedingly difficult. A dramatic example of change on retest after a new experience in the life of a first grader is shown in the following: a Negro child in an all-Negro school in a northern city was examined in interviews intended to measure racial attitudes. Negro and white dolls were used in the interviews. On the days between interviews a white substitute teacher replaced the regular teacher who was ill. A marked change in content occurred in the child's doll play. The adult white doll figured prominently in nurturant interaction with the child dolls, both Negro and white, in the second test. In the first test the adult white doll had been completely ignored. Thus the careful investigator of children's attitudes and values must be alert to more than the characteristics of his testing techniques if he is to avoid errors in research conclusions.

## Conclusions

Attitudes and values of children have, for a rather long period, occupied fringe areas in the systematic literature of child development. Their incorporation into more general developmental theory would be valuable in developmental and social psychology alike. Their usefulness has been demonstrated in investigating the social contexts of children. The intrafamilial contexts, the effects of parental handling upon children's attitudes and value systems, and the interactive effects of children's attitudes and values and parental handling upon other consequents in child development are areas in which these concepts can be given further exploration.

The investigation of inferred processes, such as attitudes and values, makes difficult demands on research technology and on the technique of the researcher; the qualities of the instrument and the context and motivation that the investigator provides are inseparable components. Children are difficult research subjects, and only the beginnings of methodological research bearing on their functioning as research subjects have been made. For example, we need to inquire much more carefully into fundamental questions, such as the conditions motivating children in research tasks. Can candy M & M's be used like food pellets with rats to reward the child and to engage and maintain his motivation in performing and answering questions? It seems doubtful. We have progressed in more sophisticated formulation of research problems. We must keep pace in our sophistication relating to the child as a participant in the more varied research in which he is now included.

No one seriously engaged in worthy research on the normal adult personality or on adult attitudes and values would place knowledge of an investigatory technique as the primary value and requirement of the investigator and knowledge of adult motivation as the secondary. Yet this ideology and practice are still current in research with children. Because children are not just simplified adults and because knowledge of the developing organism is not acquired incidentally, while plying a technique, this ideology can only impede research progress. A closer balance in the investigator of knowledge and interest in technique and theory with knowledge and interest in the child will result in sounder contributions to the psychology of children and development.

# REFERENCES

Allport, G. 1935. Attitudes. In Murchison, C. (Ed.), *Handbook of social psychology.* Worcester: Clark Univer. Press. Pp. 798–844.

———. 1942. The use of personal documents in psychological science. *Social Science Research Council Bull.,* 49, 210 pp.

Ammons, R. 1950. Reactions in a projective doll-play interview of white males, two to six years of age, to differences in skin color and facial features. *J. genet. Psychol.,* 76, 323–341.

Berelson, B. 1956. Content analysis. In G. Lindzey (Ed.), *Handbook of social psychology.* Cambridge: Addison-Wesley. 1, pp. 488–518.

Biber, Barbara, and Claudia Lewis. 1949. An experimental study of what young school children expect from their teachers. *Genet. Psychol. Monogr.,* 40, 7–94.

Bogardus, E. 1925. Measuring social distance, *J. appl. Sociol.,* 9, 299–308.

Campbell, D. 1950. The indirect assessment of social attitudes. *Psychol. Bull.,* 47, 15–38.

Chein, I., and Mary Evans. 1948. The movie study game: A projective test of interracial attitudes for use with Negro and white children. *Amer. Psychol.,* 3, 268.

Clark, K., and Mamie Clark. 1939. The development of consciousness of self and the emergence of racial identification in Negro

preschool children. *J. soc. Psychol.,* 10, 591–599.

Conn, J., and L. Kanner. 1947. Children's awareness of sex differences. *J. Child Psychiat.,* 1, 3–57.

Deri, Susan, Dorothy Dinnerstein, J. Harding, and A. Pepitone. 1948. Techniques for the Diagnosis and Measurement of Intergroup Attitudes and Behavior. *Psychol. Bull.,* 45, 248–271.

Doob, L. 1947. The Behavior of Attitudes. *Psychol. Rev.,* 54, 135–156.

Eberhart, J. 1942. Attitudes toward property: A genetic study by the paired comparison method. *J. genet. Psychol.,* 60, 3–35.

Erickson, Florence. 1958. Play interviews for four-year-old hospitalized children. *Soc. Res. Child Develpm. Monogr.,* 23, 7–67.

Festinger, L., and D. Katz. 1953. *Research methods in the behavioral sciences.* New York: Dryden. 646 pp.

Frenkel-Brunswik, Else, and J. Havel. 1953. Prejudice in the interviews of children. *J. genet. Psychol.,* 82, 91–136.

Goodman, Mary Ellen. 1952. *Race awareness in young children.* Cambridge: Addison-Wesley. 280 pp.

Grace, H., and Joan Lohmann. 1952. Children's reactions to stories depicting parent-child conflict situations. *Child Develpm.,* 23, 61–74.

Green, B. 1954. Attitude Measurement. In G. Lindzey (Ed.), *Handbook of social psychology,* Cambridge: Addison-Wesley. 1, pp. 335–369.

Harris, D., and S. Tseng. 1957. Children's attitudes toward peers and parents as revealed by sentence completions. *Child Develpm.,* 28, 401–411.

Hartley, E., and S. Schwartz. 1951. A pictorial doll play approach for the study of children's intergroup attitudes. *Int. J. Opinion Attitude Res.,* 5, 261–270.

Hartshorne, H., M. May, and J. Maller. 1929. *Studies in Service and Self-control,* New York: Macmillan. 559 pp.

Hartshorne, H., and M. May. 1928. *Studies in deceit,* New York: Macmillan. I–II, 414 pp., 306 pp.

Horowitz, E. 1936. The development of attitudes toward the Negro. *Arch. Psychol.,* 1–47.

Horowitz, Ruth. 1943. A pictorial method for study of self-identification in pre-school children. *J. genet. Psychol.*, **62**, 135–148.

——, and E. Horowitz. 1938. The development of social attitudes in children. *Sociometry*, 1, 301–338.

Heyns, R., and R. Lippitt. 1954. Systematic observational techniques. In G. Lindzey (Ed.), *Handbook of social psychology*, Cambridge: Addison-Wesley. 1, pp. 370–403.

Inhelder, Bärbel, and J. Piaget. 1958. *The teenager as logician as in the growth of logical thinking from childhood to adolescence.* New York: Basic Books. 356 pp.

Jahoda, Marie, M. Deutsch, and S. Cook. 1951. *Research methods in social relations.* New York: Dryden. I–II, 726 pp.

Kalhorn, Joan. 1944. Values and sources of authority among rural children. In K. Lewin, C. Meyers, Joan Kalhorn, M. Farber, and J. French. Authority and frustration. *Univer. Iowa Stud. Child Welf.*, **20**, 308 pp.

Kohn, M., and Eleanor Carroll. 1960. Social Class and the Allocation of Parental Responsibilities. *Sociometry*.

Krech, D., and R. Crutchfield. 1948. *Theory and problems of social psychology.* New York: McGraw-Hill. 639 pp.

Landreth, Catherine, and Barbara Johnson. 1953. Young children's responses to a picture and inset test designed to reveal reactions to persons of different skin color. *Child Develpm.*, **24**, 63–80.

Lewin, K. 1935. *Dynamic theory of personality.* New York: McGraw-Hill. 286 pp.

——. 1944. Constructs in psychology and psychological ecology. In K. Lewin, C. Meyers, Joan Kalhorn, M. Farber, and J. French, Authority and frustration. *Univer. Iowa Stud. Child Welf.*, **20**, 308 pp.

——, Tamara Dembo, L. Festinger, and Pauline Sears. 1944. Level of aspiration. In J. Hunt, *Personality and behavior disorders.* New York: Ronald. 1, pp. 333–378.

Likert, R. 1932. A technique for the measurement of attitudes. *Arch. Psychol.*, pp. 1–55.

Lindzey, G., and E. Borgatta. 1954. Sociometric Measurement. In G. Lindzey (Ed.), *Handbook of social psychology.* Cambridge: Addison-Wesley. 1, pp. 405–444.

Mead, Margaret. 1928. *Coming of age in Samoa.* New York: Morrow. 297 pp.

Meltzer, H. 1926. Talkativeness about, in relation to knowledge of social concepts in children. *Pedag. Sem.*, **33**, 497–507.

——. 1943. Differences in children's attitudes to parents. *J. genet. Psychol.*, **62**, 311–326.

Merton, R., M. Fiske, and Patricia Kendall. 1956. *The focussed interview.* Glencoe, Ill.: Free Press. 186 pp.

Morgan, P., and E. Gaier. 1957. Types of reactions in punishment situations in the mother-child relationship. *Child Develpm.*, **28**, 161–174.

Murphy, G., Lois Murphy, and T. Newcomb. 1937. *Experimental social psychology.* New York: Harper. 1121 pp.

Radke, Marian, Helen Trager, and Hadassah Davis. 1949. Social perceptions and attitudes of children. *Genet. Psychol. Monogr.*, **40**, 327–447.

Sears, Pauline. 1958. Developmental psychology. *Annu. Rev. Psychol.*, Palo Alto: Annual Reviewers. P. 135.

Seaton, J. 1949. A projective experiment using incomplete stories with multiple-choice endings. *Genet. Psychol. Monogr.*, **40**, 149–228.

Stouffer, S., L. Guttman, E. Suchman, P. Lazarsfeld, Shirley Star, and J. Clausen. *Measurement and prediction.* Vol. 4. *Studies in social psychology in World War II.* Princeton: Princeton Univer. Press. 722 pp.

Stanton, H., K. Back, and E. Litwak. 1956. Role-playing in survey research, *Amer. J. Sociol.*, **62**, 172–176.

Temple, Rita, and Elizabeth Amen. 1944. A study of anxiety reactions in young children by means of a projective technique. *Genet. Psychol. Monogr.*, **30**, 61–113.

Thurstone, L., and E. Chave. 1929. *The measurement of attitudes.* Chicago: Univer. Chicago Press. 96 pp.

Trager, Helen, and Marian Radke Yarrow. 1952. *They learn what they live.* New York: Harper. 392 pp.

Whiting, J. 1941. *Becoming a Kwoma.* New Haven: Yale Univer. Press. 226 pp.

Williams, R. 1958. Value orientations in American society. In H. Stein, and R. Cloward (Eds.), *Social Perspectives on Behavior.* Glencoe, Ill.: Free Press. Pp. 288–314.

Wolff, W. 1943. *The expression of personality: Experimental depth psychology.* New York: Harper. 334 pp.

Wright, Beatrice. 1942. Altruism in children and the perceived conduct of others. *J. abnorm. soc. Psychol.,* 37, 218–233.

Yarrow, Marian Radke, J. Campbell, and L. Yarrow. 1958. Acquisition of new norms: A study of racial desegregation. *J. soc. Issues,* 14, 8–28.

Zeligs, Rose. 1948. Intergroup attitudes of high school students. *J. educ. Psychol.,* 39, 273–280.

# chapter 17

# *Motivation*

# *and*

# *Affect*

Daniel R. Miller

*The University of Michigan*

It is striking to see how often a paper on motivation ends with the solemn protestation that the study has been an exploratory one. To demonstrate how many loose ends need tidying up, the writer usually suggests topics for further research. Often the list is a long one. The explorer of human motives and affects has good reason to qualify his empirical results. Different maps of the motivational domain present consistent pictures of a few well-traveled routes but provide only vague sketches of some areas and label others as terra incognita. As a result, the investigator often has to rely on arbitrary definitions and theoretical assumptions. His problems are further complicated by a large variety of instruments, the strengths and weaknesses of which are only partially known. Yet a perusal of studies published within the last fifteen years reveals considerable progress, not only

in the testing of traditional techniques, but also in the construction of ingenious new ones that have done much to enlarge theoretical horizons. This chapter is devoted to descriptions and evaluations of the techniques that are commonly used in the study of motivation and affect.

## *Contents of the Chapter*

### ORGANIZATION OF TOPICS

Methods for studying motivation may be divided into two general types. Some are used to elicit behavior, and some are used to measure the results. The first category consists of physical and psychological methods for creating desired conditions in one's subjects and methods for selecting groups whose previous backgrounds have created conditions of interest to the experimenter. The second includes techniques such as time samples, ratings, rankings, checklists, projective tests, official records, the interview, and the questionnaire. In applying both types of methods, investigators observe and consult with children, their peers, their parents, their teachers, and professional personnel.

This chapter has two primary parts, which are concerned with the two major kinds of methods. The parts are divided into sections, each of which is devoted to the different variants of a method. The section on verbal reports, for example, is devoted to interviews, inventories, questionnaires, compositions, and the like. Each specific technique is considered in light of the theoretical topics to which it has been applied and the age levels at which it has been tried. Purposes of studies and their results are sometimes cited when they have a bearing on the reliability, validity, or theoretical import of a method. When relevant, mention is made of the source of information, such as peers or teachers.

The primary parts of the chapter and some of the sections are concluded with evaluations of the techniques. The possible pitfalls are described not to paint a dismal picture of current methods but to stress the importance of finding the correct technique for each problem. As will become evident, the variety of promising methods offers a rosy picture of future theoretical developments. Some general methodological problems involved in the validation of tests of motivation, the selection of a sample, and the control of the experimenter's influence on results are saved for the end of the chapter.

## AGES

In line with the subject of the book, the chapter is restricted to techniques of studying the motivation of children. The label of *children* is arbitrarily restricted to subjects who have not reached the end of their eighteenth year, the age when secondary school is completed. The range from birth to 18 years is most readily split into four segments: birth to 2 years, or babyhood; 3 to 6 years, or the preschool ages; 6 to 12 years, or the first six grades of elementary school; 12 to 18 years, or adolescence. When references are made to such terms as babyhood or adolescence, they refer to the age ranges just cited. Usually the subjects' ages are given to the nearest year.

Research on adults is not considered in this chapter except for papers relevant to the methodological problems involved in studying children. It is possible that some instruments that have been tried only on adult populations would be ideally suited for research with younger subjects. But speculations on untried techniques can be misleading. The many promising ones that have been tested on juvenile populations provide the examples cited in this summary.

Three topics, values, percepts, and physiological reactions, although very relevant to motivation and affect, receive little attention in the chapter. These omissions are prompted by the detailed consideration of these topics in other chapters.

Finally, it is important to stress that this chapter does not represent a coverage of all the literature on the motivation of children. The available space would not permit even a survey of the enormous literature on only one of the methods, that of projective techniques. What has been attempted is a survey of the different kinds of methods. Representative studies of each kind of method have been cited in order to describe it and to illustrate its characteristics and its strengths and weaknesses.

### THE EXPERIMENTAL CREATION OF GROUPS

Psychologists have devoted considerable effort to methods designed to elicit certain motivational and affective states. Many of the attempts have been ingenious and effective. The different techniques may be divided into four categories, which provide the outline for this initial part of the chapter. A child can be manipulated physically by such methods as being stroked or being unsupported. He can be given some sensory stimulation, such as the sight of a smiling experimenter or of a doll with its eyes at the back of its head. He can be subjected to certain psychological pressures, such as incentives, frustrations, and conflicts. Finally, he can be manipulated by the experimenter's structuring of the interpersonal situation: the subject can be left alone; he can be allowed to interact with another person; he can be included in a group; he can be exposed to people with particular identities who behave in particular ways.

## Physical Manipulation

### ELICITING AND RECOGNIZING INNATE AFFECTIVE STATES

Simple physical stimuli were used by Watson and Morgan (1917) in one of the earliest experimental studies of human affect. Observations and manipulations of infants during their first months of life led the investigators to conclude that fear, rage, and love are part of the "original and fundamental nature of man." Signs of fear occurred in response to loss of support, loud sounds, and being jarred. Rage was usually provoked by hampered movements, and love was elicited by stroking or by manipulation of erogenous zones.

*Conditioning of Affect.* In one of the most influential papers in the history of American psychology, Watson and Rayner (1920) described the conditioning of a little boy named Albert. The unconditioned response was a loud noise, which startled the child and caused him to withdraw. First there was a number of trials, during which the loud noise was combined with the presentation of a white rat. Soon Albert shrank with fear at the sight of the animal, even when there was no sound. Whether or not the connection between the animal and the noise need be interpreted as a conditioned response is a debatable issue, but no one questions the possibility that a person can learn to fear an object because it is associated with another that was originally feared.

*Physical Stimulation of Affect.* Aside from the people who tried to check Watson's claims, few investigators have studied the affective results of physical stimulation. To investigate the causes of infants' laughter, Washburn (1929) tickled them and also raised them above her head where she jiggled them gently. Justin (1933) elicited laughter in preschool children by tickling them with an ostrich feather.

## Other Sensory Stimulation

### VISUAL STIMULI

*Laughter.* Justin (1933) tested the effectiveness of different stimuli in making preschool children laugh. The stimuli included a jack-in-the-box, a picture of a long-nosed man, a doll with eyes at the back of its head, a chair with shoes on its legs, a social smile by the experimenter, and his falling off his chair.

**Smiling.** Spitz and Wolf (1946) made a sophisticated attempt to analyze some properties of the adult's smile which elicit smiling in infants. In different sessions the experimenter first smiled, then grimaced, and finally wore a mask. Then a life-sized puppet and various inanimate objects were presented to the subjects. Between the ages of roughly 2 and 6 months the infants smiled, laughed, and gurgled when they saw the smiling, grimacing, or masked man or the puppet. None of the responses was forthcoming on presentation of such inanimate objects as a flashlight, a bell, a block, and balls. In Spitz and Wolf's opinion the infant smiles on perceiving a configuration of certain static elements within the human face.

**Fear.** Ellesor (1933) employed novel visual stimuli to elicit fear in 2-year-olds. Among the stimuli were a red devil's mask on a doll 27 inches long, a brown fur neckpiece with a mouth and glass eyes, a flashlight, and films of newborn infants and of a girl in her yard at home. At first the children whimpered, retreated, and stared. Soon, however, they approached, investigated, and played with the frightening objects. With repeated stimulation, the subjects smiled and seemed content to play with the objects.

Causes of fear in young children have also been studied by presenting the detached arm of a doll (Valentine, 1930), isolating each child, striking an iron pipe with which he was playing (Jersild and Holmes, 1935), asking him to retrieve a ball from a dark room, and placing him in a room with a stranger (Shirley, 1942; Arsenian, 1943). Reactions to strange situations and to strange people varied with age and sex of the children and with the extent of previous overprotection and rejection.

## AUDITORY AND VISUAL STIMULI

**Smiling.** Washburn (1929) elicited smiling in young infants by such methods as smiling and simultaneously making "chirruping" sounds, lowering her head to the infant's body and saying "ah-boo," suddenly reappearing from under the table saying "boo," suddenly emerging from a cupboard, clapping her hands in rhythm, playing peek-a-boo by first pulling a cloth over the infant's face and later holding the cloth in front of him, and suddenly presenting him with a mirror in which he saw himself.

## *Psychological Manipulation*

### NEUTRAL INSTRUCTIONS

**Negativism.** Relatively innocuous instructions sometimes arouse motivational states, such as negativism and attention-seeking. To investigate negativism in preschool children, Reynolds (1928) asked them to perform a number of tasks, such as imitating movements like clapping hands, repeating one- and two-digit series, and desisting from a particular activity. Bernstein (1955) proposed six tasks to his subjects: that they separate from their mothers, play with dolls, choose a piece of candy, draw a person, play with finger paints, and play with cold cream. Children who refused more than three requests were classified as negativistic.

**Attention-Seeking Behavior.** As a means of investigating attention-seeking in children between 4 and 6 years of age, Gewirtz (1956) asked them to paint at an easel in the presence of an adult as long as they wished. Then he tabulated such responses as asking questions, addressing comments to the adult, and seeking help.

## THREATENING INSTRUCTIONS

Some reactions emerge only when children are subject to stress. Only then do they experience certain types of fear; only then are they impelled to act dependently.

**Fear.** To study fears of children approximately 1 to 8 years old, Holmes (Jersild and Holmes, 1935) directed them to walk on a board which collapsed. Then he asked whether they would voluntarily walk on it a second time. He also requested them to retrieve a ball from a dark room where it had been "inadvertently" thrown, to obtain toys placed near a stranger's chair, to walk across a board 4 feet high, to pat a strange collie dog, and to get a toy from a box containing a garter snake. When a subject refused, he was urged to comply. If he was still reluctant, the examiner offered to accompany him.

**Dependence.** Employing a method similar to that of Holmes, Heathers

(1953) made his subjects walk a plank while blindfolded. The children were in the age range of the elementary school. The plank was balanced on springs, so that it could be tipped sidewise and at the end. While a subject was trying to maintain his balance, he was given the opportunity of taking the examiner's hand or of walking without help. The choice was interpreted as an index of emotional dependence or independence.

## FRUSTRATING AND THREATENING SITUATIONS

The psychological literature on anger, regression, and fear reveals that psychologists have devoted considerable thought to methods of frustrating children. Subjects have been deprived of precious objects, asked to continue indefinitely with boring tasks, forced to make unpleasant choices, and made to fail in important endeavors. Each of these techniques is now considered in turn.

**Deprivation.** Some experimenters have obviously been intrigued by the old saying that something is an easy as "taking candy from a baby." In addition to candy, children have been deprived of food, mothers, and toys, to name just a few of the varied objects.

**Food.** At different times during the feeding of a 6-month-old baby Sears and Sears (1940) removed the bottle and held it in front of him. They recorded the time it took him to cry and the frequency of his goal-directed movements, such as attempts to clutch the bottle. Davitz (1952) actually did take candy from his subjects. They were not babies, however, but children between 7 and 9 years. Prior to frustrating them, the experimenter showed them one film and then gave them some candy at the start of a second. When the film reached its climactic point, he stopped it and asked the children to return the candy. Then he ushered them into a playroom, where he told them that there would be no more candy or entertainment and that they could play with any objects.

*Toys.* One of the most influential studies of deprivation was performed by Barker, Dembo, and Lewin (1941). First the children, who were of preschool age, played with one set of toys. Then a more attractive but unavailable group of toys were exposed through a mesh screen. To study regressive reactions to frustration, the investigators tabulated signs of "primitivation" in the children's subsequent play with the original set of toys. Block and Martin (1955), Korner (1947), and Thomas (1951) also conducted investigations in which preschool children were deprived of attractive toys.

*Separation from mothers.* In an investigation of security feelings, Arsenian (1943) observed the behavior of babies in a new situation in which they were deprived of their mothers' company. The babies' responses were compared to those made in more familiar situations or in the mothers' presence. Bernstein (1955) used the request to leave the mother as part of a test of negativism.

**Satiation.** To arouse anger and such subsequent reactions as loss of control and regression, experimenters frequently ask children to continue a simple task past the point of satiation.

Among the tasks on which children have been satiated are packing spools in a rectangular rack on top of a box (Block and Martin, 1955), the crossing out of O's on pages filled with lines of randomly placed X's and O's (Blum and Miller, 1952), filling a pegboard (Burton, 1942; Yarrow, 1948), playing a very dull game with some sticks (Lerner, in Murphy 1956), and drawing a man 15 times in one sitting (Seashore and Bavelas, 1942).

**Conflict.** There are few topics with greater theoretical prominence than conflict in psychologies of motivation, learning, and psychopathology. It is surprising, therefore, that children's conflicts have not been investigated more often.

*Choice of acts.* Block and Martin (1955) offered their subjects a choice between two incompatible acts. By cranking a toy, which unloaded candy into a large vessel, each child could obtain as much as he wanted. Once he decided to taste a piece, however, he could not accumulate any more. He was thus constantly faced with the choice between further cranking and tasting the candy.

*Choice of objects.* Barker (1942) asked 10-year-old boys to choose first between two liked beverages, such as orange and pineapple juice, next between two disliked beverages, such as vinegar and a saturated salt solution, and finally between two neutral liquids. To indicate a choice, the subjects moved a lever toward a particular glass. Movements were timed by a concealed device. The data consisted of decision times and frequencies of vacillations.

Godbeer (1940) employed a similar

method with preadolescent children. Each subject sat at a table in front of a vertical board with two windows. In a control trial one window was opened, the candy was exposed, and the child was told to secure it as quickly as possible by pushing a handle. The movements of the handle were electrically timed and recorded by a concealed pantagraph, and the subject's eye movements were counted. In a second trial he was told to get the presents exposed behind both windows. He was thus torn by impulses to move the handle in the directions of different objects. In a third trial he was told that as soon as he pushed the handle for one window the shutter of the other would close. The data collected were decision times and frequencies of eye movements. Godbeer also studied choices between the dissimilar goals of gum drops and an equated number of tin soldiers and between the unclear goals contained in two small metal boxes, either of which might have contained candy.

**Creation of Failure.** *Difficult puzzles.* Since children take tests in school, there is no shortage of subjects for studies of failure. With few exceptions, however, the investigator cannot rely on school performance. Children usually differ markedly in the meaning and importance that they attribute to a test. In addition, children vary markedly in their performances. The investigator usually wants a test to have a relatively constant meaning for all subjects, he tries to arouse similar involvement in all subjects, and he attempts to control the performance. Some of the techniques of implementing these goals were used by Keister and Updegraff (1937), who asked children of preschool age to work on a puzzle box one quarter inch in depth. To be inserted in that space were ten irregularly shaped colored figures. These were one quarter inch thick and depicted interesting objects, such as a sailboat and an engine. Only with some difficulty could the figures be fitted into the box. A second test required each child to move a five-sided box with adjustable weights of 60 to 90 pounds at the ends and through the middle. Before the subject began, the box was raised momentarily to show that it covered a group of attractive toys. The child was told he could play with the toys if he could raise the box within ten minutes.

For his puzzle, Yarrow (1948) employed a tinker toy. With it, his preschool children tried to construct a simple-appearing but actually complex windmill. He measured reactions to failure by comparing the amount of aggression manifested in doll play before and after the attempt was made to construct the windmill.

*Difficult tests.* Jost (1941) induced failure by a memory task involving an exceedingly difficult set of numbers. His subjects were children of elementary-school age. First they learned a series, each unit of which was guessed before it was shown. Once the series was memorized, the subjects got a new one, which was structured quite differently from the first and was too difficult to recall.

*Timed tests.* In quite a number of investigations failures have been created by telling the subjects they did not complete the task within the required time. Zeigarnik (1927) conducted one of the earliest studies of this type. First she allowed her children, whose ages varied between 5 and 10 years, to complete half of a group of tasks that she had assigned. Then she asked the subjects to recall as many of the tasks as they could. The pattern of more recent methods of investigating selective recall was established by Rosenzweig and Mason (1934), who tried to get their subjects very ego-involved in the tasks. These investigators asked a group of crippled children to solve some puzzles and offered a prize for the best performance. The prize and the physical handicap presumably created high involvement. Like Zeigarnik, Rosenzweig and Mason permitted the completion of only some puzzles. The children tended to forget their failures, presumably because the desire to do well was so intense.

Beardslee (in Miller and Swanson, 1960) asked preadolescents to perform a series of tasks modeled after early tests of psychological abilities. The tasks included the completion of words beginning with the letters "ba," pursuit, putting a dot in each of a number of circles, rearranging scrambled sentences, supplying the missing parts of faces, mazes, coding, anagrams, and completing number series. Half the tests were interrupted before they could be completed. Gatling (1950) gave his preadolescents ten jigsaw puzzles, none of which could be completed within the time limit and five of which had no solutions. Then he compared the numbers of intropunitive and extrapunitive explanations of the results given by normal and delinquent boys.

## INCENTIVES

*Praise and blame.* There are at least two ways of getting a donkey to move. The driver can prod him or hold a carrot in front of his nose. Psychologists and educators have employed both kinds of incentive in studies of performance in school. In one of the most influential studies Hurlock (1925) used praise and blame as incentives. Her subjects were boys and girls, white and Negro, and in the third, fifth, or seventh grades of elementary school. After taking an intelligence test, one group was severely reproved for its performance. A second was warmly praised, and a third was given no evaluation and requested to take the test again. A week later all the children took another form of the test. The groups who had been reproved and praised both improved significantly more than the control group. In a more recent study Garmezy and Harris (1953) analyzed the performance of palsied children whose ages varied between 6 and 12 years. After failing on a peg board, the subjects were praised or reproved. The praise and reproof were of short and of long duration in two different conditions of the study.

*Concrete reward.* Specific objects have often served as rewards for good performances. A prize was offered by Rosenzweig and Mason (1934) and by Zubin (1932). Garmezy and Harris (1953) provided candy, and Anderson and Smith (1953) designed a test of strength so that a bell rang when the person succeeded. When he did, he received a gold star.

*Invidious comparison.* To involve subjects in a task, the investigator can encourage their competition with one another or with other groups. As a reward for competitive effort, Zubin (1932) offered a prize to each subject who surpassed the person just above him. Panlasigui and Knight (1930) produced charts depicting standards of accomplishment and the progress of individuals and the total class. Garmezy and Harris (1953) kept a score board with red masonite strips, each of which could be raised to indicate improvement. A miniature chocolate bar, the bait offered for a particular level of attainment, was attached to the score board at a specific height above the red marker. Veroff, Wilcox, and Atkinson (1953) administered a projective test to boys and girls between the ages of 16 and 18 years. To obtain an "achievement orientation," the investigators challenged the subjects to do well on an anagrams test, stating that the results would be used in a competition with another school.

*Controlling success and failure.* Various methods have been devised to hold success and failure constant so that they would have the same values as incentives for different subjects. In a study of the levels of aspiration of boys 9 to 11 years old Worrell (1956) controlled performances on three different tasks by means of prearranged sequences of scores. Anderson and Smith (1933) devised an ingenious method of controlling their subjects' method of controlling their subjects' scores on a hand dynamometer. The amount of pressure apparently activated a visible liquid column, which the experimenters could manipulate without the subjects' knowledge.

*Involvement in the task.* A child has a strong incentive to do well on a task if the results are included in official records or reflect on activities in which he must succeed. To elicit "merit involvement" on the part of his 6-to-9-year-old experimental subjects, Filer (1952) informed them that their attainments depended on their abilities. He told a control group that their performance depended upon chance. Zubin (1932) asked some subjects to sign their papers and others to leave their papers unsigned. Veroff, Wilcox, and Atkinson (1953) defined their test as one of creative imagination.

To maximize the involvement of his subjects in a task, Worrell (1956) told them that it was the most important one they would perform, that it provided the most information about skills crucial for all sports, and that he was very concerned with the task. To elicit medium involvement, he said that the task was not quite so useful as the first one and that it provided less information about a person's abilities. To minimize involvement, he said that the task was inferior to the others and was of no interest to him. Beardslee (in Miller and Swanson, 1960) attempted to get her subjects involved in a test by first asking them about ambitions and probable future jobs. Then she said that their performance would provide a good indication of their promise in their chosen fields.

*Temptation.* Long ago the story of Adam and Eve made man keenly aware of the strong incentives provided by some temptations. Temptations offered by experimenters have varied with the topics under study. In one investigation of the aggression of 3- and 4-year-old children, the experimenter sat opposite a child and built a pile of eight red bricks (McKee and Leader, 1955). After two minutes she left, saying that she needed equipment from the next room. From that vantage point, she made a complete record of his behavior and comments. Many children yielded to temptation and knocked down the bricks.

In "temptation" studies the subject is usually tempted to violate the conditions of a task. Dennis (1955), for example, invited his seventh and eighth graders in Hopi schools to take a test with their eyes closed. If they looked, their scores exceeded the upper limits that could be attained by anyone who followed instructions. Grosser, Polansky, and Lippitt (1951) provided temptation by means of a confederate, who pretended that he was a subject. After playing an interesting and competitive game of darts, the boys were assigned a dull task of drawing figure eights. At this point the experimenter left the room. The confederate stopped work a number of times, groaned with fatigue, and finally began to play the game of darts.

## PARTICIPANTS IN THE STUDY

Regardless of the technique of manipulating behavior, decisions have to be made about the identity and behavior of people with whom the subjects are to interact. A number of different combinations of personnel have been used by various experimenters.

*Solitude.* To study the fears of preschool children, Holmes (in Jersild and Holmes, 1935) left them alone for two minutes. Arsenian (1943) separated a number of children from their mothers and left them alone in a playroom for five minutes. The solitude thus signified separation and, possibly, deprivation of love or protection.

*Child and adult.* Most often the child is with the experimenter, who engages in some action like smiling or asking the child to pet a dog. Sometimes, however, another significant adult is introduced, either in place of the experimenter or as a third person. Holmes (in Jersild and Holmes, 1935) obtained the children's reactions to a stranger. Merrill (1946) investigated the behavior of preschool children with their mothers. Each mother was left alone with her child for half an hour. Before the first session, she was asked to behave as though she were in the same room with him at home and unoccupied by household duties. Before the second session, it was inferred to mothers in the experimental group that their children's performance had not provided an altogether satisfactory sample of their potentialities.

Little and Cohen (1952) investigated the levels of aspiration that asthmatics, 4 to 12 years of age, reported in the presence of their mothers. Each subject shot at a target and gave his level of aspiration after every trial. His mother watched, kept score, and wrote her own aspiration before each trial. In Sanford and Risser's study (1948) it was the mother who performed the task and the child who observed. Following the task, the child was asked to recall the different activities in which the mother had been engaged. The object of this request was to study the child's selective recall of completed and uncompleted tasks.

*Child and experimenter's confederate.* A relatively infrequent but fruitful combination of personnel has involved the subject and a confederate or confederates of the experimenter. Grosser, Polansky, and Lippitt (1951) employed a confederate who tempted subjects to engage in forbidden activities, and Lippitt (1939) coached his collaborators in methods of creating autocratic and democratic atmospheres. In a recent investigation with children 12 to 14 years of age Brigante (1958) employed three confederates as "judges" of his subject's knowledge of sports. One judge was rewarding, one was neutral, and one was punishing. Later the experimenter obtained the subjects' impressions of the judges.

*Child and child.* Not uncommonly, the second person in an investigation is another child. To investigate overt, friendly behavior, Mengert (1931) observed the reactions to each other of 2-year-old children who were put together for twenty-minute periods. To study ascendance, Jack (1934) paired each child successively with each of ten others in a preschool group. A pair was allowed to play together for five minutes in a sandbox with three sets of toys.

## Advantages and Disadvantages of Experimental Manipulation

### TOPICS REQUIRING EXPERIMENTAL TREATMENT

Records of behavior in natural situations do not permit an adequate exploration of certain types of phenomena. Observations of reactions to failure provide a good example. On first consideration, observations of children when they take tests in school would seem to provide important information about reactions to threat of failure. Yet such information is sometimes not relevant to the questions of the study. To begin with, failure is relatively infrequent in schools; serious failure is rare. Hence, if an investigator concentrates on reactions to failure, he may have to wait a long time before he gets an adequate number of cases. He may also find himself handicapped by the different meanings that the same test may have for various children. The results of some tests are hard to interpret because of complex subtests, unusual ranges of scores, or types of scores that make it difficult for children to compare themselves with one another or with an ideal norm.

Very difficult and very easy tests also create problems in interpreting results. A good example is provided by the average discrepancy in experiments on level of aspiration. If the test is too easy, a low discrepancy can have a number of meanings. A person may have done much better than he thought he had a right to expect; hence he did not anticipate that he would improve very much. It is also possible that his scores were so close to the ceiling of the test that even the highest possible aspiration still resulted in a low discrepancy (Ausubel, 1951). Or he may have had a predisposition to set low goals for himself—the usual meaning of a low discrepancy.

Even children who understand the meaning of a score may not take it as a true reflection of ability if they have not had sufficient time to study or if the test is excessively difficult. In the latter case, most children are discouraged and find it easy to blame the test rather than themselves for their poor performances.

A subject is likely to be more concerned with doing well on a challenging or interesting test than on a dull or meaningless one, and his self-esteem will be more effected by the results. Involvement in a test also fluctuates with inner values and interests as well as external incentives. Performance on verbal tests is often devalued by people from the working class (Davis, 1948). A test often has differential appeal to various children, depending on their interests. A boy who hopes to become a physician, for example, may not be at all depressed if he does poorly on a test of artistic skill, even if the test is a challenging one. The same performance may be very disturbing to a boy who intends to become a professional illustrator.

All of these variables—the interest, importance, and difficulty of a test, the clarity of results, the child's concern with his performance, and the actual amount of success and failure—can be controlled in a careful experimental design. Most of the variables can be held constant by the designs of the instrument and the instructions. Interest and importance can be maximized or varied by instructions designed to implement these ends. Failure and success can be manipulated by such methods as pre-arranged scores and the use of a timed test. The extent to which the investigator has succeeded in controlling non-experimental variables can be evaluated in a pilot study.

## THE PLANNING OF EXPERIMENTS AND PREVIOUS RESEARCH

In deciding on the design of his experiment, an investigator can often profit from findings reported in the literature. The value of such findings can be illustrated by results pertaining to a common problem in designing studies of conflict. In much of this research the subject is asked to choose one of two objects. It may be the investigator's intention to compare the choices between attractive objects and between unattractive ones. In such a study, the objects themselves should be comparable, and their relative attractiveness or unattractiveness has to be held constant if it is not to influence the results. How can one tell which variables of objects affect their comparability or relative attractiveness? A number of leads are provided by empirical studies, some of which are cited here.

*Availability.* The relative attractiveness of objects seems to depend in part on their availability. To study this variable, Wright (1937) offered each of a group of preschool children one of two lollipops which were suspended from strings. One lollipop was 11 inches away and within reach of the subject, and one was 11 inches beyond reach. Eleven of the 16 children selected the lollipop that was beyond their reach. From this result, Wright concluded that an obstructed goal has a stronger positive valence than a more accessible goal. He gave similar interpretations to the results of two other experiments. In one the children could select the available toys or the toys in a room that could be entered only after removal of bars from the door. The majority of the children tried to get the toys behind the door. In a second experiment the subjects ranked the desirability of two groups of toys, one inside a wire cage and one outside the cage. In a majority of instances the toys in the cage were given first preference. Only when an available toy was a means to a goal rather than a goal in itself was it selected in preference to a toy behind a barrier.

Also relevant to availability is the finding of Irwin, Gebhard, and Mildred (1946) that objects are preferred if they are to be kept rather than given to others. Irwin, Armitt, and Simon (1943) have reported that objects are preferred if they are to be obtained immediately instead of being available later.

*Association of object with other sources of gratification.* Filer (1952) found that when objects could be earned by the skillful playing of a game they were chosen over objects that anyone could obtain. Another kind of reinforcement was reported by Lambert and Lambert (1953), who asked each of their preschool children to exchange a red token for a white token and then to exchange the white one for a gumdrop. The children estimated the sizes of the two tokens from memory by adjusting the sizes of circles of light on a ground-glass screen. Assuming that recalled sizes are indexes of attractiveness or importance, it is interesting to note that the white tokens, which were closest to the reinforcing candy, were overestimated more than the red ones.

*Substitutability.* Comparability and relative attractiveness have also been studied in research on substitution of objects. To explore the substitutes of preschool children, Sliosberg (in Barker, Kounin, and Wright, 1943) first allowed each subject to take some candy into his mouth. Then the experimenter asked him to put it down and take pieces of cardboard similar to the candy in size but not in shape. Most subjects refused the cardboard. During a play session they did accept cardboard as food for a doll. They also accepted a paper ball as a present for a doll. In short, the simulated food could not satisfy a real need and could not be substituted for a real satisfier, but the simulated food could satisfy an unreal need. When the children were building with blocks, they accepted pebbles as substitutes but not wooden animals. The animals could not be used because they had fixed meanings. For the same reason, the children would not accept wooden animals in place of cars.

## THE MEANING OF EXPERIMENTS TO THE SUBJECTS

When a psychologist succeeds in controlling all variables but the experimental one, he can confidently attribute the resultant variation to his manipulations. If he is clear about the meaning of the experimental variable, he can measure it objectively and manipulate it in a manner that has identical effects on all subjects.

So goes the ideal version of an experiment. Sometimes this version comes close to describing the actual events. More often, complications arise. What is particularly hard to satisfy is the criterion that the situation be identical for all subjects. The difficulty stems from the existence of a large number of variables. The experimental results may be affected by other motives, the personality of the experimenter, the nature of the situation, and differences in the children's backgrounds (Miller and Swanson, 1960). So complex is the social situation alone that the investigator can never hope to control all the nonexperimental variables that might conceivably affect his results. The best he can do is to control some of the more obvious potential sources of error variance.

Among the myriad variables in human behavior, some of the most difficult to assess are those that affect the subject's interpretations of the experimental situation and procedure. Sometimes these interpretations are very different from the experimenter's. As a result, the findings are overgeneralized or misinterpreted in other ways.

*Previous Experiences.* The extent to which the subject's interpretations can affect results is illustrated by some of the findings in studies of goal preference and incentives. As has been indicated, Wright (1937) concluded that an available object is less attractive than a less accessible one: children prefer to work for a goal that is hard to attain rather than one that is easy to attain. On repeating some of Wright's studies, Child (1946) obtained different results. His subjects, who varied in age between 2 and 8 years, chose the more available objects. Child then proposed a number of possible reasons for the discrepancy in results of the two studies. In developing his explanation, he made one basic assumption: differences in past experience cause subjects to differ in their interpretations of the same situation. Some children, he thought, may have been challenged by their parents to overcome obstacles and then rewarded for successful efforts. Such subjects probably favored less accessible goals to a greater extent than children who had not been challenged and rewarded. In the experiment the latter may have found more interest in goals that were there for the taking than in the less accessible goals. It was also possible, Child thought, that some subjects had become satiated with the easily available objects because they were used every day. The ones behind barriers may have been intriguing because of their novelty.

Studies of incentives are also plagued by differential reactions to standard manipulations. Suppose a teacher has just blamed a child for a poor performance. How will the child react? In part, his response will depend on the meanings and values he ascribes to the verbal incentive. In part, his response will depend on the teacher's previous inclination to be complaining or supportive.

*Personality.* The child's personality also influences his reaction to blame. Blaming can elicit self-dissatisfaction if it is congruent with his own standards about achievement. Blaming can also gratify desires for attention or privilege. Research has indicated that in response to negative statements subjects with personality problems of excessive anxiety do poorly in learning tasks (Bird, 1927; Grace, 1948). Blamed introverts do well on a cancellation test (Forlano and Axelrod, 1937). In view of the many variables that can affect interpretations of verbally stated incentives, it is not surprising that studies of praise and blame have produced complex and somewhat inconsistent results.

*Artificiality.* The artificial, even bizarre, qualities that may have to be imposed on the situation by necessary controls or manipulations are a possible pitfall of experimentation. Such qualities may arouse feelings in children such as self-consciousness, anxiety, and even fear. One wonders what children must have felt when they were ushered into a room stripped of furniture and saw two lollipops hanging from the ceiling or when they were offered cardboard in place of candy. Of course, these designs represented the halting steps of a new discipline. In the twenty years since such research was done psychologists have generally shown increasing sensitivity to children's interpretations of tasks.

*Pretesting.* The many uncontrolled sources of error, particularly those arising from the differential feelings, interpretations, and motives aroused in subjects by experiments, point to the importance of a critical and occasionally neglected step in empirical research. It is not enough for an investigator to assume that children will in-

terpret a technique in the anticipated manner. He needs independent evidence of the meaning the children assign to a task and of the feelings it elicits in them. Such information can usually be obtained in a pilot study.

## METHODOLOGICAL CONTRIBUTIONS OF EXPLORATORY INVESTIGATIONS

In exploring the history of a science, one typically finds a sequence of investigations, each of which introduced new and sophisticated methods and controls and produced results that required modifications of earlier conclusions. Such a stream of research was initiated by Watson's pioneering study of innate affective states and their arousal. To test the validity of Watson's findings, Sherman (1927) asked a group of judges to interpret emotional expressions of infants by observing them directly and in motion pictures. It was possible to reproduce accurately the affects originally studied by Watson because he had conscientiously defined their characteristics in some detail. He had described rage, for example, in such terms as stiffening of the body, slashing movements of arms and hands, kicking, holding the breath, and screaming. When Sherman obtained judgments, he introduced a number of important controls. Emotional reactions were observed both with and without indications of the preceding stimulation and with and without sound.

Considerable doubt was thrown on Watson's conclusions by the observers' inability to agree in their identifications of emotions depicted in the film. There was not even a consensus when the babies themselves were observed, even though they could be heard and their facial color could be seen. One finding was particularly damaging to Watson's claims. When the stimuli and emotional responses were transposed in the movie, the judges' guesses were usually more appropriate to the incorrect stimuli than to the infants' affects.

Subsequent research has cast even more doubt on the validity and reliability of Watson's results. To determine the connection between restriction of movement and unlearned rage reactions, Pratt (1932) held the arms and noses of 67 infants. In 96 per cent of the cases the infants drew back their heads, hunched their backs, and indulged in restless and nonspecific body movements. When he held the infants' arms, there was no resistance or action in 58 per cent of the cases. A few of the remaining subjects flexed their arms, but most of the reactions were described as minor.

To verify Watson's claims about the unlearned sources of fear, Irwin (1932a) subjected infants to loud noises from a cabinet held 4 inches from their heads. Body jerks were recorded on a moving polygraph tape. Startle reactions were usual, but they were never accompanied by crying or by manifestations of fear. In another investigation (1932b) Irwin dropped infants 2 feet from a supine position. When they were younger than 1 month, they made no overt responses in twelve per cent of the trials and gave some reactions in 88 per cent of the trials. About half the instances of movement involved the

arms and legs, and only three per cent were accompanied by crying.

Obviously Watson's findings were not supported by the results of the subsequent investigations. The emotions he thought he was observing could not be reliably identified under more controlled conditions. The associations that he found between certain stimuli and extreme affective states, such as rage and strong fear, were not obtained when his experiments were repeated. Although these results may seem disappointing, they demonstrate three of the primary assets of well-designed experiments. First, Watson defined his operations very carefully, so that his studies could be repeated and new controls inserted. Second, he described his findings in some detail, so that considerable doubt could be cast on their validity by the absence of supportive evidence in subsequent studies. The fact that noncorroborative as well as corroborative evidence was relevant to the validity of Watson's predictions is an advantage of no small importance. Few investigators have succeeded in formulating predictions that could be disproven or the validity of which could be called into question by lack of supportive evidence. Finally, Watson developed useful techniques that have been improved by subsequent investigators. The lack of support for Watson's conclusions applies not to the assumption of innate affective reactions but only to the connections he thought he found between certain stimuli and innate emotional responses. For some years the interest in innate reactions lay dormant. Now that the topic has been revived by the challenging observations of ethologists the methodological gains resulting from the studies of affect should provide future investigators with some tested techniques for studying the affective responses of infants.

## PRACTICAL PROBLEMS

It probably helps an investigator to clarify his thinking about his methods if he plans an ideal study of children's motives. If he is at all practical, he will keep in mind the possibility that particular conditions in the school or home may force him to lower his sights. The occasional necessity of compromising with one's methodological standards can be humiliating and frustrating. The frequency with which experienced researchers have had to make such compromises probably accounts for their tolerance of some common weaknesses in studies that neophytes are sometimes inclined to condemn.

An investigator who collects data in schools must often design his study with an eye to limitations of space and of the students' time. He may be allowed only two hours with each child, and the only free room may be the dispensary, which the nurse has to enter every twenty minutes.

Even if the investigator has carefully explained the reasons for his presence in the classroom, he may find, months after the data were collected, that the teacher thought he really was there to evaluate her performance and that he was reporting his findings to the principal. Her anxieties may have been communicated to the subjects and have created an atmosphere that interfered with the purposes of the experiment.

The unforseen events that can eliminate all possibility of conducting the experiment or that may require a radical revision of the design are a constant bother to the investigator. It may be impossible to collect data on a particular day because special tests have been scheduled for all the schools in the city. There are usually some sick students who cannot be seen later because they have heard about the procedures. Materials needed for the research may not have been delivered on time. When such emergencies occur, the investigator often has to make immediate judgments about the part of the study that he will sacrifice or about the changes he will make in the methods in order to compensate for the damaging omission of important controls.

Fathers create their special practical problems. A foreign visitor once asked the writer why American child psychologists are always studying the male offspring of female parents. The reasons for selecting female parents seem obvious. Fathers work all day and are often not available at night because they are busy with other activities, tired, cannot tear themselves away from the television set, or are convinced that the rearing of children belongs to the woman's sphere of activities. Mothers are usually more cooperative. Many are alone for a good part of the day and usually welcome a visitor, particularly one who asks them about their lives.[1]

---

[1] As for the tendency to select boys rather than girls, psychologists have this because most of the theories of personality are fairly specific about the development of males but contain few or no observations about the development

Mothers, too, can create difficulties for the interviewer. Occasionally one unburdens herself to such an extent that she makes the inexperienced interviewer fearful that he has disturbed her unduly. It is also not unknown for an interviewer to have difficulty in extricating himself from a home without offending a woman who has been talking about herself and her family for two hours and seems eager to continue for two more.

During visits to families many other kinds of practical problems can arise. Their variety can be suggested by a few examples. Some parents avoid the investigator for fear he is a bill collector or an encyclopedia salesman; some are uncooperative because they do not want their children to take time off from their homework and their music lessons; some women are unavailable because they have to clean house; some are defensive or evasive about topics that have aroused guilt; some insist on witnessing the testing of the child despite the examiner's plea for privacy.

It is possible to avoid one practical type of difficulty that occurs when data are collected in schools. When there is a large group of subjects, the students' grapevine will probably carry an account of the procedure through the school in a very short time. If the subjects are seen individually or in small groups, so that the examination takes some time, most of the children will enter the experimental room with a picture of the methods, often a distorted one. If the subjects' preconceptions are accurate, a corroboration of the hypothesis may establish not its validity but the efficiency of the grapevine in describing the ways children were supposed to behave.

It is often possible to prevent mature subjects from gossiping. Older children are inclined to cooperate with an examiner who asks them not to talk about the procedure and who explains the reasons for the secrecy. Such appeals are not effective with young subjects, but the damage of the grapevine can be circumvented by the simultaneous use of many examiners. Ten examiners, for example, can see two groups of ten children individually, one group immediately after the other. Twenty children can thus be seen under conditions that preclude communication prior to testing. If the examiner limits the number of subjects in a school to those who can be seen in two contiguous sessions, he can be certain that no children had previous knowledge of his methods.

## EXPERIMENTAL SAMPLES

In many experiments it is not possible to obtain more than one sample of the subjects' behavior. It may not be possible to repeat the method of manipulating subjects without changing its meaning. Repetition may also be prevented by the complexity, costliness, and the time-consuming nature of the procedures. Compared to many experiments, then, techniques such as ratings and time samples have more of a chance of being reliable because they are based

---

of females. Even in the old nursery rhyme the composition of the boys is described in such specific terms as "snakes and snails and puppy dog tails"; the description of girls begins with "sugar and spice" but then ends vaguely with "everything nice."

on a considerable sampling of behavior.

Limitations in sampling provide a special problem in experimental studies of motives, which are dispositions that can be expressed in many different ways. Consequently, a number of different manifestations of a motive may be needed before it can be identified reliably, and one or a few samples of behavior may be mislabeled. This weakness in experimental studies of motivation was invoked by Blum and Miller (1952) to explain the marked differences they obtained in the number of significant relations between their behavioral criterion of orality and their experiments, on one hand, and between the same criterion and variables such as teachers' ratings and time samples. The experiments yielded results close to chance, whereas the ratings and time samples yielded results that exceeded chance considerably. It is possible that the two methods differed with respect to validity. Yet the care with which they were designed and pretested led the investigators to attribute the results not to difference in validity but to the unreliability inherent in the limited sampling that was possible in the experiments.

## Natural Experiments

In the typical experiment the investigator attempts to manipulate two or more groups in contrasting ways and predicts probable differences in reactions. Certain kinds of manipulations are not possible or feasible because they are unethical or because they create anxiety in parents, teachers, or other adults. Instead of manipulating subjects, the investigator can test his hypotheses by studying children whose behavior has been affected by known experiences. This section is concerned with the selection of groups whose characteristics have been determined by conditions that occurred before the investigation was planned. Such a selection takes advantage of "natural experiments."

## Past Events

### EXPERIENCES IN THE HOME

Relationships with parents and experiences during the early years of life have been invoked frequently to explain the origins of children's later behaviors. Parents are usually ready to supply information about topics such as methods of child rearing and the early illnesses and trauma of their offspring. Besides supplying information to interviewers (Sanford et al., 1943; Sears, Maccoby, and Levin, 1957), parents have rated their children (Cattell and Coan, 1957) and kept records of different kinds of behavior (Jersild and Holmes, 1935).

### TRAUMATIC EVENTS AND NEGLECT

Most of the papers on trauma are by psychotherapists, and the method of obtaining data has typically been clinical observation of behavior. The trauma of operations have been studied by a number of investigators. Langford (1937), for example, reported that after operations, particularly those initiated with ether anaesthesia, children were inclined to suffer from attacks of anxiety. On observing children before and after tonsillectomies and adenoidectomies, Jessner, Blom, and Waldfogel (1952) found an increase in psychopathological reactions following the operations.

Understimulation by adults and parental neglect have also been investigated as sources of children's pathologies. Spitz (1946) explored the origins of marasmus, a condition involving abortive development of affects and motives, among other symptoms. He and Wolf investigated the connection between anaclitic depression and the sudden separation of babies from their mothers at about the sixth month (1946). Freud and Dann (1951) made clinical observations of six children who had spent most of their first three years in a concentration camp. There they had received minimal care from a variety of adults. In addition to their anxieties and regressive behaviors, the children showed a strength in their attachments to each other that was surprising, in view of their initial lack of consistent personal relationships.

Harsh parental practices provide a third source of data relevant to the origins of trauma. Huschka (1942) found an association between coercive bowel training and the subsequent tendencies toward frequent expressions of fear and rage. Redl and Wineman (1951) described many of the later problems of children who were abused in their early years.

## PHYSICAL PATHOLOGIES

From information that a child has had a particular illness or physical disability, one can often infer the nature of his experiences and their probable effects on his motives and feelings. Between their second and fourth years, children who developed constipation or colds, or had been in accidents, displayed a marked increase in temper outbursts (Goodenough, 1929). According to Greenacre (1944), children who in their early years had to tolerate physical restraints, such as metal leg braces or corsets, were predisposed to develop catatonia in late adolescence. Molitch (1937) reported a significant association between hypogonadism and rate of delinquency, and Little and Cohen (1952) found a significant difference between the aspirations of asthmatic and nonasthmatic children.

## SOCIAL POSITIONS AND CATEGORIES

The fact that a child is a particular sex or in a particular social class or society means that he has had to satisfy standards that differ from those required of people of another sex or social class or society. A number of investigators has compared members of socially recognized groupings to investigate the nature of their previous experiences and the motivational results. Since standards of achievement are seldom so high for girls as they are for boys, it is not surprising that, at different age levels, girls have lower levels of aspiration than boys (Walter and Marzolf, 1951).

According to sociological accounts, members of the middle class are trained to regard cleanliness as an important value and to inhibit the impulse to be messy. Such reports led Alper, Blane, and Abrams (1955) to measure fastidiousness in the painting done by children from the two social classes. It has been claimed by ethnologists that Hopi children are successfully trained to achieve self-respect by self-abnegation. To test this claim, Dennis (1955) compared Hopi and white children of the same ages with respect to their levels of ambition.

## *Observation of Behavior*

### DEVELOPMENTAL OBSERVA-TIONS IN DIFFERENT SOCIETIES

Ethnologists are interested in the contrasting practices of subgroups in our own society and of people in different societies. Some ethnological reports seem relevant to principles of motivation that may apply cross-culturally. The swaddling of infants in Albania (Greenacre, 1944), for example, and the thumping of the heads of Siouan children to prevent them from biting their mothers' breasts (Erikson, 1945) have a bearing on the relation between degree of parental restraint and directness of anger. The socialization of aggression among the Dobuans (Fortune, 1932) and among the Zuni (Benedict, 1934) provides information about the connections between different kinds of projection and the stability of social organizations.

### OBSERVATIONS OF GENERAL TRENDS WITHIN A SOCIETY

Many investigators have compiled records of the modal social behavior of children in various age groups in the United States or in a western European country. Representative of the results are the studies of Bridges (1933), who observed young infants, Isaacs (1933), who concentrated on children at the preschool level, and Gesell and Ilg (1946), who observed preschool children and those in the elementary grades. Each investigator kept detailed records of different kinds of behavior. Bridges, for example, attempted to learn about the typical reactions of babies in a hospital for foundlings. Her observations were made in many kinds of situations and were reported in terms of the modal infant. In the third month, she noted, the average infant usually stops crying at the sound of a comforting voice or when someone approaches; in the sixth month he cries and draws away on seeing an approaching stranger. In the fourth and fifth months the baby struggles and yells if something he wants is taken away, and he responds to an appreciative smile with playful attention.

### SPECIAL SITUATIONS

The restriction of observations to specific environments sometimes helps to clarify the behavior under study. Many investigators have conducted their research in the playroom or the classroom because these environments are sufficiently constant to permit reliable interpretations of certain kinds of behavior. Time samples during the free play of preschool children have been particularly popular with many investigators. Heathers (1955) tabulated instances of dependence, such as the seeking of approval, and instances of independence, such as resisting the interference of another child. Marshall and McCandless (1957) compared the frequencies of contacts with peers and with adults in order to study relations between social acceptance by other children and dependency. Beaver (1932) used the number of contacts with other children as an index of initiative.

Schools sometimes provide unique situations which the alert investigator can exploit for purposes of testing his hypotheses. Having noted that 2- and 3-year-old children need their teachers' help to put on or remove snow suits, Fales (in Anderson, 1940) used responses to offers of assistance as his measure of level of aspiration. The initiative shown by some children in opening zippers, getting arms out of coats, and hanging caps on hooks revealed that even subjects of such young ages had different aspirations for specific activities. Dillon (in Murphy, Murphy, and Newcomb, 1937) observed the sexual expression of 3- and 4-year-old boys and girls in a nursery school. During nap time the children undressed completely. Autoerotic activity was observed occasionally, but heterosexual play was rare.

## SPECIAL OCCASIONS

Certain unique events have particular significance for some motives. Arsenian (1943), Heathers (1954), and Shirley (1942) investigated the anxiety expressed by young children when they first came to a clinic and were separated from their mothers. Subjects in the three investigations varied between .1 and 7 years. Goodenough (1929), Levy and Tulchin (1923), and Thomas (1929) studied the resistance of babies to taking tests. The investigators were interested in such characteristics as cooperativeness, emotional disturbance, and self-consciousness.

## Studies of Previously Established Groups: Assets and Liabilities

The use of groups that already have the attributes of interest to the investigator allows him to study variables the manipulations of which are ruled out by ethical considerations. Even if he could, no experimenter would want to traumatize children by arranging for cruel parental treatment or by depriving them of their normal amount of hormones. It is, unfortunately, all too easy to find children who have already been traumatized or who were hypogonadic before the research was begun.

The selection of special groups sometimes has another advantage. The data that they provide about the more extreme forms of behavior may facilitate the development of new psychological principles. Research on pathological subjects and certain primitive groups has contributed much valuable information about the origins of some motivational states, which was not available before such groups were compared with normal subjects in American society.

Studies of pre-established groups have one serious drawback. The many uncontrolled variables sometimes make it difficult to interpret the results. A significant difference between children from two social classes, for example, can be explained in terms of a considerable number of antecedent variables. There is always a question whether the difference is not attributable to some variable that was not controlled. The simultaneous analysis of a number of interacting background factors sometimes changes the conclusions derived from analysis of only two variables. B. Allinsmith (in Miller and Swanson, 1960) found that social class and directness of expressed aggression were not significantly related to each other until she held intelligence constant. When Miller and Swanson (1958) controlled social class and "integration setting," previously significant differences in child-rearing practices among different ethnic and racial groups were no longer significant.

Another problem in using existing groups results from the fact that many are very large. One cannot hope to test all asthmatics or all people in the middle and working classes. The individual investigator does not even command the resources to obtain a stratified sample of the middle and working classes in a particular urban area. Given the limitations of his sample, it is often hard for him to determine the extent to which his findings apply to all members of a social class. It is similarly difficult to tell whether the results obtained from a particular sample of asthmatics can be generalized to all people with the disease or only to those in the same social class and with the same range of intelligence as subjects in the sample.

Pre-established populations can have another serious limitation. Samples of these populations can be biased to an undetermined extent by the uncooperativeness of some members. The very children who are too frightened to participate in a study of neglected children, for example, may have been the most neglected in the population.

Unfortunately many investigators have not been sufficiently sensitive to such issues of sampling and control. It has been all too common for observers to develop norms for a total age group by observing infants in a foundling home, to investigate child-rearing practices by interviewing parents in the upper-middle class, or to arrive at a general conclusion about an alien society after having lived with a few families. Recently there has been a trend toward increasing methodological sophistication, but there is still much room for improvement in sampling practices.

## METHODS OF OBTAINING AND MEASURING SUBJECTS' REACTIONS

### VERBAL REPORTS

The most obvious method of finding out what a subject is thinking or feeling is to ask him. For reasons that will be summarized after the following survey of techniques, developmental psychologists have not been strongly inclined to conduct verbal inquiries into children's motives or affects. Personality questionnaires and inventories have gained in popularity as methods for obtaining information from older children. The objectivity of these instruments probably accounts for their appeal. Individual interviews have been employed less frequently, and only occasionally have children been asked to fill out rating scales or check lists. Subjects' reports have been most frequently sought in studies of affective reactions. The different techniques are illustrated in the order of their degree of structure.

## LESS STRUCTURED METHODS

*Compositions.* To investigate anger, Bovet (1923) asked schoolboys to write compositions about fights. In his instructions he asked for the reasons for combat and the description of a fight from beginning to end.

*Interviews.* Jersild and Tasch (1949) interviewed children between 6 and 18 years about the happiest days of their lives. Reasons for the happiness were tabulated for four age groups. Hicks and Hayes (1938) talked to children in the seventh to twelfth grades about their reasons for worry and the anger-provoking actions of other people.

## OBJECTIVE METHODS

*Ratings.* Jersild, Goldman, and Loftes (1941) asked fifth and sixth grade children to tell whether each of 25 situations was a frequent, occasional, or infrequent cause of worry. As part of their study of masculinity and femininity, Terman and Miles (1936) gave an inventory of emotional reactions to

boys and girls in the seventh and eleventh grades. The subjects rated the degree of emotion they experienced in 34 situations, each of which was described with a view to arousing an emotion such as anger, fear, disgust, or pity. Hess and Goldblatt (1957) asked adolescents to rate themselves and to predict how they would be placed on the same scales by their parents. Self-percepts and anticipated ratings were also obtained from the parents. Subjects indicated their positions on scales varying between such extremes as self-controlled and wild, loving and angry, and serious and frivolous.

*Interviews and Questionnaires.* Sources of anxiety were the topics of an interview schedule that Ort (1952) administered to adolescent boys. The questions, most of which could be answered by *yes, no,* or an indication of doubt, pertained to sex, personal habits, aggression, and honesty. Hurlock and Klein (1934) administered a questionnaire about adolescent "crushes" to boys and girls in high schools, and Finger (1947) asked college students to fill out a questionnaire about sexual practices, beliefs, and emotional reactions in the first years of adolescence.

## STANDARD INVENTORIES

*Adolescent.* Subjects' verbal reports are probably sought more often by adjustment inventories than by any other methods. A number of inventories has been used in studies of preadolescent and adolescent subjects. A few examples of the more carefully standardized tests are Washburne's Test of Social Adjustment (1935), Mathews' revision of Woodworth's Personal Data Sheet (1923), and Cowan, McClellan, Pratt, and Skaer's schedule (1935), which is an adaptation of Thurstone's personality schedule and is designed to be administered to subjects between the ages of 12 and 16 years.

Two popular inventories initially standardized on college populations, Mandler and Sarason's questionnaire for test anxiety (1952) and Taylor's test of manifest anxiety (1953), have also been validated with high-school populations. Both tests were significantly related to the duration of exposure required for correct recognition of tachistoscopically presented words (Sarason and Gordon, 1953). Test anxiety was significantly related to recognition threshhold for certain words (Smock, 1956). When asked to squeeze a dynamometer as soon as they heard a buzzer, high-school students with high anxiety scores on Taylor's scale had significantly greater amplitude scores than a less anxious group (Castaneda, 1956). The latter had the greater speed of reaction at the weak intensity and lower one at the strong intensity.

*Younger Subjects.* Rogers' Test of Personality Adjustment (1931) is one of the most commonly employed with children in the upper grades of elementary school. Items are phrased in terms of maladjustments at school, at home, and in the family. Castaneda, McCandless, and Palermo (1956) developed a form of Taylor's scale for subjects in the fourth, fifth, and sixth grades. Forty-two items in the scale pertain to anxiety, and eleven comprise a lie scale. To validate the test, the authors conducted a careful set of studies

that might well serve as a model for authors of other tests. Compared to children with low anxiety scores, children with high scores did poorly on the difficult components of a specially designed psychomotor task but were superior on the less difficult ones (Castaneda, Palermo, and McCandless, 1956). In learning by trial-and-error, less anxious subjects were consistently superior to more anxious ones (Palermo, Castaneda, and McCandless, 1956). There were no significant correlations between test anxiety and school achievement or intelligence for fourth- or fifth-grade boys. Correlations were moderate to high for fourth-grade girls and for sixth-grade students (McCandless and Castaneda, 1956). It seemed probable that very anxious children would be handicapped in social relationships with peers. Significant negative associations between the manifest anxiety scale and popularity, as measured by sociometric status, were found for fourth-grade boys and all children in the fifth grade but not for children in the sixth grade (McCandless, Castaneda, and Palermo, 1956).

## Evaluation of Verbal Reports

Many investigators are chary about using verbal reports because of their many sources of invalidity. For a child's verbal report to be accurate, he must be aware of his reactions, they must lend themselves to verbalization, and he must have the necessary descriptive terms in his vocabulary. Such conditions are satisfied most readily in interviews with adolescents. Younger children often find it difficult to describe a feeling or judgment because they are not sufficiently practiced in putting their reactions into words. They also tend to be more swayed by their emotions than are older subjects. Finally, any procedures used with young children are time-consuming because they do not read well enough to take a written test. In view of these limitations, it is not surprising that verbal reports are seldom sought from subjects below the fifth grade.

Even when children have the capacity for verbal introspection, shame or fear or anxiety about certain motives and feelings can produce distorted accounts and even a deliberate withholding of some feelings. Taylor's scale, for example, is effected by the tendency to avoid self-criticism (Jessor and Hammond, 1957).

The possible connection between resistance and ratings is illustrated in Brigante's study (1958) of boys between 12 and 14 years of age. Selected because of their high interest in sports, the subjects were tested on their knowledge of this subject by three judges. One judge was rewarding, one was neutral, and one was punishing. There were virtually no differences in the ratings of judges when the boys answered direct questions such as, "Do you think Mr. —— is a friendly or an unfriendly sort of person?" The differences in ratings became very significant, however, when the questions took an indirect line, such as, "How do you think the other two judges feel about Mr. ——?"

Anxiety about some motives can sometimes lead to their repression.

In reading about children's reports of fears, it is well to remember Freud's patient, Little Hans, who suffered from a phobia (1924). Had the child been asked, he would have reported a fear of horses. He could not have reported that horses had been unconsciously substituted for his father, the original object of the fear. Strong affective and motivational states, particularly forbidden ones, are often subject to such defensive distortions. If a person has projected his hostile feelings, he sincerely attributes them to someone else; if he has reversed them, he can only report very positive feelings to the object.

There are special difficulties about answers to objective inventories. One problem is created by the lack of any provision for answers differing from those provided in the test. No matter how a question is asked, there is always a danger that its phrasing will prejudge the issue in a manner that distorts the respondent's intentions. A child may be disinclined to admit that he does cross the street in order to avoid people because he does it for reasons other than shyness. But there is no way for him to describe his reasons or the people who elicit this behavior. Hence he feels that the answer is *yes* in one sense and *no* in another. Since he thinks that saying he is doubtful would be misleading, he is not at all clear about the answer he should mark on the test.

Another difficulty about inventories stems from their impersonal character. The subject gives his responses not to a sympathetic listener but to an anonymous reader. Would not any child feel uncomfortable about revealing his secret fears or his forbidden aggressive impulses under such circumstances, particularly when the answers may be read by school authorities? If the test is given to a group of children, there is usually little time for questions, so that it is difficult to determine the subjects' rapport or to learn about different interpretations of the same item.

## Projective Verbal Techniques

### SOCIAL CONVERSATION

Smith (1933) analyzed reasons for criticism mentioned in sentences spoken by children between 2 and 6 years of age. Fisher (1934) collected stenographic records of children's speech and then computed the proportion of negative comments. Hicks and Hayes (1933) coded more and less desirable ways of expressing aggression in junior-high-school classroom discussions.

### RESPONSES TO PROJECTIVE QUESTIONS AND RIDDLES

Material with motivational significance may also be inferred from expressions of wishes, statements of desired changes in the self, and earliest recollections. Winker (1949) obtained this information from boys and girls between the ages of 7 and 16 years. Wolfenstein (1954) investigated the reactions to anxiety of 5-to-12-year-old children by asking them to tell the jokes and riddles they liked best. On obtaining a joke or riddle, she inquired into its meaning and the subject's associations. A similar method of analyz-ing the motivational appeal of proverbs was employed by Shimkin and Sanjuan (1953) in their research on responses to anxiety in rural Russia.

### VERBAL TESTS

*Reinterpretation of Other Tests.* When taking a nonprojective verbal test, subjects may unintentionally reveal attributes that are irrelevant to the original purposes of the instrument. In their answers to Pressey's Interest Attitude Test, adolescent delinquents significantly exceeded normal subjects in references to topics such as jail, death, sin, murder, suffering, and guns (Durea, 1933). Apparently the delinquents were very preoccupied with the most direct forms of aggression.

*Signs of Emotional Instability on Intellectual Tests.* Bühler (1938) Bijou (1942), Pignatelli (1943), and Granick (1955), among others have investigated the possibility that a broad scatter of scores and poor performance on certain subtests of intelligence are characteristic of emotionally disturbed or anxious subjects. Both Granick and Pignatelli, who reviewed the literature, came to the conclusion that the results thus far have been equivocal. Although there are suggestive trends, no clear-cut signs of anxiety or maladjustment have been established.

*An Objective, Projective Test.* Scoring patterns that the subjects cannot anticipate also provide the basis for analyzing responses to Krout's Personal Preference Scale (1954). This instrument was standardized on subjects 14 years old and above. A subject is required to indicate whether he likes, dislikes, or feels indifferent to such activities and objects as sleeping alone in a house, sucking candy, eating crunchy foods, reading ancient history, and raising money for charity. Among the scoring categories are certain motivational states, levels of psychosexual fixation, masculine and feminine identifications, and maturity. The test discriminated significantly between normals and neurotics, between both and schizophrenics, and between males and females. In support of the test, Krout also described a number of cases whose scores were significantly related to independent criteria.

## FREE ASSOCIATION

Jung's method (1910) has seldom been employed with children, probably because of doubt concerning their capacity to cooperate. The suitability of the technique to adolescents has been demonstrated by Fauquier (1939), who administered the stimulus words *hate, fear, love,* and *desire* to two groups of 15-year-old boys. Compared to uninstitutionalized normal subjects, a higher proportion of institutionalized delinquents gave associations expressing hatred of persons, violence, and fear of animals.

## Story Techniques

What could be more natural for children than listening to stories or making them up? Such activities are familiar and entertaining and make it easy for children to talk without being self-conscious. This survey of story techniques begins with the relatively unstructured request to tell a story about anything, continues with more structured techniques, such as the completion of standard themes, and ends with objective methods that provide the subjects with standard choices.

## TELLING STORIES

*No Assigned Themes.* As a means of studying the time orientations of subjects who were 8 to 10 years of age, Leshan (1952) asked them to "tell me a story." He anticipated that children from the middle class would think in terms of long time periods, since such an orientation would implement their concern with self-control in the service of future goals. As he predicted, subjects from the working class had a much narrower time span and a less definite picture of the future than did subjects from the middle class. In their research on time span Barndt and Johnson (1955) found that delinquents between the ages of 16 and 18 years could not start a story on their own. When they were provided with a neutral theme about two boys who were walking along a street near the edge of a town, the subjects were then able to complete the story. The results were analyzed with respect to time spans and references to crime and unhappy endings.

*Assigned Themes.* Wright (1942) investigated the reactions to conflict of children between 5 and 8 years of age by asking them to tell a story about a toy. First the children ranked 11 toys in order of preference. Next, each child was shown the toys he had ranked most and least attractive and asked to select one for himself and one for another child. Following the choice of gifts, each child was asked to tell a story about one of three toys, two of which had been in the initial pair and one of which was new. The selection of a preferred or rejected toy as a topic for story telling was done twice. Stories were analyzed for frequency and degree of conflict.

## REACTIONS TO STORIES

*Children's Responses to a Story.* To explore the emotional reactions of 4-year-old children and their mothers to the birth of siblings Wolfenstein (1946) requested the mothers to read a story to their offspring and to report the ensuing events. The investigator also observed the children's behavior during play sessions before and after the reading. The story described a child's version of his mother's pregnancy, the birth, and the return of the mother and baby from the hospital. Wolfenstein tabulated different reactions to the story and related the results to such factors as sex, presence of siblings, circumstances under which the story was read, and mothers' attitudes toward their children's ambivalence.

*Memory of a Story.* To elicit material relevant to the problems of emotionally disturbed children, Despert and Potter (1936) asked them to reproduce a story they had previously heard. Frenkel-Brunswik (1949) used the same method to investigate the emotional aspects of prejudice in young adolescents. The story began with the description of 11 children, one of whom was a

Negro and another of whom was Jewish. Different children were then described as being aggressive or protective to three newcomers, whose attempts to defend themselves were futile. The story was read once and the subjects were then asked to reproduce it in writing. Children high in prejudice significantly exceeded those low in prejudice in distortions, references to hostility, and recall of undesirable facts and unfavorable comments about the Negro. Children low in prejudice recalled the stories with greater accuracy and displayed more awareness of individual differences.

## COMPLETION OF THEMES WITH MINIMAL STRUCTURE

*Incomplete Sentences.* Investigators differ in the amount of structure they provide in story tests. In some instances lengthy plots are produced in order to limit the subjects to only a few endings. In other instances fragments of sentences are presented in order to broaden the range of possible endings. The second approach may be illustrated by a method used by Sanford et al. (1943), who investigated the motives of children between the ages of 5 and 14 years. Items in the sentence completion test were structured in three ways. A situational pressure was described in one type of item, which was designed to elicit the expression of a relevant need: "Seeing that he was ignored, John. . . ." Some children ended this theme with descriptions of aggressive departures from the room or with tearful appeals. A second type of item began with a reference to a need and called for the description of a situational pressure: "She almost choked with rage when. . . ." Representative endings to this item included accusations of stealing and of the reading of one's diary by a brother. A third kind of item was phrased ambiguously, and its construction required a reference to some motive in the ending: "James's purpose in going there was to. . . ." Answers to this item included the needs to find out whether accusations were correct, to acquire a dog, and to behave aggressively.

*Fables.* Duss (1940), a pioneer in the construction of the story-completion test, created a group of incomplete fables. These were translated by Despert (1946), who used them to investigate the emotional problems of stuttering children. The fables were all short and could be completed by children from 6 to 15 years of age. One fable begins with a funeral going through a village street. People ask about the identity of the dead person; somebody says it is a person in the family who lives in this house. Then the examiner asked who it was and encouraged the subject to talk about the person. Despert interpreted the endings in terms of such categories as death wishes, guilt feelings, Oedipus complex, sibling rivalry, and jealousy toward parents.

Friedman (1952) constructed his own fables for boys and girls between the ages of 5 and 16 years. To elicit castration anxiety, he told two fables, one about a monkey with a pleasing tail to which something happened and one about a puppy who liked to watch his long tail wag but found it looked different one day.

*Incomplete Short Stories.* As part of his study of castration anxiety, Friedman (1952) also told a story about a child whose finger itched and who scratched and rubbed it all the time, even when the parents warned against it. Again, the subjects were asked to tell what happened. A theme designed to elicit oedipal reactions concerned a child who enjoyed himself alone in the park with one parent. On returning home, the child encountered the other parent, whose face did not look the way it usually did.

In an effort to test the validity of certain psychoanalytic conceptions of pregenitality, Miller and Stine (1951) designed a story-completion test for children between 7 and 14 years of age. The story beginnings portrayed situations that are common sources of anxiety, according to psychoanalytic theory. In the theme pertaining to castration anxiety, for example, a child was warned by his teacher not to touch some machinery, was curious, and decided to investigate. In the theme about sibling rivalry a hungry child could not be fed by his mother until she had first fed the baby. The test also contained themes pertaining to oral sadism and phallic tendencies. Some of the signs of pregenitality tabulated by the authors were magical thinking, anality, passivity, and running out of the field. In a subsequent investigation of "oral character" (Blum and Miller, 1952) the frequency of oral references in the story endings written by third graders was negatively related to a criterion of orality but an interpretive analysis of the endings was positively related to the criterion.

# PARTIALLY STRUCTURED STORIES

*Rated Story-Beginnings.* Graham, Charwat, Honig, and Weltz (1951) studied aggressive responses to different amounts of provocation. Their subjects, who were between 12 and 14 years of age, were asked to complete statements in terms of the heroes' probable actions. Each statement described a hostile act and the individual who committed it, and each act had been rated for degree of aggressiveness. The test was designed to cover five degrees of aggressiveness. Every degree was combined twice with each of five individuals: parents, authorities, siblings, friends, and inferiors. An analysis of the findings revealed that frequency and degree of aggression varied significantly with directness of aggression expressed in the attack and with the power of the attacking individual.

*Incomplete Longer Stories.* To study the defenses against aggression of preadolescent boys, Beardslee (in Miller and Swanson, 1960) administered a story-completion test. The hero of each story was very attached to an adult and was seriously but unintentionally inconvenienced by him. Considerable detail was included in the story beginnings in order to maximize endings about techniques of resolving conflict. In the coding of endings, frequencies of defenses, such as turning on the self, reversal, and rationalization, were tabulated.

*Story Completion with Guided Questions.* Sargent's Insight Test (1953), a method of story completion with guided questions, was adopted for children by Engle (1958). The endings were given in response to such questions as, "What did he do?" and "How did he feel?" The questions about feelings was not asked after the third item. In some representative themes the hero always gets good marks in spelling but fails on one test, sees a big boy beating up a smaller one, and finds out that some children had been saying bad things about him. Engle adopted Sargent's elaborate scoring system, which includes types of relationships, aggressive, passive, and evasive reactions, amounts and categories of different affects and defenses, indices of conflict, and various indicators of maladjustment.

In an investigation of the independence of children in elementary school Boehm (1957) supplemented a story-completion test with more detailed guided questions. In one story a boy was unsure about the best methods of decorating a room and decided to seek advice. To delimit the themes in a subject's endings, Boehm first asked him to mention someone from whom the boy might get advice. After the subject answered, she said the hero was able to consult either a very artistic student or a homeroom teacher who did not know much about art. The subject was then asked to name the one whose advice the hero took. There followed other questions about his selection among conflicting opinions and his feelings about the person whose advice was not followed. Another story was about a boy who became involved in a fight and had given his opponent a bloody nose. The questions pertained to the hero's feelings, his choice between the advice of a teacher and a friend about techniques for mollifying the victim, his reaction to the victim's advice to forget about the incident, and the kind of atonement necessary to allay the hero's guilt. Results were analyzed in terms of the objects of dependence, degree of independence of judgment, and the autonomy of conscience.

## OBJECTIVE STORY TESTS

To study the resolution of conflict in early adolescence, Seaton (1949) constructed a story-completion test with multiple-choice endings. In one story a boy accidentally collides with his mother. As a result, she says he cannot go to the movies, as she has promised, and that he must go to his room. The subject was asked to choose one of three possible endings: the hero goes to his room and wonders why he always does the wrong thing; he questions the punishment and points out that the collision was an accident; he goes to his room but thinks the treatment was mean and unfair. Endings were coded in terms of such categories as self-blame, blame of others, hostility by means of an external agent, verbal aggression, and resistance to temptation.

Schroeder and Hunt (1957) explored the defenses of adolescent boys by means of an objective scale. For each of ten items that described different kinds of failure, the subjects chose one of two alternative endings. The endings were predominantly intropunitive, extrapunitive, or impunitive. Choices were significantly related to flexibility in actual shifts from one ego-involving activity to another, to the Taylor scale, and to the level of aspiration.

## Projective Pictures

The commonest way of eliciting a subject's projections is to present him with a relatively unstructured visual stimulus: a clear picture with an ambiguous meaning, a vague picture of people, a cartoon of animals who are free to express many impulses barred to human beings, or even vaguer stimuli such as ink blots or cloud pictures. When projective techniques first burst forth on the psychological world, they seemed to offer access to people's private worlds, both conscious and unconscious. Many psychologists hoped the new techniques would markedly expand the theoretical horizons of perception and motivation. For the most part, such hopes have not been realized. There is now considerable evidence that conscious resistance affects the results of tests and that they are not so sensitive to some kinds of unconscious impulses as was once hoped. Little progress has been made in the clarification of basic theoretical problems, such as the meaning of projection and the emotional significance of color. Although an impressively large number of projective techniques has been proposed, their standardization and validation has tended to be fragmentary or lacking. At present, it is possible to summarize the projective picture tests that have had most influence on motivational research by discussing three types of instruments. One is the Thematic Apperception Test and related techniques, a second embraces the various tests consisting of cartoons and drawings, and the third is the Rorschach Test.

## THEMATIC APPERCEPTION TEST AND RELATED TECHNIQUES

Probably the most influential and most frequently used of the projective techniques has been the Thematic Apperception Test (Morgan and Murray, 1935), which contains 20 cards for children. Subjects are instructed to interpret the action, to tell what the characters are thinking and feeling, and to give imaginary constructions of the preceding events and the final outcomes. The stories are scored in terms of needs, press, and outcomes.

*Use of Parts of the Test in Research.* Most investigators administer only those cards and score those needs and press required to test particular hypotheses. Mussen and Naylor (1954) for example, employed a curtailed form of the test to explore the aggression of working-class boys between the ages of 9 and 16 years. A majority of the subjects were having difficulties with educational or legal authorities because of antisocial behavior. Ten of the 20 cards were administered, and the stories were coded for only two needs. One was aggression, which was tabulated when references were made to such acts as fighting, killing, criminal assault, getting angry, quarreling, criticizing, and resisting coercion. Because the authors felt that the overt expression of aggression depends, in part, on fear of punishment, they also tabulated references

to such punishments as assault, threat, quarreling, deprivation of privilege, and rejection.

*Combination of Standard Pictures with New Ones.* Investigators frequently add new pictures to the ones supplied by Murray. To test children between 5 and 14 years, Sanford et al. (1943) supplemented the standard set of pictures with another group in which a child was the central figure. The stories were interpreted in accordance with Murray's system. In order of frequency, the most commonly expressed needs were aggression, acquisition, autonomy, affiliation, succorance, and passivity. The least frequently expressed needs were order, infavoidance, exhibition, blamescape, understanding, and counteraction.

In their research on physical maturation and personality, Mussen and Jones (1957) used nine pictures from the standard TAT (Murray, 1943), five pictures from a 1938 version of the test, and five new pictures designed to highlight the motives to be analyzed. Written stories were obtained from physically retarded and physically advanced 17-year-old subjects. Themes of the two groups were then compared with respect to feelings of personal inadequacy, parental rejection, the inclinations to escape and defy parents, and the needs for affiliation and aggression.

*Scoring Methods.* A number of new systems for scoring the Thematic Apperception Test has been prompted by differences in purpose and population from the ones of Murray's research and by fruits garnered from clinical practice with his instrument. Henry (1947) has developed one of the more sophisticated systems. In his research he compared personalities in different societies and also traced the associations between the culture and different aspects of personality within each society. The subjects were Hopi and Navajo children between the ages of 6 and 18 years. Because the scoring system was being applied to stories of children from alien cultures, the dimensions had to have the same meanings in the two societies. The scoring system also had to be quite detailed because Henry intended to study the organizations of total personalities. To that end, he classified each subject with respect to such varied topics as mental capacities, richness and originality of imagination, motivational and emotional ties with peers and adults at home and in school, defense mechanisms, and conflicts between white and native identifications. To analyze such material, he defined criteria for coding both form and content. Some aspects of form coded were length of story, originality, rhythm, level of organization, and language structure. Among the categories of content were the motives, actions, and thoughts of characters in interpersonal situations, the emotional interplay between persons, conflict and the substitutes for forbidden impulses, and insight into emotional bases of action. The scoring was done with reference to the age and sex norms for each picture. Subjects were rated on each variable. Eighty-three per cent of the ratings agreed with some other source of data, such as the Rorschach Test, a life history, a free drawing, and a battery of tests devoted to emotion, moral standards, and the making and changing of the rules of games.

*The Achievement Motive.* An investigator sometimes finds that he gets better results with pictures selected because of their relevance to his topic than he does with the original TAT cards. To measure the achievement motive, McClelland et al. (1953) selected a special set of pictures, which portrayed people doing various kinds of manual and intellectual work. In a typical picture two men in working clothes are standing next to a machine, which appears to be some kind of press. When the test was administered to high-school freshmen, the reliability of the scoring, as measured by the agreement between raters, was .96. Scores were significantly related to incidental learning but not direct learning (Karolchuck and Worrell, 1956). Correlations of school grades and intelligence with the achievement motive were low to moderate.

*A Scale for adolescents.* To establish norms for adolescent boys and girls, Veroff, Wilcox, and Atkinson (1953) repeated the original method of standardizing the test of achievement motivation with a high-school population between the ages of 16 and 18 years. Scores were obtained with two types of instructions. First the test was administered with instructions calculated to produce a relaxed orientation. Then it was administered with achievement-orienting instructions. Under the relaxed condition, boys' scores were significantly lower than they were with the achievement orientation. Girls' scores under the initial instructions were so high that they could not increase on the second test.

*The scoring system.* Although the promise of test of the achievement motive has been demonstrated in a number of studies, recent investigations by MacArthur (1953) and by Karolchuck and Worrell (1956) indicate the desirability of refining the scoring system. The results of both investigations suggest that the current scores have at least two relatively independent components. One, the expectancy of goal achievement, is expressed in descriptions of mastery and of positive goal states. Another, which Moulton (in Atkinson, 1958) has called the fear of failure, is expressed by references to obstacles and to anxiety about the achievement of goals. Moulton has created a scoring system for fear of failure. He tabulates only nonpositive references to the goal and to the techniques of implementing it.

## OTHER TESTS WITH REALISTIC PICTURES OF PEOPLE

*Adolescents' Fantasies.* Symonds (1949) designed a special set of pictures for adolescents and standardized his instrument by administering it to boys and girls in junior and senior high schools. Among the more frequent motivational and emotional themes that occurred in the stories were aggression, eroticism, anxiety, altruism, ambition, and repentance. The commonest environmental themes pertained to family relationships, economic issues, punishment, separation, accidents and illnesses, and school. Norms were provided for each of the themes, and Symonds recommended that picture-story material be interpreted in the light of individual case histories.

*A Test of Oedipal Problems.* To obtain stories related to the Oedipus complexes of subjects between 5 and 16 years of age, Friedman (1952) made up two sets of pictures, one for boys and one for girls. In each set one picture depicted a father, a child with a broken toy, and a staircase in the background; another picture portrayed a child standing at a door and looking toward his mother; a third depicted two parents facing a child on the floor. After the set had been administered, Friedman asked each subject to name the parent in the picture whom the child loved better and the parent who loved the child better. Stories about the pictures were coded in terms of such categories as homosexual versus heterosexual choice, constructive action by a parent, frequency of conflict themes for a card, and frequency of references to the father ascending the staircase. The ascent was interpreted as a symbolic reference to the sexual act.

*Aggression to Authority.* Johnson and Stanley (1955) used a sophisticated design to select items for a study of aggression. The investigators first planned 24 pictures, which represented different combinations of three characteristics: the provoking agent, who was male or female; threat, which was high or low; and power, which was high or low. There were eight possible combinations of the three dichotomized variables. A picture could portray a man with low power and high threat, for example, or a woman with high power and low threat. In a pretest the authors asked 18 graduate students to judge the amount of power and threat suggested by each picture. Since the sex of the main character was obvious, it did not have to be rated. The investigators then eliminated eight pictures, one from each of the eight sets with the same combination of variables, about which the judges disagreed most with the original classification. The final form of the test, then, consisted of 16 pictures with two categories of sex, of power, and of threat. The test was administered individually to delinquent and nondelinquent boys between the ages of 10 and 12 years, and the responses were rated on a five-point scale of submission-hostility. In the analysis of data the investigators computed associations involving submission-hostility, sex, power, and threat, and their interactions.

## CARTOONS OF HUMANS

One reason for giving projective tests is to obtain material that the subject will not give voluntarily, either because he deliberately withholds it or because it makes him so anxious that he unconsciously distorts it. To minimize the effect of such resistances, investigators have created tests with cartoons or with drawings of animals rather than of people. It is assumed that unusual-looking anonymous figures or drawings of animals will not make a subject self-conscious or arouse anxiety in him about his own motives and feelings.

*Direction of Aggression.* Rosenzweig (1948) one of the pioneers in the development of cartoon tests, devised a form of his Picture Frustration Study for children between 4 and 13 years of age. Each cartoon depicts a hero who is being provoked by the action of another person. Rosenzweig and Rosenzweig (1952) found that extra-punitiveness gradually diminished with increasing age and that there was a progressive increase of indirect expressions of aggression. These trends were less marked for maladjusted than for well-adjusted children.

*Misbehavior and Punishment.* Morgan and Gaier (1956) constructed a special cartoon test, the Punishment Situation Index, depicting actions that are commonly punished. There are two sets of ten cartoons. Each set portrays such situations as a possible physical injury to a child, an unfavorable relationship with a sibling, destruction of the parents' personal possessions, a bad report card, a disordered room, and stealing. After the subject described what was happening in the picture, he was asked what his mother would say if he were the person in the picture, what he would say to his mother, what his mother would do, what he would do, how he would feel if his mother acted in the way he anticipated, and how he thought his mother would feel.

## CARTOONS AND DRAWINGS OF ANIMALS

Animals have the special virtue of being natural objects of identification for children and adults. It is commonly assumed that both will be readily involved in the task of telling stories about animals.

*Psychosexual Development.* To measure different aspects of psychosexual development, Blum (1949) constructed the Blacky Pictures. Blacky, the hero, is a dog. Incidents involving him and members of his family are portrayed in 12 cartoon drawings. From the subjects' stories and responses to the subsequent inquiry, the author inferred the strengths of oral eroticism, oral sadism, anal sadism, Oedipal intensity, masturbation guilt, castration anxiety, penis envy, positive identification, sibling rivalry, guilt feelings, positive ego ideal, masculine and feminine, and love object, masculine and feminine. The author devised scoring criteria and obtained norms for each picture. Instead of computing correlations with independent criteria, such as clinical ratings or psychiatric diagnosis, Blum offered strong evidence for construct validity. When psychosexual categories were correlated, almost all the results were consistent with psychoanalytic principles. Instances of such evidence were the significant correlations between anal expulsiveness and sibling rivalry and between penis envy and narcissistic love object in females.

Cava and Raush (1952) used the Blacky Pictures to study the identifications with fathers of boys in the twelfth grade. Subjects were classified as having more or less conflict on the dimensions of oedipal intensity, castration anxiety, identification, and ego ideal. As anticipated, the less the conflict, the greater was the perceived similarity between the subjects' responses to the Strong Vocation Interest Test and the responses they attributed to their fathers. The trends were significant, however, only for the dimensions of castration anxiety and of total identification.

Also psychoanalytic in orientation is Bellak and Bellak's (1950) Children's Apperception Test. Stories about the animals in the pictures were coded for orality, anality, sibling rivalry, Oedipal conflict, aggression, fear, sexuality, and identification with mother and father. Frequencies and relative intensities of responses to each picture by children in the preschool years were reported by Byrd and Witherspoon (1954). On the basis of their attempt to obtain normative data, these authors concluded that the test was most effective in eliciting information about orality, aggression, and relations with parents, and less adequate in producing material about sibling rivalry, fears, and sexuality. Byrd and Witherspoon also noted that judgments of parental identification had low reliability and that the only adequate interpretations of toilet cleanliness and oedipal dynamics were derived from pictures designed to elicit stories about these topics.

## MOTION PICTURES

***Motion Pictures versus Stills.*** On comparing the stories told by tenth graders about silhouette motion pictures and matched stills, Eiserer (1949) discovered that films were superior in eliciting expressions of needs and press, interpretable content, and stories that were more projective than descriptive.

***A Filmed Puppet Show.*** Eiserer's results should motivate others besides Haworth (1957) to study filmed projective methods. Haworth made a film of a puppet show called "Rock-a-Bye Baby," which was originally written by Woltman (in Bender and Woltman, 1936). Sibling rivalry was the theme of this 35-minute film, which begins with Caspar, the hero, calling a witch to get rid of his baby sister. In subsequent scenes the witch puts a spell on the milk, the baby falls ill and is rushed to the hospital, Caspar kills the witch, the baby is restored to health, and Caspar gets his parents' love. Haworth stopped the film at the point when the baby is taken to the hospital and asked the children to finish the story as a group. Then the rest of the film was shown. Finally, the subjects were seen individually and interviewed. At that time the investigator asked them to give their reactions to the show and to describe Caspar's thoughts about his mother, father, baby sister, and the witch. Other questions pertained to the necessity of Caspar being punished, his probable answer if his mother asked about the reasons for the baby's becoming well, and predictions of subsequent events. From the subjects' answers, Haworth derived signs of defensiveness, sibling rivalry, autoeroticism, obsession, Oedipal conflict, and superego development. Norms were established by testing one group of relatively normal children between 4 and 10 years and another group of children in therapy who were between 4 and 9 years.

## AN OBJECTIVE PICTURE TEST

A creative attempt to construct an objective test of anxiety was made by Temple and Amen (1944) and Dorkey and Amen (1947). Intended for preschool children, the instrument consisted of two series, each containing 14 pictures. Each picture depicted a particular kind of relation between two children or between a child and an adult. Some of the themes were scolding, neglect, and aggressive attack. In every picture the area of one person's head was left blank. From two faces, one happy and one sad, the subject selected the most appropriate one for the blank space. The proportion of unhappy faces chosen to complete the pictures was the anxiety score. Norms were compiled for each picture, but they were based on few cases. For children 2 years of age, the correlations between test scores and teachers' ratings of anxiety was .59.

## Inkblots

### RORSCHACH TEST

*Norms for the Preschool and Elementary Grades.* For reasons to be discussed below, the Rorschach Test has been used less frequently in studies of children's motives and affects than have the other popular projective techniques. A careful standardization of the method is available in the publication of Ames, Learned, Metraux, and Walker (1952), who tested 25 boys and 25 girls at each year level from 2 to 10 years. The authors described their procedures very carefully, but the sample was not at all representative of the general population. Three fourths of the children were above average in intelligence and from the middle class. In addition, the restricted geographic region from which the subjects were selected—Connecticut and New York—raises doubts about the applicability of the norms to children in different areas, such as the southeastern or mountain states.

*Norms for Adolescents.* Some of the studies of adolescents suggest the need of a special set of Rorschach norms for these subjects. Compared to Beck's normal adult group, Hershenson's (1949) adolescents produced a lower mean percentage of good, pure form and much more white space. As these signs are interpreted by the investigator, they signify that, compared to adults, adolescents display greater emotional distortion, lack of conscious control, and rebelliousness. McFate and Orr (1949) analyzed sex differences in the Rorschach records of adolescents in the California Guidance Study. Compared to the boys, the girls produced significantly more color, which indicates emotionality, and significantly fewer signs of anxiety.

*Clinical Reports.* A number of papers on the Rorschach Test has been devoted to the dynamics of an individual person. Sometimes the reports have been developmental. Typical is Allen's analyses of nine quarterly records obtained from a girl between the ages of 2.6 and 4 years (1955). As she grew older, the extratensive method of relating to her environment became increasingly prominent, and the author felt that she showed increasing control over emotionality without inhibiting her ability to make warm personal ties.

*Validation of Signs.* Working with boys and girls in the fourth grade, Broida and Thompson (1954) attempted to validate certain Rorschach signs of "insecurity" by analyzing their associations with reactions to psychological stress. Among the signs of insecurity were pure color, color-dominated form, color shock, a re-

stricted range of content, a large number of rejections, and few movement responses. The authors used two criteria for reactions to stress. One was the teachers' list of such responses as crying, autistic gestures, mobility, rigid approach to a test, and anxiety. The second criterion consisted of teachers' ratings of subjects on 12 scales of insecurity by Swift. The Rorschach signs were not significantly related to either teachers' observations or ratings on Swift's scale, although these two criteria were significantly related to each other. In short, it was possible to predict reactions to stress from teachers' ratings of children's insecurity in the classroom but not from the children's performances on the Rorschach Test.

## Drawing and Painting

### SCORING CRITERIA

Impressed by the extent to which artistic productions reveal the personality dynamics of children, a number of clinicians have attempted to standardize techniques of scoring paintings and drawings. Many psychologists who have employed artistic productions in research on motivation or affect have used the scoring criteria of Alschuler and Hattwick (1947). The validities of certain signs in this scoring system were investigated by Thomas (1951), who compared the paintings of children frustrated by the sight of inaccessible toys with the paintings of a nonfrustrated group. Thomas also compared the paintings produced by subjects of different ages; the age range was 2 to

5 years. Frustration was not significantly related to regressive shifts in hue or line. Age differences in form level agreed with Alschuler and Hattwick's picture of developmental changes, but age differences in color and line did not.

## PAINTING STYLE

*Fastidiousness.* Alper, Blane and Adams (1955) applied Alschuler and Hattwick's criteria to the analysis of artistic style. Their subjects were nursery-school children in the middle and working classes. From class differences in techniques of child training, especially those aimed at cleanliness, the authors deduced that children of white-collar workers would be more fastidious and inhibited in style of finger painting than would children of blue-collar workers. The predictions were generally supported by the results. Compared to the subjects from the working class, the ones from the middle class were more inclined to put colors down separately, mix colors indiscriminately, name a free painting, wash up on their own, avoid covering the whole sheet of paper, and avoid painting with warm colors. The investigators interpreted the cool colors favored by children in the middle class as signs of depression, poor adjustment, and controlled reactions. The separate placement of colors was attributed to a sense of order and cleanliness and to repression of the desires to smear and soil. Indiscriminate mixing of colors seemed to reflect the repressed desire for smearing, and the limited coverage of the drawing paper was interpreted

as a sign of withdrawal and emotional dependence. To determine how color was applied when dirtiness was not an issue, the investigators asked the children to draw with crayons. As anticipated, the socioeconomic differences obtained with paints were no longer significant.

*Conceptual Orientation.* McNeil (in Miller and Swanson, 1960) compared the paintings of preadolescent boys from the middle and working classes. His purpose was to analyze the strength of their "conceptual" orientations: their inclinations to communicate by means of concepts. The boys were asked to depict the feelings of anger, fear, happiness, and sorrow. Each feeling was illustrated by a concrete situation. In the direction to portray extreme anger, for example, the boys were asked to convey how they felt when ". . . you see a boy beating up your little dog or . . . a reckless driver has just missed you with his car." Subjects were asked not to paint a person expressing each emotion but rather to convey the ideas and feelings behind it. Guided by the literature on artistic productions, McNeil developed six criteria for conceptual and nonconceptual orientations. He assumed, for example, that a very conceptual person would be inclined to use paint only, to portray unrecognizable objects, to paint with at least four of the five colors, and to cover most of the sheet. Among the signs of a nonconceptual orientation were the outlining of shapes with black and the painting of small compositions. Although the results produced the anticipated associations, they were not so marked as those McNeil obtained with other techniques of measuring the conceptual variable.

## Play Techniques

### METHODS OF INTERPRETATION

The meaning of play has been the subject of many publications, some dating back to the nineteenth century. In clinical work with children play provides the primary source of information for both diagnosis and psychotherapy. Probably the most influential publications in more recent historical times were Freud's descriptions of Little Hans' phobia (1924) and of a child's play with a spool (1920). The importance of play therapy to people with different theoretical predilections has resulted in a variety of interpretive systems. Among the psychoanalytic orientations, those of Anna Freud (1926) and Melanie Klein (1932) have been most influential. Researchers have also found much of interest in the more eclectic scheme that Lowenfeld proposed for interpreting her World Test (1939) and in Erikson's system (1940) of analyzing play.

### FREE PLAY

Unlike the Europeans, most American investigators have been partial to objective methods and to the phrasing of hypotheses in terms of behavioristic learning concepts. In great part, the influence of learning theorists can be traced to their concern with clarity of concepts and their success in developing fruitful operational defini-

tions. Such assets have made the volume on frustration and aggression by Dollard, Doob, et al. (1939) a handbook for many students of social behavior. These authors defined a set of propositions that have been used by a number of investigators in interpreting aggression in play.

*Aggressive Behavior.* In a majority of American studies the variables are analyzed in terms of relative frequencies. Usually the criteria for tabulations are carefully defined. In designing studies, most investigators aim at the direct measurement of behavioral units but do not shy away from inferences about internal states. Representative of the American orientation to play are the following three studies of aggressive behavior, attitudes, and fantasies.

Levin and Sears (1956) investigated some antecedents of aggression in a group of 5-year-old children by observing their behavior during two twenty-minute sessions of doll play. Action during the play was divided into units; each child was classified in terms of the proportion of aggressive units in a session. To measure amount of aggression, the investigators tabulated attempts to irritate, hurt, injure, punish, frustrate, or destroy dolls or equipment. In the analysis of results relations were computed between frequency of aggression and such variables as sex of subjects and of punishing parents and birth order of subjects.

*Negative Attitudes.* Moustakas (1955) compared the "negative attitudes" expressed in play by well-adjusted and disturbed 4-year-olds. Each subject had four sessions, all of which were recorded on tape and by a stenographer. The first and third sessions provided the data for the study. From these data, 241 negative attitudes were reliably identified and rated for intensity of expressed feelings. Compared to the normal children, the disturbed ones expressed a significantly greater number of negative attitudes with more intense feelings. The commonest negative attitudes were diffuse hostility, hostility to home and family, and anxiety about orderliness and cleanliness.

*Fantasies of Aggression.* Wenar (1956) studied the aggression of 8-to-10-year-old children with motor handicaps. He observed the subjects as they played with the World Test. In analyzing the results, he focused on fantasies of destruction. These included fantasies about war, fighting, fires, accidents, sickness, and zoos or jungles with fighting, biting, or escaping wild animals, fire houses, hospitals, sailors, and policemen. In addition to destruction, Wenar also analyzed protective defenses and lack of over-all adjustment. Evidence of the latter consisted of aggressive worlds, empty worlds with few pieces and categories, closed worlds with many fences, rigid or overly symmetrical worlds, and disorganized or chaotic worlds with many fences. The frequency of fences was interpreted as an index of impulsivity and excessive anxiety about the importance of control.

## DOLL PLAY WITH STRUCTURING QUESTIONS

*Sibling Rivalry.* Numerous investigators have presented their subjects with a limited number of play materials and structured the situation further by asking a series of specific questions. In some cases the dolls were identified and descriptions were given of their relationships to each other before the questions were asked. Levy (1937) employed such a method to investigate sibling rivalry. The range of his subjects' ages was 2 to 14 years. Play was limited to three dolls, which were identified as a mother, a baby, and a child the same sex as the subject. The examiner said that the mother had to feed the baby. Pointing to her chest, he noted that she had no breasts, and suggested that he and the child make some. The examiner shaped one out of clay, and the child shaped the other. After the breasts were attached to the mother doll, her arms were put around the baby doll. The examiner then said that the sister or brother had seen the new baby at the mother's breast for the first time and asked what the sibling did. Next, the child was instructed to translate his description into action with the dolls. From time to time, other questions were asked with a view to encouraging the expression of rivalry. The examiner might even quote the older child as saying, "That bad, bad baby at my mother's breast!"

Levy classified all the activities of each subject into five general categories. One was the prevention of hostility to objects by such techniques as denial, withdrawal, distracting play, and leaving the room. A second covered the different forms of attack, and a third, the direction of hostility, included such objects as self, baby, mother, and breasts. A fourth category applied to techniques of restitution, such as making the sibling "good" or putting back the breast, and a final category involved methods of self-defense, such as impotence and rationalization.

**Directness of Aggression.** Fite (1940) used a semistructured method of doll play to study directness of aggression in children's relationships with peers and with adults. First the examiner asked whether she should make her doll hit the subject's doll. Then she asked him what he thought about hitting and if it was all right to hit other children. These queries were followed up by requests to justify his positions and to explain their sources. Next, he had to say whether it was all right to hit if the other child attacked first. Finally he was requested to make his doll hit the examiner's.

**Responses to Frustration.** Lerner (in Murphy, 1956) first gave each child some attractive new toys, such as a Mickey Mouse, some trucks, and a toy telephone. Then he raised some questions. He might ask what he should do, or he might try to get the child to say which toys were his and which were the examiner's. Once ownership was established, the investigator wanted to know whether his toys or the child's were nicer. He might end by saying he was going to play with all the toys and that the child should watch. Such procedures were repeated with different groups of toys. Then the child was given a chance to create a "selective play fantasy" involving himself and the examiner. Lerner inferred the child's methods of overcoming frustration from reactions such as competition, intrusion, desertion, and obligation. There

seemed to be three general styles of reaction to frustration. One consisted of ego-extending, ego-intruding, and ego-shielding responses. Another consisted of reciprocal actions, such as ego-fusing, ego-sharing, and ego-supporting. The third included ego-retreating, ego-recoiling, ego-destroying, and other passive actions.

## HIGHLY STRUCTURED PLAY AND REAL SITUATIONS

**Frequency of an Act.** Blum and Miller (1952) provided a group of third-grade children with an apparently limitless amount of ice cream shortly after they had eaten an ample lunch. The ice cream was packed in 1-ounce cups. Only one cup was available at a time, so that it was easy to record the quantity consumed by each child. Since the children had just eaten, the investigators assumed that the consumption of ice cream indicated not hunger but strength of oral passivity. The amount consumed was significantly related to nonpurposive mouth movements and to some of the behavioral characteristics, which, according to psychoanalytic theory, are part of the constellation of the oral character.

**Inhibition About Engaging in a Legitimate Act.** The destructiveness of preschool subjects was given free scope by Stone (in Murphy, 1956), who invited them to break some balloons. When a child refused, he was given a more pressing invitation. If he was still reluctant, the examiner asked if he should break them. With further refusal, the child was told that the balloons belonged to the examiner, that there were many, and that it was all right to break them. If there was still a show of reluctance, the examiner broke one when the child was not looking. Then the child was asked how the balloon had broken, if he did it, if it was fun, if more should be broken, and so forth. Stone recorded the total sequence of events and various indications of emotional tension, anxiety, and guilt.

In a game of collisions Lerner (in Murphy, 1956) moved a toy train on a track toward an approaching train that a preschool child was pushing. The purpose of the exercise was to see how the subject would act when the trains met. In two other situations the examiner's doll stopped the child's car and the child could not put his doll into a doll house because it belonged to the examiner.

*Style of Action.* Bernstein (1955) recorded amount of smearing during finger painting and play with cold cream. Smearing, which was taken as a sign of anality, was not significantly associated with a history of coercive toilet training.

*Choice Between Alternative Acts.* In one form of projective test the child has to make a choice between alternatives. To diagnose type of orality, for example, Bernstein (1955) said his subjects could have either a lollipop or chocolate. A decision to suck the lollipop was classified as oral-passive; the eating of chocolate was classified as oral-sadistic.

*Choice Plus Style of Action.* At each of ten positions on a floor Ackerman (1937) placed a toy, parts of which were assembled, and a disassembled replica. When a child came to a position, he had to decide whether he would put a toy together or pull one apart. Some of the coding categories were constructive and destructive impulses, ineffectiveness because of extreme orderliness, and constructive play with destructive motives. The investigator provided criteria for scoring each item. Results were interpreted in such terms as patterns of aggressive expression, conscience, level of aspiration, and dominant emotion. On comparing degree of constructiveness of maladjusted and well-adjusted children, Ackerman obtained significant differences for subjects between 3 and 6 years but for no other groups up to 16 years of age.

## BEHAVIOR IN PLAY AS AN INDICATOR OF CHANGE

*Deprivation and Regression.* All the experiments to be described in this section have similar designs. First, the investigators conducted a play session. Then they created a frustrating situation. Finally, there was a second play session. To assay the effects of frustration on motivation or affect, the investigators assessed the changes from the first to the second sessions of play. In their research on the regression of preschool children, Barker, Dembo, and Lewin (1941) predicted a decrease in the constructiveness of play following frustration. Constructiveness was rated on a seven-point scale. To frustrate the children, the investigators exposed a number of highly attractive, inaccessible toys behind a wire-net partition. Events in each play session were recorded by an experimenter and by an observer behind a one-way screen.

During the period of frustration the subjects significantly increased attempts to penetrate the barrier, to mix play with other diversions, and to leave the experimental situation. There was a significant decrease in the types of play to which the subjects gave their complete attention.

*Failure and Aggression.* Yarrow (1948) tested the effect of different kinds of failure on the aggressiveness that preschool children expressed in play. The subjects participated in two thirty-minute sessions of doll play. Between the sessions, members of the control group spent fifteen minutes in solitary play with tinker toys and with a simple jigsaw puzzle. The productions were praised liberally. Members of a failure group were given tinker toys and requested to duplicate the complex model of a windmill; toward the middle of the session, the examiner disparaged the children's efforts. Members of a satiation group were asked to work on a large peg board. They continued until either they refused despite the experimenter's insistence, or thirty minutes were up. Play before and after the frustrating experiences was rated for intensity of aggression.

*Training and Aggression after Frustration.* In an ingenious experiment Davitz (1952) demonstrated that training can affect the reactions to frustration of 7-to-9-year-old children. One group of subjects was given practice with aggressive games; another was helped to perform constructive, cooperative tasks. A typical aggressive game was Break the Ball. Each subject was provided with a pingpong ball, which was placed on the floor and could not be touched by hand. The object of the game was to break somebody else's ball while protecting one's own. In a second game each subject competed physically with the others to cover a very small spot on a mat with his body. In a third game each subject had to rip a piece of cloth from another subject's arm and retain the cloth on his own arm.

The second group of children worked cooperatively on the drawing of murals and the solution of jigsaw puzzles. During these activities all aggressive behavior was discouraged, and constructiveness was praised. To frustrate both groups, Davitz stopped a film at a climactic point and deprived each subject of some candy that he had previously received. Play before and after frustration was then rated for aggressiveness and constructiveness. The subjects trained in aggression were more aggressive after frustration than those trained to be constructive. The constructively trained subjects were more constructive after frustration than those trained to be aggressive.

## Congruence Between Projective and Social Behavior

Projective tests were originally devised for purposes of clinical prediction. From the test protocol, the psychologist obtained information that he used as a basis for estimating the patient's cooperation, his probable defenses, his ego strength, and other structural or behavioral characteristics of relevance to prognosis. The researcher, too, employs projective tests as predictive instruments. On learning that a child has expressed much aggression in his play with dolls, an investigator often infers a disposition, which he anticipates will also be manifested in verbal or physical attacks on adults or peers. To be more accurate, the typical investigator used to do so more often than he does now. The assumed relations between projective protocols and actual behavior were based on two premises. It was assumed that the stronger the need, the more frequent or the more emphatic would be its expression on the test. It was also assumed that the higher the score on the test, the more strongly or frequently the need would be manifested in actual social behavior. Research on projective tests has revealed that these premises are based on too simple a picture of the connections between test performance and behavior.

*Contradictory Evidence.* Under some conditions, the frequencies and intensities of test responses are valid prognostic indices of actual behavior. Walker (1951) found that ratings of hostility in Rorschach protocols were significantly related to ratings of actual hostility. Most of the evidence, however, indicates the lack of a simple association between responses to tests and social behavior. In the study by Sanford et al. (1943) the needs expressed in various projective tests were not related to behavior in any consistent manner. Symonds (1949) discovered an inverse relation between the frequency of a need in adolescents' stories and its overt manifestation. In his opinion, even a strong need that receives sufficient expression in behavior does not have to be expressed in fantasy.

Only suppressed needs require such internal outlets.

In Korner's research (1949), the hostility that preschool children expressed in play was consistent with the results of a story-completion test. But the relations of play and stories to the subjects' overt manifestations of frustration and to parents' ratings to such behavior were quite low. Jensen (1957) administered the TAT to three groups of boys between 15 and 17 years. According to their teachers, one group was aggressive and was in trouble in school, a second group was aggressive but their behavior was not antisocial, and a third group was passive. Neither a direct nor an inverse relation existed between aggression on the TAT and the expression of the need in school.

## THE MEANING AND CODING OF A NEED

The results of Davids, Henry, McArthur, and McNamara (1955) indicated that clarification of theory and greater refinement in the coding of projective tests might contribute to an increase in predictive efficiency. Aggression on a projective test is often tabulated without regard to the direction with which it is expressed. The investigators found that amount of aggression in self-ratings was related to direction of aggression against others on the TAT but not to the total quantity.

## STIMULATION AND CHANGES IN TEST SCORES

Some of the investigations revealed a direct correspondence between the stimulation of a need and its expression on a projective test. When deprived of food, subjects increased their references to food in the TAT (Sanford, 1937). When criticized continually by the examiner under conditions that permitted no outlets other than story writing, subjects increased their references to aggressive words in protocols of the TAT (Bellak, 1944). When given instructions calculated to create a relaxed orientation, boys got significantly lower scores on the achievement motive than they did when they were challenged to do well and had performed a competitive task before taking the projective test (Veroff, Wilcox, and Atkinson, 1953).

*Conditions under Which Direct Manifestations Are Avoided.* Not always has arousal been followed by an increase in the direct manifestation of a need or affect. It was necessary for Clark (1952) to measure strong sexual needs not by their direct manifestations in TAT stories but by their symbolic forms of expression. In coding strong feelings of guilt, Allinsmith (in Miller and Swanson, 1960) had to take into account both their direct and their indirect manifestations. Feasibility of expression as well as avoidance may affect the reaction to arousal. Evidence provided by Brozek, Guetzkow, and Baldwin (1951) suggests that arousal may not be reflected on a projective test if there is no possibility of gratifying the need. While on a semistarvation diet for 24 weeks, their subjects, unlike those of Sanford (1937), did not increase their perception of food in Rorschach cards.

## DISPOSITION VERSUS BEHAVIOR

*Impulse and Expression.* One factor underlying the occasional disparity between projective tests and behavior is suggested by the findings of Lindzey and Tejessy (1956). Of ten signs of aggression on the TAT, few were significantly related to extrapunitiveness or intropunitiveness in behavior but most were significantly related to self-ratings of aggression. In other words, the subjects knew what they wanted to do but did not necessarily follow their impulses. Tests results thus signify dispositions but not necessarily their forms of overt expression. In fact, as already mentioned, the expression may be exceedingly indirect if it is not feasible or not compatible with the moral standards of the child or his parents and the motivational state is strong.

*Age, Disposition, and Control.* The curvilinear relation sometimes obtained between aggression in fantasy and in behavior provides one kind of evidence that strong, forbidden responses are often inhibited by subjects taking projective tests. Preschool children whose behavior was rated by Bach (1945) at either extreme of aggression expressed more of this motive in doll play than the children who were rated as moderate. On giving the Rorschach Test to subjects between 9 and 15 years of age, Smith and Coleman (1956) discovered that very aggressive behavior was associated with medium hostility; nonaggressive behavior went with high or low ratings. Although the trends in both studies are curvilinear, the results are not congruent, a fact that may be attributed to age differences in the two samples. In the preschool group high scores in aggression during doll play were associated with either high or low ratings of behavior. In the pre-adolescent group high hostility scores on the Rorschach Test were associated with low ratings of overt aggression. Older subjects had had more practice than the younger subjects in controlling their aggression and were probably more adept at curbing their immediate impulses, particularly the stronger ones, by deliberate inhibition or defensive distortion.

## AVOIDANCE AND DIRECTNESS OF EXPRESSION

*Disposition, Fear, and Behavior.* Direct evidence of the effect of avoidance on direct expression has been provided by two studies. Mussen and Naylor (1954) investigated the aggressive fantasy of boys in the working class who were between 9 and 15 years and in difficulty because of antisocial behavior. When scores on the TAT were high, rated behavior varied with the fear of punishment expressed in the stories. If the fear was strong, the subjects were not rated as being very aggressive. Only if the fear of punishment was weak were high scores on the test congruent with rated behavior.

Similar conclusions can be derived from Lesser's research (1957). For those of his 10-to-13-year-old subjects whose mothers had encouraged aggression, he obtained a correlation of .43 between the expression of the need in TAT stories and in behavior. For boys

with discouraging mothers, the correlation was minus .41. If aggression had been encouraged, overt aggression was significantly correlated with extrapunitiveness and intropunitiveness on the Picture Frustration Test. If aggression had been discouraged, the correlations were not significant. Apparently children who have become anxious about their aggression avoid its direct forms in overt behavior and sometimes when taking tests. It seems necessary for an investigator to obtain information about the subjects' previous training or their internalized standards if he hopes to avoid misinterpreting some of the low projective scores for forbidden needs. Such scores have at least two meanings. The subjects' needs may actually be weak, or they may be strong but not expressed directly because of the deterring effects of stronger avoidance responses.

*Other Interacting Variables.* Fear of punishment is one of a number of variables that affect the association between the expression of aggression in fantasy and overt behavior. Otis and McCandless (1955) studied two others. The investigators frustrated preschool children with two of Lerner's blocking methods (in Murphy, 1956). Despite repeated frustrations, the subjects varied markedly in their expressions of dominant-aggressive and compliant-submissive responses. The variations were significantly related to two needs, power-dominance and love-affection, on which the subjects were rated by teachers. Children with high need for power were high on aggression during frustration and increased their scores during the second half of the series. The submission scores of these subjects were low during frustration and dropped rapidly after that. Children with low need for power were low on aggression. Strong need for love-affection was associated with frequent submission and infrequent aggression in play.

The current evidence thus seems to indicate relatively complex relations between the expression of needs in projective tests and in behavior. Overt expression may be effected by fear, moral proscriptions, the feasibility of certain actions, and competing needs. An investigator would do well, therefore, to think about the third or fourth variables that may affect the way in which the need is expressed. If he does not take the interacting variables into account, he is decreasing his chances of obtaining significant results. Of course, his results may still be significant if he is lucky enough to have stumbled on one of the simpler associations between projective expression and social behavior or if he has unwittingly chosen conditions under which the interacting variables were held constant. If significant results are not to be fortuitous, the investigator must develop acumen in selecting variables that affect the association between fantasy and overt expression.

## Structure of Projective Tests

Except for the TAT, few of the standard projective tests popular with clinicians have been employed very much in research on motives and affects.

Initially, investigators tried the standard tests, since they provided many measures of different needs, objects, affects, defenses, and perceptual styles. As time went on, the clinical instruments gave way to others designed for particular topics and particular populations. Researchers have shown most partiality to techniques such as story completion and play, the forms of which can be tailored to the particular hypotheses. The investigator who analyzes behavior in play can choose the number and type of dolls and can define the activity to restrict the subjects' range of response.

## DEGREE OF STRUCTURE

*Ambiguity and the Goals of Research.* It is the vagueness and the many details in projective pictures and inkblots that are of most value to the clinician. When given a picture of two adults, both of whom are doing different things with a number of instruments, a subject can respond to many different details (Miller and Swanson, 1960). He can concentrate on one or both people, a utensil, a clock in the background, or even a shaft of light. Psychologists assume that forces within the subject prompt him to select particular stimuli and some of their attributes from the total picture and to organize them in a manner that reflects the nature of those forces.

All the content in a subject's stories is grist for the clinical mill. All the information about different needs, defenses, and affective states has a bearing on the structure of the subject's personality, his dynamics, and his prognosis. But much of the story content is of no use to the researcher, who is interested not in everything he can find out about one person but in a few variables, possibly even one. From all the projective material he chooses the references that help him to rank the subject on the experimental variables.

*Choice of Stimuli and Validity.* The traditional projective test is most fallible when it is used to rank all subjects on a variable. If a subject has selected his own stimuli and given them his own meanings, there is no guarantee that all or any of his associations will be pertinent to the problem of the study. In fact, there is a number of reasons why a child's fantasy or behavior may not be pertinent to the investigator's interest. The child may be high on a need but get an invalidly low score because he is consciously or unconsciously suppressing references to it or distorting it. He may get an invalidly low because the test contains few stimuli relevant to the topic of the research.

*Interpretation of Protocols and Ambiguity.* When he interprets the subjects' responses to ambiguous stimuli, the investigator must sometimes assume they have a "common meaning." Card IV of the Rorschach Test, for example, is supposed to signify the father to most subjects (Levy, 1958), and a number of latent meanings has been proposed for cards of the TAT (Henry, 1956). Yet the more ambiguous the stimulus, the smaller the probability of a common meaning for all subjects (Heath, 1958).

*Structured Projective Instruments.* To benefit from the primary asset of projective tests, one must use stimuli with some ambiguity so that the sub-

ject can make a choice that reflects the nature of his motive. To rule out responses that are irrelevant to the study, one must use items with particular kinds of structure. Some experimenters have tried to achieve these goals by working with the more structured items of traditional tests. From the TAT, Mussen and Naylor (1954) selected the cards that seemed most likely to elicit particular needs and affects. Other experimenters have devised their own tests. To elicit feelings about oral sadism, Blum (1949) used a picture of an angry dog biting a collar. To obtain expressions of sibling rivalry, Levy (1937) showed each child a mother doll feeding a baby and then asked the subject what he would do. Such stimuli are far less ambiguous than an inkblot or a picture of a vague figure in the darkness. So clear are the meanings of themes that even a lack of response can be interpreted with some confidence. Despite their structures, such tests retain one advantage of a projective test: they still permit the subject a range of reactions.

*Constructing an Unambiguous Test.* Allinsmith (in Miller and Swanson, 1960) has discussed the advantages of the structured story-completion test and some of the difficulties of designing one. He was concerned with the strength of guilt feelings expressed in response to stories about immoral behavior. To make it clear that the hero was motivated by guilt rather than fear, the investigator defined the specific violation of a moral standard in each story beginning. The violations were of a kind that could not be detected. Each theme specified the act, the extent of the violation, the motive behind it, and the relationship between hero and victim. These facts were included in order to insure a comparable interpretation of the story by all subjects. Among the other variables listed by Allinsmith as requiring control in projective tests of guilt feelings were the hero's initial wish and his intention when he committed the act, the sex of the victim, symbolic connotations of the violation, and the order of stories. The satisfaction of so many criteria requires considerable work in the writing of stories and in conducting pilot studies. But if the investigator has even moderate success, he can collect final data with some confidence that he has eliminated one possible source of error. He will have specified the facts, both implicit and explicit, so that they will be hard to misinterpret. All subjects, then, will write endings with reference to approximately the same event.

*Multiple Choice Endings.* It is sometimes difficult to choose between a partially structured but open-ended test and one that is completely objective. Advantages of objective tests, like high reliability, ease of administration, and automatic scoring, are too well known to require discussion here. The disadvantages of objective tests require more attention. The most obvious one is the sacrifice of the most commonly mentioned asset of projective tests: the subject's freedom to select the stimuli to which he will respond. The more structured the test, the more limited is the subject in his attempts to organize his percepts. If the test is completely objective, he cannot even give responses that the examiner did not anticipate.

It is sometimes possible that a list of alternative answers provided by the examiner will change the subject's frame of reference. He may not have thought of some of the answers in the test, or he may have thought of similar ones with slightly different meanings. If his own answers are not on the list, he may have no choice but to check the closest alternatives, even if they misrepresent his reactions. If his reactions seem pathological in comparison with some of those furnished in the test, he may become anxious and, for conscious or unconscious reasons, choose the more socially acceptable answers.

Although the potential problems that have been listed require the investigator's careful consideration, they do not preclude the use of objective projective tests. Unlike the clinician, the researcher is not necessarily interested in many free associations or in the dynamic organization of a mass of material. If he is sufficiently ingenious and he conducts a careful pilot study, he can construct endings that are relevant to the topic under investigation, are phrased in terms that are familiar to most subjects, and include most of the reasonable alternatives. If his subjects have not reached adolescence, he can often count on their being relatively naïve about the psychological significance of the endings. Younger subjects are usually less guarded than older ones. In sum, objective tests have their assets and their liabilities. An investigator can make an intelligent choice of a test only after careful consideration of such issues as his hypotheses and his population.

## CONTENTS OF TESTS

*Animal and Human Characters.* In addition to the structures of empirical tests, their contents have provided investigators with a number of challenging empirical problems. It is often assumed that animal characters elicit more self-revealing information than human characters. A test with pictures of rabbits elicited longer stories from children between 5 and 10 years of age than TAT cards (Bills, 1950), but the animal stories did not yield the same trends as the stories obtained from the TAT. Nor did the animal stories of a group of third graders yield the same trends as their behavior in play therapy (Bills, Leiman, and Thomas, 1950).

Of course, the playroom and the TAT both differ in stimulus value from pictures of animals. In comparing stories about animals and people, Biersdorf and Marcuse (1953) tried to control differences in the stimulus values of the pictures. These investigators constructed a special set of pictures, which, with one exception, were identical with the CAT cards, even in the emotional expressions of the characters. The exception: the special pictures portrayed people instead of animals. There were no significant differences between the two tests on such quantitative measures as response time and number of ideas. Mainord and Marcuse (1954) administered the CAT and the special cards to a group of disturbed boys and girls whose average age was seven years. Again there were no significant differences in the quantitative measures derived from the two tests, but ratings of the clinical usefulness of the results favored the cards with human figures. Light (1954) and Furuya (1957) found that stories based on pictures of human beings exceeded CAT stories in the expression of feelings, number of conflicts, and amount of dynamically interesting content.

In most studies, then, pictures of people have been equal or superior to the animal pictures in eliciting material of interest to the psychologist. Murstein (1959) summarized much of the literature on the structure and content of projective tests. His review led him to conclude that the most productive pictures are only moderately ambiguous and portray culturally acceptable human beings who are not so similar to the subjects as to create self-consciousness.

*Type, Quantity, and Presentation of Toys.* The content of the play situation has also been the subject of empirical work. Both the preference for toys (McDowell, 1937) and attention span for them (Moyer and Gilmer, 1955) varied with age. The choice of toys and their use in play also varied with sex differences (McDowell, 1937) and with the amount of available equipment (Johnson, 1935). When many materials were provided in a playground, the children devoted themselves primarily to these objects. With less equipment, the children were not so inclined to play with toys and were more likely to initiate social contacts, play games, and display aggressive behavior.

The kinds of toys and the ways in which they are presented may affect style of play. When play materials were organized as part of a conventional house, children expressed more aggression than they did when the materials were just spread on the floor (Pintler, 1945). Dolls like the subjects' own family constellations elicited more direct aggression than standard figures (Robinson, 1946). Realistically clothed dolls and recognizable furniture stimulated more exploratory behavior but less systematic arranging by subjects than undressed stuffed dolls and blocklike, ambiguous furniture (Phillips, 1945).

## SOURCES OF ERROR IN THE TESTING SITUATION

In discussing the results of different projective techniques, Lerner (in Murphy, 1956) noted that children often express a need on one test but not on another. He also observed that reactions to tests differ in accordance with the sex of the examiner, the child's previous experience with the test, and even the day or the particular time of day. When such sources of variance are large, the results may reflect the attributes of the situation more than the enduring traits of the subjects. The error variance can often be diminished by the addition of certain controls to the design. Some of the needed controls have already been mentioned. Others suggested by studies of the potential sources of error in the testing situation are now considered.

*The Examiner's Influence on Play.* When the examiner was an interested and approving onlooker, subjects expressed more thematic aggression, more nonstereotyped play, and more changes in themes than they did when they had minimal interaction with the examiner (Pintler, 1945). Amount of contact with an examiner also affected behavior during play (Phillips, 1945). From the first to the third sessions there was a significant increase in aggression and decreases in exploratory behavior and stereotyped thematic play. But, when Siegel (1957) eliminated the examiner, the aggression decreased in the second session. In Siegel's opinion, the presence of an adult motivates the child to abdicate control. If the child is alone, his guilt becomes aroused when he is tempted to engage in disapproved acts. Since the amount of temptation increases with time, he becomes less aggressive from one session to another.

*The Examiner's Influence on the Rorschach Test.* It is commonly recognized that scores on an intelligence test vary with differences in the examiner's behavior (Sacks, 1952). The variation is probably greater for projective tests. The potential effect on projective protocols of the examiner's personality is illustrated by the study of Sanders and Cleveland (1953). Rorschach Tests were administered with a standardized inquiry by nine examiners to randomly assigned, normal subjects. Of 38 scoring categories, there were 20 on which the subjects varied significantly, depending on the examiners who had done the testing. The protocols also varied with the subjects' impressions of the examiners' hostility and anxiety and with scores on these variables computed from Rorschach Tests that the examiners had taken before they received clinical training.

*Conditions of Administration.* Other studies suggest the existence of additional sources of error. Rorschach scores varied markedly, depending on whether or not the subjects were very ego-involved in the test and whether it was defined as a measure of intelligence, nervousness, or imagination (Calden and Cohen, 1953). Scores on the TAT differed for group and individual methods of administration (Sarason and Sarason, 1959).

*Socioeconomic Backgrounds.* Subjects' protocols can vary with personal attributes other than aspects of personality. In verbal projective tests the performances are often related to the subjects' socioeconomic backgrounds. Reissman and Miller (1958) postulated that the contrasting stories often told by subjects from blue-collar and white-collar backgrounds may result from differences in willingness to participate, capacity to establish rapport with the examiner, verbal skill, and previous experience in making up stories about pictures. The fact that people in the pictures appear to come from the middle class may also help subjects from that socioeconomic level to be productive.

Social backgrounds are also mirrored by responses to the Rorschach Test. Compared to the white-collar workers, manual laborers gave more signs of maladjustment, produced fewer responses, and made fewer references to color or movement. Reissman and Miller were inclined to attribute the frequent signs of stress in the Rorschach protocols of manual laborers to their lack of familiarity with tests in general. It will apparently be necessary to develop special norms for subjects from the working class.

## OBSERVATIONS AND REPORTS ABOUT CHILDREN

Most of the methods mentioned thus far are feasible when subjects are available, able, and willing to produce some special form of behavior: to discuss their fears, to finish a story about a curious boy and some dangerous machinery, to break balloons, to play with toys.

In some types of investigation it is not feasible to manipulate subjects physically or psychologically. They cannot be put into special situations or even asked any questions. There are many possible reasons for such prohibitions. It may not be advisable to disturb children who have just had an operation; a clinician may fear that testing will interfere with psychotherapy; the children may have so many assignments at school that they cannot spare the time needed for participation in the study.

Even when the subjects are not available for manipulation and testing, it may still be feasible for the investigator to observe them or to get impressions of them from people who know them well. This concluding section is devoted to the different sources of information about children. The sources to be discussed are the investigator, teachers, parents, and peers. Included in the discussion of each source are suggested techniques for obtaining the information and representative topics that have been investigated by such techniques.

## *Experimenter's Observations*

### SUBJECTIVE APPROACHES

*Anthropological Observation.* Ethnological accounts of child development sometimes provide valuable links between social structure and motivation. Such a linkage is illustrated by Henry's description (1944) of the sexualized aggression of Pilagá children, Bateson and Mead's portraits (1942) of parental teasing and emotional development in Bali, and Asch's evidence (Murphy, Murphy, and Newcomb, 1937) of non-competitiveness in the conversations of Hopi children.

*Clinical Cases.* So large is the current clinical literature on children's problems that it is not possible to do more in the available space than suggest some of the different topics. Some typical clinical reports are those of Levy (1937) on affect hunger, Redl and Wineman (1951) on the control and defenses of children who have suffered years of abuse and neglect, and Smalley (1930) on variations in sibling rivalry with sex, age, and intelligence.

*Clinical Observations of Specific Events.* Subjective observations of children can be quite productive when applied to circumscribed and clearly defined topics. An interest in the congenital aspects of sucking, for example, led Ribble (in Hunt, 1944) to observe 600 neonates for signs of exaggerated sucking activity. Jessner, Blom, and Waldfogel (1952) compiled case studies of children before and after tonsillectomies and adenoidectomies.

Clinical reports are usually couched in terms of particular theoretical positions and convey the impression that the writers may not have paid sufficient attention to phenomena that are not covered by the theory. The disinclination of some ethnologists to specify their psychological assumptions creates problems of interpretation for the readers of field studies. Other common failings of both anthropological and clinical reports are a lack of precise definitions of psychological concepts, a paucity of cases, an insensitivity to the representativeness of the sample, claims of significance without supporting statistical evidence, and a lack of control groups. Despite such deficiencies, anthropological and clinical studies often contain fruitful hunches, some of which are later transformed into testable hypotheses by resourceful experimenters.

### COMBINATIONS OF SUBJECTIVE AND OBJECTIVE METHODS

*Continuous Parallel Records.* The goal of objective analysis is coveted by virtually all investigators, but many disapprove of the rating or tabulating of variables at the time of the original behavior. The disapproval seems cogent when applied to studies of complex reactions or to studies in which there are many coding categories. In both kinds of research the judges may become very uncertain about their evaluations or even about the facets of the situation requiring most attention.

To prevent such confusion, the investigator can gather continuous stenographic records of events and then interpret the results at his leisure. In his investigation of autocratic and democratic group atmospheres Lippitt (1939) compiled records of the conversations and activities of groups of 10-year-old boys. Among the data were a running account of social interactions, a minute-by-minute analysis of group structure, notes on changes in the group's atmosphere, and a continuous stenographic record of all conversations. It was this kind of information that he analyzed when he tabulated the frequencies of such reactions as aggressiveness, competitiveness, persecution of scapegoats, and frustration because of lack of structure.

*Specimen Records.* Barker and Wright's (1954) specimen records and the method of coding them represent the most sophisticated use to date of the continuous record as a means of analyzing motives and affects. Each specimen record referred to all the events observed in a defined situation during a period of thirty minutes or less. The observer dictated the results immediately after the period was over. A supervisor then raised questions about the points he did not understand, and the observer added information to the record in order to eliminate sources of confusion.

In the analysis of results the record was divided into natural episodes, each with its settings, behavior, and objects. The analytic code contained a category of matrix factors, such as action sequence, strength of motivation, centrality of motivation, and social field potency. Another category consisted of modes of action, such as dominance, aggression, resistance, submission, nurturance, appeal, and avoidance. There were also action attributes, such as pressure, affection, mood, and evaluation. Finally, there was a category of aggression, including attacks, their end, spontaneity, and emotional concomitants.

*A Time Sample of Continuous Records.* In her study of the behavioral problems of elementary-school children, Young-Masten (1938) employed a combination of time-sample and continuous record. Each child was the object of at least ten fifteen-minute observations. When at all possible the observations were spread over every activity of the school program. During each session an attempt was made to record all the overt behavior of the child. Unlike Barker and Wright, Young-Masten did not make inferences about underlying motives. Once the records were compiled, they provided the basis for listing each child's unacceptable behaviors, such as talking without permission, standing up in one's seat, and pushing.

## THE STRENGTHS AND WEAKNESSES OF SUBJECTIVE METHODS

It is common among toughminded social scientists to stress the weaknesses of subjective methods. There is no gainsaying the seriousness of some of the defects. The frequency with which case studies depend on unchecked recall by biased informants, the lack of precautions concerning halo effects, the ease with which observations can be stretched and tailored to fit the procrustean bed of a preconceived theoretical system, the usual stress on qualitative judgments and relative lack of concern with frequencies, the omission of critical facts because the collection of data was not planned with sufficient care—these and other damning comments are often made about some kinds of subjective observation.

A survey of the literature on children's motives and affects conveys the impression that many investigators, particularly those with positivistic orientations, are far more aware of the serious weaknesses than of the strengths of subjective methods. As a result, such methods are sometimes used without sufficient care or rejected when they could be very useful to the investigator. It is important, then, to list their assets as well as their liabilities.

Often mentioned as an asset of subjective observation is the fact that it permits an analysis of events in natural units. Such units may be quite small or quite large and may vary with the situation. If molar units are necessary, events do not have to be distorted by arbitrary atomistic analysis.

When an observer keeps records of total situations, he can later view each event in its context. The information about events in all their complexity also makes it possible to study their continuity. The completeness of the record facilitates analyses of genotypic forces.

These, then, are some of the assets claimed for subjective methods. But do the assets compensate for the serious liabilities? The answer is positive for some topics. Few objective methods can do justice to the complexity and organization of some complex phenomena, such as those typically encountered in a clinic. Subjective methods, with all

their defects, are particularly helpful during the initial exploration of a topic. Such methods may provide the original hunches that are later to be defined as testable hypotheses.

## Check Lists

### NATURAL SITUATIONS

*Emotional Adjustment to Nursery School.* If the investigator is clear about his operations and they are not very complex, he can obtain a great deal of information in a relatively short time by means of a check list. Heathers (1954) used a check list to evaluate the initial adjustments of 2-year-olds to a nursery school. Among the behaviors that he looked for in each child were hiding to avoid the trip, resisting attempts to dress him, seeking reassurance or comforting, crying, calling to mother, and clinging to mother.

*Aggression.* Dawe (1934) analyzed the quarrels of preschool children during free play by means of a combined record blank and check list modeled after Goodenough's (1931). The research was restricted to conflicts about possessions, physical violence, interference with an activity, and difficulties in social adjustments among children. The data were coded in terms of such categories of people as precipitator and nonparticipator and such categories of behavior as aggressive, retaliative, passive, and objecting.

### CONTRIVED SITUATIONS

*Ascendance.* Jack (1934) successively paired each of a group of preschool children with each of ten others and observed the play of each pair with three sets of toys in a sandbox for a period of five minutes. Eight categories of ascendant behavior were tabulated. They were verbal attempts to secure play materials, forceful attempts to secure play materials, success in securing play materials, defending or snatching back materials taken from one's possession, verbal attempts to direct behavior of the companion, compliance by the companion with one's direction, forbidding, criticising, or reproving the companion, and providing a pattern of behavior which the companion imitates.

*Fear.* Holmes (in Jersild and Holmes, 1935) observed children in the age range of 1 to 8 years and filled out check lists to describe their behavior when they were placed in such threatening situations as being left alone for a few minutes, deprived of support on a collapsing board, and asked to retrieve a ball from a dark room. Each subject was classified as performing the act without hesitation, performing it but after some delay or after an intervening act, performing it with the help or company of the experimenter, or completely refusing to try.

## Investigator's Ratings

### STANDARD PERSONALITY SCALES

*The California Inventory.* Rating scales are among the most popular techniques for collecting data about motivation. Of the personality scales that have been carefully standardized,

the best known are the California Behavior Inventory (Conrad, 1932; Read, 1940) and the Fels Child Behavior Scales (Richards and Simons, 1941). From Conrad's original instrument, Read collected the items judged by a group of experts as being most important for the study of the general adjustment and the personality makeup of children. For each trait in the inventory, the rater is presented with the definitions of two ends and the middle of a seven-point scale. Items are phrased in terms of situations commonly found in nursery school. Some of the items are persistence in the face of difficulty, happiness, desire for affection, emotional inhibition, suspiciousness of people, quarrelsomeness, and nervous habits.

*The Fels Scales.* There are 30 Fels Scales. According to the authors, the scales are suitable for children in preschool or in the first four grades. In deciding on the rating of a trait, the judge makes a choice from four or five cues that are placed at appropriate points on a line. Each cue is indicative of a degree of the trait. The position of the cue on the line was determined by judges' ratings in accordance with the procedure developed by Champney (1941). The scales cover such traits as affectionateness, aggressiveness, competitiveness, cruelty, emotional control, friendliness, and vigor of activity. Reliability coefficients for individual items are in the upper .70's or above; the mean is .89. A multiple factor analysis of the scales revealed three factors. One is desirable, mature behavior, such as competitiveness, friendliness, and leadership. A second is defined in such terms as independence, nonconformity, and antagonism and is illustrated by such traits as aggressiveness, cruelty, lack of emotional control, and jealousy. The third factor, lack of social apprehensiveness, is exemplified by cheerfulness, curiosity, and a sense of humor.

## SCALES DEVELOPED WITHIN RESEARCH PROJECTS

*Strengths of Motives.* Frenkel-Brunswik (1942) asked three judges to rate the motives of a group of preadolescents and adolescents on five-point scales. The nine motives, which were derived from Murray's list, were autonomy, social ties, achievement, recognition, abasement, aggression, succorance, dominance, and escape. The judges, who had known the subjects for a number of years, were asked to rate underlying motives and also variables of social behavior. The combined ratings for the three judges had reliabilities of the order of .70 for all categories but autonomy and succorance. The analysis of the data revealed that the same motivational state could be expressed in a number of forms. Girls high on abasement, for example, were high on manifestations of altruism or insecurity or both.

*Affective Reactions.* Arsenian (1943) used a ten-point scale to rate the security of 1-to-3-year-old children in a strange playroom. The scale varied from crying at one extreme to a free approach at another. Children were in the room for intervals of five minutes, during which time they were observed through a one-way screen.

A lack of security might also be at-tributed to the elementary-school children who got high scores on Young-Masten's rating sheet for symptoms. Four-point scales were used to rate children on traits such as sulkiness, nervousness, stubbornness, and giggling. In studies of preschool children Mc-Hugh (1943) rated their degree of shyness and negativism and Duffy (1930) rated their excitability.

To develop an index of regression, Barker, Dembo, and Lewin (1941) rated the constructiveness of children's play on a seven-point scale. Schiff, Dougan, and Welch (1949) used a clinical rating of anxiety as a criterion for a study of the psychogalvanic response and the electroencephalogram. The patients and normal subjects in this study were between the ages of 7 and 16 years.

## Time Samples

### SUBJECTIVE OBSERVATION

A time sample provides an objective basis for the ranking of subjects on a dimension. In devising a method, the investigator has to define his terms and to decide on the minimal number of observations and their duration. Both differ greatly in various studies, usually as a function of the problems being investigated.

*Short Periods.* Green (1933) made very short observations of the quarrels of preschool children. Such events are very tempestuous. They flare up suddenly and often run their full course within a matter of seconds. It was not necessary, therefore, for the investigator to observe a child for more than thirty seconds at a time. The sample of behavior was always taken in a free-play period when there was maximal opportunity for open aggression. The data consisted of tabulations and of subjective observations. Information was gathered about the nature of the activity, the subject's companions, the name of the aggressor, the manner in which antagonism was expressed, and the subject's reactions. From the different observations, Green developed indices of friendly and quarrelsome contacts and a ratio of quarrelsome contacts to cooperative play. The reliabilities of these indices varied between .77 and .90.

***Longer Periods and Specimen Records.*** In contrast to Green, who was interested in a more circumscribed topic, Young-Masten (1938) studied behavior problems in elementary-school children. Such problems can be manifested in different ways and can vary markedly in duration. Since she hoped to obtain data about many kinds of misbehavior, she observed each child for fifteen minutes at a time and attempted to spread her ten observations among all the activities of the school program. She did not classify the difficulties beforehand and make objective observations. Instead, she recorded all the overt behavior of a child during the period of observation. Later she identified different behavior problems from a perusal of the records.

## OBJECTIVE RECORDS

***Social Contacts.*** Mengert (1931) studied the overt friendly behavior of paired 2-year-old children by means of twenty-minute time samples. Beaver (1932) tabulated the initiation of social contacts by 2-to-4-year-old children by means of five-minute time samples during free play.

***Aggression.*** In a study of the aggression of children between the ages of 2 and 4 Body (1955) obtained daily samples of seven and one-half minutes for eighteen days. A sample was broken up into three periods, each lasting two and one half minutes. Included in the tabulations were four categories each of physical and verbal aggressions toward teachers, children, and objects. Lippitt (1941) investigated hostility in the behavior of preschool children by getting time samples of one minute per day over a period of thirty days. Walker (in Dawe, 1934) studied quarrels of preschool children by placing them in a room in pairs for six minutes, providing toys, and recording aggression every five seconds. Among his categories were screaming, pleading, and passive relinquishment.

***Dependence.*** To record social interactions between preschool children and between children and adults during free-play periods, Marshall and McCandless (1957) made a minimum of 50 two-minute observations of each child over a period of one calendar month. The investigators tabulated associations between subjects, friendly and neutral approaches, conversations lasting one half minute or more, and hostile verbal or physical behavior. An index of dependence was developed to analyze the data. It was the sum of the interactions with adults proportional to the length of observations.

*Oral Tendencies.* As part of an investigation of nervous habits of normal children in elementary school, Olson (1929) obtained time samples of oral gestures like thumb sucking. He found that the frequency of oral gestures was negatively correlated with nutritional status in children between the ages of 7 and 13 years and that it was high among overweight children between 10 and 12 years. Blum and Miller (1952) measured orality by means of eight two-minute samples of such nonpurposive mouth movements as thumb sucking, lip licking, tongue rolling, and bubbling. The frequency of these movements was significantly related to the amount of ice cream consumed when sated and to teachers' ratings of eagerness for lunch.

*Affect.* Swan (1938) used five-minute samples to collect data on the facial expression of emotion during periods of free play. Her children varied between 2 and 4 years of age. In a study of emotional instability in preschool children Lee (1932) collected three-minute time samples of shifts in mood. Each sample was divided into 12 fifteen-second units. For each unit, a judgment was made on a seven-point scale, ranging from audible expression of rage or grief to audible expression of pleasure. The scores consisted of frequency in shifts of mood and average mood level. To learn about the initial adjustment of children to nursery school, Highberger (1955) obtained 20 six-minute time samples of the aggression, initiative, and anxiety revealed in the incidents that occurred over the first nine days.

## USES AND ABUSES OF TIME SAMPLES

The time-sampling method has most of the assets of check lists and rating scales: it is simple and not very time consuming, it is objective, and it lends itself to quantitative analysis. It has a special asset: it is based on many reactions of a subject over a period of time. As a result, it is a good representative measure, and it permits the analysis of variability from day to day.

Like check lists and rating scales, time samples have their liabilities. They provide data that can be interpreted in many ways, they omit information about context. When misused, they can present an oversimplified picture of an event, and they can be affected by the observer's bias.

Usually, tabulations require quick judgments, so that time samples cannot be too complicated. A common error in planning the collection of time samples is the inclusion of too many categories. The observer can attend to only a limited number of events. Beyond the limit, his ratings become unreliable.

Time samples are more useful with observable than inferential material. When an investigator's hypothesis requires some inference, he must decide whether to retain the method of time sampling, shift to another method, or jettison the hypothesis. Such a decision had to be made by Swan (1938), who could not get sufficient agreement among observers in their ratings of aggression, affection, or general bodily activity. She decided to eliminate these variables. It was certainly an asset of the technique that it permitted the assessment of reliability. But the decision to abandon part of the study because the time sample did not provide sufficiently reliable information suggests that the method may not have been the most appropriate one for the research. Although the final study produced valuable data about the affect that could be studied in terms of facial expression, information was lacking about some of the original problems of the research. Another investigator might have been inclined to change the method or to add another.

Time sampling is not suited to some kinds of topics. Failure, for example, occurs so infrequently in many schools that a random sampling of behavior during the administration of tests is likely to miss critical incidents. The method of time sampling is also not suited to subtle and complex types of events, which can have varying meanings and which are spread over time units of varying duration. Expressions of sympathy, for example, can take many forms. They can include a fleeting smile, an earnest discussion, and assistance with work. The duration of each form of expression is not necessarily a good index of the strength of sympathy: the fleeting smile may express more sympathy than assistance with physical labor. Tabulations within standard units of time do not provide a meaningful comparison of degree of sympathy in the smile and the earnest discussion.

## Records of Professional Agencies

Quite a variety of records have been consulted by investigators interested in the origins and development of motives and affects. An interest in the jealousy of young children led Sewall (1930) to search the records of a clinic and a nursery school for information about competition among siblings. Bernstein (1955) consulted medical records about the early feeding of his subjects, and Page (1941) perused the records of social agencies to learn about the early frustrations of children who were later classified as aggressive and withdrawn. School records provided Sanford et al. (1943), with data about emotionality and needs, such as those for recognition, play, and nurturance.

## Teachers and Professional Personnel

### INTERVIEWS, QUESTIONNAIRES, AND REPORTS

Spitz and Wolf (1949) consulted nursing personnel concerning the frequencies of rocking and of genital play at different times during the first year. Sanford et al. (1943) conducted monthly interviews with teachers to obtain information about the needs of children in elementary school, and Hurlock and Klein (1934) administered questionnaires to principals, teachers, and counselors about the "crushes" of boys and girls in high school.

*A Structured Interview with Special Informants.* Some investigators have devised special interviewing methods, which are structured to elicit very concrete examples of the traits being investigated. Flanagan's critical-incident technique (1954) is such a method. By means of it, an interviewer can interrogate an observer about incidents that are important to the understanding of a particular topic. First, the observer is asked to make several judgments in order to establish the meaning of the topic. The relevance of different actions to a particular motive, for example, can be explored by such judgments. The informant is then asked to describe the actions in detail: the times and conditions, the persons involved, their locations, their behaviors, and so forth.

Turner (1948) used a similar method to obtain information about the altruism of children between the ages of 9 and 16 years. The items of a questionnaire on altruism provided the basis for interviews with a special group of informants. These people were selected because they knew the subjects well, did not have any need to protect them, and were able to communicate the required information. Items in the interview referred to seven classes of situation, among which were competition with others, frustration, and personal threat. The aim of the interview was to obtain descriptions of concrete situations encompassed by the definition of each item. On the basis of each description, Turner classified the actions as egoistic, of doubtful meaning, or altruistic with respect to the underlying motive. Scores on the test correlated .55 and .47 with ratings of emotional

stability and .47 and .42 with freedom from antisocial tendencies.

## RATINGS

*Ascendance.* It is not at all difficult to train teachers to make reliable ratings, since they are accustomed to making comparisons among their pupils. Jack (1934) obtained teachers' ratings of the ascendance of preschool children. The subjects were rated on five-point scales for such traits as insisting on one's own right to material, directing the activities of companions, and helping with the enforcement of the group's rules. The ratings correlated .81 with the ascendance manifested in an experimental situation.

*Dependence and Aggression.* Beller (1955) asked teachers to rate preschool children on dependence, independence, and aggression. Most of the individual scales had reliabilities above .80, a fact that is attributable to the care with which the categories were defined. Each scale was introduced by a question specifying the instrumental activity believed to be an aspect of a particular motive. The question was followed by a paragraph describing examples of activity, actions not in the category, and other clarifying information. The scales had seven points, the extremes of which were *very often* and *very rarely*. Subsumed under striving for dependence were scales for such variables as seeking help, seeking recognition, seeking attention, and seeking to be near others. For independence and achievement, ratings were obtained of such reactions as the derivation of satisfaction from work, attempting to overcome an en-

vironmental obstacle by oneself, and
taking initiative in carrying out one's
own activity.

*Affective States.* To measure the insecurity of fourth graders, Broida and
Thompson (1954) asked teachers to fill
out 12-point scales for such variables
as dependence, fear of things, reaction
to criticism and responsiveness to emotional stimulation. In a study of fear-
arousing communications Janis and
Feshbach (1954) first asked the teachers of high-school students to select
subjects who were hyperemotional or
excitable. The investigators then compared the responsiveness to different
communications of this extreme group
with the responsiveness of the less emotional subjects.

## CHECK LISTS

*Aggression and Dependence.* Livson
and Mussen (1957) had teachers fill out
a daily check list and then independently rank preschool children at the end
of the week. Among the items on the
check list for aggressive behavior were
interference with others' activities,
teasing or insulting, quarreling, and
physical attacks. Typical items on the
check list for dependence were the
seeking of physical contact, wanting to
go home, "helpless" crying, and asking
permission unnecessarily. The median
of the reliability coefficients for aggression was .80, and the median for
dependence was .48. To increase the
low reliability of the pooled ranks for
dependence, the investigators excluded
those cases about which the observers
showed most disagreement.

## Parents

## INTERVIEWS

*Early Training.* Parents are often interviewed about their children's behavior at home and about their important
experiences in earlier years. Interviewers have tended to concentrate on the
parents' techniques of child rearing,
such as the timing of weaning, preferred
methods of discipline, and methods of
teaching responsibility for various
household tasks. In a number of studies
these methods have been traced to indices of social background, such as social class, bureaucratization of father's
job, race, religion, and ethnicity (Davis
and Havighurst, 1942; Miller and Swanson, 1958; Sears, Maccoby, and Levin,
1957). In some investigations parents'
methods have been related to the subsequent characteristics of the children.
On questioning a group of mothers
about the early history of their offspring, Levy (1928) found a significant
association between reported deprivation of normal sucking opportunities
in babyhood and the later incidence of
thumb sucking. Allinsmith (in Miller
and Swanson, 1960) found a number
of significant relations between the
harshness of weaning and toilet training
reported by mothers and their children's
moral standards in early adolescence.
In Bernstein's research (1955) mothers'
reports of coercive toilet training were
significantly related to the anxiety that
the children later manifested when
separated from their mothers, to signs
of immaturity in drawings of a person,
and to the negativism expressed when
asked to take some tests.

*Motives and Affects.* Dameron (1955) obtained reports from mothers about their methods of teaching emotional self-restraint, and Sewall (1930) sought information about competition with siblings. Sanford et al. (1943), conducted free interviews with mothers and also asked direct questions about their children's needs. Sears, Maccoby, and Levin (1957) conducted interviews with mothers and made inferences about their children's dependence, sex, aggression, and conscience.

*Pathological Traits.* Mothers can usually give reliable reports about the presence of certain discernible symptoms. Moncur (1955) asked mothers of stuttering children to provide evidence of such difficulties as weeping, emotional vomiting, and nightmares. Long (1941) requested parents to fill out an anonymous questionnaire concerning such undesirable behavior as fears, dawdling, and boastfulness. Then he analyzed the age distributions of the reported reactions. Michaels and Goodman (1934) questioned parents of children between 6 and 16 years about the frequencies of such pathological traits as enuresis, thumb sucking, tantrums, and sleep disturbances.

## PARENTS' RECORDS

*Anger.* In a study of the expression of anger in preschool children, Goodenough (1931) asked the mothers of her subjects to keep records of the frequency, duration, and causes of outbursts. To get reliable data for each child, the investigator requested the mothers to keep records over a four-month period. The outbursts were most frequent at meals and during illnesses and became less explosive and more focused with increasing age.

*Fear.* Jersild and Holmes (1935) obtained parents' records of their children's expressions of fear. The range of subjects' ages varied between 1 and 8 years, and the records were collected over a period of 21 days. In the description of each incident a parent included the place and time, the child's activities, the persons present, the apparent causes of fear, and the child's reactions. Two judges agreed in 90 per cent of their ratings of fear.

*Children's Questions.* Davis (1933) asked mothers to keep records of the questions asked by children between the ages of 3 and 12 years. Most of the questions referred to actions, but many suggested different kinds of motives. The records were analyzed in terms of the categories of people to whom the questions were addressed. The categories included mothers, fathers, all other adults, children of the same age, older children, younger children, animals, dolls, and no one in particular. Still needed is an exploration of the overt and symbolic content of questions. Judging from the clinical literature, such content offers a mine of information about children's motivational and affective states.

*Letters.* In her study of social development Isaacs (1933) exploited an unusual source of information about children. She analyzed letters from mothers and nurses, who described various kinds of behavior in children and asked for practical advice. The letters provided interesting evidence of the kinds of motives and affects that create anxieties in adults and that may provide foci of difficulty in children's relationships with authorities.

## Peers

### INTERVIEWS

How can one get the most valid information about a subject from other children who know him? The interview has a number of serious drawbacks with juvenile informants, especially when the research pertains to affects and motives. These are loaded topics, and the average child lacks the objectivity to converse about them. His anxiety may be considerable if the questions pertain to his friends or even his schoolmates. Children who become anxious often become blocked or incapable of visualizing the interpreter's purpose. For such reasons, the interview has been used with decreasing frequency in recent years, and primarily in studies of adolescents.

### SOCIOMETRIC CHOICES

The sociometric method is probably the commonest current method of obtaining information about children from their peers. The assets of this method are best illustrated by examples of its use in research.

*Pictures.* When children are very young, they cannot be depended on to remember all the people in a social group. Lists are no help as reminders when subjects have not yet learned to read. To overcome these difficulties, Biehler (1954) used pictures. Each subject was asked to look at three pictures, each of which portrayed two children at play. In every picture the children lacked heads. After putting a picture of the subject's head on one of the figures, the investigator asked him to select a picture of another child's head for the other figure. Choices by children showed agreements of 72 and 76 per cent with time samples of the choices made during free play.

*Verbal Requests.* Gray (1957) did not need to use pictures with her children, who were in the sixth and seventh grades. She obtained information about aggression and withdrawal by means of a verbal sociometric technique. To identify the most aggressive children, she asked each subject to name the people who broke the rules of the school and of games. To identify withdrawing children, she asked about the boys and girls who stayed out of games. As measured by repetitions of the choices, the reliability of aggression was significant for the total group.

*Verbal Portraits.* To obtain a sociometric rating, the examiner sometimes presents a verbal portrait of a particular type of child and then asks the subject to name people in his group who fit the portrait. Lesser (1957) employed this technique to study direct and indirect aggression in children between the ages of 10 and 13 years. Havighurst and Taba (1949) presented their 16-year-olds with descriptions approximately a paragraph in length and asked the subjects to name the portrayed persons.

### ASSETS OF SOCIOMETRIC CHOICES

Sufficient examples of the sociometric method have been presented to illustrate the reasons for its popularity. First, the descriptions of traits are provided by the investigator and not the respondent. This procedure relieves the respondent of the burden of verbalization. All he has to do is match each description with one or more persons. Next, the respondent is asked not to discuss a specific child but to pick the people in a group with certain attributes. Hence he is not likely to feel that he is telling tales about a particular person. He is also providing information, which, when combined with the reactions of others in the group, will enable the investigator to compare a subject's ranking with those of other children. The data consist of choices or of ratings, which make them easier to analyze than the more varied content of an interview. In many cases the child is motivated to give a valid description of others because his responses may determine who will sit next to him in class or who his partner will be in play activities.

### SOME GENERAL IMPRESSIONS OF RESEARCH ON MOTIVATION AND AFFECT

A survey of methods would be incomplete if it did not list common pitfalls and sources of confusion. Foremost among the difficulties is a lack of consensus about conceptions of motivation and affect. Another vexing problem concerns the methods of validating tests of complex phenomena, which can be manifested in many different kinds of behavior. Finally, there are questions about the choice of subjects; particularly, the extent to which characteristics such as age, sex, social class, and availability of subjects should determine the selection of a sample.

## Problems of Definition

Although this is a volume on methods, it is necessary to raise certain theoretical issues that are pertinent to the design of investigations and the interpretation of results. Some of the most perplexing problems in studies of motivation and affect arise because of a lack of consensus about definitions. Some conceptions of motivation are so broad that it is difficult to tell what they exclude. A psychologist who cannot understand a subject's behavior, for example, often assumes that more information about his past experiences or his current unconscious reactions would reveal an underlying motive. Such a definition of motivation covers virtually all behavior but reflex action.

The problem of definition is not limited to the generic meaning of motivation. Names of specific motives seem as numerous and as arbitrary as the names of stars. In line with differing theoretical assumptions about components and origins of motives, they have been identified in psychological, behavioral, and phenomenological terms. Various concepts refer to such aspects of motives as hereditary characteristics, affects, incentives, objects, acts, and goals. Some concepts are as specific as needs for money and for a friend's company; others are as general as the need for consistency and the death instinct.

# DEFINITIONS AND CODING
# OF AGGRESSION

The lack of consensus about nomenclature and theoretical premises creates some practical difficulties in the planning and interpretation of research, difficulties that are all too evident in the literature on aggression. Sometimes the same term has been applied to concepts that were obviously intended to have different meanings. In the Fels Scales (Richards and Simons, 1941), for instance, the reactions subsumed under aggression are closer in meaning to what is ordinarily understood as initiative. Sometimes different terms have been applied to the same concept. Many of the items in Jack's code for ascendance (1934) would ordinarily be assigned to the motive of aggression. Often a form of behavior, which different psychologists are ready to define in the same way, is given different underlying interpretations. Negativism has been interpreted as an expression of aggression by Fisher (1934), of shyness by Goodenough (1929) and of anxiety by Reynolds (1928).

Investigators have shown some agreement in their connotative definitions of aggression but not enough to establish a common position with respect to denotative definitions and operations. The latter have tended to vary with the level of abstraction, the scope of the investigator's conception, and the extent to which it was conceived in terms of observable behavior rather than an underlying disposition. Frenkel-Brunswik's definition (1942) encompassed one of the broadest range of acts. She viewed aggression in terms of a goal, the desire to deprive others. Aggression, she thought, refers not to behavior but to an underlying predisposition, which can be expressed in many kinds of acts. She did not think that the motive could be measured validly by ratings of overt behavior. Her estimates of the motive consisted of intuitive judgments based on many kinds of acts in a variety of situations.

Frenkel-Brunswik considered a broader range of acts than did Allinsmith (in Miller and Swanson, 1960), who concentrated on the directness with which aggression is expressed. Her coding system consisted of categories of directness, each of which was defined in terms of specific acts. Still more restricted was the definition of Mussen and Naylor (1954), whose code gave more weight to acts calculated to inflict injury on an organism or its surrogate. The instrumental acts used in Beller's definition (1957) represented the most direct forms of aggression, although he provided for the possibility of displacements.

Disagreements about the definition of a motive have also led to differences in the codes for what was purported to be the same concept. The code of aggression employed by Graham, Charwat, Honig, and Weltz (1951) did not include hurting oneself; Mussen and Naylor's did. Mussen and Naylor did not include reactive helpfulness in their code; Allinsmith did. Only the most speculative comparisons of the studies of aggression are possible when they have differed in their operational definitions.

## VALIDATING TESTS OF MOTIVES

***Development of Criteria.*** When psychologists disagree about definitions, there can be no generally acceptable criteria for validating tests. Even if there were agreement, validation would still be hampered by the very nature of motives. They are conceived not as acts but as dispositions, which can be expressed in many ways. Frequency of fighting would be a poor criterion for a test of aggression, a motive that can also take overt unbelligerent forms such as excessive friendliness and depression. A better criterion would encompass the different manifestations of the motive, indirect as well as direct.

***Arousal.*** Some investigators have attributed face validity to tests of motives if they were given before and after the motives were actually aroused. The data consisted of discrepancies between two scores. Such a technique also has its problems, some of which can be illustrated by a hypothetical study of aggression. The investigator must create conflict about the aroused anger or it will be turned against him instead of being expressed on the test. If the guilt is very strong, the aggression may be distorted defensively so that there are few direct manifestations of it on the test. It is not easy to succeed in the delicate task of arousing just the right amount of anger and guilt. A second difficulty is created by unanticipated reactions to the provocation. Some children may not become angry but may welcome the punishment as atonement for guilt, and some may react with masochistic pleasure.

***Construct Validity.*** Because of the difficulty of devising good independent criteria, investigators have been showing an increasing tendency to justify tests by construct validity. The fact that different sets of empirical results derived with an instrument are consistent with an underlying theoretical system is taken as evidence not only in support of the theory but also of the probable validity of the instrument. Of course, there are pitfalls in the use of such evidence. A few findings may be consistent with some of the investigator's theoretical premises but may have meanings that are related less to his theoretical scheme than to others that he did not consider. This lack of a necessary connection may help to account for the difference in frequencies of significant Rorschach validities obtained by the different methods. A survey of the Rorschach literature by Levy and Orr (1959) reveals that many more significant results were reported for construct than for predictive validity. The chances were better than two to one that the hypotheses of the study would be supported by evidence in favor of construct validity. With an independent criterion, however, the odds were almost two to one against significant results. The less favorable results with predictive validity may also reflect the difficulty of establishing good criteria for complex reactions to the Rorschach Test, such as color shock (Baughman, 1958) and extratension.

## VALIDITY AND THE RELATIONSHIP BETWEEN SUBJECT AND EXAMINER

Ideally, an investigation should be experienced in the same way by all subjects. Careful planning is needed to approximate that ideal in studies of motives and affect, since there are many sources of variance. The interaction between subject and examiner is a frequent source of uncontrolled error. If the subject is ashamed of some of his associations, for example, he may be tempted to modify them in the direction that will win the investigator's respect. If the subject has been removed from a cherished activity, such as swimming, he may become covertly uncooperative.

Even subtler interpersonal influences may affect a subject's responses. A number of investigations indicate that results can differ as a function of such variables as the sex of examiner, his overt and covert personality traits, the subject's private definition of the task, and his involvement in it (Miller, 1953).

*Validity of Methods of Manipulation.* Despite the many possible interpersonal sources of error, very few of the experimenters who have manipulated their subjects have attempted to find out whether the methods had the anticipated effects. Attempts to frustrate subjects or to vary their involvement in different tasks, for example, have seldom been followed by inquiries into degrees of resultant frustration or involvement. When the hypotheses about the effects of frustration have been confirmed, the validity of the techniques of manipulation has usually been taken for granted. There are some notable exceptions to this practice. To judge the effects of their technique, Barker, Dembo, and Lewin (1941) compared regressive reactions with amounts of frustrated behavior elicited by two

degrees of frustration. To judge the effects of two sets of instructions intended to produce different degrees of ego involvement, Calden and Cohen (1953) obtained reports of involvement from subjects who had been given the different instructions.

## Selection of Subjects

### AVAILABILITY AND REPRESENTATIVENESS OF SPECIAL POPULATIONS

Often studies that have been carefully planned in other respects have produced questionable results because too little time was devoted to consideration of the sample. A review of developmental studies of motives and affects conveys the impression that some populations were selected primarily because they were available. Staffs of psychology departments have been inclined to employ easily obtained captive populations, usually college sophomores or children from nursery schools in college towns. Such groups have tended to have high IQ's and to come from the middle class.

Availability of a sample is no small advantage in conducting research. When an investigator does not have to spend much time in finding children, he can devote most of his efforts to the planning of the study and the analysis of data. But availability can be given undue weight as a selective criterion. Subjects in a college nursery school are not representative of the total population of children, and it is often hazardous to generalize results obtained from such samples. It is probable, for example, that their average need for achievement will be quite high. It is also probable that they will favor indirect forms of aggression more than a group of children from the working class will. The acts that one observes in a college nursery often have a different significance than they would in a nursery for children from the working class. The son of a white-collar worker who habitually resorts to direct forms of aggression is likely to be more pathological than a child from the working class who behaves in the same way.

## HOMOGENEITY OF SPECIAL POPULATIONS

The college sophomore and the child in the college nursery have an additional disadvantage in research—their homogeneity in certain traits. Because of the narrow ranges, the probability is small that such traits will be related significantly to antecedent variables. It is not surprising, for example, that so many studies of the levels of aspiration of college sophomores reveal few significant associations with antecedent variables. The narrow range of ambitions in such a sample may be imagined from the fact that people in the second year of undergraduate school have been ambitious enough to complete elementary school, get good enough grades to be admitted to academic secondary schools, do well enough there to be graduated and to be admitted to universities, and, finally, to pass enough courses in their first year to attain the status of sophomore. In sum, the investigator increases the probability of

nonsignificant results when he restricts his subjects to those in a particular social class or within a narrow range of intelligence.

## AGE LEVELS

How old should one's subjects be? Obviously, the answer depends on one's hypotheses. In selecting children to test his hypotheses, the investigator would do well to consider some of the characteristics of children at different stages of development. Subjects at each stage have their advantages and disadvantages. Children in the preschool and even early school years, for example, have the assets of being relatively naïve and credulous. As a result, they accept at face value many instructions and situations that might make older children skeptical or uncooperative. It is also relatively easy to establish relationships with young children and to stimulate their interest in activities from which motives and affects can be inferred. In the nursery school and the initial grades of the elementary school the curricula are flexible, and most teachers are not reluctant to spare children for an experiment during school hours. Finally, young subjects are often easy to obtain because they are members of captive populations.

Young children also have their limitations. First, they cannot read. Hence they cannot be given paper-and-pencil tests in a group, and research with them is often more time consuming than research with older groups. Also contributing to the complication of obtaining data from young subjects is their limited ability to concentrate on a topic.

The investigator has to be sensitive to the duration of each child's span of attention and to the periods when he is attending. Considerable time must be allowed, therefore, for the collection of certain kinds of information that require the subject's participation. Third, young children are not accustomed to describing their feelings verbally, particularly to strangers. A few shy children cannot ever relax with a stranger. Most subjects can be cooperative, even spontaneous, if they have a few sessions with the observer. Finally, their limitations in the ability to communicate their feelings verbally makes it necessary to study their affects and motives indirectly.

Adolescent subjects can read and can concentrate on a task for some time, and many of them are accustomed to introspecting and expressing themselves verbally. Hence they can often be seen in groups, given written tests, and asked questions about complex experiences.

It is somewhat difficult to obtain adequate samples of older adolescents in the working class because they have left school. A difficulty that arises in the testing of adolescent subjects is their occasional lack of cooperation. Their negativism may take such forms as ambivalence, rebelliousness, cynicism, and sophisticated boredom. The negativism is only one manifestation of a general increase in certain conflicts. In adolescence children are trying to develop new identities. They cannot express their needs and affects as children, nor have they mastered the more mature forms of behavior. Sex and ambition and aggression represent perplexing problems and are connected with

emotional disturbances. Subjects in their teens are often understandably reticent about discussing certain affects and motives.

Preadolescent children, between 9 and 13 years, deserve more attention from psychologists than they have received thus far. Most children of these ages still have the naïveté and the immaturity of more youthful subjects. The writer has found them very credulous, and very cooperative after receiving chocolate bars. Since attendance at school is still compulsory, the populations of children in these intermediate years contain adequate proportions of potential subjects from all social classes. Children in this age group read and possess a fair amount of skill in verbal communication. Hence many of them can be given paper-and-pencil tests in groups.

## The Current State of Developmental Research

The literature on motivation and affect leaves one in a far from pessimistic frame of mind. Of the more recent developments, the most striking is the accumulation of a great variety of tested methods. Also impressive are the manifestations that each generation of psychologists has benefited from the achievements and errors of their predecessors. Many of the techniques described in the last decade, for instance, represent the achievement of a double goal that was seldom attained by earlier investigators. Most of the techniques have permitted objective measurements of results without oversimplications of the motives and affective states that were being studied.

American investigators have revealed increasing tendencies to define concepts with some rigor and to justify operations in terms of theoretical and developmental considerations. A number of studies has begun to unravel some of the current tangle of theoretical terms and premises. It is now apparent, for example, that independence and dependence are not opposites (Beller, 1955; Heathers, 1955). The quality of current developmental research on motivation and affect reveals a growing competence with both theory and methodology. It is a competence that promises a steady progress toward the goal of establishing empirically tested theoretical systems.

## REFERENCES

Ackerman, N. W. 1937. Constructive and destructive tendencies in children. *Amer. J. Orthopsychiat.* 7, 301–319.

Allen, R. M. 1955. Nine quarterly Rorschach records of a young girl. *Child Develpm.*, 26, 63–69.

Alper, Thelma G., H. T. Blane, and Barbara K. Abrams. 1955. Reactions of middle and lower class children to finger paints as a function of class differences in child-training practices. *J. abnorm. soc. Psychol.*, 51, 439–448.

Alschuler, Rose H., and La Berta B. Hattwick. 1947. *Painting and personality.* Vol. I, II. Chicago: Univer. Chicago Press.

Ames, Louise B., Janet Learned, Ruth Metraux, and R. N. Walker. 1952. *Child Rorschach responses: Development trends from two to ten years.* New York: Hoeber.

Anderson, C. 1940. The development of a level of aspiration in young children. Unpublished doctoral dissertation. State Univer. Iowa.

Anderson, H. H., and R. S. Smith. 1933. Motivation of young children: The constancy of certain behavior patterns. *J. exp. Educ.*, 2, 138–160.

Arsenian, Jean M. 1943. Young children in an insecure situation. *J. abnorm. soc. Psychol.*, 38, 225–249.

Atkinson, J. W. (Ed.) 1958. *Motives in fantasy, action, and society.* Princeton, N.J.: Van Nostrand.

Ausubel, D. P. 1951. Prestige motivation of gifted children. *Genet. Psychol. Monogr.*, 43, 53–117.

Bach, G. R. 1945. Young children's play fantasies. *Psychol. Monogr.*, 59, No. 2.

Barker, R. G. 1942. An experimental study of the resolution of conflict by children. In Q. McNemar and Maud A. Merrill (Eds.), *Studies in personality.* New York: McGraw-Hill.

———, Tamara Dembo and K. Lewin. 1941. Frustration and regression. *Univer. Iowa Stud. Child Welf.*, 18, No. 1.

Barker, R. G., J. S. Kounin, and H. F. Wright (Eds.). 1943. *Child behavior and development.* New York: McGraw-Hill.

Barker, R. G., and H. F. Wright. 1954. *Midwest and its children. The psychological ecology of an American Town.* Evanston, Ill.: Row, Peterson.

Barndt, R. J., and D. M. Johnson. 1955. Time orientation in delinquents. *J. abnorm. soc. Psychol.*, 51, 343–345.

Bateson, G., and Margaret Mead. 1942. *Balinese culture: A photographic analysis.* New York: N. Y. Acad. Sci.

Baughman, E. E. 1958. The role of the stimulus in Rorschach responses. *Psychol. Bull.*, 55, 121–147.

Beaver, A. P. 1932. The initiation of social contacts by preschool children. *Monogr. Soc. Res. Child Develpm.*, No. 7.

Bellak, L. 1944. The concept of projection: An experimental investigation and study of the concept. *Psychiatry*, 7, 353–370.

———, and Sonya S. Bellak. 1949. *Children's Apperception Test* (C. A. T.). (2nd ed.) New York: C. P. S.

Beller, E. K. 1955. Dependency and independence in young children. *J. genet. Psychol.*, 87, 25–35.

Beller, E. K. 1957. Dependency and autonomous achievement striving related to orality and anality in early childhood. *Child Develpm.*, **28**, 287–315.

Bender, Lauretta, and A. G. Woltmann. 1936. The use of puppet shows as a psychotherapeutic method for behavior problems in children. *Amer. J. Orthopsychiat.*, **6**, 341–354.

Benedict, Ruth. 1934. *Patterns of culture.* Boston: Houghton Mifflin.

Bernstein, A. 1955. Some relations between techniques of feeding and training during infancy and certain behaviors in childhood. *Genet. Psychol. Monogr.*, **51**, 3–44.

Biehler, R. F. 1954. Companion choice behavior in the kindergarten. *Child Develpm.*, **25**, 45–50.

Biersdorf, K. R., and F. L. Marcuse. 1953. Responses of children to human and animal pictures. *J. proj. Tech.*, **17**, 455–459.

Bijou, S. W. 1942. The measurement of adjustment by psychometric pattern techniques. *Amer. J. Orthopsychiat.*, **12**, 435–438.

Bills, R. E. 1950. Animal pictures for obtaining children's projection. *J. clin. Psychol.*, **6**, 291–293.

——, C. J. Leiman, and R. W. Thomas. 1950. A study of the validity of the TAT and a set of animal pictures. *J. proj. Tech.*, **6**, 293–294.

Bird, G. 1927. Personality factors in learning. *J. Pers.*, **6**, 56–69.

Block, Jeanne., and B. Martin. 1955. Predicting the behavior of children under frustration. *J. abnorm. soc. Psychol.*, **51**, 281–285.

Blum, G. S. 1949. A study of the psychoanalytic theory of psychosexual development. *Genet. Psychol. Monogr.*, **39**, 3–99.

——, and D. R. Miller 1952. Exploring the psychoanalytic theory of the "oral character." *J. Pers.*, **3**, 287–304.

Body, Margaret K. 1955. Patterns of aggression in the nursery school. *Child Develpm.*, **26**, 3–11.

Boehm, Lenore. 1957. The development of independence: A comparative study. *Child Develpm.*, **28**, 85–92.

Bovet, P. 1923. *Fighting instinct.* London: Allen and Unwin.

Bridges, Katherine M. B. 1933. A study of social development in early infancy. *Child Develpm.*, **4**, 36–49.

Brigante, T. R. 1958. Adolescent evaluations of rewarding, neutral, and punishing power figures. *J. Pers.*, **26**, 435–450.

Broida, D. C., and G. G. Thompson. 1954. The relationship between certain Rorschach "insecurity" hypotheses and children's reactions to psychological stress. *J. Pers.*, **23**, 167–181.

Brozek, K., H. Guetzkow and M. V. Baldwin. 1951. A quantitative study of perception and association in experimental semistarvation. *J. Pers.*, **19**, 245–264.

Bühler, Charlotte. 1938. The ball and field test as a help in the diagnosis of emotional difficulties. *Charact. & Pers.*, **6**, 257–273.

Burton, A. 1942. The aggression of young children following satiation. *Amer. J. Orthopsychiat.*, **12**, 262–268.

Byrd, E., and R. L. Witherspoon. 1954. Responses of preschool children to the children's Apperception Test. *Child Develpm.*, **25**, 35–44.

Calden, G., and L. B. Cohen. 1953. The relationship of ego involvement and test definition to Rorschach Test performance. *J. proj. Tech.*, **17**, 300–311.

Castaneda, A. 1956. Reaction time and response amplitude as a function of anxiety and stimulus intensity. *J. abnorm. soc. Psychol.*, **53**, 225–228.

——, B. R. McCandless, and D. S. Palermo. 1956. The children's form of the manifest anxiety scale. *Child Develpm.*, **27**, 317–326.

Castaneda, A., D. S. Palermo, and B. R. McCandless. 1956. Complex learning and performance as a function of anxiety in children and task difficulty. *Child Develpm.*, **27**, 327–332.

Cattell, R. B., and R. W. Coan. 1957. Personality factors in middle childhood as revealed in parents' ratings. *Child Develpm.*, **28**, 439–458.

Cava, Esther L., and H. L. Rausch. 1952. Identification and the adolescent boy's perception of his father. *J. abnorm. soc. Psychol.*, **47**, 855–856.

Champney, H. 1941. The measurement of parent behavior. *Child Develpm.*, **12**, 131–166.

Child, I. L. 1946. Children's preference for goals easy or difficult to obtain. *Psychol. Monogr.*, 60, No. 4.

Clark, R. A. 1952. The projective measurement of experimentally induced levels of sexual motivation. *J. exp. Psychol.*, 44, 391–399.

Conrad, H. S. 1932. The validity of personality ratings of preschool children. *J. educ. Psychol.*, 23, 671–680.

Cowan, Edwina A., Minerva C. McClellan, Bertha M. Pratt, and Mae Skaer. 1935. An adolescent personality schedule. *Child Develpm.*, 6, 77–87.

Dameron, L. E. 1955. Mother-child interaction in the development of self-restraint. *J. genet. Psychol.*, 86, 289–308.

Davids, A., A. F. Henry, C. C. McArthur, and L. F. McNemara. 1955. Projection, self-evaluation, and clinical evaluation of aggression. *J. consult. Psychol.*, 19, 437–440.

Davis, A. 1948. *Social-class influences upon learning.* Cambridge: Harvard Univer. Press.

——, and R. J. Havighurst. 1942. Social class and color differences in child-rearing. *Amer. Soc. Rev.*, 7, 370–382.

Davis, Edith A. 1933. The form and function of children's questions. *Child Develpm.*, 3, 57–74.

Davitz, J. R. 1952. The effects of previous training on post-frustration behavior. *J. abnorm. soc. Psychol.*, 47, 309–315.

Dawe, H. C. 1934. An analysis of two hundred quarrels of preschool children. *Child Develpm.*, 5, 139–157.

Dennis, W. 1955. Are Hopi children noncompetitive? *J. abnorm soc. Psychol.*, 50, 99–100.

Despert, J. Louise. 1946. Psychosomatic study of fifty stuttering children. *Amer. J. Orthopsychiat.*, 16, 100–113.

——, and H. W. Potter. 1936. Technical approaches used in the study and treatment of emotional problems in children. Part I: The story, a form of directed fantasy. *Psychiat. Quart.*, 10, 619–638.

Dollard, J., L. Doob, N. Miller, O. Mowrer, R. R. Sears, C. S. Ford, C. I. Hovland, and R. T. Sollenberger. 1939. *Frustration and aggression.* New Haven: Yale Univer. Press.

Dorkey, M., and Elisabeth W. Amen. 1947. A continuation study of anxiety reactions in young children by means of a projective technique. *Genet. Psychol. Monogr.*, 35, 139–183.

Duffy, E. 1930. Tensions and emotional factors in reaction. *Genet. Psychol. Monogr.*, 7, No. 1.

Durea, M. A. 1933. Personality characteristics of juvenile delinquents. I. A method for the selection of differentiating traits. *Child Develpm.*, 4, 115–128.

Duss, L. 1940. La Méthode des fables en psychanalyse. *Arch. Psychol., Genève.* 28.

Eiserer, P. E. 1949. The relative effectiveness of motion and still pictures as stimuli for eliciting fantasy stories about adolescent-parent relationships. *Genet. Psychol. Monogr.*, 39, 205–278.

Ellesor, Martha V. 1933. Children's reactions to novel visual stimuli. *Child Develpm.*, 4, 95–105.

Engel, Mary. 1958. The development and applications of the Children's Insight Test. *J. proj. Tech.*, 22, 13–25.

Erikson, E. H. 1940. Studies in the interpretation of play: I. Clinical observations of play disruption in young children. *Genet. Psychol. Monogr.*, 22, 557–671.

——. 1945. Childhood and tradition in two American Indian tribes, *Psychoanal. Study Child.*, 1, 319–350.

Fauquier, W. 1939. The measurement of attitudes of delinquent and normal boys by use of an associational technique. *Child. Develpm.*, 10, 231–239.

Filer, R. J. 1952. Frustration, satisfaction, and other factors affecting the attractiveness of goal objects. *J. abnorm. soc. Psychol.*, 47, 203–212.

Finger, F. W. 1947. Sex beliefs and practices among male college students. *J. abnorm. soc. Psychol.* 42, 57–67.

Fisher, M. S. 1934. Language patterns of preschool children. *Monogr. Soc. Res. Child Develpm.*, No. 15.

Fite, Mary D. 1940. Aggressive behavior in young children and children's attitudes toward aggression. *Genet. Psychol. Monogr.*, 22, 151–319.

Flanagan, J. C. 1954. The critical incident technique. *Psychol. Bull.*, 51, 327–358.

Forlano, G., and H. C. Axelrod. 1937. The effects of repeated praise or blame on the performance of introverts and extroverts. *J. educ. Psychol.*, **28**, 92–100.

Fortune, R. F. 1932. *Sorcerers of Dobu*. New York: Dutton.

Frenkel-Brunswik, Else. 1942. Motivation and behavior. *Genet. Psychol. Monogr.*, **26**, 121–265.

———. 1949. Intolerance of ambiguity as an emotional and perceptual personality variable. *J. Pers.*, **18**, 108–143.

Freud, Anna. 1926. *The psychoanalytic treatment of children*. London: Imago.

———, and Sophie Dann. 1951. An experiment in group upbringing. *Psychoanal. Study Child*, **6**, 127–168.

Freud, S. 1922. *Beyond the pleasure principle*. London: Hogarth.

———. 1924. *Collected papers*, Vol. III. London: Hogarth.

Friedman, S. M. 1952. An empirical study of the castration and oedipus complexes. *Genet. Psychol. Monogr.*, **46**, 61–130.

Furuya, K. 1957. Responses of school children to human and animal pictures. *J. proj. Tech.*, **21**, 248–252.

Garmezy, N., and J. G. Harris, Jr. 1953. Motor performance of cerebral palsied children as a function of their success or failure in achieving material rewards. *Child Develpm.*, **24**, 287–300.

Gatling, F. P. 1950. Frustration reactions of delinquents using Rosenzweig's classification system. *J. abnorm. soc. Psychol.*, **45**, 749–752.

Gesell, A. L., and Frances L. Ilg. 1946. *The child from five to ten*. New York: Harper.

Gewirtz, J. L. 1956. A factor analysis of some attention-seeking behaviors of young children. *Child. Develpm.*, **27**, 17–36.

Godbeer, E. 1940. Factors introducing conflict in the choice behavior of children. Unpublished doctoral dissertation, Yale Univer.

Goodenough, Florence L. 1929. The emotional behavior of young children during mental tests. *J. juv. Res.*, **13**, 204–219.

———. 1931. *Anger in young children*. Minneapolis: Univer. Minnesota Press.

Grace, Gloria L. 1948. The relation of personality characteristics and response to verbal approval in a learning task. *Genet. Psychol. Monogr.*, **37**, 73–99.

Graham, Frances K., Wanda A. Charwat, Alice S. Honig, and Paula C. Weltz. 1951. Aggression as a function of the attack and the attacker. *J. abnorm. soc. Psychol.* **46**, 512–520.

Granick, S. 1955. Intellectual performance as related to emotional instability in children. *J. abnorm soc. Psychol.*, **51**, 653–656.

Gray, Susan W. 1957. Masculinity-femininity in relation to anxiety and social acceptance. *Child Develpm.*, **28**, 203–214.

Green, E. H. 1933. Group play and quarreling among preschool children. *Child Develpm.*, **4**, 302–307.

Greenacre, Phyllis. 1944. Infant reactions to restraint. *Amer. J. Orthopsychiat.*, **14**, 204–218.

Grosser, D., N. Polansky, and R. Lippitt. 1951. A laboratory study of behavioral contagion. *Hum. Relat.*, **4**, 115–142.

Havighurst, R. J., and Hilda Taba. 1949. *Adolescent character and personality*. New York: Wiley.

Haworth, Mary R. 1957. The use of a filmed puppet show as a group projective technique for children. *Genet. Psychol. Monogr.*, **56**, 257–296.

Heath, D. 1958. Projective tests as measures of defensive activity. *J. proj. Tech.*, **22**, 284–292.

Heathers, G. 1953. Emotional dependence and independence in a physical threat situation. *Child Develpm.*, **24**, 169–179.

———. 1954. The adjustment of two-year-olds in a novel social situation. *Child Develpm.*, **25**, 147–158.

———. 1955. Emotional dependence and independence needed in nursery school play. *J. genet. Psychol.*, **87**, 37–57.

Henry, J., and Zunia Henry. 1944. Doll play of Pilagá Indian children. *Res. Monogr., No. 4, Amer. Orthopsychiat. Assoc.*

Henry, W. E. 1947. The Thematic Apperception Technique in the study of culture-personality relations. *Genet. Psychol. Monogr.*, **35**, 3–135.

———. 1956. *The analysis of fantasy*. New York: Wiley.

Hershenson, Jeanne R. 1949. Preference of

adolescents for Rorschach figures. *Child Develpm.*, **20**, 101–118.

Hess, R. D., and Irene Goldblatt. 1957. The status of adolescents in American society: A problem in social identity. *Child Develpm.*, **28**, 459–468.

Hicks, J. A., and M. Hayes. 1933. The verbal responses of junior high school pupils in classroom discussions. *Child Develpm.*, **4**, 176–182.

———. 1938. Study of the characteristics of 250 junior high school children. *Child Develpm.*, **9**, 219–242.

Highberger, Ruth. 1955. The relationship between maternal behavior and the child's early adjustment to nursery school. *Child Develpm.*, **26**, 49–61.

Hurlock, Elizabeth B. 1925. The value of praise and reproof as incentives for children. *Arch. Psychol.*, No. 71.

———, and E. R. Klein. 1934. Adolescent "crushes." *Child Develpm.*, **5**, 63–80.

Hunt, J. McV. (Ed.) 1944. Personality and the behavior disorders. New York: Ronald.

Huschka, Mabel. 1942. The child's response to coercive bowel training. *Psychosomat. Med.*, **4**, 301–308.

Irwin, F. W., F. M. Armitt, and C. W. Simon. 1943. Studies of object-preferences: I. The effect of temporal proximity. *J. exp. Psychol.*, **33**, 64–72.

Irwin, F. W., and Mildred E. Gebhard. 1946. Studies in object-preferences: The effect of ownership and other social influences. *Amer. J. Psychol.*, **59**, 633–351.

Irwin, O. C. 1932a. The latent time of the body startle in infants. *Child Develpm.*, **3**, 104–107.

———. 1932b. Infant responses to vertical movements. *Child Develpm.*, **3**, 167–169.

Isaacs, Susan. 1933. *Social development in young children: A study of beginnings.* New York: Harcourt, Brace.

Jack, Lois M. 1934. An experimental study of ascendant behavior in preschool children. *Univer. Iowa Stud. Child Welf.*, No. 3.

Janis, I. L., and S. Feshback. 1954. Personality differences associated with responsiveness to fear-arousing communications. *J. Pers.*, **23**, 154–166.

Jensen, A. R. 1957. Aggression in fantasy and overt behavior. *Psychol. Monogr.*, **71**, No. 16.

Jersild, A. T., B. Goldman, and J. J. Loftus. 1941. A comparative study of the worries of children in two school situations. *J. exp. Educ.*, **9**, 323–326.

Jersild, A. T., and F. B. Holmes. 1935. Children's fears. *Monogr. Soc. Res. Child Develpm.* No. 20.

Jersild, A. T., and Ruth J. Tasch. 1949. *Children's interests and what they suggest for education.* New York: Teach. Coll., Columbia Univer. Bur. Publ.

Jessner, Lucie, G. E. Blom, and S. Waldfogel. 1952. Emotional implications of tonsillectomy and adenoidectomy on children. *Psychoanal. Study Child*, **7**, 126–169.

Jessor, R., and K. R. Hammond. 1957. Construct validity and the Taylor Anxiety Scale. *Psychol. Bull.*, **54**, 161–170.

Johnson, M. W. 1935. The effect on behavior of variations in the amount of play equipment. *Child Develpm.*, **6**, 56–68.

Johnson, O. G., and J. C. Stanley, 1955. Attitudes toward authority of delinquent and nondelinquent boys. *J. abnorm. soc. Psychol.*, **51**, 712–716.

Jost, H. 1941. Some physiological changes during frustration. *Child Develpm.*, **12**, 9–15.

Jung, C. G. 1910. The association method. *Amer. J. Psychol.*, **21**, 219–269.

Justin, Florence. 1933. A genetic study of laughter-provoking stimuli. *Child Develpm.*, **3**, 114–136.

Karolchuck, Patricia A., and L. Worrell. 1956. Achievement motivation and learning. *J. abnorm. soc. Psychol.*, **53**, 255–257.

Keister, Mary E., and Ruth Updegraff. 1937. A study of children's reactions to failure and an experimental attempt to modify them. *Child Develpm.*, **8**, 241–248.

Klein, Melanie. 1932. *The psychoanalysis of children.* London: Hogarth.

Korner, Anneliese F. 1949. *Some aspects of hostility in young children.* New York: Grune & Stratton.

Krout, M. H., and Johanna K. Tabin. 1954. Measuring personality in developmental terms: The Personal Preference Scale. *Genet. Psychol. Monogr.*, **50**, 289–335.

Lambert, W. W., and Elisabeth C. Lambert. 1953. Some indirect effects of reward on children's size estimations. *J. abnorm. soc. Psychol.*, 48, 507–510.

Langford, W. S. 1937. Anxiety attacks in children. *Amer. J. Orthopsychiat.*, 7, 210–218.

Lee, Mary A. M. 1932. A study of emotional instability in nursery school children. *Child Develpm.*, 3, 142–145.

Leshan, L. L. 1952. Time orientation and social class. *J. abnorm. soc. Psychol.*, 47, 589–592.

Lesser, G. S. 1957. The relationship between overt and fantasy aggression as a function of maternal response to aggression. *J. abnorm. soc. Psychol.*, 55, 219–221.

Levin, H., and R. R. Sears. 1956. Identification with parents as a determinant of doll play aggression. *Child Develpm.*, 27, 135–153.

Levy, D. M. 1928. Finger sucking and accessory movements in early infancy: An etiological study. *Amer. J. Psychiat.*, 7, 881–918.

———. 1937. Studies in sibling rivalry. *Res. Monogr., No. 2, Amer. Orthopsychiat. Assoc.*

———, and S. H. Tulchin. 1923. The resistance of infants and children during mental tests. *J. exp. Psychol.*, 6, 304–322.

Levy, E. 1958. Stimulus-values of Rorschach cards for children. *J. proj. Tech.*, 22, 293–296.

Levy, L. H., and T. B. Orr. 1959. The social psychology of Rorschach validity research. *J. abnorm. soc. Psychol.*, 58, 79–83.

Light, B. H. 1954. Comparative study of a series of TAT and CAT cards. *J. clin. Psychol.*, 10, 179–181.

Lindzey, G., and Charlotte Tejessy. 1956. Thematic Apperception Test: Indices of aggression in relation to measures of overt and covert behavior. *Amer. J. Orthopsychiat.*, 26, 567–576.

Lippitt, R. 1939. Field theory and experiment in social psychology: Autocratic and democratic group atmospheres. *Amer. J. Sociol.*, 45, 26–49.

———. 1940. An experimental study of the effect of democratic and authoritarian group atmospheres. *Univer. Iowa Stud. Child Welf.*, 16, No. 3, 43–195.

Lippitt, Rosemary. 1941. Popularity among preschool children. *Child Develpm.*, 12, 305–332.

Little, Sue W., and Louise D. Cohen. 1952. Goal setting behavior of asthmatic children and of their mothers for them. *J. Pers.*, 19, 376–389.

Livson, N., and P. H. Mussen. 1957. The relation of ego control to overt aggression and dependency. *J. abnorm. soc. Psychol.*, 55, 66–71.

Long, Alma. 1941. Parents' reports of undesirable behavior in children. *Child Develpm.*, 12, 43–62.

Lowenfeld, Margaret. 1939. World pictures of children. *J. med. Psychol.*, 78, 65–101.

Mainord, Florence R., and F. L. Marcuse. 1954. Responses of disturbed children to human and animal pictures. *J. proj. Tech.*, 18, 475–477.

Mandler, G., and S. B. Sarason. 1952. A study of anxiety and learning. *J. abnorm. soc. Psychol.*, 47, 166–173.

Marshall, Helen R., and B. R. McCandless. 1957. Relationships between dependence on adults and social acceptance by peers. *Child Develpm.*, 28, 413–419.

Mathews, Ellen. 1923. A study of emotional stability in children. *J. Delinqu.*, 8, 1–40.

McArthur, C. C. 1953. The effects of need achievement on the content of TAT stories: A re-examination. *J. abnorm. soc. Psychol.*, 48, 532–536.

———. 1955. Personality differences between middle and upper classes. *J. abnorm. soc. Psychol.*, 50, 247–254.

McCandless, B. R., and A. Castaneda. 1956. Anxiety in children, school achievement, and intelligence. *Child Develpm.*, 27, 378–382.

———, and D. S. Palermo. 1956. Anxiety in children and social status. *Child Develpm.*, 27, 383–391.

McClelland, D. C., J. W. Atkinson, R. A. Clark, and E. L. Lowell. 1953. *The achievement motive.* New York: Appleton-Century-Crofts.

McDowell, Marion S. 1937. Frequency of choice of play materials by preschool children. *Child Develpm.*, 8, 305–310.

McFate, Marguerite Q., and Frances G. Orr. 1949. Through adolescence with the Rorschach. *Rorschach Res. Exch.*, 13, 302–319.

McHugh, G. 1943. Changes in IQ at the public school kindergarten level. *Psychol. Monogr.*, 55, No. 2.

McKee, J. P., and Florence B. Leader. 1955. The relationship of socio-economic status and aggression to the competitive behavior of preschool children. *Child Develpm.*, 26, 135–142.

Mengert, I. G. 1931. A preliminary study of the reactions of two-year-old children to each other when paired in a semi-controlled situation. *J. genet. Psychol.*, 39, 393–398.

Merrill, Barbara. 1946. A measurement of mother-child interaction. *J. abnorm. soc. Psychol.*, 41, 37–49.

Michaels, J. J., and S. E. Goodman. 1934. Incidence and intercorrelations of enuresis and other neuropathic traits in so-called normal children. *Amer. J. Orthopsychiat.*, 4, 79–106.

Miller, D. R. 1953. Prediction of behavior by means of the Rorschach Test. *J. abn. soc. Psychol.*, 48, 367–375.

———, and Margaret E. Stine. 1951. The prediction of social acceptance by means of psychoanalytic concepts. *J. Pers.*, 20, 162–174.

Miller, D. R., and G. E. Swanson. 1958. *The changing American parent*. New York: Wiley.

———. 1960. *Inner conflict and defense*. New York: Holt.

Molitch, M. 1937. Endocrine disturbances in behavior problems. *Amer. J. Psychiat.*, 93, 1175–1180.

Moncur, J. P. 1955. Symptoms of maladjustment differentiating young stutterers from nonstutterers. *Child Develpm.*, 26, 91–96.

Morgan, Christiana D., and H. A. Murray. 1935. A method for investigating fantasies. *Arch. Neurol. Psychiat.*, 34, 289–306.

Morgan, Patricia K., and E. D. Gaier. 1956. The direction of aggression in the mother-child punishment situation. *Child Develpm.*, 27, 446–457.

———. 1957. Types of reactions in punishment situations in the mother-child relationship. *Child Develpm.*, 28, 161–166.

Moulton, R. W. 1958. Notes for a projective measure of fear of failure. In J. W. Atkinson (Ed.), *Motives in fantasy, action, and society*. Princeton, N. J.: Van Nostrand.

Moustakas, C. E. 1955. The frequency and intensity of negative attitudes expressed in play therapy: A comparison of well-adjusted and disturbed young children. *J. genet. Psychol.*, 86, 309–325.

Moyer, K. E., and B. H. Gilmer. 1955. Attention spans of children for experimentally designed toys. *J. genet. Psychol.*, 87, 187–201.

Murphy, G., Lois B. Murphy, and T. M. Newcomb. 1937. *Experimental social psychology*. New York: Harper.

Murphy, Lois B., et al. 1956. *Personality in young children*. Vols. I and II. New York: Basic Books.

Murray, H. A. 1943. *Thematic Apperception Test manual*. Cambridge: Harvard Univer. Press.

Murstein, B. I. 1959. A conceptual model of projective techniques applied to stimulus variations with thematic techniques. *J. consult. Psychol.*, 23, 3–14.

Mussen, P. H., and Mary C. Jones. 1957. Self-conceptions, motivations, and interpersonal attitudes of late- and early-maturing boys. *Child Develpm.*, 28, 243–256.

Mussen, P. H., and H. K. Naylor. 1954. The relationship between overt and fantasy aggression. *J. abnorm. soc. Psychol.*, 49, 235–240.

Olson, W. C. 1929. The measure of nervous habits in normal children. *Inst. Child Welf. Monogr. Ser.*, No. 3. Minneapolis: Univer. Minnesota Press.

Ort. R. S. 1952. A study of role-conflicts as related to class level. *J. abnorm. soc. Psychol.*, 47, 425–432.

Otis, Nancy B., and B. R. McCandless. 1955. Responses to repeated frustrations of young children differentiated according to need area. *J. abnorm. soc. Psychol.*, 50, 349–353.

Page, R. M. 1941. Aggression and withdrawal in relation to possible frustrating factors in the lives of children. Unpublished doctoral dissertation. Northwestern Univer.

Palermo, D. S., A. Castaneda, and B. R. McCandless. 1956. The relationship of anxiety in children to performance in a complex learning task. *Child Develpm.*, 27, 333–337.

Panlasigui, I., and F. B. Knight. 1930. The effect of awareness of success or failure. *Twenty-ninth Yearb. Nat. Soc. Stud. Educ.*, Part II, 611–621.

Phillips, Ruth. 1945. Doll play as a function of the realism of the materials and the length of the experimental session. *Child Develpm.*, 16, 123–143.

Pignatelli, Myrtle L. 1943. A comparative study of mental functioning patterns of problem and nonproblem children, seven, eight, and nine years of age. *Genet. Psychol. Monogr.*, 27, 69–162.

Pintler, Margaret H. 1945. Doll play as a function of experimenter-child interaction and initial organization of materials. *Child Develpm.*, 16, 145–166.

Pratt, K. C. 1932. A note upon the relation of activity to sex and race in young infants. *J. soc. Psychol.*, 3, 118–120.

Read, Katherine H. 1940. Significant characteristics of preschool children as located in the Conrad Inventory. *Genet. Psychol. Monogr.*, 22, 455–487.

Redl, F., and D. Wineman. 1951. *Children who hate.* Glencoe, Ill.: Free Press.

Reissman, F., and S. M. Miller. 1958. Social class and projective tests. *J. proj. Tech.*, 22, 432–439.

Reynolds, M. M. 1928. Negativism of preschool children. New York: Teach. Coll. Contr. Educ., Columbia Univer., No. 288.

Ribble, Margaret A. 1944. Infantile experience in relation to personality development. In J. McV. Hunt (Ed.), *Personality and the behavior disorders.* New York: Ronald.

Richards, T. W., and Marjorie P. Simons. 1941. The Fels Child Behavior Scales. *Genet. Psychol. Monogr.*, 24, 259–309.

Robinson, Elizabeth F. 1946. Doll play as a function of the doll family constellation. *Child Develpm.*, 17, 99–119.

Rogers, C. R. 1931. Measuring personality adjustment in children nine to thirteen years of age. New York: *Teach. Coll. Contr. Educ.*, Columbia Univer., No. 548.

Rosenzweig, S., Edith E. Fleming, and Louise Rosenzweig. 1948. The children's form of the Rosenzweig P-F Study. *J. Psychol.*, 26, 141–191.

Rosenzweig, S., and Gwendolyn Mason. 1934. An experimental study of memory in relation to the theory of repression. *Brit. J. Psychol.*, 24, 247–265.

Rosenzweig, S., and Louise Rosenzweig. 1952. Aggression in problem children and normals as evaluated by the Rosenzweig P-F Study. *J. abnorm. soc. Psychol.*, 47, 683–687.

Sacks, Elinor L. 1952. Intelligence scores as a function of experimentally established social relationships between child and examiner. *J. abnorm. soc. Psychol.*, 47, 354–358.

Sanders, R., and S. E. Cleveland. 1953. The relationship between certain examiner personality variables and subjects' Rorschach scores. *J. proj. Tech.*, 17, 34–50.

Sanford, N., and J. Risser. 1948. What are the conditions of self-defensive forgetting? *J. Pers.*, 17, 244–260.

Sanford, R. N. 1937. The effects of abstinence from food upon imaginal processes: A further experiment. *J. Psychol.*, 3, 145–159.

———, M. M. Adkins, R. B. Miller, E. A. Cobb, et al. 1943. Physique, personality and scholarship. *Monogr. Soc. Res. Child Develpm.*, 8, No. 34.

Sarason, Barbara R., and I. C. Sarason. 1958. The effect of type of administration and sex of subject on emotional tone and outcome ratings of TAT stories. *J. proj. Tech.*, 22, 333–337.

Sarason, S. B., and E. M. Gordon. 1953. The test anxiety questionnaire: Scoring norms. *J. abnorm. soc. Psychol.*, 48, 447–448.

Sargent, Helen D. 1953. *The Insight Test: A verbal projective test for personality study.* New York: Grune & Stratton.

Schiff, Ethel, Catherine Dugan, and L. Welch. 1949. The conditioned PGR and the EEG as indicators of anxiety. *J. abnorm. soc. Psychol.*, 44, 549–552.

Schroder, H. M., and D. E. Hunt. 1957. Failure-avoidance in situational interpretation and problem solving. *Psychol. Monogr.*, 71, No. 432.

Sears, Pauline S., and H. Levin. 1957. Levels of aspiration in preschool children. *Child Develpm.*, 28, 317–326.

Sears, R. R., Eleanor E. Maccoby, and H. Levin. 1957. *Patterns of child rearing.* Evanston, Ill.: Row, Peterson.

Sears, R. R., and Pauline S. Sears. 1940. Minor studies of aggression: V. Strength of frustration-reaction as a function of strength of drive. *J. Psychol.*, 9, 297–300.

Sears, R. R., J. W. M. Whiting, V. Nowlis, and Pauline S. Sears. 1953. Some child-rearing antecedents of aggression and dependency in young children. *Genet. Psychol. Monogr.*, 47, 135–234.

Seashore, H. E., and A. Bavelas. 1942. A study of frustration in children. *J. genet. Psychol.*, 61, 279–314.

Seaton, J. K. 1949. A projective experiment using incomplete stories with multiple-choice endings. *Genet. Psychol. Monogr.*, 40, 149–228.

Sewall, M. 1930. Some causes of jealousy in young children. *Smith Coll. Stud. Soc. Wk.*, 1, 6–22.

Sherman, M. 1927. The differentiation of emotional responses in infants. I. Judgments of emotional responses from motion picture views and from actual observations. *J. comp. Psychol.*, 7, 265–284.

Shimkin, D. B., and P. Sanjuan. 1953. Culture and world view: A method of analysis applied to rural Russia. *Amer. Anthrop.*, 55, 329–348.

Shirley, Mary M. 1942. Children's adjustments to a strange situation. *J. abnorm. soc. Psychol.*, 37, 201–217.

Siegel, Alberta E. 1957. Aggressive behavior of young children in the absence of an adult. *Child Develpm.*, 28, 371–378.

Smalley, R. E. 1930. Two studies in sibling rivalry: II. The influence of differences in age, sex, and intelligence in determining the attitude of siblings toward each other. *Smith Coll. Stud. Soc. Wk.*, 1, 23–29.

Smith, J. R., and J. C. Coleman. 1956. The relationship between manifestations of hostility in projective tests and overt behavior. *J. proj. Tech.*, 20, 326–334.

Smith, Madorah E. 1933. The preschool child's use of criticism. *Child Develpm.*, 3, 137–145.

Smock, C. D. 1956. The relationship between test anxiety, "threat-expectancy," and recognition threshold for words. *J. Pers.*, 25, 191–201.

Spitz, R. A. 1945. Hospitalism. *Psychoanal. Study Child*, 1, 53–74.

Spitz, R. A. 1946. The smiling response: A contribution to the ontogenesis of social relations. *Genet. Psychol. Monogr.*, 34, 57–125.

——, and Katherine M. Wolf. 1946. Anaclitic depression: An inquiry into the genesis of psychiatric conditions in early childhood. *Psychoanal. Study Child*, 2, 313–342.

——. Autoeroticism. *Psychoanal. Study Child*, 3 and 4, 85–120.

Swan, Carla. 1938. Individual differences in the facial expressive behavior of preschool children: A study by the time sampling method. *Genet. Psychol. Monogr.*, 20, 557–650.

Symonds, P. M. 1949. *Adolescent fantasy: An investigation of the picture story method of personality study.* New York: Columbia Univer. Press.

Taylor, Janet A. 1953. A personality scale of manifest anxiety. *J. abnorm. soc. Psychol.*, 48, 285–290.

Temple, R., and Elisabeth W. Amen. 1944. A study of anxiety reactions in young children by means of a projective technique. *Genet. Psychol. Monogr.*, 30, 61–113.

Terman, L. M., and Catherine C. Miles. 1936. *Sex and personality: Studies in masculinity and femininity.* New York: McGraw-Hill.

Thomas, D. S. 1929. Some new techniques for studying social behavior. *Child Develpm. Monogr.*, No. 1.

Thomas, R. M. 1951. Effects of frustration on children's paintings. *Child Develpm.*, 22, 123–132.

Turner, W. D. 1948. Altruism and its measurement in children. *J. abnorm. soc. Psychol.*, 43, 502–516.

Valentine, C. W. 1930. The innate bases of fear. *J. genet. Psychol.*, 37, 394–420.

Veroff, J., Sue Wilcox, and J. W. Atkinson. 1953. The achievement motive in high-school and college-age women. *J. abnorm. soc. Psychol.*, 48, 108–119.

Walker, R. G. 1951. A comparison of clinical manifestations of hostility with Rorschach and MAPS test performances. *J. proj. Tech.*, 15, 444–460.

Walter, L. M., and S. S. Marzolf. 1951. The relation of sex, age, and school achievement to levels of aspiration. *J. educ. Psychol.*, 42, 285–292.

Washburn, Ruth W. 1929. A study of the smiling and laughing of infants in the first year of life. *Genet. Psychol. Monogr.*, 6, 397–539.

Washburne, J. N. 1935. A test of social adjustment. *J. appl. Psychol.*, 19, 125–144.

Watson, J. B., and J. J. B. Morgan. 1917. Emotional reactions and psychological experimentation. *Amer. J. Psychol.*, 28, 163–174.

Watson, J. B., and R. Rayner. 1920. Conditioned emotional reactions. *J. exp. Psychol.*, 3, 1–14.

Wenar, C. 1956. The effects of a motor handicap on personality: III. The effects on certain fantasies and adjustive techniques. *Child Develpm.*, 27, 9–15.

Winker, J. B. 1949. Age trends and sex differences in the wishes, identifications, activities, and fears of children. *Child Develpm.*, 20, 191–200.

Wolfenstein, Martha. 1946. The impact of a children's story on mothers and children. *Monogr. Soc. Res. Child Develpm.*, 11, No. 1.

Wolfenstein, Martha. 1954. *Children's humor.* Glencoe, Ill.: Free Press.

Worell, L. 1956. The effect of goal value upon expectancy. *J. abnorm. soc. Psychol.*, 53, 48–53.

Wright, B. A. 1942. Altruism in children and the perceived conduct of others. *J. abnorm. soc. Psychol.*, 37, 218–233.

Wright, H. F. 1937. The influence of barriers upon the strength of motivation. *Contr. Psychol. Theor.*, 1, No. 3.

Yarrow, L. J. 1948. The effect of antecedent frustration on projective play. *Psychol. Monogr.*, 62, No. 6.

Young-Masten, Isabel. 1938. Behavior problems in elementary school children. *Genet. Psychol. Monogr.*, 20, 123–181.

Zeigarnik, B. 1927. Ueber das Behalten von erledigten und unerledigten Handlungen. *Psychol. Forsch.*, 9, 1–85.

Zubin, J. 1932. Some effects of incentives: A study of individual differences in rivalry. New York: *Teach. Coll. Contr. Educ.*, Columbia Univer., No. 532.

# chapter 18

# The Appraisal of Personality Characteristics in Children

Urie Bronfenbrenner and
Henry N. Ricciuti
*Cornell University*

This review of methods for the appraisal of personality characteristics in children is distinguished by three features: it is variable-oriented, child-oriented, and theory-oriented. The first feature refers to the fact that major consideration is given primarily to those procedures that have been explicitly designed for measuring particular variables. Generalized techniques for the appraisal of personality *in toto*, such as the CAT, the Rorschach, and the World Test, are not treated here, especially since they are dealt with elsewhere in this book. The review is child-oriented in that we have restricted ourselves only to those methods that have been specifically devised or adapted for use with children. Thus we make only passing references to procedures that

were designed primarily for adults but happen also to be applicable to adolescents or older youngsters. Finally, our approach is theory-oriented out of necessity. We found that we could not evaluate techniques for appraising personality in children without first analyzing conceptually both the kinds of variables that investigators wished to assess and those that they were in fact measuring.

Even when one restricts oneself only to those methods of personality assessment that meet our criteria of being variable-oriented and child-oriented, the number of "eligible" traits and techniques is far beyond the scope of a single chapter. Accordingly, we have resorted to the usual expedient employed by the researcher confronted with an impossibly large universe—sampling. Our sample in this instance is "stratified" rather than random; specifically, we have selected for intensive consideration three variables—*aggression, anxiety,* and *motivation for achievement*—which represent something of the range of personality characteristics that have been measured in children and each of which has been studied by a variety of techniques.

The chapter is organized in five major sections:

1. The first presents what is intended as a theoretically neutral conceptual analysis of types of personality characteristics.

2. Here we consider the major strategies employed for the analysis of personality characteristics in children, the assumptions on which these strategies are based, and the dangers inherent in these assumptions.

3. A statement of the criteria em-

ployed in selecting variables and techniques for consideration and an outline of the steps to be followed in evaluating each variable and the techniques employed for its measurement.

4. The main body of the chapter analyzes the major concepts and techniques currently employed in the measurement of three representative variables: *aggression, anxiety,* and *motivation for achievement*. This evaluation is carried out in the light of the concepts and criteria outlined in the first three sections. Implications for use of the techniques in research and practice are examined.

5. An examination of the general implications suggested by the intensive analysis of the selected variables and techniques and directions for future development.

## THE NATURE OF PERSONALITY CHARACTERISTICS

The conceptual framework we have employed for the analysis and classification of personality characteristics is by no means new; rather it is a synthesis gleaned from a variety of sources, the most important being the contributions of Allport (1937), Murray (1938), Sanford et al. (1943), Goodenough (1949) and, most recently, Baldwin (1955, 1958). We may begin by noting that the term "personality characteristic" is used, explicitly or implicitly, to refer to a wide range of properties of a person. Nevertheless, these diverse uses have one feature in common; underlying all is some kind of *dispositional construct*, in Carnap's (1936,

1937) sense of this term. To put the matter more precisely, *a personality characteristic ordinarily implies a tendency toward behavior associated with a particular person under a given set of conditions*. Most commonly, this behavioral tendency refers to a disposition to act on the part of $S$, the person himself. For example, Mary cries whenever she sees another child crying, Tom avoids the company of boys his own age. For reasons that we shall indicate later, we also wish to consider as a personality characteristic any tendency of $S$ to evoke a particular response in others under a given set of conditions. For example, John is picked on by boys of his own age, Tom is "mothered" by females older than himself. All together, we have found it necessary to distinguish three types of personality characteristics, which we designate as *response tendencies, motives,* and *stimulus characteristics*. The first two refer to dispositions toward action on the part of $S$ himself, the last to tendencies to evoke responses in others.

## RESPONSE TENDENCIES

Here it is the specific behavior elicited that is relatively invariant. Every time the response tendency is activated, the person tends to do exactly the same thing. There is no modification of response in order to achieve a particular goal or end-state. For example, Baby Sam cries when not fed for several hours, Mary reacts impulsively in new situations, John shows anxiety signs when separated from his mother. Many response tendencies may, in fact, bring about a particular end-state: the baby's crying will often lead the mother to feed it. The crucial criterion for a response tendency, then, is not whether the behavior is adaptive or nonadaptive (it may be either), but whether the particular behavior evoked tends to be the same under similar stimulus conditions. The reader will recognize that many emotional characteristics of the type that Allport (1937) subsumed under the term temperament, such as energy level, speed of response, irritability, and mood, fall under the rubric of response tendencies as here defined.

## MOTIVES

With motives, it is the goal or end-state that is invariant rather than a specific mode of response; the person may resort to a variety of actions to achieve the goal. For instance, Henry strives to excel in any activity in which he engages, Mary tries to comfort anyone who is hurt or unhappy. In both of these examples the particular acts in which the child engages may differ from one situation to the next. On one occasion Mary may feed a hungry dog, on another, get a Band-Aid for a hurt child, and, on a third, perhaps even fight a bully attacking other children. The consistency manifested is with respect to the particular end-state—that of relieving the pain or discomfort of others. This goal or end-state may be positive as well as negative; for example, Tom avoids the company of girls.

In the case of motives, then, the specific behavior manifested constitutes an instrumental act that may vary markedly from one situation to the next. A motive, therefore, cannot be inferred from a single piece of behavior, since both response tendencies and motives may lead to the same specific act. Thus the crying of a hurt child may reflect simply the disposition to cry in response to pain or may represent an instrumental act, in the service of a dependency motive, aimed at getting help from others. To establish the existence of one or the other type of disposition requires additional evidence either that the child tends to cry in response to pain in a variety of situations irrespective of the consequences or that he consistently engages in a variety of behaviors having in common the feature that they elicit attention and assistance from others. Lacking such additional evidence, it is easy to err by inferring the existence of one type of disposition when only the other in fact exists. As we shall see when we begin to look at specific techniques, the readiness to assume motives where only response tendencies are actually present is particularly common.

## STIMULUS CHARACTERISTICS

The distinction between response tendencies and motives on the one hand and stimulus properties on the other parallels Allport's differentiation (1937) between "biophysical" and "biosocial" characteristics. In the belief that the former are no less social than they are physical and that the latter are as much physical as social, we have eschewed Allport's terminology and substituted our own. One can argue, as Allport does, that to view biosocial characteristics as aspects of personality is illegitimate, since they refer primarily not to attributes of $S$ but to the effect of these attributes on others. We nevertheless wish to retain the concept of stimulus characteristics in our analysis for three reasons. First, there is the purely practical consideration that a number of widely used techniques of personality assessment do in fact measure primarily not attributes of $S$ but the effect of these attributes on others (for example, sociometric indices of acceptability). Second, there is a theoretical argument: much of human behavior, being social in character, implies reciprocal expectation and response. When, for example, we describe a child as influential or irritating, we are referring not merely to characteristics of $S$ but also to the response that $S$ is likely to evoke from others. The principal basis for wishing to maintain the distinction, however, is methodological, since the failure to differentiate between $S$'s own behavioral tendencies and the responses that he elicits from others can contribute to ambiguity and error in present-day procedures for the appraisal of personality characteristics, especially in children.

Having described three major types of personality characteristics and emphasized the differences between them, we would now call attention to certain features that they share in common. First, since all three are dispositions that are manifested only under a given set of circumstances, the frequency of overt expression depends in part on the number of times the person is subjected to these instigating conditions. Thus some response tendencies, such as smiling, may be evoked many times in the life of a person; others,

like fainting under stress, only once or twice. The frequency with which an act occurs, therefore, is not exclusively a property of the disposition but also a function of the situation. A disposition is no less a disposition if it occurs only once (or perhaps never) in the course of a lifetime. Second, although from a theoretical point of view a disposition may remain a property of the person for only a short period of time (e.g., a matter of hours or minutes), interest customarily focuses on dispositions that are relatively enduring (i.e., they last for a period of years). Finally, and most important, personality characteristics, being dispositional constructs, cannot be observed directly; their existence must be *inferred* from certain operations performed under specified conditions. These operations and inferences constitute the major strategies that underlie specific techniques of personality assessment. We turn next to a consideration of these strategies and the assumptions on which they are based.

## STRATEGIES AND UNDERLYING ASSUMPTIONS IN THE ASSESSMENT OF PERSONALITY CHARACTERISTICS

*The Problem of Construct Validity.* In attempting to measure behavioral dispositions, the investigator is confronted with an issue which, though it has haunted psychology since its beginnings, has been given systematic formulation only in recent years. This is the problem of "construct validity," of inferring "the degree to which the individual possesses some trait or quality (construct) presumed to be reflected in the test performance" (APA Technical Recommendations, 1954). The concept of "construct validity" was first introduced formally in the report of the APA Committee on Psychological Tests (APA Technical Recommendations, 1954). The most definitive analysis, however, appears in the subsequent paper by Cronbach and Meehl (1955).[1] Echoing the Committee report, these writers take issue with the traditional view that a measuring technique is adequately validated simply by correlating it against a single external criterion. Such a procedure is appropriate, they assert, only when the investigator is interested solely in predicting the criterion behavior and has "no concern whatsoever with the type of behavior exhibited in the test." Whenever "the trait or quality underlying the test is of central importance," we are faced with the problem of "construct validity," and the single criterion approach is no longer sufficient nor absolutely necessary. Instead, the investigator is called upon to marshal all available evidence, both logical and empirical, in support of the argument that the test measures what it purports to measure. Correlations with external criteria are but one possible source of corroborative evidence. Cronbach and Meehl cite five common methods of construct validation.

1. *Correlational matrices and factor analysis.* If two tests are presumed to measure the same construct, a correlation between them is predicted. . . . A matrix of intercorrelations often points out prof-

[1] A recent review of principles and methods of construct validity is provided by Clark (1959).

itable ways of dividing the construct into more meaningful parts, factor analysis being a useful computational method in such studies.

2. *Group differences.* If our understanding of a construct leads us to expect two groups to differ on the test, this expectation may be tested directly. . . .

3. *Studies of internal structure.* For many constructs, evidence of homogeneity within the test is relevant in judging validity. . . . Negative item-test correlations may support construct validity provided that the items with negative correlations are believed irrelevant to the postulated construct and serve as suppressor variables.

4. *Studies of change over occasion.* The stability of test scores ("retest reliability") may be relevant to construct validation. Whether a high degree of stability is encouraging or discouraging . . . depends upon the theory defining the construct. . . . More powerful than the retest after uncontrolled intervening experiences is the retest with experimental intervention . . . the experimenter validates by determining whether the test can detect induced intraindividual differences.

5. *Studies of process.* One of the best ways of determining informally what accounts for variability on a test is the observation of the person's process of performance (pp. 287–289).

The foregoing list of methods is by no means exhaustive. Particularly pertinent to the validation of personality measures in children, for example, is the demonstration that the variable being measured shows developmental trends and antecedents that are consistent with the theory of the nature and genesis of the variable. The general strategy of construct validation is well summarized by the authors of the APA *Technical Recommendations* (1954) when they state, "Essentially, in studies of construct validity, we are validating the theory underlying the test" (p. 14).

*Construct Validity of Behavioral Dispositions.* The general problems of construct validity are further complicated when the characteristic being assessed is a behavioral disposition, for this type of construct requires somewhat more involved operations and attendant assumptions. These requirements for establishing the existence of a behavioral disposition are easier to state than to meet. Since a personality characteristic involves a tendency toward action associated with S under given conditions, it is necessary to show that the particular behavior does in fact occur whenever S is found or placed in specified conditions. Ideally, this requirement is met by direct observation of S over a period of time under a variety of circumstances. If the specified behavior is then observed only under the specified conditions, the particular personality characteristic may be said to exist.

These ideal criteria are obviously difficult to establish. Not only is the procedure of direct observation expensive in time and money, but there is always the chance, since one cannot observe all possible situations, that the inferred personality characteristic is actually either more general or more specific than is believed.

Moreover, although the method of direct observation over extended times and settings has been employed on occasion (e.g., Murphy, 1937), ordinarily the investigator resorts to other, less demanding procedures, which, though more practicable, inevitably entail further assumptions, hence scientific risks.

Whatever method is employed for the assessment of personality characteristics, two general kinds of assumptions are made, explicitly or implicitly. Each type has its dangers and difficulties.

1. *The assumption of specificity.* To identify a personality characteristic, it is necessary to specify both a particular kind of behavior and a particular type of situation in which this behavior is evoked. Accordingly, in applying any method of personality assessment, it is necessary to assume that *the behavior and situation being observed are representative of the particular class of behaviors and situations in which one is interested and not some broader class or mixture of classes.* If this assumption is not warranted, then the measuring procedure being employed is not a valid one.

*Example.* An index of aggressiveness based on the number of times a child attacks other children may be a function not only of the child's tendency toward aggressive behavior but his general rate of activity. (For this reason, aggressiveness is often measured as a percentage of all acts exhibited in a given time interval.)

2. *The assumption of generality.* This assumption represents the opposite side of the coin from the first. In employing any assessment technique, one must assume that the behavior and situation being observed are generalizable to the broader class of behaviors and situations in which one is interested. In point of fact, the observed behavior may be highly specific to the particular situation in which it is elicited or to the psychological state of the subject at the time.

*Example.* Level of aspiration as observed in a given experiment may not be a pervasive aspect of S's behavior but specific to the task employed (e.g., dart throwing).

We shall now examine the application of these generic assumptions in each of the major approaches commonly employed for inferring personality characteristics.

***Sources of Data.*** We shall discuss strategies as they relate to the various sorts of data utilized as the bases for inference. The data are of four types.

1. *Observations of behavior in selected situations* (typically one situation only). This method compromises with the ideal in reducing the variety of situations and the period of time over which S is observed. The situation selected may be taken from life or contrived as an experiment. In either case, both major assumptions apply, and the corresponding pitfalls increase as a direct function of the restrictiveness of the situations selected in variety and time span. Thus, to return to the example of level of aspiration, the fewer the tasks employed and the number of replications, the greater the risk in generalizing to other situations.

2. *Reports of behavior.* In the case of children, these are typically obtained by questionnaires or interviews with the subject, his parents, teachers, or others who know him well. Here the assumption of specificity takes a special form and brings its special problems of validity; namely, the investigator assumes substantial correspondence between verbal report and overt behavior. The content of the report is assumed to be determined primarily by the behavior that actually occurred at another time rather than by immediate circumstances or orientations of the respondent. It is well recognized, however, that considerable violence is done to this assumption by distortions of fact. These may arise from a variety of sources: ignorance, faulty observation, failure to understand the question, and deliberate or unconscious bias as a function of the respondent's own needs and behavioral dispositions. A special form of this last source of error is the *response set* or tendency to answer questions in a particular manner without regard to the specific content of the item. Response sets can be a serious contaminating influence in reports of behavior, especially when the reports are obtained as responses to

a structured questionnaire. The distortions are likely to be even more marked, however, in reports of attitude rather than action. Accordingly, we defer systematic consideration of response sets to the next section, which deals with the measurement of behavioral dispositions from statements of attitude.

3. *Reports of attitude.* Inferences about personality characteristics are frequently made from the subject's stated preferences or opinions as recorded in interviews or questionnaires or as reported by others. Except in the relatively rare instances in which the investigator's interest is confined strictly to the subject's verbal response per se, the use of attitude data as a basis for inferring personality characteristics rests on the assumption that the professed attitude reflects a disposition to act in accordance with the opinion expressed. Apart from the requirements of construct validity imposed by this hypothesis, attitude measures of personality are, as already mentioned, highly susceptible to the contaminating influence of response sets. The full extent, variety, and subtlety of this influence have come to be recognized only in recent years. For systematic analysis of the various types of response sets and of methods for taking them into account, the reader is referred to the technical papers of Cronbach (1946, 1950), Bass (1955, 1956), Edwards (1957), Christie et al. (1958), Bronfenbrenner et al. (1958) and Bronfenbrenner (1958, 1960b). For present purposes, it will suffice to call attention to five of the commonest kinds of response set:

*a. Stereotypy.* The tendency to give the same response to every question.

*b. Acquiescence.* A special type of stereotypy in which the respondent consistently tends to say "yes" or to agree.

*c. Expressiveness.* Willingness or inclination to take a strong or intense position, whatever its content or direction.

*d. Favorability.* The tendency to view one's self or others in a favorable light.

*e. Social desirability.* The tendency to

give the response that is most socially acceptable.

As is readily apparent from the foregoing examples, response sets are actually personality characteristics in their own right. Although in some instances they may reflect goal-oriented dispositions (e.g., the desire to make a good impression), response sets are ordinarily invariant, stimulus-specific forms of behavior, hence constitute examples of the type of disposition we have called "response tendency." In a recent article Loevinger (1959) has pointed to the special importance of response sets in the study of personality development in children. She argues that the gradual increase, between the ages of 8 and 13, in the tendency to describe one's self favorably (Getzels and Walsh, 1958) and the subsequent decrease in this same tendency over the college years (Sanford et al., 1956) can be viewed as a reflection of the normal course of ego development in children. "At the lowest point there is no capacity to conceptualise oneself; at the midpoint there is a stereotyped, usually conventional and socially acceptable self-conception; and at the highest point a differentiated and more or less realistic self-concept." More typically, however, response sets are not of interest in their own right but function as confounding factors giving a false stability and generality to measures intended to assess variables far more specific than a generalized pattern of verbal response. Although structured questionnaires and interviews are particularly susceptible to these contaminating effects, non-directive, projective-type approaches are by no means immune to their influences.

4. *Projective responses.* These are ordinarily obtained by specially designed techniques (e.g., story-completion, doll play, drawings), although any kind of behavior, including responses to structured questionnaires, may be used as the basis for projective analysis. What distinguishes the projective technique from other methods is a special form of the assumption of generality. Specifically, projective tech- niques are assumed to reflect dispositions that are not given free and direct expression in everyday behavior. Accordingly, one cannot postulate, as one does with the preceding methods, a continuity in kind between the behavior exhibited in the projective test and in other situations. Nevertheless, a certain systematic relationship is implied, namely, the *projective response is presumed to reflect a personality characteristic that manifests itself in a different but yet theoretically consistent fashion in real-life situations.* The validity of a projective technique as a measure of the personality characteristic depends on the demonstration of this systematic relationship.

In a searching essay on "The Appraisal of Child Personality," Goodenough (1949) employed the term "sign" to designate that feature of a projective response that is taken as an indicator of some underlying behavioral disposition, or as she called it, "conduct tendency."

Because the projective significance of his response is ordinarily not apparent to the respondent, it is easy to dismiss or overlook the possibility that distortions or response sets, willful and otherwise, may plague such techniques no less than they do more conventional procedures. It is nevertheless a fact that projective techniques are highly susceptible to confounding influences from such factors as vocabulary level, verbal fluency, level of abstraction, and stereotypy of response. Specific instances of such sources of error will be noted as they occur in relation to particular techniques.

Whatever the source of the data, variations occur also in the unit of measurement employed and the level of inference it implies. For example, in analyzing observations of behavior, the investigator may work from a "verbatim" record of specific acts or episodes, as in the studies of Barker and Wright (1951, 1954) or, following the method of Bales (1950), acts may be classified, as observed, into higher-order categories such as "shows tension" or "shows solidarity." More commonly, however, an even more "global" unit is employed; that is, observers are asked to rate on the basis of general impressions gleaned from an entire behavior protocol or from observations over an extended period of time. In such instances, not only is the chain of inference longer and less explicit, but there is an increased danger of distortion from halo effects (which, incidentally, are good examples of stimulus characteristics).

The same range in units of measurement and levels of inference is found with other sources of data as well. Thus measures of attitude may be based on responses to specific items or on self-ratings on highly abstract variables. Similarly, one may analyze projective responses at a very molecular level, as exemplified in the work of McClelland, Atkinson (McClelland et al., 1953; Atkinson, 1958) and their colleagues, or, following the earlier practice of Murray (1938) and Sanford et al. (1943), rate the projective protocol as a whole. As we shall indicate in our discussion of specific techniques, each approach has some advantages and some shortcomings.

## SELECTION OF VARIABLES AND METHOD OF EVALUATION

*Criteria for Selection.* Our aim is to evaluate, in the light of the conceptual distinctions and methodological criteria outlined above, examples of the most widely used and most promising strategies and techniques currently available for measuring personality characteristics in children. Since practical considerations preclude the examination of all possible personality characteristics and available techniques and since many such procedures are treated extensively in other chapters of this book, we focus attention primarily on a few selected variables and methods meeting the following criteria:

1. The variables examined must, insofar as possible, be representative of the major types of personality characteristics that have been (and are likely to continue to be) the focus of attention in work with children.

2. The variables examined must have been investigated through a variety of techniques representing the major approaches and problems currently encountered in the measurement of personality characteristics in children.

3. The assessment techniques themselves must have been devised or adapted to measure the specific variable in question. Procedures designed to provide a global picture of personality or to yield measures on a wide variety of dimensions are thus excluded from consideration.

4. The method must have been originally devised or specifically adapted for use with children. Procedures primarily designed for adults are not dealt with here, even though they may be applicable to adolescents or older children.

5. The method must meet conventional criteria of psychological measurement, e.g., the specific procedures for applying the technique must be described and consideration given to problems of validity and reliability.

*The Variables To Be Examined.* A review of research studies utilizing methods meeting the foregoing criteria brought to light three general types of variables for which specific measuring techniques had been developed for use with children. We may refer to these characteristics as *emotional orientations*, *social orientations*, and *task orientations*. The first category includes variables such as anxiety, guilt, orality, and psychological sexuality, which are primarily intrapsychic in nature or imply disposition toward the self. The second group is interpersonal and social in focus and encompasses such attributes as aggressiveness, affiliation, authoritarianism, and identification. Finally, there are problem-centered orientations such as motivation for achievement, intolerance of ambiguity, and creativity. Although the three groups of variables pose many of the same theoretical and methodological issues, each appears also to have certain special features. Accordingly, in order that our selection might be at least in small measure representative of the variety of problems to be encountered, we have chosen one variable from each group. In each instance the variable chosen was the one that seemed to have been studied most intensively with the greatest variety of techniques and that lent itself best to the exposition of the major conceptual and technical problems involved. The measuring procedures to be examined, then, are those that have been devised for assessing children's *aggressiveness*, *anxiety*, and *motivation for achievement*.

**Method of Evaluation.** The following procedure is employed in evaluating existing techniques for assessing the foregoing variables:

*Step 1.* A brief theoretical analysis of the variable to delineate its status in terms of the concepts outlined under the heading The Nature of Personality Characteristics.

*Step 2.* A factual description of each technique used for assessing the variable, together with basic data available on standardization, validity, reliability, etc.

*Step 3.* Analysis of the explicit and implicit assumptions underlying the technique with the aim of determining what aspects of the theoretical variable each technique is in fact measuring.

*Step 4.* Implications of the analysis for application of the technique in research or clinical practice.

*Step 5.* Suggestions for improving existing methods for measurement of the variable.

## METHODS FOR THE ASSESSMENT OF SPECIFIC PERSONALITY CHARACTERISTICS

### AGGRESSIVENESS

The appraisal of aggression confronts us with most of the theoretical and methodological problems discussed in the preceding sections; hence it represents a particularly useful point at which to begin our discussion of techniques for evaluating specific personality characteristics. As ordinarily defined, the construct of aggression subsumes any action, thought, or impulse, the presumed aim of which is physical or psychological injury, either real or symbolic, to an individual or surrogate. This typical conceptualization places primary emphasis upon aggression as a *motivational* disposition, as we have defined this term earlier. In common practice, for example, where observations of a variety of specific aggressive behaviors are made, principal interest is usually centered upon the implications of such behaviors for the individual's hostile intent. But an important difficulty may arise with an uncritical application of this approach, namely, that behaviors classified by an observer as "aggressive" may actually be response tendencies rather than instrumental activities in the service of aggressive motivation. In very young children, for instance, one may see "destructive" behavior, such as knocking over block towers or cutting up clay figures, which, under some circumstances, may actually represent characteristic modes of manipulating material objects (i.e., response tendencies) rather than hostile acts reflecting an impulse to hurt or injure. In appraising aggressiveness in children, then, it is important to attempt to differentiate between behavior that reflects the presence of aggression as a motive and phenomenologically similar behavior that is essentially a response tendency. The task is by no means an easy one, but it deserves considerably more attention than has typically been devoted to it.

Turning to the sources of data utilized for the appraisal of aggression, we find that only three of the four sources previously described are frequently used: (1) systematic direct observation of the subject's aggressive behavior, (2) reports or judgments of aggressiveness by others having varying degrees of contact with the subject, and (3) the individual's projective responses. Relatively little use has been made of reports of attitudes in the appraisal of aggression, probably because of the assumption that it is difficult to obtain valid self-descriptions of an impulse like aggression, which is subject to a good deal of social inhibition and control.

The obvious variety in the sources of data just mentioned immediately raises the question of the equivalence of measures of aggressiveness obtained by these very different approaches. It is well known, for example, that the relationship between fantasy aggression (as revealed in projective responses) and overt aggression is by no means simple or easily predictable. This is one illustration of the more general problem of the complex relationship between motives and their expression in behavior (Sanford et al., 1943; Lindzey, 1952; McClelland, 1958a; Atkinson, 1958), a problem to which we return repeatedly in subsequent discussion.

In the paragraphs that follow illustrations are presented of the principal techniques that have been used for the appraisal of aggression. As before, procedures are grouped according to the sources of data upon which they rely.

*Systematic, Direct Observations of Aggressive Behavior.* A number of promising techniques have been developed and applied for the purpose of measuring individual differences in amount and types of aggressive behavior by systematic, direct observation in naturalistic settings. Typically, these techniques involve the determination of the frequency of occurrence of a variety of specific kinds of aggressive behavior, as noted by trained judges working over a number of time periods. The observations may consist of detailed, running narrative accounts, which are subsequently analyzed for the occurrence of aggressive acts (e.g., Jersild and Markey, 1935; Lewin, Lippitt, and White, 1939), or, as has become more common, the observer may directly classify and tabulate the various defined types of aggressive behavior as they occur (e.g., Sears et al., 1953; Walters et al., 1957). The use of specific categories of aggressive behavior permits meaningful differentiation among qualitatively different forms of aggression, for example, verbal or physical, and among different objects of aggression, such as persons or inanimate objects. The frequencies of occurrence of such behavior units, separately and/or in aggregate, may then be used as indices of aggressiveness for each child.

As an illustration of an extremely careful systematic application of this approach, the reader is referred to the study by Sears, Whiting, Nowlis, and Sears (1953). These investigators classified the aggressive behavior of nursery-school children in six categories.

1. *Injury to person* (including hurting someone, getting someone punished, damaging another's property, derogating status).

2. *Discomforting another* (including threatening gestures and language).

3. *Insuring compliance with demands.*

4. *Destruction of inanimate objects or constructions* (in the form of displaced aggression or nondirected aggression).

5. *Having object in own possession* (taking things away from another).

6. *Removal of immediate or anticipated frustration* (removing barriers, minimizing injuries from another person, maintaining status as in "saving face," taking back an object that has been previously taken away by someone else, retaliation).

A child's score for each category was the number of occurrences of the defined type of aggressive acts during 16 fifteen-minute periods of observation, and a total aggression index was obtained by summing the scores for all categories. (It should be noted that indices of this kind may be complicated by differences in children's activity level.)

With careful definitions of the observational categories to be used and with sufficient training of judges, it is possible to achieve a satisfactorily high degree of interobserver agreement with techniques involving direct observation. In the study just described, for example, two judges simultaneously and independently classifying the behaviors of 43 children over 74 fifteen-minute observations achieved percentages of agreement varying from 67 to 100 for the six aggression categories, with an average agreement of 86 per cent.

The success with which the method of direct observation can be used in appraising any phenomenon depends not only upon the conceptualization and definitions of the categories for classifying behavior, and upon the interjudge reliability of the category system, but also upon the strategy for sampling of observations; that is, the number, duration, and spacing of the behavior samples to be observed. This fundamental problem in the methodology of observational procedures is dealt with elsewhere in the present volume (Chapter 3). It is mentioned briefly here, however, because of the known variation in aggressive behavior in specific situations. If one wishes to obtain indices of broad generality, one needs to sample fairly large segments of the child's behavior in a variety of situations, and it is necessary that the sampling of such situations be reasonably comparable from child to child.

The direct classification and tabulation of aggressive behaviors as they occur by means of a prearranged system of categories has many methodological advantages. For some purposes, however, the investigator may gain by recording relatively detailed narrative descriptions of the behavior under study and the setting in which it occurs, with the coding and tabulation of specific categories of behavior occurring later. The principal advantage of such an approach is that it includes a description of the situational context in which the aggressive behavior takes place. Moreover, it permits sequential analyses of changes in behavior, without necessary loss of the quantitative treatment of the various categories of aggressive acts under study (e.g., Jersild and Markey, 1935).

Finally, an approach of this type makes possible the differentiation between aggressive dispositions as response tendencies and as motives. For example, one could evaluate each child's record for the extent to which it reveals a variety of aggressive behaviors across different situations, with invariance of goal [i.e., hostile intent or injury to another (aggressive motive)], as distinguished from a specific type of aggressive behavior occurring frequently but only in a particular situation. Without such analysis, two children with quite different behavior protocols reflecting different kinds of disposition might conceivably achieve the same over-all aggressiveness score on the basis of mere frequency of occurrence of behavioral acts. To the authors' knowledge, such analyses of observational data have not yet appeared in the research literature.

*Reports or Judgments of Aggressiveness from Others.* One step removed from the direct observation of aggressive behavior is the familiar method of asking judges to make ratings of aggressiveness. Such judgments usually require the rater to summarize in quantitative form a variety of cumulative, relatively uncontrolled observations and impressions.[1]

Among the earliest attempts to set up carefully defined scales for judging various kinds of aggressive behavior (as well as a variety of other traits) are the Fels Child Behavior Rating Scales (Richards and Simons, 1941) and the California Behavior Inventory for Nursery School Children (Conrad, 1932, 1933; Read, 1940). The revised Fels Child Behavior Rating Scales[2] contain four scales in the area of aggression: one is concerned with the frequency of aggressive behavior, another with the success or lack of success of the child's aggression against others, a third describes his reaction to aggression by others, and a fourth evaluates the extent to which the child tends to elicit aggressive behavior directed toward him. The last scale constitutes an excellent example of aggression as a stimulus characteristic. Each scale has

---

[1] There have been many extended treatments of the methodological problems involved in the construction and use of rating and ranking methods (e.g., Thorndike and Hagen, 1955; Guilford, 1954). The reader is referred to these for detailed consideration of technical issues.

[2] Fels Research Institute, Yellow Springs, Ohio.

a general definition, as well as five defined cue points, and the rater makes his judgment at any point on a graphic continuum.

The previously mentioned study of Sears et al. (1953) illustrates the effective use of rating scales to obtain judgments of aggressiveness from nursery-school teachers. Each of 13 scales, assumed to represent various instrumental activities subserving aggressive motivation, was described in detail. Ratings were made on a seven-point graphic scale, four points being defined in terms of frequency of occurrence.[1] With adequate training and experience in the use of the scales, pairs of teachers were able to achieve a satisfactory degree of agreement in rating children's aggressiveness (r's from .66 to .98). The final rating used was the sum of the judgments by the two teachers. As previously mentioned, children's aggression was also appraised in this study by means of a direct observational technique. The correlations between the observational measures and the teachers' ratings of total aggressive behavior were .64 for boys and .48 for girls. These correlations provide evidence supporting the construct validity of both techniques as methods for appraising aggressive behavior.

A number of promising techniques have been utilized to obtain estimates of the aggressive behavior of older children. Mussen and Naylor (1954), for example, used daily behavior reports (made by attendants and a handicraft

[1] The complete definitions of the scales are not found in Sears (1953) but are available elsewhere (Beller, 1948).

teacher over a two-week period) of the aggressive behavior among delinquent boys (ages 9 to 15) living in cottage groups. Each report consisted of a check list of 12 specific kinds of aggressive behavior, and the observer indicated which types of behavior had occurred each day. In addition, at the end of a week, the observer rated each boy on five scales representing different aspects of aggression. Although no data are reported on interjudge reliability for these indices, they apparently possess some validity as measures of aggression, since they revealed consistent relationships with independent estimates of fantasy aggression. Thus they appear to represent a promising practical approach to the problem of getting estimates of overt aggression from lay observers, based on day-to-day association.

Several other investigators have dealt effectively with the problem of obtaining estimates of specific types of aggressiveness from teachers. Thus frequency of fighting behavior shown by boys in the first three grades was rated by teachers in a study by Kagan (1956). A more global approach, aimed at differentiating socially acceptable and socially unacceptable forms of aggressive behavior in high-school boys (15 to 17 years old), is illustrated in the recent work of Jensen (1957). He used a combination of nominating and rating techniques by teachers to identify contrasting groups of high-school boys classifiable as "aggressive-bad," "aggressive-good," and "passive." Each teacher named five boys most closely fitting the descriptions of the aggression types and also ranked the boys and filled out descriptive check lists containing various items of aggressive behavior. From these data, the investigator picked relatively homogeneous groups of boys representing each of the three types of aggression "syndromes."

As we move further away from quantitative judgments on various defined variables, we approach the appraisal of aggression as a stimulus characteristic, evaluated in terms of the relatively long standing impression a child has made on other children. In a current research study Eron and others (1958) have used the familiar "guess who" technique in order to obtain criterion measures of aggressiveness based on peer nominations of third-grade children. After considerable pretesting, the investigators found 26 specific items of aggressive behavior on which children could agree quite well in making their nominations (e.g., "Who starts a fight over nothing?" "Who grabs things from other children?"). Further, the items could be grouped into clusters having median interjudge reliabilities in different classrooms ranging from .85 to .92. For total aggression scores thus obtained, the correlation with teacher ratings of aggression was .63. Although there are methodological problems involved in the use of peer-nominating techniques, such as the lack of comparability of frequency of nomination scores obtained in groups of different size and composition (Bronfenbrenner, 1945), this approach can be used profitably (Beswick and Cox, 1958).

Having dealt with evaluations and reports of children's aggressive be-havior by trained observers, by teachers, and by classmates, we now turn briefly to a source of information that is literally "closest to home": the child's mother. Although there has always been some skepticism with regard to the accuracy of mothers' reports concerning various aspects of their children's behavior, some investigators have found this a useful approach (e.g., MacFarlane et al., 1954; Sears, Maccoby, and Levin, 1957), particularly if one uses careful interviewing and rating methods to obtain the data. When reports from mother are used to supplement data on aggression obtained from other sources, they may contribute additional information of considerable importance. Taken by themselves, however, they would generally appear to represent material of uncertain objectivity and validity.

**Projective Responses.** It is probably safe to say that this source of data has been by far the most widely used by investigators concerned with the appraisal of aggression. Such usage reflects the view of aggression as a motive subjected to considerable social control and inhibition; hence it is not readily accessible to more direct methods of study. In the paragraphs that follow representative projective approaches are discussed under the headings of picture-interpretation methods, sentence-completion methods, and play methods.

**Picture-Interpretation Methods.** Since the classical work of Murray and his collaborators (1938), the Thematic Apperception Test (1943) and a variety of similar picture-interpretation techniques (Hartwell et al., 1951; Symonds, 1949; Bellak, 1954) have been widely used as methods for the global appraisal of personality in children. In this context, specific assessments of the strength and quality of aggressive motivation have sometimes been made by having skilled judges make subjective ratings on the basis of their interpretation of the total protocol (e.g., Sanford et al., 1943; Frenkel-Brunswik, 1942).

However, there has been an increasing tendency for investigators to utilize picture-interpretation methods in a more focused manner. Mussen and Naylor (1954), for example, in the study of 9-to-15-year-old boys previously mentioned, obtained a measure of fantasy aggression by counting the number of times aggressive acts by the hero or leading character occurred in the subject's stories on ten selected TAT pictures.

The following were considered acts of aggression: fighting, killing, criminally assaulting; getting angry, hating, quarreling, cursing, criticising, blaming, ridiculing; breaking and smashing objects; escaping restraint, running away, resisting coercion; being negativistic, resisting authority, lying, cheating, stealing, gambling; forcing someone to change his behavior or ideas; domineering or restraining someone; suicide, self-injury, self-deprecation (p. 236).

The measures of aggressive motivation thus obtained were significantly related to the indices of overt aggression obtained from observers' reports, as described previously (p. 783), and the relationship was even stronger when joint consideration was given to fantasy aggression and to anticipated punishment of aggression expressed in the TAT stories. Subjects with high fantasy aggression and low fear of punishment showed more overt aggressive behavior than those with little fantasy aggression accompanied by high fear of punishment [see also discussion of Hollenberg and Sperry study (1951) on p. 790]. The authors rightly point out that their findings must be regarded in part as a function of the lower-class sample with which they deliberately elected to work, since

. . . earlier studies have shown that in other social classes and age groups the relationship between covert and overt aggression may be negligible or even negative. These findings may not be at all applicable to members of a social class which has rather rigid taboos against the expression of aggression, or to older people whose internal controls of aggressive expression may be more firmly established (p. 239).

This study provides convincing evidence that fantasy measures of aggressive motivation have promising validity for predicting overt aggression. At the same time, it should be pointed out that such measures may be valid under some circumstances and not under others because of the complex relationship between motives and their expression in behavior, in part as a function of the situational context. For example, a more recent study by Jensen (1957) reports no relationship between amount of fantasy aggression revealed in ten TAT pictures and overt aggressive behavior judged by teachers (see pp. 783–784). In contrast with Mussen and Naylor's research, however, Jensen's study involved older subjects (15 to 17 years), presumably representing a different social class, a different set of TAT pictures (which were group-administered), a different scoring method (each story being rated from o to 10 for amount of aggression), and different criterion measures of overt aggression. Despite the lack of relationship between amount of fantasy and overt aggression, Jensen did find that boys who showed aggressive behavior of a socially unacceptable sort had more stories without punishment or defense against aggression than boys expressing socially acceptable forms of aggression. At the same time, the "aggressive-bad" group showed more freedom in expressing themselves by stories containing socially disapproved themes and language. This study again underscores the importance of examining picture-interpretation material specifically for content involving punishment or control of aggression. At the same time, it points to the potential value of analyzing stories for certain expressive qualities viewed as "overt" behavior samples (e.g., tabooed language and themes).

Kagan's study (1956) is representative of the current interest in the use of pictures specifically designed for appraising a particular motive. Working with 118 boys in grades one to three, he presented 13 pictures, each containing a boy in situations varying in ambiguity with respect to the suggestion of a fighting theme (none actually showed a fight in progress). Arguing that we need to emphasize greater precision in our analyses of aggressive fantasy and behavior, Kagan found a significant relationship between a simple count of the fighting themes in the boys' stories and ratings of frequency of fighting behavior obtained from teachers. He also reports evidence

that other categories of aggressive fantasy (e.g., stealing) were not related to overt aggression as manifested by fighting behavior. This study demonstrates the desirability of going beyond indices of aggression based on general categories (such as those used by Mussen and Naylor) to deal more systematically with specific kinds of aggression, both in fantasy and in overt behavior. In this way, we may hope to increase our understanding of the processes interconnecting behavior in these two spheres.

The findings reported by Kagan also suggest that pictures with more obvious aggressive content are preferable for differentiating between groups varying in amount of overt aggression. This work is illustrative of the increasing attention investigators are directing toward the general methodological problem of the relation between picture cues and the content of the fantasies they evoke (e.g., Atkinson, 1958, pp. 596–683).

Another recent development that points toward more refined quantitative methods for appraising aggression, as well as other motives, is represented by Lesser's attempt (1958) to apply Guttman's scaling method (1950) in evaluating children's fantasy aggression. Using ten specially constructed pictures administered to 72 boys, ages 10 to 13, Lesser was able to construct a reasonably satisfactory Guttman scale of fantasy aggression. These pictures had previously been used to obtain a gross measure of fantasy aggression that had shown promising relationships to indices of aggression in overt behavior.

A method employing picture cues of

a highly structured type is the Children's Form of the Rosenzweig Picture-Frustration Study (Rosenzweig et al., 1948). This instrument is an adaptation of the adult form of the test (Rosenzweig, 1945) and is designed for children from 4 to 13. It contains 24 cartoonlike drawings depicting a child in a mildly threatening situation involving another person, and the subject is asked to indicate what the child might say. Each response is scored for direction of aggression (outward, inward, or minimized and glossed over) and kind of reaction to frustration. The P-F technique is more amenable to quantitative scoring and statistical treatment than many projective methods, and initial norms are available for 131 boys and 125 girls from 4 to 13. Evidence of the test's construct validity, however, is still unclear and is limited for the most part to the results of comparisons between grossly contrasted groups, such as clinic and nonclinic cases (Rosenzweig and Rosenzweig, 1952) and delinquents and nondelinquents (Norman and Kleinfeld, 1958). If supported by further evidence of construct validity, the P-F technique would appear to be a useful research instrument for the appraisal of aggressive reactions to frustration.

*Sentence-Completion Methods.* The method of story or sentence completion has seen rather wide clinical use as a projective technique for global personality assessment (e.g., Rohde, 1946; Rotter and Rafferty, 1950; Sargent, 1953). One of the important advantages of this method is the possibility it offers for structuring the incomplete sentence or story to elicit responses that are relevant to a particular area of interest. For example, Graham et al. (1951), constructed 50 incomplete sentences, each of which portrayed a person as an object of aggression. The subject was to complete each statement by indicating the most likely way a person might act in such a situation. The aggressive situations were systematically varied with regard to the role of the one who is being aggressive (e.g., parent, sibling, friend or classmate, authority, and inferior) and the degree of aggressiveness shown (hitting, bawling-out or making dirty cracks, talking-about behind back, giving nasty looks, and not-liking). For instance, "When John's mother hit him, he . . ."; "The colored kid called him names, so Ricky . . ."; "When her mother bawled her out like that, Thelma . . ." (p. 513).

The 50 incomplete statements just described were administered to about 100 boys and girls in the seventh, eighth, and ninth grades, and all responses judged to be aggressive (i.e., involving injurious effect) were scored for strength of aggression with a high degree of interjudge agreement. The investigators were primarily concerned with the relationship between strength of aggressive response and the type and strength of instigation, *within the verbal material used.* Consequently, they provide no data on the relationship between the projective measures of aggression and independent indices of aggressive behavior. At the same time, however, the theoretical consistency of the results obtained suggest that a carefully constructed sentence completion test of this type may possess considerable construct validity and warrants further exploration.

*Play Methods.* For a good many years the play interview has been one of the most widely used clinical methods for the appraisal of young children's personality (Levy, 1936, Erikson, 1940; Murphy et al., 1956). In this technique, which commonly combines diagnostic and therapeutic functions, the child is encouraged to play with a variety of materials (family dolls, clay, paints, toys, etc.) by an adult examiner who assumes a generally permissive, understanding, nonjudgmental role. The adult may enter into the play in a variety of ways, by making encouraging comments, asking questions, or interpreting the child's feelings.

More recently, investigators have attempted to develop and exploit the play interview as a controlled, systematic research instrument for appraising child personality (Bach, 1945; Pintler, 1945; Sears, 1947; Lynn and Lynn, 1959). These more structured approaches usually involve uniform presentation of standard sets of play materials, most often family dolls, and systematic procedures for categorizing and evaluating the child's behavior in quantitative terms. (For an unusual and provocative quantitative treatment of play-interview-behavior items, the reader is referred to the study by Carroll and Levin, 1956.)

The controlled doll-play interview has had particularly wide application in the study of aggression in children. A good illustration is the structured doll-play technique described by Sears (1951) and utilized in a number of recent studies on aggression (e.g., Sears,

Whiting, Nowlis, and Sears, 1953; Levin and Sears, 1956). The material consists of a miniature six-room roofless "house" containing realistic furniture that is set up on the floor and five dolls that are easily recognizable as father, mother, boy, girl, and baby. The examiner urges the child to play with the dolls and the house they live in and interacts with the child by means of encouraging comments, continued attention and interest, etc., to stimulate continued play with the dolls. At the same time, the examiner makes an observational record of the child's aggressive play, which permits coding of aggressive acts with respect to (1) frequency or amount, (2) direction (i.e., agent and object of aggression), (3) type or content, and (4) latency (time elapsing before occurrence of the first aggressive act). Each subject receives two twenty-minute sessions of play, usually on consecutive days.

Sears (1951) conducted an extensive methodological and normative study with the technique just described, which was administered to 150 boys and girls 3 to 5 years of age. She found that independent observers could categorize the occurrence of various types of aggressive acts with a high degree of agreement (82 per cent) and that children maintained reasonably similar relative positions with regard to the amount of aggression shown in the two sessions ($r$'s $= .73$ for boys, .49 for girls). The doll-play technique that Sears utilized is thus seen to have appreciable interjudge as well as test-retest reliability, and it represents an extremely useful technique for the appraisal of aggression as expressed in play.[1]

Other types of play materials and procedures have also been used in controlled or semicontrolled techniques for eliciting and evaluating aggression. For example, Siegel (1957) observed the aggressive play of pairs of preschool children who were left alone for fourteen minutes with instructions to play freely until the examiner returned. A standard set of play materials was provided, including rubber daggers, clay, toy telephones, rubber sponges, small toy vehicles, a doll bed and a doll, and inflated balloons. During each twenty seconds of play, two observers independently rated each child on a four-point scale for level or intensity of aggression and level of anxiety and guilt over aggression. Total score for the child was simply the sum of these ratings for the entire observation. Interobserver agreement for these total scores was very high ($r = .97$ for level of aggression and $.77$ for anxiety and guilt). Siegel's method is of particular interest, since it permits expression of fantasy as well as overt aggression with a greater variety of play materials than is typically provided in standardized doll play and without the presence of an adult. At the same time, it utilizes ratings of the intensity of behavioral units of aggression, which may eventually provide more valid measures of strength of aggressive motivation than

[1] The Levin and Sears study (1956) provides additional normative data on 379 5-year-olds and generally confirms the evidence just cited in regard to the reliability of the doll-play technique.

are obtainable from indices relying on frequency alone.

Another interesting variant of the play method is represented in the technique devised by Stone (1956), in which children are provided with an opportunity to break inflated balloons under varying conditions of adult encouragement or permissiveness. Although not yet highly developed as a standardized method, this technique appears to represent a potentially promising semistructured, miniature-situation approach to the analysis of children's aggressive behavior. One of the difficulties with techniques of this sort, as well as the more structured play methods, is the previously discussed problem of determining whether behavioral acts classed as "aggressive" reflect response tendencies rather than motives implying hostile intent.

Although doll play and related techniques are typically classified under the rubric of "projective techniques," it should be noted that in contrast to the predominantly verbal responses usually elicited by most projective methods doll play evokes both *verbal* fantasy and fantasy *behavior*. The child can actively make the dolls play imaginary roles of various sorts, while at the same time he can directly express his own aggression against the dolls, toy furniture, the examiner, etc. Because the doll-play technique can elicit samples of fantasy and even overt aggression so directly, it has usually been regarded as having a high degree of intrinsic validity in its own right; thus doll-play aggression has served as the major dependent variable of interest in a number of studies (e.g., Siegel, 1956; Levin and Sears, 1956;

Sears, Pintler, and Sears, 1946). For the most part, such studies have yielded theoretically congruent results that lend support to the construct validity of the doll-play measures. For example, Hollenberg and Sperry (1951) found that the frequency of doll-play aggression was greatest for children experiencing high punishment for aggression and high frustration in the home, whereas it was lowest for children experiencing little punishment and frustration. Similarly, Sears et al. (1953) found a positive relationship between severity of punishment for aggression in the home and amount of children's doll-play aggression, although in a later study (Levin and Sears, 1956) this relationship was true for girls only.

Although these findings support the construct validity of doll-play measures, it should be recognized that the relationship between aggression in doll play and in natural social situations has not yet been widely investigated. Hence the question of the generality or specificity of the indices of aggressive motivation revealed in play remains a problem for further study. All in all, however, structured play techniques for appraising aggression in young children represent valuable research methods that have already been subjected to considerable technical study as research tools and have demonstrated their usefulness in theoretical studies of fantasy aggression.

### Evaluative Summary

It is apparent from the foregoing discussion that although many promising techniques for the appraisal of aggression in children have been developed the research worker will find relatively few refined psychometric instruments available. To some extent, this state of events reflects the over-all status of psychological measurement in the field of personality study. In addition, however, the paucity of standardized techniques is partly due to the complex nature of aggression as a psychological variable.

Viewed as a motive, aggression is typically subject to a variety of social inhibitions and controls from many sources. Consequently, aggressive impulse may manifest itself in many different forms, some obvious, some subtle, and its overt expression will vary greatly, depending upon the nature of the situational conditions and the repertoire of control mechanisms that the child has learned to invoke on the basis of previous experience. Some children with considerable aggressive motivation may reveal aggressive behavior very rarely, and then only under special circumstances, so that virtual absence of overt aggression does not necessarily imply absence of aggressive impulse.

When we consider overt behavior that is phenomenologically classifiable as "aggressive," we are faced with the problems of deciding whether such behavior reflects the presence of aggressive motivation, with explicit or implicit hostile intent, or whether it should be regarded as a nonmotivational response tendency. We sometimes have the additional complication of "aggressive" behavior, which subserves some other motive such as the need for dominance or mastery.

Problems such as these pose obvious and formidable difficulties for the investigator insofar as the methodological assumptions of generality and specificity are concerned. He needs to be aware, for example, that if he relies only on behavioral measures of aggression his measures may reflect the specific situational conditions to a high degree. If he bases his estimates on projective responses primarily, these may tell him very little about the person's aggressive behavior. These and similar difficulties suggest that the most theoretically meaningful and practically useful appraisals of aggression are likely to be obtained in a multifaceted approach, which combines observations and reports of behavior and projective responses obtained across a variety of situational contexts. Such "triangulation" would enable the investigator to evaluate not only the strength of aggressive motivation but also the types of stimuli most likely to instigate aggression, the kinds of controls a child imposes under different circumstances, and variations in overt aggression that occur as a function of all of the preceding factors. It is recognized that the approach just described is methodologically expensive in terms of time, money, and technical skills. When practical considerations preclude such strategy, it is suggested that the investigator employ at least two measures of aggression, one based on observations or reports of behavior, the other on projective responses.

Research workers may find some of the specific techniques discussed in this chapter usable in the manner in which they were originally employed (e.g., the observational method used by Sears et al., 1953, and the TAT measures of Mussen and Naylor, 1954). In other instances the investigator may wish to adapt a technique to fit his particular research needs. In either event the researcher should take appropriate measures to insure adequate reliability of administration and scoring before undertaking operational use of any of the techniques mentioned. Most of the methods described in the chapter have either been shown to have adequate interjudge reliability or appear to be reasonably capable of meeting this requirement.

Finally, it should now be apparent that one cannot evaluate adequately the validity of any techniques here described in terms of a relationship to a single empirical criterion. Rather one needs to look for different kinds of evidence to indicate that the method possesses some construct validity (see earlier discussion of this concept). Whenever such evidence has existed for the techniques reviewed, it has been cited in our discussion. It should be remembered, however, that even a technique possessing promising construct validity may yield measures that do not have a high degree of generality across situations. Once again, then, we are led to the conviction that whenever possible the appraisal of aggression in children should be undertaken with the simultaneous application of measures based on observations and reports of behavior as well as projective responses, all examined across a variety of different situations. This variation might be supplied by nature, by contrived experiment, or preferably by both. In short, we see the methodological gains of the future lying in a multifaceted approach that fuses experimental, observational, and testing methods.

## ANXIETY

The term "anxiety" has been widely used with a rather large variety of connotative and denotative meanings. In what appears to be its most general meaning and commonest usage, anxiety refers to an affective state of the individual, characterized by fearfulness, apprehension, or dread. Following the original suggestion of Freud (1935), many workers have found it both theoretically and practically useful to distinguish between a generalized state of apprehensiveness, in which the individual's anxiety is not restricted to any particular object or class of objects (Freud's "free-floating" anxiety), and fearfulness or apprehension attached to particular objects or situations.

Although some investigators emphasize this distinction, the custom is by no means universal, and the terms are often used interchangeably. Thus even a brief review of the research literature reveals the variety and ambiguity of conceptualizations and operational techniques used by different investigators. Although research workers are tending increasingly to designate the specific types of anxiety, which their instruments presumably measure (test anxiety, audience anxiety, sex anxiety, etc.), mere absence of such a specific modifier does not necessarily mean that the instrument measures generalized anxiety; rather it may only reflect the fact that the nature of what

is being measured is not exactly clear.

This lack of conceptual and operational consistency is eloquently noted and condemned by Cattell and Scheier (1958), who are particularly critical of the use of single measures of anxiety.

. . . each test in splendid operational insularity spawns its own possibly unique species of "anxiety," while the researcher whose "pet" test it is often seems to believe it is the only species of anxiety, and soon proceeds to assume that all other "anxieties" behave just as it does (p. 352).

Although one might argue with these authors' recommendation of factorial studies as the optimal approach for achieving conceptual clarity in the field, their concern with the multiplicity of concepts and instruments in anxiety research is one in which all investigators in this area must share.

To turn directly to this problem, according to our conceptual analysis, anxiety appears to have been regarded primarily as a response tendency and a motive rather than as a stimulus characteristic. It is our impression, moreover, that a great many measuring techniques deal with both aspects of anxiety at the same time, and, although it is difficult to separate the two conceptually and operationally, we feel that it is important to attempt to do so. Thus a person characterized by anxiety as a response tendency would be one who brings to all situations as a dispositional quality an affective state of fearful or anxious expectation. Similarly, an individual who reacts only to specific types of objects or situations with fearfulness may be regarded as manifesting a specific type of anxiety as a response tendency. In either case, anxiety is expressed in part in the affective state of the individual and in part in a variety of physiological and motor responses, all of which may affect the individual's performance in various activities or tasks.

In contrast, when one deals with various patterns of response that serve the function of reducing, eliminating, or avoiding anxiety, then, it seems to us, one is viewing anxiety as a motive rather than as a response tendency. Many important kinds of adaptive as well as maladaptive behavior are known to function in this manner, from simple flight or avoidance through subtler devices of inhibition and control to the more complex mechanisms of defense. Obviously, anxiety could not operate in this way as a motive unless it had also been present as a disturbing response tendency. Nevertheless, two persons having similar levels of anxiety, operating as a response tendency, may still be quite different in terms of the extent to which anxiety operates as a motivating factor in their behavior. In our appraisal of anxiety in children, then, we would do well to ask not only "how anxious or fearful is this child?" but also "to what extent and in what way does his anxiety serve a motivating function in his behavior?" Most of our assessment techniques have tended to mix these two aspects of anxiety in a single measure, with more weight usually being given to the first than to the second, particularly in objective tests.

Once one accepts the notion that it is important to evaluate anxiety both as a motive and as a response tendency, one is faced with the rather formidable prospect not only of evaluating the level and type of anxiety present but also of appraising the adaptive mechanisms, controls, and defenses with which the individual handles his anxieties or fears. How essential this broader approach may be depends in large part upon the degree to which measures of anxiety as response tendency, expressed without reference to motivational components, do in fact show appropriate relationships to psychologically relevant criteria.

Before turning to such questions, we must first examine the techniques and sources of data available for measuring individual differences, both in general and in focused types of anxiety. As before, we shall confine ourselves primarily to those techniques that have been specifically designed to measure anxiety. Thus we eliminate from consideration more global measures dealing with such broad concepts as neuroticism, security-insecurity, and adjustment, which may reflect anxiety along with many other variables.

The sources of data most commonly utilized for the measurement of anxiety in children seem to have been reports of behavior or attitude from the child himself, or sometimes from an adult, and projective response behavior. Relatively little use has been made of direct observations of behavior for arriving at quantitative indices of anxiety, although some techniques that utilize this source of information appear to have some merit for future work on the problem.

*Self-Reports of Behavior and Attitude.* A great deal of concerted research effort has been directed toward the development of questionnaire measures of anxiety in children. Sarason and his associates have been involved in a long program of research on test anxiety and its correlates in college students and, more recently, in children. As their principal measure of "test" anxiety, these investigators developed a 30-item "Yes-No" questionnaire, which is "concerned with attitudes toward and experiences in test and test-like situations" (Sarason et al., 1958, p. 105). For the most part, the questions focus upon anxiety as response tendency, since they ask about affective, physiological, and motoric manifestations of anxiety (e.g., Do you worry a lot before you take a test? When the teacher says she is going to find out how much you have learned, does your heart begin to beat faster? When . . . , do you sometimes feel that the hand you write with shakes a little?). The questions are read aloud by an examiner, and the test can be group-administered effectively to children as young as first graders.

Sarason and his colleagues have administered this questionnaire to large numbers of school children from grades one to five, and they have diligently explored the relationships between their test-anxiety measures and a wide variety of psychologically relevant criteria, based upon both field and experimental studies. The results of these studies are summarized briefly in one of the more recent publications of this group (Sarnoff et al., 1959). The test has very satisfactory reliability (both split-half and test-retest), and the over-all results of the research done with it suggest, for the most part, that the questionnaire is tapping a psychologically meaningful anxiety manifestation in elementary-school children, although the relationships with appropriate criteria are rarely very large and not always as expected. The test-anxiety measures (TA) show a low positive relationship to teacher's anxiety ratings, and they tend to be correlated negatively with both measured IQ and school achievement (Sarason et al., 1958) as well as with performance in experimental situations requiring new learning (Waite et al., 1958). In samples of both English and American children, TA scores tend to increase from the first to the fourth grade. Also, English children had higher mean TA scores than American children, although their general anxiety levels (as measured with a short general anxiety questionnaire) were equivalent, as predicted on the basis of the presumably greater importance of school examinations for the young school child in England (Sarnoff et al., 1958).

Some of the research on the Test-Anxiety scale illustrates rather complex problems of a general sort that tend to plague the investigator concerned with the appraisal of personality characteristics, such as anxiety, even with structured questionnaires. In a recently reported study (Sarnoff et al., 1959) the test-anxiety scale was given to English children at the end of the fourth-grade year and then again the following February, a week before a presumably highly anxiety-arousing standard classroom examination (the "11+"). Instead of finding a rise in test anxiety as the examination became imminent, the investigators found that the scores of both boys and girls dropped significantly. In their interpretation of this puzzling result the authors suggest that the drop in scores might reflect an increase in the "normal" defensiveness that ordinarily tends to produce a drop in mean scores upon retesting (Lighthall et al., 1960). If this interpretation is correct, the authors rightly point out, "we are obliged to acknowledge that, under certain circumstances, the TA scale may be measuring defensiveness as well as test anxiety."

It will be recalled that this is precisely the kind of problem we referred to in our discussion of the importance of trying to deal separately with anxiety considered as response tendency and as motive. The experience of the Sarason group suggests that even when an instrument is intended to deal primarily with anxiety as response tendency (in the sense that it asks about feelings under various hypothetical conditions) the test responses may at the same time reflect various adaptive mechanisms that subjects invoke in coping with anxiety. This problem may have been one of the factors responsible in part, at least, for the absence of a significant relationship between TA and scores on the 11+ examination in England, in contrast with results obtained with American children.

Problems such as response set and item characteristics, as factors determining TA questionnaire responses, are reportedly being thoroughly analyzed by the Sarason group. One of their most consistent findings, which may be more thoroughly explained when these analyses are completed, is that girls get higher test-anxiety scores than boys in both England and America. The authors suggest that this may be due to the greater social acceptability of expressions of worry and concern from girls than from boys.

In summary, the bulk of the findings obtained with the test-anxiety questionnaire suggest that this is a useful research instrument with reasonably good construct validity, dealing with a relatively specific and important type of anxiety manifestation in young school children. (Correlations between test anxiety and general anxiety are reported as about .55.) One of the most impressive features of the work of the Sarason group is the broad variety of psychologically relevant criteria against which the validity of the instrument is continuously being evaluated. One wonders, however, whether an extensive and productive research program of this sort might not have been even more fruitful had it been possible simultaneously to study and validate several appraisal techniques representing different approaches to the measurement of anxiety, rather than placing major emphasis upon a single approach represented by the short questionnaire.

Another rather widely used questionnaire measure of children's anxiety is the Children's Manifest Anxiety Scale (CMAS), developed by Castaneda, McCandless, and Palermo (1956) for use primarily with fourth-, fifth-, and sixth-grade children. This 42-item questionnaire represents a children's form of the Taylor Manifest Anxiety Scale (Taylor, 1953), which in turn was derived from the Minnesota Multiphasic Personality Inventory. The questions deal with reported physiological and psychological concomitants of generalized anxiety, worrisomeness, etc.

(e.g., I blush easily, My hands feel sweaty, I get angry easily, I often do things I wish I had never done). It is of interest that this scale was developed primarily to provide a measure of general drive level or strength of motivation in experimental studies on the relationship between drive strength and performance in children.

Numerous studies have indicated that the CMAS has some interesting relations to criteria of various sorts. For example, as predicted on the basis of similar studies with adults, anxious children were found to perform less well than nonanxious children on relatively difficult and complex learning tasks, although anxiety seems to facilitate certain kinds of simple learning (Castaneda, Palermo, and McCandless, 1956; Palermo et al., 1956). High anxious children tend to show more perceptual rigidity and greater speed of perceptual closure on experimental tasks than do low anxious children (Smock, 1958). Test scores also tend to be negatively correlated with measures of both IQ and school achievement, as well as sociometric standing (McCandless, et al., 1956a,b).

The test appears to have satisfactory test-retest reliability, correlations ranging between .70 and .94 over a period of one week (Castaneda, McCandless, and Palermo, 1956), and between .59 and .91 over a one-month period (Palermo, 1959). As in the case of the test-anxiety scale developed by the Sarason group, girls tend to achieve higher CMAS scores than boys, but no increases in score with age over the fourth- to sixth-grade period were found. Although the authors have incorporated a brief lie scale in the questionnaire, problems of response set still remain for further study.

In general, the results obtained with the CMAS suggest that it is tapping meaningful anxiety manifestations in children with some validity, and it may therefore be used with profit as a research instrument. Perhaps because of the original interest in the scores as measures of drive strength in experimental studies, the criteria against which the test has been validated do not appear to have represented a very broad range of theoretical constructs about anxiety *as* anxiety. Consequently, as is true of any instrument of this type, continuing construct validation of the test as a measure of anxiety is highly desirable.

A final illustration of a promising questionnaire measure of a specific form of anxiety is the Audience-Anxiety Scale in the Children's Audience-Sensitivity Inventory, described by Paivio, Baldwin, and Berger (1959). The Audience-Anxiety (AA) Scale consists of 16 questions designed specifically to evaluate the child's predisposition to react with anxiety in audience situations in which his performance is observable by other individuals. When administered to several hundred third-, fourth-, and fifth-grade children, the AA scale had a split-half reliability of .80, whereas a six-month test-retest comparison yielded a reliability of .54. Encouraging support for the construct validity of this instrument comes from the significant negative relationships found between audience-anxiety measures and ratings of children's willingness to volunteer for public performance in a summer camp "skit-night" program ($r$'s $= -.35$ for boys, $-.45$ for girls). It is of further interest to note that in this same study the test-anxiety questionnaire of the Sarason group yielded correlations very similar to those just mentioned ($-.36$ and $-.39$), whereas the Children's Manifest Anxiety Scale, which is a measure of generalized anxiety manifestations, had similar but somewhat lower correlations ($-.29$ and $-.26$) with this particular criterion. These findings support the notion that relationships tend to be higher when both test and criterion measures are specifically designed or selected to deal with a designated type of behavior. That these three measures of anxiety have a good deal of common overlap, however, despite the correlational differences just mentioned, is revealed in the intercorrelations among them, based on 421 children in the third to tenth grades (AA correlates .74 with TA and .62 with CMAS; the latter two correlate .70).

The three questionnaires just discussed appear to be promising instruments for obtaining measures of self-reported anxiety as response tendency. They have the advantage of being objectively scorable and group administerable. However, they share the problems of response set and are dependent upon the capacity and willingness of the subject to report accurately feelings and experiences presumably indicative of anxiety as an affective state with its physiological and motor concomitants.

*Reports of Behavior from Others.* Turning from the child's self-reports about anxiety reactions, we find that investigators have sometimes been able to obtain useful information about a child's anxieties from observations and impressions of teachers, parents, or other adults. Effective use of parental reports on children's specific fears is illustrated in the familiar work of Jersild and Holmes (1935), who asked parents to record the frequency of occurrence of various fear reactions during a period of twenty-one days. This type of approach, which asks for parental reports of specified behaviors over a period of time, might well be more fully explored as a means of providing measures of individual differences in anxiety level and manifestation, although the investigator would need to be a bit wary about the reliability and validity of such parental reports.

The use of carefully constructed and administered rating scales frequently makes it possible to obtain valuable judgments on children's personality characteristics from teachers or other adults who have opportunity for lengthy periods of observation and contact with the subjects. A good illustration of the construction and application of such scales in the evaluation of the behavior of nursery-school children may be found in the previously mentioned work of Conrad (1932, 1933) and Read (1940). Among the rating scales used by these investigators are several that deal with anxious behavior: (1) suspiciousness of people, (2) apprehensiveness, (3) fear in response to bullying, threatening commands, etc., (4) fear in nonsocial situations, and (5) elaboration or indirectness of response to fear. The last-named scale is of particular interest, since it deals with a motivational aspect of anxiety, that is, how the child adapts to fear, rather than with anxiety as a response tendency, which is essentially the object of the first four scales. The two extremes of this scale are defined as follows:

1. Reacts to fears by a relatively indirect (compensatory or "sublimated") response; e.g., by showing off in other directions; by bravado; or by other similar subterfuge designed to conceal the fear from the child itself, and from others. . . . 7. Reacts to fears by a simple, frank, direct response. Child either cries, whimpers, etc., or else directly resists the fear. Does not resort to attempts at concealment or "sublimation" of response (Read, p. 481).

The scales are carefully defined in behavioral terms and are accompanied by very detailed instructions to the teachers to provide a common basis for making judgments, factors which undoubtedly contributed to the demonstrated effectiveness with which they can be used. These rating scales thus offer both specific techniques, which the investigator may find useful for appraising anxious behavior in nursery-school children, and suggestive models for the development and use of similar scales applicable to older children.

Less elaborate scales than those just described have also been used with some effectiveness in evaluating anxious behavior of second-to-fifth-grade children. In the work of Sarason et al. (1958), the investigators compared children's test-anxiety scores with ratings made by teachers on 17 items describing various specific kinds of anxious behavior in the classroom situation (e.g., "does the child exhibit unwarranted fidgeting . . . squirming, restless behavior . . . when called upon to recite in class"; "does the child work better in a situation in which he can take his time than in one in which there is time pressure?"). Although there is no report given of the reliability of the ratings thus obtained, the fact that they correlated significantly, although not substantially, with the questionnaire measures suggests the potential usefulness of such judgments.

A final illustration of the use of reports about children's anxiety from adults is found in the study of the audience-anxiety questionnaire (Paivio et al., 1959). These investigators took advantage of a naturally occurring situation in which boys and girls at a summer camp were asked to volunteer to perform publicly on a "skit night." Camp counselors were asked to rate the children in terms of their willingness to volunteer for this public performance, and the measures thus obtained, even though relatively crude, correlated meaningfully with the questionnaire scores.

In general, it is our feeling that the research worker would do well to exploit more fully, as a source of data on children's anxious behavior, the considered judgments and reports of observers who have the opportunity of fairly long-term contact with the subjects over a variety of situations. Although there are important problems involved in eliciting reliable and valid information from this source, with proper training of judges and with appropriate instruments it should be possible to utilize this source of information profitably to obtain data on anxiety considered as both response tendency and motive.

*Projective Responses.* Among the most widely used techniques for appraising anxiety in children are the various global projective methods, which evolved as diagnostic testing procedures in the clinical evaluation of individual children and adults. Although such techniques involve a high degree of subjectivity and for the most part cannot yet be regarded as well validated, quantitative measuring devices, they do offer two potential advantages. First, because of the indirect nature of the approach, they presumably permit the child to express various kinds of anxiety manifestations that he might not reveal directly when questioned or observed. Second, the projective methods tend to focus attention upon anxiety as *motive;* that is, they are frequently concerned not only with the level and nature of the subject's anxieties but also with the various ways in which the subject tends to cope with or respond to anxiety. Because of these characteristics, it is to be hoped that the gradual refinement of some of the projective techniques in the direction of greater objectivity and quantification, along with systematic validation studies, may eventually produce highly useful methods for the measurement of anxiety as *motive* and as *response tendency.*

There have already been some promising attempts to structure and systematize projective techniques along the lines just indicated. Two of the studies already mentioned in the discussion of aggression (Mussen and Naylor, 1954; Siegel, 1957) illustrate how one can derive from projective techniques measures reflecting the degree to which anxiety serves as an inhibiting or control factor in the expression of aggressive impulses. Mussen and Naylor simply counted the number of times the "hero" in ten TAT stories was subjected to punishment "press" and used this as a measure of the subject's fear of punishment. It will be recalled that their prediction of overt aggressive behavior was improved when they considered not only the subject's level of aggressive motivation but also his anxiety about punishment.

Siegel used the controlled-play situation to obtain measures of aggression and indices of anxiety and guilt during the play of pairs of children. Observers made ratings every twenty seconds in which their judgments of anxiety, inhibition, or guilt were guided by a list of specific behavioral signs adapted from the work of Ryder (1954). The list included "escape behavior; tense, stiff, or awkward movements; incompleted or blocked aggressive acts; self-directed hostility; moralistic comments; nervous mannerisms, tics, thumb-sucking; tense facial expression . . . halting play at sound of footsteps at door" (p. 375). Siegel was primarily interested in changes in children's play from a first- to a second-play session a week later and found significantly less aggression as well as less anxiety in the second session than in the first, which suggests that her anxiety measures were reflecting concern with expressed aggression. It is our feeling that methods of this sort, which concentrate upon specified behavioral signs of anxiety in a controlled situation, are of potentially great promise and should be more fully exploited as techniques for the measurement of anxiety.

Apart from technical considerations of method as such, the two studies just mentioned illustrate rather nicely, we think, the kind of concern with anxiety as *motive*, which we have been stressing as an important conceptual approach to the measurement of anxiety. Both studies are concerned with the anxiety that is associated with the expression of a particular motive (i.e., aggression) and the possible controls or inhibitions that such anxiety tends to produce in the behavior of the individual. It is this sort of information about the manner in which anxiety motivates or influences the adaptive responses of the individual that we believe must be assessed more effectively, along with the individual's anxiety level or anxiety proneness.

A final illustration of a projective technique that was specifically structured to yield measures of anxiety in young children may be found in the interesting pictorial method described by Dorkay and Amen (1947) and previously investigated by Temple and Amen (1944). The test consists of 14 pictures portraying a child in familiar situations of various kinds, either with another child or an adult. The face of the child in the picture is left blank, and at the top of the picture two heads are drawn, one with a happy and one with a sad expression. The subject is asked in each case, "What kind of a face do you suppose this child will have, a happy face or a sad face?" Although anxiety scores based on nursery-school children's choices had low test-retest reliabilities over a three-month period, correlations with teachers' ratings of anxiety were promising (.28 for original and .59 for retest scores). Structured projective techniques of this sort seem worth exploring further for appraising anxiety in very young children.

*Direct Observations of Behavior.* It is interesting to note that very little use has been made of systematic observations of behavior in natural settings as a basis for measuring anxiety in children. In part, this reflects the nature of the anxiety construct, which is difficult to operationalize in terms of a narrow range of behavioral manifestations easily amenable to direct observation. It is obvious that if one child in the classroom manifests anxiety by withdrawal, another by hyperactivity, and another by immature attention-seeking it is difficult to make up a set of categories that would apply equally to all children.

Observation of children's behavior in contrived situations is a source of data that has been used with considerable profit. Siegel's study of aggression and anxiety by means of a controlled play technique (1957), which we discussed as a projective method, may be regarded as a good illustration of direct behavioral observation in a contrived setting. A considerably greater degree of situational structuring is found in the direct confrontation techniques used by Jersild and Holmes (1935) in their familiar studies of children's fears. Each child was exposed to a variety of potentially anxiety-arousing stimuli (e.g., loud sound, height, snake), and his reactions were carefully observed. Although these methods were not developed to provide measures of individual differences in anxiety-proneness and although formidable difficulties are involved in contriving such potentially fear-producing situations appropriate for various age levels, and which can be presented to children unobjectionably, it appears to us that a more intensive exploitation of this kind of approach might well be worthwhile. Even though such techniques may not be practical for obtaining routine measures of anxiety, they might well serve as supplementary measures or as criteria against which to evaluate the construct validity of operationally more convenient appraisal techniques. Methods of this sort may have the added advantage of permitting more systematic study of the motivational implications of anxiety, in terms of the nature of the individual's adaptive responses to anxiety arousing stimuli.

An illustration of a contrived situation of the kind just discussed may be found in the work of Levin, Baldwin, Gallwey, and Paivio (1959). These investigators, who were interested in "public" and "private" story-telling performances by 10-to-12-year-old children, used the number of errors in the child's speech when performing before an audience of six adults as one measure of "audience stress" produced by the situation. The relationships between these behavioral indices of a specific type of anxiety and questionnaire measures of "self-consciousness" (apprehensiveness about one's evaluation by others) and "exhibitionism" (positive attitude toward public exposure of the self or a self product) are such as to encourage further development of contrived situations to provide behavioral measures of particular anxiety manifestations.

Closely related to behavioral observations of anxiety in contrived situations is the use of performance on "objective" tests of various sorts. The work of Cattell and his associates (1955, 1956) provides one illustration of this approach, which has potential but not yet demonstrated validity. These workers have made available for research use experimental batteries of objective tests to measure a variety of personality factors in children (11 to 16) and adults, including a set of ten intended to provide a measure of "anxiety to achieve." The anxiety tests are primarily paper-and-pencil techniques, yielding scores such as susceptibility to annoyance, honesty in admitting common frailties, acceptance of good aphorisms, and emotionality of comment. Although the appropriateness of these particular tests for measuring anxiety in children is open to serious question, in part because they are based almost entirely on factor analyses with adult subjects, the methodological goal toward which the tests were aimed is an important one, that is, the measurement of anxiety by means of objective instruments requiring neither deliberate self-evaluation nor projective responses. We believe that the likelihood of this goal being attained will depend on the degree to which the objective tests are based upon significant theoretical constructs and hypotheses about the nature of anxiety and its manifestations.

### Evaluative Summary

Our review of techniques for the measurement of anxiety in children leaves us in much the same position as we found ourselves after evaluating procedures for the appraisal of aggression. Although some promising techniques have been and are being developed, there is relatively little available in the way of standardized measuring instruments possessing a high degree of construct validity. To a large extent, the measurement difficulties reflect the conceptual and theoretical problems that face anyone attempting to deal systematically with the objective appraisal of anxiety. There is, for example, the important question of distinguishing between generalized, or "free-floating," anxiety and more specific anxieties or fears. Another fundamental problem is that of differentiating between level of anxiety (viewed as a response tendency) and typical modes of coping with anxiety or characteristic effects of anxiety on adaptive behavior (anxiety viewed as motive). It is virtually impossible, we believe, to assess level of anxiety without at the same time dealing with behavior that to some extent reflects the nature of the person's controls over anxiety. Even if it were possible to measure pure level of anxiety, which some of our questionnaires attempt to do, one wonders how meaningful such measures can be unless one also knows something about the individual's modes of adaptation or inhibition.

It is our belief that separate evaluations providing both kinds of information will be needed in order to make valid predictions about behavior. For example, some questionnaire measures of anxiety as response tendency correlate negatively with examination grades, yet certain very anxious children do very well on examinations. The prediction of behavior for these children might be considerably improved if we knew how the child coped with anxiety in stressful situations. Such information might be provided by observations of the child in contrived or natural situations, by carefully obtained ratings from teachers, etc. Similarly, as the complex relationships between anxiety and performance on experimental tasks of learning, perception, and problem solving become increasingly clarified, it may well be that such tasks may themselves provide valuable supplementary indices of anxiety.

The task that we have posed is obviously not a simple one. We feel, however, that the problem can be approached fruitfully by means of a strategy that involves the simultaneous application of a selected variety of the kinds of methods previously discussed, with the aim of evaluating the level and specific nature of the child's anxiety as well as how he adapts to it and how it influences his performance.

## MOTIVATION FOR ACHIEVEMENT

The last decade has seen a resurgence in American psychology in the study of task-oriented behavior and motivation. This resurgence has been spearheaded primarily by the work of McClelland and his colleagues (McClelland et al., 1953; Atkinson, 1958) in the development of methods for the assessment of human motives by the analysis of fantasy productions. The motive studied most intensively by such methods, and the one for which special techniques have been devised for use with children, is *need achievement*.

Any theoretical analysis of this variable is complicated by the studied avoidance in the most recent publications of McClelland and his colleagues of any attempt to define the concept of motive in a priori terms. We quote McClelland:

> But what is a motive? Is it not desirable to define what is being measured before trying to discuss ways of measuring it? There are theorists who have proceeded in this way. . . . The approach to be followed here is more empirical, less prejudicial in advance as to what the characteristics of a motive will turn out to be. At the outset it takes no position as to whether, for example . . . motives drive or direct, or whether they are temporary states or enduring dispositions of the organism. To a certain extent, such questions can be answered only *after* one has a measure of motivation, not before (1958a, p. 8).

As one of the present authors has written elsewhere (Bronfenbrenner, 1960a), this view placed McClelland in a position analogous to that of psychologists who define intelligence as "that which is measured by an intelligence test"; a motive thus becomes whatever is measured by the methods that McClelland and his colleagues employ. Accordingly, before we can attempt a theoretical analysis, we must reverse our usual procedure and examine the techniques utilized for measuring *n* achievement in children. Three such procedures, utilizing projective materials, have been developed: the first employs verbal cues instead of pictures as stimuli (Lowell, 1950; Winterbottom,

1953; 1958), the second relies on the analysis of graphic expression (Aronson, 1958; McClelland, 1958), and the third involves an adaptation of a doll-play technique (Melville, 1959).

*The Method of Verbal Story Cues.* Faced with the fact that young children often fail to respond satisfactorily when pictures are used to elicit thematic apperception (as in the standard McClelland procedure), Lowell (1950) introduced the use of verbal cues as stimuli for evoking imaginative stories from a sample of Navaho ninth-graders. The same procedure was adopted, with minor modifications, by Winterbottom (1953; 1958) in what to date is the most comprehensive investigation of *n* achievement in young children. The subjects, 29 8-year-old, middle-class boys, were asked to make up stories in response to an "idea" presented orally by the examiner and consisting of such brief verbal cues as "a mother and her son," "a boy who has just left his house," "brothers and sisters playing, one is a little ahead," and "a young man with his head resting on his hands." Following the practice commonly employed for validation by the McClelland group, Winterbottom obtained stories under both "relaxed" and "achievement-oriented" conditions. In the first the task was presented as a game, with every effort being made to put the subject at ease and to reduce as much as possible any "test atmosphere." Following the "relaxed" stories, the child was given a "puzzle test" (a form board), which would "tell how smart he was"; he was told further that he should try his best because he was to be compared with others in his class. After three minutes of work on the test, a second set of stories was collected. Both sets were scored according to the achievement criteria developed by McClelland et al. (1953), and Atkinson (1958). The fundamental requirement is evidence in thematic context of "concern over competition with a standard of excellence." Such concern may be reflected in references to needs, goals, obstacles, positive or negative affective states, instrumental activity, etc. Each of these features receives unit weight in each story, with a possible range of 13 points per story.

*Results.* The interjudge reliability for total score based on stories written by the 8-year-old boys was highly satisfactory ($r = .92$). McClelland and his co-workers regard an increase in score from the relaxed to the aroused condition as primary evidence for the validity of the method. This criterion is met in the present instance, although, as Winterbottom acknowledges, some question can be raised, since the two sets of verbal cues employed had not been shown to be equivalent. Further evidence for construct validity is found in correlations with presumed antecedent and consequent measures. Thus, when cases were divided at the median into high and low groups, mothers of high need achievers reported significantly more demands for independent accomplishment before the age of 8 than did mothers of low need achievers; the former also evaluated their children's accomplishments more favorably and used physical expressions of affection to reward achievement. As for the children themselves, high need achievers

worked more independently and persistently in the testing situation and were rated by teachers as trying harder, taking more pleasure in success, more independent, and more popular. Similar correlates of high $n$ achievement are reported in a recent study by Rosen and D'Andrade (1959) with a sample of 9-to-11-year-old boys. The fact that these investigators successfully used the usual TAT procedures rather than verbal story cues suggests that the picture method for measuring $n$ achievement may be applicable with boys at this and perhaps even younger age levels.

The impact of these impressive findings is tempered somewhat by the results of a follow-up study recently completed by Feld (1959), who tracked down and retested 17 of Winterbottom's original cases six to eight years later. Unfortunately, the retesting was done not with the method of verbal cues employed originally but with TAT pictures as stimuli. The correlation with the boys' $n$ achievement scores obtained earlier was significant only under the achievement-oriented conditions. The obtained $r$ of .38 "compares favorably with test-retest reliabilities previously reported for much shorter time intervals" (Chapter 3, p. 4). The measures of need achievement at adolescence, however, failed to show significant relationships either with the original, retrospective, or current reports of mother's behavior toward the child. That the mothers' behavior reported six years earlier has relevance to some present characteristics of her son is indicated by the high correlation ($r =$

—.70) between independence training before the age of 8 and the boys' test anxiety as measured in adolescence.

*Problems of Validity.* With these methods and results in mind, we may now return to the question of just what is being measured by McClelland's technique and Lowell and Winterbottom's adaptation of it. The fact, reported by Winterbottom and Rosen and D'Andrade, that scores derived from story protocols do predict concurrent achievement-oriented behavior in preadolescent boys is reassuring. It is unfortunate that Feld's study did not include measures of performance at adolescence that could serve as criteria for evaluating the predictive power of both the earlier and current measures of $n$ achievement. But, in any event, such correlations with external criteria are not in themselves sufficient to establish the validity of the method. To begin with, there is the question of specificity: to what extent may the technique be measuring variables other than a disposition to achieve. The question is raised in part by work done by McClelland and his followers subsequent to the completion of Winterbottom's study. Thus papers included in Atkinson's compendium (1958) call attention to the influence of protocol length, sequence of stimuli, and choice of pictures as factors affecting the $n$ achievement score. In addition, a number of the studies point to the importance of distinguishing between *fear of failure* versus *hope of success* as components in the conventional $n$ achievement index. The issue of extraneous variables, however, can be raised on a still broader level, especially when measures of this sort are being applied to children. To what extent, for example, are individual differences in score a function of variation not in motives but in abilities. Apart from the influence of general intelligence, there are the more specific developmental phenomena of progressive differentiation in the capacity for time perspective, conception of causal relationships, attribution of intent, etc. All of these abilities would appear to be involved in the production of thematic content scorable for $n$ achievement.

Finally, even though the issue may not be relevant for McClelland, we must pose the question of the extent to which the $n$ achievement score measures what, in our terminology, are response tendencies rather than motives. For example, as one of the present authors has pointed out elsewhere (Bronfenbrenner, 1960a), one could argue that the effect of the arousal procedures employed in the McClelland technique is to make certain experiences cognitively salient. To push the argument one step further, perhaps fantasy materials predict behavior principally to the extent that they are autobiographical; e.g., the child who has succeeded in the past is more likely to tell stories about success and to succeed in the immediate future. Alternative hypotheses such as these once again call attention to possible pitfalls in the current tendency in psychological research to interpret fantasy materials solely or primarily in motivational terms.

*The Method of Graphic Expression.* Questions of this same kind can be raised even more forcefully with respect to the second technique for measuring need achievement adapted for use with children. This is the method of graphic expression developed by Aronson (1958). Using two abstract designs consisting of children's scribble patterns, this investigator sought "to discover empirical relationships between $n$ achievement and various modes of graphic expression" (p. 252). There were no a priori hypotheses. The designs were exposed tachistoscopically to male college students for whom $n$ achievement scores had previously been obtained with the conventional TAT procedure. Immediately after exposure, students were asked to reproduce what they had seen. Cross-validation with four additional samples of college students revealed five major features of graphic expression distinguishing high from low $n$ achievers: the high $n$ achievers used more discrete versus fuzzy, overlaid lines, left less unused space, preferred diagonal configurations to straight ones, and drew more S-shaped figures and fewer multiwave formations.

Aronson cites as one of the primary virtues of his technique the fact that it is applicable to young "preliterate" children. Acknowledging that "it is a very large jump indeed" from male college students to 5-year olds, McClelland (1958b) employed Aronson's technique, with some modifications, in a study of motivational correlates of risk-taking in 26 kindergarten and 32 third-grade children. No breakdown on sex is given—a surprising omission in view of the admitted inapplicability of Mc-

Clelland's technique with female subjects (McClelland et al., 1953, p. 173). The stimulus card was presented for three seconds, and children were asked to "make scribbles like these; if you can't remember all of them, make up your own." Since children drew far fewer identifiable forms than adults, the last three of the five criteria were combined into a single composite "form score." When applied to the drawings for Aronson's original college sample, this new score yielded a correlation of .36 with the original measure of graphic expression, a result that indicates very little overlap between the two measures. Reliability across two designs was .38 for the 9-year-old group but only .13 for the kindergarteners. McClelland believes that the latter value is "a serious underestimate of the true correlation caused by the coarse grouping of results and also by the two deviant cases in a very small sample" (p. 313). Although he goes to some length to support his argument that the true reliability of the doodle measure of $n$ achievement "is somewhere around .40," the present authors remain unconvinced.

The evidence offered for validity is little more encouraging. The argument that "the doodle measure is reflecting $n$ achievement, since it increases with age" arouses more doubts than it allays, since it raises once again the question of the influence on test performance of differential capacities for form perception, motor coordination, spatial organization, and the like. The fact that the doodle measure of $n$ achievement showed a correlation of only .08 with

IQ for the third-grade sample is somewhat reassuring, although it may be attenuated by the low reliability of the method. Unfortunately, IQ scores were not available for the more crucial kindergarten group.

Similar considerations apply to what McClelland regards as the most important evidence for the validity of the technique, the relationship between the doodle measure of need achievement and risk taking. McClelland had hypothesized that children high in need achievement would prefer to take moderate risks as opposed to long shots or sure bets. This prediction was substantially confirmed in both age groups. Again the question may be raised whether factors other than $n$ achievement reflected in the index of graphic expression may account for the obtained relationship. Consider, for example, the substantial research evidence, noted by Atkinson (1958, p. 337), to the effect that anxious persons tend to show extremes in level of aspiration, setting their goals either very high or very low. Atkinson explains this highly reliable finding as a reflection of differences in $n$ achievement, on the assumption that nonanxious "normals are relatively more positive in their motivation in achievement-related situations" (p. 337). An equally plausible alternative hypothesis explains this same difference as a direct function of anxiety. It is noteworthy in this connection that graphic features such as those scored by Aronson as uniquely relevant to low $n$ achievement are interpreted in the Bender-Gestalt test, a task similarly involving reproduction of abstract designs, as indices of anxiety level and immaturity (Pascal and Suttell, 1951).

***The Measurement of Achievement Motivation through Doll Play.*** Melville (1959) has recently adapted Sears' method of doll-play analysis (Sears, 1951) to provide measures of achievement fantasy. Using a doll house constructed to simulate the classroom of a modern elementary school, she devised reliable scoring procedures for a number of variables, two of which are presumed to be directly related to achievement:

*Work routine*, thematic, which must be verbalized or clearly indicated. The teacher may be the agent, "The teacher says 'now do your number work' "; a child may be the agent of such actions as "The boy is doing his seat work," "This little girl is having her reading turn." The principal or parent may come to school to see the children do their work. For purposes of this study with young children, "work" may be "choosing time," organized games, painting, as well as the more academic work of reading and number work.

*Achievement.* Someone expends effort, evaluates, compares school work with some standard of quality. "The boy is working *hard* on his seat work"; "The principal comes over and looks at the kids' work to see *how good* they are doing" (pp. 25–26).

For a sample of 48 first and second graders, percentages of agreement by two observers, who classified behavioral units into seven different categories, ranged from 80 to 94. To correct for individual differences in total productivity, the score for each category was expressed as a fraction of the total number of behavioral units produced by the child. Results of the technique were validated against systematic observations of the children's school behavior over a five-day period. In each grade youngsters were divided into upper and lower thirds, on the basis of percentage of time spent in "industrious" behavior. These "high" and "low" groups were then compared for differences in fantasy scores. Although both the *work-routine* and *achievement* categories from the play session showed differences in the predicted direction, only the work routine was reliable. The *achievement* score also yielded positive but nonsignificant relationships with teacher judgments of motive strength but gave inconsistent results in predicting achievement-test scores when intelligence was held constant.

In one respect, however, the high and low industry groups did exhibit reliable differences associated with the achievement-fantasy score. Over the three play sessions, the high group showed a significant increase in achievement fantasy, whereas the low group did not. Also, when in the last session the children were given achievement-oriented comments (e.g., "I'll bet that teacher wants those children to do their very best work."), only the high group showed a significant rise in achievement fantasy. These findings led Melville to conclude, ". . . it is not in mere use of the achievement category, but rather in . . . changes in the use of this category from session to session and with additional achievement stimulation that one should seek to measure an achievement motive in this kind of fantasy setting" (p. 51).

Melville's findings once again raise the question of the extent to which measures of the disposition to achieve reflect what we have called response tendencies rather than goal-oriented motives. Thus, particularly in children, one can conceive of a characteristic way of behaving, involving industry and persistence, that is not necessarily oriented toward attaining a particular end or standard of performance. Indeed, to judge from the name that Melville applies to her index of overt behavior ("industriousness") and to its operational definitions, this kind of response tendency would seem to constitute a major component of the criterion against which the fantasy measures were validated. Consistent with this view is the finding that differences in fantasy between high and low industry groups were greater for the *work-routine* category, which emphasized being busy, than for the *achievement* category, which calls for activity involving comparison with "some standard of quality."

How might one distinguish a goal-oriented motive from a generalized response tendency? One possible approach is suggested by Melville's finding that although the high and low groups did not differ in over-all achievement score the high group showed greater increases from situation to situation, especially in response to achievement-oriented comments from the experimenter. Presumably, a child with a strong response tendency toward hard work and persistence would tend to behave in the same way in every situation. One who is motivated to achieve, however, would become diligent primarily in those situations that call for the attainment of a goal of a high standard of performance. Indeed, taking a leaf from the work of both Melville and McClelland, one might argue that the most appropriate index of an achievement *motive*, as distinguished from a response tendency, would be the increase in achievement imagery from the "relaxed" to the "aroused" condition.

This line of reasoning is strikingly consistent with the theoretical model developed in a series of papers by Atkinson (1958) in his attempt to reconcile the paradoxical findings obtained in studies of *n* achievement (as measured from the TAT) and level of aspiration. Atkinson argues convincingly that scores from level-of-aspiration experiments cannot be interpreted as measures of motive strength. Rather they are resultants of an interaction of three factors—motive strength, expectancy (defined as the subjective probability of success or failure), and incentive ["the magnitude of the reward or potential satisfaction should the expected consequence occur" (p. 288)]. He proposes further that the strength of the achievement motive is reflected in the steepness of the incentive gradient between success and failure; persons highly motivated to achieve perceive a much steeper affective or choice gradient than those with low motivation. Atkinson suggests a number of experimental procedures for measuring the slope of this gradient, most of these techniques being adaptations of methods utilized by the McClelland group for validating the TAT measure of *n* achievement. The possibility that such direct behavioral methods might prove superior to the now conventional projective techniques is not considered.

*Toward Behavioral and Experimental Measures of Achievement Motivation.* Yet a number of recent researches with children suggest that this possibility offers considerable promise. We have already mentioned the observational measures of "achievement motive strength" utilized by Melville for validating her doll-play technique. These measures are being developed in a comprehensive program of research on "achievement and self-esteem motivation" in children being directed by Pauline Sears at Stanford University (Sears, 1957). Although a detailed account of these procedures is yet to be published, preliminary data cited by Melville indicate highly satisfactory interobserver reliability (*r*'s ranging from .67 to .90 in three first- and second-grade classrooms) for samples taken over a five-day period.

A less structured approach based on summary ratings as against direct observation is represented by the work of Beller (1957), who developed a series of rating scales for use by teachers in rating "autonomous achievement striving" in children 2 to 6 years of age. Specific variables rated include satisfaction derived from work, carrying out of routine tasks, overcoming obstacles, taking initiative, and completion of activity. Interjudge reliabilities for the five subscales range from .67 to .80. The ratings were substantially independent of similarly constructed ratings of dependency.

As Sears notes in the initial publication on her research (1957), such naturalistic observational methods have practical and theoretical limitations. The methods are expensive both in time and money and yield measures that tend to be multidimensional. Nevertheless, they provide an appropriate point of departure for the clarification of concepts and the subsequent development of more economical and rigorous experimental techniques.

Indeed, the development of such techniques is already under way. To begin with, as one of the present authors has noted elsewhere (Bronfenbrenner, 1960a), a number of the experimental procedures utilized by McClelland and his colleagues as validating criteria for fantasy measures offer promise as indices of motives in their own right. The manner in which such procedures can be adapted for use with children is well illustrated in the experiments of Sears and Levin (1957) on level of aspiration. These investigators set for themselves the goal of developing six tasks, each of which would involve graded levels of difficulty, be relatively unfamiliar, and yet be sufficiently simple, absorbing, and challenging to yield valid and reliable results with preschool children. Their findings indicate that, by and large, the experimental procedures met these exacting criteria. Moreover, although devised for studying level of aspiration, the procedures lend themselves nicely to the kinds of theoretical and operational distinctions required for differentiating achievement-oriented motives and response tendencies.

Perhaps the best example of progress and potential in the experimental analysis of achievement motivation and its antecedents is found in the work of Rosen and D'Andrade (1959). These investigators tested 140 boys between the ages of 9 and 11 with the TAT measure of $n$ achievement in order to select a sample of 40 extreme high and low scorers pair-matched for age, race, IQ, and social class. In order to study the behavioral correlates of $n$ achievement both in children and their parents, Rosen and D'Andrade then devised a series of ingenious experimental procedures, two examples of which are given here:

1. *Block Stacking.* The boys were asked to build towers out of very irregularly shaped blocks. They were blindfolded and told to use only one hand in order to create a situation in which the boy was relatively dependent upon his parents for help. His parents were told that this was a test of their son's ability to build things, and that they could *say* anything to their son but could not touch the blocks. A performance norm was set for the experiment by telling the parents that the average boy could build a tower of eight blocks; they were asked to write down privately their estimate of how high they thought their son could build his tower. The purposes of this experiment were (*a*) to see how high were the parents' aspirations for and evaluations of their son, e.g., if they set their estimates at, above, or below the norm; (*b*) to see how self-reliant they expected or permitted their son to be, e.g., how much help they would give him.

2. *Anagrams.* In this task the boys were asked to make words of three letters or more out of six prescribed letters: G, H, K, N, O, R. The letters, which could be reused after each word was made, were printed on wooden blocks so that they could be manipulated. The parents were given three additional lettered blocks, T, U, and B, and a list of words that could be built with each new letter. They were

informed that they could give the boy a new letter (in the sequence T, U, B) whenever they wished and could say anything to him, short of telling him what word to build. There was a ten-minute time limit for this experiment. Since this is a familiar game, no efforts were made to explain the functions of the task.

The purposes of this experiment were (a) to see how self-reliant the parents expected their son to be, e.g., how soon they would give him a new letter, how much and what kind of direction they would give him, if they would keep him working until he got all or most of the words on the list or "take him off the hook" when he got stuck. And (b) to obtain, by scoring interaction between the subjects, measures of the affect generated by the problem-solving process, e.g., the amount of tension shown by the subjects, the positive and negative remarks directed toward one another (pp. 191–192).

The results of these experiments showed consistent differences in the behavior of both boys and parents in the two $n$ achievement groups. As in the Winterbottom (1953) study, high $n$ achievers were characterized by persistent striving and general competitiveness; they built higher towers of blocks, worked faster, and accomplished more. An important added feature of the Rosen study is the inclusion of controls for IQ; hence Rosen can legitimately conclude that "the superior performance of high $n$ achievement boys appears to be more a function of greater self-reliance and zest in competitive activity than of intelligence (p. 199). Similarly, parents of the high $n$ achievement boys tended to be more competitive, show more involvement, have higher aspirations for their sons, set up standards of excellence even where none

was given, etc. In addition to similarities, important differences were found in the behavior of the two parents. Mothers of high $n$ achievers differed from those of the controls in being both more rewarding and more "pushy." In contrast, their husbands, although similarly setting high standards, gave their sons greater autonomy; they tended "to beckon from ahead rather than push from behind" (p. 216).

In terms of our interest, the most important contribution of Rosen and D'Andrade's research does not lie in its substantive findings nor even in its implications for the construct validity of McClelland's fantasy measure of $n$ achievement. In our view, the greatest promise of the study lies in its demonstration of the applicability of experimental procedures for the measurement of achievement motivation in children under conditions simulating real-life situations. Noteworthy in this regard is the fact that Rosen administered all of his experiments not in the laboratory but in the homes of his subjects—"usually in the kitchen."

While pointing to the promise of behavioral and experimental measures of the disposition to achieve, we would emphasize the importance of continuing to improve and refine the instruments already available for the study of achievement motivation through fantasy. Much is to be gained by the practice employed in the major studies we have reviewed of using both overt and fantasy measures with the same subjects. But merely to note a low but significant correlation between the two and to go no further is to stop short at the very gate of scientific understanding. In our judgment, it is precisely from the study of the interaction of behavior in fantasy and overt action in a variety of situational contexts that we stand to learn most about the nature and measurement of human motives and their expression.

## PITFALLS AND PROSPECTS

Having examined intensively a wide variety of techniques employed for measuring three rather different types of personality variables in children, we feel some obligation, in concluding our discussion, to consider existing methods as a whole and to call attention to recurring problems and possibilities. To begin with the debit side of the ledger, in the course of our review we found ourselves referring time and again to many of the same blind alleys and sources of confounded measurement. Chief among these are the following:

1. Reliance on purely empirical approaches to the construction and validation of measuring techniques without prior and continuing conceptual clarification of the precise variable or variables to be measured. Especially questionable in this regard is the practice of accepting mere predictive power as sufficient evidence for establishing the construct validity of a method.

2. Failure to consider and control the extraneous variables that may in fact be measured by a particular technique. Common sources of such confounding include response sets (such as acquiescence, social desirability, or general level of productivity), factors associated with broader social influences (such as class and culture), and, especially in the case of children, differential levels of psychological development (e.g., capacities for motor coordination, form perception, and concept formation). In particular, the tendency to interpret projective responses solely in motivational terms may becloud the operation of cognitive factors that account appreciably for individual differences in test performance.

3. Reliance on measurements by a single technique applied in a single situation often far removed from the context in which the variable appears in the day-to-day life of the child. Given the fact that the behavior of children is even more likely to be affected by immediate environmental events than the behavior of adults, the practice of interpreting results of questionnaires and projective techniques as reflecting primarily enduring personality characteristics without sufficient regard for the influence of momentary situational conditions or more stable social contexts has probably done much to retard the development of more adequate measuring techniques in which environmental variation could be controlled, or systematically varied, through experimental manipulation.

Although the foregoing defects are still to be found in many current studies, there is evidence of increasing methodological sophistication and ingenuity among behavioral scientists working with children. The following are among the most promising developments in this respect.

1. A trend away from traditional mechanistic methods of test construction, with their single-measure indices of reliability and validity, toward multiple approaches for establishing the construct validity of the theory underlying the measuring instrument. In this connection, the effort to distinguish between what we have called response tendencies and goal-oriented motives would seem to be potentially fruitful.

2. Investigation of a particular variable simultaneously through fantasy and overt behavior with the aim not merely of demonstrating a positive correlation between the two but of exploring the

situational conditions and processes that appear to account both for the continuities and discontinuities in the two spheres of expression.

3. The effort to supplement traditional objective and projective instruments with systematic behavioral observations and experimental procedures that are sufficiently simple and attractive to be applicable to children but permit controlled manipulation of situational factors.

4. The articulation of social and cultural variables into the procedures employed for the appraisal of personality characteristics. In many instances such articulation can be accomplished only by statistical design rather than experimental manipulation.

If we are correct in our vision of trends to come in the measurement of personality characteristics in children, one fact seems clear—the world of child psychology, like the rest of science, will be requiring new and more complex concepts, techniques, and research designs that are at once imaginative, rigorous, and appropriate to the demands of an expanding universe.

## REFERENCES

Allport, G. 1937. *Personality*. New York: Holt.

American Psychological Association. 1954. Technical recommendations for psychological tests and diagnostic techniques. *Psychol. Bull.*, **51**, Supplement.

Aronson, E. 1958. The need for achievement as measured by graphic expression. In Atkinson, J. W. (Ed.), *Motives in fantasy, action, and society*. Princeton, N. J.: Van Nostrand. Pp. 249-265.

Atkinson, J. W. (Ed.). 1958. *Motives in fantasy, action, and society*. Princeton, N. J.: Van Nostrand.

Bach, G. R. 1945. Young children's play fantasies. *Psychol. Monogr.*, **59**, No. 2.

Baldwin, A. L. 1955. *Behavior and development in childhood*. New York: Dryden.

———. 1958. The role of an "ability" construct in a theory of behavior. In D. C. McClelland, A. L. Baldwin, U. Bronfenbrenner, and F. L. Strodtbeck, *Talent and society*. Princeton, N. J.: Van Nostrand, Chapter 5.

Bales, R. F. 1950. *Interaction process analysis*. Cambridge, Mass.: Addison-Wesley.

Barker, R. G., and H. F. Wright. 1951. *One boy's day*. New York: Harper.

———. 1954. *Midwest and its children: The psychological ecology of an American town*. Evanston, Ill.: Row Peterson.

Bass, B. M. 1955. Authoritarianism or acquiescence? *J. abnorm. soc. Psychol.*, **51**, 616-623.

———. 1956. The development and evaluation of a scale for measuring social acquiescence. *J. abnorm. soc. Psychol.*, **53**, 296-299.

Bellak, L. 1954. *The Thematic Apperception Test and the Children's Apperception Test in clinical use*. New York: Grune & Stratton.

Beller, E. K. 1948. *Dependency and independence in young children*. Unpublished doctoral thesis. State Univer. Iowa.

———. 1957. Dependency and autonomous achievement striving related to orality and anality in early childhood. *Child Develpm.*, **28**, 3, 287-315.

Beswick, D. G., and F. N. Cox. 1958. Reputed aggression and dependence in children. *Austr. J. Psych.*, **10**, 2, 144-150.

Bronfenbrenner, U. 1945. The measurement of sociometric status, structure and development. *Sociometry Monogr.*, **6**. New York: Beacon House.

———. 1958. The study of identification through interpersonal perception. In R. Tagiuri and L. Petrullo, *Person perception and interpersonal behavior*. Stanford, Calif.: Stanford Univer. Press. Pp. 110-130.

———. 1960a. An achievement creates a need. (A review of Atkinson's *Motives in fantasy, action and society*.) *Contemp. Psychol.*, **5**, 65-68.

———. 1960b. Personality and participation. *J. soc. Issues*, **15**, in press.

Bronfenbrenner, U., J. Harding, and M. Gallwey. 1958. The measurement of skill in social perception. In D. C. McClelland, A. L. Baldwin, U. Bronfenbrenner, and F. L. Strodtbeck. *Talent and society*. Princeton, N. J.: Van Nostrand. Chapter 2.

Carnap, R. 1936. Testability and meaning. *Phil. Sci.*, 3, 419–471.

———. 1937. Testability and meaning. *Phil. Sci.*, 4, 1–40.

Carroll, J., and H. Levin. 1956. A method for determining the polarity of behavior items. *Child Develpm.*, 27, 427–438.

Castaneda, A., B. R. McCandless, and D. S. Palermo. 1956. The children's form of the manifest anxiety scale. *Child Develpm.*, 27, 317–326.

Castaneda, A., D. S. Palermo, and B. R. McCandless. 1956. Complex learning and performance as a function of anxiety in children and task difficulty. *Child Develpm.*, 27, 327–332.

Cattell, R. B., et al. 1956. *Handbook for the objective-analytic personality test batteries*. Champaign, Ill.: Institute for Personality and Ability Testing.

Cattell, R. B., and W. Gruen. 1955. The primary personality factors in 11-year-old children, by objective tests. *J. Pers.*, 23, 4, 460–478.

Cattell, R. B., and I. H. Scheier. 1958. The nature of anxiety: A review of thirteen multivariate analyses comprising 814 variables. *Psychol. Rep.*, 4, 351–388.

Christie, R., J. Havel, and B. Seidenberg. 1958. Is the F scale irreversible? *J. abnorm. soc. Psychol.*, 56, 143–159.

Clark, C. A. 1959. Developments and applications in the area of construct validity. *Rev. Educ. Res.*, 29, 84–105.

Conrad, H. S. 1932. The validity of personality ratings of nursery school children. *J. educ. Psychol.*, 23, 671–680.

———. 1933. *The California behavior inventory for nursery school children*. Berkeley: Univer. Calif Press.

Cronbach, L. J. 1946. Response sets and test validity. *Educ. psychol. Measmt.*, 6, 475–494.

———. 1950. Further evidence on response sets and test design. *Educ. psychol. Measmt.*, 10, 3–31.

Cronbach, L. J., and P. E. Meehl. 1955. Construct validity in psychological tests. *Psychol. Bull.*, 52, 281–302.

Dorkey, M., and Elizabeth W. Amen. 1947. A continuation study of anxiety reactions in young children by means of a projective technique. *Genet. Psychol. Monogr.*, 35, 139–183.

Edwards, A. L. 1957. *The social desirability variable in personality assessment and research*. New York: Dryden.

Erikson, E. H. 1940. Studies in the interpretation of play. *Genet. Psychol. Monogr.*, 22, 557–671.

Eron, L., L. O. Walder, J. H. Laulicht, and F. Hladky. 1958. The psychosocial development of aggressive behavior in children. *Proceedings, Rip Van Winkle Clinic*, 9, 16–35.

Feld, S. 1959. Studies in the origins of achievement strivings. Doctoral dissertation, Univer. Michigan.

Frenkel-Brunswik, Else. 1942. Motivation and behavior. *Genet. Psychol. Monogr.*, 26, 121–265.

Freud, S. 1935. *A general introduction to psychoanalysis*. New York: Liveright.

Getzels, J. W., and J. J. Walsh. 1958. The method of paired direct and projective questionnaires in the study of attitude structure and socialization. *Psychol. Monogr.*, 72, No. 1.

Goodenough, Florence L. 1949. The appraisal of child personality. *Psychol. Rev.*, 56, 123–131.

Graham, F. K., W. A. Charwat, A. S. Honig, and Paula C. Weltz. 1951. Aggression as a function of the attack and the attacker. *J. abnorm. soc. Psychol.*, 46, 512–520.

Guilford, J. P. 1954. *Psychometric Methods*. New York: McGraw Hill.

Guttman, L. 1950. Chapters 2, 3, 6, 8 and 9. In S. A. Stouffer et al., *Measurement and prediction*. Princeton, N. J.: Princeton Univer. Press.

Hartwell, S. W., M. L. Hutt, G. Andrews, and R. E. Walton. 1951. The Michigan Picture Test: Diagnostic and therapeutic possibilities of a new projective test in child guidance. *Amer. J. Orthopsychiat.*, 21, 124–137.

Hollenberg, E., and M. Sperry. 1951. Some antecedents of aggression and effect of frustration in doll play. *Pers.*, 1, 32–43.

Jensen, A. R. 1957. Aggression in fantasy and overt behavior. *Psychol. Monogr.*, 71, No. 16.

Jersild, A. T., and F. B. Holmes. 1935. Children's fears. New York: Columbia Univer. Press. Child Develpm. Monogr., No. 20.

Jersild, A. T., and F. V. Markey. 1935. *Conflicts between pre-school children.* New York: Columbia Univer. Press. Child Develpm. Monogr., No. 21.

Kagan, J. 1956. The measurement of overt aggression from fantasy. *J. abnorm. soc. Psychol.*, 52, 390–393.

Lesser, G. S. 1958. Application of Guttman's scaling method to aggressive fantasy in children. *Educ. psychol. Measmt.*, 18, 3, 543–552.

Levin, H., A. L. Baldwin, M. Gallwey, and A. Paivio. 1960. Audience stress, personality, and speech. *J. abnorm. soc. Psychol.*, in press.

Levin, H., and R. R. Sears. 1956. Identification with parents as a determinant of doll play aggression. *Child Develpm.*, 27, 135–153.

Levy, D. M. 1936. Hostility patterns in sibling rivalry experiments. *Amer. J. Orthopsychiat.*, 6, 183–257.

Lewin, K., R. Lippitt, and R. K. White. 1939. Patterns of aggressive behavior in experimentally created "social climates." *J. soc. Psychol.*, 10, 271–299.

Lighthall, F. F., K. S. Davidson, R. R. Waite, S. B. Sarason, and I. Sarnoff. 1960. The effects of serial position and time interval on two anxiety questionnaires. *J. genet. Psychol.* In press.

Lindzey, G. 1952. Thematic apperception test: Interpretive assumptions and related empirical evidence. *Psychol. Bull.*, 49, 1–25.

Loevinger, Jane. 1959. A theory of test response. In *Proceedings, 1958 invitational conference on testing problems.* Princeton, N. J.: Educational Testing Service.

Lowell, E. L. 1950. A methodological study of projectively measured achievement motivation. Unpublished Master's dissertation, Wesleyan Univer.

Lynn, D. B., and R. Lynn. 1959. The Structured Doll Play Test as a projective technique for use with children. *J. proj. Tech.*, 23, 335–344.

McCandless, B. R., and A. Castaneda. 1956a. Anxiety in children, school achievement, and intelligence. *Child Develpm.*, 27, 379–382.

———, and D. S. Palermo. 1956b. Anxiety in children and social status, *Child Develpm.*, 27, 385–393.

McClelland, D. C. 1958a. Methods of measuring human motivation. In J. W. Atkinson (Ed.), *Motives in fantasy, action, and society.* Princeton, N. J.: Van Nostrand, Chapter 1.

———. 1958b. Risk taking in children with high and low need for achievement. In J. W. Atkinson (Ed.), *Motives in fantasy, action, and society.* Princeton, N. J.: Van Nostrand. Pp. 306–321.

———, J. W. Atkinson, R. A. Clark, and E. L. Lowell. 1953. *The achievement motive.* New York: Appleton-Century-Crofts.

MacFarlane, J. W., L. Allen, and M. P. Honzik. 1954. *A developmental study of the behavior problems of normal children between twenty-one months and fourteen years.* Berkeley: Univer. Calif. Press.

Melville, C. P. 1959. A study of overt and fantasy expressions of variables related to young children's motivation toward working industriously in school. Unpublished doctoral dissertation, Stanford Univer.

Murphy, Lois B. 1937. *Social behavior and child personality.* New York: Columbia Univer. Press.

———, et al. 1956. *Personality in young children.* Vol. I. New York: Basic Books.

Murray, H. A. 1938. *Explorations in personality.* New York: Oxford Univer. Press.

———. 1943. *Thematic Apperception Test: Manual.* Cambridge, Mass.: Harvard Univer. Press.

Mussen, P. H., and H. K. Naylor. 1954. The relationship between overt and fantasy aggression. *J. abnorm. soc. Psychol.*, 49, 235–240.

Norman, R. D., and G. J. Kleinfeld. 1958. Rosenzweig P-F study results with minority group juvenile delinquents. *J. genet. Psychol.*, 92, 61–67.

Paivio, A., A. L. Baldwin, and S. Berger. 1959. Measurement of children's sensitivity to audiences. Unpublished manuscript.

Palermo, D. S. 1959. Racial comparisons and additional normative data on the Children's Manifest Anxiety Scale. *Child Develpm.*, 30, 53–58.

———, A. Castaneda, and B. R. McCandless. 1956. The relationship of anxiety in children to performance in a complex learning task. *Child Develpm.*, 27, 333–339.

Pascal, G., and B. J. Suttell. 1951. *The Bender-Gestalt test: its quantification and validity for adults*. New York: Grune & Stratton.

Pintler, Margaret H. 1945. Doll play as a function of experimenter-child interaction and initial organization of materials. *Child Develpm.*, 16, 145–166.

Read, K. H. 1940. Significant characteristics of pre-school children as located in the Conrad Inventory. *Genet. Psychol. Monogr.*, 22, 455–487.

Richards, T. W., and M. P. Simons. 1941. The Fels Child Behavior Scales. *Genet. Psychol. Monogr.*, 24, 259–309.

Rohde, A. R., 1946. Exploration in personality by the sentence completion method. *J. appl. Psychol.*, 30, 169–181.

Rosen, B. C., and R. D'Andrade. 1959. The psychosocial origins of achievement motivation. *Sociometry*, 22, 185–217.

Rosenzweig, S. 1945. The picture-association method and its application in a study of reactions to frustration. *J. Pers.*, 14, 3–23.

———, E. E. Fleming, and Louise Rosenzweig. 1948. The children's form of the Rosenzweig Picture-Frustration study. *J. Psychol.*, 26, 141–191.

Rosenzweig, S., and Louise Rosenzweig. 1952. Aggression in problem children and normals as evaluated by the Rosenzweig P-F study. *J. abnorm. soc. Psychol.*, 47, 683–687.

Rotter, J. B., and J. E. Rafferty. 1950. *The Rotter Incomplete Sentences Blank: Manual*. New York: Psychol. Corp.

Ryder, J. M. 1954. Aggression with balloons, blocking, and doll play. In Lois M. Stoltz et al. *Father relations of war-born children.*

Stanford, Calif.: Stanford Univer. Press. Pp. 212–243.

Sanford, N., M. Adkins, R. B. Miller, and E. Cobb. 1943. Physique, personality and scholarship: A cooperative study of school children. *Monogr. Soc. Res. Child Develpm.*, 8, No. 34.

Sanford, N., M. B. Freedman, H. Webster, and D. Brown. 1956. Personality development during the college years. *J. soc. Issues*, 12–70.

Sarason, S. B., K. S. Davidson, F. K. Lighthall, and R. R. Waite. 1958. A test anxiety scale for children. *Child Develpm.*, 29, 105–114.

Sargent, H. 1953. *The Insight Test*. New York: Grune & Stratton.

Sarnoff, I., F. K. Lighthall, R. R. Waite, K. S. Davidson, and S. B. Sarason. 1958. A cross-cultural study of anxiety amongst American and English school children. *J. educ. Psychol.*, 49, 129–136.

Sarnoff, I., S. B. Sarason, F. K. Lighthall, and K. S. Davidson. 1959. Test anxiety and the "eleven-plus" examinations. *Brit. J. Educ. Psychol.*, 29, 9–16.

Sears, Pauline S. 1951. Doll play aggression in normal young children: influence of sex, age, sibling status, father's absence. *Psychol. Monogr.*, 65, No. 6.

———. 1957. Problems in the investigation of achievement and self-esteem motivation. In M. R. Jones (Ed.), *Nebraska symposium on motivation*. Lincoln, Neb.: University of Nebraska Press. 5, 265–339.

———, and H. Levin. 1957. Levels of aspiration in preschool children. *Child Develpm.*, 28, 3, 317–326.

Sears, R. R. 1947. Influence of methodological factors on doll play performance. *Child Develpm.*, 18, 190–197.

———, Margaret H. Pintler, and Pauline S. Sears. 1946. Effect of father separation on preschool children's doll play aggression. *Child Develpm.*, 17, 219–243.

Sears, R. R., Eleanor E. Maccoby, and H. Levin. 1957. *Patterns of child rearing*. Evanston, Ill.: Row, Peterson.

Sears, R. R., J. W. M. Whiting, V. Nowlis, and Pauline S. Sears 1953. Some child-rearing antecedents of aggression and dependency in young children. *Genet. Psychol. Monogr.*, 47, 135–234.

Siegel, Alberta E. 1956. Film-mediated fantasy aggression and strength of aggressive drive. *Child Develpm.*, 27, 365–378.

——. 1957. Aggressive behavior of young children in the absence of an adult. *Child Develpm.*, 28, 371–378.

Smock, C. D. 1958. Perceptual rigidity and closure phenomenon as a function of manifest anxiety in children. *Child Develpm.*, 29, 237–247.

Stone, L. J. 1956. Experiments in group play and in readiness for destruction. In Lois B. Murphy et al. *Personality in young children.* Vol. I. New York: Basic Books.

Symonds, P. M. 1949. *Adolescent fantasy: An investigation of the picture-story method of personality study.* New York: Teach. Coll., Columbia Univer. Press.

Taylor, J. A. 1953. A personality scale of manifest anxiety. *J. abnorm. soc. Psychol.*, 48, 285–290.

Temple, R., and Elizabeth W. Amen. 1944. A study of anxiety reactions in young children by means of a projective technique. *Genet. Psychol. Monogr.*, 30, 59–114.

Thorndike, R. L., and Elizabeth Hagen. 1955. *Measurement and evaluation in psychology and education.* New York: Wiley. Pp. 311–332.

Waite, R. R., S. B. Sarason, F. K. Lighthall, and K. S. Davidson. 1958. A study of anxiety and learning in children. *J. abnorm. soc. Psychol.*, 57, 267–270.

Walters, J., et al. 1957. Affectional and aggressive behavior of preschool children. *Child Develpm.*, 28, 15–26.

Winterbottom, M. R. 1953. The relation of childhood training in independence to achievement motivation. Unpublished doctoral dissertation, Univer. Michigan.

——. 1958. The relation of need for achievement to learning experiences in independence and mastery. In J. W. Atkinson (Ed.), *Motives in fantasy, action, and society.* Princeton, N. J.: Van Nostrand. Pp. 453–478.

Zuckerman, M., J. Norton, and D. S. Sprague. 1958. Acquiescence and extreme sets and their role in tests of authoritarianism and parental attitudes. *Psychiat. Res. Rep.*, 10, 28–45.

part V

# The Study
# of the Child's
# Social Behavior
# and
# Environment

chapter 19

# Children's Groups

George G. Thompson
*Ohio State University*

The scientific study of children's groups has been a relatively neglected area of inquiry during the last ten years. It was brilliantly launched just prior to 1940 by the investigations of Lewin and his students (Lewin, Lippitt, and White, 1939; Lewin, 1946; Lewin, 1948). Then came World War II and the shifting of Lewin's creative efforts toward the influence of democratic leadership and social climate on the morale and efficiency of *adult* groups. This marked the beginning of the "group dynamics" nucleus and cast the die in the direction of the many insightful investigations of adult groups by Bavelas, Cartwright, Festinger, Lippitt, and associates. The study of children's groups waned in popularity within the group dynamics movement.[1]

The years following World War II were also marked by another trend, which encouraged a preference for the

[1] A few of Lewin's students maintained an active interest in children's groups. See Barker and Wright, 1954; and Polansky, Lippitt, and Redl, 1950.

study of adult rather than child groups. Large congressional appropriations were made to the various branches of the armed services to subsidize psychological research on behalf of our national defense. It is understandable that the armed services were interested primarily in studies employing young adults as subjects. Carter's investigations of the dynamics of "leaderless" groups, supported by the Office of Naval Research, were conducted with young adults (Carter et al., 1950, 1951). The classic Ohio State investigations of leadership were heavily subsidized by military funds (Shartle, 1952; Hemphill, 1949). The "sociometric" procedures, which were initiated by the study of children's groups (Moreno, 1951, 1953; Jennings, 1950), were extended theoretically and operationally in adult groups (Gardner and Thompson, 1956; Taguiri, 1952) because of the available funds for research with military defense implications.

The last four or five years have seen some important changes in our national policies related to research subsidy. The National Science Foundation supports "pure" research with no stated biases toward subjects of any species of whatsoever level of maturity. The now flourishing National Institutes of Mental Health have no explicit policies that favor the study of any particular aged subjects. The U. S. Office of Education research program definitely *favors* investigations of child subjects. The current *Zeitgeist* thus augurs well for a revival of research interest in children's groups. Indeed, with ample funds now available for research with child subjects, we may see some of the previously deflected experimenters returning to the study of younger subjects because of the alleged greater simplicity of the child's behavior.

Whether the study of children's groups will again become "fashionable" and demand the interests of a fair share of our scientists remains to be seen. However, one thing is very clear. Much progress has been made during the last ten years in research theory and methodology by investigators using *adult* subjects. There are now many techniques to be adapted for use with younger subjects by the psychologist primarily interested in the dynamics of children's groups. There are many hypotheses whose generality over the developmental span must be investigated. New and provocative theories of the dynamics of social interaction and group processes have been proposed, which may, or may not, be helpful in future studies of children's groups. These conditions dictate the format and contents of a large part of this chapter on research procedures for the study of children's groups. Any attempt to restrict the discussion to those methods that have proved their usefulness in the study of *children's* groups would neglect the most fruitful aspects of presently available methods for group study.

## RESEARCH IS NEEDED

To the impassive and disinterested scientist, "research is its own reason for being." The curiosity of the inquiring mind is insatiable and leads man toward the observation and manipulation of almost every discriminable aspect of his surroundings. He has an intense need to "understand" as well as a strong need to manipulate his environment toward conditions most favorable to his "happiness." The study of children's groups is related to both these needs.

***Theoretical Problems.*** The *developing* abilities of the human organism for social interaction are obvious, even to the casual observer. The young infant lacks the necessary perceptual and motor skills for anything but the most primitive of symbiotic relationships with his mother—the *social* authenticity of which remains in doubt. The preschool years are marked by an ever widening array of social skills. The phonemes appear spontaneously as the infant's neuromusculature matures; they become differentially patterned through learning experiences into a functional communication system. How much of a language repertory is necessary before young children become responsive to each other in a group situation? Studies of 2-year-old children show that they are largely involved in solitary and/or parallel activities within a social grouping (Parten, 1932). Is this because they lack the necessary language skills to influence and be influenced by each other? Or is it because they lack the developing skills of socioempathy? Murphy has shown that the perception of a companion being in distress, which is necessary for the social response of sympathy, does not make its appearance until around the fourth year (Murphy, 1937). This is about the same age when fairly sustained cooperative undertakings are observed among preschool children (Parten, 1932). What perceptual and motor skills are required before the "group properties" of cohesion (French, 1941), contagion (Polansky, Lippitt, and Redl, 1950), "fight and flight" (Bion, 1952), and so on, make their appearance? When do children acquire the need to be in the company of their peers, and what social-emotional variables influence the acquisition of this need? Answers to these questions, which are based on solid research findings, are not as yet available. Observations of young children in the *Kibbutz* of Israel (Faigin, 1958; Rabin, 1957) suggest that they may be responsive to the "social climate" of their peers at a very early age. However, the relevant variables need a systematic examination with appropriate control groups before one's scientific curiosity can be reasonably satisfied.

The foregoing unanswered questions could be raised in analogous fashion throughout the later periods of the developmental years. With the increasing maturity of the growing child, even more questions about the dynamics of children's groups become important. The following are only a small sample of those that pique the curiosity of an observer of children's social relations when they are in the company of their peers. What developmental and social variables initiate the sex cleavage in children's spontaneous play groups during the preadolescent years? Do the same variables function to modify the social climates of those formal groups (e.g., the classroom) in which children of this age are forced into social interaction? What perceptual, motor, and other abilities and interests promote the greater "social maturity" of the female in our culture as contrasted with

her male peer? Could this usual state of affairs be modified experimentally? What developmental and social variables are related to the adolescent's withdrawing from formally organized social groupings (e.g., Boy Scouts, Girl Scouts, etc.) in favor of less "formally organized" groupings (e.g., the gang)? What social variables in group functioning predispose adolescents toward the invention and use of new verbal concepts?

The many dimensions of group life during childhood deserve study in their own right. The questions raised represent only a very few of the unknowns. The unknown is always tantalizing to the scientist, so there can be little doubt that children's groups will eventually be studied as intensively, and with at least an equal profit to man's knowledge, as the complex social interactions of ants, bees, chickens, and dogs.

## METHODOLOGICAL ADVANTAGES

There is a hard core of American psychologists who believe that research progress can best be expedited by concentrating our efforts first on the behavior of infrahuman subjects by constructing an explanatory model for "simple" organisms and then revising and expanding this model, as subsequent research may dictate, to explain the more "complex" behavior of man. These psychologists have traditionally selected the white rat as an appropriate experimental subject. If one accepts the validity of this approach, he can make an equally strong case for studying the dynamics of children's groups prior to the presumably more difficult task of identifying and measuring the dimensions of social functioning within groups composed of adults.

An argument can be made that the psychological defenses of children will have been less frequently practiced than those of adults. Hence the available behaviors from which the scientist must make his inferences will be more direct and spontaneous. Although this may in fact be a defensible argument, it is practically and operationally not demonstrable at our present state of ignorance about the functioning of social groups at any level of maturity.

Another methodological advantage that is sometimes claimed for the study of children's groups is their readier availability and a greater ease in manipulating the conditions important to their functioning. There seems to be some justification for the first part of this claim, although college sophomores may still be preferred because of their greater proximity to the typical university laboratory. The second alleged advantage seems unwarranted. Children are generally less tolerant than adults about anything that bores or frustrates them. If group conditions become uninteresting or unduly frustrating, they are more prone than adults to withdraw (either overtly or covertly) from the group. For example, in one of Lewin's authoritarian groups a boy who became a scapegoat for his companion's aggression quit the group (Lewin, Lippitt, and White, 1939). In addition, there are some ways of manipulating the social conditions of adult groups that no one as yet has been ingenious enough to

adapt for use in the study of children's groups. A good example is the introduction of a "ringer" or "stooge" into the adult group, either to make undetected observations or to play a social role important to the group's functioning (Festinger, 1953).

In general, it may be concluded that there are no *demonstrated* advantages for furthering scientific knowledge by the study of child as contrasted with adult groups. The investigator who elects to do research with children's groups may be legitimately influenced in this direction by any of the following conditions: he may be most interested in studying developmental variables affecting social groups during the accelerated growth period of the early years of life; he may have readier access to child subjects; he may find it more personally rewarding to do research with children; or he may wish to throw light on some pressing social problem whose solution would help to advance the happiness and adjustment of many children. As a group, child psychologists have been characteristically most highly influenced by the last condition—the need to help children.

One distinct methodological advantage in the study of children's groups is the urgency with which teachers, parents, and youth counselors regard their practical problems in the area of social psychology. This sense of urgency can be used to advantage in securing the cooperation of individuals responsible for the supervision and guidance of children's groups. However, the investigator must be able to project a sincere concern about the importance of the applied problems if he hopes to gain full-fledged cooperation.

Individuals who work with children in group situations *are* faced with a host of unsolved problems. They are forced to adopt rule-of-thumb procedures to maintain interest and "discipline" because no sure guide lines have been established in the research literature.

Consider the plight of the conscientious teacher who must interact daily with some 30 to 40 children in a group situation. She has some vague impression that she should be "democratic" toward the group, arrange the curriculum to meet the largely unknown needs of each and every pupil, promote cooperative efforts without destroying individual initiative, and all the while see that her pupils do not damage school property or disturb the classroom across the hall. A formidable assignment!

The recreational supervisor is faced with similar problems, with perhaps a little less pressure to maintain "discipline." However, he is confronted with an equally difficult task that is partially solved for the teacher by laws of compulsory school attendance. The recreational leader must find ways and means of maintaining a high level of interest and individual satisfaction within his group or it will dwindle away. Like the teacher, he falls back on rule-of-thumb devices, such as badges, intergroup competitions, and so on. Are these approaches the most effective ways to solve his problems? Perhaps, although they are frequently ineffective. Controlled research is necessary to isolate the relevant social variables and then

to vary them systematically to see how they influence the structure and dynamics of different kinds of recreational groupings.

The psychologist who does therapy with children in group situations is in a somewhat more favorable position than the teacher or recreational supervisor. He has usually been well trained in observational methods, so that he is more prone to develop and modify his rule-of-thumb guides with experience. However, he is forced to "play by ear" and sometimes adopts regrettable group procedures. He is potentially a significant contributor to knowledge about the structure and dynamics of children's groups, although his atypical subjects may distort or conceal many of the primary dimensions of group functioning.

What are some of the problems whose solutions would have practical implications for these teachers and counselors of children? Are there hints in the available research literature on either children's or adults' groups that may promote and expedite our groping toward valid and useful generalizations? Let us consider a small sample of the problems that have attracted the interests of socially oriented psychologists.

## GENERAL RESEARCH APPROACHES

It has now become conventional to speak of three general approaches to the study of human behavior. This rubric serves to limit the boundaries of the present discussion.

The normative-descriptive study of children's groups in their naturalistic setting is employed as a first approximation to the identification of the most significant variables in group functioning. It has been used to describe the structure and dynamics of such diverse children's groups as adolescent gangs (Thrasher, 1927), communal living within the *Kibbutz* in Israel (Faigin, 1958), group process involving both children and adults in a small town (Barker and Wright, 1954), infant-nurse relationships within nurseries (Dennis and Najarian, 1957), and so on. Since this approach is usually applied far and wide over diverse cultural and social conditions and since it generally enjoys the "fresh-naïve-look" of phenomenology, it always bears the potential of uncovering heretofore hidden or neglected variables important to group functioning. The special characteristics and techniques peculiar to the normative descriptive or "ecological" approach are discussed at length in Chapter 3 of this book.

The correlational approach may, or may not, utilize existing children's groups as research subjects. Its distinguishing characteristic is the attempt to identify covariances among the variables related to group structure and dynamics or covariances between these variables and certain manipulable dispositional conditions such as type of adult leadership. An example of the latter is the established covariance between the number of "dominative" overtures made by different classroom teachers and the dominative responses of their pupils (Anderson, 1939). The inference is then drawn that adult domination tends to produce pupil domination. A good example of the study of

covariances of variables within group functioning is Hemphill's (1949) correlational analysis of the relationships between several group dimensions (homogeneity, stability, etc.) and members' relationships with the group (participation, dependence, etc.). Another example is Cattell and associates' (1953) factor analysis of 80 groups on 93 variables (including behavior ratings, group judgments, and motor performances), which resulted in the identification of 15 factors considered important to the description of group structure and dynamics (e.g., group elation, recklessness, and intrinsic synergy). The correlational approach is time-honored in psychology, geology, astronomy, and under any conditions in which it is difficult (or impossible) to manipulate the conditions predispositional to the variance of some dimension of interest.

A substantial number of psychologists like to bring nature into the experimental laboratory. They prefer to follow the pattern of physics and chemistry rather than that of astronomy or geology. They attempt to control all but a very few of the "independent" variables, then systematically to vary these conditions in an effort to determine the covariation of selected "dependent variables" (e.g., to vary the size of a group systematically and to observe any correlated changes in the formation of subgroups during free discussion periods). Although the control group is not a necessary component of the experimental method, it is a common adjunct, since it provides a reasonable estimate of the influence of the variables not under the experimenter's control. Another method of control is to have several groups exposed to the same, but differentially ordered, experimental conditions (e.g., Group A is exposed to conditions X, Y, and Z in that order; Group B to Y, Z, and X in that order; and Group C to Z, X, and Y in that order). This is the so-called counterbalanced experiment. This method produces unknown interaction effects, the results of which may support spurious inferences.[1] Despite its obvious operational complexities the experimental method can be used to pinpoint covariances with the greatest rigor. The contributions of experimental studies to our knowledge of psychophysics, learning, and psychophysiology have been most impressive. Can the social psychology of group behavior be expected to draw with equal success on experimental procedures of this type? It is too early to say, but it can be stated that controlled experimentation with children's groups has been conducted with signal success. (See Roseborough, 1953, for an excellent summary of experimental studies.)

A vexing problem in each of these research procedures, when applied to the study of children's groups, is estimating the limits of the obtained generalizations. Although this problem is common to all of science, it seems especially troublesome in the study of group behavior because there are so many parameters potentially important to patterned relationships among process variables. For example, to mention only a few possibilities: the numerical size of the groups, the sex of the members, the ages of the members, the sub-

culture from which the members are drawn, the "intrinsic" interest of group activities to the members, special abilities of the members, such as intelligence, motor skills or handicaps, emotional disturbances, and so on, through many more conditions and all of their possible combinations. It would be a Gargantuan and futile undertaking to conduct investigations that would exhaust all of the combinations of parameters potentially important to any generalization about the structure or dynamics of children's groups. Fortunately, such a program is not demanded. Any generalization is always subject to restriction by conflicting findings from studies involving similar parameters; and any "law," "principle," or "trend" remains forever hypothetical in its generality and adequacy. This state of affairs is a continuous stimulant to the seasoned scientist but may be a depressing reminder to the beginning investigator who hopes to "solve" his problem once and for all by a "crucial" experiment. The inductive-deductive-inductive processes by which generalizations are drawn, hypotheses proposed, and theories constructed are never static in a growing science that promotes its own ends by the logical and operational tools it invents.

## SELECTING OR CREATING GROUPS

It will be assumed that the experimenter has selected some important problem for study on the basis of a preferred theory or in response to a pressing problem in group instruction, management, or supervision. He knows

[1] See Campbell (1957) for an excellent discussion of experimental design in group studies.

what variables he wishes to study but is relatively unfamiliar with the lore of selecting or creating groups of children with whom to work. How can he best proceed?

*Selecting Appropriate Groups of Children.* If the experimenter is primarily interested in the functioning of some type of existing group, such as a delinquent gang, a classroom, or a formally organized recreational unit, its composition is largely determined for him. Under these conditions his problem is to select a sample of the available groups in such a way that his findings can be maximally generalized to this class of children's groups.

There are two widely practiced procedures among social scientists in selecting the sample of groups to be studied. The first is based on sheer expedience. The investigator selects all, or part of, the groups that are near at hand. This approach will limit his generalizations to the groups studied unless he can demonstrate that those under investigation are very similar in many ways to a larger and reasonably well defined population of groups. This demonstration permits tentative generalization of findings.

A more defensible procedure for selecting groups to be studied consists of drawing a representative sample stratified on those variables considered relevant to the dimensions of group structure and dynamics under investigation. Judgments about relevance may be based on the findings of prior research or on theoretical assumptions. A good model for this type of selection can be found in the work of authors of standardized achievement tests devel-

oped for use in our nation's classrooms (Kelley, 1953).

Another feature that must be considered in the selection of existing groups is their accessibility for study. Beyond obtaining the necessary permission and cooperation of the groups and their sponsors, there is the more difficult problem of securing observations without destroying the properties of the group being studied. Although this is a problem in any investigation, it may be especially troublesome in working with existing groups whose members will naturally be curious about the experimenter's special interest. For example, an informally organized boys' gang that tolerated an experimenter's intrusion would probably be atypical to an extreme degree. Ways must be found to make the investigator's presence acceptable and "natural" so that the variables being studied are not distorted by the acts of observation.

*Groups for Experimental Purposes.* For the study of many problems in group structure and dynamics, there are advantages in creating special groups. This was the experimental procedure followed in the now classic studies of democratic and authoritarian leadership (Lippitt, 1940). The boys for each of the clubs were selected so that they had a common sociometric structure in the classrooms from which they were drawn.

If the experimenter decides to create his own groups, he must be mindful of several conditions that may influence their functioning—or even their continuing existence throughout the desired experimental period. There must be reasons for creating groups that are acceptable to their members in order to avoid "artificiality." These reasons will vary from community to community, for they should be contingent on the particular mores, folkways, and general styles of living prevalent in the subcultures from which the subjects are selected.

In order to maintain the group, the experimenter must arrange for activities that are intrinsically interesting to the children involved. If this cannot be effected, there will be disruptive absences or drop-outs that may have serious influences on the functioning of the groups being studied.

If the investigation involves the comparison of outcomes or ongoing processes for experimental and control groups, the experimenter who creates his own groups is called upon to demonstrate the comparability of the members on *all* variables judged to be relevant. For example, this might involve

**TABLE 19-1. DESCRIPTION OF ADULT-LEADER'S FUNCTIONS IN THE AUTHORITARIAN, THE DEMOCRATIC, AND THE LAISSEZ-FAIRE GROUP ATMOSPHERES STUDIED BY LEWIN AND HIS STUDENTS**

| Authoritarian | Democratic | Laissez-Faire |
|---|---|---|
| 1. All determination of policy by the leader | 1. All policies a matter of group discussion and decision, encouraged and assisted by the leader | 1. Complete freedom for group or individual decision, with a minimum of leader participation |
| 2. Techniques and activity steps dictated by the authority, one at a time, so that future steps were always uncertain to a large degree | 2. Activity perspective gained during discussion period. General steps to group goal sketched, and when technical advice was needed the leader suggested two or more alternative procedures from which choice could be made | 2. Various materials supplied by the leader, who made it clear that he would supply information when asked. He took no other part in work discussion |
| 3. The leader usually dictated the particular work task and work companion of each member | 3. The members were free to work with whomever they chose, and the division of tasks was left up to the group | 3. Complete nonparticipation of the leader |
| 4. The dominator tended to be "personal" in his praise and criticism of the work of each member; remained aloof from active group participation except when demonstrating | 4. The leader was "objective" or "fact-minded" in his praise and criticism and tried to be a regular group member in spirit without doing too much work | 4. Infrequent spontaneous comments on member activities unless questioned and no attempt to appraise or regulate the course of events |

From Ralph White and Ronald Lippitt, Leader behavior and member reaction in three social climates. In Cartwright and Zander (1953) with permission of authors and Row, Peterson and Company.

a demonstration of comparable ages, IQ's, socioeconomic status, sociometric relationships, skills, and the like. This is no easy assignment; therefore, success in securing comparability of subjects is usually approximate. Since it has been shown that only *one* member with strong social influence can have far-reaching effects on group structure and dynamics (Festinger, 1953), the importance of member comparability in especially created groups cannot be over-estimated.

## EXPERIMENTAL PROCEDURES

The most important work in the experimental manipulation of "group atmospheres" was initiated by Lewin and carried on by his former students. Prior to Lewin's formulations, there were some empirical guides, such as those of Thomas (1929), Jack, (1934), and Page (1936); however, these investigators failed to conceptualize the pervasive and dynamic social interactions that define the broad spectrum of "group atmosphere" or "social climate."

Let us take a look at Lewin's procedures for influencing group structure and dynamics by the induced social forces of democratic, laissez-faire, and authoritarian leadership. The adult leaders were especially trained to produce the group atmospheres described in Table 19-1.

It was postulated and verified that the leader's behavior would induce social forces that would influence the group members' responses to each other and to the leader, so that the group atmosphere would be somewhat self-propelling once it was set in mo-

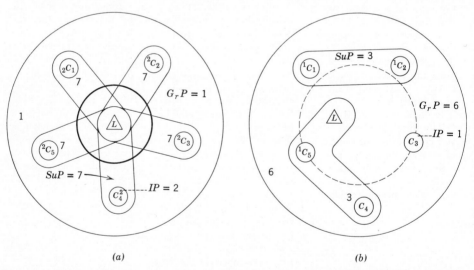

(a)                                          (b)

Fig. 19-1. Subgrouping and potency of the group as a whole in (a) an autocratic and (b) a democratic setting. (From R. Lippitt. 1940. An experimental study of the effect of democratic and authoritarian group atmospheres. *Univer. Iowa Stud. Child Welf.*, 16, 133–135. As adopted for use by K. Lewin, Behavior and development as a function of the total situation. In L. Carmichael (Ed.). 1954. (2nd ed.) *Manual of child psychology.* With permission of the University of Iowa and John Wiley and Sons, Inc.

tion. Observational procedures were adopted to describe the social process within the ongoing group atmospheres (e.g., subgroupings, expressions of "we-ness," hostility, and dependence on leader) and to assess the *over-all* effects of each atmosphere on group functioning. One of the types of differential influence of autocratic and democratic settings is presented schematically in Fig. 19-1.

Several of Lewin's students have successfully influenced group processes in a predictable way by manipulating selected independent variables. For example, Thompson (1940) was able to produce an underpriviledged minority in a larger group of 10-year-old children by prejudicial adult leadership. The children in the privileged majority continued to discriminate against the minority members, even when the leader was absent from the group. This shows something of the self-sustaining forces that can be induced into a group situation. Wright (1940) showed that adult-induced frustration may produce an increment in the friendship between two children if they "see themselves opposed to the adult." French (1944) showed that "organized groups" (previously organized in social structure) evidenced more interdependence and motivation than socially restrained, unacquainted groups when confronted with a frustrating puzzle and an experimentally produced fire.

Many subsequent investigators have utilized stress conditions to influence social processes within a group. Bishop (1951) showed that experimentally produced negative attitudes of mothers toward their preschool-aged children's

behavior resulted in more inhibition and non cooperation in their children. Deutsch (1949) utilized several groups of five adults each to study the effects of intergroup and intragroup competition on group functioning (group solutions to puzzles and human relations problems). Observation sheets, nine-point rating scales, weekly questionnaires, and postexperimental questionnaires were employed to assess group processes and outcomes. It was concluded that intergroup competition favored more within-group cooperative interrelationships and greater organizational productivity. Grosser, Polansky, and Lippitt (1951) have shown that the impulsive initiation of acts by paid subjects is effective in overcoming the restraints of other children by a process that they describe as "behavioral contagion." Hare (1953) has demonstrated that boy leaders trained for participatory leadership have more influence on group functioning than boys trained for supervisory leadership. Lanzetta and associates (1954) have found that threats toward either the group as a whole or to any of its members had a negative effect on interpersonal relations and the effectiveness of the group. All of these studies are illustrative of the many ways that an experimenter can influence the structure and dynamics of group functioning by experimental procedures.[1] The

[1] See L. Festinger. 1953. Laboratory experiments. In L. Festinger and D. Katz (Eds.), *Research methods in the behavioral sciences.* New York: Dryden. Pp. 136–172. This is an excellent discussion of such laboratory procedures as use of paid participants, false reporting, and pre-experimental instruction of leaders or members.

possible techniques seem limited only by the experimenter's ingenuity and the theoretical "meaningfulness" of the induced social forces.

## DIMENSIONS OF GROUP FUNCTIONING

The following is not an exhaustive survey of the concepts that have been proposed to describe group processes; rather it is a selection of those dimensions about which considerable empirical research data are now available. The present discussion should not be interpreted as implying that all of these variables have found a permanent niche in behavioral science or that the most important variables are now known. Research with groups is of recent origins, and there is every reason to believe that it is still essentially exploratory-descriptive in scope.

*Cohesiveness.*[1] Cohesiveness encompasses the properties of a group (such as goals, type of organization, and status in the community) in combination with the needs of an individual, which may be expected to be met by belonging to the group (for example, affiliation, recognition, succorance, and the like). "The cohesiveness of a group, thus, is the resultant of all the forces acting on all members to remain in the group." (Cartwright and Zander, 1953.)

[1] The definition of this concept (and of that immediately following) is based on D. Cartwright and A. Zander (Eds.), 1953. *Group dynamics: research and theory.* Evanston, Ill.: Row, Peterson. The serious student of the structure and dynamics of children's groups will do well to master the contents of this volume.

Research findings and theoretical analysis point toward a number of variables related to degrees of group cohesiveness. The members may be attracted by each other as individual personalities, by the activities supported by the group, or by both conditions. Cohesiveness based on the functioning of different patterns of social variables produces different patterns of communication and interpersonal attractions. Cohesiveness that is a function of the intrinsic needs of members results in different group processes than cohesiveness based on social forces exerted by external authorities (e.g., the differences between a classroom and an informally organized gang). Cohesiveness is enhanced by cooperative relationships, by some external threats to the group's existence, and by some external evaluations of a favorable type. Cohesiveness is diminished by interpersonal conflicts and frustrations within the group, by unpleasant assignments, and by some types of negative evaluations from outsiders. Whether the concept of cohesiveness is largely descriptive of a large class of patterned functions or has some "unitary" invariant properties such as general intelligence remains in doubt (Gross and Martin, 1952). Nevertheless, the concept has stimulated some very fruitful investigations (e.g., Fessenden, 1953; French, 1941; Schachter et al., 1951; Thibaut, 1950).

*Group Pressures.*[2] Although many formally organized groups (e.g., the classroom, the Boy Scout troop, and the Sunday-school class) exert fairly

[2] Cartwright and Zander, 1953.

obvious pressures on their members by chartered intent, informally organized groups may exert equally strong, or stronger, pressures on their members for uniformity of behavior, attitudes, standards of excellence in performance, and so on. It seems reasonable to infer that these social pressures serve two general functions important to the group: "to help the group accomplish its purposes, and to help the group maintain itself as a group" (Cartwright and Zander, 1953).

Many ingenious experiments have been conducted to investigate the antecedents and consequences of group pressures. The techniques adopted by Asch (1951), by Festinger, Schachter, and Back (1950), and by Lippitt et al. (1952) should be especially noted. In a general summary Cartwright and Zander (1953) note that the strength of social forces of the individual member toward uniformity and conformity is probably determined by the following conditions: the attraction of the group for the member, the importance of the issue on which conformity is demanded, an awareness that the standard for conformity is unanimously supported by other members, and the size of the group exerting the forces toward conformity.

The special characteristics of those social pressures that fail to effect unanimous conformity or that result in the formation of "splinter" subgroups are largely unknown. However, such variables as differential perceptions, attractiveness of the group, differential punishments for nonconformity, differential rewards for yielding, and so on, have been proposed as possible explanations. This aspect of the functioning of group pressures offers an especially attractive area for further research—indeed, exploratory research in *children's* groups.

**Leadership.** Considerable research has been conducted over the years on the influence of different kinds of adult leadership on the structure and dynamics of children's groups; however, relatively little has been done to investigate the dimensions of a child member's leadership in children's groups (Parten, 1933; Hanfmann, 1935). The *developmental* aspects of the leadership function have been grossly neglected in the last decade, a period during which psychologists have exerted substantial amounts of energy to study leadership in *adult* groups. The findings of studies with adults should, however, provide a rough blueprint for investigations that would have a developmental perspective.

The evidence for a general "trait" of leadership is not convincing. An individual who is a leader in one group may not be a leader in a group with different goals. For example, Carter and associates (1950) found, from their factor analysis, two different kinds of leadership ability—an "intellectual leadership" factor and a "doing things with one's hands leadership" factor. It seems probable that there is even a greater variety of leadership abilities. Hence the most fruitful *exploratory* research in children's groups might be the study of variables related to different types of leadership.

**Group Structure.** Group structure defines the patterning of social relations within a group. Who prefers the companionship of whom? Who has the greatest influence or "power" over whom? Who communicates most with whom? Which members are most frequently found within a common sub-grouping? Information related to the answers to these and similar questions falls under the general rubric of "group structure."

Group structure is the one dimension in group processes for which reasonably reliable and useful scales have been developed (Jennings, 1950; Northway, 1952; Gardner and Thompson, 1959a). Advances in sociometry have stimulated a great deal of research with which the reader may become familiar by reading the various issues of the professional journal *Sociometry*. The properties of several instruments for measuring group structure are discussed in a later section of this chapter. Suffice to say at this point that social-relations scales have been a boon to research on the social structure of groups.

**Dimensions of Group Structure and Dynamics.** Space does not permit a discussion of the many identifiable properties of group functioning. Social communication (Back, 1951; Festinger, 1950, 1951), socioempathy (Barker, 1942; Borgatta, 1954), communication patterns (Bavelas, 1950; Heise and Miller, 1951; Leavitt, 1951), and social perception (Tagiuri, 1952) are among the many dimensions that have attracted the attention of investigators.

The thoughtful analysis by Hemphill and Westie of some of the salient dimensions of group structure and dynamics is a rough chart of the variables that merit immediate study. They have developed scales for evaluating the following dimensions of group functioning:[1]

1. *Autonomy* is the degree to which a group functions independently of other groups and occupies an independent position in society. It is reflected by the degree to which a group determines its own activities, by its absence of allegiance, deference and/or dependence relative to other groups.

2. *Control* is the degree to which a group regulates the behavior of individuals while they are functioning as group members. It is reflected by the modifications which group membership imposes on complete freedom of individual behavior and by the amount or intensity of group-derived government.

3. *Flexibility* is the degree to which a group's activities are marked by informal procedures rather than by adherence to established procedures. It is reflected by the extent to which duties of members are free from specification through custom, tradition, written rules, regulations, codes of procedure, or even unwritten but clearly prescribed ways of behaving.

4. *Hedonic Tone* is the degree to which group membership is accompanied by a general feeling of pleasantness or agreeableness. It is reflected by the frequency of laughter, conviviality, pleasant anticipation of group meetings, and by the absence of griping and complaining.

5. *Homogeneity* is the degree to which members of a group are similar with respect to socially relevant characteristics. It is reflected by relative uniformity of members with respect to age, sex, race, socio-economic status, interests, attitudes and habits.

6. *Intimacy* is the degree to which members of a group are mutually acquainted with one another and are familiar with the most personal details of one another's lives. It is reflected by the nature of topics discussed by members, by modes of greeting, forms of address, and by in-

[1] From Hemphill and Westie (1950) with permission of authors and *The Journal Press*.

teractions which presuppose a knowledge of the probable reaction of others under widely differing circumstances, as well as by the extent and type of knowledge each member has about other members of the group.

7. *Participation* is the degree to which members of a group apply time and effort to group activities. It is reflected by the number and kinds of duties members perform, by voluntary assumption of non-assigned duties and by the amount of time spent in group activities.

8. *Permeability* is the degree to which a group permits ready access to membership. It is reflected by absence of entrance requirements of any kind, and by the degree to which membership is solicited.

9. *Polarization* is the degree to which a group is oriented and works toward a single goal which is clear and specific to all members.

10. *Potency* is the degree to which a group has primary significance for its members. It is reflected by the kind of needs which a group is satisfying or has the potentiality of satisfying, by the extent of readjustment which would be required of members should the group fail, and by the degree to which a group has meaning to the members with reference to their central values.

11. *Size* is the number of members regarded as being in the group.

12. *Stability* is the degree to which a group persists over a period of time with essentially the same characteristics. It is reflected by the rate of membership turnover, by frequency of reorganizations and by constancy of group size.

13. *Stratification* is the degree to which a group orders its members into status hierarchies. It is reflected by differential distribution of power, privileges, obligations, and duties and by asymmetrical patterns of differential behavior among members.

14. *Viscidity* is the degree to which members of the group function as a unit. It is reflected by absence of dissension and personal conflict among members, by absence of activities serving to advance only the interests of individual group members, by the ability of the group to resist disrupting forces, and by the belief on the part of the members that the group does function as a unit.

Each of these dimensions is represented by a series of items (e.g., for *Control:* "Activities of the group are supervised," and "Members fear to express their real opinions"), which are rated by an observer of the group on a five-point scale ranging from "definitely true" to "definitely false."

The scales have adequate reliability, yield scores showing a high degree of agreement between respondents describing the same group, and with a few exceptions have low intercorrelations among themselves. (Hemphill and Westie, 1950.)

## GUIDE TO THE OBSERVATION OF GROUP BEHAVIOR

This important topic has been so ably discussed by Heyns and Zander that many of their comments are presented here in only slightly abridged and adapted form:[1]

The importance of theory in the design of experiments is often neglected. We need only point out here that the theoreti-

[1] From R. W. Heyns and A. F. Zander, Observation of group behavior. In L. Festinger and D. Katz (Eds.), 1953. *Research methods in the behavioral sciences.* New York: Dryden. Pp. 398–415. (With permission of authors and publisher.) The investigator who has had no previous experience in the use of rating and category approaches to the description of group processes may read the original report in its entirety with profit. The excerpts reported here will serve as a helpful review and summary for all investigators interested in the measurement of group processes.

cal framework plays a central role in determining the decision which the experimenter must make in developing his methodology. This is particularly true with respect to selection of the behavior to be observed or rated and the definition of the categories into which these behaviors are to be placed. Without a knowledge of the purpose of the experiment or research and the theoretical setting in which the experiment takes place, no one can prescribe for an experimenter the dimensions with which he ought to be concerned, or the amount of inference he ought to require of his observers. The experimental design and the specific hypotheses to be tested will dictate the level of reliability of observed data which will be necessary. Many other decision implications of the theoretical framework could be stated; several of these will be made explicit in the discussion of decision areas which follows.

## THE FRAME OF REFERENCE

In the interests of reliability, observers must be clear about the dimension to be observed and about the vantage point they are to use in observing, recording, coding, or rating it. Observers may be instructed, for example, to observe the social interaction along the dimension of interpersonal affect—i.e., the extent to which the members of the group are personally fond of each other. As the dimension is fairly clear, the question arises whether the observers are to react to the observed behavior as if they are participants or whether they are to identify with the actor, making inferences about his motives. These are different frames of reference. Many others are possible.

## SIZE OF UNIT

After the experimenter has determined the dimensions along which he wants ratings or categorization, he faces the problem of determining the size of the unit of behavior to be rated or categorized.

Failure to state clearly to the observers the precise limits of the unit of observation is a frequent source of unreliability. The reliability of the coding depends in part on the reliability of deciding what constitutes a unit of behavior.

Roughly speaking, the size of the unit may vary from a single act—for example, the contribution of a single participant—to a total period of interaction. Time sampling (categorizing or rating units of time distributed randomly over the total action period) is an intermediate technique. This can obviously include a single act or all acts.

In categorization, the selection of the size of unit is not independent of the category system itself. This has led to a fairly common practice of defining units in some such fashion as this: "any act which is classifiable into a single category." Failure to consider this aspect in the definition of units will perforce affect reliability. Thus, in practice, experimenters dealing with verbal behavior of members of problem-solving groups have often found it impossible to deal with a total simple participation as the unit. A lengthy verbal statement too frequently contains elements which permit classification in several categories.

## SAMPLING METHODS IN OBSERVATION

It often happens that one cannot, or does not want to, record all of the behavior that takes place in a given situation. This may occur because the meeting lasts too long to observe continuously, too many persons are present, interactions come too rapidly to record, or for any of a variety of reasons. In such a case we are forced to develop a method of obtaining a representative sample of the behavior being observed. This can be done in a number of ways: (1) Attention can be concentrated on the behavior of a few of the members, ignoring the others present. (2) Attention can be directed to each person, or to a number of persons in the group, each for a given length of time. (3) The whole observation instrument can be divided into parts and the social setting can be observed in terms of each part of the observation schedule for a standardized length of time. (4) Observations can be made only when certain key behaviors have been introduced into the meeting. (5) The most frequently used system for obtaining representative samples of the behavior being observed is the time-sampling system, in which a standardized time unit is selected during which observation takes place. The assumption is that these parts will be an adequate description of all of the events.

In general, it is risky to use sampling procedures unless one has an adequate theory to guide the selection of the sample. As an illustration, let us assume that we wish to observe a number of behaviors in a group but for some reason it is necessary to use a time-sampling procedure. We make the decision to observe in terms of a certain set of categories for five minutes, skip ten minutes (during which we may be observing with a different set of "spectacles") and return for another five minutes with the original categories, and so on. Any social situation, however, is a changing set of activities, and we may discover that certain events occur during the ten minutes we are not observing which distort the representativeness of the records made during our time samples. Thus, we would rightly be suspicious of the adequacy of our data. We could have avoided this difficulty if we had had some notion of the range of possibilities of crucial changes in this group which could affect the adequacy of our time samples and had arranged our sampling procedure in such a way that it covered all of the crucial differences which may have distorted the representativeness of our time sample.

Another problem one may encounter while using time sampling is that the psychological meaningfulness of the behavior being observed may be destroyed. For example, rating a group's reactions to a given act of a leader may not give a mean-ingful picture; that is, it may be atomistic or incomplete. When one observes the complete sequence of events in a group's reaction to a leader's act before recording anything, however, it is possible to rate or otherwise record the behavior in a way that includes all of the group's reactions and all of the implications of these actions.

## TRAINING OBSERVERS

The use of group observers means that we are using people as measuring instruments. A good measuring instrument is one which will accurately measure at various times what it is supposed to measure. If a person is to become an "observing instrument," he must be trained to see what it is required that he see. This may be a simple or a complex task, depending upon the data needed. It is an important phase of the preparation of a study using group observers and cannot receive too much attention. A well-developed observation schedule will be only as good as the skill of the persons who are asked to use it.

In general, one can expect that the observers will have the greatest problems on those categories which require integration or collation of complex phenomena. They will have the least difficulty, in contrast, with those events which are simple objective occurrences which require little insight or sensitivity on the part of the observer. Studies of coder reliability (Guetzkow, 1950) have found that there is most disagreement on data which are complicated and demand much inference. Since an observer functions as a highly trained coder, it is quite likely that he will have similar problems.

This suggests that the skills required of an observer cannot be performed by all persons equally well, quite aside from the academic training they may have had. One may find that a group of observers has comparable ability to understand the phenomena involved in a study and to discuss them intelligently but that some of them may not be able to "see" these things in a group of interacting people. A study by

Luszki (1950) provides some insights which are relevant. She found that there is a positive relation between sensitivity to the feelings and emotions of others (empathic ability) and the ability to "see" what is happening in a social situation. Persons with good empathic ability (1) are better able to see what is happening in the role performance of others, (2) have good personal adjustment, as measured by the instruments used in the study, (3) have insights into themselves which are similar to the evaluations made of them by others, (4) have more stable, positive, and secure feelings about the self and somewhat favorable perceptions of others, (5) have a more consistent and more favorable perception by others.

## RELIABILITY

The reliability of observational instruments has been much more a matter of concern to investigators of social behavior than has validity. For purposes of exposition it may be useful to make a distinction that is not often made. In assessing the reliability of a system of social observation, it is necessary to differentiate the reliability of the behavior being observed from the reliability of the categorization or rating which is made of that behavior. In other words, the reliability of the observer and of the behavior are separate problems. It is clear, of course, from this distinction that the consistency of behavior is a substantive problem, whereas the consistency of an observer is a methodological problem. Once the consistency of an observer has been established, it becomes possible to tackle the problem of the consistency of the behavior.

The task of assessing degree of agreement among observers, in the case of a category system, breaks down into at least two separate reliability problems. The first is the extent of agreement among observers with respect to the number of units coded. This is essentially the extent to which the observers agree as to the boundaries of the unit which is to be categorized. Guetzkow (1950) has pointed out, as has Bales

(1950), that unreliability in this area is an important factor affecting the reliability of categorization itself. It seems clear that until there is rater agreement as to the boundaries of units to be categorized, there is little purpose in assessing rater agreement on categorizing. The second principal task in assessing reliability is to determine the extent to which observers agree on the category or rating they assign to a specific unit of behavior.

The most frequently used statistic in appraising degree of agreement between observers has been the correlation coefficient. This is especially useful, provided the assumptions underlying its use can be met, because the extent of agreement that is being obtained can be evaluated in terms of a fixed standard. It is a separate question, however, whether in a given case one needs a correlation of 0.7, 0.8, or 0.9 to be certain that one's degree of agreement is satisfactory. It is apparent that the question immediately becomes: satisfactory for what? In other words, the experimenter or investigator must ask himself the purpose of his observational scores. His theory will indicate the extent to which large or small differences are to be expected. It is a truism that where fine differentiation is necessary the scores must be more reliable than where gross differences can be expected. It is impossible to state categorically that observational scores should be at such and such a level of reliability to be useful, for the usefulness of a score depends on the use to which it is to be put.

The second principal statistical device which has been utilized in characterizing amount of agreement between observers has been a percent-agreement score. This is essentially a matter of computing the percentage of the total number of items which were classified in the same way by the two observers or by all the observers combined. Guetzkow (1950) has provided statistical devices for evaluating the level of agreement.

Bales (1950) illustrates the use of the chi square to evaluate degree of observer agreement. He points out that his use of chi square is different from the more conventional applications, since his use applies it to a situation which does not represent random sampling. The principal advantage of chi square is that it does not require the assumptions of the usual parametric techniques.

It seems useful to point out that the investigator ought to be concerned with the reliability of the measure *actually used* in the analysis of the data. For example, it is a matter of *relative* unimportance whether observers agree with respect to the number of units of behavior assigned to a specific individual if the score with which the investigator is concerned is the number of units in each category made by the group as a whole. In that case the reliability of individual scores is not of concern as long as high group reliability is present. Another illustration is the reliability of the categorization of each unit as opposed to the reliability of a category score for an individual. That is, the agreement between observers as to the percentage of responses categorized in each of the categories in the system may be very high even though the observers show relatively low agreement on the categorization of each item. This condition occurs, of course, only when the errors of categorization are fairly random. The point is, however, that the investigator must ask himself what score he is going to use and must then assess the reliability of that score.

## THE RELATION OF THE OBSERVER TO THE GROUP BEING OBSERVED

One of the most frequent questions addressed to the investigator who reports a study which used observers is: "Did the presence of the observers influence the behavior of the group?" Usually he must answer that he has no evidence that the observers influenced the results in any way, but that they might have. It is quite conceivable that the presence of an observer may be an important variable. This depends upon the nature of the group, the type of observation, the nature of the group's activity, the nature of the variables being observed, and a number of other things. Arsenian (1943) found that the simple presence of an adult sitting near the door seemed to lend assurance to a group of nursery-school children. Yet the presence of observers was a threat to young boys at a summer camp, according to Polansky (1949). The influence of observers is a methodological problem which needs more careful study.

Deutsch (1949) found that the members of small groups which met frequently over a period of three weeks were aware of the presence of observers at the beginning of their work together but had become almost oblivious to them by the end of that period. Half of these groups were constructed in such a way that the members cooperated with one another to achieve a common goal; the rest of the groups were in a situation in which the members competed with one another. It is interesting to note that the competitive groups were much more conscious of the observers than were the cooperative groups. Thus, procedural differences within a group may influence the way in which the observers are perceived.

Polansky (1949) noted that changes took place in the perception by boy campers of the purpose and role of cruising observers. Early in the summer, research observers were well accepted by the campers, who had been told that the strangers were neutral persons who were interested in learning how they could improve the camp. By the third week, however, they had become the objects of aggression by many of the boys. The observers decided that their role was too ambiguous and represented a threat to these boys, many of whom were rebellious against adult authority. It was felt that the campers were projecting their feelings of hostility toward adults onto the observers. After the observers changed their behavior to become more warm, human, and friendly, they found that they were no longer rejected by the campers.

Naturally, we must be cautious about generalizing from such an experience as this. In a laboratory situation, for example, where the group members are working toward a decision, it would no doubt be quite disruptive for an observer to indicate that he feels warm and friendly toward the participants. In short, in some situations we may want one perception of the observer; in another situation we may need quite a different one.

Bales (1950) has used observers in a wide variety of laboratory arrangements. They have sat with the group, or behind a one-way screen with the group aware they are there, or behind the screen with the group wondering whether they are there. He has found no difference in the behavior of the groups which could be attributed to the influence of these various positions of the observers.

Thus, it appears that group observers sometimes influence a social situation. When in doubt, it is wisest to explain the function of the observers to the group in some way that does not spoil any necessary naïveté of the subjects. The observers will do best, barring any special conditions such as those met by Polansky (1949), by showing all of the external signs of a piece of furniture. If they behave like a person who is having no reactions to the events being observed, the group members will perceive them as such. For most situations that is probably best.

## SCALES FOR MEASURING THE SOCIAL STRUCTURE OF GROUPS

The social structure of groups can be described and evaluated by general observational procedures. However, it is often convenient to use the verbal responses of the children themselves to make inferences about the structure of the groups in which they hold membership. "Sociometric" instruments are convenient and useful for a number of reasons. They provide data that have been shown to be related to several other important dimensions of group processes, such as morale, group effectiveness, and patterns of communication. They tap a residue of social-relations tendencies that are usually difficult to sample in direct observations of social behavior. They provide reasonably reliable measures of what has been shown to be a fairly stable component of human-response tendencies. They can be employed in comparable form over a wide age-range of subjects; hence they have been useful in describing developmental trends in social relations (Thompson and Horrocks, 1947; Horrocks and Buker, 1951).

*"Nominating" or Partial-Rank-Order Procedures.* Although the "social distance" scales of Bogardus (1933) had priority in this category, the sociometric techniques of Moreno (1951, 1953) have been by far the most influential in stimulating a mass of studies about the social structure of groups (Criswell, 1943; Loomis and Pepinsky, 1948; Lindzey and Borgatta, 1954).

The partial-rank-order approach proposed by Moreno is simple and flexible.[1] It consists of any desired number of questions such as the following: "Whom would you most like to have sit next to you in this classroom (or other group)? "Whom would you most like to have go with you on a picnic (or on a dangerous military mis-

[1] The directions for administering sociometric tests of the partial-rank-order type and a convenient form for recording the obtained nominations is now commercially available (Bonney and Fessenden, 1955).

## TABLE 19-2. THE GENERAL FORMAT OF A TYPICAL SOCIOMETRIC QUESTIONNAIRE OF THE PARTIAL-RANK-ORDER TYPE

| A. Whom would you most like to have sit next to you in this classroom? | B. If you were going on a picnic, whom would you most like to have go with you? |
|---|---|
| 1st choice ...................... | 1st choice ...................... |
| 2nd choice ...................... | 2nd choice ...................... |
| 3rd choice ...................... | 3rd choice ...................... |

sion, or to a party, and so on)?" "To whom do you talk most frequently?" "Who is your best friend?" And so on through the gamut of possible social relationships.[2]

Answers to questions of the forego-

his first, second, third, fourth, and fifth choices (or some smaller, or larger, ordering), or he may be asked to list as many individuals in a preferred order as he wishes.[3]

The obtained data are usually tabu-

Nominations Received

| Individual | R.A. | C.C. | J.H. | B.K. | R.L. | J.M. | G.P. | A.R. | S.S. | F.T. |
|---|---|---|---|---|---|---|---|---|---|---|
| Ralph A. | | I | | I | I | | | | | |
| Carl C. | I | | | | | | I | | | I |
| John H. | | I | | | I | | | I | | |
| Bill K. | | I | | | I | | | I | | |
| Ray L. | I | I | I | | | | | | | |
| Jim M. | | I | | | I | | I | | | |
| George P. | | I | I | | I | | | | | |
| Art R. | | I | | | I | | I | | | |
| Sam S. | | I | | I | I | | | | | |
| Frank T. | I | I | | | I | | | | | |
| Total number of nominations received | 3 | 8 | 3 | 2 | 8 | 0 | 3 | 2 | 0 | I |

*(Left margin label: Nominations Made)*

Fig. 19-2. A matrix of nominations in a Boy Scout group of 10 members, with three choices permitted each member in response to, "Whom would you most like to have as your buddy on an all-day hiking trip?"

ing types may be solicited by interviews or by written forms similar to the one presented in Table 19-2. The respondent may be requested to give

lated in a matrix similar to the one presented in Fig. 19-2. They are also often

[2] It should be noted that these questions may also be phrased in a negative way; e.g., "Whom would you *least* like to have sit next to you?"

[3] Lippitt and associates (1952) have used photographs to help subjects identify other members of the group in the early stages of camping experience. McCandless and Marshall (1957) have also used photographs to help offset the "out of sight, out of mind" tendencies among preschool-aged subjects.

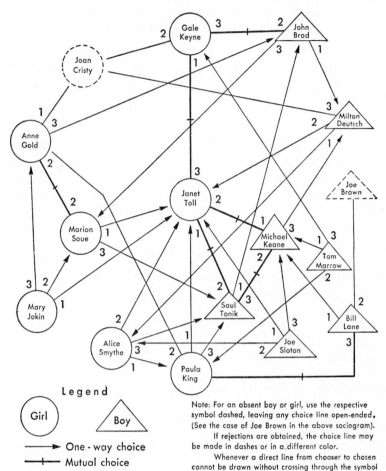

Legend

Girl

Boy

———► One - way choice

———┼— Mutual choice

1, 2, or 3 = order of choice

Note: For an absent boy or girl, use the respective symbol dashed, leaving any choice line open-ended. (See the case of Joe Brown in the above sociogram).

If rejections are obtained, the choice line may be made in dashes or in a different color.

Whenever a direct line from chooser to chosen cannot be drawn without crossing through the symbol for another individual, the line should be drawn with an elbow, as in the case of Bill Lane to Paula King.

Fig. 19-3. The social structure of one classroom. The data for this sociogram were obtained by asking each pupil to make first, second, and third choices among his classmates for a particular social activity. From Jennings (1948). With permission of the American Council on Education.

plotted in a sociogram like that shown in Fig. 19-3.

The obtained data may be manipulated in a number of different ways to describe several properties of group structure or to define the individual member's social relationships with other members in the group. Experi-

menters have been unusually ingenious in developing social-relations indices based on the partial-rank-order approach (*partial* listing in rank order) to sociometry (see Proctor and Loomis, 1951, for a summary).

For example, in instances in which the interest is in cliques of preferred companions or in describing networks of communication within the group Luce and Perry (1949) have developed a method for identifying n-chains and cliques by squaring .and cubing the matrix of intersubject preferences (see also Festinger, 1949). Festinger, Schachter, and Back (1950) used this method of matrix multiplication to advantage in describing the patterns of social interconnections existing in a multiple-unit housing project. Although this approach does not make available any information that could not be obtained by a sustained inspection of the matrix, it does provide a straightforward procedure for identifying social interconnections in a rigorous way. The availability of electronic computers greatly expedites the squaring and cubing of matrices obtained for conventional-sized small groups.

Another index of social relations has been of enduring interest to investigators with a primary concern for the individual's status or social position within a group. As may be seen in Fig. 19-2, it is relatively simple to sum the nominations in a given column and thereby find out how frequently the particular person associated with that column has been selected as a preferred companion by all other members of the group. When all of the columns are summed for a typical matrix, the resulting "scores" of social preference or "acceptability" usually comprise a highly skewed distribution. Three or four members receive over half of the votes and a few individuals may receive only one or two nominations, or none at all.

It has become conventional in soci-

ometry to speak of "stars" (individuals with many nominations) and "isolates" (individuals receiving few, or no, nominations). How many nominations, or how few, define a star or an isolate in a given-sized group making a definite number of nominations? Bronfenbrenner (1945) has proposed one solution to this problem. His method, described as a "deviation from chance expectancy" approach, involves fitting a Pearson Type III function to the obtained nominations and defining stars and isolates as falling within given restricted areas at appropriate ends of the theoretical distribution. Although this approach does constitute an unambiguous method for defining certain levels of social status, or acceptability, within a group, it does not always provide an unambiguous or psychologically meaningful basis for identifying stars and isolates (Thompson, Bligh, and Witryol, 1951).

The partial-rank-order approach (*partial* listing in rank order) to the measurement of group structure has the advantage of simplicity in both data procurement and analysis. However, its simplicity makes it vulnerable to a large number of deficiencies. The reliability and stability of some of the obtained social-relations indices are reasonably high, but the stability of the individual nomination is highly variable (Witryol and Thompson, 1953). It suffers all of the deficiencies of an ordinal scale. For example, it cannot be legitimately employed to compare the social-relations position or status of individuals who are members of nonoverlapping groups; nor can it be used to compare the social structures of different groups.[1] These shortcomings have prompted a number of investigators to attempt to find more defensible methods for describing the social structure of small groups.[2]

**The Syracuse Scales of Social Relations.** The Syracuse Scales were designed to overcome some of the deficiencies of the now traditional sociometric procedures. They were constructed to reflect specific individual needs rather than the more generally defined social situations of conventional sociometry. They involve each respondent's adopting a reference population that extends beyond the group being studied, so that the social structures of different groups can be meaningfully compared. The bisection procedures and the forced choices built into the rating procedures result in highly reliable and stable information about *each* of the social "interconnections" within a group. The following is a brief description of these new scales:[3]

To overcome some of the deficiencies of the traditional sociometric procedures, standardized instruments called the *Syracuse Scales of Social Relations* have been

[1] See Gardner and Thompson (1956) for a discussion of the metric and psychological deficiencies of the partial-rank-order approach to sociometry.

[2] The paired-comparison approach (Witryol and Thompson, 1953) is not elaborated as a measure of group structure because the data obtained by its use are relevant only to the social acceptability component. It does provide highly reliable and stable information for this purpose.

[3] From Gardner and Thompson (1959a) with permission of authors and The World Book Company.

constructed and are available for use with elementary, junior high, and senior high school pupils. The *Syracuse Scales* present social situations each one of which elicits responses calling for the satisfaction of *one* particular psychological need. For example, one situation requires the pupil to rate his classmates as kind, sympathetic friends to whom he would go in time of trouble (need-succorance). His ratings are made in reference to a scale of all persons he has ever known.

Figure 19-4 shows the frame of reference set up by Johnny F., a fifth grade pupil. From among all the persons he has ever known, he has selected his mother as the person he would *most* like to have help him when he is troubled by some personal problem. He has written her name in the "five-star" box at the top of the rating sheet above the word MOST. He next chose Alice, one of his classmates, as the person who seems to be *least* interested in helping him. He has entered her name in the "one-star" box above the word LEAST. Johnny decided that his Uncle Joe was about *medium* or in the middle for helping him when he is in trouble; that Dan, one of his classmates, was about halfway between his mother and his Uncle Joe; and that Neighbor Jones was about halfway between Alice and Uncle Joe. He has written these names in the appropriate boxes.

The five names which Johnny has written in the boxes at the top of Fig. 19-4 constitute the frame of reference for his evaluations of his classmates. He has rated each of his classmates as being nearest to one of these five persons. As can be seen in Fig. 19-4, he decided that Edith A. was a little *less good* than Neighbor Jones, so he drew a circle around the words "Less Good." He considered Joan E., pupil No. 5, as medium but a little better than Uncle Joe, so he drew a circle around the word "Better" in the column under MEDIUM. He evaluated all of his classmates in this fashion.

Since the *Syracuse Scales* use a frame of reference that extends beyond the class-

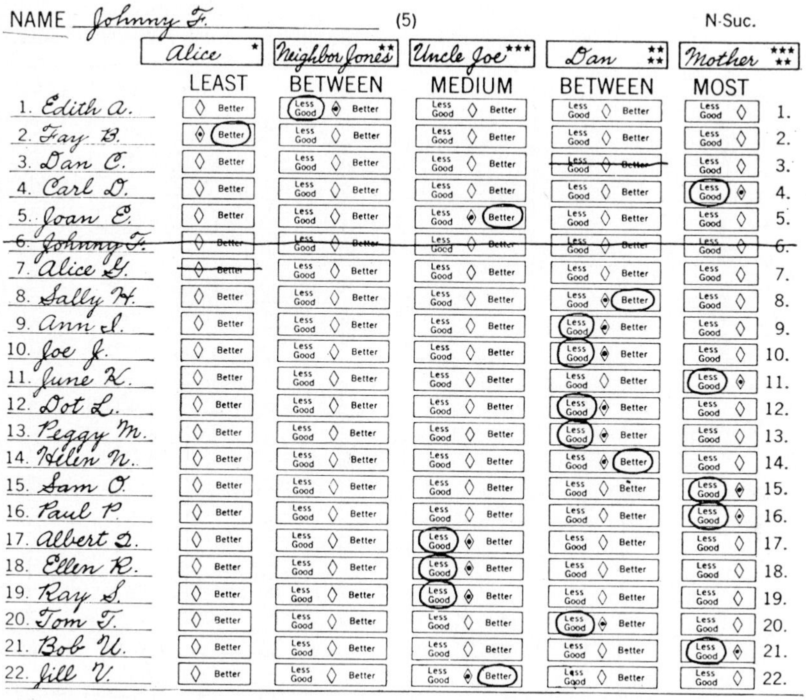

NAME *Johnny F.* (5) N-Suc.

| | *Alice* * LEAST | *Neighbor Jones* ** BETWEEN | *Uncle Joe* *** MEDIUM | *Dan* **** BETWEEN | *Mother* ***** MOST | |
|---|---|---|---|---|---|---|
| 1. *Edith A.* | | (Less Good) | | | | 1. |
| 2. *Fay B.* | (Better) | | | | | 2. |
| 3. *Dan C.* | | | | ~~Less Good ◊ Better~~ | | 3. |
| 4. *Carl D.* | | | | | (Less Good) | 4. |
| 5. *Joan E.* | | | (Better) | | | 5. |
| ~~6. *Johnny F.*~~ | ~~◊ Better~~ | ~~Less Good ◊ Better~~ | ~~Less Good ◊ Better~~ | ~~Less Good ◊ Better~~ | ~~Less Good ◊~~ | ~~6.~~ |
| 7. *Alice G.* | ~~◊ Better~~ | | | | | 7. |
| 8. *Sally H.* | | | | (Better) | | 8. |
| 9. *Ann I.* | | | | (Less Good) | | 9. |
| 10. *Joe J.* | | | | (Less Good) | | 10. |
| 11. *June K.* | | | | | (Less Good) | 11. |
| 12. *Dot L.* | | | | (Less Good) | | 12. |
| 13. *Peggy M.* | | | | (Less Good) | | 13. |
| 14. *Helen N.* | | | | (Better) | | 14. |
| 15. *Sam O.* | | | | | (Less Good) | 15. |
| 16. *Paul P.* | | | | | (Less Good) | 16. |
| 17. *Albert Q.* | | | (Less Good) | | | 17. |
| 18. *Ellen R.* | | | (Less Good) | | | 18. |
| 19. *Ray S.* | | | (Less Good) | | | 19. |
| 20. *Tom T.* | | | | (Less Good) | | 20. |
| 21. *Bob U.* | | | | | (Less Good) | 21. |
| 22. *Jill V.* | | | (Better) | | | 22. |

Fig. 19-4. The frame of reference and the ratings of Johnny F., a fifth-grade pupil, on the *Syracuse Scales of Social Relations*. From Gardner and Thompson (1959a). With permission of authors and the World Book Co.

room membership, it is possible to compare the social relations status of a pupil in a number of subgroups to which he belongs—classroom, clubs, athletic groups, etc. The pupils he selects as desirable for satisfying one need may be a very different group from those he chooses as desirable for a second need. In like manner, the frame of reference he sets up for one need may also differ considerably from that set up for the second need.

For a particular need situation, each pupil makes a rating of *every* other pupil on a scale ranging from LEAST to MOST. Figure 19-5 shows the ratings that Tommy Adams, a fifth-grade pupil has given to each of his classmates on the *need succorance* scale. A scoring guide has been applied which can be used to convert Tommy's ratings to numerical scores. Thirteen numerical scores, ranging in value from 5 to 85 are marked off on the *Scoring Guide* to correspond to the ratings in the reference scale.

In the illustration, Tommy has rated Phil B. as the person whom he would most like to have help him when he is in trouble and has placed this pupil's name in the 5-star box above the word MOST. A numerical score of 85 would be assigned to this *rating*. Tommy has rated Ray M., pupil No. 9, as a "Better" than MEDIUM person for satisfying his need. A score of 50 corresponds to this rating. In like manner, a score of 20 would be assigned to Tommy's rating of Cathy S. and a score of 10 to his rating of Betty O.

The rating that a pupil *receives* from each of his classmates can be assigned a numerical value in a similar fashion. When these scores are transferred to a pupil's test booklet, it becomes a complete record

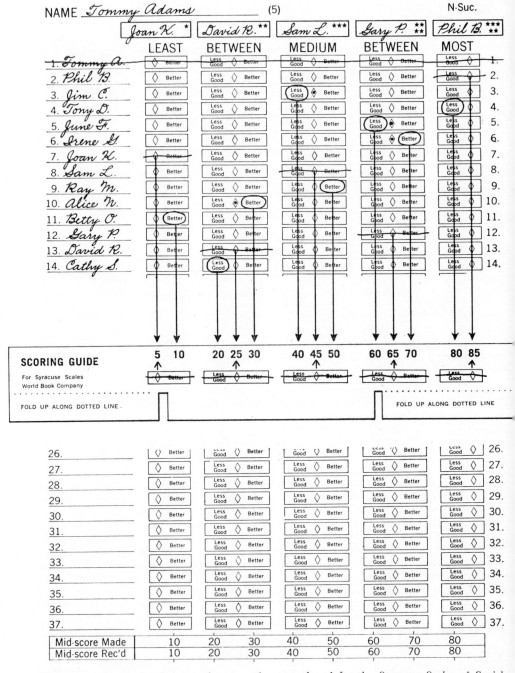

Fig. 19-5. An example of the scoring procedures employed for the *Syracuse Scales of Social Relations*. From Gardner and Thompson (1959a). With permission of authors and the World Book Co.

of the ratings he makes of his classmates and the ratings he receives from them.

The numerical scores can be used to determine a pupil's average score for ratings made and for ratings received. These average scores are referred to as mid-scores and represent the median or middle score. The mid-score of ratings made by Tommy Adams is 45, the seventh score, since Tommy rated 13 classmates.

The mid-score of the ratings that a pupil makes and the mid-score of the ratings he receives can be interpreted not only in terms of the average scores of his classmates but also in terms of percentile norms obtained from a large group of pupils at his own grade level. These social-relations norms, based on over a thousand pupils at each grade level, are similar in type to those provided with standardized achievement tests.

Norms are also provided in which the *class average* is used as a unit, so that the teacher can compare the average social-relations status of her class with the large

## SCALES FOR MEASURING SOCIAL ROLES

The partial-rank-order procedures employed in Moreno's sociometric approach have also been adapted for the measurement of social roles, or reputations, in children's groups. In this latter usage the children's nominations are used as a metric for describing an individual's behavior tendencies and social roles as they are viewed by all other members of the group.

*The "Guess Who?" Approach.* This technique, which has been used at least since the time of Hartshorne and May's early investigations of character development, presents each member of the group with a series of social role descriptions similar to those presented in Table 19-3. The subject is asked to list

**TABLE 19-3. THE GENERAL FORMAT OF THE "GUESS WHO?" APPROACH TO THE MEASUREMENT OF SOCIAL ROLES WITHIN A GROUP**

A. Here is someone who always knows what to do so everyone will have a good time at a party. Guess who?

. . . . . . . . . . . . . . . . . . . . . . . . . . . . . . . . . . . .

. . . . . . . . . . . . . . . . . . . . . . . . . . . . . . . . . . . .

. . . . . . . . . . . . . . . . . . . . . . . . . . . . . . . . . . . .

B. Here is someone who is always bossing others around and telling them what to do. Guess who?

. . . . . . . . . . . . . . . . . . . . . . . . . . . . . . . . . . . .

. . . . . . . . . . . . . . . . . . . . . . . . . . . . . . . . . . . .

. . . . . . . . . . . . . . . . . . . . . . . . . . . . . . . . . . . .

number of classes included in the normative group. Research has shown that this information is related to group morale (Gardner and Thompson, 1956).

"Chums," "triangles," and "cliques" are graphically represented, using methods similar to those utilized in sociograms. In addition to a sheer representation of mutual attractions, the magnitudes of the reciprocal ratings also indicate the strength of the social bonds that hold the members of such subgroups together.

as many of his fellow group members as he thinks fit each of these descriptions.

The metric for each social role, or description, is simply the number of nominations received by each member of the group. Data obtained in this fashion have been used to plot developmental trends in a number of investigations (Jones, 1943; Kuhlen and Lee,

1943; Tryon, 1939). Descriptions of this type have also been collected into relatively homogeneous groupings to study the more *general* reputations of group members (deGroat and Thompson, 1949; Meyer and Thompson, 1956). The reliability and stability of indices based on "Guess Who?" procedures are generally satisfactory for correlational purposes and for group comparisons.

***Ratings of Social Roles and Group Climates.*** Ratings tend to yield reliable and useful information in direct proportion to their clarity and the insightfulness of the raters. The rating scale accepts the validity of the statement "Man is the measure of all things" at face value and in its most primitive form. Ratings are generally employed for descriptive and evaluation purposes when the attribute being studied is not yet amenable to more indirect forms of measurement. (See Chapter 11 of Guilford, 1954, for a sophisticated discussion of rating scales and their proper use.)

A variation of the ratings approach, and one that has gained in favor during the last two decades, is the method of categorization of observations according to an a priori system. The frequency of behaviors assigned to different categories provides the metric for individual and group comparisons. Because Withall's category system is typical of the more carefully conceived approaches, it has been selected for illustrative purposes. Withall's approach involves a rater (or raters) distributing a teacher's (or teachers') statements made within a classroom into the following categories:[1]

Category 1. Learner-supportive statements or questions. These are teacher-statements or questions that express agreement with ideas, actions or opinions of the learner, or that commend or reassure the learner. Agreement is frequently expressed by a monosyllabic response such as "Yes," "Right," "Uhuh," and the like. Commendation or reassurance may be stated in terms of

   (*a*) class-accepted criteria or goals, or
   (*b*) the private goals and subjective criteria of the teacher.

The *dominant intent* of these statements or questions is to praise, encourage or bolster the learner.

Category 2. Acceptant or clarifying statements of questions. These are teacher-statements or questions which

   (*a*) accept, i.e., evidence considerable understanding by the teacher of, or
   (*b*) clarify, i.e., restate clearly and succinctly in the teacher's words, the ideational or the feeling content of the learner's statements. The *dominant intent* of these teacher-responses is to help the learner gain insight into his problem, i.e., define his "real" problem and its solution in more operational terms.

Category 3. Problem-structuring statements or questions. Problem-structuring responses by the teacher offer facts or ideas or opinions to the learner about either (i) phenomena, or (ii) procedures, in a non-threatening and objective manner. These responses contain *no* element of advising or recommending the adop-

---

[1] From Withall (1952) with permission of author and *Educational and Psychological Measurement*. It should be noted that this category system is not restricted to use in a classroom setting. It could also be employed in any group in which the emphasis is upon an instructional program.

tion of certain ideas or procedures. Problem-structuring responses are frequently posed as questions which seek further information from the learner about the problem confronting him; or they may be statements which offer information to the learner about his problem. The learner is free to accept or to reject in part or in entirety the facts or opinions that are presented to him. Problem-structuring responses may be questions which the teacher asks either (*a*) to further increase his own understanding of what the learner has said or (*b*) to increase the precision of the learner's statement of the problem. Problem-structuring responses are problem-centered rather than either teacher- or learner-centered. Nevertheless the *dominant intent* is to sustain the learner by facilitating his problem-solving activities.

Category 4. Statements evidencing no supportive intent. These statements are neither teacher-centered, nor learner-centered, nor problem-centered. They constitute a small percentage of the total teacher-responses. These responses include statements in which the teacher (*a*) questions himself aloud, (*b*) repeats verbatim a statement that the learner has just made, (*c*) uses a polite formality, (*d*) states an administrative or procedural detail such as "We'll meet in Room 25 tomorrow."

Category 5. Directive statements or questions. These are teacher-statements or questions which advise the learner regarding a course of action or his future behavior; they either narrowly limit his choice or offer no choice. These statements recommend to the learner the facts or procedures that the teacher proffers him. These statements or questions convey the impression to the learner that the teacher expects and hopes that he will follow her prompting and that she will approve if he does. The *dominant intent* of these responses is to have the learner take up the teacher's point of view and pursue a course of action that she advocates.

Category 6. Reproving, disapproving or disparaging statements or questions. By means of these statements a teacher may express complete or partial disapproval of the ideas, behavior and personality foibles of the learner. The teacher's internalized societal values largely enter into these responses. By means of these statements some teachers believe they are fulfilling their responsibility of inculcating in young people society's standards of acceptable behavior and achievement. The *dominant intent* of these statements is (*a*) to represent to the learner societal values as the teacher perceives them, (*b*) to admonish the learner for unacceptable behavior and to deter him from repeating it in the future, (*c*) to impress on the learner the fact that he has not met the criteria for successful achievement which the teacher sets up.

Category 7. Teacher-supportive statements or questions. These are statements or questions in which the teacher refers to himself and expresses a defensive attitude, or refers to his present or past interests, activities, or possessions with the purpose of reassuring himself and of confirming his position or his ideas in the eyes of those around him. The *dominant intent* of these teacher-responses is to assert, to defend or to justify the teacher. Statements in which the teacher perseverates on an idea, a belief or a suggestion fall into this category. By "perseverate" we mean a persisting in and a reiteration of an idea or opinion despite additional data which calls for a re-examination of the original idea or opinion.

An application of this rating, or categorization, approach to a sample of 271 teacher-statements yielded a split-half reliability of .90. The mean percentage of agreement between four raters and the investigator was found to be 65, with a range of 53 to 77 per cent. These findings demonstrate something of the power of the categorization approach when it is skillfully conceived and administered by well-trained judges.

Thelen and Withall (1949) have shown that the foregoing rating scheme yields data that are in rough agreement with pupils' responses as measured by an "audience-reception" technique (pupils push buttons to indicate their differential reactions to the social-emotional climate of the classroom). Wrightstone (1951) has proposed a somewhat different technique for measuring the social climate of a classroom, and Horowitz and Cartwright (1953) have suggested that projective methods may be used to advantage in describing the more general properties of a group. Gardner and Thompson (1956) have successfully employed a number of novel approaches to the measurement of *esprit de corps* morale within a group (e.g., estimates of asymptotes of pleasant and unpleasant recall functions and patterning of values produced in defense of group's continuing existence).

## "BACKGROUND" LITERATURE FOR RESEARCH

Research without a theoretical frame of reference is becoming relatively rare in social psychology. The advantages of a guiding theory have become so obvious to investigators that the majority hesitates to conduct empirical studies that have no explicit theoretical home. It is fortunate for the beginning student with a primary interest in children's groups that the background literature on group structure and dynamics is now readily accessible.

The following "books of readings" edited by highly competent investigators of group processes provide a modest-sized but very usable library: Cartwright and Zander (1953), Festinger and Katz (1953), Guetzkow (1951), Hare, Borgatta, and Bales (1955), Lazarsfeld and Rosenberg (1955), Miller (1950), Sherif and Wilson (1953), Sullivan (1952), and Tagiuri and Petrullo (1958).

## REFERENCES

Anderson, H. H. 1939. Domination and social integration in the behavior of kindergarten children and teachers. *Genet. Psychol. Monogr.*, 21, 287–385.

Arsenian, J. M. 1943. Young children in an insecure situation. *J. abnorm. soc. Psychol.*, 38, 225–249.

Asch, S. E. 1951. Effects of group pressure upon the modification and distortion of judgments. In H. Guetzkow (Ed.), *Groups, leadership, and men.* Pittsburgh: Carnegie Press. Pp. 177–190.

Back, K. W. 1951. Influence through social communication. *J. abnorm. soc. Psychol.*, 46, 9–23.

Bales, R. F. 1950. *Interaction process analysis: A method for the study of small groups.* Cambridge, Mass.: Addison-Wesley.

Barker, R. G. 1942. The social interrelations of strangers and acquaintances. *Sociometry*, 5, 169–179.

———, and H. F. Wright. 1954. *Midwest and its children: The psychological ecology of an American town.* Evanston, Ill.: Row, Peterson.

Bavelas, A. 1950. Communication patterns in task oriented groups. *J. acoustical Soc. of Amer.*, 22, 725–730.

Bion, W. R. 1952. Group dynamics: A review. *Int. J. Psychoanal.*, 33, 235–247.

Bishop, B. M. 1951. Mother-child interaction and the social behavior of children. *Psychol. Monogr.*, 65, No. 11.

Bogardus, E. S. 1933. A social distance scale. *Sociol. soc. Res.*, 17, 265–271.

Bonney, M. E., and S. A. Fessenden. 1955. *Bonney-Fessenden Sociograph*. Los Angeles, Calif.: California Test Bureau.

Borgatta, E. F. 1954. Analysis of social interaction and sociometric perception. *Sociometry*, 17, 7–32.

Bronfenbrenner, U. 1945. The measurement of sociometric status, structure and development. *Sociomet. Monogr.*, No. 6.

Campbell, D. T. 1957. Factors relevant to the validity of experiments in social settings. *Psychol. Bull.*, 54, 297–312.

Carter, L. F., W. Haythorn, and M. Howell. 1950. A further investigation of the criteria of leadership. *J. abnorm. soc. Psychol.*, 45, 350–358.

Carter, L. F., W. Haythorn, E. Shriver, and J. Lanzetta. 1951. The behavior of leaders and other group members. *J. abnorm. soc. Psychol.*, 46, 589–595.

Cartwright, D., and A. F. Zander, (Eds.). 1953. *Group dynamics: Research and theory*. Evanston, Ill.: Row, Peterson.

Cattell, R. B., D. R. Saunders, and G. F. Stice. 1953. The dimensions of syntality in small groups. *Hum. Relat.*, 6, 331–356.

Criswell, J. H. 1943. Sociometric methods of measuring group preferences. *Sociometry*, 6, 398–408.

deGroat, A. F., and G. G. Thompson. 1949. A study of the distribution of teacher approval and disapproval among sixth-grade pupils. *J. exper. Educ.*, 18, 57–75.

Dennis, W., and P. Najarian. 1957. Infant development under environmental handicap. *Psychol. Monogr.*, 71, No. 7.

Deutsch, M. 1949. An experimental study of the effects of cooperation and competition upon group processes. *Hum. Relat.*, 2, 199–231.

Faigin, H. 1958. Case report: Social behavior of young children in the Kibbutz. *J. abnorm. soc. Psychol.*, 56, 117–129.

Fessenden, S. A. 1953. An index of cohesiveness-morale based on the analysis of sociometric choice distribution. *Sociometry*, 16, 321–326.

Festinger, L. 1949. The analysis of sociograms using matrix algebra. *Hum. Relat.*, 2, 153–158.

Festinger, L. 1951. Informal communications in small groups. In H. Guetzkow (Ed.), *Groups, leadership and men: Research in human relations*. Pittsburgh: Carnegie Press. Pp. 28–43.

———. 1953. Laboratory experiments. In L. Festinger and D. Katz (Eds.), *Research methods in the behavioral sciences*. New York: Dryden. Pp. 136–172.

———, and D. Katz. 1953. (Eds.) *Research methods in the behavioral sciences*. New York: Dryden.

Festinger, L., S. Schachter, and K. Back. 1950. *Social pressures in informal groups: A study of human factors in housing*. New York: Harper.

Fiedler, F. E. 1954. Assumed similarity measures as predictors of team effectiveness. *J. abnorm. soc. Psychol.*, 49, 381–388.

French, J. R. P., Jr. 1941. The disruption and cohesion of groups. *J. abnorm. soc. Psychol.*, 36, 361–377.

———. 1944. Organized and unorganized groups under fear and frustration. *Univer. Iowa Stud. Child Welf.*, 20, No. 409, 229–308.

Gardner, E. F., and G. G. Thompson. 1956. *Social relations and morale in small groups*. New York: Appleton-Century-Crofts.

———. 1959a. *Syracuse scales of social relations. Manuals for elementary, junior high, and senior high levels*. Yonkers, N. Y.: World Book.

———. 1959b. Measuring and interpreting social relations. *Test service notebook*, No. 22. Yonkers, N. Y.: World Book.

Gross, N., and W. E. Martin. 1952. On group cohesiveness. *Amer. J. Sociol.*, 57, 546–554.

Grosser, D., N. Polansky, and R. Lippitt. 1951. A laboratory study of behavioral contagion. *Hum. Relat.*, 4, 115–142.

Guetzkow, H. 1950. Unitizing and categorizing problems in coding qualitative data. *J. clin. Psychol.*, 6, 47–58.

——— (Ed.). 1951. *Groups, leadership and men: Research in human relations*. Pittsburgh: Carnegie Press.

Guilford, J. P. 1954. *Psychometric methods*. New York: McGraw-Hill.

Hanfmann, E. P. 1935. Social structure of a

group of kindergarten children. *Amer. J. Orthopsychiat.* **5,** 407–410.

Hare, A. P. 1953. Small group discussions with participatory and supervisory leadership. *J. abnorm. soc. Psychol.,* **48,** 273–275.

———, E. F. Borgatta, and R. F. Bales. (Eds.) 1955. *Small groups: Studies in social interaction.* New York: Knopf.

Heise, G. A., and G. A. Miller. 1951. Problem solving by small groups using various communication nets. *J. abnorm. soc. Psychol.,* **46,** 327–335.

Hemphill, J. K. 1949. Situational factors in leadership. *Ohio State Univer. Bur. Educ. Res. Monogr.,* No. 32.

———, and C. M. Westie. 1950. The measurement of group dimensions. *J. Psychol.,* **29,** 325–342.

Horowitz, M., and D. Cartwright. 1953. A projective method for the diagnosis of group properties. *Hum. Relat.,* **6,** 397–410.

Horrocks, J. E., and M. E. Buker. 1951. A study of the friendship fluctuations of preadolescents. *J. genet. Psychol.,* **78,** 131–144.

Jack, Lois M. 1934. An experimental study of ascendant behavior in preschool children. *Univer. Iowa Stud. Child Welf.,* **9,** No. 3.

Jennings, H. H. 1948. *Sociometry in group relations: A work guide for teachers.* Wash., D. C.: Amer. Counc. Educ.

———. 1950. *Leadership and isolation.* (2nd ed.) New York: Longmans, Green.

Jones, H. E. 1943. *Development in adolescence.* New York: Appleton-Century-Crofts.

Kelley, T. L., et al. 1953. *Stanford achievement test manual.* Yonkers, N. Y.: World Book.

Kuhlen, R. G., and B. J. Lee. 1943. Personality characteristics and social acceptability in adolescence. *J. educ. Psychol.,* **34,** 321–340.

Lanzetta, J. T., D. Haefner, P. Langham, and H. Axelrod. 1954. Some effects of situational threat on group behavior. *J. abnorm. soc. Psychol.,* **49,** 445–453.

Lazarsfeld, P. F., and M. Rosenberg, (Eds.). 1955. *The language of social research: A reader in the methodology of social research.* Glencoe, Ill.: Free Press.

Leavitt, H. J. 1951. Some effects of certain communication patterns on group performance. *J. abnorm. soc. Psychol.,* **46,** 38–50.

Lewin, K. 1946. Behavior and development as a function of the total situation. In L. Carmichael (Ed.), *Manual of child psychology.* New York: Wiley. Pp. 791–844.

———. 1948. *Resolving social conflicts: Selected papers on group dynamics.* New York: Harper.

———, R. Lippitt, and R. K. White. 1939. Patterns of aggressive behavior in experimentally created "social climates." *J. soc. Psychol.,* **10,** 271–299.

Lindzey, G., and E. F. Borgatta. 1954. Sociometric measurements. In G. Lindzey (Ed.), *Handbook of social psychology.* Cambridge, Mass.: Addison-Wesley. Pp. 405–448.

Lippitt, R. 1940. An experimental study of the effect of democratic and authoritarian group atmospheres. *Univer. Iowa Stud. Child Welf.,* **16,** 43–195.

———, N. Polansky, and S. Rosen. 1952. The dynamics of power: A field study of social influence in groups of children. *Hum. Relat.,* **5,** 37–64.

Loomis, C. P., and H. B. Pepinsky. 1948. Sociometry, 1937–1947: Theory and methods. *Sociometry,* **11,** 262–286.

Luce, R. D., and A. D. Perry. 1949. A method of matrix analysis of group structure. *Psychometrika,* **14,** 95–116.

Luszki, M. B. 1950. Empathic ability and social perception. Unpublished doctoral thesis, Univer. Michigan.

McCandless, B. R., and H. R. Marshall. 1957. A picture sociometric technique for preschool children and its relation to teacher judgments of friendship. *Child Develpm.,* **28,** 139–148.

Meyer, W. J., and G. G. Thompson. 1956. Sex differences in the distribution of teacher approval and disapproval among sixth-grade children. *J. educ. Psychol.,* **47,** 385–396.

Miller, J. G. (Ed.). 1950. *Experiments in social process.* New York: McGraw-Hill.

Moreno, J. L. 1951. *Sociometry, experimental method and the science of society.* Beacon, N. Y.: Beacon House.

———. 1953. *Who shall survive?* (Rev. ed.) Beacon, N. Y.: Beacon House.

Murphy, Lois B. 1937. *Social behavior and*

*child personality: An exploratory study of some roots of sympathy.* New York: Columbia Univer. Press.

Northway, M. L. 1952. *A primer of sociometry.* Toronto, Canada: Univer. Toronto Press.

Page, M. L. 1936. The modification of ascendant behavior in preschool children. *Univer. Iowa Stud. Child Welf.*, 12, No. 3.

Parten, M. B. 1932. Social participation among preschool children. *J. abnorm. soc. Psychol.*, 27, 243–269.

———. 1933. Leadership among preschool children. *J. abnorm. soc. Psychol.*, 27, 430–440.

Polansky, N., W. Freeman, M. Horowitz, L. Irwin, N. Papania, D. Rapaport, and F. Whaley. 1949. Problems of interpersonal relations in research on groups. *Hum. Relat.*, 2, 281–291.

Polansky, N. A., R. Lippitt, and F. Redl. 1950. An investigation of behavioral contagion in groups. *Hum. Relat.*, 3, 319–348.

Proctor, C. H., and C. P. Loomis. 1951. Analysis of sociometric data. In Marie Jahoda, M. Deutsch, and S. W. Cook (Eds.), *Research methods in social relations: With especial reference to prejudice.* New York: Dryden. Pp. 561–585.

Rabin, A. I. 1957. Personality maturity of Kibbutz (Israeli Collective Settlement) and non-Kibbutz children as reflected in Rorschach findings. *J. proj. Tech.*, 21, 148–153.

Roseborough, M. E. 1953. Experimental studies of small groups. *Psychol. Bull.*, 50, 275–303.

Schachter, S., N. Ellertson, D. McBride, D. Gregory. 1951. An experimental study of cohesiveness and productivity. *Hum. Relat.*, 4, 229–238.

Shartle, C. L. 1952. Ohio State leadership studies. *Engng. Exp. Station News*, Ohio State Univer., 24, 16–21.

Sherif, M., and M. O. Wilson (Eds.). 1953. *Group relations at the crossroads.* New York: Harper.

Sullivan, D. F. (Ed.). 1952. *Readings in group work.* New York: Association Press.

Tagiuri, R. 1952. Relational analysis: An extension of sociometric method with emphasis upon sociometric perception. *Sociometry*, 15, 91–104.

Tagiuri, R., and L. Petrullo (Eds.). 1958. *Person perception and interpersonal behavior.* Stanford, Calif.: Stanford Univer. Press.

Thelen, H. A., and J. Withall. 1949. Three frames of reference: The description of climate. *Hum. Relat.*, 2, 159–176.

Thibaut, J. W. 1950. An experimental study of the cohesiveness of underprivileged groups. *Hum. Relat.*, 3, 251–278.

Thomas, D. S. (Ed.). 1929. *Some new techniques for studying social behavior.* New York: Teach. Coll., Columbia Univer. Press.

Thompson, G. G., H. F. Bligh, and S. L. Witryol. 1951. A critical examination of several methods of determining levels of social status. *J. soc. Psychol.*, 33, 13–32.

Thompson, G. G., and J. E. Horrocks. 1947. A study of the friendship fluctuations of urban boys and girls. *J. genet. Psychol.*, 70, 53–63.

Thompson, M. M. 1940. *The effect of discriminatory leadership on the relations between the more and less privileged subgroups.* Unpublished doctoral dissertation, State Univer. Iowa.

Thrasher, F. 1927. *The gang.* Chicago: Univer. Chicago Press.

Tryon, C. M. 1939. Evaluations of adolescent personality by adolescents. *Soc. Res. Child Develpm. Monogr.*, 4, No. 4.

Withall, J. 1952. Assessment of the social-emotional climates experienced by a group of seventh graders as they moved from class to class. *Educ. Psychol. Measmt.*, 12, 440–451.

Witryol, S. L., and G. G. Thompson. 1953. A critical review of the stability of social acceptability scores obtained with the partial-rank-order and the paired-comparison scales. *Genet. Psychol. Monogr.*, 48, 221–260.

Wright, M. E. 1940. *The influence of frustration upon the social relationships of young children.* Unpublished doctoral dissertation, State Univer. Iowa.

Wrightstone, J. W. 1951. Measuring the social climate of a classroom. *J. educ. Res.*, 44, 341–351.

chapter *20*

# *Interpersonal Behavior*

William W. Lambert
*Cornell University*

## *The Problem*

In this chapter we discuss how we can study the interpersonal behavior in which children are involved. Although this may appear to be an easy thing to do, most active researchers would agree that, next to children's motives, it is the most tangled and difficult area of study in all of child development. Furthermore, there is a sense in which most of the techniques we have developed in this area are short-cut methods that permit us to work in the general realm of the "interpersonal" but that also usually evade some of the important problems.

First we wish to create a "sense of problem" about interpersonal behavior because there is no doubt that there is a number of exciting and subtle issues here. Then we must look at what we now have available to work with.

The writer wishes to record his appreciation of the ideas and help that have come from the staff of the Cornell-Harvard-Yale study of socialization in five cultures and from Elisabeth C. Lambert and A. L. Baldwin. He takes all responsibility for what is said here, however.

Finally, we speculate concerning the costly and complicated techniques that the future may bring, which will permit a more direct attack on the problems of this area.

It is necessary, however, to outline the focus of the present discussion because so much space in this book is devoted to what is broadly referred to as the "interpersonal" or "social" aspects of a child's development. Sociometric, projective, and experimental methods are all used to study a child's relationships with others, as are the observational techniques discussed by Wright (Chapter 3). We limit the discussion in this chapter to what some people have done in order to observe as directly as possible the social interaction of children, which involves such behavior as aggression, dominance, sociability, helpfulness, and competition.

This discussion may be somewhat more substantive than some of the other topics in this book, since it focuses as much on a rather homogeneous set of phenomena as it does on methods and techniques. Since the emphasis here is on direct observation, such devices as sociometry, doll play, and the TAT are less relevant, for those devices permit a study of interaction more indirectly or at a farther remove from its actual occurrence. Doll play may be an excellent device for studying aggressive relations in the fantasy of children, and sociometry may permit a map to be drawn of the relationships children report to others that they are engaged in. The focus in this chapter, however, is on how an investigator can record in a reliable and valid way the relationships that a child engages in as seen by a "trained observer" rather than by the

854

child himself. No doubt there are relationships, for example, between the actual aggressive behavior of a child or a child's peer group and his fantasy, and there is undoubtedly great overlap between the relationships a child sees himself in and those that a scientific observer would see. But these are research questions that cannot be decided a priori. The one kind of data can validate the other, so to speak, although investigators often place a premium on the "actual" behavior and the "scientifically observed" relationship as being the criteria against which other techniques are judged. This is our major focus.

The present aim is broader than the issues of "how to see behavior in the raw" or how to validate other measures. We hope to discuss the methods of studying interpersonal behavior in such a way that we may be able to improve our chances of relating our records of these occurrences to the situational and antecedent conditions that give rise to them. The aim of the study of child development is not merely to record the daily life of a child, nor is it merely to assist in the task of developing tests. It is to use records and tests in the context of the analysis of determinants of the phenomena that records and tests are theoretically stated to reflect. Our long-range intention must be "causal" or "antecedent-consequent" analysis, so that observational methods must be tied closely with good design of studies with as much use of experimental method as the question under consideration permits. We reiterate this emphasis throughout this chapter.

## SOME KINDS OF INTERPERSON ACTION UNITS

Figure 20-1 presents one way of representing an interpersonal-behavior situation to which we frequently refer in this chapter. The figure represents three persons in interaction: person $(P)$ who is usually the "subject" in child development studies; other $(O)$ who is any other person with whom the child is seen as interacting, mother, father, sibling, etc; and a "third person" $(TP)$ who is often involved when we consider a total interaction because he may be the recipient of a "displaced aggression" that arises from the interaction of $O$ and $P$ or he may be the person who rewards or punishes both $O$ and $P$ because of what they have done in the interaction.

Each of these three individuals is in a "social or physical situation," which in part determines what will go on. Arrows with dashed lines radiate from the situation "box" of the diagram to impinge upon the "external instigations" that are working on each actor. These arrows represent the situational influences that comprise part of the external instigation. If, for example, all three are in a church, the situation will arouse inhibitions (or *be* inhibitions, depending on one's theory of stimulation) with regard to the loudness with which they talk and with regard to certain topics of conversation or forbidden actions. These situational components of the "external instigations" are called "external" here only because they can be varied by taking the actors out of church or by varying such matters as whether a service is in progress.

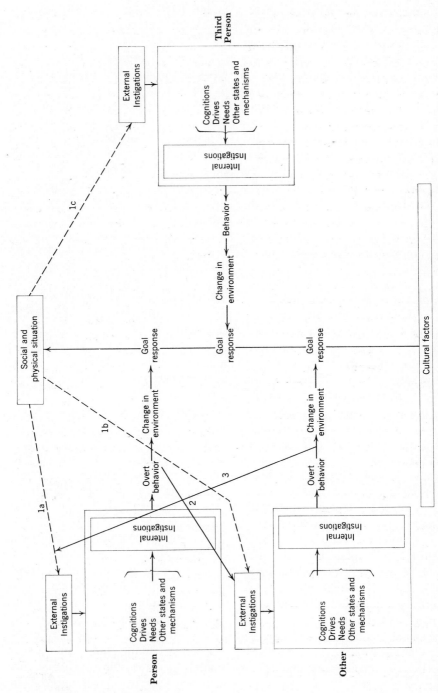

Fig. 20-1. A schematic representation of the setting of the interpersonal behavior involving a subject (*P*), another person (*O*) and a third person (*TP*) and of some of the elements involved in the analysis of such interpersonal behavior.

The bottom box of the figure refers to "cultural factors," which impinge upon the situation box to help define the social situation to the actors or to help the scientific observer predict which aspects of the social or physical situation will impinge upon them. We have also represented the box of the cultural factors as somehow encompassing the total diagram. We do this because we still know so little about how these factors operate. There are many definitions for the notion of "culture" and many ways in which it is viewed as affecting action. Sometimes it is seen as determinative of the entire pattern of Fig. 20-1. Sometimes it is seen as being involved in the past learnings of each actor so that it is reflected in the cognitions and needs or other states of each actor. Sometimes it is seen as "defining" what should be done by each actor at the moment. There is also much vagueness about just what (short of everything) "culture" determines. We will not try here to resolve such large issues nor to prejudge any direct empirical issues on this score. We may say, however, that "being in a church situation" has different effects on the external instigations for actors if the church is Buddhist rather than Greek Orthodox—assuming that the actors have learned the difference. We include "cultural factors," therefore, in at least this sense. Although we intend nothing mystical, we must accept some vagueness and some ambiguity in regard to these factors because of our present lack of knowledge and lack of agreement on the use of terms.

The diagram in Fig. 20-1 implies or assumes an objective approach to the study of interaction. This is not because of dogma or because of any belief that this is the "best" way to approach these matters. The objective view is adopted for two reasons. The first is that it is very difficult to diagram interaction in a simple way by using a subjective approach because one would have to have a number of diagrams for each of the three actors in Fig. 20-1—the view of each with regard to the other two, plus diagrams representing what each thought that each of the others saw in him, and so on. This is too complicated for the requirements of the present problem.

The second reason is simply that our state of knowledge in child development with regard to "internal instigations" (cognitions, needs, drives, and other states and mechanisms) that occur inside the actors is not yet adequate to treat them *in principle* as other than inferences made by the "independent" observer. That is, we can decide that a child is aware of the fact that he is in church because he tells us he is or on the basis of this statement and other behavior of his. In either case it is safest to view the decision as a deduction or an inference and state as clearly as possible the basis for the decision. The objective approach functions as a constant reminder to tell others the bases of our inferences. A subjective approach can do this too, of course, but we would then have to add a whole series of diagrams to reflect what the scientific observer saw in the situation that led him to be able to determine how each actor saw the situation. Figure 20-1 is this last kind of diagram, especially for the reader who likes to draw "field diagrams" or use other kinds of subjective definitions for the things in the "internal instigation" boxes. Figure 20-1 will merely remind such a reader as well as ourselves that he must *also* use operational definitions for such states in order that we can understand him more fully.

In short, we recognize that different aspects of a social situation will be "taken up" by different actors in Fig. 20-1. We do this, for example, by characterizing the arrows emanating from the situation box as (1a) for $P$, (1b) for $O$ and (1c) for $TP$. Such a notation solves no problems, but it may state some. There is a similarity in the influence of the social or physical situation (and via these, of culture) on the different actors. There is also, sometimes at least, a difference. It is a problem of how well we *can* measure these influences and how much of such measurement we have really done that is involved here, not whether the influences *really* reside in the situation or in the behaving actors. The "influence" might be measured in the situation itself, in the physical stimuli impinging upon the actor(s), within the actor himself (inferred from antecedent-consequent relationships), or by the arbitrary (but creative and useful) tools devised by the scientific observer, including his own judgment (checked for reliability and for validity). The cosmology of the place of measurement is not so important as the brute question, "Have we *any* way of measuring the influence of these things we think may be important so that we can get a notion how important they *are?*"

The reader should note that we have made a place for three general sources of influence that make up the "external instigations" for an actor. We have already discussed the cultural and social or physical sources of variance. The third source of influence is what is done immediately by other people that is apperceived by the actor. We have placed two arrows numbered (2) and (3) to illustrate this source of variance. The first of these (2) could take the concrete form of an act by $P$ whereby he asks help from $O$; the second of these arrows emanates from $O$'s behavior—helping, for example—which provides the conditions for $P$ to obtain what he wanted help to get; that is, this act of $O$ helps to provide the occasion of a goal response for $P$. Such arrows, of course, select somewhat arbitrarily certain things that occur in order to give them special attention. The "asking" behavior of $P$ may also impinge on him as well as on $O$ as a self-initiated external instigation, just as the act (3) of helping does that $O$ then emits. In the case of the first (2), once $P$ has asked for help, the probability of his asking again may be increased or decreased, depending, for example, on the strength of his "need for nurturance" or of his "need for independence." This probability of "asking again" may also vary with the social situation (there may be rules against seeking help, for example, in a sport situation) or as a function of culture (there may be a general cultural value that rules out asking for help except in dire necessity). It may also vary, of course, with whether or not the request and the immediate problem that gave rise to the request is satisfied by $O$.

These considerations begin to lead us toward the complexities involved in attempts to study "interaction" directly, to which we shall soon turn. We shall not dwell, however, on the arbitrariness implicit in our arrows, since this is an aspect of all attempts to deal analytically and scientifically with any phenomenon. It is always necessary to leave out of consideration not only many aspects of the "concrete case," whose function we do not yet know, but also a good many things that we already know may be partly determinative. It does no good to argue that "the more we can observe and cogitate on, the better" because there is no way of knowing, a priori, what is relevant, and the addition of "some more" that is irrelevant may merely frustrate the researcher and rule out his discovery of the clarity or order that otherwise might be there. We should also remind ourselves that our techniques of measurement, our theories, and our available statistical models always have a limit on what they can handle.

Returning to Fig. 20-1, the external instigation is seen as influencing the internal instigation(s) to lead each actor to behave overtly in such a way that this behavior could, in principle, be seen by an independent observer. Two clarifying statements are called for with regard to this complicated process. First, there are many problems involved in this exchange. Theoretical differences exist as to assumption on such issues as whether external or internal instigations are more important (either in general or with regard to specific classes of interactions), how to conceptualize the components of internal instigation, how to conceptualize the interactions among such components, etc. Second, great restrictions exist in solving such problems because of the limits of our measurement skills.

Our second statement is a reminder that most of the components of internal instigation are inferred by the observer. This means that they should ideally be indexed or varied independently of the particular interaction observed if they are to be used rigorously in an explanatory way. If the hypothesis, for example, is that a child's interaction with another person is dependent upon the child's knowledge (cognition) about that person, then we should ideally be able to report both the interaction and the child's knowledge by the use of separate and independent operations. There is more than one way of doing this. The ideal approach would be to control the children's acquisition of relevant knowledge prior to the interaction, thus providing both a measure of the degree of knowledge as well as an experimental control over its acquisition. Sometimes we can only study the past history of the children with regard to such knowledge and make an inference (using what we already know or hypothesize about child learning and development) as to what the state of knowledge is at the time of the observation of the interaction. It is not our present problem to decide which of these independent indexing methods is best. It is necessary to point out that some such operations are called for, and the more there are, the firmer the interpretation of our finding will be. The same holds true with regard to the components of external instigation, except that sometimes these can be varied more directly (though not necessarily more easily), for example, when we first study a child interacting in church and then remove him to a playground.

Returning once more to Fig. 20-1, it should be noted that the scheme includes two further elements for each of the actors. The first of these is the reference to "changes in environment" that occur as the result of behavior on the part of an actor. This refers to a wide array of possible things and can be used theoretically in several ways. One fruitful way is that of Sears (1951) who finds it useful to point out that one of the usual changes in the environment that occurs following an aggressive act is a sign of pain in the person toward whom the aggression is directed. This sign of pain is sometimes a necessary condition for a goal response to occur, and it may itself take on value and become a source of satisfaction to a child under certain conditions.

Following the change in environment comes the goal response, if the interaction is a "successful" one for the actor. If the child wanted or at least asked for help and received it, this occurrence is a goal response (so that the instrumental act of O provides the goal response for P). If the help is successful in solving the original problem (which may have been either externally or internally instigated), this may also be considered as an additional goal response—"getting the task finished." Such usages depend on what theory one is entertaining, upon what categories one is using, and, of course, what one assumes can be abstracted from the concrete flux and flow of action with the method being used.

Some "goal responses" are, of course, not available or may not be noticed by the independent observer. Perhaps the child who asked for help did so mainly to keep O from doing something else or to dominate him. Part of the problem of methods in this kind of problem involves the question of how to arrange a study to provide either direct "noticing" or a basis for inference of such goal responses. Theoretically, it may be the case that a child who asks for help in order to dominate may have tendencies to seek help, as well as a particular form of cupidity strengthened. If the observer is set for one and not the other, he is not necessarily wrong in what he does record but may have missed something else.

In the present state of our efficiency in research this may not be important at all, unless, of course, it so happens that the problem at hand is to predict P's future succorant tendencies from effects of present interaction and such predictions would be improved by knowing when succorance has become strongly associated with dominance. This may be a fault of theory, rather than of the method of observation. Of course, it may be the case that P asks for help in a sports situation for achievement purposes as well as for dominance (and succorance), and there may be three goal responses occurring almost at the same instant. Even if the observer is set for all three and the theory for prediction is quite adequate, the reliability may drop drastically because one observer cannot attend to such complexity. Here observation method is at fault, and another observer or two or a different research design may be called for, as we suggest later in this chapter. There are always limits, however. The "totality of interaction" is never available for direct study, and the notion of the "total field" will always retain an immense component of "extra meaning" that is not realized (and probably not realizable) in measurement terms.

If the import of Fig. 20-1 is now more or less clear, let us use it to help outline some of the kinds of interperson units that have been studied or that might be studied. Discussion follows the order of complexity of such units.

*Single Acts.* It is often the case that the observer is set to observe the occurrences of a certain class of act, engaged in by $P$ or $O$ or both, or to observe the occurrence of that class of act in a whole group. In fact, the observer may be set to record occurrences of a number of such categories at the same time. The main characteristic of this kind of unit is, however, its extreme simplicity when viewed in the context of Fig. 20-1. When he is recording, for example, the frequencies of aggression or dominance in terms of single acts, the observer is watching the totality of the interaction as shown in Fig. 20-1, but he is recording only some of the acts of $P$, using the totality for purposes of assuring himself that he is categorizing

correctly. He may be recording from an a priori or an empirical check list, which may be either detailed and specific or quite general.

Suppose $O$ and $P$ are playing a game and $P$ asks $O$ for help. An observer who is set to record dependent acts may be poised to record this as one, but he may desist when he notices smiles on the faces of both and immediately recognizes that this is a joke where both actors apparently know the rules that obviate such help. Such is the context, in part, and such is the way the context may be utilized by the observer. Since the act has something to do with dependency—it is a "succorance joke," so to speak—it may become recorded if the categories the observer is utilizing have a place for it. Otherwise it may be left out altogether or wrongly included.

Single-act recording is probably the simplest and most reliable way to go about studying something about interpersonal relations. But there is a sense in which it has very little to do with anything "interpersonal" at all. The researcher is also very limited in the uses to which he can put the data that emerge from such records. Both points call for a bit more expansion.

First, single-act records are interpersonal only insofar as the actors are directing their "single acts" toward one another and insofar as the observer is making use of cues in the total context that do not appear on his record. As we shall see, there are many other senses in which they are not "interpersonal" at all but are usually placed in this general category because the category of acts studied often has a social sounding name rather than because the unit of recording used is actually social in its content.

Second, single-act records can lead an unwary analyst into difficulties in interpretation. Suppose the observer is following children around, one at a time, in order to study the individual differences in their succorant behavior.

Even though his records include a good sampling and are reliable, he will have difficulty in inferring that the differences are due to differences in the children because he cannot partial out the differences that might be due to the instigations to succorance that the children met. The least succorant of children might display a good deal of this behavior if they met a number of extreme problems during the recording session.

Such worries can be greatly reduced, of course, if the observation takes place under experimental conditions in which the instigation is kept carefully controlled or is equated in some way for each subject. When we consider this case, we see how this form of "interpersonal" study is much the same as that used in most individual laboratory study of animals or humans. The barpress of a rat is formally similar and differs mainly because it is directed toward a physical rather than a social object and is usually recorded by a mechanical counter rather than by the human observer.

Single-act records can also be used to characterize some groups in which children work or play. One nursery-school group may show more frequent aggressive acts than another, and single-act recording may reliably and validly reflect this fact. Such records, however, will usually permit very little analysis of the reasons for such group differences: for instance, different teachers, more frustrating play conditions, the presence of one or two bullies, or an average difference in one or more personality traits in the children studied. Analyses of these kinds call for a more complex form of recording or a carefully manipulated experimental design.

*Interactions.* When we talk about interactions, we are referring to situations in which two (or more) children are being observed and in which the recorded unit includes facts about the behavior of more than one child. This kind of unit can take many specific forms but often involves in terms of Fig. 20-1 at least as much as the arrows in that figure imply. Examples of interactions might be the following: $O$ asks for help and $P$ helps; $O$ strikes $P$ and $P$ retaliates; $O$ orders $P$ to do something other than what he is doing and $P$ complies. Such are the minimum requirements of *interact* recording as we mean it here—it is action that involves at least two persons. It is a double or compound act, so to speak, rather than a single one.

Let us quickly make one further and important distinction regarding the recording of *sociological* interactions. The difference has to do with whether or not one or more of the subjects who are being observed are "replaceable." Sometimes both $O$ and $P$ are in principle completely replaceable by a different $O$ and $P$. Suppose one is interested in studying the effect of a physical setting on interaction. The observer might place himself first in a sample of large playgrounds and then in a sample of small ones, recording all cases of aggressive interactions that occur. Since the analysis is going to be made in terms of settings, there is no need to record the proper names of any of the children involved. The observer is set to record any of a number of actions, retaining the relationships between instigation and action in the record. In our sense, all pairs of actors are replaceable with any other pair.

The analysis can then focus on the effects of size of playground on instigations (e.g., the number of verbal and physical "assaultings"), on retaliation (the proportion of retaliations to assaultings), or on simple frequency of aggressive actions. We assume that other control issues have been met, such as size of the group of children and socioeconomic area from which the children are drawn. In terms of replaceability, the study is a sociological or a social-psychological one. This observational unit is often what is referred to as the basis of an analysis of role behavior, in which $P$ is a policeman, for example, and $O$ is a motorist, but $O$ is no particular motorist and $P$ is no particular policeman.

A middle case occurs when $P$ is not replaceable, whereas $O$ is replaceable. Such is the case when $P$'s proper name is recorded, and the observer is watching both what he does and what others do to him with an interest in making a diagnosis of $P$'s personality on the basis of such "input-output" information. In such a case it is not necessary to record the proper names of the various Others with whom $P$ has com-

merce. It is sufficient to record the age of $O$, the relative status of $O$, or, perhaps, whether or not $O$ is a friend of $P$. The Others are replaceable, whereas $P$ is not, since he ($P$) is either an end of study in himself or is one of those selected as representative of an age or population group and therefore a number of different observations must be referred to him. He is replaceable only in the statistical sense.

A completely *interpersonal* study of interaction is a very different and a rather rare thing. Here neither $O$ nor $P$ is replaceable. This might occur when the observer is interested in watching friendships or in long-term relationships in a family group. Let us consider the second case. The observer will feel called upon to record the proper names of all family members who appear in interaction with $P$ or with any one of them who is being viewed as $P$. The fact that $P$ is being asked to help an "older boy" is not enough—the observer is interested in the fact that the older boy is $P$'s brother Peter, whose relationships with $P$ have become strained, perhaps because of the arrival of a new family member or because the relationship between the parents of these two children has been deteriorating in some manner. In this case the observer will want to record, at a minimum, the names of $P$ and of $O$, the instigations involved, the behaviors such instigations invoked, and the name of the person who created the instigations in the first place.

A complete interpersonal interaction is a complex unit even in its simplest form and may require a number of observers for its adequate coverage. Each of these observers must supply coordinated bits of information, which will go to make up the interpersonal interact. It may also be achieved by one observer who samples the interactional life of first one then another member of the family, viewing each in turn as $P$ in Fig. 20-1. It is then extremely vital that the proper names of $O$'s be recorded, and the interpersonal interaction of $P$ with each $O_1$, $O_2$, etc., may need to be cross-filed with the data collected for $O_1$ and $O_2$ when they were serving as $P$.

A sample of *interpersonal interacts* is therefore a far cry from a sample of single acts or even from a sample of sociological interacts. None of these is *generally* more "correct" than another, but for any given research question one may be adequate, another may be quite inadequate, and the third may be overadequate and wasteful of observing time and of analysis time. As we shall see, child development has hardly begun to collect the information necessary to make researches efficient in this regard, and such efficiency will not emerge without help from statisticians, theorists, and experts in study and design.

*Interpersonal Activities.* There are many units of "interpersonal behavior" that call for much less fine texture in the record than is called for in the units we have so far described. Take, for example, the observer who is interested in recording the interpersonal *relations* between two boys or in a group of boys. It may be silly to attempt to record all the instigations or actions that occur between or among these actors when the fact that they are "playing together" or are "meeting together" or

are "getting together to fight" against some other group is sufficient. In these cases the fact of contact of some duration is sufficient, and the rate of such contact, the initiator of such contact, etc., can provide indices of the strength or frequency of the relationship's occurrence.

It is to these broader aspects of interpersonal relations that the various forms of sociometric questions are usually directed. Here we ask $P$ to tell us whom he would choose, or would like to choose under certain conditions, for companionship in various activities, such as going to the movies or having a roommate. There is reason to hope that systematic study of the relation between what $O$ replies to such a question and what he does in directly recorded interaction (either *in naturo* or where social setting is controlled) might provide more knowledge of the values of sociometry and also provide substantive findings regarding "shyness," "status striving," and the general relation between wishing and acting. Such study depends in part on recordings of what we shall call *interpersonal activities.* We do not mean to rule out the possible value of our finer-textured units from this kind of endeavor. If $P$ chooses $O$ as a roommate and initiates such an actual relationship, observation of the interpersonal interactions may provide a basis for diagnosis of the reasons for the choice and indices that can be related to other aspects of the personalities of the two actors or to the longevity or success of the relationship.

*Sociological Activities.* Closely related to interpersonal activities are the units of "interpersonal behavior," which are characteristics of collectivities and which, like interpersonal activities, avoid the fine texture of the interaction that occurs between members of the collectivity. If, for example, an observer records the fact of the meeting of the Winthrop Street Baptist Church, he has provided a fact helpful in constructing certain kinds of indices. He may ignore (or not know) the additional fact that no one at this particular meeting was present at the last one (replaceability) or that this was a particularly friendly meeting, marked by a high frequency of single acts of sociability, the initiation of a number of reciprocal interpersonal activities and a high number of interpersonal interacts of the form in which $P$ reminds $O$ of past kindnesses on the part of $O$. The fact of the occurrence of the social pattern (i.e., that the church meeting was held) may be sufficient if one is comparing the Baptist pattern with, say, that of the Methodists in terms of frequency.

One final remark is called for about these kinds of units, which we have briefly outlined. This listing in no sense exhausts the possibilities but merely outlines some important kinds of units in a manner that is useful to us in keeping our focus on the direct observation of "interpersonal" phenomena. Past research designs have combined various of these units, and there is no reason why future ones may not do so even more if adequate statistical and study designs can be devised. Substantively, the phenomena of this realm have hardly been explored, much less mapped, and almost all probably have

some usefulness with regard to some hypothesis.

In a sense we have started with something less than an "interpersonal behavior" (single-act records) and ranged beyond it to sociological activities in outlining units. Such "bracketing" of the problems has been done to provide perspective; it has also been done because the task of our topic embraces this wide range. We shall focus as much as possible, however, on the middle of this range—on the methods available for the direct study of interactions.

It is perhaps worth pointing out here that most of the work of experimental behavior psychologists has been focused on units like the "operant" response. The usual procedure is to select a response class (single-act unit) and to study the conditions for its occurrence, its suppression, its weakening, its strengthening. Such systematic work has led to very fruitful description of the properties of such a class. Similar fruitfulness has come from systematic analysis of behavior at a choice point. Such work should certainly not be lost when we broaden our sights to these larger and more complicated units. Probably, interactions have all the properties of operants and many others as well. Their description and eventually their experimental manipulation may make clear properties that even operants have but that cannot be discovered in the noble isolation from everyday action that is the usual fate of operants.

At the other end of this continuum lies, of course, the huge problems of the recording and analysis of intergroup relations, international relations, intercultural relations, and, perhaps before too long, the new field of interplanatary relations. To date, methods of direct systematic observation have been extremely rarely used in these fields, in which the sample survey questionnaire, scholarly perusal of documents and first-hand accounts, and occasional content analysis of recorded conferences are the presently preferred techniques. As progress increases toward the development of experimental paradigms of the situations referred to by these terms, any findings of lasting value that arise from the study of children's interpersonal behavior may become directly relevant, and categorial systems developed in child study may suggest solutions to problems in the study of the larger aspects of the interplay of parents. But international relations and the study of child development are areas of study that we presently see as only too far apart for common discussion although Barker (1957) has begun work on putting them together.

## Strategy Issues in the Direct Study of Interpersonal Behavior

We have so far discussed some of the kinds of units that one can study directly in children's interpersonal behavior. In some cases, at least, the next step in planning a research would be to plunge into the issue of what aspects or attributes of such units one wished to study and what specific categories of observation one might wish to utilize. In this chapter, however, we shall delay such discussion in order to consider first some of the fascinating and complicated issues of the strategy of measurement and recording in this field. These strategy matters are important to the design of studies, second in importance only to the tools of adequate theory or a good clear preliminary empirical question.

## SAMPLING OF INTERPERSONAL BEHAVIOR

*Sampling Single Acts.* The research question that motivates a study determines to some extent the kind of sampling one will want to do. Barker and Wright (1955), for example, are interested in describing the psychological world of the children of a Midwestern United States town. The population, which they wish to sample, is a matter of the several million "episodes" of behavior that involve children in a given year. Their main emphasis is ecological —a desire to reflect accurately the life of children in a town, according to a set of categories they argue are "natural" ones. Whether or not they achieve a sampling of their population or whether their categories are "natural" relative to nature or only to their implicit and explicit theoretical interests, their strategy is based on this aim and guided by it in good part. It takes the direction of obtaining total day records for a sample—or at least a range—of children in the town of different ages, sex, etc.

Although it is very easy to become fascinated by the wide-ranging aim of such a study, and thereby approve of its strategy, these are not the only aims, the only categories, or the final strategy even for those aims and categories. By way of contrast, let us consider a much more specific, yet equally legitimate, research problem. Suppose one's research aim is limited to the single acts *initiated* by a sample of *P*'s in the relative absence of direct instigation from others. The theory may further specify the situations of such action by two classes: situations in which *P* is in interaction with peers (i.e., children of roughly the same age) and situations in which *P* is interacting with parents. The children themselves may be divided into two groups on the basis of their being samples of two populations: those with parents who have punished them physically for aggressive behavior toward these parents and those who have not been so punished (based on a previous sample of a sample of all the parents of a town or of a subgroup of a town). Furthermore, the hypothesis being entertained may specify an interest only in aggressive acts instigated by *P*, as compared to all other acts instigated by him. The theoretical considerations may further rule out any aggressive or other acts instigated by *P* in the midst of long interaction sequences but include those that arise after pauses in the interaction of a certain duration (based on some as-yet-undeveloped theory of memory span for immediate interaction). These last considerations help to keep the observed units independent of one another. The problem is reduced by the (rare) clarity of the theory to one of obtaining a sample of the things *P* initiates following such pauses, and this

may be done by spot checking (walking past *P*'s play ground and visiting his home at preset intervals), by staying with the child for relevant periods of his day, etc.

Such assistance from theoretical considerations as this example assumes is still extremely rare in the field of child development. A survey of the literature shows that the aims of most studies are less clear regarding aim, the categories are usually constructed for purposes of exploration rather than to test hypotheses, and sampling considerations are usually much less in the foreground. Finally, it is the rare researcher who would engage in such a costly procedure as direct observation with the faith in the value of the hypothesis that such an investment calls for. Most researchers would usually content themselves with ratings by, or interviews with, teachers and parents, or they may content themselves more by the use of experimental tests in which a parent is present and is then replaced by a peer or two. He then hopes that the findings are representative of the unstudied question of the spontaneous instigations by *P* in his daily life in these two kinds of situations. Such a situation is not so much to be deplored as to be understood. What is usually done is often right and proper, but for some purposes it is often incomplete or inefficient.

***The Sampling of Instigations.*** The strategy of a researcher is only slightly different when the question is one of trying to sample the pressures or instigations on a child. Theory may again help limit the task by limiting the situations under which such sampling needs to be done, or it may specify the classes of instigative act more or less closely. Such specification may take a general form, such as "impositions," "opportunities" (see Baldwin, 1955, pp. 131 ff.), "lures," and inferred internal instigations, or it may make further distinctions within these or other general categories, such as "blocking of activity of $P$," "attacking $P$," or "initiating help for $P$." If the observer is comparing two groups in terms of the pressures of certain kinds placed on children, then, in terms of Fig. 20-1, these pressures or instigations come not only from initiations or retaliations from $O$ but also from the third party of that figure. Consider the case in which $O$ attacks $P$ but in which $P$ is punished by the mother (third party) for retaliating to $O$'s onslaught. Such actions are often vital if groups or individuals are being studied over time, since theoretically these effects of $O$'s own actions are important psychological instigators to learning and conflict.

The aim of sampling is to render equally probable the presence in the sample of each of the kinds of things considered important. When one is studying instigations, there is a wide array of possible important instigation sources. This array is so wide that to some researchers the task seems hopeless. Perhaps one of the rarely mentioned effects of Freudian theory was to convince some researchers that mothers and fathers were such important sources of instigation that most others could be ignored. This at least helped lead to empirical observations, whether the theory was correct or not. The problem here is that for every

category of single acts that one considers, such categories multiply when situation factors, factors describing who $O$ is, etc., are considered. If a researcher is interested in comparing, for example, the occurrences in two nursery schools of instigations of the type "assault upon $P$ by an older child, the older child being a sociometrically chosen friend," the classification may have become so refined that an observer would have to be present for many hours before such a case would occur. Of course, such a type of instigation may be exactly the vital one for theoretical analysis. Three things can be done in such cases (short of giving up the endeavor altogether): the theory can be developed to handle more general classes that provide more frequent occurrences; a pretest may be used in which a child is followed around so that the observer can estimate where such occurrences are most probable; or the whole study might be shifted as soon as possible to a more experimental arrangement, so that the probability of such occurrences could be increased at the will of the experimenter.

One simplifying possibility should be mentioned in connection with the sampling of instigations, which also holds for the sampling of "single acts by $P$." This is the situation that arises when a sample of $P$'s has been selected from some population of children and in which a number of these $P$'s interacts frequently with one another. Then, if each child is being followed one at a time, what $P$ does to $O$ by way of instigating him can also be recorded as an instigation at the same time that $O$'s instigations of $P$ are being recorded. There are occasions when this may save recording time; there are also occasions, however, when this may be more trouble in analysis than it is worth. If, for example, the $O$ in the foregoing case is being time-sampled on a different schedule, the additional information obtained while sampling $P$ may merely confuse this time sampling. Further, the independence of such observations may be jeopardized unless great care is taken to make sure that what $P$ does to $O$ is not directly related to what $O$ has done (or will do) to $P$ that is also recorded as an instance. This double recording becomes clearly valuable when *interactions* are being studied and when the hypothesis calls for the interactions to be used to infer traits of personality in $O$ and $P$. This is discussed below.

One additional warning about studies that involve the sampling of instigations: any analysis of the external instigations that impinge upon $P$ is limited indeed, unless the study design permits the analysis of some of the conditions that lead to such instigations. Consider a study in which mothers' behavior toward $P$'s (i.e., their children) is being sampled and the differences in the instigations are being related to $P$'s behavior on a TAT (or to $P$'s own behavioral *initiations*). Once the analysis is done and the relationship reported, the researcher may well want to explore the issue of *why* some mothers "wheedle" or "coerce" more than others, and the researcher may then wish to relate such "instigations of $P$" to personality traits, situational factors, or broader family relationships. Such questions may focus upon the immediate instigations that impinge upon the

mother and that in turn lead to the instigations of $P$ already recorded. Such explorations may be ruled out, unless the broader scene was recorded in which mothers are viewed as $O$'s upon whom other $O$'s impinge and who in turn impinge in certain ways upon $P$'s (their children). In short, a study of a mother's *interaction* may be the best strategy to pursue when in search of a portrait of the external instigations that are visited upon the child.

We must quickly add, however, that if the hypothesis deals only with the relationship between the distribution of certain classes of instigations that impinge upon a child and his subsequent TAT or doll-play performance the test of the hypothesis should not be jeopardized merely to obtain exploratory data. It might be best to limit observation to the "instigations by mother of $P$" and interview the mother on the other matters. Observation is a costly procedure, and our methods are still distinctly limited in their ability to capture the broader reaches of the "structure of an event."

At a practical level, the recording of instigations is beset with the recurring fact that $P$ often acts without any apparent *external* instigation. This is the case that may arise when $P$ joins a group by verbally attacking one of the members of the group or when $P$ has been playing quietly alone and suddenly rises up and, for no apparent reason, decides to destroy the next child's sand castle. This problem arises more clearly when the researcher is interested in *interactions*, but it is sometimes germane even when only external instigations are being studied. First of all, it can lead to errors in recording external instigations. If a researcher is watching $P$ mainly in order to "catch" the instigations that impinge upon him and if $P$ suddenly initiates an act with no apparent external instigation, then the fact that some other child had suddenly changed his place of play may appear in retrospect to be the instigation to $P$ to go and strike his neighbor. This is a problem that only careful observer training and clear definition of instigation classes can overcome.

A more insidious problem sometimes arises. Suppose the recorder is working with a conceptual scheme that *defines* instigations in terms of their inferred or observed effect on $P$. It is quite sensible in some theories (including common sense) to suggest that a "frustrating instigation" is not frustrating to $P$ unless $P$ shows by his behavior (anger, aggression, leaving the field) that it is so. In short, instigations are viewed by the researcher as "perceived or apperceived—by the subject." These, of course, are a subclass of instigations, but they are sometimes defined in such a way that they are a subclass so close to $P$'s action as to be almost equatable with it (an easy way indeed to get high correlations between "instigation" and a particular class of action). Except where this issue is not important to the hypothesis under test, it is the "duty" of a theory or of an operational procedure to state what a stimulus is, and this can rarely be left to the subject to do for us. We must in the long run judge the state of our field in part by the degree it can unequivocally state that "it is this physical pattern of energies or this situational factor—measured

independently of $P$—or this cultural factor or this personality factor measured such-and-so that disposes $P$ toward behavior of class X or that changes in such-and-such a way the *probability* of his behaving according to class X."

Regardless of how we go about defining or pointing out instigations, we should expect $P$ to act sometimes in the apparent absence of such things, and, if, shortly after he has initiated an aggressive act, we note that someone is hitting him (in return), it is wise to have distinctions in our categories for such self-initiated retaliations, which otherwise might merely appear to be cases of poor $P$ being picked on by his neighbors. These retaliations, which arise from $P$'s own initiations, may have different effects on $P$. He may, for example, be feeling guilty by then.

***Sampling Interactions.*** There are two importantly different strategies involved when the sights are raised for capturing interactions. The one is involved when interactions are being recorded for purposes of studying personality differences among children; the other is used when the study aims at characterizing diads, groups, settings, or cultures.

In the first instance, in which the aim is to characterize the action tendencies of individuals (or more complicatedly, their *interaction* tendencies), theory may specify cultural factors, and the only problem is that of arranging the external instigation situations for each child so that the full range of action (or interaction) tendencies is possible. This permits the internal instigating (or personality) factors to express themselves in determining differences in the distribution of actions or interactions obtained from one child to the next. The best way to handle this problem, short of having more knowledge than we usually have, is to provide a representative array of instigations but to have them the same for each child. This is, unfortunately, a contradiction in itself, since a "representative array" of instigations that would fit the everyday life of one child would not necessarily be representative of the instigations in the everyday life of the next; yet, unless we use the "same" array of instigations for measuring, we lose one of our bases of comparison. There is an indeterminacy here, since a child who meets a limited array of instigation situations in real life (compared to the next child) may have personality properties of a certain kind or intensity just because of the limitedness of the array he usually meets! Perhaps the best compromise available for nomethetic study is to provide a representative array of external instigations that would fit the everyday life of a *modal* child of the group or an array of instigations that would fit the everyday life of *all* the children in the group, dropping out those instigations that are rare.

Such considerations lead rapidly toward the simplifications of our usual test procedures, in which we attempt to provide the same "standardized" external instigations to all subjects, letting what is "in them" determine the distribution of answers. It is even sometimes argued that it is wise to control on the "reportable" reception of the external instigations by the subject or, more broadly, the perception of the external instigation. This is one of the virtues of the laboratory or clinic situation for testing, as long as the operation used to make the stimulus "graspable" does not itself deform the response distribution too much. If, in an intelligence test, we rule out all questions (external instigations) that the subject cannot cognize, then we may have limited the range of responses that define the kinds or degrees of "intelligence" so that it no longer fits with the theory with which we started. The report "I am confused by the question" may be a valuable clue to intelligence.

These test criteria raise problems for direct observation. In fact, they usually raise such complicated questions that this form of validation is often completely avoided. Such avoiding is often the better part of valor but not when the theory or measurement under test is supposed to apply to everyday behavior. The only way to test the assumption that "this hypothesis applies to everyday behavior" is to order or categorize everyday behavior and find out. Direct observation is one of our ways of doing exactly that. The problems must sometimes be faced.

In practical terms, the problems too often arise after the data have been collected—in the analysis phase—as any experienced statistician would sadly tell us. Suppose a researcher has time-sampled the interactive behavior of a carefully selected sample of subjects—recording all the data necessary to an analysis of both instigations and resulting actions. The data are all in, the observers have gone home, and suddenly it is discovered that there are only four cases of "$O$ attacks $P$" for child $A$, none for child *B* or *C*, 15 for child *D*, etc. The analysis sometimes has to stop at this point, and it is necessary to fall back on the still more mysterious process of "ratings" in order to save the research. Such problems can be avoided by careful research strategy. If one is aware ahead of time of at least some of the crucial instigation classes in which the researcher is interested and if the observations are analyzed, at least roughly, for the occurrences of these in the time-sampled material, then extra recording can go on for those children who, for example, are infrequently attacked by peers. Further recordings may be obtained for all children in situations in which rare instigations are more frequent. If a careful record is kept of the protocols taken according to the sampling schedule, and which went beyond the schedule, then the latter can be included for studying the personality dispositions of the children (the ratio, for example, of retaliations to attacks), whereas they could be left out of the analysis of the sample of everyday pressures or of the interactions that characterize the sample of the child's life. Such planned checks on the incoming data may even be formalized by the use of sequential analysis, which could save time and money by giving estimates on how soon a given instigation category is going to be filled (or not filled).

In the example immediately above we have dealt with a research case in which both personality study and representativeness of instigations are involved. Relatively few studies of personality attempt to achieve the latter. Situational representativeness rarely goes beyond the time sampling of a few situations and that usually involves observing the child at play with his peers or occasional observation at school or at home. In most Western European countries the home is viewed by parents and researchers as a bit too sacred to permit one-way screens or even the randomly timed presence of a silent observer. It is probable that some personality development problems can best be studied in societies in which the privacy of home life is less highly valued.

Representativeness of settings or situations is generally ignored for a more insurmountable reason—there is a dearth of adequate analysis of the problem at both the empirical and theoretical levels. Barker and Wright (1955) have made a valiant effort in this direction, but despite their interesting index of the similarity between two "settings" for action the categorizing of the settings themselves is still at an extremely empirical descriptive level. We are still awaiting, from whatever source, some generally useful methods for "placing" settings (and their attendant instigations) in various conceptions of "social space." It is largely on these issues that the operational value of Parsons' patterns variables (Parsons and Shils, 1951) may be evaluated as far as child development is concerned. In the meantime however, we need a number of alternative theoretical approaches to these problems. Such theoretical contributions could have a very salutary effect on our strategies in the observation of interpersonal behavior.

In research cases in which only personality differences are involved the main focus is on the distribution of things done by *P* to a given class of instigation, which is compared to the distribution provided by another *P*. When we are sampling the interactions that occur in a group, then, as in the case of the Murphy study on sympathetic behavior (Murphy, 1937), the observer is set to note *all* occurrences of a certain class of instigations (in that case, forms of "distress" in any *O*) during the time sampled. When two groups are being compared, in short, the representativeness of both the instigation and of the responses to the instigations are equally vital, since the minimal unit under study is an instigation-action unit.

Such equal emphasis on instigation and action defines what we referred to as the second basic strategy in the sampling of interactions, and we shall discuss other strategy factors in considering this case. First, however, let us pause again on this issue of the unit to be observed. The minimal unit is, in the Murphy study, "distress in *O*, sympathetic or nonsympathetic behavior in *P*." This permits analysis of the personality dispositions of the various *P*'s, assuming that the frequency of instigations is equal or at least large enough for each. It permits also the comparison of two groups in terms of the frequency of occurrence of such units. It permits, in addition, the analysis of the "initiation of signs of distress" by the various *O*'s, provided proper names are always part of the protocol. However, full analysis of the conditions under which the various *O*'s initiate signs of distress is not possible unless the observer is also set to record all instances of the occurrence of "instigations to *O* to initiate signs of distress such as hurts, frustra-

tions, etc." A matrix of group structure is also possible with these data, in terms of who gives sympathy to whom, viewed simply as a description of the present group in action.

Our point here, however, is to ponder some possibilities that are not usually considered. If the unit is expanded to include not only distress in *O* and *P*'s response but also *O*'s response to *P*'s response (or, whenever necessary, the behavior of a third party in bringing the sequence to an end, for example, when the teacher intervenes to comfort *O*), the additional analyses are possible. It would be possible to study the success *O* has with showing distress in terms of whether he gets comfort or not and whether the comfort tends to come from peers or adults. Such analysis might provide a basis to follow the changes in *O*'s distress-showing behavior tendencies as a function of whether such tendencies are rewarded or not rewarded. Further, knowing how *O* responds to sympathy or lack of sympathy may not only provide a check on the classification of his signs of distress but also a basis for an inference of his intention in making the original outcry. If he is quickly or easily "pacified" by help or sympathy, then the strength of his succorance need may be inferred and compared with that of the child who maintains the succorance demand as long as it brings help or attention. Such inferences would require independent measurement in the long run.

In terms of Fig. 20-1, there is no end but that of practicality to the exact size of units of action that might be useful for some purposes. Some children are characterizable as leaders who like to *initiate* interaction sequences that are long and complicated, yet may have importance as dimensions of personality. A given $P$ may show persistence in initiating a form of imaginative play, which may aim to include all the other children present, may or may not involve content of a reciprocal, aggressive, or dominating nature, and may extend over days instead of hours. It is not only "leaders" who initiate long interaction sequences, of course. Some children initiate play patterns of a form that permits them to follow some more imaginative child or merely to watch while some conflict or constructive play emerges from the watcher's initiation.

The usual considerations involved when children are being sampled to represent a town, city, or tribe are age, sex, socioeconomic status of the family, and the placement of the child in the family. We shall not discuss these points, since they are (in principle) part of the strategy of any research in child development. What we would like to point out is that there are practical as well as theoretical issues involved in the selection of the population out of which the sample is to be drawn. The issue of the "population" is usually a very bewildering one in a science in which the theory being tested is often couched in universal terms ("all children tend to regress in their play when frustrated") but in which the subjects available to test the theory are very limited in number and representativeness. Some researchers dream of a national sample as the ideal, others limit their aims to a city or town or even a school, and still others dream of a world-wide sample of children for a study. It should be said that none of these populations is sacred. If the hypothesis contains within it certain recognized population limits ("all children who grow up in the United States tend to regress in their play when frustrated"), then the population problem is clear. There has been an increasing tendency to place "cultural" as well as national limits on hypotheses in child development, but our general ignorance on the specific import of such factors leads more often to vagueness on these issues.

Some of these matters are discussed in a useful way by Whiting et al. (1953), who recommend a "primary sampling unit" as a reasonable population focus for some kinds of child-development studies. Such a unit has a number of virtues, which are not discussed here. It has one lack of virtue as presently formulated in publications. This is that for complex research designs, in which several variables are to be analyzed to bring out the interactions among the variables, the number of children available in a PSU may be too small. There is one consideration, however, that may have important consequences, even for one-variable studies of interpersonal behavior. This is that the PSU may facilitate the study of interpersonal interactions and interpersonal activities because any given $P$ is usually found interacting with the same $O$'s. This means that a given sample of $P$'s instigations and/or reactions may include a sufficient number of interactions between that *P* and his particular friends to provide a basis for such additional analyses. All of this possibility arises from the smallness of the PSU and from the criterion of sociometric homogeneity called for by this "population" unit. The possibility of such additional analyses cannot, of course, be assumed, but such considerations may prove important in developing multipurpose research designs in the future.

It is interesting to consider the future problems in the strategies that may be evolved in attempts to define the population from which PSU's themselves, or some similar units, should eventually be sampled. Perhaps Murdock (1957) has come closest to this with his notion of a world ethnographic sample, but much further work will have to be done to carry his large idea into use in complex modern societies. It is interesting that the technology of the sample survey has so often focused on "national" samples, possibly because of the relatively atheoretical quality of most of the work done and because of the importance of national power units in current applied work. Such a population definition should by no means become assumed as the most useful or "natural." Research endeavors, which are guided by more theory, may eventually require or find "natural" a number of different notions on this score. Since work done by the use of direct observation has not yet found any ready definition of research efficiency, as has perhaps occurred in the use of the sample survey, new notions of populations and of subunits may be developed

that may prove of general value in behavioral science.

## STRATEGY ISSUES IN RECORDING INTERPERSONAL BEHAVIOR

There are several issues of a strategic sort involved in deciding what kinds of records to take while observing children's interpersonal behavior. These issues include whether or not to try to record everything that goes on, to permit inference in the protocols, to use preset categories or leave the categories to be developed a posteriori, and to try to save the time and cost of an analysis phase in the research by providing the recorder with preset forms or IBM cards that are punched while observing.

There is no absolute answer to any of these questions, and the dearth of methodological research makes even partial answers difficult. Let us consider some of them, however, in the hope of creating a "sense of problem" for at least those readers to whom these problems are new.

The major strategy issue, with regard to field recording of interpersonal behavior, is that between an approximation to "total records" and the use of preset categories. Let us state again our opinion that the mystic notion of some absolute totality of record should be discarded. If so, we can define the "total recording" approach more usefully as one in which the observer is set to record a rather wide array of interpersonal phenomena in a form that necessarily calls for a further analysis stage. This can then be compared to the strategy of using precoded categories to avoid such an additional analysis state.

A number of rather imponderable issues then arise, imponderable at least in terms of our present methodological knowledge. One thing seems to be clear at first blush, however, and that is that when a very few categories of action are being observed preset codes can be very efficient compared to total records. Observer reliability can be extremely high, a costly phase of research involving protocol analysis is avoided, and statistical analysis can be effectively speeded. It might also be said that the researcher is left with no more data than his theory calls for—assuming that he has such a theory.

On the other hand, if a large number of categories is being observed, then it may be better to try to record a good deal of the flow of action in a manner that is determined more by the requirements of reliable and valid recording (whatever they may be) than by the requirements of efficient analysis. Despite the much higher cost in this strategy, the virtues are many, particularly in exploratory stages of research in a given area. One can change his categories of analysis if he has such rich protocols to work from. This is helpful in exploratory work but dangerous in hypothesis testing, unless the bases of such decisions to change the categories are purely measurement criteria and the change is not done in such a way as to improve the probability of upholding the original hypothesis. It is also possible that in the use of an additional analysis phase the reliability of the final categorizing may be improved, since the task can be done

under conditions in which speed is not so important. This depends upon how well the coders are trained, of course. There is also some reason to hope that protocols collected under what we are calling a "total recording" set may provide some fairly permanent data to which a wide array of category systems can be applied. We discuss this hope further in subsequent sections of this chapter.

Another virtue of the "total record" is that it can provide some kinds of data that are rarely achieved with the use of preset categories, except perhaps when the preset categories are all-inclusive. Consider a research case in which a given $P$ is being observed systematically and in which both "instigations" (or at least the basis for an analysis of instigations) and $P$'s actions are recorded. Compared to other $P$'s, this $P$ may be found to initiate many helpful acts toward others. According to some rules of inference, he would then be considered as a highly nurturant child. If the protocols include data on a wide array of other kinds of actions, however, such data may provide the basis for a measure of this $P$'s general activity level, as compared to the other $P$'s. It may then be discovered that relative to all his initiations his helpful initiations are a very small proportion indeed—although they are higher in absolute frequency than those of others. It may then appear to be more reasonable to place him in the "low nurturance" group of children for purposes of analysis. Furthermore, if the research is focused on this $P$'s place in the group interaction, then his helpful initiations relative to all the initiations of all the *P*'s studied may also place him high or low, depending on whether or not these other initiations are available for index construction.

There is an additional feature to total records, which, though imponderable in any case, is sometimes of great value. If the record of interaction is kept in this way, it is possible to change a definition of a particular category in the analysis stage, thus improving reliability of coding and the fitness of the code to the hypothesis under test. This arises because the cues to be utilized for categorizing are available for such reshuffling, and their presence provides the researcher with an opportunity to report in great detail just what the contents of a category are. This may facilitate communication and may increase the possibility of exact replication of studies.

The recording of "cues" so that they may be perused at leisure is a virtue that may, of course, be purchased at great cost. How many cues are lost in such recording that might be utilized by an observer who is set for on-the-spot categorizing? Under what conditions are more cues recorded under a "total set" than are noted by a preset categorizer? How speedy is the observer's reception of interpersonal behavior? How important is having time to receive information for categorizing as compared to "total" recording? What are the reliable and valid cues to watch for or to record for a given class of behavior? Most of these are unanswered research questions. Mead (1953) has provided a clear example of the ethnographic value of the use of cameras and tape recorders as well as a

larger number of observers in attempts to capture more of the action for later analysis. There are still, however, few systematic studies of the value such devices add to direct observation. (See Heyns and Lippitt, 1954.)

Let us turn to the issue of "inference or no inference" in the basic protocols. In its absolute form, of course, the argument is rather empty, and the discussion should rest on a clearer definition of such terms as "inferring," "deducing," and "inducing" than we will attempt here. It seems clear, at least, that the more complex the judgment required of an observer, the more the chance for difference to occur in the judgments of two observers, unless the observers have been trained to differentiate the particular complex pattern. This may mean that the judgments are more in error or that the phenomenon being judged is too complicated to be encompassed *in toto* by one human's span of apprehension. Perhaps the two disagreeing observers are seeing correctly two or more facets of the phenomena or are responding to different kinds of information in the action being observed. As soon as we put the problem in such modern terms as "there is always a limit to the momentary capacity for information reception," then we commence to see the enormity of our ignorance regarding what is going on in the observation situation. In short, only basic theory-directed research on the process of observing and recording, and on the process of learning to observe and record, will ever provide us with other than facile verbal solutions to this dilemma. How can we specify the kinds and contents of "cues" that must be recorded or observed so that we can reliably and validly infer that two people are angry at one another? How many forms of "anger" expression are there? Is the matter one that should be viewed in terms of "arousal," for which instruments of a more physiological kind might be more fitting? Having decided some of these issues, we could then turn to a consideration of how adequately a human observer can function as a recording instrument for such events and approximate a clear answer to questions of how fast and how complicatedly he can operate. Such research has hardly begun, at least in any form of direct use for naturalistic observation.

In the meantime, however, observation will continue. When theory is adequate to specify what should be observed and recorded, then the only issue is that of reliability (and attendant issues of reportability and replication). When theory is not adequate to the task (as is so often the case), then all the researcher can do is develop a "feel" for the phenomena he is interested in and develop his observation method accordingly, hoping that basic research will prove him correct in the long run. As Heyns and Lippitt (1954) and Gellert (1955) have suggested, recent practice has been to let "theory" or the "feel" discussed above determine what is to be attempted in observing interpersonal behavior rather than let the matter be decided totally by the reliability obtainable between two independent observers. Perhaps the modicum of success achieved in studies of direct observation means that there is more information about motives, feel-

ing, and intentions that is "imminent in behavior" than we have generally supposed. This cannot yet be formally documented, but it may be that this is a constructive assumption to make.

There are degrees of inference, probably; or, in more everyday terms, some judgments are more complicated than other judgments. It is here that researchers who have used some form of total recording have made their compromise. Observers are often asked to record "what is said and done by each actor" (the overt behaviors of Fig. 20–1). They are asked also to record adjectives, adverbs, or other inferences but to place them in parentheses ($O$ struck $P$; $P$ smiled (painfully)). The "insights" are recorded, at least, and can be used as the coding rules permit. Sometimes inference goes further, as when, in the Bales technique, an observer is expected to make category placements of particular communicative acts according to their function in the group process—a rather complicated judgment but one in which a surprising degree of observer reliability can be obtained under the right conditions (Bales, 1950). Most observers of behavior are still queasy, about records that might read, "$O$'s libido cathected $P$; $P$ set up a defense (sublimation) and talked rapidly." It is difficult, however, to rule out such records on rational grounds, particularly if theory calls for such inference and if the record is reliable and provides indices that relate meaningfully to other kinds of indices. Is an inference to the "cognitive field" of a child so different in kind from an inference to an unconscious state? Common sense suggests that if protocols are to read like this last one then they should include "what *O* said and did" in some other sense as well as in the sense outlined above. In short, whenever our language of description wanders too far from that mysterious realm of "everyday discourse," we should spice it with terms from "everyday discourse" for the help of those colleagues who have not yet learned our more special theoretical language. Later in this chapter we turn to this issue and discuss our best guess as to how far we might be able to go in the recording of interpersonal behavior with just "everyday discourse," though even this can be viewed as hardly more than a temporary stop-gap (Heider, 1958) or at best as a source of hypotheses for basic research of the kind we have described so briefly.

*Field Strategy.* There are practical as well as theoretical issues in the following questions, which arise in most research in interpersonal behavior. How many observers? Where should they be placed to observe? How many children should they watch? How long should they watch at a time?

Let us first consider some of the possibilities of error in the observer-subject relationship itself, avoidance of which may sometimes determine the answers to such questions as those above. One source of error is that of the effect of a particular observer on a particular kind of child; another is the consistent differential effect of different observers on all the children. The first of these can be controlled or studied only by the systematic use of a number of observers or by the use of a one-way vision screen. This source of variance

can never be *completely* ruled out except by statistical means. The second is handled in the same way but with at least one complication. This is the fact that shifting observers keeps up the children's interest in these novel stimuli longer than if one observer is used and he becomes part of the "background" as Spiro (1958, p. 465) has described so clearly. It is probably worthwhile to spend many days or weeks having children become habituated to an observer before recording starts, as recommended in the field guide for the Cornell-Harvard-Yale Socialization Study (Whiting et al., 1955). Even this precaution may not be enough. The writer recalls vividly how the interest shown in him by a group of nursery-school children continued to grow for several weeks. He never managed to become part of the background because he was observing the children in an experiment in which the children received candy on a random reinforcement basis!

Another source of error is the effect of the children, so to speak, on the observer. This can take many forms, but one of the more dramatic has been described by Campbell (1959) as an error that arises because of the order in which stimuli to be judged are presented. Professors who visited one Russian city first found it drabber than the second one they visited, whereas those who visited the second city first found it drabber. Such errors unquestionably occur in the observation of interpersonal behavior. They can be controlled at least in part by planning the order with which a given observer watches particular children, groups, or settings.

In an unpublished research work done at Cornell, in which whole families were observed, John Harding employed a design that required a number of observers, a simplified version of Bales' category system, and a time-sampling procedure in which each observer watched one family member for two minutes, then shifted systematically to other members. A counterbalanced design helped to control at least some observer errors that arise from order effects. Gellert (1955, pp. 185–186) has compiled a useful list of 13 additional sources of observer error, which the careful research strategist will wish to peruse before considering the field plan a final one.

Let us now return to some of the questions raised at the beginning of this section. It should now be clear that it is difficult to make the job of direct observer of interpersonal behavior one for a single man. Even if no attempt is made to provide interobserver reliability estimates for more than a small portion of the observation, the kinds of errors outlined above suggest that it may usually be better for at least two observers to spend less time at what one could do less well with more time. But the number of observers needed depends upon how complex the judgment task is, how many categories of behavior are being observed, how many actors must be watched in order to obtain the necessary information, and, of course, on how ambitious the unit of observation is, among other things. It is strange that animal psychologists, who often observe rather simple actions or interactions, have developed the

most objective means of recording, although it is also true that a pigeon in a Skinner box can peck away at a spot at a rate impossible to count unaided. At the other extreme, however, it is only fair to say that some anthropologists—particularly Mead (in Carmichael, 1954)—have developed highly ingenious and careful methods for recording the rather complex occurrences at tribal rituals, including the use of a good many brass instruments. Modern television reporting may be the current apex of field recording methods. Television recording of the tribal rituals of more complex cultures may someday be useful to all students of human behavior. Television coverage of even a baseball game is no one-man job. If only the frequency of dependent and aggressive behavior of a particular child in nursery school is wanted, then one man may do very well.

How many children or children and adults can one person observe? Many of the foregoing considerations apply to this question also. The clearer and simpler the cues to be observed, the more available and geographically concentrated the action under perusal; the simpler the unit of observation, the more homogeneous the goals of the action, etc., the more people can be observed. Whiting reports that one observer could reliably record two classes of action of several children in the Iowa studies directed by Sears et al. (1953), but that when instigations were added to the task and nine categories with a quasi-total recording set were introduced, as in the Cornell-Harvard-Yale Socialization Study, then no more than one person could be observed at all reliably (Whiting, 1959). In that project, we should also report, there were usually two field personnel involved before a protocol was finally written up. Although more complex, this was a procedure somewhat akin to that of Barker and Wright (1955), in which the observer is queried on particular points by another person while preparing the final draft of the protocol. This last is a notion that (like so many others) deserves methodological research in its own right.

The question of how to place the observer or observers relative to the actor (or actors) leads us to suggest the following analogy with the problem of defense in the game of basketball. One technique is to have one man follow his opposite number wherever that actor goes. This is called a "man-to-man defense." Another strategy is to employ a "zone defense," in which a defender watches over whatever goes on in a given area of the playing field, regardless of who is doing it. Barker and Wright have employed both strategies, at least in principle. The *One Boy's Day* (Barker and Wright, 1951) approach is a man-to-man observation; their later work, with its heavy emphasis on "setting," includes some analyses that are akin to "zone" methods, in which, ideally, an observer stands in Kane's drug store and records what goes on regardless of who does it.

Either of these placements of the observer can achieve an adequate sample of the behavior of the children in a group in the sense of sociological single acts or sociological interactions. Zone observation, however, may make analysis of personality differences more difficult, since the observer must know so many names and because much reshuffling and cross-filing of data would be necessary. It provides data, however, in a form that may facilitate an analysis in which an inference to the group may be made easier—since a given observer's protocols may provide a fair time sample of "what instigations and/or reactions occurred at 'Kane's Drug Store' (or in this area of the play school)."

Many more strategies are possible, of course, many of which have not even been tried seriously. It is possible, for example, to divide labor by having one observer look for instigations and another for resultant or contiguous action. Another would be to have one observer specialize in one class of instigation, while the other watches for something else. Still another variation would be to have a pair of observers watching a pair of actors, with one of the observers trying to watch the things that $P$ watches and to record what $P$ does and the other trying to look where $O$ does. Coordination of such protocols, their statistical analysis, and the research designs that would be necessary in order to rule out various observer errors would present many fascinating problems.

Possibly a definition of efficiency in the observation of interpersonal behavior will arise by maximizing the values of different possible strategies for a given research problem. In the Cornell-Harvard-Yale study it was hoped that the field strategy would permit the sampling of both instigation and action of nine behavior systems, with man-to-man observation within pre-arranged (and representative) settings. It was further hoped that these settings were representative of fairly clear sub-units (PSU's) of strategically selected cultures. It will be interesting if this was achieved. Spiro (1958) has reported on observations obtained by use of a rather complicated strategy in which man-to-man observation was inter-spersed with observation of particularly relevant instigation situations, both of these set within a rather constant use of ethnographic observation. His re-marks on the differences between sys-tematic observation and observation of the usual ethnographic sort are par-ticularly valuable (see Appendix).

### Clues Used in Observing Interpersonal Behavior

At the heart of most definitions of the categories into which observed be-haviors are sorted lies the issue of the cues observers should be attuned to while observing. Considering the case of the recording of single acts is fruit-ful in clarifying some basic distinctions, which may also prove useful when more complicated units are being dealt with. We have made a place for these distinc-tions in Fig. 20-1 by the use of the entities "P's response—environmental change—goal response" in describing P's (and the others') action. Let us outline some of the implications of these entities for the choice of more or less ambitious aims in the cues to be utilized in observation of single acts.

## MOVEMENTS DIRECTED TOWARD THINGS AND OTHER PEOPLE

Some words in our everyday lan-guage refer to movements in space-time of an actor, such as "kick," "strike," "push," and "pull." These terms refer, with some vagueness or ambiguity, only to the movements in space-time co-ordinates. Such movements are the classical ideal data of some forms of behaviorism, and the coordinates repre-sent for some psychologists the basic coordinates for the description of action in the sense that "observable behavior" is limited to movements that, in prin-ciple at least, can be reduced to such terms. This has been an idea of great importance in the development of modern psychology, holding out as it does the lure of an objective and strictly public referent for our behavior cate-gories.

The history of this idea should be written and its present place evaluated, but we shall not attempt such a task here. There are two remarks, however, that we would like to make on the topic, even at the risk of superficiality. In an important sense this idea has been applied more superficially than wisely to observation work, and in some respects it has only recently been applied at all. Let us expand briefly.

In work on behavior observation we often interpret the notion of movement (and the scientific principle regarding its objectivity) as counseling us to "record the actual movements and noth-ing more." This is a very simple render-ing of the notion we have outlined, since we have suggested that our records should *in principle* be reducible to movement terms in space-time, not that the protocols be rendered in nothing but space-time terms. It is interesting that the purists in this regard have never worked out a serious, generally useful language of "merely movement," nor have they approached movements of people with the kind of analytic intention toward developing basic units in the way linguists have brilliantly done in their treatment of the sounds emitted by people. Short of having such a pure movement language, or a set of generally accepted units such as the linguists have, it has been sensible, perhaps, to try to keep to terms that refer as much as possible to "what the subjects *do*." The hope has been that such a set in the observer will call out in him his naturally coded terms for describing movement. He will record "*P* struck *O* in the face with the flat of his hand" rather than "*P* struck *O* in the face with clear intention to hurt." The trouble is, of course, that within a given "behavioral language" it may be quite reasonably possible that there are "movement components," which might validly (either conceptually or directly) distinguish between a hurting act that was intended to hurt and one that was not so intended. Primitivizing the set of the observer may merely rule out the recording of solid empirical facts, which our natural movement language code may be inadequate to capture. Perhaps the nearest we could come would be something like this: "*P* struck *O* in the face with the palm of his hand, but with that characteristic decrease in speed, as the palm approached the face, which usually means that a modal *P*'s intention is to be *playfully* aggressive." The statement would ideally end with a reference to some unwritten "dictionary of movement" in which the correlation between the decrease in speed and the intention (directly or conceptually measured) is quoted. In short, we have lost much in the observation of movements because we have hardly begun to face the complexities and the fascinating research problems involved in untangling our language code from the phenomenon we wish to code.

Two factors have probably encouraged our naïvete on these matters. The first is the fact that in important experimental work we can focus on a fairly limited set of movements or actions, properties of which can be automatically measured and used as dependent variables. Second, in this way it is possible (by the use of some implicit assumptions) to work with movements or actions in such a clearly objective manner that the broader implications of the relation of the position to our usual language codes need not be faced. The observation of interpersonal relations in everyday or even laboratory settings brings all these implications clearly into the open. For such purposes even the purest behaviorist must "botanize," despite Skinner's well-taken worries on this score (1938), and such botanizing will either be done well or it will be done in a naïve manner, which may cover up a good many of the phenomena that occur in a replicable and ordered way even in our "usual" space-time coordinate system.

So we have argued that the implications of a behaviorism of the observation of interpersonal behavior have hardly begun to be investigated, much less "*used*." There may well be limits to how much of the action of children can be caught by protocol sentences, which are, in principle at least, reducible to sentences having to do with movements in space-time. We just do not know. It may, of course, turn out to be rather impractical to make such an attempt with some categories or properties of interpersonal behavior, since the complexity of the movement pattern corresponding to the property may be very great and may change greatly from child to child. There is some hope, however, in the linguistic approach by researchers like Hockett (1958), who suggests that at least for English speakers there may be fairly reliable psychophysical aspects of speech pauses, which may reflect such subtle matters as the fact that someone has "changed his mind" in the middle of a sentence.

Past attempts to keep observation categories close to movements have often been accompanied by a relentless search for high reliability in the records. Two such criteria used too stringently can serve to lead research up a path toward highly specific indices and categories that predict only themselves and that do not satisfy legitimate curiosity regarding other aspects of the interpersonal behavior of children. Such emphases, although they should not be lost sight of, may well be held in abeyance for a time in order that the complexities of interpersonal interactions and such matters may be explored.

Bott (1933) is quoted by Gellert (1955):

In surveying the results presented (in various studies), it is evident that effort has been focussed, first on the reliability of observers, which is regarded as the basic condition of reliability in further studies. Constancy of the data has received the next amount of attention, but the difficult question of validity has been passed over with comparatively little study. We would like to suggest a reversal of this order; that is, that attention should be focussed on discovering what units of behavior have representative and predictive significance in relation to the whole of the child's behavior. When this has been done, it will next be in order to proceed with detailed studies of the consistency of the behavior items. The training of observers can then be persisted in till a sufficient reliability has been reached. If interest is focussed first on the training of observers, there is danger that the elements of observation are so reduced in the interest of reliability that they are largely emptied of significance. On the other hand, if significance can be demonstrated with observations which have only a modicum of reliability, it is safe to conclude that a more rigorous control of procedure will only heighten the significance of what has already been demonstrated to have meaning in relation to the whole of the child's behavior (p. 184).

It may be valuable at this point to make a distinction that seems to be rather important in any future search for movement-pattern correlates to theoretically important aspects of interpersonal behavior of children. To some this reduces to a problem in the "perception of action or behavior" by an observer, calling for experiments of the usual perceptual variety, ideally psychophysical in method. Such an interpretation of the problem may be a costly error because of the limited resources of information and procedure usually permitted a subject who is "perceiving" someone else's action. The subject in an experiment needs to be granted the status of a "scientific observer" before such psychophysical relationships become directly useful to the improvement of behavior observation techniques. Regardless of the logical or doctrinal issues in this distinction, the "scientific observer" is usually permitted to record copiously, to make systematic (often statistically complicated) inferences, and to use all modern technical means to get information about what the "object of judgment" is doing. It is the rare study in the "perception of persons" or "perception of behavior" that permits such extensive behavior on the part of the subject or observer. It is just such procedures that are at issue in our present problems —not merely simple percepts based on relatively little information. Psychophysics must become more complicated in its operations in order to become usefully "global" in this area.

## EXPRESSIVE ACTS

Some of the energy transformations or movements that children and adults engage in or find themselves doing have little to do with changing the environment or with obtaining resources. In fact, probably more often than not, these things are not even meant to be communicated to others but are often the crucial cues that provide others

with an interpretation of large segments of the interpersonal behavior of the actor who emits them. We shall refer to these events as "expressive acts" merely because this term comes closest to the meaning we intend, even though it is far from accurate. Perhaps our very ignorance of these events makes it difficult to find a more useful word. One of the main troubles with the term "expressive movements" is that it has been used in personality study to refer vaguely to the personal style that sets a person apart, often uniquely, from others. With the broadened perspective of our modern social-psychological or communication approach to personality, such usage is too limiting and constraining. Some expressive acts or movements are possibly as much shared and equally as objective and general as "forms of request" in language or modes of chopping down trees in motor behavior.

Consider, for example, Hockett's statement that grows out of his intensive experience in trying to use linguistic and other tools to name some of the interactional modes that occur in a psychiatric interview.

In one brief episode—about three seconds long—in a taped psychiatric interview which I have been studying, the patient goes through an observable process of emotional editing. She manifests, in turn, the signs of three different nameable emotional reactions to what has gone before. The only way I can understand this episode is to assume that the patient cannot know what emotion she "feels"— that is, which emotion is culturally appropriate to the setting—without trying a bit of each and judging it by feedback. The manifestation is at a lower power level, giving the impression of a sort of pastel kaleidoscope of emotionality; but the power level is not so low as to render the sequence indetectable (1958, p. 11).

Although, like any class of behavior, "editing behavior" can be studied in terms of individual differences or even unique patterning, there is no necessity to do so. What is needed is the description of the linguistic and other movement patterns that correspond to the subtle activity of editing (or at least vary the way they should according to some *theory* of editing); this category can be studied, presumably, in any person and with all the methods available to any general behavioral phenomenon. Such research as that of Hockett and the attempts of Birdwhistle (1952) to develop methods for a purely movement-based study of interaction may provide us with some important categories for the study of interpersonal behavior of exactly this kind.

Another problem with our term "expressive acts" is that it is often used solely in the context of a trait or dispositional psychology, in which we study a person's expressive actions during interactions solely to obtain indices of supposedly deeper intervening traits. We wish merely to point out that, here again, this is not the only service to which such indices can be put. They may serve as independent or dependent variables in their own right. They may also serve to enhance the reliability and validity of more complex interpersonal categories into which we may wish to place movements and actions.

The potential value of expressive acts or movements as dependent, nomothet-ically viewed variables in their own right is clearly shown in a study by Levin et al. (1959). They tape-recorded speeches made by children under various audience conditions, then had two coders, working independently, score the following categories: (1) length of speaking in seconds; (2) number of words uttered; (3) number of stutters; (4) prolongations (like "speeeech"); (5) shifts (starting a word or sentence and shifting before the utterance is finished, as "the b-girls want"); (6) sighs; (7) pauses (any cessation of speech for two seconds or more was scored, and the actual length of the pause was timed); (8) word whiskers (these are the ubiquitous "uhs" around words); and (9) catches in the voice. They found the lowest correlations between the scores of the two coders was .80 and the highest was above .90. They were able to show that these indices were sensitive to systematic changes in audience conditions and that they were also sensitive to differences in certain personality properties of $P$'s, measured independently.

***Acts Which Have Certain Visible Effects on Others.*** The basic units of many category systems for the observation of interaction include reference to actions of $P$ that have certain visible effects on others. Such units are a subclass of what are usually termed "instrumental acts," and we have made a place for this category in Fig. 20-1 by noting the "change of environment" that follows an action. Some observers have even tried to be systematic in constructing categories that have as their referents such observable changes in the environment. These categories have a certain elegance from a neobe-haviorist point of view, since they permit definitions of actions that do not require a detailed description in terms of movements but still permit an immediately observable datum that defines the class of actions under study. This is the case in which responses are defined as "the number of times an animal managed to push down a bar" or "the speed with which the rat ran to the goal box at the end of the maze." It is also the case in which observers define aggression as "that class of acts wherein the behavior of $P$ causes signs of pain in $O$" or in which dependency is recorded as "that class of acts of $P$ that elicits helpful actions from $O$."

A great many of our everyday terms for action refer at least in part to the effects of behaviors. This means that categories defined in this way are close to our usual language codes, at least in English, and represent one level of refinement above everyday usage. This may have both advantage and disadvantage in training observers. Observers need not be so well trained to record these kinds of behaviors as they must to record expressive actions, but they must practice ignoring some of the cues they habitually use in observing behavior in everyday life.

The visible effects of a child's actions on others have considerable theoretical importance in some conceptual schemes. If they happen also to be the effects that are visible, or at least apprehended by the child, then they may be the things that will become important aims of the child's striving behavior (learned goals or subgoals), or they may provide a fairly objective referent in analyses of the reinforcements that maintain the child's relationships with particular or generalized others. If a child, for example, plays often with children who do provide help when he asks for it (or when he merely gestures for it or shows some signs of need) but tends to drop out of diads in which such effects are not forthcoming, then we have information about the child and also about his interpersonal relationships.

This example points up one of the problems of categories defined in terms of the effects of $P$'s behavior on others (or the physical environment). This problem is that the observer would often like to have a record of the *attempts* at succorance as well as the failures and successes in order to make ratios of attempts to successes and failures to predict the development of interpersonal associations based on partial or total reinforcement of "dependency needs." To achieve such additional recorded information, at least one and possibly two further kinds of categories of actions must be considered.

***Acts Which Usually Have a Certain Effect on Others.*** One step toward the fuller information called for in the foregoing example is to set the observer to look for acts that *usually* have a certain effect on others, whether they succeed in any particular case or not. There is a limited, but fairly large, number of ways, for example, by which $P$ can *usually* hurt another. One is to hit the other physically, and this is a clear and objectively recordable class of complex movements. But suppose a very young child strikes a very much bigger and older child and merely achieves a laughing retreat from the other? In such cases the important thing is that in terms of the usual "language of action" there is an interesting disjointedness in this interaction, which requires that we distinguish attempt from effect if we are to describe the matter with fidelity. *P*'s act of hitting can only be placed in the category "aggressive," in which it probably belongs (particularly if *P* continues to try to hurt and says angry things at the same time, despite *O*'s laughter and retreat), if we refer it to the aggression category on the basis that such acts (or movement patterns) *usually* achieve hurt in others.

There are at least two ways of providing a rationale for placing the ineffectual but usually hurting act into the aggression category. One is to refer to a table that shows that such acts usually (statistically) are followed by visible signs of hurt in most others. The other is to refer to the conventional "language of action" for which, unfortunately, no dictionary has yet been written but on which most experienced members of a culture might well agree. The code for such a language is probably pretty much a learned thing, and it would be very helpful indeed to have age-norm data on this learning, since very young children may be behaving in such a way that the adult or mature code can serve merely as a source of observer reliability but provide no validity.

*Acts Which Achieve (or Usually Achieve) an Inferred Effect on Others.* In the last two categories we have discussed we have assumed that there is (or usually is) a visible effect on *O*

following *P*'s action, which can be recorded and which can even serve as the defining characteristic of the category. One of the main problems in the observation of interpersonal behaviors is the brute force that often there are effects that are not immediately visible or that may never become visible. If, for example, a very large boy strikes a rather small one with all his strength, we would expect that even if the small chap laughs he has been "hurt." His laugh may, of course, have a different intonation or stress pattern, which may be a reliable sign of the otherwise invisible "hurt," or he may laugh first and then grimace or cry, providing visible indices of the class of "visible hurtings." Fortunately, young children often carry their feelings "on their sleeves," so to speak, but it would be naïve to hope that this would always be the case. The observer then must have recourse to the mysterious process of "inferring that *O* is hurt," and this is often done with considerable interrater reliability. The mysteriousness of the process arises because the observer often cannot state the objective basis of the inference. The trouble with the process arises when the basis of inference shifts, thus destroying the systematic quality of the report in the protocol. Suppose the beleaguered younger child in our example gives no cues in his reaction that he is "hurt," other than the visual signs that some of his skin has been temporarily displaced by the fist of the older boy. The observer may decide that the young fellow is hurt because of the very strength of the blow, because some onlookers gasp in apparent sympathy, because he feels that he himself would feel hurt by such a blow, or because of the clear signs provided by the older boy that he clearly intended to hurt the younger. Any or all of these sources may provide a tentatively valid contextual basis for inferring the hurt of the brave young chap: there is probably no way of knowing for sure. But it would be most uncomfortable if the observer later ran a correlation between "inferred achievement of hurt in interaction" and "inferred intention to hurt in interaction" and discovered a high intercorrelation that was in large part due to the fact that the information regarding the intention of the large boy was also used in judging the hurt in the other.

A good deal of the time spent in training observers should be spent in differentiating the classes of information to be used for making, for example, inferences of hurt. Usually the direction of such specification will be toward becoming sensitive to the expressive acts of the other or to higher-order patterns or even "higher-order variables" that are involved in such action. Unfortunately, we lack terms for most of these or the knowledge on which to base a scientific language. Until such language has been developed, or until the knowledge has been gained, probably the second best strategy is to train observers to be sensitive to their own empathic response, assuming that they share the same codes with the other about whom they are making an inference. Such empathic methods place great stress, of course, on the observer and the persons observed having the same cultural and language background and argue for the use of trained native observers in doing work in foreign cultures.

***Interacts in Which the Inferred Intent of P Has an Inferred Effect on O.*** The full complexity of the operations involved in recording interpersonal behavior becomes clear when we analyse a unit in which the observer reports, for example, that "P responded with a (hidden) anxiety to the aggressive intention of O." There is no doubt that we make judgments of this double-pronged, two-person, double-inference kind in everyday life and that we do it with some (unknown) degree of fidelity. But it is also quite true that we make a good many errors in often unknown places. It may also be true that we make fewer errors than some people think we do; such, in fact, would be the present writer's bias. Such considerations, however, provide only a background for a scientific strategy but can never replace a strategy in which the degree of error, as well as the information used for the inference, is known.

In a sense, the scientifically trained observer is given more to go on than the participant in interaction has. He is, for example, permitted to remain detached from the ongoing action. He is, however, also called upon to provide more than the participant usually has to do. He must state the basis for his inferences and, preferably, the further evidence that can provide a check on the name he gives to the inference—the further implications of its substantive content, so to speak. The raw data in a behavior protocol are only as good as the information used in recording them, and this in turn has import only insofar as the inference is shown to be useful in ordering interpersonal phenomena so that they bear on our theories and assumptions. It is probably the best strategy, therefore, to have the observer record as fully as possible the information available about $P$ and about $O$ from which an inference is made. He can then also record, probably in parentheses, the inference that comes to mind. The final inference can be made more systematically by a coder, who can apply the kinds of rules that can, for example, make sure that the information regarding the intent of $O$ is not also the only source of the inference to the effect on $P$ and vice versa. The final judgment on the entire procedure is left to the outcomes of the research in which the theoretical import and degree of ordering of the data can be evaluated.

The extra coding operation may be extremely costly, as we have mentioned before, and calls for costly verbatim records, which, in their turn, may keep the observer from noting some of the subtler cues that should go to make up the record. This may merely mean that nature happens to be a rather difficult task-mistress, who requires much in payment for relatively little. Inventiveness is desperately needed in order to cut down the exorbitant cost of obtaining good behavior records.

**Quantification of Single Acts.** Any one or all of the foregoing distinctions may be used to attempt to define a unit single act. Once this is done in a clear way, then additional properties of the act may be scored. If the act is defined, for example, in terms of "its visible effect or its usual effect or meaning" [Heyns and Lippitt (1954) refer to this as recording while taking the role of the "generalized other"], then the additional properties may include degrees or kinds of intensity, latency, intention, inferred effect, probability, etc. This is one approach to the quantification of action and often leads to the characterization of the single-act unit in ways similar to Gellert's definition:

Any scorable action, terminated by interruption by $O$, or by changes of intent, direction, or additions of new ideas by $P$ (i.e., "Let's put on the shoes, and then let's play house," is *two* units). If a series of interacts turn into a ritualistic, repetitive game, only the first two scorable units are recorded for each subject (1956, p. 12).

The last point is, of course, arbitrary, but it is clear, and the *number* of repetitions may be recorded and explored as to its usefulness as a personality, diad, or group property.

There are many other approaches to quantification. One may, for example, take very short time samples, as did Bishop (1951), who recorded the state of mother-child interaction every five seconds regardless of whether a change such as that required by Gellert had occurred. She therefore emerges with a measure of the percentage of total time filled by a certain kind of activity by mother or child. This has the advantage of clarity in terms of time but makes it more difficult to rule out ritualistic repetitions as Gellert wishes to do. In the long run, issues of this kind must be decided by the scientific utility of the scores obtained. On this score, both Bishop and Gellert, as we shall see, were able to obtain high reliability and were also able to test important hypotheses with their measures.

We have reiterated in this chapter that considerations such as those in this section, which have to do with the definition of the informational basis for single-act scoring, are related to the problem of scoring *interacts*, but they do not solve it by any means. We shall discuss some recent attempts to deal more directly with this complex problem.

## Typical Sets of Categories for Recording Interpersonal Behavior

So far in this discussion we have attempted to create a sense of problem regarding the study of interpersonal behavior, we have discussed some of the possible kinds of interaction units that have been or could be studied, we have outlined some strategic questions involved in planning research of this kind, and, finally, we have looked at close quarters at the kinds of units out of which interaction categories can or have been built. It is now time to list some of the categories with which researchers in child development have had experience. Our aims here are not only to provide useful categories for further research but also to show how some of these categories represent the distinctions we have made so far in this chapter.

It is not our aim to give an exhaustive list of categories but rather to illustrate the issues involved in using them in research. We shall also point out in passing the kinds of criteria that should be considered in using the category systems we shall outline or in developing new category systems.

In our discussion of the kinds of concrete information for which observers may be set to record, we focused upon particular kinds of information. We discussed expressive acts or movements as distinguished from the visible effect of an act on someone else. Some kinds of interpersonal or personality theory might require that a category set should be consistently defined in terms of only one or another of the kinds of information available to the observer. In that case consistency is certainly a virtue. We see no reason, however, to criticize empirically derived or, for that matter, theoretically derived category sets merely because they do not remain consistent in this sense. In fact, it will be interesting to comment on the mixtures of such information that creep into various categories in the sets we shall describe. The close and intimate contact with interpersonal behavioral phenomena, which comes from hundreds of careful observations, is a positive source of possible inductive truth that any empirical scientist must respect. In fact, theories about what information should be accepted or rejected in this realm are probably still less powerful than the detailed information that emerges from direct observational experience. As we have mentioned above, it is still incumbent upon a scientist to state as fully as possible the classes of information used in a study.

Gellert (1955) has listed seven major divisions into which observational research in child study has fallen in approximate order of the emphasis they have received. Her breakdown is interesting: (1) affiliation (sociability, friendship, popularity, ethnocentricity); (2) aggression (conflicts, anger); (3) ascendency (rivalry, demands); (4) conformity and cooperativeness (compliance, helpfulness); (5) fear and insecurity (tension, clinging tendency); (6) extraversion-introversion; (7) sympathy and social sensitivity. She suggests that the emphasis in research to date on these particular dimensions of interpersonal behavior has been determined by such matters as the relevance to broad theoretical interests, the pressure of educational, social, and clinical problems, by the fact that these behaviors command attention, and finally by expediency. She ponders the further question of such uniformity in the variables that have been investigated and bemoans the lack of imagination so far displayed in this sphere. We feel similarly and wish to make clear that the category systems that follow should not be assumed in any sense to be tools around which even a major portion of future research should revolve. The area of interpersonal behavior in children has hardly been tapped, and we hope our preceding discussion has helped to make this fact more salient.

## THE RELATION OF STRATEGY TO CATEGORY SYSTEMS

Many of the situations and strategies we have discussed are those in which a child's interpersonal behavior might be studied. We have distinguished between the use of a priori categories and those used to code a fairly verbatim protocol. Presumably, either of these categories could be used to record aggressive single acts, aggressive interactions, aggressive activities, or aggressive relationships. Presumably, each of these might be used to study sociological (or cultural) aspects of aggressive interpersonal behavior (in which $P$ and $O$ are replaceable in principle, except that they may have some property such as a role or status relation to one another or a friendship relation) or the more directly interpersonal aspects (in which at least $P$, and possibly $O$ and $TP$ as well, is in an important sense not replaceable). The last category would also include the very frequent case in which a set of categories has been worked out for the purpose of recording the interaction of a child with his parent or with his teacher or psychiatrist but under the conditions that *both* remain unreplaceable during the observations. Finally, we have outlined two possible tactics of observation, the man-to-man method as compared to the zone method, and we have named a number of kinds of information for which an observer might be set.

These distinctions can help to classify studies in which children are observed, and they may even prove useful to those who are planning research in this area by helping them to make the data fit more closely their theory or question of interest. They are not necessarily useful *in toto* for classifying category schemes. This is because a given category scheme (a priori or a posteriori) might be used for a good many or even all of these purposes. If we permute some of the major distinctions in the foregoing paragraph, we emerge at one end with a study "focused on sociological single acts based upon an inference regarding the visible or usual effect of the acts of $P$ with the use of a zone observation tactic," whereas at the other end we emerge with a study "focused on interpersonal interactions based upon information regarding the instigations directed toward $P$, his response (visible or usual effect of same), and the response of $O$ (or of $TP$) to the behavior of $P$ obtained by a man-to-man tactic." It is quite conceivable that the same category set could be used in both of these otherwise quite different studies. If, for example, the content of interest were aggression, then the same categories could be used for recording the behavior of the two kinds of $P$'s in these studies. It might also be the case that the categories for recording instigations directed at $P$ would be the same, except for a residual category for non-aggression, because of the broadly reciprocal quality of aggression interaction. Finally, the effect acts (the counter-response of $O$ or the intervention of $TP$) would be largely the same except for the same residual category.

There is considerable independence between the kinds of categories one uses and the other parameters that describe a study. Consider the category system of Bales (1950). It is basically a system established on information regarding the usual effect (i.e., meaning) of the actions of $P$ and is most often used to record the frequency of the single acts of a group of essentially replaceable $P$'s. It is possible, however, to record interpersonal single acts by the simple expedient of keeping track of who "sends" the single act and who "receives" it, and this is often done in fact. The category sets could also probably be used in some cases to record units of interacts by keeping the records so that instigation-reaction-effect reaction could be retained as a unit. Perhaps some changes would be needed for this last purpose. We shall therefore discuss some category systems in terms of the content of the phenomena recorded, but we shall also point out some of the uses to which the category system has been put according to our other dimensions. We shall be particularly careful to point out the content and strategy limitations of present existing category systems.

## OBSERVATION OF AGGRESSIVE INTERACTION

Faigin (1958) has used a set of categories to study the frequency of aggressive behaviors displayed by the children of two different *Kibbutzim* in Israel. The categories were worked out prior to the beginning of observation, and time samples were taken of the behavior of each individual child in ten- or fifteen-minute time units. She obtained, in all, three hours of systematic observation on each child, the time periods being allotted to the various activities in which the child spent his day: free play, organized play, meal time, and getting up in the afternoon period. The observer reliability of the categories of aggressive responses ranged from 75 to 95 per cent, using this formula: per cent agreement is equal to the number of agreements of two observers divided by the number of agreements plus the number of disagreements. When the subcategories were totaled to provide a total score, the agreement was found to be 92 per cent.

Faigin's study is of interest partly because of the relatively young age of the children, the range being 19 to 38 months at the time when the study was begun. The categories she used were (1) physical aggression, which she defined as hitting for the purpose of hitting or hurting, apparently utilizing information regarding the intention of the child; (2) instrumental aggression, which is defined in terms of hitting or pushing in order to obtain some other goal such as a toy, play space, or attention, apparently utilizing information regarding the visible effect or usual effect of hitting or pushing movements; (3) defense of toys; (4) defense of self; (5) aggression to objects; (6) aggression to smaller children; (7) verbal aggression; (8) disobedience. In her research report Faigin does not go into the definitions used for more than the first two categories, partly because the frequency of any but the first two was so small that the main effect was their lack of occurrence, possibly due to the extreme youth of most of her subjects. She also found that half the children expressed very little or no physical aggression and that 18 out of the 31 children displayed almost no instrumental aggression. These categories produced a considerable range of individual differences but showed no differences between Kibbutzim, which led to the interpretation that the instigation to aggression is due to factors other than, or in addition to, the frustrations inherent in group living, since the social and cultural environment of the Kibbutzim differed considerably. It is also interesting that among children of the age Faigin studied there was a significant negative relationship between the total aggression scores and those for dependency. Other studies, with older children, tend to find a low or medium positive relationship. This leads Faigin to the suggestion that at this earlier age dependency and aggression are alternative responses to frustration and that the children who have been successful in using one or the other type of response seem to persist in its use.

An important study of children's interpersonal aggression is the Iowa study of Sears et al. (1953). Among other measures taken on the 40 children (21 boys, 19 girls) involved in the study, each child was observed for 16 fifteen-minute periods and his aggressive behavior was recorded in six categories. These categories are fairly homogeneously defined as being in "the nature of instrumental acts designed by the child to place himself in such context with another person as to provide gratification of the acquired drive of aggression." The categories utilized for aggression were (1) injury to person (including hitting someone, getting someone punished, damaging another's property, or derogating status). This category appears to refer to the physical effects of a child's actions, except for the last example in which judgment must be made of verbal behavior on the basis of its usual effect or meaning to the recipient. (2) Discomforting an-other (including threatening gestures and language); (3) insuring compliance with demands; (4) destruction of in-animate objects or constructions (in the form of displaced aggression or nondirected aggression); (5) having object in own possession (taking things away from another); (6) removal of immediate or anticipated frustration (removing barriers, minimizing injuries from another person, maintaining status, as in "saving face," taking back an object that has been previously taken away by someone else, and retaliation). It is interesting to note that these cate-gories are delicately worded in terms of the change in the environment that follows behavior and that this corre-sponds to a basic element in interac-tion analysis, as displayed in Fig. 20-1. The attempt here is to capture the num-ber of times the child maneuvers a change in the environment, which puts him close to a theoretically important goal response. There is little doubt that a great deal of information from vari-ous aspects of the context is necessary for making the judgments called for in these categories. However, by using the same formula as Faigin did to cal-culate reliability, Sears et al. were able to report that the mean agreement on the six aggression categories was 86 per cent, with a range of 67 to 100 per cent. The agreement on the total ag-gression score was 91 per cent.

The interest of the observers in the Sears study was not sociological, but individual and psychological. They de-sired to use the frequency of aggres-sion as an index of the strength of a child's aggression drive. The categories do not systematically take instigation into account, nor is any additional scor-ing of the length of an act or of its intensity attempted. The authors, how-ever, were not unaware of the need for control of instigation to aggression. They attempted to make the condi-tions of observation as comparable for each child as possible. They propor-tioned the observations according to the total time spent by preschool groups in settings of free play, story and music, and art. They also at-tempted to ensure that the conditions would allow for maximal interaction among the children and teachers, with minimal interference on the part of the teachers on the action of the chil-dren.

Two additional methodological re-marks seem called for with regard to this category system. The first is that a correspondence of +.64 was reported between the total frequency of ob-served aggression and the combined scores on ratings of aggression provided by teachers. The second is that the aggression scores correlate highly with a rating of the activity level of a child, and the authors report that the direct observations (since they were pure fre-quency measures) were more influenced by activity level than were the teach-er's ratings. The last two points are based on the data for the boys in the sample, but they also hold with some-what less clarity for girls. These re-marks provide a basis for the sugges-tions we made earlier in this chapter with regard to providing residual cate-gories in observation, which will give an index of activity level, or to achieve somewhat the same effect with a rating. The Sears study had the positive value of being theoretically guided so that it is possible to report that the validity of the observations is somewhat strengthened by the fact that these indices behaved, at least to some degree, the way the theory called for.

## Observation of Dominant and Submissive Behavior

Dominant or ascendant behavior has been studied a number of times by direct observation methods. Some of the important studies in this regard have been those of Jack (1934), Page (1936), and Anderson (1937, 1943). But our present discussion will be limited to the more recent work of Gellert (1956), both because she built upon the work of past students of these classes of behavior and because the criteria by which she judged the fruitfulness of her category system can provide some useful hints for future work in other areas of interpersonal behavior. She outlines the criteria she used for selecting the variables for her study, suggesting that behavior systems should have the following properties:

1. The behavior systems should be universal. They should not be peculiar to a particular *kind* of social situation nor to a special group nor to a stage of genetic development.

2. The behavior systems should have attained a demonstrable degree of consolidation.

3. It should be possible to divide the behaviors described into comparable units.

4. Instigations and opportunities for exhibiting the acts to be studied should be numerous and, if possible, controllable.

5. The behaviors in question should be overt and maximally unequivocal.

6. For the sake of economy, the behaviors studied ought to have theoretical interest beyond the study of variability, per se.

She evaluates the dimensions for variables of dominance and submission systems in the light of each of these criteria. Gellert's treatment of the second and third criteria in the foregoing list are particularly interesting, as is the fact that her category systems have been used to record both free play observations and observations of children under experimental conditions. We shall return to these points after outlining her category systems for dominance and submission. Her preliminary a priori category systems follow, being partially quoted:

### Domination Categories

*Mandate, positive.* Spontaneous order or suggestion: "Come here," "Let me take it," "Put it down."

*Mandate, negative.* "Don't," "Stop," when they are used as an order rather than in the context of an altercation or as defense against clear domination on $O$'s part.

*Dominates play; instructs.* Attempts to gain precedence in play; pushing $O$ out of the way; changing what $O$ has just built; grabbing toys $O$ is using *in order to use them;* initiating rules or referring to real or contrived "adult established rules" in order to direct play; also verbal threats to gain control; also instructions; also giving permission or assigning roles in play.

*Suggests orientation.* This is a gentler, or more genteel, form of domination than the preceding ones. It includes suggestions to which qualifications such as "please," "O.K.?," "Would you like," or "Let's" are appended or prefixed.

*Countermandate.* Domination in response to domination, noncompliance, or frustration occasioned by *O*. Any scorable form of domination or noncompliance on *O*'s part may provide a stimulus to a countermandate. Also, conditional surrender: "I will, *if* you . . . ," "I'll give it to you later . . ."; also, counter-suggestions; also counteraggression, counterteasing, counterboasting, etc.

*Calls attention.* "Look at . . . ," "See what I made," "Hey. . . ."

*Boast.* Favorable comparison of self with other child; also of self's prowess, property, or creations.

*Tease.* Initiating a threatening gesture made "in fun"; name calling; derogation of *O* or of *O*'s property or efforts.

*Aggression, per se.* Physical aggression, when it seems to be *spontaneous* or mainly with intent to hurt rather than in the course of conflicting aims in play, etc.

*Noncompliance; self-defense.* Resistance to *O*'s domination, per se, not in conjunction with attempts to counterdominate. Persistence in the direction of own activity in the face of *O*'s attempt to change it; defense of self, property, or rights.

### Submission Categories

*Comply; submit.* Complying in response to *O*'s directions or domination or bid for attention; obeys or accepts *O*'s impositions passively, desists, gives in; concedes actively in response to *O*'s domination; does not defend self, property, or rights.

*Agreement, verbal.* Verbal concession, not accompanied by active compliance of any other sort, in response to domination.

*Asks permission, directions, or orientation.* Almost any question is included here.

*Imitates.* Spontaneously copies what *O* is doing or saying.

*Withdraws.* As a result of conflict or dominance of *O*, *P* leaves play area, or what he is playing with, without expressing objections.

Having devised these categories for the observation of children, Gellert considered the next logical task, that of testing the psychological coherence of each of the sets of categories, a criterion that relatively few sets of categories have ever had to face. She did this in the following way:

> The best test of common motivation for a series of acts is to vary the conditions that are thought to evoke them. For instance, if increased domination by *O* raises the degree of *P*'s submission, there should tend to be an increase, for *P*, of unit acts in all the categories listed under submission (1956, Appendix).

In the case of dominance, one of the main findings of her study was that as *O*'s relative dominance decreases *P*'s relative dominance increases. She therefore compared the scores of *P*'s when paired in a partly structured experimental situation with more dominant *O*'s with the scores of *P*'s when paired with less dominant *O*'s and demonstrated a positive direction of change in *all* the subcategories of dominance. A similar test was applied to submission. Another of her findings was that "as *O*'s dominance decreases *P*'s submission score will decrease." She found a consistent decrease in all subcategories of submission when *P* was paired with a less dominant *O* than when *P* was paired with a more dominant *O*. The second method, a weaker one, which she used to check on the psychological coherence of her categories, was to compare the correlation with the total score of each behavioral system taken as a whole. Although all the correlations were in the expected direction, there was a great deal of variation found in the extent of the relationship. She therefore retained only those categories that correlated at a level of significance of 5 per cent or less with the over-all scores. This led her to drop *calls attention* and *aggression* and *countermandate* and *noncomply* from the categories that made up her composite dominance score. Countermandate and noncomply were considered together under a third heading, *resistance* and viewed as a separate behavioral system in testing the substantive hypotheses of her study. On the same grounds, Gellert dropped the category *imitate* from the submission heading and also deleted *withdraw* because it was too rare to be useful.

Gellert made a consistent effort throughout her observations to discriminate between the intent and the effect of each act. Behavior was always scored from the point of view of the actor rather than the recipient of an interact; thus an attempt on the part of *P* to take away *O*'s toy was scored as *dominates play*, whether it was successful or not. The average in observer reliability between Gellert and her two assistants was .81 and .84, respectively, the interobserver reliability being computed by this formula: twice the number of agreements divided by twice the number of disagreements, plus A's omission, plus B's omissions. The *omissions* were unit acts recorded by one observer but not by the other. Agreements were the number of scores per category that were recorded by both observers. These reliability data were obtained when observers were watching two children in the experimental play situations. The category system was also designed to record the behavior of only one child at a time in samples obtained in the free-play period in the children's nursery school. Since only 15 of the 50 children who took part in the experimental observations were also recorded in the free play, the comparison of findings is unfortunately not very meaningful. However, the systematic observations in conjunction with ratings and with the systematic experimental pairing of children for comparison purposes permitted Gellert to test several hypotheses concerned with general principles of interaction.

These hypotheses have much to do with the implications of Fig. 20-1 in that they show quite clearly and explicitly some of the ways in which the overt or scoreable behavior of *P* is a function of social-setting factors and of the properties of *O* and *TP*. Since Gellert worked within a very restricted cultural group (unless we view families or groups of families as having different cultures, as Roberts (1951) has suggested), she was unable to vary these factors systematically.

## OBSERVATION OF DEPENDENT BEHAVIOR

A number of category sets have been developed for the observation of dependent behavior in children in either laboratory or everyday-life situations. Sometimes these categories have been developed for observations of diads; for instance, when the child is interacting with one parent or with a teacher or psychiatrist. Dependency categories of this kind are illustrated in a subsequent section.

The Iowa study of Sears et al. (1953) called for the observation of dependency according to five categories, which are analogous to those discussed for aggression. In fact, observation was done with both sets of categories as part of the set of the observers. The dependency categories were also "of the nature of instrumental acts designed by the child to place himself in such contact with another person as to provide gratification of the acquired drive of dependency." The five categories were as follows: (1) touching or holding, in which the child is conceived as displaying evidence of dependency drive when he behaves in such a way as to secure touching or holding from another person; (2) being near; (3) securing positive attention (including praise, talking, playing such an institutionalized dependent role as the baby, inviting cooperative activity, asking questions unrelated to ongoing activity, giving unasked for information); (4) securing reassurance, information, or consolation (including apologizing, asking permission, voluntary conformity, asking protection, asking for help or guidance); and (5) securing negative attention (by disruption and aggressive activity and defiance). A total dependence score for each child was secured by summing the frequencies of the foregoing categories for 16 fifteen-minute periods. The mean interjudge agreement on the five dependency categories was 91 per cent; with a range of 76 to 100 per cent. The agreement on the total dependency score was 94 per cent.

In this group, in which the ages ranged from 3 years, 4 months to 5 years, 5 months, there was a significant difference in the frequency of dependency behaviors, more dependency toward teachers being shown by girls than by boys. A similar difference was found for the rated dependency measures. The correlations between observed total dependency and the ratings of dependency were only +.44. The observed dependency score correlated, as did the aggression scores, with the rated activity level of the child. In the case of the girls, there was a zero correlation between the total rated dependency and observed dependency. The problem in this case appears to reside in the judgment of the teachers with regard to negative attention-seeking on the part of girls. To quote the authors' interpretation: "It is as if the teachers, who were women, saw negative attention-getting girls as being aggressive but not dependent, while they saw such boys as being both aggressive and dependent." (Sears et al., 1953, p. 158.) Although the authors worry about the inexactness of the dependency observations when viewed as indices of the drive construct to which the theory referred, the results based on these measures were to some extent consistent with what the theory predicted.

Gewirtz (1956) has developed more pointed categories for categorizing specifically the *attention seeking* of young children in a free-play experimental setting in which only one adult was present and the children were engaged one at a time in the activity of painting. Despite the fact that the categories were developed to some extent for use in this limited situation, we include them here because they represent one of the directions in which interests in child-observation study will go in the future—toward more careful specification of more restricted aspects of behavior systems. Gewirtz developed six observational categories for scoring the attention-seeking behaviors of the children, three of them for the purpose of capturing verbal behavior and three for the capturing of non-verbal behavior. We include here brief definitions and examples of the categories.

1. *Comments.* Included in this category were casual remarks (never urgent), which usually required no response from the adult. "Typically the child made his remark and either just continued on to another remark or resumed his painting."

2. *Questions.* This category included casual questions, "never urgent, which required only brief replies from the adult."

3. *Attention seeking.* "Included were responses characterized by urgency, apparently designed for active notice from the adult. The adult's overt responses indicated, in a manner appropriate to the child's request, that he was attending to the child."

4. *Glances.* "Included were the child's glances and stares at the adult, which involved no verbal accompaniment, required no responses from the adult, nor initiated sequences of interaction when it was apparent to the child that his glance had been noticed by the adult."

5. *Paintings.* "When a child informed the adult that he had completed a painting, the adult removed it from the easel, attached a blank sheet of newsprint in its place, and wrote the child's name in a corner of that sheet. The number of paintings on which the child worked during the session was recorded."

6. *Time.* This category refers to the time that elapsed from the moment the subject first arrived at the easel until he stated that he no longer wished to paint.

Gewirtz reports the usual indices of percentage observer agreement for these categories, and he also reports computations of percentage observer agreement when disagreement included those of omission as well as of commission. A disagreement of commission is indicated when two judges assign a particular event to different categories, whereas a disagreement of omission refers to the case in which one observer assigns a particular event to a given behavior category and the other omits that event entirely. The percentage-agreement figures are not extremely high but seem adequate for the purposes of Gewirtz' study (Gewirtz, 1956, p. 21). He further reports the correlations of the scores obtained for the six dependence variables for the 56 children in his sample. The correlations show two clusters of measures, the first involving reliable intercorrelations among the three indices of verbal attention seeking and the second involving reliable intercorrelations among the three nonverbal indices. The only index showing reliable correlation in both clusters was the number of paintings done by a child in a given sitting. It may also be useful to point out that category 3, attention seeking, proved to be most sensitive in reflecting the effects of the independent variables employed by Gewirtz in his experimental design.

These categories may not be directly useful in all studies of dependency, since they were constructed for an extremely limited interaction situation. However, it is just such categories as this that have reasonable reliability and are related in a reasonable way to experimental variations in settings that may provide rich categories in future studies.

## OBSERVATION OF SYMPATHETIC BEHAVIOR

One of the classical studies in interpersonal behavior, and a study of great yield, is the analysis of sympathetic behavior in children's play groups by Lois Barclay Murphy (1937). This study ranged from extensive exploratory observation of children, mostly between 2 and 4 years of age, to experiments or "framed situations," which increased the frequency per unit time of the phenomena of interest. Interviews with parents, parental records, and ratings were also used at one point or another.

The observation method used was that of objective diary records of responses of $P$ to distress situations occurring spontaneously in the play groups. Because of the low frequency of occurrence of "distress situations," it was felt that it was possible to obtain protocols of *all* occurrences of these situations and to record the "total setting" of the distress, the behavior of the "stimulus children," the response of the other children, and teacher suggestions or interference that might have a bearing on the behavior of the children who responded to distress situations. In short, there was an attempt to record almost all of the elements outlined in Fig. 20-1, which were relevant to "distress" in $O$ and the subsequent behavior of $P$ and $TP$. We do not know to what extent other instigating situations, which also lead to "sympathetic" behavior on the part of $P$, were overlooked because of the focus on "distress" instigations. But the long qualitative exploratory procedure probably led to a broadening of the meaning of "distress situation" and possibly some refinement of the notion of "sympathy response" to provide a scientifically valuable denotation of an important instigation-response unit, at least for some purposes.

Murphy gives us the following classification of "the most characteristic stimuli for sympathetic responses among the preschool children."

*Physical cause.* (1) Accident; (2) attacked by child; (3) physical discomfort (cold, uncomfortable position, caught in play apparatus, etc.).

*Mental distress.* (1) Toy snatched or threatened; (2) play hampered or intruded upon; (3) disciplined; (4) separated from mother, father, etc.; (5) fear.

*Emotional expression without knowledge of stimulus.* (1) Crying; (2) holds hands over face; (3) pained expression—inhibition of crying.

*Evidence of injury without evidence of present pain.* Sore lip, mercurochrome, bandage, etc.

*Wishes, needs.* (1) Expressed wish ("I want . . . ," "Help me," or some action that reveals want or need); (2) unexpressed wish or need, assumed or implied; (3) precarious situation (need of care).

*Adult in distress or want.* Chiefly physical danger or physical need.

*Animal in distress or want.* Physical danger, need such as hunger, real or supposed attack by another animal or human being.

Murphy's corresponding list of responses to the "sympathy stimuli" follow:

*Helps.* (1) Helps out of physical distress situation—picks child up after falling; (2) helps with play—gives toy, plays with child, pushes swing, helps climb.

*Removes or attempts to remove cause of distress.* (1) "Stop it!" "Don't!" to aggressor of other child; (2) pushes away child attacking another (when this solves difficulty); (3) explains child's attitude to adult causing resistance; (4) removes cause of physically distressing situation—removes a tricycle from fallen child, gets out of child's way, uncatches child's foot; (5) stops play when it is in opposition to other child's need—e.g., stops jumping on board while child climbs off.

*Comforts.* (1) Pets, pats, hugs, kisses; (2) reassures, e.g., "I won't hurt you"; (3) expression of solicitude, e.g., "That's too bad," "That hurts, doesn't it?"

*Punishes cause.* (1) Attacks the aggressor of the other child before the aggressor has withdrawn, but not thereby remedying the difficulty; (2) attacks aggressor of other child after difficulty; (3) speaks sternly to aggressor (after difficulty); (4) retaliates on aggressor (does to aggressor what aggressor did to first child).

*Protects, defends.* (1) Defense of other child's material; (2) "It belongs to . . . ," ". . . was using that," "You can't have that"; (3) helps other child hold toy against aggressor; (4) "Don't hurt . . . ," "Don't touch . . ." (before difficulty occurs but is imminent); (5) retrieves snatched property for other child; (6)

explains other child's wants to aggressor; (7) verbal defense of other child: "He *can* get in," "That's not Jenny—she's crying"; (8) protects from hurt—catches child as he falls.

*Warns.* (1) Warnings of doubtful motive—"Look out," "Watch out," etc.; (2) sympathetic warnings: "You might hurt yourself," "You might fall."

*Tells adult or other child.* (1) "Look at . . ."; (2) "He's crying"; (3) "He wants. . . ."

*Questions.* (1) "Why is he crying?" (2) "Did it hurt you?" (to child); (3) "What are you going to do about it?" (to teacher); (4) "What's the matter?" (to animal or to a child).

*Anxious, disorganized.* (1) Stares with anxious expression; (2) evidence of worry, shakes head, frowns, lips pressed together, etc.; (3) cries, whimpers.

*Suggests or effects solution.* Tells adult to keep other child out of danger; tells child how to get out of the situation.

She also categorizes certain "nonsympathetic" or egocentric responses to distress situations:

*Laughs.* (1) Scoffs, criticizes; (2) laughs, smiles; (3) contrasts own behavior ("I don't cry").

*Dramatic.* Uses situation to play own role, usually dominating.

*Sadistic-destructive.* (1) Attacks child in distress or his material; (2) attacks child who helps child in distress; (3) teases, e.g., makes loud noise at.

*Ambiguous.* (1) Stares; (2) comments on situation (usually not addressed to anyone).

To some analysts, of course, these categories cut across other ways of categorizing these behaviors. In case of controversies of this sort, only recourse to the kinds of criteria quoted from Gellert can lead to a suspension of argument. Besides, that which cross-cuts other ways of thinking, along with the categories that are so crosscut, may continue to provide useful data. The main problem in the Murphy study is a limitation set up by the fact that although the main interest was in sympathetic behavior as a category of interaction, or at least as a phenomenon of interaction, it was basically observed as "merely" a stimulus-response entity —as a "sympathy-expressing" behavior, which was a response to "distress" in someone else. The limitations set up are, first, that only limited aspects of individual differences can be analyzed with this kind of unit and, second, that the full possibilities of interaction analysis cannot be explored. Murphy states the first limitation.

Of course, inferences regarding the *degree* of sympathy of the children are difficult to draw, since we have no measure of the *opportunities* for sympathetic responses; all we have is a rough statement of the proportion of the child's nursery-school life which is occupied by the sorts of behavior we have grouped under this heading (1937, p. 122).

Despite this limitation, Murphy developed "observation scores" on sympathy by weighting the total number of sympathetic episodes recorded for each child for the hours observed. It is very interesting that these scores correlated around +.80 with the (highly reliable) teacher's ratings. Furthermore, the odd-day, even-day reliability coefficient for the observation scores was +.94 and +.99 for two different groups of children. Murphy herself is led to remark in a footnote (p. 163) that the "ratings on an inventory (of objective items of behavior) by teachers or observers who have watched the children

over a period of months may be more valid than some of the procedures now in use of obtaining samples of behavior by so-called objective recording techniques." Such a conclusion appears rather problematic. The high correlations between the rating scores and the observed (categorized) behavior may have been due to the fact that each was based on the raw frequency of the empirical occurrence of the sympathetic response class (itself highly correlated with activity level and therefore with "visibility") rather than on some ratio of "opportunity" to be sympathetic to the number of sympathetic responses. In short, Murphy was very sensitive to the conditions for the instigation of sympathy, but "distress" was used as an aid in the recording of sympathy rather than as another parameter in itself of the total situation. It is to the latter problem that some recent explorations have been turned.

Murphy's study is extremely rich in information and description (as well as wisdom) regarding the behaviors that were "caught" in her categories. In all her considerations of sympathetic episodes in what we have termed a sociological manner (comparison of frequencies in groups, according to age, intelligence, etc.) there are rich suggestions if the report is read with a sensitivity to the possible effect of activity level. The study is a landmark in the area of interpersonal relations.

## OBSERVING PARTICULAR DIADS OR TRIADS

In our highly selective outline of typical category systems we have so far dealt mostly with systems that have been constructed with a particular class of behavior in mind. In recent years, however, there has been an interesting tendency to develop category systems for the study of particular diads or triads, in which content of the categories is important, of course, but in which the outstanding characteristic is that they are developed for handling intensively the behavior of two people at a time. A very impressive work of this kind is that of Barbara Merrill Bishop (1951), done under the direction of Robert Sears at the Iowa Child Welfare Research Station. Bishop's aim was to develop a category system for the study of parent-child relationships under varying degrees of controlled experimental conditions. The most elaborate set of categories is those for recording mother-child interaction, which are probably also useful for recording a child's interaction with any other adult as well, if the hypotheses call for the contents that Bishop is interested in. But whether one is interested in Bishop's contents or not, the categories and their apparent research success provide an example of our increasing sophistication in handling subtle aspects of behavior in an objective manner.

Bishop states the aims of her categories:

The categories had originally been selected partly on theoretical and partly on empirical grounds. From a theoretical standpoint it was desired to have categories which would reflect accurately the different amounts and kinds of influence the adult's behavior had on the child, i.e., the stimulus properties of her behavior. From an empirical standpoint it was necessary to select categories that were clearly definable, easily recorded in the intricacies of social interaction, and sufficiently comprehensive to express all possible behavior incidents that would appear during the play session (p. 8).

Despite her general worries about rating methods, she has included rating scales in several of the behavior categories in order to capture the subtler concomitants of the objective behavior. We shall not include all of her rating distinctions, but in the following brief description of her behavior categories we mention the kinds of distinctions she made.

Bishop's categories for describing the mother's behavior begin with three that describe the behavior of the child as well, then go on to eleven additional major categories reserved for only the mother's behavior. The categories are (1) out of contact, where the mother is sitting apart from $C$ and is either doing something on her own or silently watching; (2) contact, where $M$ is in contact with $C$ either verbally or physically or both; (3) playing interactively, where the mother plays as though she were another child; (4) teaching, where $M$ gives information to $C$ for the purpose of increasing his knowledge; (5) helping, where $M$ gives physical help to $C$; (6) structurizing, where $M$ facilitates activity on the part of $C$ in a manner that stimulates independent thinking in $C$ and leaves the responsibility of decision to $C$ (a rating is used here to distinguish between a suggestion for which $C$ has the option of acceptance and the giving of incomplete cues that call for some individual thinking on the part of $C$); (7) directing, where the mother states specifically the course she wants $C$ to follow (ratings are used here to distinguish five points along a continuum from $M$ anticipating noncompliance through matter of fact directing to angry demand); (8) interference, where $M$ interferes with $C$'s activity with intent of stopping it (ratings are also used here to distinguish similar points from those under directing); (9) restriction, where $M$ modifies $C$'s behavior but does not stop it; (10) interfering by structurizing, where $M$ points out undesirable consequences of a course of action, but the final decision is left to $C$; (11) criticism, where $M$ criticizes plans or punishes $C$ (here ratings are used to distinguish intense from mild statement from actual physical punishment); (12) praise or affection, where $M$ praises or gives encouragement to $C$, including patting or hugging $C$ (ratings of two kinds are used here, the first to distinguish praising $C$'s activity as compared to providing reassurance and the second to distinguish points on a dimension, from mother complying to $C$'s demand, through submission to enthusiastic response to $C$'s stimulation in a spirit of having fun with $C$); (13) noncooperation, where $M$ ignores or refuses to comply or accept stimulation from $C$ (ratings are used again to distinguish five points on a continuum, from simply ignoring through noncooperation to angry nonacceptance).

We list here only the major category totals for the 15 categories that are used specifically for recording the child's behavior: (1) seeking information, (2) seeking help, (3) suggestions,

(4) seeking attention, (5) seeking contact, (6) directing, (7) interference, (8) restricting, (9) criticism, (10) seeking praise, (11) praise, (12) asking permission, (13) indications of anxiety (where $C$ expresses concern over consequences of his activity), (14) cooperation, and (15) noncooperation. Rating scales or further subcategories were also used for all but six of these categories.

Bishop's method of recording was to use one block square for each five seconds of thirty-minute play sessions. The observer was behind a one-way screen, and five-second intervals were signaled by an automatic light. The observer recorded the status of the interaction (or at least of the first stimulus-response that occurred) in the five-second interval. The time interval was short enough so that there were very few instances in which one or two symbols did not completely describe the observed behavior as far as the categories were concerned. The observer reliability was correlated by dividing the number of agreements between two observers by 360, which is the number of five-second intervals in thirty minutes. The total reliabilities averaged .87, and Bishop has reported the reliability for each category as well (1951, p. 12). The reliabilities for the ratings averaged .88. On the whole, the experimental setup and the categories provided a situational framework to the mothers, which evoked and recorded behavior in a half-hour session that was rather highly consistent under repetition in another session on a different day. The average correlation for the 34 mothers (computed by major categories) was .71. A similar statement can be made with regard to the repetition of the child's behavior in two sessions, in terms both of frequency and reliability.

Using this procedure, Bishop was able to investigate hypotheses regarding correlations existing between mother and child behavior, individual differences among mothers and children, and indications of stimulus generalization on the part of the child when he was tested in a similar way in the company of a neutral adult female who was a stranger to him. This work is of the kind that leads to new developments in a field, and we shall report subsequently on two further category-system developments, which have grown out of Bishop's excellent start. We have mentioned that this approach characterizes one way in which interpersonal interaction can be quantified, while at the same time retaining by the use of ratings some of the qualitative dimensions of action. The scoring technique provides a kind of continuous record; it displays a careful sensitivity to the problem of instigation and presages later attempts at the development of an interact unit that retains characteristics of the successive flow of interaction.

Henrietta Smith (1958) has recently used some of Bishop's categories for a study of the dependency behavior of children in interaction with their mothers, which is interesting on two counts: it is interesting as a methodological study, and it included a different manner of scoring that brings up the possibility of studying *sequential* aspects of mother-child interaction.

This last aspect, although not fully utilized in her analyses, may be one of the new important developments in scoring interpersonal behavior. In order to achieve a parsimonious and precategorized record of the sequence of theoretically relevant action, Smith dropped the five-second time record of Bishop and substituted for it a scoring sheet containing a column for each category. The behavior of both mother and child was recorded, the units being set down in rows in the order of occurrence. This recording procedure makes it possible to indicate number and nature, as well as sequence, of the scored elements for each person. Smith recorded the interaction of thirty minutes with the child (18 girls and 12 boys). The children's ages ranged from 3 to 4.1 years. The mothers were observed for thirty minutes from behind a one-way screen and then for an additional fifteen minutes during which the mother was requested to fill out a questionnaire sheet while still in the presence of her child. This permitted an experimental measure of her behavior towards the child's dependency solicitations while she was busy.

The main content interest of Smith's study was to compare the usefulness of the observation procedure with ratings obtained from open-ended interviews with the mothers on comparable category topics. She reports interobserver reliability varying from .75 to 1.00, depending upon the category, with the over-all average over all categories used in five sessions of .94. She also reports significant correlations in a number of the mother-behavior categories from the first fifteen minutes to the second fifteen minutes of the observed sessions. The scores on the third fifteen-minute session (when the mothers were busy) were studied to determine which mothers changed the most. Only six mothers changed their scores more than one standard deviation from the mean in 40 per cent or more of the categories. The responses of these mothers on the open-ended interview were studied, and it was discovered that these six mothers were consistently within one sigma of the mean on ten interview questions, five of which were judged to involve some anxiety and five, which were considered to be neutral, selected at random. Smith's analysis along these lines led her to suggest that these six women who changed so much in their behavior toward the children when they were experimentally caused to be busy are "defensive mothers," who had entered the observations with a strong set to behave in a certain way while under observation but who were forced to reflect some of their more usual behavior when their set was experimentally altered. Smith concludes that such "defensive mothers" can possibly be more easily discriminated by the change in their behavior under observation conditions than by the answers to interview questions, since they were all close to the mean in the interview answers, though discrepant from the mean in behavior when they were busy. On other grounds, however, the interview was found to be equally useful in reflecting early findings with regard to the immediate instigating conditions to dependency behavior as well as to some of the home-condition antecedents.

Smith used 15 categories drawn from Bishop's categories described above, plus one category, which was used to record positive social interaction of a verbal sort, that was not concerned with dependency behavior. She used four categories for children's behavior and 11 categories for the behavior of the mother. The mothers' behaviors, which were considered theoretically relevant, were those that served as either stimulus or response to the child's dependency behavior or that were related to forms of control of the child's behavior. We shall not list Smith's categories here, since the major points of interest in this study are (1) that portions of someone else's category systems can be used effectively for more limited theoretic purposes; (2) that by giving up the small time-sample feature of Bishop's approach sequential aspects of interaction can be recorded, including the *possibility* of drawing from the record higher-level units, such as interacts or interact sequences in the sense of these terms discussed in the first part of this chapter; (3) the study provides a nice example of how observation records can be integrated with a study that has antecedent-consequent as well as experimental features.

The most ambitious attempt at the development of objective scoring categories to grow out of Bishop's work is reported in a paper by Moustakas, Sigel, and Schalock (1956). The aim again is to develop categories for recording adult-child interaction. Bishop's categories were used as a point of departure but were then refined, the definitions clarified, and numerous categories added "to make our schedule more inclusive, detailed and widely applicable" (p. 110). A scale for recording anxiety and hostility was added. Since much thought, experience, and hard work have gone into the development of this set of categories and since the reliability seems to be quite adequate, anyone planning observation work on child-adult diads should seriously consider using this system to provide continuity and comparability in research.

Such a decision, however, must be made with the knowledge that considerable time will have to be spent in training observers, since the system involves a total of 89 adult and 82 child categories as well as anxiety-hostility ratings. Furthermore, the categories are of various kinds, calling for attention to all of the classes of information that we have discussed in outlining different ways of defining individual acts. For example, several categories involve an attempt to elicit a particular kind of response or behavior by the adult or the child. These "stimulus categories" are (1) seeking information, (2) seeking help, (3) seeking reassurance, (4) seeking recognition, (5) seeking praise, (6) seeking affection, (7) seeking reward, and (8) seeking permission. This requires attentiveness on the part of the observer to information regarding the observable intention or the "usual intention" of the actors. Other categories, such as those involving "orienting and directing," appear to be judged more in terms of the visible effect or usual affect of overt actions. The attempt to "objectify" in defining the categories appears to lead to a focus on verbal social behavior, and although nonverbal matters are probably a help in categorizing they are not specifically included in the definitions. The authors suggest that meaningful behavior of the kind that involves tone gestures, postural signals, and facial expressions might be the subject of further construction of categories.

The actual recording procedure used by Moustakas et al. is modeled after that of Bishop. The basic unit is a five-second time interval, which is reported by putting symbols on a printed square on the recording sheet. Symbols referring to the various categories of behavior are placed in different positions in the square or above the square, according to set rules. For example, the first act by either person in a five-second interval is placed in the upper left of the box. It is not quite clear whether or not this act is always an "instigating" one. This seems in places to be implied by the writers, but since they are not focused conceptually upon what we have called an interact, involving an instigation-reaction unit, this question might be further clarified in future work for at least some theoretical purposes. The location in the square of behavior subsequent to this initial entry depends upon whether the adult or the child provides the initial behavior. If the adult provides the initial behavior, the child's behavior is recorded in the lower right corner of the square. If the child provides the initial behavior, the adult's behavior is always recorded above the square. Only the adult's behavior can be recorded in the space above the square, and only the child's behavior can be recorded in the lower right corner. Such conventions provide the eye with easy access to information that facilitates plucking out five-second intervals in which the child or the parent is the initiator, but it sharply limits the *number* of persons whose behavior can be recorded. Such a scoring procedure is obviously not set up for solving the problems of recording interpersonal interacts in a playground situation such as that which interested Murphy. Squares do not have enough corners for dealing with three or more people, and the complexity of the placement code could quickly become a deterrent to interobserver reliability.

The procedure here permits the recording of more than one sequence within a five-second interval; for instance, when the mother is engaged in a common activity with the child and also chats about something else. It has not been elaborated, of course, to capture the double or triple functions or the nuances involved in a particular act.

When an interaction takes more than five seconds to complete, the same symbols will appear in the next five-second square. Although the present writer has not actively worked with the Bishop scoring procedure, nor that of Moustakas et al., he feels that there might occasionally be confusion in *interact* analysis in deciding whether a particular series of squares, which may retain the same scored form for three five-second intervals, is in fact the same series of acts. That is, there seems to be some need for symbols that would differentiate when one interact of the same form leaves off and another identical-looking interact begins (as called for in Gellert's unit rules). Such considerations would arise only when someone was interested in using this kind of record for analyzing the properties of interacts (such as their extent in time) or the antecedent situational or cultural conditions for a particular class of interacts (i.e., instigation-reaction units or instigation-reaction-effect act units). What is needed here perhaps is further movement in the direction of placing within Bishop's form of analysis the possibilities for the description of the sequence of events in an interaction situation that we found in Smith's approach. Moustakas et al. have done something in this direction for the case of diad observation. A truly general useful set of categories may call for assuring the virtues of Smith's approach along with the virtues of Bishop's elements or time units but at the same time, solving problems that will permit observations of larger groups or at least of individuals studied by the man-to-man strategy acting within larger groups, such as classrooms, playgrounds, or family settings.

Moustakas et al. present data regarding the reliability of the adult and the child categories, and except for cases in which a category has not yet been observed to occur these reliabilities generally work quite adequately (Moustakas et al., 1956, pp. 129–30). They have reported data on therapist-child interaction and mother-child interaction in a playroom as well as mother-child interaction in the home. Although we would feel better about these categories if they had been shown to provide the basis for constructing categories to measure entities in systematic theory, there is little doubt that such attempts as this will soon be available because these categories obviously reflect much experience and wisdom in the observation of interpersonal behavior.

Strodtbeck (1958) has developed an interesting use of the Bales scoring categories (Bales, 1950) in connection with the problem of quantifying the power relationships in a family. In this case, the experimenter and his assistant visited the homes of a sample of school children from Jewish and Italian ethnic backgrounds. A questionnaire was administered to the mother, father, and son, the answer sheets were collected, and the assistant compiled a set of items that were then discussed by the three members of the family. He selected items for family discussion with an eye to creating three coalitions of the following types: (1) mother and son agree, father disagrees; (2) father and mother agree, son disagrees; and (3) father and son agree, mother disagrees. The family members then moved into position around a tape recorder and were asked to try to agree on one position on the issue that would best represent the family's opinion, if this were possible. The family members were reminded of their individual answers on the previous questionnaire. The experimenter and the assistant then retired to an adjacent room and worked at the controls for the recording equipment until the family had come to some decision. For most families, it was possible to go through this procedure nine times, providing three replications of each coalition type. All protocols were scored directly from the recordings and were not transcribed; the catego-ries developed by Bales were used for interaction recording.

These categories are discussed in an illuminating way by Heyns and Lippitt (1954). Despite the name Bales has given the method, the basic unit recorded is a communicative act of the kind that we have called a single act, and it is scored on the basis of its meaning to the observer "in the role of the generalized other." The scoring also calls for the observer to judge the function of the act with reference to the group problem. These requirements, plus the fact that the scoring system is limited almost completely to verbal behavior in a discussion situation, places limits on its usefulness for child-development study. The category system has some elegant properties, however, and observers who are well trained can achieve considerable reliability. The number of categories (12) is extremely parsimonious compared to the large number involved in the foregoing system.

Strodtbeck's method of obtaining a quantified index of family power was to assign arbitrary scores to the final family decision, so that winning or holding one's position when in the minority is weighted more heavily when one is an isolate than when one is a member of the larger coalition. Another way to devise a power score is to analyze the total number of acts initiated by each member of the family during the discussion. According to Strodtbeck, "Previous research leads one to expect that persons who talk most should have most power in the sense of winning the most decisions" (p. 165). In addition to this kind of index, the use of the Bales categories enables one to arrive at an index of "supportiveness," in which "we utilize jointly the information concerning the originator and target of each act, as well as the category in which it is placed, to form an index which reflects the tendency of a particular actor, number one, to give positive responses to the attempts at problem solution by another actor, number two" (1958, p. 167). This index is constructed somewhat indirectly (since the basic unit is not that of the interact in our sense) by subtracting the sum of the "negative acts" from person one to person two from the sum of the positive acts and the total is divided by the number of acts from person two to person one in the problem-solving categories of Bales's system. We shall not attempt to summarize the findings in Strodtbeck's study that are related to these indices except to say that the indices act in such a way that they may be very valuable additions to our tools in the study of interpersonal behavior. They might be even more valuable, of course, if the technique were used to retain sequence to provide direct classification of interact units for construction of indices.

## OBSERVATION OF "INTERACTS" IN EVERYDAY SETTINGS

The category systems described above were *selected* because they illustrate a range of problems and procedures in the technical problems of observation method. Observations have been made in free-play period (the Iowa study, Gellert's work, Murphy's study), in homes (Strodtbeck, Moustakas et al.), in a range of everyday life situations (Faigin), under laboratory conditions (Bishop, Smith, Gewirtz). We have also shown how category systems vary from those that focus upon very specific behaviors of the simple act or movement kind (Levin et al., Gewirtz) to general purpose categories that may serve several theories and may also serve to measure more than one kind of unit (Moustakas et al., Bishop).

It is to this point that we wish to turn for a moment: there seems to be an interesting sequence of development in our observation techniques over the last twenty years or so, and the development seems to center particularly around attempts (1) to solve the problem of the control of external instigations; (2) to record explicitly such instigations; (3) to search for efficiency by the use of precoded categories; and (4) to acquire an increasing sophistication with regard to issues of sampling. The first two tendencies are interwoven with the challenge of learning how to record the interact as a unit in an efficient manner. Murphy used the relatively inefficient diary method to capture "interaction," but the notion was not achieved operationally because instigations were merely recorded as (largely) a help in defining the single-act class of "sympathy behavior." The Sears group (Iowa studies) were very sensitive to instigation control but worked mainly on controlling the social structural (and cultural) sources of external instigation. They did not *control* the interpersonal sources, as in the case in which

"*P* acted aggressively in retaliation to *O*'s instigation," nor did they vary it systematically. The laboratory experimenters who also observe interpersonal behavior have, of course, achieved much more control or variation of instigation sources but usually within the limits of the "rules of standardized testing," which, as we have suggested, have their limits of usefulness. The first real approach to a solution occurs, as we have seen, in Bishop's work, but here the unit act used was really a unit *time* measure, and changes would have to be made in order to achieve a clear and interpretable interact record. We suggested some of these changes in our discussion of the intriguing categories of Moustakas et al. Smith's work suggested the possibilities of an efficient sequential record, although she has not yet displayed what could be done with such added power. Finally, in Moustakas et al. we see the near realization of an interact sequential record for the diad.

But it is only for the diad that these advances have been partly achieved. It is interesting that the final category system, which we shall discuss—that for the Cornell-Harvard-Yale Socialization Study—attempts to utilize and broaden these gains by trying to capture interacts (in the sense of instigation-reaction-effect act units) as they occur in a sample of a child's life in a number of important "settings" and for a number of different cultures (PSU's). In order to do this, it was necessary to go back to a somewhat improved version of the old diary method ("total record" set).

The total project (see Whiting et al.,

1955) was organized around a conceptualization of nine behavior systems or sets of behavior dispositions, each of which was defined as integrated around a particular motive. These behavior classes are aggression, sociability, nurturance, succorance, independence, achievement, obedience, responsibility, and self-reliance. The study design included other data obtained in a number of ways, but major emphasis was placed on systematic behavior sampling of 12 five-minute periods spread over several weeks for 24 carefully sampled children (12 boys, 12 girls; 12 younger, 12 older) in each of five (later six) societies.

The field workers spent considerable time before leaving the country in becoming trained in observation methods and worked over the definitions of the behavior systems by use of multiple examples, much discussion, and practice in observation with children in the United States. Tentative definitions of the major instigators were worked out that were consistent with theory and with the contents of the interview used with the mother. The instigating situations of particular importance were *O* hurts *P*, *O* insults *P*, *O* hurts self, *O* has difficulty, *O* asks for help, *P* hurts self, *P* has difficulty, *O* tries to dominate *P*, *P* breaks rule, *O* tries friendly approach, *O* reprimands *P*.

Arriving in the foreign culture, the field personnel worked with bilingual assistants for several months before attempting observations and watched for examples of the response classes and of the instigating classes. The classification problem was in a sense an iterative one. They were "set" to record all instances of the response classes and to capture the sequence and context of events in order that the instigation might be reconstructed in case it was not of the theoretically expected class. A child might display aggression, for example, not because he had been "picked on" or frustrated but as a response to a friendly advance from a younger child. Sometimes when $O$ is hurt, $P$ hits him (because $O$ had been careless), etc. The records of verbatim verbal and nonverbal behavior included a "cast" of all people who were present and a sketch of the physical setting. Interpretations and inferences were included but placed in parentheses.

The record was typed and sent to a central office for coding, and the coding was done by people who had been intensively trained and who read the field notes for the culture and other relevant material. The coder then "mapped" out the interaction sequentially, using a column for each actor and a row for each act. This permitted the coder to abstract out those interacts that were of any theoretical relevance. The coder was in search of any act on the part of $P$ or $O$ or of any $TP$ that was theoretically relevant and, in the case of the last two, also had something to do with $P$. In other words, if any instigation, any response of $P$, or any effect of any response of $P$, or any combination thereof, was of theoretical interest, it was retained for purposes of analysis.

It was necessary, of course, in cases in which, for example, only the response of $P$ was relevant, to provide categories for the (otherwise) irrelevant instigation and effect acts. Thus the category system grew toward a rather broad and possibly fairly "generally useful" system. It was elaborated particularly in the direction of forms of control and of discipline.

The information regarding the instigation (including the category "no *external* instigation"), the reaction of $P$ (including the possibility of "no act of $P$" or "$P$ ignores"), and the effect act (if any) were coded for placement on an IBM card. Such a card—an "interact" card—is the first approximation to this level of analysis, exploratory and costly though it may be, and the use of these cards may provide a stimulus to our theoretical and practical imagination regarding new possibilities in the study of interpersonal behavior.

The information mentioned above is merely the nucleus of "fact" around which the interact card is organized. The card is literally filled with additional information—eighty columns of it. Some of this information is, in fact, the basis for new kinds of exploration. It includes, for example, the place in the sequence of interacts of the particular interact on "this card"—its number, so to speak, in the five-minute observation time.

It was also early recognized that a particular act (on the part of $P$ or $O$ or of $TP$) might deserve more than one classification. Therefore, the IBM interact card includes such considerations in the form of adverbs, which, so to speak, "modify" the main classification of an act. Suppose $P$ initiates a request for help in an angry and demanding manner. It is, then, a "succorant response," but it is also done "aggressively" or "dominantingly" or both of these (there is provision on the card for "triple adverbs"). These adverbs were quite important, for as long as the first adverb on at least one basic act in the interact was theoretically relevant then the total interact was kept for analysis.

Let us review briefly the other kinds of information included on the card. There is information about $P$ himself (age, sex, etc.); the setting of the action is there (play, work, authority present or not, at home, etc.); the size of the group $P$ is in is there; the identity of the instigator (at least in relation to $P$ or to the society—but he is replaceable in any other sense); the act of $O$ is coded; the purposive nature of the instigating act is separately coded (was the act accidental, instrumental, imitative, retaliatory, etc.); the adverbs for the instigating act are coded; the intensity of the act is coded. All of this information is present for each of the basic elements of the interact, that is, not only the instigating act but the response of $P$ and the effect act that flows from $P$'s act. Repetitions of the same interact within the five-minute period were weeded out in order to keep independent the interacts retained.

The purpose of all this is to provide, in effect, the possibility of analyzing the impact on the behavior of $P$ of aspects of all of the major elements involved in our diagram in Fig. 20-1: culture, setting, identity of $O$ (or $TP$), immediate social structure, instigating act of $O$ (if any), and (for some analyses) the effect act. The IBM card will eventually contain background information on $P$, providing at least one independent check on some of the *internal* instigations that might be acting in $P$ to help determine his behavior. Given such a card, all of the kinds of analyses that were discussed in the first two sections could, in principle, be done and a number of different kinds of hypotheses investigated. All, that is, except one kind of analysis, as we shall see. Further, these "exploratory" cards have been obtained at a great price in energy and money because of the costly recording and coding procedures that had to be used at this stage in the technical history of observation methods. Thirty thousand IBM cards emerged from this analysis of the data from six societies or PSU's (one each from the United States, India, Mexico, Okinawa, the Philippine Republic, and Africa). And much must be done before we will know what these particular cards can tell us.

## Summary and Discussion

In this chapter we have attempted to create a "sense of problem" regarding the strategies and techniques involved in the direct study of interpersonal behavior. Having provided a scheme (Fig. 20-1) for analyzing an interaction situation, we outlined a number of kinds of unit that might be abstracted from such a situation for study, ranging from a single act of one actor through an interact encompassing aspects of the energy displacements of two or more actors, to interpersonal activities and relationships. The focus of the remainder of the chapter was on the first two of these.

A number of aspects of strategy in this research realm were discussed, as were some of the practical problems. This led to a discussion of some of the different ways in which single acts can be defined in terms of the source of "information" used for classification and to a discussion of the further quantification of unit acts and of interacts.

A discussion of a selected group of category systems followed. An attempt was made to outline a historical development, so that new inventions in technique, which had been tried first with inefficient methods, could then be consolidated into efficient techniques that usually involve precoded category systems. Historical development toward operational recognition of momentary instigations as a parameter or variable in its own right was emphasized. Recent developments appear to achieve an approximation to this end but at a cost in efficiency and with problems still present regarding the independence of informational sources (Whiting et al., 1955; Moustakas et al., 1956) and the fact that one technique (Moustakas et al.), though efficiently precoded, is too limited in the number of people who can be recorded. The other, though broader in its grasp, still leans on the more costly method of post-recording coding.

As we move toward efficiency in these regards, it should be pointed out that there will be an increasing need for better statistical models to help solve problems. It will be necessary to solve problems inherent in multiple contingency (see, for example, Sutcliffe, 1957) and to investigate the implications of the concepts of experiment-wide error (see Ryan, 1959) when applied to studies with a number of different dependent variables. Progress must be made in the direction of comprehending the implication of Kish's (1958) analysis of the problem of estimating confidence limits when simple random sampling is given up in favor of more complex designs.

At the risk of being oracular, let us end on a note regarding future developments. Once we get to know more about the possibilities involved in the analysis using interacts, we may then wish to analyze these units (or those more complex) in their own right. This will lead to the solution of how to include the immediate instigations (working on two or more people) that predispose a diad or triad toward a particular class of interacts. This may be the next big step beyond the compass of present methods.

The step prior to that, however, will probably be to render interact recording, itself, efficient by the use of precoded categories, while at the same time retaining the additional information needed for making inferences to the personality of $P$, the settings of $P$'s action, the modal personality for a group, and the social or cultural contributions to "external instigation."

Let us hope that these developments can be achieved in conjunction with some agreement on one, or a series, of generally useful categories, so that the values of replication and of cumulation in research can be enhanced.

# REFERENCES

Anderson, H. H. 1937. An experimental study of dominative and integrative behavior in children of preschool age. *J. soc. Psychol.*, 8, 335–345.

———. 1943. Domination and socially integrative behavior. In Barker, Kounin, and Wright (Eds.), *Child behavior and development*. New York: McGraw-Hill. Chapter XXII.

Baldwin, A. L. 1955. *Behavior and development in childhood*, New York: Dryden.

Bales, F. 1950. *Interaction Process Analysis*, Cambridge, Mass.: Addison-Wesley.

Barker, R. G., and L. S. Barker. 1957. Behavior units for the comparative study of cultures. Palo Alto, Calif.: Center for Advanced Study in the Behavioral Sciences.

Barker, R. G., and H. F. Wright. 1951. *One boy's day*, New York: Harper.

———. 1955. *Midwest and its children: The psychological ecology of an American town*. Evanston, Ill.: Row, Peterson.

Birdwhistle, R. L. 1952. *Introduction to kinesics* (an annotation system for analysis of body motion and gesture). Louisville, Ky: Univer. Louisville.

Bishop, Barbara M. 1951. A study of mother-child interaction. *Psychol. Monogr.*, 65, No. 11 (Whole No. 328).

Bott, Helen M. 1933. Method in social studies of young children. *Toronto Univer. Stud. Child Develpm. Ser.*, 1. Toronto: Univer. Toronto Press.

Campbell, D. T. 1959. Invited address to the Amer. Anthrop. Assoc.

Faigin, H. 1958. Social behavior of young children in the *Kibbutz*. *J. abnorm. soc. Psychol.*, 56, 117–129.

Gellert, Elizabeth. 1955. Systematic observation: A method in child study. *Harvard Educ. Rev.*, Vol. XXV, No. 3, 179–195.

———. 1956. Patterns of dominance, submission, and resistance in the interaction of young children. Doctoral thesis, Graduate School of Education, Harvard Univer.

Gewirtz, J. L. 1956. Three determinants of attention-seeking in young children. *Monogr. Soc. Res. Child Develpm.*, XIX, 59, 2.

Heider, F. 1958. *The Psychology of Interpersonal Relations*. New York: Wiley.

Heyns, R. W., and R. Lippitt. 1954. Systematic observation technique. In G. Lindzey, (Ed.), *Handbook of Social Psychology*, Vol. I. Pp. 370–404. Cambridge, Mass.: Addison-Wesley.

Hockett, C. F. 1958. Ethnolinguistic implications of studies in linguistics and psychiatry. Georgetown Univer. Speech presented to the Institute of Language and Linguistics.

Jack, Lois M. 1934. An experimental study of ascendent behavior in preschool children. *Univ. Iowa Stud. Child Welf.*, 9, 7–65.

Kish, L. 1957. Confidence intervals for clustered samples, *Amer. soc. Rev.*, 22, 154–165.

Levin, H., A. L. Baldwin, M. Gallwey, and A. Paivio. 1959. Audience stress, personality and speech (in preparation). Cornell Univer.

Mead, Margaret. 1954. Research on primitive children. In L. Carmichael (Ed.), *Manual of child psychology*, New York: Wiley. Pp. 667–706.

Moustakas, C. E., I. E. Sigel, H. D. Schalock. 1956. An objective method for the measurement and analysis of child-adult interaction, *Child Develpm.*, 27, 2, 109–134.

Murdock, G. P. 1957. World ethnographic sample. *Amer. Anthrop.*, 59, 664–687.

Murphy, Lois B. 1937. *Social Behavior and Child Personality*. New York: Columbia Univ. Press.

Page, M. L. 1936. The modification of ascendant behavior in preschool children. *Univer. Iowa Stud. Child Welf.*, 12, 3.

Parsons, T., and E. A. Shils (Eds.). 1951. *Toward a general theory of action*. Cambridge, Mass.: Harvard Univer. Press.

Roberts, J. M. 1951. *Three Navajo households. A comparative study in small group culture*. Cambridge, Mass.: Peabody Museum Papers, Vol. XL, No. 3.

Ryan, T. A. 1959. Multiple comparisons in psychological research, *Psychol. Bull.*, 56, 26–47.

Sears, R. R. 1951. Social behavior and personality development. In T. Parsons and

E. A. Shils (Eds.), *Toward a general theory of action*, Cambridge, Mass.: Harvard Univer. Press. Pp. 465–476.

Sears, R. R., J. W. M. Whiting, V. Nowlis, and Pauline S. Sears. 1953. Some child-rearing antecedents of aggression and dependency in young children. *Genet. Psychol. Monogr.*, 47, 135–234.

Skinner, B. F. 1938. *The behavior of organisms. An experimental analysis.* New York: Appleton-Century-Crofts.

Smith, Henrietta. 1958. A comparison of interview and observation measures of mother behavior. *J. abnorm. soc. Psychol.*, 57, 278–282.

Spiro, M. E. 1958. *Children of the Kibbutz.* Cambridge, Mass.: Harvard Univer. Press.

Strodtbeck, F. L. 1958. Family interaction, values, and achievement. In D. C. McClel-land et al., *Talent and Society*. Pp. 135–194. Princeton, N. J.: Van Nostrand.

Sutcliffe, J. P. 1957. A general method of analysis of frequency data for multiple classification designs. *Psychol. Bull.*, 54, 2, 134–137.

Whiting, J. W. M. 1959. The observation of children's behavior—a cross-cultural approach. Paper delivered before the American Psychological Association.

———, et al., 1953. *Field manual for the cross-cultural study of child rearing.* New York: Social Sci. Res. Council.

Whiting, J. W. M., I. L. Child, and W. W. Lambert, et al. 1955. Field guide for a study of socialization in five societies. Cambridge, Mass.: Laboratory of Human Development. (Mimeo.)

# chapter 21

# Contributions of Anthropology to the Methods of Studying Child Rearing

John W. M. Whiting
Beatrice B. Whiting
*Harvard University*

The contributions of anthropology to the study of child rearing may be divided into three categories—conceptual, methodological, and substantive. On the conceptual side, the field of anthropology has contributed the concept and analysis of culture. On the methodological side, anthropologists have developed the ethnographic interview, participant observation, and the genealogical methods. On the substantive side, the major contribution of anthropology has been to report a range of variation in many child-rearing practices that goes far beyond any found within Western European society and thus provides a framework for defining cultural variables that are not bound to

a single society. It is our purpose to discuss each of these classes of contributions in order.

## CONCEPTS

Anthropologists, like other social scientists, have been concerned with human behavior and, like other social scientists, have reported norms and variations in the behavior of people belonging to various societies the world over. They have even at times been concerned with the behavior of individual members of these groups, as evidenced by the numerous biographies and life histories they have produced. Their methods of observing, recording, and assessing human behavior are not strikingly different from those of other behavioral scientists, such as sociologists and social psychologists. In fact, they generally have not been nearly as systematic in sampling and counting or describing the norms and variations of behavior. Where they have, however, made a unique conceptual contribution is in the formulation of the shared symbolic determinants of behavior, which, in our view, is the essential feature of the concept of culture.

Although, as we explain below, this concept is often used to include overt behavior, and even the products of behavior such as artifacts, we feel that its essential contribution lies in providing a method for coding and classifying the shared ideas of the members of a society or group, rather than in describing norms of behavior, and it is this view of culture that we would like to present here.

The concept of culture as it is used today is generally attributed to the

British anthropologist, E. B. Tyler in his classic work *Primitive Culture* (1871). His much cited definition provided the original impetus for a way of looking at social life that has persisted among anthropologists for the last seventy-five years. Many books and articles have been written to suggest modifications and elaborations of his formulation, the latest and most exhaustive being *Culture, A Critical Review of Concepts and Definitions*, by Kroeber and Kluckhohn (1952). It is not appropriate in this chapter to review the various points of view and nuances that have been given to the concept but rather to describe the features of the concept of culture to be used. These features are technology, ethnoscience, and ethics. Each of these symbolic or cognitive systems is presumed to influence the customary behavior of the members of any society. The elements of these systems consist of cultural units, shared habits, or customs. Each of these units, however, has different attributes, and we have chosen to label them, respectively, techniques, beliefs, and values.

A technique is a recipe for action. Techniques are found in cook books, books on infant care, and manuals on how to operate a car. If you wish to bake a cake, "take three eggs, a cup of flour, etc." "To wean a child, first, withdraw the two A.M. bottle, feed orange juice from a spoon, remove the bottle at the noon feeding, and feed milk from a cup, etc." A technique does not imply moral compunction. There is no implication that anyone should bake a cake or ought to drive a car— simply that this is the way people in

this society do drive cars and bake cakes. The manual on child care, however, is likely to contain not only techniques but also beliefs and values. A technique should also be distinguished from a skill. The fact that a given individual knows how to bake cakes or drive a car is of a different order. It is a statement on the behavioral rather than on the cognitive level. A technique is something that is or can be stated in the language of the society in which it exists. Some techniques are covert; that is, the members of the society are not constantly aware of them. However, a deviation from a technique would be recognized immediately, and the technique could be formulated and stated by a member of this society if it were brought to his attention. The recognition and definition of techniques and their transmission to the next generation is, of course, one of the most important aspects of the process of socialization.

Belief, the second major type of custom, may be defined as a statement of the relationship between events. For instance, greenheaded flies bite, the east wind brings rain, sinners will suffer in hell, and 6-year-old children will get sick with less than ten hours of sleep a night are examples of beliefs. Whether or not they are true is irrelevant. Every culture has a set of beliefs about the social and the spiritual environment that may be defined as the ethnoscientific and religious dogma of the culture. This set of beliefs is the second major aspect of the culture that must be transmitted to the children of the new generation.

Values comprise the third basic type

of custom. A value, as it is used in this chapter, may be defined as a statement that attributes goodness or badness to any event. Thus murder is bad; honesty is good, people should be successful, a man ought to obey the law, and children should love their parents are all statements of values. All of the values held by the members of a given society may be said to comprise the ethical system of that culture. The transmission of values to children is generally held to be one of the most important duties of a parent and the one most difficult to accomplish.

Each of these three types of custom is internally organized in a somewhat different manner. Techniques are organized so that the responses they specify usually achieve the desired result in the most efficient manner and are thus subject to pragmatic test. A technique that does not work is often abandoned, but many magical rituals, such as rainmaking or water dowsing, have surprising persistence in the face of failure.[1]

There are two primary principles that govern the organization of a belief system—that of coherence and of correspondence. In other words, beliefs in any given system ordinarily do not contradict one another, nor are they in general stated so that they are clearly false in terms of empirical reality. They may, however, be stated in such a way that it is difficult to sub-

ject them to empirical test. This is particularly true with respect to beliefs about the spirit world. Statements about the supernatural are, by definition, such that they are not directly subject to empirical test. In all societies ghosts and spirits are incorporeal. Perhaps because such beliefs cannot be tested, they tend to be all the more logically consistent with one another, and thus magical belief systems generally are beautifully coherent.

Values systems are still further removed from empirical fact. Although coherence characterizes a values system, correspondence with empirical reality does not. Whether an event is good or bad cannot be tested in the same way that a belief is. In other words, values cannot be false. They can only be accepted or rejected, usually on the basis of their consistency or inconsistency. Again, in contrast to beliefs, values are generally given priority with respect to one another.[2] Although one may be skeptical with respect to some beliefs and hold them in doubt, there is a great number of beliefs about which the members of any society are certain. Values, however, even those most strongly held, are continuously being opposed to one another and reviewed with respect to the strength with which they are held. For example, in our society, it is held to be wrong to lie and to be bad to hurt another's feelings. What does one do in a situation in which one must either lie or hurt somebody's feelings?

The pragmatic test is thus applied to

[1] The resistance of culture to change, particularly the persistence of belief systems and value systems, is presumed and not discussed in detail here, largely because the precise reasons for such persistence are not well understood.

[2] Beliefs do have, however, a priority of a somewhat different order, that is, the certainty with which they are held.

techniques, the test of coherence to both techniques and values, the empirical test to beliefs, and, finally, values are ordered with regard to the strength in which they are held. Thus the customs that comprise a culture are not a simple list of items but systems of techniques, beliefs, and values, each integrated in accordance with respect to its own principles.

Not only are each of the foregoing systems internally integrated, but each type of custom is systematically related to the others and each performs a different function in guiding action. If one wishes to sail a boat, the acceptance in the first place of a large number of beliefs is required. First, that the boat will not sink or capsize; that the sail, if held at a certain angle will propel the boat; that the wind blows laterally to the earth rather than up and down; that the rudder will guide the boat; etc. Certain techniques are also accepted. "If you wish to turn to starboard, push the tiller to port." "In sailing into the wind, maximum speed is obtained when the sail is sheeted in just so that it doesn't luff." Comparably, in the field of child training one may believe that physical punishment administered at the moment of transgression teaches a child to perform desired acts or, contrariwise, that such punishment teaches only the avoidance of transgression but not the desired habit; or, again, it is useful only as a teaching technique when the child is more than 2 years old. Values are also involved. In the first instance, the act of sailing itself is generally considered to be good by those who sail, although, of course, others may feel that it is an inefficient

means of getting somewhere. In the child-training example the acts desired or not desired involve a decision relating to value judgments. Furthermore, one may have values as to whether physical punishment is good or bad for the child in general. These values may outweigh the belief that physical punishment is an effective way of teaching.

Quite clearly, the techniques, beliefs, and values described here are very closely related and are often in practice very difficult to distinguish one from another. In fact, all three are often implied, if not explicitly stated, in any given sentence. It is, we think, useful to distinguish them not only because of the different integrating principles but because they form in combination a blueprint for action that has been called the custom complex (Whiting and Child, 1953).

## THE CUSTOM COMPLEX

For the visually minded, the organization of the customs that comprise a custom complex, together with the way in which they are related to one another and to behavior, is presented in the diagram on p. 922.

To elucidate the diagram, let us take the example of the influence of a custom complex upon the responses of an individual. Let us suppose there is a 4-year-old American middle-class boy who is playing with a toy car in the living room at 6 o'clock in the afternoon and that his mother enters the room and says, "Put away your toys now and wash your hands for supper." This situation calls forth a

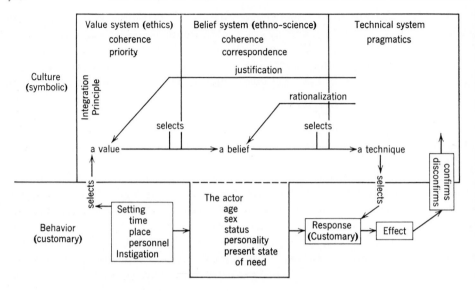

Chart of the ethnographic domain

number of values for the child: it is fun to play; it is bad to wash your hands; it is good to obey. Let us suppose that obedience is the strongest value and is therefore selected. The next problem for the child is to formulate a plan whereby he can obey and at the same time maximize his value that hand washing is a nuisance. He then calls upon his belief system— that if he goes into the bathroom and runs the water and makes splashing sounds his mother will think that he has obeyed her. This belief selects his technique, and he goes into action. The effect of this response, however, may be either that his mother is taken in by his behavior, which confirms his splashing technique, his belief that he can fool his mother, and his value compromise, or that she will say to him, "Look at your hands. You didn't really wash them." This puts a strain on his

cognitive system. Something went wrong. He may say to himself, "I guess I didn't splash loud enough—my technique was bad." Or he may say to himself, "I guess I can't fool my mother that way," and modify his belief system. He may say, "I guess it's best to do just what mother says after all," and obedience moves up in his value system and not washing hands, relatively speaking, moves down.

Now, suppose the mother asks him, "Why did you wash your hands that way?" If the boy replies, "I thought I could fool you," this would be, in our scheme, a reference to his belief system and *rationalization* of his action. If, however, he says, "But, I don't like to wash my hands," this would be a reference to his value system and a *justification* in our scheme.

It may seem from this example that we are talking just about the cognition of an individual child, and in fact we are. Culture as we see it operates in just this way. It is only the extent to which the members of a society share their systems of values, beliefs, and techniques and the extent to which these are customary rather than idiosyncratic matters that carries them beyond the realm of individual psychology.

Culture thus provides a cognitive map or blueprint, which governs the action of the members of every society, and the transmission of this blueprint is the rather imposing task faced by any parent if he wishes to bring up his child to be an adult who can operate effectively in his society.

The custom complex, however, is but a beginning. It describes the blueprint for but a single action of a single category of persons in a single situation. Custom complexes are, however, organized into roles that are played in institutional settings. Most readers will be familiar with the concept of role, and it need not be elaborated here. We would simply define it as all the customs that a given society expects an individual to accept and perform in a given status, which is in turn a part of a given institution. We would adopt, with slight modification, Malinowski's (1944) definition of an institution as being a group of people occupying different statuses (personnel), who are expected to perform certain roles defined in terms of techniques (norms and rules), agreeing upon certain values, and accepting certain beliefs (charter).

Roles and institutions thus bring a new principle of integration into culture. They refer to individuals working together toward a common end and assume agreement among the individuals as to certain beliefs, values, and techniques. In other words, these concepts refer to the effect of society in integrating the customs that comprise a culture. In sum, a culture consists of a set of customs, which may be divided into techniques, beliefs, and values that are in turn integrated into the systems of ethnoscience, ethics, and pragmatics. Customs are combined into roles that are combined into institutions. We feel that anthropologists, in isolating the concept of culture and by studying its manifestations in societies the world over, have brought a perspective that has enabled them to make a contribution to a more precise understanding of that which is transmitted to a child in any society by those responsible for child rearing. Furthermore, the concept of culture focuses attention not only on the overt behavior of parents in training their children but on the cognitive map that influences the content of what is transmitted, the techniques the parents employ, and their behavior as role models.

This view of culture as essentially symbolic or cognitive will not be agreed upon by many nor perhaps by most anthropologists. They say quite legitimately that anthropology is concerned with behavior as well as ideas, and this is, of course, true. It is fruitless to quibble over labels, and if one wishes to use the term culture to refer both to the symbolic and the behavioral, this is also legitimate. This analysis would suggest only that the symbolic and behavioral aspects of culture be distinguished. We would suggest the term *customary behavior* to refer to action that has been selected in the manner indicated in our chart—that is, by reference to the cultural symbolic systems or cognitive maps. Both, together with the relationship between them, may be taken as the *ethnographic domain*. Idiosyncratic, or noncustomary behavior, could then refer to action in which this process of selection has not taken place or is not used as an explanatory principle. In the examples to be given, both cultural data, e.g., beliefs, values, and techniques, and customary behavior are reported.

## CULTURE
## AND CUSTOMARY BEHAVIOR:
## ILLUSTRATIONS

Consider, for example, the beliefs concerning the nature of a child and how they may influence the teaching techniques employed by parents. Rajput mothers in a northern Indian village believe that the fate of a child is written on his brow at birth—that not only his physique but his temperament and behavior are predetermined (Triandis and Hitchcock, ms.). Mothers in a small New England town, on the other hand, report the belief that an infant is born "a bundle of potentialities" and that his personality and behavior are the result of the molding of these potentialities by parents, teachers, and peers (J. and A. Fischer, ms.). Mothers should seek to discover the latent potentialities and should be attuned to every indication the child gives, should look to the school psy-

chologists and his battery of tests, and to any other available information so as to know how to help the child to realize these potentialities. It is not surprising that the child-training techniques employed by the Indian mothers differ from those of the New England parents nor that the interest in and anxiety about child rearing is far greater among the New England mothers. The Indian mothers showed little interest in the questions asked by the ethnographer and found it hard to believe that anyone would travel so far to do research about such a subject. They were laconic in their answers and had few rationalizations or justifications for their actions as compared to their New England counterparts, who were eager to discuss the subject and anxious for new insights and advice.

In the field of learning mothers also held different beliefs. Indian mothers believe that their children learn from observation and that direct tuition or verbal communication is not necessary. New England mothers put great faith in the spoken word and in demonstrating with constant verbal statements and explanations. Related to these belief systems is the greater use of reasoning and lecturing by the New England mothers and the more frequent use of physical punishment and threats by the Indian mothers.

Okinawan mothers make a sharp distinction in the nature of children according to age. They consider any child under five as "senseless" and incapable of learning right from wrong. They excuse many of the transgressions of such "senseless ones." Once the child is sent off to school, however, and becomes a first grader, he is expected to learn to behave and is constantly told that he now is capable of "knowing better" (T. and H. Maretzki, ms.). This belief in the changing nature of a child with maturation is shared by parents in many societies. It is paralleled in our society by those who believe that the superego is not developed until around 6, when the oedipal complex is resolved.

It is sometimes the case that seemingly identical behavior on the part of parents is rationalized by different beliefs and justified by different values. In a study of child-training practices among three culturally divergent communities in the Southwest of the United States it was found that most nursing infants in the Texan and Mormon communities slept in the parental bed (Whiting et al., ms.). The Mormon mothers stated that they kept the infants in bed to keep them warm. The rationalizations and justifications of the Texan informants were more varied; some stated that they were afraid that the child would roll out of bed if he were alone; others that it was easier to nurse during the night. Crowded living conditions seemed, however, to account for the Texan sleeping patterns, since all families living in houses with three rooms or less took their infants into the parental bed, whereas three of the four families which had four rooms or more did not do so. Furthermore, several Texan informants reported disliking the lack of privacy. It appears that the Texan ideal would be for the infant to sleep alone. Mormon mothers evidently have the value that it is good to sleep with the infant and do so even though they have adequate space for the baby to have his own crib.

A similar contrast can be made between physical punishment as administered by the Rajput Indian mothers and the Mixtecan mothers of Juxtlahuaca, Mexico (Romney, ms.). In discussing such punishment, the Rajput mother is apt to justify striking the child because of her own anger at misbehavior. The Mixtecan mother, on the other hand, more often justifies the punishment in terms of teaching the child how to behave. Furthermore, the Mixtecans believe that the emotion of anger causes illness. The Indian mothers, although claiming to disapprove of the expression of anger, are constantly fighting among themselves and yelling at their children. The differences in beliefs, and the consequent difference in expressiveness, undoubtedly explain to some degree the differences in the aggressive behavior of both Mixtecan and Rajput children and adults and suggest that isolated behavior out of the context of the total custom complex may be less predictive of behavior.

## METHODOLOGY

Since description of culture has been one of the major interests of anthropologists, they have developed methods for obtaining data that are somewhat different from those employed by other social scientists. Whereas the sociologist and social psychologist are concerned with describing the frequencies with which certain types of customary behavior are manifested in a given society and presenting them in terms of their distribution, the anthropologists, as indicated above, are concerned more with determining the typical and agreed-upon beliefs, values, and techniques. Since their realm has been the ethnographic description of people little known to the western world, they have been less concerned with variations among the individual members of the societies that they have studied. To say that middle-class American children are usually brought up by their own parents is not a particularly interesting or dramatic statement. Social scientists who have studied our society take such a fact for granted and have concerned themselves with the effect of such matters as "broken homes." To say, however, that an Ojibwa child is brought up by his grandmother from the time he is weaned and may live in a different village from his own parents' from that time forth is of interest, even though, and this is reported to be the fact, this custom is not practiced by all or even a majority of Ojibwa families (Barnouw, 1950). That it is a custom, and that any Ojibwa family who practiced it would not be looked upon as deviant, is the sort of statement that is generally made by anthropologists and can be said to be descriptive of Ojibwa culture.

To obtain such data as this, two techniques have been developed that represent the contributions of anthropology to the methodology of social science. These are the *ethnographic interview* and *participant observation*.

The ethnographic interview (Paul, 1953; Maccoby and Maccoby, 1954) differs from other interviews in a number of respects, perhaps the most striking of which is the status relationship between ethnographer and informant. A doctor interviews his *patients*, a social worker interviews *clients*, a sociologist or social psychologist interviews *respondents*. In each of these cases the interviewer has a status vis-à-vis the person interviewed that implies greater expert knowledge and more control of resources. The ethnographer is also acknowledged as an expert by his informant, but not with respect to the subject under discussion. He describes himself as knowing about the culture of other peoples but as being ignorant of the culture being studied. He is careful to acknowledge the superior expert knowledge of his informant with respect to the subject under discussion. The status relationship is thus more nearly one of equality than that used in other social science interviews.[1] An ethnographer, for example, having some knowledge of how canoes are built the world over, may go to the most expert canoe-builder of the tribe he is studying and tell him, "I have come to you because of your expert knowledge and wish you to tell me how to make a canoe." This is quite different from a doctor asking his patient to relate his symptoms or a pollster asking a respondent how he voted in the last election.

To ask an informant for cultural data requires that the questions be put somewhat differently from an interviewer

---

[1] This idea was suggested to us by Professor Cora DuBois in personal communication.

asking a respondent about his, that is, the respondent's, attitudes or opinions. When the question, "What do you think about such and such?" is asked of an informant, the "you" is meant to refer to the members of his society or group. When the same question is asked of a respondent, the "you" refers to the respondent himself. An informant replies to a question from an ethnographer, "We bring up our children this way," whereas a respondent replies, "I bring up my children this way."

The syntax of the role relationship between ethnographer and informant requires that the ethnographer be a member of a different society from that of his informant. For example, if an American middle-class interviewer asked an American mother how American middle-class mothers brought up their children, the informant would look at the interviewer in amazement and say, "You know as well as I do." If the same question had been asked her by a Chinese anthropologist, or even by an interested Britisher, the question would make sense, and she would reply accordingly. It is quite understandable then that the ethnographic interview was developed by anthropologists working in unknown cultures rather than by social scientists working within the framework of their own society.

In addition to having the status of expert to expert, to asking questions phrased in terms of the generalized "you," and being an outsider, the ethnographer often defines his status outside the society in which he is interviewing. It is understood that a doctor, social worker, or pollster seeks information, and these statuses are well known to the members of our society. Outside the western world, however, the professional seeker of information is not a familiar status. This fact is exemplified by an anthropologist who overheard two Australian aborigines talking about him as they sat around a campfire believing him to be already asleep. Said one to the other in Pidgin English:

What name this fellow man?
Me no savvy, I think he belong government?
No got—he no belong government. I think he belong mission.
No got—he no belong mission. Him no talk all the same man belong mission. You think he belong business?
No, me savvy! Him, he man belong nothing, that's all.
True too much, him, he man belong nothing.

Not all anthropologists define themselves as "belonging nothing," but many find this a very useful status, which, like the stranger at *The Cocktail Party*, elicits information that would not be given even to intimate friends. It is well known that many anthropologists are "adopted into the tribe" and given kinship status within it. This, however, is generally recognized by both sides to be a pseudo-matter to be talked and joked about rather than to be taken as a serious set of mutual obligations. An anonymous relationship with an informant, such as is described above, is difficult, if not impossible, to establish if one is working in one's own society; and, again, it is understandable that this should be uniquely characteristic of the ethnographic interview.

One final word should be said about the ethnographic interview. Although this characteristic is not unique, in this kind of interviewing an ethnographer generally works with an informant over a long period of time. He may often work with one informant daily for weeks or return to him frequently for long sessions over a period of years. It is not unusual for an anthropologist to discuss a topic with an informant for an afternoon, to spend the evening typing up and checking over his notes, and to return the next day to a discussion of the same topic with the same informant, filling in gaps and straightening out ambiguities that appeared to him during the course of working up his notes. As a corollary to this procedure, the ethnographic interview is not standardized in the same manner that respondent interviews of sociologists and social psychologists are. Such standardization as there is takes the form of detailed topical outlines, which have been developed over the years. As ethnographic data have accumulated, the universal problems for which every culture has some solution have become apparent and a list of these topics or problems form a guide to the ethnographer as he works with an informant. *Notes and Queries* (1951), first published in 1888, by the Royal Anthropological Institute of Anthropology of Great Britain, is one of the most widely used of such topical guides and is now in its sixth edition. The *Outline of Cultural Materials* (Murdock, 1950) is another useful general guide. In addition to this, there

are many field guides or outlines for special topics. The *Field Manual for the Cross-Cultural Study of Socialization* (Whiting et al., 1953), a preliminary mimeographed draft published by the Social Science Research Council, is an example of a specialized outline relevant to the topic of this chapter.

Participant observation is the second major method that is generally credited to the field of anthropology. Florence Kluckhohn (1940) discusses this method in detail in an article well worth reading. It is difficult to define this method precisely, and perhaps the best general description of it is that the ethnographer participates in the daily life of the people in such a way that he learns the roles he is permitted to play by actually performing them and learns their reciprocals by actual interaction with members of the society. To use participant observation successfully as a technique, the ethnographer must be very sensitive to the sanctions that are applied to him. If he makes an error, or behaves improperly, he must also be sure that his status in the society is such that the sanctions will be applied to him. An experience that one of the authors had while working with Kwoma in New Guinea is an example (Whiting, 1941). These people wore no clothing, and the ethnographer found himself gazing at some of the fair maidens of the tribe. After about two months, he noticed that there seemed to be some rather rigid rules of etiquette requiring that men, when visiting a house, should sit on the edge of the porch facing outward; the women sat around the fire behind the men's backs. Furthermore, he noticed that if a man and woman met on the path she would turn aside and stand with her back to the path until the man had passed. He would then stop, and they would carry on any conversation facing away from one another. The ethnographer then checked these observations with one of his informants and verified them. He asked why he had not been told about his impropriety; whereupon his informant replied, "Well, after all, you're a white man and you don't know any better."

The status of an ethnographer as a participant observer is similar to that of a child. He is putting himself in a position to be socialized: that is, to be instructed with respect to proper behavior, to practice whatever roles are appropriate for him, to err, to be successful, to be rewarded and punished, so that eventually he may live in the society as a full-fledged member. This final aim has seldom been accomplished by professional anthropologists, but, during the course of living in the field for eighteen months to two years, many have learned large segments of the culture of a society in this way. Insofar as he is successful, an ethnologist becomes not only a reporter on the society but an informant. An anthropologist in the field does not rely solely upon participant observation or informant interviewing but uses them both in conjunction to construct the "invisible pattern" that orders the behavior of the members of a society. Malinowski (1935) in an excellent discussion of ethnographic field method describes this process as follows:

The observer should not function as a mere automaton; a sort of combined camera and phonographic or shorthand recorder of native statements. While making his observations the field-worker must constantly construct: he must place isolated data in relation to one another and study the manner in which they integrate. To put it paradoxically one could say that "facts" do not exist in sociological any more than in physical reality; that is, they do not dwell in the spatial and temporal continuum open to the untutored eye. The principles of social organisation, of legal constitution, of economics and religion have to be constructed by the observer out of a multitude of manifestations of varying significance and relevance. It is these invisible realities, only to be discovered by inductive computation, by selection and construction, which are scientifically important in the study of culture (p. 317).

This method of combining participant observation and informant interviewing gives the ethnographic interview a structure all its own. The topics to be discussed are often suggested by recent events rather than by some predetermined plan. It has been argued that the lack of standardization of the ethnographic interview brings into question its scientific usefulness. Since the ethnographic interview is designed to get at materials at the cultural level rather than at the level of individual differences, the problem of standardization is somewhat different. It is our opinion that internal consistency in material gathered from one or two informants over a period of months and then checked with observations of behavior will add to the validity on a cultural level of material gathered by a carefully designed questionnaire given to a large number of subjects in a single interview. Such criticisms, however, should not be taken lightly, for if the study of children is to become legitimately scientific the question of validity of reporting is clearly of prime importance. In the early days of anthropology, in particular, and unfortunately even today, we find such statements as the "Mbongo-Mbongo never punish their children." All too frequently such statements have been refuted by later work and were, in all probability, based upon the fact that the parents seemed kind to their children and the reporter could not remember having observed any parent spanking her child. It is unfortunate for the field of child development that it is only recently that child rearing has become accepted as a legitimate and necessary part of the description of a culture; hence standardized methods are only now being developed for obtaining data on this aspect of life. With respect to the gathering of cultural materials on other aspects of life, anthropologists have developed certain techniques of checking the validity of their data. Similar techniques may be borrowed and utilized in the study of child rearing.

Kinship systems have for a long time been the most carefully described aspects of the culture and of the customary behavior of primitive peoples. This has been in a large part attributable to the development of the so-called genealogical method, which was first described by Rivers (1914). The method consists of asking an informant to name and place on a genealogical tree all of his kinsmen. After he has named and identified them by sex, age, and blood or affinal relationship, then

and then only does the ethnographer ask his informant what kin term he uses to refer to and/or to address each of them and what behavior is expected or most frequently occurs in their interaction. When an informant's family tree has been established, that is, when all his blood relatives and affines have been named, then the essential features of social structure can be explored.

To which of these people must you show respect?

Which of them must show respect to you?

Which do you help when they are in trouble?

Which of them can you call on for help when you are in trouble?

Which of them do you have the right to discipline?

Who can discipline you?

Which of these people must you avoid?

Which of these people may you marry?

Which are you sociable with?

It can be seen that all questions relevant to the socialization process, insofar as they affect kinsmen, can be concretely described by the use of this method—that is, the relatives who are the caretakers, the disciplinarians, the educators, and the playmates. This method can be easily extended to cover nonkinsmen, important in the socialization process. One would ask an informant to give the names of neighbors, colleagues, friends, teachers, and then proceed to ask him the same questions concerning his interaction with them as those described for kin relationships.

It can be seen that this is essentially a reversal of the sociometric method as it is generally used. Instead of asking a child to name the best friend in his class, to name those whom he likes in his class, or who like him in the class, the investigator using the genealogical method would ask his child informant first to name each member of his class and then proceed to question him concerning his relation to each person named. For example, if Joe is one of the persons named, he would ask these questions:

Do you play with him?
Do you fight with him?
Do you boss him around?
Does he boss you around?
Do you avoid him?

It can be seen from this description that the method is appropriate to arrive at both the symbolic attributes of a social system, which we have called culture, and to the typical interactions of individuals who occupy reciprocal kin relationships. In other words, this method has been used to arrive at both the cultural and behavioral aspects of the ethnographic domain.

Since ethnographers have found it useful, when describing kinship and social structure, to start with naming names and collecting many instances of concrete relationships to arrive at the general features of the system rather than attempting to ask an informant about the general features directly, we feel that this method might well be most profitably employed in a study of the socialization process.

The procedure of arriving at general concepts by induction from concrete instances has been used by anthropologists to describe other features of the ethnographic domain than that of social structure. Although extensive work has not been done in this area, the method can well be applied to de-

termining the meaning of emotional concepts. Instead of asking an informant to define aggression, let us say, one might proceed in the following manner: ask an informant to give a list of native terms referring to emotions such as anger, hurt feelings, fear, shame, and happiness and then ask him to give concrete instances in which each of the native terms could be applied appropriately to the feeling that the informant had in these instances. In this way, an operational definition of the emotional categories recognized and distinguished in any culture can be derived. It may well be that the distinctions that seem self-evident to us are not the same in other societies.

Although anthropologists have generally not been self-conscious with respect to the problem of sampling, they have been quite consistent in their procedures. In the first place, they have chosen a group for intensive study, which consists of a relatively small number of people, generally less than 50 or 60 families living in a hamlet, band, or barrio. A complete census is generally taken of this group and a complete genealogical chart of their kin relationships is drawn up. If the group is sedentary, a map and village plan is made to show the range of fields, buildings, paths, and public places. Since it is ethnographic protocol to stay in the field for at least a year, the field worker generally knows every member of the group by name and has talked with most of them. Although he may have used the majority of adults as informants on one or another aspect of the culture, he generally works intensively with but a few of them. Some anthropologists have obtained a great majority of their information from a single informant, but more generally an anthropologist works extensively with five or six informants, using them to check one another. Although anthropologists often report their findings to be representative of a larger society than the village, band, or barrio they have intensively studied, it is our opinion that their reports should more properly be referred to the smaller group, and with respect to such a group the informal methods of sampling used are generally quite adequate (Whiting et al., 1953).

Living as an anthropologist does with a small group for a year or more provides a validity check that is often not recognized. If two members of the society are interacting in the presence of on-lookers and this audience pays little or no attention to the interaction, it can be taken as being within the bounds of custom. From the cultural point of view, there are as many affirmations of the customary nature of the event as there are people present. Any anthropologist who has been in the field can report the strong and immediate audience reaction to events that are outside the permitted range of custom (Whiting, 1941).

As we suggested in our discussion of the complex nature of culture, an ethnography must be more than simply a record of events. These events must be classified and their structural and functional relationships explored and presented. It is our view that the most useful ethnographic reports contain both concrete observations and interpretations. A good example of this is Margaret Mead's reports on the Arapesh, which range from her circumstantial "Diary of Events in Alitoa," published in the American Museum monograph series (1947), to her interpretation of the Arapesh in *Sex and Temperament in Three Primitive Societies* (1935). Anyone writing an ethnography, whether he wishes to be mainly circumstantial or largely interpretive, should in any case be sure to make this clear. Nothing is more annoying, when abstracting ethnographic data, than to read a paragraph that might contain either the carefully checked opinions of a number of native informants or the ethnographer's unchecked opinion arrived at after he had left the field. We do not wish to imply by this that such *post hoc* interpretations are invalid or useless. On the contrary, we feel it is the responsibility of any good cultural reporter to make such interpretations. The wisdom of the historian who distinguishes history from historeography and interpretation from documentation may well be borrowed here.

Before concluding our discussion of method, mention should be made of the phenomenon of culture shock. No matter how objective an anthropologist feels himself to be as a consequence of his graduate training or previous field experience and no matter how much he knows in advance about the culture he is studying, there comes a time, generally in the first few weeks, when some event or events produce a violent emotional reaction in him. This reaction is difficult to describe and probably differs from one person to another, but it is ordinarily a combination of disgust, apprehension, or anger and a sense of guilt for having such feelings.

Obviously, if one is to be a successful field worker, this sense of shock cannot persist, and anthropologists have adopted different methods of defending themselves against it. The relation between a field worker's strongly held personal values and those represented in the culture he is studying is a matter of great methodological importance, which, unfortunately, has never been systematically studied. Informal and unsystematic reports by ethnographers suggest that many different types of defense may be employed. Rationalization, repression, avoidance of disturbing parts of the culture, and projection have probably all been employed. A systematic attempt to keep complete personal diaries, especially during the first months of field work, and a careful study of a number of such documents would be invaluable.

Not only does the type of defense vary, but also the aspect of the culture that provides the shock. One field worker may be disturbed by dirt and disease, another by violence, still another by a feeling of being excluded, and yet another by lack of privacy. That these defenses and shock areas influence the perception and the interpretation of certain custom complexes is not surprising.

## VARIATIONS IN CHILD-REARING PRACTICES

The many studies of child life and child rearing that have been made by anthropologists in societies all over the world represent perhaps the most valuable contribution of anthropology. These studies describe a range of beliefs, values, and behavior not found in our society. The comparison of these accounts suggests variables that are not obvious to students who confine their work to Western European societies.

Although there were some early ethnographic accounts that gave a creditable description of child life, for example, Junod (1927), the first monograph to focus on child life was Margaret Mead's study of preadolescents in Samoa (1927). She, and those anthropologists who became interested in the field of culture and personality, produced some of the best early descriptions. In the last twenty years there has been a steady increase in the number of accounts of child life. As in the other branches of anthropology, each good monograph increases the range of topics and areas covered by subsequent field workers.

If children are studied within the confines of a single culture, many events are taken as natural, obvious, or a part of human nature and are therefore not reported and not considered as variables. It is only when it is discovered that other peoples do not follow these practices that have been attributed to human nature that they are adopted as legitimate variables. In addition, even when individual variation among parents within western society suggests the presence of an important variable, the range of variation is often very small in contrast with its range in the societies of the world at large.

An example of such a variable is the

age at which a child is weaned. With our clocks and calendars, it seems obvious that this is a meaningful transcultural variable, but it turns out not to be so simple as it seems. A cross-cultural study of weaning now in progress at the Laboratory of Human Development, entitled *The Meaning of Weaning*, indicates that western culture is relatively unusual in determining the age for weaning by the calendar. If the age of the child is a factor, this is measured in other areas of the world by maturational events rather than by months. Of 106 societies in the sample, 30 of them used a maturational event as a basis for weaning. Five of these 30 weaned when the child began to cut his teeth, and the other 25 were distributed among such maturational events as crawling, toddling, walking, or talking. Neither the age nor the maturity of the child, however, provides the occasion for weaning in most societies. It is determined, rather, by social events, such as the mother's pregnancy or by the birth of a younger sibling. Thirty-three of our sample of societies weaned the child sometime during the mother's pregnancy and 23 at the time of the birth of a sibling. If societies wean their children on the basis of maturational age, a reasonable estimate in terms of months can be established. If, however, pregnancy or the birth of the next sibling is the occasion for weaning, the conversion is more difficult. Even with no conscious policy of spacing children, implemented by abstinence or contraception, the time following childbirth in which a woman is able to conceive is apparently quite varied. There is some

evidence that prolactin, the hormone related to milk production, is, to some extent at least, antagonistic to the production of sex hormones, and cross-cultural evidence suggests that in societies without a post-partum sex tabu or contraception the average spacing of children is about two years, or approximately nine months after the child begins to get most of his sustenance from supplementary foods rather than from his mother's milk. This interpretation needs much more careful checking before it is taken as established in any sense. Even if it were true, however, there is much greater variation in the time of the mother's next pregnancy than there is in the child's cutting his teeth or learning to crawl. Those societies in which children are weaned at the mother's next pregnancy should have a much greater variance in the age of weaning than those who wean by some maturational event, even though the average age may be the same.

Those societies that have a long postpartum sex tabu, and nearly half of the societies in the world have such a tabu lasting for a year or more, generally wean their children at the moment the post-partum sex tabu terminates. This conjunction is a nice illustration of the effect of beliefs upon customary behavior. In many of these societies, particularly those situated in the tropics, there is a belief that sexual intercourse sours a mother's milk, and she therefore abstains in order to insure the health of her nursing infant. As soon as the child is weaned, however, this reason no longer obtains, and sexual intercourse is resumed.

Thus the age of weaning, looked at cross culturally, may depend upon various beliefs and upon either maturational or social events. The range of variation within any society and between societies is also much greater than could be imagined if one studied it within Western European society alone. The effect of this extended range may have unexpected consequences, such as the curvilinear relationship with the emotional disturbance of the child that was pointed out by Whiting (1954). A child, for example, is most disturbed if he is weaned around 18 months. To be weaned earlier or later than this is progressively less disturbing.

It is impossible in the space of this chapter to present all the variables reported by anthropologists that might be relevant and important to the study of child rearing. We would like to select those that at present seem to be the most neglected because of the nature of Western European society. It is our belief that they suggest variables for isolation and study that will be useful in the understanding of human behavior. These variables stem primarily from a comparative analysis of social structure.

## HOUSEHOLD COMPOSITION

Although there is some variation in household arrangement in our society, by far the majority of children are brought up in a home that consists solely of a father and mother and unmarried sons and daughters—the so-called nuclear family household. This arrangement of people under a single roof is by no means universal. A recent examination of households of a sample of 565 societies, representing a sample of world cultures (Murdock, 1958), indicates that only slightly more than a quarter of them have this arrangement. Various forms of extended family households, that is, in which either the married sons or the married daughters remain living in the house of their parents, are commoner, and the mother-child household in which the father sleeps either in a hut or at the men's clubhouse is nearly as common. The following table indicates the distribution of household arrangements in this world sample.

| | |
|---|---|
| Extended | 161* |
| Nuclear | 141 |
| Mother-child | 123 |
| Polygynous | 89 |
| Communal | 11 |

* This includes large extended families with three generations of nuclear families, lineal households with two generations, and stem family households, in which only the oldest or youngest married son or daughter lives in the household.

The infant's world and its effect on socialization should be profoundly different for households with such different groupings. A Siriono child growing up in a communal household in which a whole band of 20 or 30 families sleep (Holmberg, 1946) has quite a different experience from a Gusii child who grows up in a hut with only his mother and his sisters and brothers under 7 (LeVine, ms.), or, again, the Zuñi child who, in addition to his mother and father and siblings, shares a roof with his mother's parents and her married sisters and their children (Roberts, 1956). Since he calls his maternal aunts by the same term as he calls his mother and since they share with the real mother the responsibility of care and discipline, it is as though a Zuñi child were brought up by many mothers.

Perhaps the most curious arrangement in the eyes of one brought up in our society is the polygynous household. In its commonest form, this consists of two sisters married to the same man and living in the same house. Although the rivalries that we expect from our vantage point are apparently held in check to make such an arrangement viable, there is evidence that hostility among co-wives is not naturally absent and is often projected in the form of a strong belief in witchcraft.

The importance of household composition is more obvious when we consider that it defines both the number of people with whom the child interacts and the physical nature of the setting in which he is socialized. Status relationships among members of the household and their roles in socialization are important variables for child rearing for two quite different reasons. In the first place, the persons with whom a child has intimate contact and who control resources for him are the most important models for identification (Whiting, 1959a). Thus in a mother-child household the mother is the sole model for identification and the sole object of cathexis. The problem of cross-sex identification for a male brought up in this kind of household is great, and these societies find it necessary to develop techniques for changing the boys' object of identification before adulthood (Whiting et al., 1958). The frequency of mother-child households in our own society, particularly in lower-class groups, in which divorce and desertion are very frequent, is just beginning to be recognized and its effects are being studied. Preliminary findings indicate that here also there are problems of cross-sex identification (Miller, 1958; Rohrer and Edmonson, 1960).

An example of the influence of status in the household on one's role in socialization is exemplified by a cross-cultural study of the function of grandmothers in child rearing (Apple, 1956). A grandmother who is titular head of a household is likely to function as a disciplinarian, whereas one with less status is more likely to function only in a nurturant caretaking role. The locus of responsibility for caretaking and the relative authority within the household is a variable which child psychologists have recognized. The variations in patterns, however, are greater than in non-Western European societies, in which women are the primary caretakers and disciplinarians, for example, but have low status in the society as a whole. They may have difficulty in controlling their male children, especially in latency and preadolescence. This is a problem for the Rajput mothers (Triandis and Hitchcock, ms.).

In three communities in the southwestern United States differences in authority patterns have been shown to have an interesting effect (Whiting et al., ms.). In one group of Mormon origin the father is clearly in authority. In a second group of migrants from Texas matters of import are discussed between father and mother, and thus authority can be said to be shared. In the third group, the Zuñi Indians, the authority in the household is vested in the grandmother. When preadolescent children in these three groups were asked, "If a magic man could change you into a mother, a father, a brother, or a sister, which would you choose to be?" most children chose to be a relative of the same sex as themselves. Several Mormon girls, however, chose to be a brother, and several Zuñi boys chose to be a sister. No cross-sex choices were made by Texan children. Thus the authority structure of the household seems to influence sex preference.

## SLEEPING ARRANGEMENTS

Another important aspect of the household is the pattern of sleeping arrangements during infancy. We are not referring here so much to the recent interest in methods of swaddling that has been held by some to be a major determinant of national character (Gorer, 1949; Mead, 1954) but rather to the question of who shares the bed and bedroom with a child from birth until he is grown up. A recent cross-cultural study (Whiting et al., 1958) indicates that in a great majority of societies an infant sleeps in the same bed with his mother during the time that he is nursing. It is only rarely (in less than 10 per cent of the cases) that he has a crib or cradle of his own, and only in Western European societies, notably middle-class America,

does an infant ever have a bedroom of his own. In approximately one half of the societies under consideration the father also shares the bed with mother and infant. Sleeping arrangements for older children also vary. They may continue to share a bed or sleeping platform with their mother, with both parents, or move to one of their own. Boys and girls are generally segregated at sometime before adolescence, but the age at which this occurs varies considerably from one society to another. This segregation sometimes takes the extreme form of a child not being permitted to sleep in the same house as his mother or sisters after he reaches a certain age, and sometimes this change of residence may involve moving to a separate village—in matrilineal societies often to the house of his mother's brother.

Here again the persons with whom a child shares the intimacy of a bed seems to have a profound effect on the development of his personality. It is our view that the nature and resolution of the oedipus complex is determined by social arrangements at night rather than during the day. It is then that intimate and intensive interpersonal feelings within the family are expressed rather than during the casual, busy day when adults are concerned with making a living.

The number of people who share a household and the nature of the spatial arrangements also have a demonstrable effect on the timing and techniques of socialization and on the values that are felt to be most important to transmit to the child. For example, weaning and independence training are earliest in nuclear family households, apparently because the father and child are competing for the nurturance of a single woman, who, unlike the woman in the extended or polygynous family, has no other woman to help her. Similarly, when there are many hands to do the work, children's help will not be required so early. The economic role of both men and women is a variable, which, in conjunction with household arrangements, seems to predict not only the age of independence training but the age of responsibility training. Among the Rajput mothers of northern India (Triandis and Hitchcock, ms.), where a married woman often lives with her mother-in-law and sisters-in-law in an enclosed courtyard and seldom leaves it and where there are lower caste servants, independence and responsibility training are late; young girls do little housework, their mothers discouraging rather than encouraging their participation in food preparation, cooking, and other tasks. The situation is similar in other societies with large extended households when there are many hands to do the work. In Okinawa (Maretzki, ms.), on the other hand, where the women usually live with their husbands and perhaps their mothers-in-law and do a large part of the agriculture and help in the lumbering, both boys and girls are expected to baby sit and do household chores at an early age; similarly, in a Texan homestead group, in which the mother in a nuclear family household helps with the farming, children are expected by the age of 6 or 7 to do regular tasks (Whiting et al., ms.).

Similarly, household arrangements influence the age and severity of aggression training and the techniques parents employ in training for control. Children's aggression is most severely prohibited in societies with extended family households (Murdock and Whiting, 1951). Apparently, hostilities must be controlled when so many people are living under one roof; and it is disruptive if the mother is expressive in her efforts to teach the child control. More indirect methods are used in the extended household. A Zuñi mother will ignore an aggressive child or threaten him with a supernatural agent—the "scare kachina," a god impersonated by a Zuñi man, rather than yell at him or spank him (Whiting et al., ms.). In contrast, the use of physical punishment occurs most frequently in societies with mother-child households, in which the mother apparently can "blow her stack" without disturbing anyone else.

Settlement patterns, or the clustering of households, also have an effect on child rearing. Once a child can get about, the nature and composition of play groups will be determined not only by the spatial pattern of households but by the kinship and social structure bonds relating the members of the settlement. A child in a village with closely packed houses, with many children of his own age nearby, will lead quite a different life from the child raised in a household distant from others or a child raised in a small nomadic band. The isolated child is likely to spend much more time alone or with adults than with his age mates. It is not surprising that self-reliance tends to be more emphasized in his case, whereas responsibility to the group is more highly valued in the village life.

In closely settled areas, however, the social life of the child may be limited by other social-structure variables. If a society has a caste or class subgroup living in close proximity, the rules pertaining to adult social participation may be reflected in the composition of the play groups. Thus among the Rajputs (Triandis and Hitchcock, ms.) children are discouraged from playing with members of lower castes and are allowed to treat these children in domineering and aggressive ways not approved of within their own caste group. The play groups tend to follow lineage ties; families are related through the males and often live in adjacent houses.

Similarly, social classes and ethnic and religious groups in our own society influence play groups. In some cases younger children from divergent groups intermingle, but conflicts between the beliefs, values, and child-rearing practices of the groups often lead to tension and conflict. These cultural differences sometimes result in the kind of clique structure found in urban public schools.

When subgroups are important in the social structure, ostracism from one's group becomes a serious matter, and parents often use the threat of abandonment by this group to control their children's behavior. Thus a Rajput mother will reprimand her child by calling him a "leatherworker" or a member of the lowly sweeper caste, implying ostracism from his own group; or an Okinawan will chide her child by calling him a "kindergarten child," implying loss of status from the age

group to which he rightfully belongs and with whom he spends the majority of his waking hours; or an American mother will call her child "cheap," implying behavior of a lower social class. Among the Zuñi, where the pueblo is an isolated subgroup in the American Southwest, parents will advise their children to behave well so that "They," i.e., the Zuñi, will help them (Whiting et al., ms.).

One's position in the hierarchy of castes or classes may have profound effects on child rearing and personality, as has been suggested by studies of Negroes in our society by Kardiner (1951). A similar effect is seen in the personality of a Mixtecan living in a minority subgroup in a barrio of the Mexican town of Juxtlahuaca (Romney, ms.).

In summary, the anthropologist's analysis of household arrangements, residence patterns, and larger settlement patterns with associated status and kin relationships has isolated variables that are important to the study of child rearing. One of the authors (Whiting, 1959a) recently discovered a convincing example of the importance of these variables in an attempt to predict the occurrence of the practice of a patient accepting blame for his illness, a measure developed by Whiting and Child (1953) as an index of guilt. It was shown in Whiting and Child that early socialization predicted high guilt. When this factor is combined with monogamous family structure, which also predicts high guilt, the association is much stronger than with either factor alone.

As already suggested, intimately associated with social structure is the environment and economy of a society. Analysis of variables along these dimensions has also proved profitable. In environments, for example, in which the habit and economy make nomadic life a practical adjustment, the women usually carry the gear while the men march ahead with their weapons in hand, both for defense against enemies and for hunting. Families traveling in this manner with few beasts of burden or conveyances cannot afford to have two children who cannot walk. Children are, therefore, spaced by means of a post-partum sex tabu, which lasts from three to four years; and to save carrying extra food for the young child the nursing period is prolonged. It is interesting to note that a similar pattern of prolonged dependency also occurs in the tropics. Here, however, the long post-partum sex tabu and the prolonged nursing period seem to be associated with infant diseases, which are apparently held in check by prolonged nursing and caretaking.

Another example of the interdependence of environmental and social structure variables is the relationship between temperature, household type, and child-training practices. Since extended family households are, economically speaking, the cheapest per capita way to provide heat and shelter for the adults of a society (there is one house for five or more adults as against one house for two adults in the nuclear family household), they are found more often in cold climates, especially where there is a lack of building materials. We have discussed the child-training practices associated with extended

families. In temperate zones, where the people live a settled life in nuclear family households, weaning and independence training are early. It is interesting to note McClelland's findings (McClelland and Freidman, 1952) that early independence training is associated with high need achievement.

The activities of children are also influenced by the natural environment. Climate, of course, will determine how much time a child will spend out of doors. The presence of dangerous fauna or natural phenomena may limit the extent of freedom. If the climate is favorable and there are few dangers in the environment and if wild foods may be gathered and eaten, the range of territory over which children are allowed to wander may be exceedingly great—as reported by Margaret Mead (1927) in her study of Samoa. In New England man-made dangers, such as automobiles and thoroughfares, and concepts, such as private property, limit the freedom of children. The danger of the environment may be supernatural as well as real. Thus among the Ilocano-speaking Tarongans of Northern Luzon (Nydegger, ms.) it is believed that the environment, though realistically not particularly threatening, is peopled by spirits who must be handled with caution. Children are afraid to wander away from the security of their hamlets, whose members are usually related families. The Tarongans also fear the supernatural powers of people from other hamlets, and the children learn to distrust and fear all strangers. Such projected fears may be related to the type of socialization of sex and aggression and social structure variables (Whiting, 1959b).

Whether the determinants are the result of the settlement pattern, economics, or environment, the play setting available to children will have effects on their socialization and behavior. Of particular importance is the length of time spent in activities that are not directly supervised by adults. The Mixtecan boy and girl (Romney, ms.), who are encouraged, persuaded, and forced to stay in the family patio until the age of 7 or 8 and play with their brothers, sisters, or cousins within earshot of the mother or some other relative (lest they get into fights with other children), are in striking contrast to their Okinawan counterparts (Maretzki, ms.) and Gusii (LeVine, ms.) age mates. Okinawan children, who have been members of large play groups since the age of 3, play without adult supervision, and the Gusii have been out herding the cattle and playing with infrequent supervision.

Recent studies of the influence of setting on children's behavior (Barker and Wright, 1954) would indicate that analysis of the consequences of the amount of time spent in different settings might prove valuable to students of child development. It may be, for example, that the kinds of self-control that children learn are related to these settings. Children who are constantly under adult supervision may have less practice in self-control and may be more responsive to direct threats of injury and abandonment. Children who spend the majority of their time with peers may also be more responsive to socialization by age mates.

In addition to and related to the so-

cial-structure, economic, and environmental variables, which have been suggested by comparative studies of child-rearing practices in nonwestern societies, there are variables relevant to the timing of socialization, to variations in the abruptness of the changes in the demands made of a child, to variations in the behavior expected of different sex and age groups,[1] and to variations in the techniques employed by socializing agents. Many of these variables have been suggested in the foregoing discussion. Again, the range of variation suggests new parameters for analyzing child rearing. Time and space prohibit the discussion of all these variables. We would like in conclusion to touch briefly on two aspects of socialization techniques that are not characteristic of our society.

One of the techniques of training of particular interest frequently used in nonwestern societies is the change of setting and/or caretakers at a time when there is a change in the demands made upon a child. For example, a technique of weaning a child from the breast is to send him to the house of a

---

[1] See in particular the cross-cultural study by Barry, Bacon, and Child (1957), who rated 110 societies on the age and sex differences in the demand made in regard to nurturance, obedience, responsibility, self-reliance, and achievement. They found that although boys and girls were generally treated the same in infancy there was a general tendency toward higher demands for nurturance, obedience, and responsibility in girls and toward self-reliance and achievement in boys. The greatest sex difference occurred in those societies whose economy required superior strength and in those societies in which there were large family groups with high cooperative interaction.

relative to stay until he is accustomed to doing without his mother's milk. Usually the child returns home when he has given up fussing and is moved to sleep with his father, brother, or sister or into a bed of his own. New caretakers may enter the life of the child at this time—siblings take over this responsibility for periods of time during the day.

One of the most dramatic cases of change of setting and agent is that of the Ojibwa child who at weaning moves permanently to the home of her grandmother, who becomes the mother surrogate.

Changes of residence also occur in late childhood and early adolescence. This is more frequent among boys than girls. In some societies with matrilineal descent boys are sent to live with their maternal uncles, who take over the role of disciplinarian and teacher (Malinowski, 1927). In other societies the move is associated with the separation of the sexes. In Africa the boys may move into a house of their own (Le-Vine, ms.), or, more drastically, they may set up a village, returning to eat in rotation at the houses of their parents and eventually marrying and setting up housekeeping in their own settlement (Krige and Krige, 1943). A similar function is performed in England in the boarding school.

A second interesting phenomenon not found in European societies are changes of status with maturation and their formal celebration. Initiation ceremonies are the most dramatic example of such "rites de passage" and generally include isolation from the opposite sex, hazing, instruction in new role behavior, and sometimes genital or other body mutilation. It is interesting to note that those societies in which the child is closely associated with the mother during a prolonged infancy are the most likely to have such ceremonies (Whiting et al., 1958). In many societies marriage and the marriage ceremony mark dramatic changes of status and role.

## Summary and Conclusions

In conclusion, we suggest that students may find the concept of the culture complex, with its analysis of values, beliefs, techniques, justifications, and rationalizations, and the methods devised by anthropologists to get at these, helpful in the study of child development. We also suggest that the comparative study of child life in non-European societies indicates the presence of important variables that have been overlooked and that may prove very useful in the prediction of human behavior.

## REFERENCES

Apple, Dorrian. 1956. The social structure of grandparenthood. *Amer. Anthrop.*, LVIII, No. 4.

Barker, R. E., and H. P. Wright. 1954. *Midwest and its children.* Evanston, Ill.: Row, Peterson.

Barnouw, C. 1950. Acculturation and personality among the Wisconsin Ojibwa. Amer. Anthrop. Ass., *Memoir No. 72.*

Barry, H. A., Margaret K. Bacon, and I. L. Child. 1957. A cross-cultural survey of some sex differences in socialization. *J. abnorm. soc. Psychol.* 55, No. 8.

Fischer, J. L. and Ann Fischer. In Beatrice B. Whiting (Ed.), *Child-rearing in six societies*. In preparation.

Gorer, G. 1949. Some aspects of the psychology of the people of Great Russia. In *The American Slavic and East European review*. 7, pp. 155–166.

Holmberg, A. R. 1946. Nomads of the long bow: The Siriono of Eastern Bolivia. Smithson. Inst. soc. Anthrop., *Publica. No. 10*.

Junod, H. A. 1927. *The life of a South African tribe*. (2nd rev. ed.) London: Macmillan. 2 vols.

Kardiner, A., and L. Ovesey. 1951. *The mark of oppression: a psychological study of the American Negro*. New York: Norton.

Kluckhohn, Florence R. 1940. The participant-observer technique in small communities. *Amer. J. Sociol.*, 46, No. 3.

Krige, E. J., and J. O. Krige. 1943. *The realm of a rain-queen*. London: Oxford Univer. Press.

Kroeber, A. L., and C. Kluckhohn. 1952. Culture: A critical review of concepts and definitions. *Pap. Peabody Mus.*, Vol. XLVII, No. 1.

LeVine, R. A., and Barbara LeVine. In Beatrice B. Whiting (Ed.), *Child-rearing in six societies*. In preparation.

McClelland, D. C., and G. A. Freidman. 1952. A cross-cultural study of the relationship between child training practices and achievement motivation appearing in folktales. In G. E. Swanson, T. M. Newcomb, and E. L. Hartley. *Readings in social psychology*. New York: Holt. Pp. 232–243.

Maccoby, Eleanor E., and N. Maccoby. 1954. The interview: A tool of science. In G. Lindzey (Ed.), *Handbook of social psychology*. Cambridge: Addison-Wesley. Vol. 1. Pp. 449–487.

Malinowski, B. 1927. *Sex and repression in savage society*. New York: Harcourt, Brace.

———. 1935. *Coral gardens and their magic*. New York: American Book. Vol. I.

———. 1944. *A scientific theory of culture*. Chapel Hill: Univer. North Carolina Press.

Maretzki, T., and Hatsumi Maretzki. In Beatrice B. Whiting (Ed.), *Child-rearing in six societies*. In preparation.

Mead, Margaret. 1927. *Coming of age in Samoa*. New York: Morrow.

Mead, Margaret. 1935. *Sex and temperament in three primitive societies*. New York: Morrow.

———. 1947. Diary of events in Alitoa. *Anthrop. Papers, Amer. Mus. Nat. Hist.* Vol. 40. Part 3.

———. 1954. The swaddling hypothesis: Its reception. *Amer. Anthrop.*, 58, No. 3.

Miller, W. B. 1958. Lower class culture as a generating milieu of gang delinquency. *J. soc. Issues*, 14, 5–19.

Murdock, G. P., et al. 1950. *Outline of cultural materials*, New Haven: Human Relations Area Files.

Murdock, G. P., and J. W. M. Whiting. 1951. Cultural determination of parental attitudes: The relationship between social structure and parental behavior. In M. J. E. Senn (Ed.), *Problems of infancy and childhood*. New York: Josiah Macy Jr., Foundation. Pp. 13–80.

———. 1957. World Ethnographic Sample, *Amer. Anthrop.*, LIX, No. 4.

Nydegger, W., and Corinne Nydegger. In Beatrice B. Whiting (Ed.), *Child-rearing in six societies*. In preparation.

Paul, B. D. 1953. Interview techniques and field relationships. In A. L. Kroeber (Ed.), *Anthropology today*. Chicago: Univer. Chicago Press. Pp. 430–451.

Rivers, W. H. R. 1914. *Kinship and social organization*. London: London School of Economics, *Studies in economic and political science*, 36.

Roberts, J. M. 1956. Zuni daily life. *Lab. Anthrop. Notebook #3*, Univer. Nebraska.

Rohrer, John H., and Munro E. Edmonson. 1960. *The eighth generation: cultures and personalities of New Orleans Negroes*. New York: Harper.

Romney, A. K., and Romaine Romney. In Beatrice B. Whiting (Ed.), *Child-rearing in six societies*. In preparation.

Royal Institute of Anthropology. 1951. *Notes and Queries*, London: Routledge and Kegan Paul.

Triandis, Leigh M. and J. Hitchcock. In Beatrice B. Whiting (Ed.), *Child-rearing in six societies*. In preparation.

Tyler, E. B. 1871. *Primitive culture*. London: John Murray.

Whiting, J. W. M. 1941. *Becoming a Kwoma*.

New Haven: Yale Univer. Press.

———. 1954. The cross-cultural method. In G. Lindzey (Ed.), *Handbook of social psychology*, Cambridge: Addison-Wesley.

———. 1959a. Sorcery, sin, and the superego: A cross-cultural study of some mechanisms of social control. In *Symposium on motivation:* Univer. Nebraska Press. Pp. 174–195.

———. 1959b. Resource mediation and learning by identification, typescript, Laboratory of Human Development, Harvard Univer.

———, H. F. Antonovsky, E. H. Chasdi, and B. C. Ayres. The learning of values. In E. Z. Vogt, and J. M. Roberts, *Peoples of Rimrock* (Vol. I), Final Report of the Harvard Values Study, manuscript.

———, et al. 1953. Field manual for the cross-cultural study of socialization, New York: Social Science Research Council.

Whiting, J. W. M., et al. *The Meaning of Weaning.* Research in progress, Laboratory of Human Development, Harvard Univer.

———, and I. L. Child. 1953. *Child training and personality*, New Haven: Yale Univer. Press.

———, and Roy G. D'Andrade. 1959. Sleeping arrangements and social structure: A cross-cultural study. Presented at American Anthropological Association Annual Meetings, Mexico City, December.

———, R. Kluckhohn, and A. Anthony. 1958. The function of male initiation ceremonies at puberty. In Eleanor E. Maccoby, T. Newcomb, and E. Hartley (Eds.), *Readings in social psychology.* New York: Holt. Pp. 359–370.

# chapter 22

# *The Measurement*
# *of*
# *Family Life*
# *Variables*

Lois Wladis Hoffman
Ronald Lippitt
*University of Michigan*

There is a variety of approaches to the study of the family. Sociologists and anthropologists have often been concerned with the family as a social system or as an institution within a society. Recent years have seen an increased interest in the family as one type of small group with its own patterns of functional and structural characteristics. Other approaches, which are more psychological, treat the family as an interpersonal system of dyadic relations or focus on the personality and behavior of individual family members.

Aside from the way in which the family is conceptualized, approaches differ along other dimensions. For example, some investigators have a predominantly taxonomic and descriptive interest in the family, whereas others

have primarily an analytic interest in the dynamics of family process and socialization. Still others are largely interested in a diagnostic approach to the understanding of family pathology and health.

In this chapter we shall restrict our focus to the study of various aspects of family life as they are related to the child's behavior and development. Specific techniques of measurement are discussed in previous chapters. Our interest here is to illustrate the application of these methods in the study of linkages between family-life and child-behavior variables. The goals are twofold:

1. To present a schema for classifying concepts in family research and to ilustrate how the concepts at each level have been measured and used for linking family variables and child-behavior variables.

2. To review some of the methodological problems that seem to be unique or more focal to research on family life.

## A CAUSAL SEQUENCE SCHEMA

As a schema for classifying research designs and procedures, we have chosen a sequence of causality that goes from the most general and causally distant variables and moves by steps through variables that are more specific and causally closer to the child's personality and behavior. The schema we are using is as follows:

*Parental Background.* This category includes such variables as the parent's national origin, educational history, and early relations with own parents.

*Current Family Setting.* Included here are such variables as culture, social class, occupation, temporal setting, rural-urban-suburban location, and physical characteristics of home and neighborhood.

*Family Composition.* This includes family size, ordinal position of child, age and sex distribution of siblings, presence or absence of certain family members, and special status of family membership (e.g., adopted).

*Relationships between Parents.* This includes such variables as power relations, decision-making patterns, division of labor, the communication pattern, degree of consensus, and the affective relationship.

*Personal Characteristics of Parents.* This cluster includes those psychological characteristics of parents not specifically oriented toward the parental function, such as general personality structure, religious values, social attitudes, and philosophy of life.

*Child-Oriented Parental Attitudes.* Included here are child-rearing goals, concepts about the parent role and child role, attitudes toward parenthood, attitudes about discipline techniques, and acceptance or rejection of the child.

*Overt Parental Behavior Patterns.* Here we include child-rearing and training practices, influence and discipline techniques, responses to child behaviors, changes or inconsistencies in behavior patterns, and types of conflicts with the child.

*Child's Orientation toward Parents and Siblings.* This includes a large set of variables, such as perceptions and evaluations of parent behavior patterns, attitudes toward parents and sibs, perception of parent feelings and attitudes

toward the child himself, and perceptions of the relations existing between parents and among all family members. This level in the sequence already involves the child's response to the family situation.

*Overt Child Behavior toward Other Family Members.* We include here categories of child response to others, such as reaction to discipline, and spontaneous initiated actions, such as attention-demanding behavior, hostility, and affection.

*Personal Characteristics of the Child.* Here are included a variety of variables, such as intelligence, physical characteristics, ego structure, superego formation, conception and evaluation of the self, emotionality, and basic need tendencies.

*The Child Away from the Family.* This focuses on the child's attitudes and behaviors in areas other than the family, such as interaction with peers and the child's behavior at school.

## THE USE OF THE CAUSAL-SEQUENCE SCHEMA

In looking for studies to illustrate this schema, we have been interested in those that make some linkage between one or more levels of family variables and one or more levels of child variables—especially when the attempt is made to clarify the processes intervening between these two levels. We have felt free, however, to use studies that stop short of making the bridge to child variables, when this seemed necessary to illustrate the measurement of certain important concepts.

## INTERVENING PROCESSES OR LINKING MECHANISMS

Almost any study that attempts empirically to test a relationship between family variables and child variables is potentially interesting. It seems to us, however, that the major need is for studies that use some conceptual model for the intervening processes and attempt to clarify and test the model by appropriate measurement operations.

A wide variety of theoretical models has been used, either explicitly or implicitly, to clarify the intervening processes between the family-life situation and the development of the child. There are cognitive learning models that stress the importance of the stimulus patterns available for the child to learn; reinforcement learning models that emphasize the effects of patterns and intensities of rewards and punishments; interpersonal relationship models that emphasize one or another aspect of the emotional dynamics of the relationship as the channel of influence. For example, a particular parent-child relationship may be seen as leading the child to act out with others the emotional frustrations experienced in the relationship, or it may be seen as creating in him the need to replicate the same relationship with others. Another linkage process model often used is that of the child's identification with one or both parents, along with notions about the nature of the internalization processes involved.

Some investigators have focused on pathologies or discontinuities in the socialization process. They point, for example, to the critical phenomenon of early mother-child separation or to affective deprivation resulting from parent rejection. Others have focused on variables that are more sociological, such as environmental deprivation with respect to learning experiences or subcultural stimulus patterns that promote directions of socialization counter to those promoted and approved by the larger society.

There is no paucity of theories to explain the effects of the family on the child, but there is a paucity of empirical research connected with these theories. Perhaps one of the most frequent problems with existing research is the size of the "causal jump" in the sequential framework. Too broad a jump, without operationalizing the intervening steps, makes it difficult to infer whether any particular finding may be regarded as evidence for one or another linking process. The size and nature of the causal jump, along with the problems in the measurement of variables necessary for all conceptual approaches, is an important focus of this chapter.

## Family Variables: Measurement and Linkage

### PARENTAL BACKGROUND

Studies that relate parental background to child variables need to stop on their way at some other point in the causal sequence. There is almost always an intervening variable or hypothetical construct that reconceptualizes the parental background to a more genotypic and less "distant" level in relation to the child. For example, analytic writers (Erikson, 1946; Hellman, 1954) may discuss the relationship between early experiences of the parent and the child's psychological state, but these background factors are seen as operating through their effects on the parent's personality, which in turn affects the parent's interaction with the child. Or the parent's early experience may be seen as affecting his marital relationship, which in turn plays a role in the child's personality development.

Sears (1950) discusses the effects of a discrepancy between the parent's social-class background and current class status on the child's dependency behavior, the intervening variables in this case being sensitivity to approved methods of child rearing and whether or not the child was fed on demand. Spiegel (1957) and Kluckhohn (1958) have studied the effects of the parent's cultural background on the child, but again through other variables, such as current value conflict and family disequilibrium. Similarly, Baruch (1937) related the parents' early home environment to the child's adjustment through the intervening variable of the marriage relationship. Several investigators have studied the influence of education on the parents' child-rearing attitudes and behavior (Bouck, 1936; Elder, 1949; Staples and Smith, 1954; Schaefer and Bell, 1958; Burchinal, 1958a,), which in turn are presumed to affect the child's development.

Glueck and Glueck (1957) found a relationship between the juvenile delinquency of the mother and the juvenile delinquency of the son and suggest that the relationship takes place through the mother's current instability, which is assumed to have carried through from her past. Miller and Swanson (1958) use rural-urban background of parents and whether they were foreign or American-born as measures of current "entrepreneurial" or "bureaucratic" settings, which they believe have significance for child-rearing patterns.

Thus the studies relating parental background variables to the child's development have found it necessary to pass through a more current aspect of the family situation. Starting from the more remote level of parental background, however, does lend a certain richness to family studies. More importantly, it ties them to a wider context and suggests avenues by which historical change and idiosyncratic variations in family structure occur. Some researchers (e.g., Ackerman and Sobel, 1950; Spiegel, 1957) feel that to understand the child as a functional part of the family group a study must take account of the history of that group, including the parent's background, so as to gain the necessary understanding of the child's current experiences in the family.

The measurement of certain parent-background variables, such as education and place of birth, is relatively simple. Respondents can report these data with only minor precautions being taken by the researcher to assure their validity. However, personal report is also the method one must usually use to obtain data about the early interactions of the parents with their own parents. Radke (1946) asked mothers and fathers to complete questionnaires about their childhood home lives. Subjects were given short declarative sentences such as "As a child I had a voice in making the family plans and decisions." Their responses were made in terms of frequency ("usually," "sometimes," "rarely") and, for some items, intensity ("very much," "somewhat," "very little"). The items in general dealt with authority and discipline patterns.

Few other measures have been developed specifically to obtain parents' perceptions of their childhoods, but there are some, such as the P.O.P. measure (Schutz, 1958), designed to elicit childhood data from adults, which could obviously be used for this purpose. Clinical interviews have also been used, especially with mothers of children in treatment, but these are usually intensive studies of only a few cases. A notable exception is Baruch (1937, 1944), who clinically interviewed a number of parents of nursery-school children to obtain parental background and marital adjustment data. She found that the parents', especially the mothers', childhood family relations related to both marital tension and the adjustment of the child.

Using recall data is usually undesirable, particularly when the events occurred many years earlier and may be emotionally loaded. Simple forgetting, conscious distortion, and repression are likely to affect the reports. Unfortunately, about the only alternative to the method of recall is the longitudinal study that continues through at least two generations. The need for longitudinal studies is great, but they pose obvious practical difficulties. There are the difficulties of maintaining contact with the families for a long time, the continued improvement of measures with those used in the past generation

often seeming obsolete in the present, the unwillingness of many researchers to commit themselves to a study of the necessary duration, and the inevitable organizational and personnel changes that also lessen the chances of research continuity. These difficulties have at times been surmounted. Certain organizations have maintained contact with families over one or more generations, e.g., the Fels Institute and the Merrill-Palmer School. When the research institute takes responsibility for the longitudinal study, the researcher involved in the earlier phases can often use the data as part of an intact research project and the data can remain with the organization for later use. The values of longitudinal studies have become increasingly apparent, and the storehouses of data that they make available have many uses in addition to that of facilitating studies involving parental background.

## CURRENT FAMILY SETTING

The family-setting variable that has probably been most frequently related to the child, directly and indirectly, is social class. Social class has been related to the child's perceptions, attitudes, personality, motivation, future expectations, and overt behavior (e.g., Lynd and Lynd, 1929; 1936; Bruner and Goodman, 1947; Centers, 1949; Rabban, 1950; Schneider and Lysgaard, 1953; Himmelweit, 1955; McKee and Leader, 1955; Hoffman and Albizu-Miranda, 1955; Douvan, 1956; Rosen, 1956; Sewell and Haller, 1956; Rainwater, 1956; Angelino, Dollins, and Mech, 1956; Remmers and Radler, 1957; Hoffman, Mitsos, and Protz, 1958.) These are all family studies in the sense that the child's social-class position is a function of his family membership, and the family is usually seen as the medium through which the meaning of the class setting is transmitted to the child.

In addition, however, a number of studies have related social class to the child-rearing attitudes and practices of the parents. (These include Davis and Havighurst, 1946; Duvall, 1946; Ericson, 1947; Hollingshead, 1949, Havighurst and Taba, 1949; McGuire, 1952; Klatskin, 1952; Oeser and Emery, 1954; Oeser and Hammond, 1954; Maccoby and Gibbs, 1954; Alper, Blane, and Abrams, 1955; Havighurst and Davis, 1955; Sears, Maccoby, and Levin, 1957; Littman, Moore, and Pierce-Jones, 1957; White, 1957; Boek et al., 1957; Miller and Swanson, 1958; Kohn, 1959b.) Some of these studies have examined the relationship between class and child-rearing variables *and* between class and child behavior. Some have related class to child-rearing variables and the latter, in turn, to child behavior. Others have stopped at the point of relating class to child-rearing variables, often inferring probable child resultants or leaving that linkage to other researchers.

The studies that directly link class to child resultants often involve the theoretical weakness that the breadth of the jump leaves open many possible alternative explanations for any empirical relationships obtained. Why does social class differentiate child attitudes and behavior? The studies of class and intrafamily variables help bridge this gap, but even these studies often involve static analyses which treat class

simply as a fixed value setting. Thus it was surprising when two studies, ten years apart, revealed different relationships between social-class and child-rearing practices (Havighurst and Davis, 1955). The original study was not based on a dynamic theory capable of incorporating changes over time. Since then, several theories have been advanced, which would account for such changes. White (1957) suggests that if the discrepancies in the two studies reflect true change, rather than mere difference in samples or methods, one explanation might lie in the different reference groups used by the classes. She found that middle-class mothers more often mention experts, other mothers, and friends as their sources of ideas about child rearing. If they mention their own parents, it is usually as a negative reference. Lower-class mothers, on the other hand, more often rely on their own inclinations and their own upbringing—using their parents as a positive reference group. Thus the lower class is less susceptible to change in child-rearing patterns, whereas the middle class responds more to expert advice and the prevailing climate of opinion.

Miller and Swanson offer another explanation, which views class differences within the context of larger societal settings they call "entrepreneurial" and "bureaucratic." They contend that the growing complexity of economic organization, the continued increase in urbanism, and the decreased rate of immigration have changed the meaning of social class. Child-rearing patterns have correspondingly changed in such a way that the child's resulting personality will enable him to pursue more effectively an occupation in the family's current setting. For example, risk taking may have been appropriate behavior for the middle class in a entrepreneurial society, but in a bureaucratic society a security orientation is more appropriate. This changed requirement is presumed to be reflected in child-rearing practices, thus fitting the child psychologically for his probable adult occupation. A similar theory of the process by which class affects child-rearing practices (Aberle and Naegele, 1952) views the parent as socializing the child for the adult role he is expected to occupy, the parent's model for this role being the one he himself occupies.

The measurement of social class has been discussed and studied for many years, but still there is no generally agreed-upon way of measuring it or even conceptualizing it. To some researchers, class represents a way of life; to some, power over resources and persons; to some, reputation or esteem. Some investigators regard class as an objective phenomenon, to others it is entirely subjective; and even those who agree on its subjectivity disagree whether it is a perception of the self or of others. The number of classes in our society has usually been placed at between two and six, although some researchers think of it as a continuous ranking system with almost as many positions as there are families to be classified. Perhaps the prototypic definitions of social class are those of Marx (1906–1909), who defines class in terms of man's relationship to the means of production, i.e., occupation; Veblen (1918), who considers consumption patterns as crucial; Warner and Lunt (1941) who define it in terms of other people's judgments of a family's prestige and esteem; and Centers (1949), who defines it primarily as the subject's self-judgment. The occupational indices most commonly used have been either the classification of the family breadwinner's occupation according to the categories used by the U. S. census (U. S. Employment Service, 1949) or a simple white collar-blue collar dichotomy. In the Veblen tradition one might count the Chapin scale (1930), which includes a rating of living-room furniture. Warner's original rating system used community informants, but because it was too cumbersome for extensive use, a scale called the Index of Status Characteristics was developed (Warner, Meeker, and Eells, 1949). This index, designed to estimate community prestige ratings, is based on a sum of weights assigned to occupation, dwelling area, house type, and source of income. Hollingshead's Index of Social Position (Hollingshead and Redlich, 1958) uses occupation, dwelling area, and education. Hatt (1950) has suggested a compromise to the use of occupation and community judgments in which occupations are rated and classified not according to the researcher's judgments but according to popular judgments. Sewell and Haller (1956), in a small community study, used teacher ratings of family status in combination with the father's occupation. Income, ethnic background, and race have also been considered as aspects of class.

Each operational definition of class,

and these include many combinations of the measures mentioned above as well as others, has its protagonist. Although the ultimate decision depends on the needs of the particular research, some help in deciding which measure to use is available in the empirical comparisons that have been made of the various indices. Nineteen class indices were interrelated by Kahl and Davis (1955). They conclude that the various indices are highly correlated, and, although two common factors could be isolated from these indices, all can be viewed roughly as representing a single dimension. This would mean that for many purposes the simplest measure, the breadwinner's occupation, would probably be sufficient. On the other hand, Haer (1957) compares several indices on their ability to predict various attitudes and behavior and concludes that Warner's Index of Status Characteristics has the greatest predictive power, with the Centers type of self-perception measure having the least. Boek et al. (1957), also report that the Warner I.S.C. was the social-class index most highly correlated with six competing indices. It should also be pointed out that, other things being equal, there is an advantage to using measures of class that will make possible comparisons and syntheses with other related studies.

Father's occupation can be conceptualized as a family-setting variable in other ways besides merely as an index of social class. Occupation could affect family life and the child by its effect on the father's personality. Thus, for example, occupations might be classified in terms of their frustration potential and their opportunities for hostility release. Such a classification, cutting across class lines, might prove to be significant for family interaction and child behavior. Using the same general theory as Miller and Swanson and Aberle and Naegele, the child's socialization might be different, depending on whether the father's occupational position depends on formal training or personal characteristics. Dyer (1956) has shown that job satisfaction of the father is communicated to the child and also affects the parents' job aspirations for the child. Bronfenbrenner (1958a) has categorized occupations into those that are quality oriented and those that are not. The first group includes occupations that involve evaluation of a concrete product, the evaluation being based on the worker's own knowledge and skill. This classification of occupations, which cuts across class lines, has been found to relate to parent-child relations, as reported by the adolescent child. Aberle and Naegele (1952), who interviewed fathers about effects of their jobs on the family, found that their respondents did not see a connection between their jobs and their homes. Their conclusion that this is perceptual blindness on the part of the subjects would suggest that this line of research might better be explored by using some theoretically based classification of occupations as the independent variable and relating it to measures of family life and child variables rather than relying on introspective reports of job effects.

Time is another family-setting variable and one which is a challenge to measure. There are many theoretical notions about the relationship between a given time period, family patterns, and child behavior, but empirical studies are few because standardized studies over the years have not been done. Ramsey and Nelson (1956), in one of the few replication studies that have been reported, compared adolescent attitudes toward the family in 1939 and in 1952. They point out that even with an exact replication there are difficulties in that the cultural meaning of words and the interpretations of questions may change over time. This would apply to longitudinal studies also. But replication and longitudinal studies are still the most promising methods for studying changes over time.

Wolfenstein (1953) and Stendler (1950) have operationalized time as a variable by studying literature about child care over several generations. Such content analyses of expert opinion are not studies of practices, of course, but Bronfenbrenner (1958a) has shown in a reanalysis of some of the studies of social class and child-rearing practices that there is a remarkable correspondence between expert opinion and reported behavior, particularly for the middle class. Bronfenbrenner has managed, by organizing existing empirical studies according to the time period the data represent and by reanalysis of the data to make the various studies more comparable, to operationalize time as a family-setting variable. He suggests that expert opinion may be the intervening variable between the time setting and the child-rearing practices.

Other methods of comparing time settings include asking adults to recall their own childhood (Radke, 1946) and comparing attitudes of grandmothers with attitudes of mothers of the current generation of children (Staples and Smith, 1954). The recall method has already been criticized; and the data gathered from grandmothers suffer in that they do not necessarily reflect the opinions of these women when they actually were mothers of young children.

Still another way of considering time as a variable is by specifying certain crucial aspects of the time period and studying these aspects as they occur currently. This is, in a sense, what Miller and Swanson have done. They have studied contemporary families, but by classifying them according to whether they are entrepreneurial or bureaucratic they are doing a time study in that the entrepreneurial represent an earlier generation in certain genotypic respects.

Studying war or depression as a current family-setting variable involves problems similar to those in a study of any time period. If there is no current war or depression, the problem is the same as studying any time period that is past. The paradox of the researcher's position was clear in the laughter of the classroom when Robert Angell said in mock solemnity that he had always hoped to do a replication of his study, *The Family Encounters the Depression* (1936). It is sometimes true, however, that a depression or other disaster will hit one community, even though the country as a whole is relatively unaffected. A confined disaster is a preferable state of affairs for the researcher, for a second community can be used as a control group. In war, and in a general depression, this is not possible. Usually, the events that preceded have to be reconstructed by subject reports, as in the case of Angell's study. The possibility that the perception of the preceding state of affairs is colored by later events is always a danger.

Other family-setting variables include culture (see Chapter 21), subculture membership, rural-urban-suburban location, neighborhood, and even the house and its physical surroundings. All the family-setting variables, like parental background, are most effectively linked to the child through intervening steps. One outstanding example is a study of achievement by Strodtbeck (1958) in which he links subculture membership to parent values and family structure, examines the relationship between each of these and child values, and links child values to the child's personality and behavior.

Most family-setting variables are not particularly difficult to measure. Measuring neighborhood can be somewhat challenging, depending on what aspect of the neighborhood is important for the theory. One might want to consider the socioeconomic status of the neighborhood, the ethnic composition, the physical facilities, the transiency, the delinquency rate, the community's perception of the neighborhood, etc. Census-tract data, interviewer ratings, use of community informants, interviews on neighborhood perceptions with a random sample of community members, and the ratio of police records of juvenile arrests (coded by neighborhood) to the number of children in a neighborhood (obtained from the school census) have all been used as measures of the neighborhood setting. Bossard (1951) has suggested a unique way of considering the house itself as a variable. He has developed a Spatial Index for Family Interaction, based on the number of persons in the household, the resultant number of interrelationships, and the number of square feet of floor space in the living quarters. He suggests that this index is related to the stresses, strains, and frustrations of family living.

## FAMILY COMPOSITION

Most of the anthropological studies of cultural groups consider family composition variables and their significance for child development. Malinowski (1927), for example, has attempted to demonstrate the cultural basis of the Oedipus complex by showing that in the Trobiand Islands, where the child's important family unit is his mother's kin group, it is the uncle, the family authority, who is the target of the male child's hostility, whereas the father is an affectionate companion. In cross-cultural studies it is difficult to demonstrate empirically the particular effects of family composition because cultures usually vary in many additional respects. Nevertheless, many valuable insights have come from cross-cultural comparisons, and the possibility of comparing many cultures, alike in some respects but different in others, is a promising area of research. Because the anthropological studies are discussed in Chapter 21, we confine ourselves here to discussing mainly variations in family composition within the conjugal family.

The nuclear family in America typically consists of a mother, father, and one or more children. However, one parent may be absent from the home permanently or temporarily, and both parents may be absent, with the conventional parental roles being taken by other adults. Sometimes the family unit includes adult members in addition to the parents and their offspring. Finally, the number of children, their sex and age, and the ordinal position of any given child may vary considerably. Each of these variations has been given a turn as an independent variable in relation to some aspect of the child's development.

*Absence of a Parent.* Authors of studies involving the father's absence from the family often begin their reports with the comment that everyone studies mother absence but few have studied father absence. Strictly speaking, this is not so. We know of very few studies of mother absence, per se, although there are studies of children reared without families in which the researcher is relatively unconcerned with the missing father and siblings. The reason for this paucity is partly that *families* without mothers are uncommon and cannot be found in concentrated groups. Maternal absence has therefore usually been studied by comparing children in institutional settings with children in intact families—natural or adopted. These studies typically relate "maternal absence" directly to data about the child and show physical, mental, and emotional retardation to be associated with separation from the family (e.g., Goldfarb, 1945; Bender, 1948–1949; Feinberg, 1954). Bowlby

et al. (1956), studied maternal separation by locating children, 7 to 13 years old, who had been separated from their families before the age of 4 and had spent a few months to two years in a tuberculosis sanitarium. Comparison between these children and a control group did not reveal differences as striking as those in previous studies, presumably because the separation in this case was not tied in with parental rejection or other emotional conflicts in the family. Heinicke (1956) has studied the *degree* of separation from family by comparing children in a day nursery to children in a residential nursery. Families were contacted before the separation, and some attempt was made to standardize the two groups so that the amount of separation was the major variable influencing differences. A very interesting study designed to obtain data on the importance of the mother is that used by Spitz (1945), in which two groups of institutionalized children were compared as to retardation. In one group, composed of children in a nursery attached to a women's prison, the mothers were present, and in the other they were not. This study gives evidence that the crucial variable is the absence of a mother or mother-surrogate. An additional piece of the puzzle is provided by an experiment by Rheingold (1956). In the experimental situation one person cared for eight babies, giving them as much individualized attention as possible. The control group included babies cared for by regular institutional routines, the caretaking acts being performed by many different persons. The dependent variable in this study was social responsiveness, and the experimental babies showed more social responsiveness, even to strangers, than did the control babies.

In reviewing these studies of mother absence or separation, it can be noted that the challenge of research is not so much in the construction of measures as in the ability to find a natural setting that itself measures the independent variables. Bowlby, concerned with isolating mother separation from the emotional factors that often precede such an event, used children who had been hospitalized for disease. Spitz, interested in distinguishing between the absence of a mother figure and institutional care, sought out an unusual situation in which the latter condition existed but not the former. The "trick" is to find natural settings, alike in some ways, but different with respect to the crucial variable under investigation. This is not an easy task. Even the Spitz study was not completely successful, for the two nurseries also differed in that the nursery attached to the penal institution was superior to the other in certain physical respects. The Rheingold study is one of the few that involved experimentation. Manipulation of family-structure variables by the researcher is usually limited to the institutional setting, and, because of ethical considerations, it is further limited to *improving* conditions. The most important problem in measuring structural variables remains that of finding experimental conditions already in existence.

The prevalent use of institutionalized children is probably one of the reasons why the actual processes that link mother absence to child personality have not been examined. Institutional-ized children are different in so many ways that specifying empirically the particular intervening variables between mother absence and the child's mal-adjustment is usually not feasible, despite the noteworthy attempts by such investigators as Spitz and Rheingold. It would be worthwhile to seek out as subjects families in which the mother is absent but the family has continued to function; for example, when the mother is hospitalized or dead. In most cases a mother substitute will have been provided, but one might still classify the mother substitutes along a number of theoretically derived criteria. Variables such as maternal employment could also be conceptualized in terms of relative degrees of mother absence.

In some ways the studies of father absence have been more fortunate. There are many natural settings that enable one to study father absence. Freud and Burlingham (1944), Bach (1946), Sears, Pintler, and Sears (1946), Hill (1949), Sears (1951), and Stolz et al. (1954), studied families in which the father was absent during the war. Tiller (1958) studied families of sailors in Norway in which the father's occupation kept him away from home for long periods at a time. Additional studies deal with situations in which the marriage has been disrupted by separation, divorce, or death of father (Sutherland, 1930; Sears, 1951). The father-separation studies, for the most part, deal with families that continued to exist and, as such, allow the researcher more readily to study father separation as an isolated variable, i.e., by comparing families that are alike in most other respects. Furthermore, the fact that families are otherwise intact has made it possible to study the effects of father separation on family interactions.

The intervening processes have included consideration of such variables as resolution of the Oedipus complex and identification, absence of a masculine model, communication of the father figure through the mother's description, the mother-child relationship that results from father absence, the presence of a grandparent, employment of the mother, and the mother's emotional state. Thus the father-absence studies compared to the mother-absence studies have left much less of a mystery concerning the processes by means of which parental absence is linked to the child's personality and behavior. The Stolz study is particularly exciting because she also deals with the father's return and the problems of readjustment, and because her design enables her to compare the child born while the father was absent with a second child born after his return and with a comparable first-born child whose father was not absent.

Before going on to sibling composition, it might be mentioned that a few studies have dealt with the presence of an extra parent figure. For example, Staples and Smith (1954) have studied the relationship between the presence or absence of a grandmother in the home and the permissiveness of the mother.

*Siblings.* Concern with sibling composition variables include family size (within the conventional nuclear family the number of children is the main source of variability), ordinal position, spacing, sex, and certain specific patterns, such as the "only" child, the adopted child, and twins. These variables have been linked to the child's personality and behavior directly and by the intervening variable of family interaction—either parent-child or child-sibling. In most studies that empirically link sibling composition directly to child variables certain assumptions are made about family interaction. However, Bossard (Bossard, 1948; Bossard and Sanger, 1952; Bossard and Boll, 1954; Bossard and Boll, 1955b) approaches the problem with what might be called a true ecological theory. Bossard's theoretical constructs include such variables as the density of interaction, the availability of supplies, and the availability of personality roles. As an example of the last, he takes up the question of personality roles in the large family. One of the reasons he gives for the personality roles of the younger children is that the other roles, such as the "social butterfly," will already have been chosen by one of the children who arrived on the scene earlier.

Koch (1954, 1955a,b, 1956a,b,c,d), on the other hand, empirically relates composition factors directly to the child data, but she organizes her relationships by means of a theory that involves assumptions about the gratifications and stresses of the child-sibling relationship and the parent-child relationship. Brim (1958) has reanalyzed some of Koch's data linking sex of sibs and ordinal position to sex-linked traits in the child. The intervening process in his theory is that interaction between two persons leads to assimilation of roles, especially the assimilation by the younger (less powerful) sibling of the role of the older. Still other studies (e.g., Lasko, 1954) have considered the relationship between ordinal position and parent-child relations without studying the traits of the child.

Sears (1950), Sears, Maccoby, and Levin (1957), and Henry (1957) have empirically studied all three steps—ordinal position, child rearing, and the child. Each of these studies considers relationships between the first step and the third, the first and the second, and the second and the third, and each is concerned with establishing linkages between ordinal position and child resultants. It is interesting to note that both the study by Sears, Maccoby, and Levin and the one by Henry address themselves to the relationship between being the oldest child and being aggressive toward authority, but each suggests a different theory to explain the relationship. For Henry, the intervening step is the fact—reported by both studies—that fathers are more likely to discipline the oldest child; for Sears, Maccoby, and Levin, the intervening step involves consideration of intersibling relationships. Both hypotheses need further testing, but the fact that two competing hypotheses have emerged from studies showing consistent patterns of findings suggests the difficulties of demonstrating linkages. A more adequate test of the Henry hypothesis might be to divide oldest children into two groups, those who are the recipients of greater father discipline and those who are not, and to divide nonoldest children into the same two groupings. If the Henry hypothesis is correct, both oldest and nonold-

est children whose fathers are disciplinarians should show more aggression than the others, and they should not be different from one another.

Methodological problems in studies of sibling composition do not lie in the measurement. Both adults and children can report family composition in response to direct questions without distortion. However, there is often a problem in locating appropriate subjects. This problem is most obvious in a study like that of Bossard and Boll (1954, 1955b), in which their sample needed to include only families with six or more living children, or in a study like that of Mowrer (1954), which analyzed relationships of 612 twins to each other, to other members of their families, and to friends. However, even in a study of more commonly occurring sibling status positions, there are difficulties when one tries to hold some aspects of sibling structure constant. A remarkably well-controlled study from this standpoint is that of Koch (1955a,b, 1956a,b,c), in which she selected a sample consisting of 384 5- and 6-year-old children from native-born, intact, urban, *two-child families*. These subjects had been selected so that it was possible to subdivide the sample into equal-sized groups based on sex, ordinal position, sex of sibling, and space between siblings. Since the first three variables were dichotomies and the third was operationalized as a trichotomy, she had 24 groups of 16 children each. By considering only two-child families, Koch immensely reduced the number of possibilities to be considered. Even so, there were 24 possibilities, and had the 384 subjects not been selected to fall equally into each classification she would not have had enough subjects in some of her groups.

The difficulties involved in such a study are obvious. Where does one obtain a large group of subjects with these particular characteristics? If a researcher is interested in obtaining a sample of 6-year-old children, he need only contract the schools to obtain concentrated groups of children who fit this classification, but *there is no natural setting in which one can readily find concentrated groups of two-child families*. This kind of problem occurs so often in family research that it will be taken up in the section dealing with general methodological problems. Suffice it to say that the researcher is indeed fortunate who is on cordial terms with the superintendent of a large school system and who is able to obtain the names and addresses of the children who have the specific characteristics he seeks.

Another very promising method of studying sibling position while controlling on other variables is that employed by Lasko (1954). She was interested in comparing first and second children *in the same family*. To understand the differences in personality between first and second children, it is important to know whether they are treated differently by their parents. Dean (1947) had already done a study that compared personality traits of siblings, using the mother's report of the differences between them as her measure. Lasko, however, had behavioral ratings of parent behavior (the Fels Parent Behavior Rating Scales). Furthermore, these data were part of a longitudinal study, home observations being made at intervals of six months. With such data, Lasko was able to compare the mother's behavior toward her first and second child *when the two siblings were the same age* and also to compare the consistency of the mother's behavior toward each child over the years. She found, for example, that parent behavior toward the first child is, on the average, less warm and more restrictive and coercive. She further found that first children are treated less consistently by their parents over the years. They start out from a more favorable position than the second child ever experiences, but by the time they are 3 or 4 they are treated less warmly than the second child is treated at a similar age. This study represents a real attempt to understand the environmental factors through which ordinal position is linked to child personality and behavior. It is interesting to note that Sears, Maccoby and Levin report no differences in maternal warmth expressed toward first and second children. Their study involves *interfamily* comparisons based on maternal interview data. Lasko's use of *intrafamily* comparisons, in combination with the use of longitudinal behavior observations, makes the Lasko study much more sensitive and capable of discerning differences.

## RELATIONSHIPS BETWEEN PARENTS

As we move down the process sequence, fewer steps are required to link the independent variable with the child. Mother-father relationship can be linked to the child almost directly by processes that are internal to the child. For example, the power relationship between the husband and wife is perceived by the child and may influence his identification choice; the division of labor between husband and wife determines in part the child's cognition of what male and female roles are; and the degree of marital tension may affect the child's sense of security. These variables might also be tied to the child less directly. Hoffman (1960), for example, suggests that when the father is dominant toward the mother she is dominant toward the child, and the child, continuing the pecking order, is then dominant toward other children in nursery school. This theory involves a more concrete step, linking the parental relationship first to the parent-child relationship and only then to the child. It is apparent from these illustrations that the husband-wife relationship is an important variable in the child's development.

To elaborate, using the theoretical model implied in the division of labor example, the family represents a model of society for the young child. Perhaps the first status in society that the child becomes aware of is sex. He learns his own sex and that of each parent. The relationship between the parents communicates to him what males and females are like and how they interact. He may learn that males are strong and dominant and females are weak and submissive, if this is the pattern communicated to him by his parents' interaction. This tells the child something about what to expect from other males and females, and, since his sex is the same as one of the parents, it also tells

him something about what should be expected of him. Furthermore, if that expectation is undesirable to him, e.g., if he is a male but perceives that males (his father) are weak, he may choose to be the opposite sex. There are two empirical studies that suggest that boys prefer the dominant parent and girls prefer the nondominant parent. Kohn and Clausen (1956) found this with schizophrenic adults recalling their childhood, and Lippitt and Hoffman (1959) found it with normal children between 8 and 12. Kohn and Clausen's study corroborated subject reports about the dominance of their parents with reports of other family members. Lippitt and Hoffman used both children's perceptions of father-mother power and mothers' reports of which parent had the major role in certain important family decisions. These findings suggest that the child's identification choice and probably also the child's adjustment to society may be influenced by whether or not the father-mother relationship in any particular family corresponds to the male-female relationships of the larger society. The Kohn and Clausen study reports that mothers of schizophrenic patients controlled more major and minor decisions in the families than the mothers of normals, and they suggest that schizophrenia is not the only maladjustment so characterized. Whether or not a cross-sex identification is the process involved in linking mother dominance to maladjustment needs further investigation.

When one considers the importance of the relationship between the mother and father for the child's development, the scarcity of studies in this area seems startling. There is a number of studies predicting *to* husband-wife power (e.g., Strodtbeck, 1951; Sharp and Mott, 1956; Heer, 1958; Blood, 1958; Wolfe, 1959; Hoffman, 1960.) Some studies establish norms about or predict to the division of functions (e.g., Herbst, 1952; Oeser and Hammond, 1954; Oeser and Emery, 1954; Johannis, 1955; Kenkel and Hoffman, 1956; Blood, 1958; Hoffman, 1960). However, omitting the studies that have dealt only with the division of certain child-rearing functions between husband and wife (e.g., King and Henry, 1955; Henry, 1956, 1957; Sears, Maccoby, and Levin, 1957), which will be considered in later sections, we find very few studies relating either husband-wife power or division of functions to the child. Aronfreed (1955) and Altucher (1956) tried to relate a child perception measure of these variables to sex identification in males, but their results are inconclusive.

Strodtbeck (1958) has studied the effects of power in the family on the child. However, the independent variable is not, strictly speaking, husband-wife power but husband-wife-son power, and the theory Strodtbeck uses to link power to child attitudes is one that involves the son's being in a reciprocal relationship to the high-powered father; that is, when the father is high powered, the son feels controlled and generalizes this to the nature of the world, believing, for example, that man is controlled by destiny.

Although there are few attempts to relate husband-wife power and division of functions to the child, there are many methods of measuring these variables.

Power is the more challenging to measure. For one thing, since power is not specific to the home setting but capable of being revealed in discrete acts, it is not limited to home observation or the questionnaire and can be measured by means of an experimentally contrived situation. An example would be Strodtbeck's revealed difference technique, which he has used in studying husband-wife power as well as husband-wife-son power. The husband and wife separately answer questionnaire items. The experimenter then presents them with one of the items about which there was disagreement and asks the couple to reconcile their differences. Their discussion is tape-recorded while the experimenter is absent from the room. The process is repeated for a given number of items, and a score is later computed for power based on which person won the other over to his view. A similar technique was used by Kenkel (1956). Married couples were asked to pretend that they had received a gift of 300 dollars and to go through the process of deciding how it would be spent. Power was measured in terms of the adopted items suggested by each spouse. Vidich (1956), without much success, tried a similar technique in which couples were asked to discuss several salient problems and to decide how they would spend an imaginary amount of money.

Interviews have also been employed to determine husband-wife power. Wolfe (1959) used a measure based on wives' responses to questions about whether they or their husbands decided each of eight important family matters, such as when to buy a car, where to live, and how much money should be saved. Answers were placed on a five-point scale from "husband only" to "wife only," and scores were added across the eight items. Heer (1958) asked husbands and wives jointly which parent won out in a case of disagreement. The Herbst Day-at-Home measure (1952) consists of a series of questions about relatively trivial household activities in which the child is asked to report who does the activity and who decides about it. It has been adapted by several researchers (e.g., Aronfreed, 1955; Altucher, 1956; Hoffman, 1960) to measure husband-wife power. Hoffman, for example, developed a scoring system whereby each pair of *doing* and *deciding* items was considered as a unit. The number of activities the mother decided but the father did was subtracted from the number of activities that the father decided but the mother did.

It is interesting and reassuring to note that the different measures of husband-wife power have been found to relate *in the same way* to many other variables. For example, father dominance has been associated with high socioeconomic status, using the Strodtbeck measure, the Wolfe measure, the Heer measure, and the Hoffman measure. The last three have also shown the same relationships between husband-wife power, on the one hand, and size of family and maternal employment, on the other.

Strodtbeck and Kenkel also analyzed the interaction in terms of the Bales (1950) categories. Thus these measures can be used to obtain data about the division of certain goal-directed and emotional functions between the husband and wife, e.g., which parent performs the integrative function of reestablishing cohesion after situations of stress.

Measuring the division of household tasks between the mother and father can be done by a relatively direct questionnaire, so long as the items are specific and are not threatening and the answers can be checked from a preconstructed list. Although there have been many variations of this technique, the prototype has been put forth by Herbst (1952). The Herbst Day-at-Home measure consists of 33 questions about different household tasks (e.g., Who mows the lawn?). Each item is followed by a list of family members, and the respondent is asked to circle the persons who always do it or whose job it is to do it, to underline those who do it sometimes or help, and to cross out all those who would never do it. (Each participation item has a counterpart that asks who makes the corresponding decision.) Herbst selected the particular items used by considering the distribution of the activities with respect to four regions—household duties, child care and control, social activities, and economic activities. He also considered a time sequence for an ordinary work day. With these two considerations in mind, he attempted to get an "unbiased, random distribution" of activities, including, however, only those that could be engaged in by either parent. This measure was actually developed for use with child respondents and, as such, might more properly belong in the later section on child perceptions. We have included it here for two reasons. First of all, with the possible exception of the child-care items, the questions concern activities that are rather objective and free of emotion for the child. The child may therefore be thought of simply as the informant about what takes place in the household. In fact, it is Herbst's opinion that the child is a better informant about such things than the parent, for parents tend to give a picture of greater mutuality and cooperation than actually exists. Second, we include it because the same measure has also been used with parents.

Several variations have been added to the original measure, e.g., a differentiation between responses when the mother and father participate in the activity *jointly* and when they participate *separately* and a check list that asks the respondent to report the frequency of each activity for each parent. The answers have been scored to give a measure of husband-wife interaction, sex-role reversal, amount of participation, areas of participation, etc. Despite several criticisms (Yamamura and Zald, 1956), this measure has received much validational support. For example, Hoffman (1960) found a relationship between a measure of sex-role reversal constructed from children's responses and the parents' responses to an attitude scale measuring sex-role ideology.

The affectional relationship between mother and father has probably been considered in child-development studies more than the power relationship or the division of functions. Certainly the analytic literature is filled with case histories that illustrate the relationship between marital tension and maladjustment of the child, and a number of theories link these two variables. Marital tension has been linked to child maladjustment somewhat directly in the theory that the child perceives the tension and therefore feels insecure and less directly in theories that state marital tension leads to parental rejection because (1) the child symbolizes the parents' inability to dissolve the unhappy marriage, (2) the child resembles the disliked spouse, (3) the child becomes the scapegoat for uncommunicated areas of marital tension, and (4) the parents have a generally low morale. It has also been suggested that disappointment in her mate leads the mother to invest too much emotion in the child. Marital adjustment might also be linked to the child by the intervening variables of insufficient or inconsistent parental authority. Finally, it is possible that marital tension and child maladjustment are spuriously associated, in that certain personality traits of the parent lead to a rejection of both spouse and child.

There are, however, very few adequate empirical studies in this area. No one really has studied the affectional relationship between the mother and father as it affects the child and also operationalized the linkages between the two. Furthermore, the studies that have tried to relate marital adjustment to parental attitudes or to child variables have produced a pattern of findings difficult to integrate.

Porter (1955) and Hawkes, Burchinal, and Gardner (1956) have examined the relationship between marital adjustment and parental acceptance of the child as measured by the Porter Parental Acceptance Scale. Porter measured marital adjustment by a modified question-naire based on previous scales developed by Terman et al. (1938), Burgess and Cottrell (1939), and Locke (1951). Hawkes, Burchinal, and Gardner developed their measure from the marriage-success indices of Burgess and Wallin (1953). Porter reports a relationship between marital adjustment and parental acceptance, using combined mother-father data. Hawkes, Burchinal, and Gardner, doing separate analyses for mothers and fathers, found no such relationship for mothers and a low one for fathers.

Turning to the studies that have examined the relationship between marital adjustment and child personality directly, we find at least two (Stroup, 1956; and Burchinal, Hawkes, and Gardner, 1957a) that suggest that no such relationship exists. Stroup tried to relate mother's marital adjustment, measured by the Kirkpatrick Interests Scale, to the child's adjustment, measured by the California Personality Scale. Burchinal, Hawkes, and Gardner tried to relate marital adjustment of both parents, measured by items from scales developed by Burgess and Wallin, to the child's adjustment, measured by the Rogers Test of Personality Adjustment.

The Baruch studies (1937, 1944), on the other hand, present a different picture. Using clinical-style interviews with both parents to obtain data about marital adjustment, Baruch tried to isolate the areas of marital tension that were important for predicting to the child's adjustment. She found tension over sex, lack of consideration, insufficient expression of affection, the as-

cendance-submission relationship, and the inability to talk things through all related to maladjustment in the child, measured by behavioral observations in a nursery-school setting. The first three tension areas she sees as similar and inter-related, and she refers to them as "security-giving factors." Ascendance is seen as an "adequacy-giving factor." The inability to talk things over is seen as a factor that intensifies the other two. She suggests that these factors are the essential aspects of the marriage relationship. In the second study (1944) Baruch examines the effects of marital tension on boys and girls separately and notes that marital tension has a greater influence on girls than on boys. This is like a replication of another finding of the study—that the mothers in her study were more influenced than the fathers by their own parents' marital adjustment. Furthermore, it ties in with studies by Toby (1957) and Nye (1958) that deal with the relationship between family disorganization and juvenile delinquency. Both investigators note that this relationship is stronger among adolescent girls than among adolescent boys. Although their explanations differ somewhat, both Toby and Nye suggest that since adolescent boys are generally unsupervised, as compared to girls, any factor that leads to a lack of supervision will disproportionately affect girls. In this sense, both investigators conceptualize marital discord in terms of less parental supervision, and explain the sex differences in sensitivity to marital discord accordingly. If the Baruch finding with preschool children is part of the same pattern as that manifested in the juvenile-delin-quency findings, it may be that the lack of supervision is not the genotypic variable. In any case, it would be worthwhile to study further the differential responses of boys and girls to marital tension.

Another sex difference reported by Baruch is that the one area of tension that influenced the adjustment of boys more than girls is ascendance-submission. This finding is especially interesting in line with our earlier discussion of mother-father power relations and identification. Is it possible that mother-dominance is a pattern more likely to lead to tension in the area of ascendance-submission? Is it possible that mother-dominance and cross-sex identification is more dysfunctional to boys' development than to girls'? Or is ascendance-submission a more salient area in general for boys? It is an unfortunate indication of the discontinuity of family research that the Baruch study has not been followed up with attempts to determine why certain areas of tension were especially crucial, to distinguish further the areas in which the children's maladjustments were manifested, and to understand the process by means of which these tensions affected the child.

It is also significant, and should be investigated further, that the Baruch study, using clinical-style interviews, found a relationship between marital tension and child adjustment, whereas the Stroup study and that by Burchinal, Hawkes, and Gardner, using marital adjustment scales, did not. This difference, in combination with the abundance of psychoanalytic case histories

illustrating the linkage of parents' marital relations to children's personality disorders, suggests that the clinical interview is better than the marital adjustment scales for detecting those aspects of marital tension most crucial to the child's development.

Nye (1957, 1958), using adolescent reports of parental adjustment, also finds mother-father tension linked to the child's maladjustment, specifically to psychosomatic illness, delinquency, and strained parent-child relations. In fact, both Nye and Landis (1955) have helped to pinpoint certain aspects of the marital tension situation by comparing child adjustment in unbroken but unhappy homes with child adjustment in broken homes and in happy unbroken homes. They find, in general, that the unhappy unbroken homes produce the most disturbance in the child. These findings may mean that on-going and continual marital tension is disturbing to the child but that once the tension is over and the parents separate he can, to a certain extent, recover, even though he has lost one of his parents. On the other hand, there is another interpretation of these findings that has significance for the validity of using the standard marital adjustment scales for child development studies: these findings might mean that *marital tension and the predivorce situation are not the same thing*. That is, it is possible that there is a kind of marital tension disturbing to the child that does not culminate in divorce. Spiegel (1957) has suggested that when areas of tension between parents are not communicated the child becomes a scapegoat. This situation is functional to the marriage but dysfunctional to the child. If there is a form of marital tension that is dysfunctional to the child but does not lead to divorce, then the inadequacy of the standard marital adjustment scales in predicting to child adjustment is explained. Most of the existing marital adjustment scales have been developed as predictors of divorce and have often been standardized and validated by comparisons between married and divorced couples. They may not be sensitive to the detection of other kinds of marital tension that do not typically culminate in divorce but are highly disturbing to the child. This raises a methodological problem and a related theoretical one. The first involves a need to develop scales to detect unhappy marriages that do not end in divorce, and the second involves a need to identify more thoroughly the different areas of marital tension and their significance.

Several of the standard marital adjustment scales have already been mentioned. Such scales include those developed by Burgess and Cottrell (1939), Terman et al. (1938), Locke (1951), Popenoe (1937), Adams (1946), and Burgess and Wallin (1953). These scales typically include items such as "How often do you kiss your mate?" and are presented with a list such as "every day, now and then, almost never." Respondents check their answers, and these are weighted and scored. The Kirkpatirck Family Interests Scale (1937) is considered more indirect. It consists of a list of activities on which the respondent is asked to check the ones he enjoys. On the opposite side of the sheet the respondent checks the ones he enjoys with his spouse. The more enjoyed activities the respondent likes to do with his spouse, the better is his marital adjustment. Taves (1948) has compared the Kirkpatrick measure with the more direct Terman scale and found the Kirkpatrick superior in several respects.

Other measures of marital adjustment use adolescent reports. Nye (1957, 1958) and Harter (1950) have used this method. Harter compared these scores to marital adjustment scores obtained from the parents. He found correlations between 0.48 and 0.58 and concludes that adolescents (high-school seniors) can give fairly accurate pictures of the degree of marital adjustment of their parents.

Bossard and Boll (1955a) have used ratings made by siblings of the married couple as a measure of marital happiness. Strodtbeck (1952) has also interviewed persons about the marital adjustment of friends. This may not be a very practical technique for general use, but it does offer possibilities for validating other measures.

## PERSONAL CHARACTERISTICS OF PARENTS

In this section we consider studies that attempt to link the parent's personality or general social attitudes (1) directly to child variables, (2) to parent child-rearing practices or attitudes without going as far in the causal sequence schema as child variables, (3) to both child-rearing orientations and child variables.

*Linking Parent Characteristics Directly to Child Variables.* The paper by Rosenzweig and Isham (1947) illustrates the attempt to jump the wide "socialization process gap" between parent personality and child personality. These writers present an analysis of the complementary personality trends in the TAT protocols of a mother and her 16-year-old son. Most of the analysis is focused on understanding the current interpersonal situation between the mother and son rather than exploring the mother's personality structure as a source of trends in the son's personality pattern, although they mention the latter as a desirable and feasible type of analysis. They feel the TAT is more suited to this kind of complementary personality analysis than the Rorschach (Buhler, 1943; Beck, 1945), "since it is more sensitive to such problems of adjustment as would involve the various members of the patient's personal world." Such analyses of "complementary patterns" do not demonstrate a definite sequence of causality nor shed light on the process involved. This requires research designs that are still largely absent from the research literature.

Frenkel-Brunswik and Havel (1953) compared the ethnocentric attitudes of parents and children as determined in interviews. The correlations between parent and child ethnocentrism were all positive and ranged from 0.20 to 0.60, but the investigators note that such figures give no insight whether ethnocentric attitudes are transmitted directly or by indirect processes. In their investigation of the same variables with a larger population Bird, Monachesi, and

Burdick (1952) found correlations in the high 0.20's between the attitudes of parents and their third-, fourth-, and fifth-grade children. These investigators, assuming a process of direct communication, believe the correlations are low because parents refrain from expressing their own attitudes to their children because of guilt or ambivalence. The question of the processes intervening in the communication of prejudice was considered with more methodological care by Radke Yarrow, Trager, and Miller (1952), as we shall see in the next section.

Several studies, for example, those by Gray and Klaus (1956) and Payne and Mussen (1956), have used the comparison between parent characteristics and child characteristics as a measure of identification. Gray and Klaus compared three different measures of identification: similarities between parent and child responses to the Allport-Vernon-Lindzey Study of Values, similarities between the child's actual responses and his perception of how each parent would respond, and the child's warmth toward his parents as expressed in sentence-completion items. They showed that for each of these measures of identification there was more like-sex parent identification. Furthermore, they showed that the three identification concepts are related but not identical. Payne and Mussen secured California Personality Inventories from adolescent boys and their parents. Identification with father was measured by subtracting the number of mother-son agreements from the number of father-son agreements. Story completions were used for obtaining the boys' imagery of parent-child relationships. They examined the relationship between the warmth of perceived parent-child relations and identification and between parent personality and identification. In addition, they obtained teacher ratings of the boys on social-emotional adjustment and related these to identification. Unfortunately, the parent personality and identification measures were not independent, since both were obtained from the responses to the California Personality Inventory. However, the idea of predicting from parent personality to identification rather than directly to child personality or behavior offers a promising line for further research.

Goodstein and Dahlstrom (1956) illustrate a different methodological approach. They selected a group of children with the same personality disturbances (stuttering) and a control group of normals and administered personality tests (MMPI) to the mothers. They found no significant differences in the personality patterns of the two sets of mothers. With this type of comparative design, it is difficult to discover the linkage between parent variables and child variables because of the complex global nature of the dependent child variable as well as the size of the jump in the socialization process.

The direct linking of parent and child characteristics seems to be a less rewarding focus for research than starting with parent characteristics and moving through intervening variables toward child personality and behavior.

*Linking Parent Characteristics to Child-Rearing Variables.* There is a variety of studies that do not attempt to relate parent characteristics to child variables but make their contribution to an understanding of the socialization sequence by studying the connection between the parent's personality or values and his child-rearing orientation or practice.

In a very interesting exploratory study Sigel and Hoffman (1956) administered 13 TAT-type cards to parents. These cards depicted all possible combinations of parents and children: mother-son, father-daughter, family scenes of parents and children, cards of children alone, etc. Projective stories were elicited, using the standard instructions. These parent protocols were related to extensive data on the influence-technique patterns used by parents with their children. The influence-technique data were secured by an interview that will be taken up later. In the pilot report the authors make predictions from the projective stories of three fathers to their interaction patterns with their preschool-age children. The analyses and predictions from the personality data were made by one judge, and a second judge independently analyzed the materials on the influence techniques used by the parent. The two sets of data were then compared. This pilot study indicates a high degree of predictive success. The investigators believe this is the result of using test stimuli corresponding in content to the area of real life under study, predicting from a coherent personality picture of the respondent, using the entire test record, and conceptualizing in advance the behavioral situation toward which the predictions are made.

Zemlick and Watson (1953) report

an interesting design for studying the mother's "psychic acceptance-rejection" as a determinant of attitudes and adjustment during and after pregnancy. TAT stories, sentence completions, and judges' ratings were used to assess the degree of rejection of femininity, sexuality, marital status, and motherhood. A separate assessment was made of psychosomatic and physiological symptoms of anxiety and disturbance. These personality variables were related to ratings of adjustment to labor and delivery and to time-sampling observations of mother-behavior patterns and verbalizations with the baby after birth. The personality measures of rejection and disturbances were positively related to problems of adjustment in the prenatal behavior patterns and attitudes of the mother but negatively related to the postnatal observations. This led the investigators to suggest that basic rejective attitudes are often expressed in overprotective maternal behavior. There are several points in this study where one might wish for more adequate procedures, but the over-all design is suggestive of the fruitfulness of studying adjacent phases of the process sequence.

Several studies have used the authoritarian-egalitarian dimension in seeking a connection between parent characteristics and child-rearing attitudes and practices. Levinson and Huffman (1955) made a methodological contribution in developing a test of Traditional Family Ideology in which the respondents indicate three degrees of agreement and disagreement with a series of items about parent-child relationships, husband-wife relationships, male and fe-

male roles, and general aims of the family. The TFI scale was found to be highly related to the Ethnocentrism $(E)$ and Authoritarianism $(F)$ scales. It also differentiated between persons with different religious preferences and practices. Hart (1957) carried the analysis further with a population of mothers of preschool children. These mothers responded to the TFI scale and the $F$ scale and also reported what they would do in response to 38 different child-behavior situations. The findings indicate a relationship between the mothers' reports of how they would behave toward their children and the authoritarian-egalitarian values measured by the tests. The investigator relates this study to those that show similarities between the authoritarianism of mothers and that of children, but notes that further data are needed to complete the causal chain.

Kates and Diab (1955) explore the relationship between the $F$ scale and Shoben's Parent Attitude Survey, which scores parent attitudes of dominance, possessiveness, and ignoring. A significant relationship was found, but the pattern for male and female respondents was markedly different. The findings fit in with the view expressed by McCandless (1958) that the link between personality needs and child-rearing philosophies may be considerably higher for mothers than for fathers, for whom there is less psychological involvement in child-rearing practices. However, whether the fact that the relationship is stronger for females is due to differences in mother and father roles or a reflection of wider sex differences is an important question that requires further research.

Shapiro (1952) used Eysenck's social and political attitude inventory to obtain scores on radicalism-conservatism and tendermindedness-toughmindedness. These scores were found to relate significantly to those obtained on an inventory of 40 child-rearing items scored on the dimensions of restrictiveness-permissiveness and objective-emotional.

Brodbeck, Nogee, and DiMascio (1956) worked with a much clearer conceptual direction, starting with Reisman's ideas of other-directed and inner-directed character structure. They studied 30 mothers with young children in homogeneous lower middle-class socioeconomic family situations. The mother checked multiple-choice responses to 39 different mother-child interaction situations in three ways: first, indicating what she actually did in these situations, second, what she thought she should do, and third, what her neighbors usually did. The authors interpret their findings as indicating that the mother's behavior patterns were more influenced by internal than external norms, although they recognize the methodological difficulty of using only mothers' reports.

Patterson (1943) found that the "neuroticism" and "dominance" scores obtained by a group of mothers on the Bernreuter Personality Inventory related to their scores on the Fels battery of Parent Behavior Ratings. The fact that high dominance scores seemed to go with positive and democratic parent-behavior patterns led the investigator to reconceptualize the dominance variable to stress the dimensions of confidence and extraversion as being implicit in the measure.

*Parent Characteristics, Intervening Linkages, and Child Variables.* A very interesting research sequence is represented by the study of McClelland, Rindlisbacher, and deCharms (1955) complemented by that of Winterbottom (1958). In the first study relationships were found between the parents' value orientations, as inferred from group membership (Protestant, Jewish, Irish-Catholic, and Italian-Catholic), and their expectations regarding the child's attaining independence, as measured by a questionnaire developed by Winterbottom. The next step in the sequence is Winterbottom's study in which middle-class mothers of 8-year-old boys reported their goals concerning 20 kinds of independence and mastery behavior and their expectations regarding the age at which their children would learn the particular behavior. Winterbottom also secured parent reports of reactions to the child when he did and did not fulfill parent expectations. Need achievement in the boys was coded from a set of stories told in response to verbal cue situations such as "A mother and her son. They look worried." Significant relationships were found between the need-achievement scores of the boys and the child-rearing orientations of the mothers. In addition, need achievement in the boys was related to teachers' ratings regarding achievement. Furthermore, Winterbottom observed each of the boys in a standardized problem-solving behavior situation and found significant relationships between the need-achievement scores and such performance variables as not requesting help, refusing offers of help, and turning down opportunities to stop for a rest. Although the samples are small and restricted in range, the two studies together present a significant model of theoretical linkage, supported by careful measurement procedures, between parental values and practices and child personality and behavior.

Strodtbeck (1958) builds creatively upon this research sequence. Instead of starting from the fact of group affiliation as a parental value index, Strodtbeck also utilized a set of value orientation scales, which differentiated between the Jewish and Italian-Catholic families in the study. A factor analysis of the value questionnaire indicated that differences in cultural and religious affiliation were reflected in values concerning mastery or rejection of fate and independence or dependence of the family. Unfortunately, this study did not include data about child-rearing practices similar to the Winterbottom questionnaire, but a significant methodological contribution was made by setting up standardized behavior situations in which the interaction between mother, father, and son could be observed in a series of decision-making situations. Strodtbeck moves from parental value orientations, to mother-father-child interaction, to values, personality, and behavior of the son. An important finding is that the son's value orientation is a function of parent-child interaction (mother-father-child power) and not a function of the parents' ideology. As Strodtbeck

remarks, "a clear case of the children believing what the parents do and not what they say." The sample is too small to permit a careful analysis of some of the relationships, but the findings and methodology suggest important vistas for future investigation.

Some of the intervening child-rearing processes between parent prejudice and child prejudice have been explored by Radke Yarrow, Trager, and Miller (1952). One hundred mothers and their first- or second-grade children were studied. Parent prejudice and child-rearing practices were measured by a structured interview schedule, which included the presentation of a number of interracial and interreligious problem situations for analysis. Parent prejudice was linked to such attitudes and practices as restriction of the child's playmates and school associations, feelings of responsibility for the development of the child's beliefs and attitudes, and differences in parental teaching about own group membership. The investigators find that parents' attitudes toward a particular racial or religious group are correlated with their children's attitudes but that there are many individual cases in which large discrepancies exist. The authors feel that a "more intensive study of the attitudes, of the individual personalities and of the relationships within the family" is needed to explain such discrepancies. The study does suggest that the transmission of attitudes and values in this area is to a high degree not direct or planned.

Behrens (1954) has attempted to connect mother's character structure to three child-rearing practices and then to child adjustment. The children ranged in age from 2 to 6. The measurements were ratings derived from extensive intake interviews with mothers at a mental-health clinic. The character structure scales focused on such variables as the mother's self-image, self-mastery, range, quality, and control of affect, and a rigidity-flexibility dimension. The same rater made ratings of whether or not parental practices in the areas of toilet training, feeding, and weaning were adapted to the child's needs. These scales ranged from neglectful to permissive behavior patterns. A series of variables designating "adequacy of adjustment" were coded from child interviews. These included security with mother, reaction to separation from mother, self-assertion, response to discipline, quality of social relationship. The general personality or character scores of the mother did not relate closely to the reported child-rearing practices nor did the various child-rearing practices, to each other. Furthermore, there was only a slight relationship between the child-rearing practices and child adjustment scores. There is, however, a high relationship between the general mother personality scores and the child adjustment scores. Behrens believes this indicates that the child is highly sensitive and responsive to unconscious attitudes of the mother, which are not revealed in child-rearing practices. It is also possible that the particular child-rearing practices selected for study were not the crucial ones or that measuring them by means of mother reports was not valid. Thus it is difficult to appraise whether in fact the mother's personality is more important

than child-rearing practices and whether it is directly transmitted to the child.

Two other studies, Stolz (1954) and Sears, Maccoby, and Levin (1957), use parent personality as assessed from parent interviews as an independent variable and link this to child variables through parent attitudes and practices. Stolz and collaborators scored their extensive father interviews in terms of the personality schema developed by Freedman, Leary, Ossorio, and Coffey (1951) to examine the relationship between the father's self-perception and his perception of his first-born child. In addition to the father personality materials, both parents reported attitudes and behaviors in such child-rearing areas as eating, sleeping, elimination, and relations with siblings. Furthermore, the attitudes and behavior patterns of the children were assessed by a variety of techniques, including behavior observation and projective situations described later in this chapter. The study consists of several discrete analyses, each focused on the comparison between war separated and nonwar separated groups. Each level of analysis is related to the major independent variable rather than being related to one another to establish a chain of causality. However, in the case study presentations, and in the theoretical sections, the chain of linkage is brought out, tying father personality (and wartime experience) to the child's personality and behavior through the father's attitude, behavior, and relationship with the child.

Perhaps the most comprehensive study of parental patterns is that of Sears, Maccoby, and Levin (1957). From an extensive interview schedule with mothers, they coded data concerning parental attitudes, practices, and child behavior. They derived several "underlying traits" by means of factor analysis. These include such variables as permissiveness and strictness, self-acceptance and self-confidence, emotional warmth, and aggressiveness-punitiveness. Since all the data are derived from mother interviews, the measures are not independent, and the study must be viewed as an exploratory one. Nonindependence of measures is of particular concern with respect to the relationship between parent personality and child-rearing practices because the personality dimensions have been derived from the data on parent practices. Nevertheless, future studies should be able to profit from the suggestions of these writers about personality dimensions of importance in the study of the socialization process. They do link their basic dimensions of parent orientation to child effects, though the latter are derived from parental reports of child behavior. In previous studies the linkage to independent measures of child behavior in projective doll-play behavior situations has been made (Sears, Pintler, and Sears, 1946; Sears, 1951).

## CHILD-ORIENTED PARENTAL ATTITUDES

Several extensive efforts have been made to develop scales of attitudes toward the parent role and toward child-rearing. Porter's (1954) emphasis was on obtaining an attitudinal index of parent acceptance of the child. He felt that such an instrument should make it possible to bypass the more complex and uneconomical behavior observations and situational measurement procedures. The measure consists of 20 descriptions of child behavior. Respondents indicate their feelings and probable behavior in each situation by selecting from the alternative responses provided. Porter found that individual responses showed a high internal consistency and that scores differentiated among parents. Burchinal (1958a) extended the methodological work with this instrument and found meaningful patterns, i.e., that mothers appear more accepting than fathers, older mothers, more accepting than younger mothers, and more educated fathers, more accepting than less educated fathers. But difficulties appeared in the use of the scale when Burchinal, Hawkes, and Gardner (1957b) attempted to use it to link parent attitudes to child adjustment variables. They found no significant connections between parents' responses to the Porter measure and children's responses to the Roger's Test of Personality Adjustment. In another more extensive analysis Burchinal (1958b) reports using both the Parental Acceptance Scale and Shoben's Parent-Attitude Survey with a group of parents and the Roger's Test of Personality and the California Test of Personality with children. Almost none of the correlations between parent-attitude scores and child-personality scores were significant. The investigators conclude that perhaps attitudes as reported by parents and as perceived by their children are different phenomena. It is also possible that parent attitudes and practices as reported by parents are significantly discrepant from actual parent-behavior patterns, or that children's personality trends as revealed by these self-report instruments may not be tapping the genotypic dimensions that are most related to parental behaviors.

Shoben's Parent-Attitude Survey (1949) taps a wider variety of attitudinal dimensions than the Porter scale. One hundred and forty-eight items were administered to 50 mothers of problem children and 50 mothers of nonproblem children. The respondents checked a four-point scale from strongly disagree to strongly agree. Eighty-five of the items were found to differentiate between the two groups of parents. These items were further subdivided into three clusters—dominance, possessiveness, and ignoring. Gordon (1957) had mothers of preschool children fill out the Shoben questionnaire before a twelve-day camp program in which both mothers and children participated. The camp staff then observed the mothers and rated them on dimensions comparable to those tapped on the questionnaire. No clear-cut relationships between attitudes and behavior were found.

Trapp and Kausler (1958) had more success in their work with 16 preschool children and their mothers and fathers. The parents answered the Parent-Attitude Survey. The children were observed at school for ten activity samples of five minutes each. Predictions were made from the parent-dominance scores and parent-difference scores to the child-behavior variable of "avoidance of adult contacts." The predictions were successful at a modest level of significance, and the combined parent scores were a more powerful predictor for children of both sexes than individual parent scores.

The study by Gordon and the one by Trapp and Kausler, considered in combination, tend to support Behrens' notion that the link between parent attitudes and the child is not through parent behavior. However, it is possible that the crucial parent-behavior areas have not been examined. Thus it may be that attitudes do affect parent behavior but that Gordon, Behrens, and others have not selected the appropriate behaviors for study.

Duvall (1946) has developed a simple method of obtaining conceptions of parenthood by getting open-ended responses to two simple questions, "What are five good things a child does?" and "What are five good things a mother does?" Responses are scored in terms of a traditional versus a developmental orientation to the parental role. Elder (1949) reports a study of 32 fathers, using this technique in addition to more extensive interviewing. He found that developmentally oriented fathers reported more interaction with their children both at home and away from home and that traditionally oriented fathers disciplined for a larger number of reasons and used a smaller variety of punishments. The methods used, however, do not permit any clear conclusions to be made, since the fathers report both the attitude and the practice data.

Schaefer and Bell (1958) have reviewed the methodological problems and conceptual ambiguities of previous parent-attitude scales and attempted to profit from these errors in developing their Parental-Attitude Research Instrument (PARI). A variety of concepts was selected from previous studies; and attitude scales of five to ten items were developed, tested for reliability, and used for comparative measurement of populations of mothers of differing education. The final scale consists of 23 subscales of five items each. A factor analysis is also reported (Schaefer and Bell, 1957); this yields five relatively independent factors, which overlap in part with the factor analysis of the Fels Parent Behavior Scales (Roff, 1949).

An interesting methodological issue is revealed by the contrasting findings of Helper (1958) and Jourard and Remy (1955). Helper obtained parent evaluations of junior-high-school children on dimensions of favorability and acceptance. The children made self-evaluations on comparable scales. The relations between the parents' evaluations of the children and the children's self-evaluations were quite low in contrast to the findings of Jourard and Remy. In Jourard and Remy's study the child reported both the self and the parent evaluation, and this may account for the high relationships found. As Helper points out, however, the children's reports may actually be more accurate measures. That is, the parent's behavior may reveal attitudes that the children perceived and report but which the parents do not acknowledge.

Cass (1952a) reports a study which attempts to link parent attitudes to parent control techniques, parent-child conflict, and the child's identification with the parent. Mothers and their teenage children answered similar attitude questionnaires, and the mother also answered a second questionnaire about her child's attitudes. One of the parent variables, mother's "awareness" of the child, was taken as the extent to which her estimates of the child's responses to the questionnaire agreed with the child's actual responses. Identification was measured in terms of the degree of agreement between the mother's own responses and the child's responses. Parent control scores were computed from questionnaires in which the children rated parental practices in a number of areas. An incomplete sentence test was used to measure parent-child conflict. The predictions were that there would be a positive relationship between the mother's awareness of the child's attitudes and the child's identification with the mother, that the relationship between awareness and identification would be higher for mothers and girls than for mothers and boys, and that low awareness and high control by the mothers would be associated with high parent-child conflict. On the whole, the predictions were supported by the data.

Some of the problems in making the jump from parent attitudes to child personality are illustrated in a study reported by Harris, Gough, and Martin (1950) in which data were obtained on child-rearing opinions and practices from mothers of children who scored high and low on an ethnic prejudice test. Parent responses were subdivided into five a priori scales: authoritarianism, permissiveness, parent-child affective closeness, parental rigidity, and "general good judgment." Very few relationships were found between these parental indices and ethnic prejudice in the children.

An interesting attempt to measure parents' achievement expectations for children is the study by Little and Cohen (1951). Thirty asthmatic and 30 nonasthmatic children, matched for age, intelligence and school placement, were present with their mothers in a target-shooting task. Before each performance, the mother wrote down her expectations of the child's performance; then the child stated his goal. The mothers of the asthmatic children had higher achievement expectations, as did their children. This method of obtaining parent and child expectations in a specific and immediate laboratory situation offers many advantages over the usual techniques of obtaining reports about general values. Distortions should be minimized both by the specificity of the verbal report and by the imminence of the child's actual performance.

## OVERT PARENTAL BEHAVIOR PATTERNS

Increasing attention is being paid to the importance and complexity of measuring parent behavior and parent-child interaction. In part, this growing interest probably stems from the rather low level of success in making direct linkages between parent personality, values, and attitudes and child personality and adjustment; and, in part, it probably reflects the theoretical and methodological interest in moving from correlational studies to more process-oriented studies of socialization. Direct observation of parent-child interaction is still rare in the research literature, as compared to the number of studies in

which categories of parental behavior are derived from parent reports or from child reports. In this section we will take up studies that use parent reports of behavior and those that use direct observations. Studies using children's reports are taken up in the following section.

***Parent Reports on Parent Behavior.*** One of the fullest questionnaires on parent behavior is that used by Radke (1946) in her attempt to link parent authority to the behavior and attitudes of young children. Each parent responded to a questionnaire of more than 100 items relating to parent practices regarding authority and discipline. Some of the items included parent perceptions of the child's responses. An oral questionnaire was used with the children, in which many of the items paralleled those on the parent questionnaire. In addition, the children were given two projective tests—one in which responses were made to pictures of pleasant and unpleasant parent-relationship situations and the other, a doll play procedure. There were also three experimental situations in which adults used different degrees of authority to get the child to comply with orders. Independent behavioral observations of the children were also obtained from teachers. Several trends appear, such as a relationship between restrictive and autocratic home discipline and the child's being passive and unpopular. However, the various steps of potential linkage—between parent-behavior report, parent perceptions of children, children's perceptions of parents, child projective-test performance, and child-behavior patterns—are explored without any central hypotheses about the processes involved.

Watson (1957) constructed a "How I am bringing up my child" questionnaire with which he obtained multiple-choice responses from parents about their ways of handling 35 common parent-child interaction situations. The responses were scored along a continuum from highly permissive to enforcing strict obedience. Fathers showed consistently higher strictness, but there was also a great deal of agreement between husbands and wives. Using only the children at the extreme ends of the strictness-permissiveness scale, the parent practice scores were related to personality and behavior dimensions of the children, as obtained from projective tests, observations of a free-play period, questionnaires on child perceptions of home discipline, and school behavior ratings by teachers. Six of the investigator's nine hypotheses relating parent behavior to child attitudes and behavior were confirmed. No doubt part of this success was achieved because extreme groups were compared, but credit should also be given to the care with which comprehensive reports on a single carefully chosen dimension were obtained from the parents.

Since the pioneering study of Levy (1928), a number of investigators have interviewed parents for reports on feeding, weaning, and early training practices and attempted to link these data to child behavior and personality. Thurstone and Mussen (1951) faced the double methodological problem of mail questionnaires and retrospective reporting in their study of child-rearing

practices used by mothers of college-age students. The attempt was made to link mother reports on feeding and weaning to measures of oral personality traits derived from TAT responses, but the findings are inconclusive. Maslow and Szilagyi-Kessler (1946) also used retrospective reports in seeking information about breast-feeding practices. Although they used interviews rather than self-administered questionnaires, their interviewers were college students, and it may be that for data of this sort questionnaires would have been preferable to using such youthful interviewers.

The studies of Wittenborn (1956), Miller and Swanson (1958), Sears, Maccoby, and Levin (1957) and Sewell, Mussen, and Harris (1955) are all illustrations of the use of carefully developed interview schedules to secure data on early training practices from parental reports. The quantitative rating scales used by Sears, Maccoby, and Levin and the intercorrelation cluster technique used by Wittenborn are good examples of the sensitive quantification of parental-behavior reports. The Sears, Maccoby, and Levin study is an impressive effort to quantify theory-derived dimensions of parent child-rearing practices and interpret the meaning of these dimensions for the process of socialization. However, they face the difficult methodological problem of not having an independent source of data concerning the child response variables. Sears et al. (1953), in an earlier study, related mothers' reports about child-rearing practices to independent measures of the child's behavior in classrooms and in standardized doll-play situations. Wittenborn, working with parents and older children (5-to-9-year-olds), used a promising multiple choice "Social Reaction Interview" with the children. The instructions were, "Let's play a game of pretending. I'll tell you what happens and you tell me all the things you would do." Then followed a series of situations to assess the dimensions of dependency, aggression, submission, sympathy, perceived strictness of training, fears, likes, and dislikes. Because all of Wittenborn's subjects were adopted children, he had the unusual opportunity to explore "heredity-free" relationships, although there are problems of selective placement. His findings are consistent with the majority of other investigators in finding moderate and scattered relations between child-rearing practices and independent measures of child variables.

One fact of great methodological, as well as theoretical, importance seems to be documented by the studies of Milton (1958), Sewell, Mussen, and Harris (1955) and Miller and Swanson (1958): intercorrelations among child-rearing practices are low. It seems probable that more genotypic psychological variables, which capture the more general and underlying meanings of child-rearing practices, need to be conceptualized and measured to make fruitful progress in linking early child-rearing experiences to later child personality.

Among the studies that start from behavior reports by parents and probe through shorter "jumps" in the socialization process sequence is a study by Dreyer (1959). Dreyer scored mother interviews for degree of "power assertion" and other parent behaviors used in handling the child's "dependency behavior." These parent-behavior measures were linked to the child's perception of authority as obtained from a picture-story test, level of aspiration as shown on a task devised by Sears and Levin, and behavior ratings made by nursery-school teachers. Significant relations were obtained between parental power assertion and the child's perception of adult authority figures as controlling rather than nurturant and as not being a source of help and support. Adult-oriented perceptions of the child were in turn related to the child's perception of himself as having difficulty in handling problem situations. These self perceptions of the child were found to relate significantly to low levels of aspiration in the behavior situation. Finally, low level of aspiration related to teacher ratings of low level of aspiration, fearfulness, lack of flexibility, and lack of popularity with other children.

An interesting attempt to obtain objective data from parent interviews is the method, first suggested by Nowlis (1952), of using detailed accounts of all parent-child interactions occurring in a single day. This technique has been used in a study of parent-influence techniques reported by Sigel et al. (1957), and by Hoffman (1957, 1960). The main part of the interview consists of the parent's describing in great detail everything that took place between him and the child throughout the day preceding the interview. For mothers, a randomly selected weekday was used; for fathers, both a weekday and a Sunday. The interviewer probed to fill in the continuity of all action sequences involving the parent and child. This kind of interview seemed to make considerable progress in coping with the three problems of forgetting, withholding of information, and unconsciously motivated distortions. The interviews were taped, transcribed, and coded for specific behavior categories. In addition, child observations were made in the nursery school. Great care was taken to have the child data collected and coded by individuals who had no contact with the parent material. In this way it was possible to confirm, in a meaningful way, hypotheses relating the reported behavior of the parents to the observed behavior of the children.

Another contribution to the study of parent-behavior patterns is the analysis by Brim (1954) of the process of innovation of a new parent-behavior pattern in child rearing. During a first interview with mothers who were having feeding problems with their children, data were collected on the methods they used. These were coded into aggressive, intermediate, and persuasive modes of feeding behavior. A common stimulus situation was introduced, which involved advice by an expert, to induce all mothers toward a more permissive behavior pattern during the eating period. Some mothers tried the new behavior and maintained it long enough so that the behavior of the child changed; other mothers tried the new behavior but gave up; and others never tried the new behavior. The differences in change of behavior pattern were successfully linked to perceived support by the husband, concern about the child's response, motivation for the current behavior pattern, influences from other sources, and prestige of the expert who had advised the behavior change. In this study some of the basic interpersonal and motivational aspects of parent-behavior patterns are brought into clear relief, and the interdependence of parent behavior and child response is highlighted in a situation in which causation can be studied without ambiguity about what is antecedent and what is consequent.

In eliciting information from parents about emotionally laden behavior situations, several investigators have explored the possibility of using less direct projective procedures. But there are serious difficulties for the investigator in knowing whether the respondent is using the projective situation to report actual behavior patterns or to express attitudes that underlie behavior patterns. Morgan and Gaier (1957) used a series of ten picture cartoons of situations leading to punishment of the child by his parents. For each picture, the respondent was asked whether or not this ever happened in his own experience, how the parent and child behaved when it did happen, and how they felt about it. Jackson (1956) used a series of 11 hypothetical situations involving parents with children (e.g., "glancing into your bedroom, you notice your 12-year-old daughter taking money from your purse"). The parents were asked to indicate what they would do in each situation, and the responses were coded along a dimension from "little pressure toward conformity" to "great pressure toward conformity." Differences were noted between the responses of the fathers and mothers, but no attempt was made to link parental behavior derived in this fashion to child variables.

*Direct Observation of Parent Behavior.* Probably the most extensive work on the assessment of parent behavior has been done in the development and use of the Fels Parent Behavior Rating Scales. This battery of rating scales was developed by Champney (1941) and modified for research purposes by Baldwin and his colleagues (1945, 1948, 1949). The procedure is a mixture of direct observation and inferences made by a home visitor in a series of visits. The observations of the mother-child interactions are informal rather than standardized, and the ratings of behavior dimensions are based partly on supplementary material obtained verbally from the mother. On the basis of the intercorrelation matrices that were obtained and from their theoretical interests, the investigators selected several parent-behavior syndromes, e.g., democracy in the home, acceptance of the child, indulgence-protectiveness, control, and activity level. These were linked with varying degrees of success to child behavior, as rated in a nursery-school situation. Baldwin (1948) makes an important contribution by showing that a difference in the total pattern of child behavior results from a difference in one of the major dimensions of parent behavior. A statistical derivation of the underlying parental-behavior dimensions in the Fels scales, using factor analytic procedures, has been reported by Roff (1949). A replication of the design used by Baldwin and his associates was done in Australia by Pentony (1956), who reports that similar relations between parent behavior and child behavior were found. This kind of research helps map out some of the dimensions needed for further investigation, but it is limited because of the lack of theory about intervening processes.

The studies of Merrill Bishop (1946, 1951) and Moustakas, Sigel, and Schalock (1956) are good illustrations of the few systematic efforts to make direct observation studies of parent-child interaction. Bishop observed mothers interacting with their preschool children in a standardized activity setting outside of the home. Her observation categories were developed around the theory that mother-behavior influences child-learning through the offering of rewards, incentives, and punishments, through the facilitation or inhibition of certain activities, and through direct and indirect influence attempts. A series of direct links were made between mother-behavior patterns and child-initiation and response behavior. The high degree of individuality of the interactive behavior patterns of the various parent-child pairs suggests that there may be considerable unconscious collusion between parent and child in developing reciprocal response patterns.

Moustakas, Sigel, and Schalock use an observation system with eight precoded dimensions of parent-child interaction, which were tested in the nursery-school playroom and in the home. There are at least two problems in the use of such systematic quantitative procedures of which these writers show full awareness. One is that the schedule leaves the investigator without any analysis of the content of communication between parent and child. The other is the problem of utilizing the postural cues and facial expressions that have become part of a communication pattern between parent and child.

Crandall et al. (1958) report a study linking parent-child interaction to the behavior of the child with peers and adults in other situations. For children of two different age levels, they related ratings of the mothers' rewarding of compliance and punishing of noncompliance in their children to observations of social interactions with adults and peers in a nursery-school and a day-camp situation. Furthermore, they showed different connections between mother behavior and child behavior at the different age levels. With such data, it is possible to begin to think with some degree of confidence about the meaning and impact of the socialization sequence through time in the development of child-behavior patterns. A great deal could be added to this kind of design by securing data from the children concerning their perceptions of and their feelings about parental expectations and behaviors.

Although most of the work on systematic observation of parent-child interaction has been with the preschool ages, the reports of Brody (1956) and Escalona and her collaborators (1953) illustrate the growing sophistication about securing psychologically meaningful "parent-practice" data by observation of the interaction between mothers and infants. Also Strodtbeck's "revealed difference" observation procedure (1954, 1958) is an important step toward improving direct observations of parent-child interaction with older children.

Brody used behavioral observations and was able to classify mothering behavior toward infants into four patterns based on the dimensions of sensitivity, consistency, and attentiveness. As she explores the degree to which the mother's behavior pattern and the infant's behavior pattern complement one another, Brody faces thoughtfully the difficulties of interpreting whether the mother's behavior pattern is a stable source of influence to which the infant is adapting or whether infant patterns of need and activity stimulate the development of adaptive mothering patterns. This is a perennial issue that suggests the importance of starting with mother-behavior patterns toward previous children, independent personality assessment, and a clear conceptualization of predictions to the pattern of interaction with the new infant.

Strodtbeck has discovered that families accept, indeed even enjoy, the standardized discussion situation that he "imports" into the home for quantitative study of family decision making. This observation procedure, discussed elsewhere in this chapter, yields scores for interaction of parents with each other and for each of them with their child. Methodological work is needed on the extent to which the data secured in these limited interaction situations is representative of a wider range of family interactions.

Although parent behavior is not the focus of their work, Barker and Wright (1949, 1951, 1954) have made a major contribution to the direct observation of family life in their studies of the child's psychological ecology. Their continuous observation of children through the day is evidence of the readiness of families to collaborate in direct observation studies. These data should provide a point of reference for future studies that will attempt to use more focused observation schedules and sampling procedures.

## CHILD'S ORIENTATION TOWARD PARENTS AND SIBLINGS

This is perhaps the broadest level in the causal sequence schema, since it includes the child's perception of the family as well as his evaluative reactions. It is also a kind of bridge between the family as a stimulus situation for the child and the child as a product of the family. The only child-response variables that we will focus on are those where the response is the child's perceptions of the family, particularly of his parents' behaviors and attitudes toward him. These perceptions might be conceived of as objective or subjective material. In cases in which the child reports the number of children in the family the response can usually be taken as objective fact, but when the child reports about the discipline patterns in his family the material is more likely to be subjective. However, even in such areas child reports may often provide valid objective data. We have already pointed out the possible advantages of child reports in our comparison of the Helper and the Jourard and Remy studies, and we take this point up again in a later section. The child's perception of the family, in any case, is an important level in the process sequence, and we have already mentioned several studies in which the research used, or might well have used, such material as the intervening variable

between the family situation and the child's behavior.

A number of studies employ the child's perception of parent behavior as the independent variable. Sometimes it is an older child or an adult trying to recall his childhood. In this case, the problems of retrospective reporting mentioned earlier apply, although there is also the possible advantage of the decreased involvement, in that history is being described rather than current happenings.

Probably the earliest research of this kind is reported by MacKinnon (1938) in a study comparing two college-student groups of violators and nonviolators of prohibitions in a test situation. Questionnaire reports were obtained from each subject concerning early parent-child relations, including the types of punishment experienced and the roles of fathers and mothers as disciplinarians. These responses were related to behavior in the experimental situation. The studies by Henry (1956, 1957), already mentioned, deal with similar variables and also use the reports of young adults.

Kohn and Clausen (1956) interviewed schizophrenic adults and a matched group of normals to obtain data on the patterns of parental authority and affection experienced in childhood. These investigators were able to check their data in some cases by interviewing siblings and in other cases by interviewing the subjects' parents. The resulting corroboration, the consistency of the findings, and their agreement with previous research suggest that retrospective reports about parent behavior may have objective as well as subjective validity.

Kagan (1956) obtained perceptions of which parent was more "friendly," punitive, and dominant. He found that both boys and girls perceived their mothers as friendlier and their fathers as more punitive and dominant but that the older children were more likely than the younger to view the same-sex parent as more punitive and dominant. In discussing whether these reports are fact or fantasy, Kagan points out, on the one hand, that the children's comments seemed to indicate that they were reporting what they felt should be the case rather than what actually was. For example, when stating that the father was dominant, they might add "because he has to work for a living." On the other hand, Kagan points out that the perception of the same-sex parent as more threatening is consistent with other data based on interviews with mothers.

Other studies using children's perceptions of parents' current behavior include those by Radke (1946) and Brown, Morrison, and Couch (1947). Radke used an extensive 53-item interview with preschool children and compared these responses to a questionnaire administered to mothers. The results indicated that "In those questions where desirability or adherence to standards entered in, almost without exception the parent represented himself in the direction of desirability, and the child represented the parents in a less favorable or 'harder' light." In the same study Radke discovered that the parents perceived their own parents as stricter than they themselves were.

Brown, Morrison and Couch developed an extensive Family Relations Questionnaire for use with children as young as 10. Some of the major parent-behavior patterns reported were participation in work and play, approval and disapproval, role in decision making, trust of the child, interparental relations, and symptoms of tension. Children responded to questions on a five-point scale from "very often" to "almost never." These reports on parental behavior were linked to personality-test data on the children and ratings by adult leaders and peers. The investigators made an effort to check the validity of the children's reports by comparing them with independent ratings of some of the families. They conclude that the children were reporting with a high degree of objective validity.

Hawkes, Burchinal, and Gardner (1957) obtained descriptions of parents from a sample of preadolescent children with a series of questions, such as "Do your parents praise you for doing a job well?", with multiple choices from "always" to "never" to be checked.

Lippitt and Hoffman (1959) have developed two reporting procedures for use with elementary-school children. One is a "Who does it?" test, in which a series of behaviors (e.g., "praises," "blames," "scolds," "laughs") are presented, and the child checks a multiple-choice form that includes mother, father, teacher, friend, brother, and sister. Responses to certain clusters of words are combined to yield scores, such as the extent to which the mother is associated with positive affect. A second questionnaire procedure entitled, "Some Kids' Parents" presents paired descriptions of parental expectations on a number of conceptual dimensions. The child checks the description that is most like his parents. The data from these two types of parent-behavior reports have been linked to independent observations of behavior with peers and teachers at school.

Gray (1959) uses Osgood's format to present young children with a series of paired adjectives representing either end of a seven-point scale (e.g., from "tired" to "full of pep"). The child checks a description of himself and of his parent. Perceived similarity to parents is used as a measure of parental identification and linked to measures of adjustment based on peer ratings, a manifest anxiety measure, and a masculinity-femininity scale.

Lyle and Levitt (1955) use an indirect procedure to obtain reports from young children on parental punitiveness. This involves a series of incomplete sentences such as, "To make me do what they want, my parents _____ _____ _____." Attributed parental punitiveness, measured in this way, was successfully linked to attitude measures of ethnocentricism-authoritarianism and to projective measures of the child's punitiveness.

Using an even freer projective procedure, Kagan (1958) obtained stories about stimulus pictures from boys in the 6-to-10-year-old range. These were scored for hostility of parent figures and dependency of child figures. The perceptions of parents measured in this way were linked to aggressive and non-aggressive behavior patterns of the children, as rated by teachers.

Alexander (1952) has standardized a series of parent-child pictures, the Adult-Child Interaction Test, for use as a TAT-type test with children to obtain data concerning perceptions of parents and parent-child relations. Sears (1948) and Stolz et al. (1954) have used projective procedures to secure reports of parent behavior from very young children. Sears used observation of a doll play situation. Stolz and her collaborators presented stories for completion and also dramatic play situations with dolls calling for completion of a series of eleven structured situations.

Ausubel et al. (1954) measured children's perceptions of their parents' evaluations of them along the dimensions of acceptance-rejection and intrinsic-extrinsic valuation. A projective test was constructed from several existing ones, such as the Children's Apperception Test and the Blacky Test. Alternative interpretations of the pictures dealing with the dimensions under investigation were presented to the child. Story-completion items were similarly administered, giving the child a choice between two alternative endings. In addition, a Parent Attitude Rating Scale, consisting of parent-attitude and behavior items reflective of acceptance-rejection and intrinsic-extrinsic evaluation, was answered by the children. Of the three measures, only the last was considered sufficiently reliable for use in the investigation. Using this measure, the child's perception of the parents as valuing him extrinsically was related to his sense of omnipotence, goal-frustration tolerance, ideational dependence, and emotional immaturity.

Lippitt et al. (1959) have used a procedure in which children from the third grade through high school filled in the segments of circles with plus or minus signs to represent the distribution of positive or negative characteristics in themselves as they feel each parent sees them and as they see themselves. This measure of perceived parental evaluation has been linked to independent measures of parent behavior and to child attitudes and behavior outside the family.

In addition to the studies of the child's perception of the family, we might have taken up studies of child evaluations such as that by Cooper and Blair (1959), which relates college students' responses on a parent-evaluation scale to the perceived similarity of parent and child values, and that by Mussen (1950), which relates negative feeling toward parents as assessed by a TAT to prejudice and resistance to change in prejudice. We might have gone into some of the family reference group research, such as the work of Rosen (1955). However, although these are important family studies, the conceptualizations involved carry us over into studies in which the child's personality and behavior are the independent variables and beyond the point where the family provides the special focus. The problems of dealing with child reports of this sort, however, are taken up at a more general level in the following section.

## Methodological Problems

We have discussed the conceptualization of those aspects of the family that are seen as important for the child and have taken up several examples of concept measurement. In this section we will take up some general methodological problems that seem particularly acute in such studies.

### ACCESSIBILITY OF DATA

An early problem the researcher must face is that of deciding how to find the families he wishes to study. Research projects often call for special groups of families, such as two-child families, families with adolescent children, working-mother families, and families of children born while their fathers were away in military service. How does one go about locating such families?

First, there is often an agency or organization that has contact with the particular group desired. For example, schools are a good starting point for getting families that include children of a particular age. The contact here is first with the child and then with his family. A nursery school for working mothers, an adoption agency, a juvenile detention home, and a maternity clinic are examples of sources for locating families with particular characteristics.

Another important source is in the use of existing records. Births, marriages, divorces, and crimes are recorded for each county. Christensen and Rubinstein (1956) used county records in Tippecanoe County, Indiana, to locate families in which the mother was pregnant at the time of marriage. By comparing marriage records to birth records, they were able to select those cases in which a child was born less than seven months after the marriage. They then located the couples through directories and interviewed them. Although their particular interest was in marriage adjustment, this same technique might be used to study the effects of premarital pregnancy on attitudes and behavior of parents.

Hospitals keep incomplete but often helpful records. "Twin" studies sometimes locate subjects through hospital records of twin births for any given year. Kaplan (1958) used hospitals to study effects of a crisis situation on families, the crisis situation being a premature birth.

Locating families through agencies having more or less recent contact with them has an advantage in that current addresses may be available. This is less likely to be true when records are used, since they often refer to events in the past. For example, locating school-age twins through their teachers and principals is much more efficient than using records. Furthermore, the agency's rapport with the subjects may facilitate cooperation (although sometimes it may hinder the openness of responses). The agency may also have on-going records from which the researcher can select particular subjects from its total group of clients.

A third method of securing subjects is to select a geographical area in which the possibility of locating the desired subjects is maximized. For example, if the researcher were interested in locating families representing a particular ethnic group, and there were no existing groups or organization through which they could be reached, he might use informants or census data to find areas in which these families were concentrated. This method is, of course, less reliable and more time consuming, since many ineligible families would have to be interviewed in the process of locating the appropriate ones.

Finally, there is an important method for locating subjects that can be used alone or in combination with the foregoing methods. This involves gathering data on more subjects than will actually be included in the study. The data collected can be minimal, designed only to determine whether or not the respondent has the qualifications required for him to be selected for further study. If the final data are relatively simple to collect, it might be more efficient in the long run to gather the complete data at the first contact, even though only the responses from the selected subjects are to be analyzed. Despite the disadvantage of requiring the collection of more data than is needed, this method has two important advantages. First, it may well be the only way of locating clusters of families that cannot be reached through agencies, records, or areas of residence. Second, it does not impose limitations with respect to the representativeness of samples as extreme as the other methods. Statistical generalization is limited to that population from which persons had a chance of being included in the sample. If the original contact were Public School No. 2, only families with a child attending that school had the possibility of being included. In Christensen and Rubinstein's study, only those who were married in Tippecanoe County, whose first child was born there, and who could be located for study had the possibility of being included. These limitations are not always serious, as we shall see later, but they are usually undesirable. The gathering of data from many subjects can follow standard population-sampling techniques and as such permit generalizing findings to a broader population and drawing conclusions less subject to error from sample bias.

Once the subjects have been located, the researcher faces another obstacle, one which stems from the aura of privacy that surrounds family life. The high value on family privacy may provide a barrier at three points:

1. Agencies may be reluctant to cooperate in the interest of protecting the privacy of the families with which they are dealing.

2. The family members themselves may not wish to reveal what goes on in the home and thus refuse to participate.

3. Even when cooperation has been agreed upon, the family members may hold certain aspects of their home life as inviolate.

The first of these problems sometimes appears to be the greatest, for organizations may be more protective of their clients' privacy than the individuals themselves. Organizational personnel sometimes assume more naïveté and even hostility toward research on the part of the clients than actually exists. School systems that are quite willing to allow researchers to administer personality tests, sociometrics, and even experiments—when the child is the only one being studied—will often be unwilling to cooperate with a study of the child's family. Even if the child is the only one in the family to be interviewed, the school may insist that if the interview touches on family life the parents must give permission beforehand. Sometimes school policy forbids giving out parents' addresses, and the original contact with the parent may have to be made in a note delivered by the child. In one school system, in which the parents' names and addresses could not be given out, the authors were allowed to give the children letters in stamped envelopes, which they addressed to their parents as an exercise in penmanship class and the school mailed.

The protectiveness of organizations is even more of a problem when social work agencies having standard obligations to protect the privacy of their clients are involved. In general, when the head of an agency is not convinced that there is something to be gained, for himself, his organization, or society, he will not risk the possibility of censure by his client. If the proposed study might be seen—even by just a few—as a violation of privacy, he is undertaking a risk. Therefore, he must be "sold" on the study before he will agree to cooperate.

One of the difficulties with limited cooperation is that it intensifies the problem of sample bias mentioned earlier. For example, in the case in which parents have to return permission blanks beforehand, bias is introduced, for some parents will not give permission or will forget to return their forms, and these persons as a group may be different from those from whom permission is received. Furthermore, it may not be possible to identify these differences and thus to appraise the nature of the bias. If the school permits the researcher to ask the children whose parents did not return permission blanks a few simple questions, such as father's occupation, mother's working status, and whether both parents live at home, these nonreturns can at least be sociologically identified.

This brings us to the second problem —that family members themselves may be reluctant to discuss family relationships. Resistance to research cooperation has often been greatly exaggerated, and the willingness of most subjects to discuss personal matters with a stranger is often a source of amazement even to the seasoned researcher. Kinsey et al. (1948) have shown that it is possible to get people to discuss their sexual behavior. Several studies have shown the willingness of respondents to take the researcher into their homes—actually as well as descriptively. (See the earlier section on direct observations of parent behavior.) One extreme example of the willingness to cooperate is shown in the work of Soskin (1959). Soskin obtained continuous recordings of the conversations of young couples during a week's vacation at a summer resort. The resort vacation was financed by the research project in exchange for the respondents' agreement to wear small tape recorders. The couples were allowed to disconnect the recorder at any time if they felt the invasion of privacy was too great, but this was done rarely,

and the respondents seemed to forget about the apparatus.

There are always some respondents who are reluctant to cooperate—those who hold such a high value on privacy that no intrusion is allowed. If the representativeness of the sample is at all important, these nonrespondents become a concern, and special efforts must often be made to obtain data from them or at least to identify them so that the limitations of generalizing from the research can be known. Although a high value on privacy may at times be the actual reason for refusal, the prevalence of a value on the sanctity of the home makes it likely that some people will use this value to clothe less acceptable reasons. For example, the actual conscious or unconscious reasons for refusing to participate in a study of family life might be anxiety about how good a job one is doing as wife, mother, husband, or father. This makes the problem of the lack of cooperation by all subjects more crucial because a bias may thereby be introduced into the sample.

There is another way in which the privacy of family life affects the individual's cooperation. A man's home is not only a castle defended against researchers but it is also defended against his neighbors. As such, there is a great deal of pluralistic ignorance about family life. A mother may know that she herself sometimes loses her temper and screams at her child, but she does not know that the lovely young mother across the street does the same thing. Since each keeps the information within the family, each considers herself inadequate. When there is communication, most people will find that others also fall short of the ideal, and they will be less ashamed of their own shortcomings. However, because there is a romanticized ideal about family life, because most families fall short of this ideal, and because of family privacy, many areas of shame exist and cause potential respondents to be inappropriately reluctant to expose themselves to the researcher.

Similar points can be made about the inaccessibility of data once the subjects have been obtained. For example, the researcher may be allowed to make observations in the home, yet be excluded from many kinds of interaction. This means that he may not be able to obtain any data on certain activities. An even more serious problem concerns the bias that results when the researcher does not take account of the possibility that he is being excluded from certain kinds of interactions and that this exclusion does not take place equally in all families.

Although these problems may be paramount in studying the family, their solutions are not essentially different from those employed in studying any area in which organizational and subject cooperation are necessary. When approaching an organization, it is important to call upon the right level first. Sometimes there will be a person specifically in charge of research. The organization will need to be assured of the researcher's professional competence, experience, and willingness to consider the needs of the organization. Often the researcher can provide some service to the organization, such as including questions that may be of use to

it or making available a report of some of the findings (with the anonymity of the individual respondent being preserved.) Most important, the significance of the study should be stressed. Usually the organizations approached will be directly concerned with children or family life, and the study should be of special interest to them.

It is usually beneficial to work with persons in the organizational structure when planning the study. Not only will such involvement help rapport, but there may be many things the researcher can gain from the planning sessions, since the persons in the organization are likely to have valuable information about the population to be studied and about many relevant aspects of the situation.

In gaining subject cooperation, a personal contact is better than one made by mail or telephone. In addition, the anticipation of being a research subject is ordinarily more negative than the actual experience. Therefore, to approach the respondent at the time one is ready to begin is sometimes more effective than asking for cooperation in advance.

Regarding the motivation of the subjects to cooperate, the pluralistic ignorance and the general anxiety around the child-rearing area operate in the researcher's favor in some respects, just as they operate against him in others. Because of parents' lack of familiarity with the manner in which other families interact and because of their extreme interest, subjects will quickly see the importance of a study in this area and will therefore be motivated to cooperate. Promising the subject a report on some of the findings will add incentive, enhance involvement, and help make him feel a part of something important. Even though the reluctance to participate may be motivated by a need for privacy, the subject's feeling of making a contribution may be as helpful in gaining cooperation as the assurances of anonymity.

The problem of adequate motivation is especially important when the study requires the cooperation of all the members of a family, for example, when they are to be interviewed or observed simultaneously. This requirement is often not in accord with the normal routines of family life. It is an inconvenience to the subjects and thus requires higher motivation than a study in which the researcher is able to adapt himself to the normal routines and time demands of the subject.

## THE FAMILY AS A SMALL GROUP

In many respects, studying the family is like studying other small groups, but it is distinct in a number of ways. First of all, although many small groups are relatively unstructured, each member in the family holds a different status. Status in the family is assigned primarily on the basis of sex and age, and only in the case of twins of the same sex does one find two members who are identical with respect to these characteristics. Because of this individuation of status and because of the small size of the group itself, the significance of each member is greater. Therefore, only families alike in composition are truly comparable.

How serious this lack of comparability is depends on the variables being studied. When the independent variable is itself some aspect of family structure, such as the ordinal position of the child, controlling on other aspects of family structure and considering more than one aspect at a time might be essential for highlighting effects. For example, the number of children in a family and the sex and age of each might need to be considered in a study dealing with the effects of sibling composition. An older sister is a very different influence on a child's development than an older brother or a younger sister. Being the second of two children is a very different experience from being the second of three or the youngest of more than two. The studies of Koch, mentioned earlier, are outstanding examples of structural controls.

Another characteristic of the family that distinguishes it from other small groups is that it has a history. The small group in the laboratory is usually newly created. Small informal groups within organizational settings, social groups, and committees may have some history, but it is of short duration as compared to families. Having a history means that many variables important for understanding a given unit of interaction are not visible to the outside observer or even available to participants. In this sense, the observer of family life is like the observer of a total society. Lack of familiarity with the group's history may cause the observer to misinterpret the significance of a given unit of behavior, just as would be so if an anthropologist studied a society in which the history and traditions were unfamiliar to him. What seems to be hostile behavior may not be hostile in the context of the family's interaction over the years and their particular language forms, mannerisms, and affective states. What seems to be an independent, power-assertive decision on the part of one member of the family may have covertly, perhaps unconsciously, taken account of the wishes of each of the other family members as they are known from the past history of the group.

The importance of family history in understanding the present interrelationships comes out clearly in the study by Spiegel and Kluckhohn referred to earlier (Spiegel, 1957). Partly because of their sensitivity to this problem, they have intensively studied the 18 families in their sample over a four-year period. They have utilized behavioral observations, participant observation, intensive clinical interviews, and questionnaires. Although their analysis is an ahistorical structural-functional one, they have used their knowledge of significant past events to grasp fully the current family interrelationships.

However, the sheer volume of data and the prolonged period of field work needed may make this wholistic kind of study impractical for most research projects. As always, the first step is to be aware of the problem and the second is to evaluate how serious it is for the particular study. The fact that the history of the group affects its present behavior and influences the relationship between independent and dependent variables is not in itself sufficient reason for complicating the research design.

A study need not take account of all the variance. On the other hand, if ignoring the historical context leads to mislabeling behavior and to superficiality, there is a real problem. This can often be handled, however, simply by supplementing behavioral measures with introspective reports by the actors. For example, an influence technique used by a parent on a child is very much affected by previous interactions between them, and the psychological meaning of the event to both may thus not be apparent from the behavior itself, but asking each of them about their thoughts and feelings in the situation may bring out as much of the missed context as the study requires.

## SOURCES OF DISTORTION IN VERBAL REPORTS

It is clear from the earlier section that the present authors differentiate the subjective from the objective family situation. This distinction is an important one. For example, several studies have found that the child will report his father as being a more active disciplinarian than will other members of the family (Kohn, 1959b; Lippitt and Hoffman, 1959). This exaggeration of the father's disciplinary functions may stem from several sources. The father's discipline may have been more severe if not more frequent; it may have been called forth at a more intense moment in the parent-child conflict, i.e., after the mother's attempts had already failed; it may have carried more authority behind it because of the perception of the father as a more powerful figure; it may have been less threatening because it did not involve the loss of love from the nuturant parent; it may have been exaggerated by the boy because of the Oedipal conflict. Whatever the reason for the perceptual distortion (assuming it is a distortion), if it is an honest report of a perception it will influence the child's behavior. Indeed, empirically it is likely to be more related to the child's personality and behavior than the actual discipline situation because it is closer in the process sequence. However, it is a subjective impression and not a measure of the actual discipline situation. Too often a stimulus-response theory about the effect of a parent action on the child is "tested" by using the child's subjective impression of the parent's action. For example, Henry (1956, 1957) uses subjective reports of parental discipline, and, though he is very careful to refer to them as children's perceptions rather than parent behavior, his theory is about parent behavior, not about children's perceptions. Furthermore, by using the same respondent to provide both independent and dependent variables, he risks the problems of variable contamination. The lure of the questionnaire, and particularly the single questionnaire, is one of the main reasons for the prevalence of family studies dealing with response syndromes rather than testing stimulus-response theories.

On the other hand, the lure of the questionnaire is realistically based. No other method of data collection is so economical. Furthermore, many of the problems involved in the use of the questionnaire or the interview stem from misuse rather than from intrinsic faults. Two common errors are made. One is the assumption that it is impossible to obtain objective material from verbal reports, and the second is that any verbal report is a legitimate subjective response. Neither of these assumptions is true, and in considering sources of distortion in verbal reports it will be clear that many apply equally, whether the researcher is interested in obtaining valid subjective or objective material.

*Deliberate Distortion.* Perhaps the most obvious form of verbal distortion occurs when the respondent does not accurately communicate what he consciously feels to be true. Deliberate falsification of this sort can exist whether the respondent is reporting an empirical fact, such as his annual income, or an emotional state, whether or not he is disappointed in his eldest son. The respondent may know the answer to both questions but refuse to communicate the true answer to the interviewer.

The need to present a desirable picture to others is especially great in matters concerning the family. It is not uncommon for married persons who have successfully communicated to their friends a picture of a happy marriage to announce suddenly that they are getting a divorce. The value on The Happy Family is so high that the family will carry on a masquerade for the outside world long after they have come to acknowledge the unpleasant facts to themselves. This is particularly true when the outsider is believed to be an expert. Parents are remarkably well informed about what a "good parent" is like. They are familiar with words like "togetherness" and "acceptance" and "love," and they are proud of their familiarity with these concepts. A person who is doing research on family life and parent-child relations is viewed as an expert on these matters and is someone whom one can impress with one's psychological sophistication and with the beauty of one's own family interactions. On the other hand, reporting undesirable aspects of one's family involves acknowledging one's own faults and the faults of other family members. Acknowledging one's own faults as a family member may involve confessing one's lack of competence, morality, and warmth. Acknowledging the faults of other family members violates the value of family loyalty.

There are many ways of handling the problem of conscious distortion. The most basic involve gaining the respondent's acceptance of the interview situation. The respondent must be convinced that his sincere response will be an important contribution, that the researcher will not pass judgment on him, that his responses will be anonymous, and that the interviewer is a pleasant person. The researcher must communicate both that the respondent is not the only one being interviewed and that his contribution is a very special one. These are the kinds of aims communicated by the word "rapport."

The wording of a question is also important in minimizing conscious distortion. There are several techniques for wording a question to make an otherwise unacceptable answer more palatable to the respondent. One common method, for example, is to make a statement before the actual question that indicates to the respondent that the answer he is about to give is perfectly acceptable and is shared with other persons. The following questions have been used by the authors:

Everyone in America, except for American Indians, can trace his family background to some other country. What would you say your nationality background is?

Most parents disagree sometimes about how the children should be handled. What are some of the things you and your husband sometimes don't agree about?

In both examples, the only purpose of the sentence preceding the actual question is to make the respondent feel freer to answer openly. The same technique of indicating that the respondent shares his situation with others can be used when a precoded list of answers is presented. In the "Some Kids' Parents" measure, mentioned earlier (Lippitt and Hoffman, 1959), the child reports parental expectations by indicating which of two positions his parents are likely to take. The child is given pairs of items such as the following:

*Some kids' parents* tell them they should try to do things the other kids want them to.
*Some kids' parents* tell them they shouldn't try to do things just because the other kids want them to.

By making each position one that others also held, it was felt that the child would be more likely to report his parents' position as he actually perceived it.

It is often important also in such precoded responses to word the alternatives as equal in attractiveness as possible without distorting the meaning. The position that seems more socially acceptable is toned down, and the socially unacceptable position is phrased as positively as possible. For example, the response, "Some kids' parents feel that children sometimes need to be spanked," is more acceptable than "Some kids' parents believe in spanking their children" (although, for isolating an extreme group, the latter might be preferable).

The position of items in a questionnaire is also important in setting the stage to encourage free communication. For example, an item that asks the child to describe something negative about his mother should be preceded by an item that allows the child to express positive attitudes. Often the researchers will include questions for the sole purpose of providing a favorable setting for the important questions that follow.

The use of indirect measures has already been mentioned and is often used to obtain freer communication about the child's family. In Douvan and Kaye's study of adolescent girls (1958), a modification of the Rosenzweig technique was used. In one item the subject was presented with a sketch showing a girl going out the door, parents sitting on a couch, and the girl saying, "I'm going over to Mary's house—all the girls are going to be there." The respondent was asked what the parents would say. The response presumably indicates something about the girl's perception of her own parents, but since it is not obvious to the respondent that this is the case the response may be less inhibited. Similarly, one might ask questions phrased in such terms as "What do most girls your age disagree with their parents about?" or "How do parents like you feel about . . . ?" Indirect measures do involve a problem in that it may be erroneous to infer that the response is a reflection of the respondent's own situation rather than an intellectual view of others or a wishful fantasy, but this can often be checked against other aspects of the total interview, and, in addition, indirect measures are at least useful for identifying salient areas in the family situation.

Hoffman (1957) suggests still another method for minimizing deliberate distortion. We have already described this interview, which has as its primary purpose the obtaining of objective data about parent-child interactions. By asking for extremely detailed descriptions of the behavior, deliberate distortion is minimized because the "set to recall details seems to result in a fragmentation of the event which weakens its Gestalt properties and thus divests it of much of the emotional meaning it would otherwise have." Thus the motivation to distort, both deliberately and through unconscious mechanisms, is less. In addition, the sheer task of recalling becomes so absorbing that the personal relevance of the material is lost to the respondent, but even if the motivation to distort persists it is extremely difficult to do so without detection when great detail is required.

The idea that breaking a pattern down to its insignificant parts avoids distortion is an important principle to employ in measurement construction and evaluation. This is the principle involved in the Wolfe measure and the Herbst measure already described. By asking specific questions and then combining them into an over-all measure, a more valid perception is obtained, assuming that these questions are sufficiently inclusive and representative. Respondents might hesitate to report, for example, that the father was highly active in household tasks conventionally thought of as feminine, but they might reveal this information if it were parceled out only in very small innocuous packages.

One final consideration in minimizing deliberate distortion involves the question of which family member should be the respondent. The Herbst measure, for example, was designed for children because Herbst felt that parents would distort responses by exaggerating the amount of joint parental action and mutual decision making. This measure was intended for obtaining objective material more than subjective and thus interest was simply in minimizing distortion. Since the information was accessible to all, the questionnaire was geared toward the ones least likely to distort. The relative naïveté of children made them, in this case, the best reporters.

In many studies the question of who shall report is predetermined by the theory. Thus, if one is predicting from a child perception of the family to a child behavior, the child is almost always the best reporter of his own perception. However, when the aim is to obtain objective data, the researcher should consider which family member would be least motivated to distort. Obviously, the least motivated persons are not always the best ones to use, for they may not have so great an opportunity to observe the situation, but occasionally the advantages of greater objectivity may be more important. For example, mothers are usually the reporters of their children's behavior rather than fathers. In addition to the fact that mothers are more available, it is usually felt that they are better informed. At least two studies (Sarason, 1958; Levitt, 1959) have shown that mothers are rather unreliable informants, and Sarason has found that fathers' descriptions of their children show a higher relationship to clinical appraisals than mothers' descriptions. The parental role is more salient to the mother's self concept than the father's, and it may be more important for her to communicate a positive picture to the "expert."

Sometimes it is possible to use more than one informant—interviewing respondents either separately or together. It should be pointed out, however, that family members are not independent reporters. Agreement represents consensus but not necessarily one arrived at by each independently. This is a problem when family members are interviewed separately and not simultaneously. The first person interviewed might discuss the topic with other family members before their interviews take place.

Bossard and Strodtbeck have already been mentioned as obtaining verbal reports on husband-wife relations by using relatives or friends of the family as informants. Although this technique is limited by the amount of knowledge friends have about intrafamily matters, it avoids to a considerable extent the problems of deliberate distortion.

*Nondeliberate Distortion.* Nondeliberate distortion can be classified into three general categories. The first involves unconscious distortion, in which the material is threatening and is therefore repressed. In this case the respondent's report is an honest communication of what he consciously believes to be true, but it is neither what is in fact true nor what at a deeper level he knows to be true. The second category involves distortion stemming from the respondent's having insufficient knowledge about the situation—either because he has had insufficient opportunity to observe or experience the relevant material or because the material was relatively trivial and has been forgotten. The third source of nondeliberate distortion is involved when the respondent has the information to report and is willing to report it, but there is a miscommunication between researcher and respondent.

It is not always possible to pinpoint the source of distortion. Take, for example, the Herbst "Who decides?" questions. If parents do report more joint deciding than is reported by children, it is quite possible that (1) this is deliberate distortion by parents in the direction of the more socially approved pattern, (2) it is an unconscious distortion of the existing asymmetric deciding pattern that is threatening to both parents, (3) the parents have more complete knowledge of the deciding process and know that what the child sees as a one-sided decision was actually discussed beforehand or was mutually decided and routinized before the child was born, or (4) certain ambiguities in the questionnaire lead adults and children to interpret the questions and the answer form somewhat differently. The greatest difficulties in interpreting data come when all four distortions are possible. It is therefore important that the researcher consider each of the four kinds beforehand and plan his research to minimize all unwanted distortions.

Distortion through unconscious motivation is not always undesirable, and some studies may call for only conscious perceptions of the family. Obtaining conscious material requires relatively straight, direct questions, whereas unconscious material involves the use of projective measures. The projective measure developed by Alexander (1952) focuses particularly on family interactions as does Blum's Blacky Test (1950), the Children's Apperception Test (Bellak and Bellak, 1949), and the Michigan Picture Test (Hartwell et al., 1951). Whether conscious or unconscious material is called for, it is important that all persons respond at the same level and that the researcher is clear about what this level is. A combination of responses is sometimes used for handling the latter problem. For example, a pattern of overidealization of parents in combination with repressed hostility can be inferred when more direct questions are answered with great praise of parents and indirect questions produce fantasies about disasters occurring to parents.

When objective data are required, unconscious distortion is as undesirable as deliberate distortion and some of the solutions suggested for the latter apply equally here—for example, asking questions that break up the Gestalt properties of an event, selecting respondents who would be less motivated to distort, and using more than one informant in a family.

Whereas both deliberate and unconscious distortion are motivated, cognitive distortion is not. A family may also be described differently by different members simply because each member experiences somewhat different aspects of it. The mother is usually home all day and the father is not. The parents are usually up after the children are asleep. Parents do not treat all their children exactly the same, and two persons do not perceive the same interaction identically. It is not surprising, then, that the correlations between different members' perceptions of their family are usually better than chance, but not high (Lippitt and Hoffman, 1959; Kohn, 1959a). When the Herbst measure was given to fathers, mothers, and preadolescent children, it was found that each tended to exaggerate his own relative participation in tasks (Lippitt and Hoffman, 1959), probably because each person is always a witness to his own acts but is not necessarily a witness to the acts of others. If the researcher is interested in perceptual material, this is not a problem. Even if the interest is in objective aspects of the family, but only relative scores are required, this may not be a serious problem *if it can be assumed that all reporters are distorting more or less equally and in the same direction.* However, when deciding which family member should be

the reporter and what one can ask of him, it is important to consider the opportunities for observation provided by the respondent's family role.

A closely related problem is that of forgetting. When adults are asked to recall their childhood or when parents report past interactions and previous attitudes toward their children, there is always the danger of inaccurate recall. Part of this may be psychologically motivated, but part may also be simply a matter of cognitive distortion. Asking about trivial experiences also invites forgetting. One way to collect data about trivial events is to ask respondents to keep a record each time they occur.

We have noted that deliberate distortion is always undesirable but that unconscious and cognitive distortion are not. Miscommunication is like the first —always undesirable. Whether a question is intended to yield subjective or objective data, it must communicate accurately. Too often a question is subject to different interpretations, and responses reflect neither differences in the situation nor in the perception but are answers to different questions. For example, if children were asked, "How often do you and your mother do things together?" some might interpret this question to include tasks and some, only social activities; some might interpret the question to mean "you and your mother alone," and some, to mean with and without other persons; some might include parallel behavior such as television-watching and some, only activities involving interaction. The answers would not be comparable or meaningful, and saying it is a respondent's perception—a subjective response—does not make it any more meaningful. Two respondents with precisely the same perception and evaluation of their interaction with their mothers, might respond differently because each has interpreted the question differently. When a vague question is to be asked, it should be followed by clarifying questions, such as in the above example, "What are these things you do together?" or "Do you wish you did more things with your mother?" The original answer may then take on meaning in the context of the later answers.

Even questions that seem simple, precise, and objective may be misinterpreted. It is therefore important to pretest all questions. "Are you employed?", for example, is not sufficiently clear to obtain information about current maternal employment. "Do you work outside your home for money at the present time?" *and* "How many hours a week?" may be necessary. Working mothers usually have a spasmodic work history, and thus the question is more ambiguous than might seem.

Prelisted response choices like "often," "sometimes," and "hardly ever" may also pose problems of communication, since the subject's reference group is unknown to the researcher. The purposes of most research are better served by specifying the reference group (e.g., "more often than most boys my age," "more often than others in my family," or "more often than I'd like") or, if more objectivity is desired, by using a list of specified frequencies such as "once a week."

Responses to open-ended questions are also capable of misinterpretation. The role of the interviewer in minimizing this is taken up by Kahn and Cannell (1957).

One special communication problem comes up in family studies when the research design calls for identical interviews with parents and children. In most studies subjects vary in intelligence and education, and it is difficult to construct questions that are comprehensible to the least educated but not overly simple to the more sophisticated and to avoid systematic distortion that stems from these differences. When the measure is to be used with adults and children, these difficulties are increased. Adults often cannot express their opinions in the simple terms that children can, and a questionnaire that communicates clearly to children might seem vague to adults and subject to varying interpretations. On the other hand, children often interpret questions more literally than adults, and this may be reflected in their answers. To compare the perceptions of parents and children, it might be more appropriate to vary the questionnaire forms in an effort to standardize the responses, rather than to standardize the questions and produce responses that differ because of question interpretation. To develop such a measure one might do pretests, using a modified form of Strodtbeck's "revealed difference" technique in which the mother, father, and child answer questionnaires separately and are then brought together to discuss their answers. In this way differences in interpretations and response sets can be studied for subsequent revision of the questionnaire.

## OBSERVATION
## OF FAMILY INTERACTION

Behavioral observations are one way to escape the difficulties of the distortion problem in verbal reports. They are usually considered a more valid means of obtaining objective data, although there are problems even here. We will discuss some of these difficulties as they occur in family studies, taking up first observations of natural interaction in the home. Then we will discuss a technique still quite new in family research —observations in artificially created situations either in the home or in the laboratory.

*Home Observations.* Behavioral observations in the home have been used for obtaining data that is objective and not filtered through the perceptions of family members. Three general criticisms have been leveled against this method: (1) the presence of the observer influences the interaction; (2) observations without introspective reports are insufficient for knowing what is in fact taking place; and (3) it is a costly way of obtaining data. We will not discuss the method of behavioral observation in any detail, since that is the special focus of another chapter, but only these difficulties as they affect the study of the child's family.

Certainly the observer is more obtrusive in the home than in other settings. Because the household normally includes few people and because of the private nature of the home, the presence of a stranger is apparent. Where there are many people, one more is less obvious than where there are normally only one or two other adults. In a setting in which strangers frequently pass by or in which a noninteracting person is an accepted part of the scene, as in certain factory settings, the observer can be absorbed into the normal course of events. But in the home the observer probably does influence the interaction. Even when, with time, the family adjusts to his presence, it is difficult to know whether they have become less self-conscious in that they have worked out patterns of interaction acceptable for the new situation or whether they have, in fact, returned to their usual patterns. Nevertheless, even if one assumes that the observer does influence the scene, how serious is this problem? How much can a family manage to conceal in this situation? The children in the family will be less affected than their parents, and, to the extent that their behavior is somewhat natural and the routine demands of the home continue, the influence of the observer may not be severe enough to invalidate the material.

The second problem, the possible need to supplement observations with introspective material, has been discussed earlier. The extent of this problem depends on the theory being studied and the inferences that are made from the observations. A theory about family life might deal only with behavioral interactions and treat the data at the behavioral level without inferring underlying affect states. In this case, no introspective reports are needed. However, if the variables deal with warmth, rejection, social climate, etc., the data would certainly be enriched by introspective reports. The fact that the family does consist, as we have pointed out, of persons who have been interacting together for some time and the fact that all the persons interacting have particular forms of expression and certain perceptual sets means that not all of what is going on can be observed. Introspective reports would not be given at the exact time of the interaction but could be given afterwards. They could be either specific to the interactions observed or reported more generally as a framework for understanding these data.

The third criticism was that behavioral observations are a costly way of gathering data. One of the assumptions behind this is that more data will be gathered than will actually be used. This problem is not entirely a function of the method but of the marriage of this method with radical empiricism. Scientists who rejected theory were unable to say what data were important and what were not. Indeed, they did not want to say it but to collect with equal enthusiasm the meaningful and the trivial. This position often stems from a special concern with collecting data quite free from the scientist's influence. Behavioral observations in the natural setting seemed to be the method freest of influence, and as a result home observation studies are often detailed accounts of every event. A single protocol may be quite interesting and suggestive of areas of study, but the sheer quantity of data along with the absence of full measures of any single variable make the material difficult to use unless it is recoded, selecting only certain parts for analysis. Thus, in the end, if the data are to be used to predict from the family situation to the child, much

of the data are never used. It is in this sense a costly way of gathering data because it is a wasteful way. Data have been gathered and processed that need not have been if the researcher had been selective beforehand and coded either larger units of behavior or only certain specified kinds of behavior.

If, however, the researcher is interested only in certain specified variables, there is another problem—namely that he may have to observe a given family for a long time before significant events take place. Observation is better suited for studying variables revealed in behavior that occurs frequently or with a predictable regularity.

Even if the variables selected for study are revealed without an indefinite period of fruitless observation and even if the observational method is geared toward efficient codification, home observations are still expensive. They require more elaborate procedures for gaining subject cooperation, more time spent in obtaining data from each family, and more highly trained persons to do the actual field work. For many research projects, however, the greater objectivity of the data and the opportunity to capture the material instantaneously in the natural setting make behavior observations well worth this expense.

***Observations in Structured Situations.*** To retain the objectivity of the observational method while eliminating the inefficiency of having to wait until significant events occur and to standardize the situation in which behavior occurs, some investigators have devised techniques whereby subjects are given a standard stimulus situation designed to elicit codable behavior immediately. The main use of this technique has been in measuring husband-wife interaction. These studies, all of which have been mentioned previously, include those of Strodtbeck (1951, 1954, 1958), Kenkel (1956), Kenkel and Hoffman (1956), and Vidich (1956). The fact that all of these researchers have been interested in measuring power relations and social-emotional roles is very likely related to the difficulties encountered in obtaining such material from verbal reports. In fact, Kenkel and Hoffman report impressive discrepancies between respondents' reports and investigators' observations in the structured situation. In addition, these data are not readily obtained from behavioral observations in the natural setting, for revealing behavioral units do not occur frequently nor at predictable times, and they may not occur at all in front of an observer. The Strodtbeck, Kenkel, and Vidich techniques have already been described. It will be recalled that the Strodtbeck technique involves confronting subjects with differences in questionnaire responses, and subjects are asked to reconcile these differences. In the other techniques subjects were asked to make certain decisions. Strodtbeck and Kenkel scored interactions for the ability of each participant to influence the other and according to the Bales categories. Both of these investigators report satisfaction with the techniques, and they appear to be measuring meaningful concepts that relate to other variables. Vidich, in a refreshingly frank report, indicates extreme dissatisfaction with the technique. Vidich states that there was a high percentage

of refusals, that couples seemed to have difficulty in understanding the task, and that the presence of the interviewer was a great source of distraction, with couples frequently trying to draw him into the conversation. The tape recorder was seen as inhibiting free communication, and interaction underwent a qualitative change when it was turned off. It seemed to the investigator that language was inappropriately formal, that extreme deference to the opinion of the spouse was used to communicate cohesion, and that, in general, the couple was giving a public performance. Most serious, Vidich reports that these difficulties occurred more with some subjects than with others, and, thus, differences between couples were, in large part, based on differences in responses to the experimental situation rather than on differences in the husband-wife relationship. The Vidich design had certain problems, it is true. The directions given to the subjects were somewhat unclear, the interviewer might better have left the room if the interview was to be taped anyway, and the technique of waiting for disagreements might not be so effective as Strodtbeck's technique of making the disagreement a fact at the start. Nevertheless, Vidich's report highlights many difficulties with this technique that are not so easily dismissed.

The major difficulties with such measures concern the artificiality of the situation. Does the contrived situation sufficiently represent the real-life situation that the resultant behavior reflects on-going patterns? For example, these measures require a discussion. If, in fact, power is asserted and not based on argument, the powerful partner in the artificial situation may not be the powerful one in real life. In addition, there is the question of motivation. The structured situation often seems like a game to the subjects, and one partner may be more involved than the other. One spouse might have little involvement in how imaginary money is spent and thus agree to all of the other's suggestions, but when the family income is at stake the interaction might be very different. The structured situation can be taken only as a measure of actual interaction when these concerns are carefully considered. Furthermore, the situation should be supplemented with reports by the subjects afterward as to how closely this interaction compares to what usually takes place in the family.

There have been few attempts to use observations in structured situations to study parent-child interactions. One outstanding example, however, is the work of Merrill Bishop (1946, 1951) referred to earlier. Bishop observed mother-child interaction in a playroom that had been specifically set up with toys and with an adult chair and magazines. The mother was told to imagine that she was in her own home and to act as she would there. Mother-child interaction was observed from behind a one-way screen for two half-hour periods. Although the mothers knew the observations were taking place, they thought the child was the object of interest to the observer. In one study (1946) a stimulus was presented before the second period to half the mothers. They were told that their children had not acted up to their true capacities. This experimental group showed increased domination over the child in the second period, whereas a control group showed no change. In another study (1951) mother-child interaction was studied in the same way, and this time it was compared to the child's interaction with a neutral adult.

These studies are interesting from two related standpoints:

1. The method of obtaining data eliminates many of the problems of verbal reports and home observations, while keeping artificiality of the situation at a minimum.

2. These are among the very few real experimental studies in this area.

These two points are related in that behavioral observations in structured situations are particularly well suited for experimental design, and Bishop's success in developing this method of obtaining data made the experimental design possible. To be sure, this method of obtaining data is not without flaws. Outside the nursery-school population, subject cooperation might be difficult to obtain. In addition, the mother's behavior might be quite different in this situation from what it is at home. A study by Schalock (1956) suggests this is true. However, it would seem that the young child is less likely to behave artificially in the situation and, therefore, (1) the child's response to the mother will itself be natural, (2) this response might indicate to the observer any tendency on the mother's part to behave in a manner unfamiliar to the child, and (3) the naturalness of the child's behavior helps to make the situation more real for the mother so that her normal behavior is more likely to be called forth. Furthermore, we have pointed out several times that the real danger of bias in the data is that the bias operates differently for different subjects. In this study comparisons are mainly for the same person under different conditions (e.g., before and after the stimulus). Thus the differential effect of bias is much less severe. In the earlier study in particular, in which Bishop has before and after measures for both the experimental group and a control group, the possibility that unequal responses to the structured situation could explain away her findings seems extremely slim. Bishop's use of behavioral observations in structured situations points this up as a very promising method for research in the family. Her demonstration of the compatability between this method and the experimental design makes it particularly exciting.

## GENERALIZING RESULTS

It has been said that psychology is the study of the attitudes of college students in introductory psychology courses. It might similarly be said that family-life studies deal with the perceptions of mothers of children in nursery schools or of children in university affiliated schools. This is a problem that plagues many of us. Essentially our concern is, to what extent can we generalize findings when the group studied is not representative of the larger population that we want to understand? The statement at the end of the report of such research that the findings cannot be generalized beyond the sample included in the study is a valid one that is often quickly ignored by the investigator as well as the reader. What is the solution? Shall we give up trying to test general hypotheses and test only hypotheses that are specific to the group under study? Or shall we engage in research only when we can study representative samples? The problem is a complicated one and the answer depends on what one is trying to study and what methods are being used.

A distinction has sometimes been made between what might be called statistical generalization and theoretical generalization (Jahoda, Deutsch, and Cook, 1951; Cartwright, 1953). If one is interested in obtaining information about populations, such as how many parents spank their children or class differences in the use of punitive discipline, statistical generalization is paramount. In such studies, representativeness of sample is crucial, for the data have no meaning beyond the population the sample represents. However, when one is studying relationships between variables, e.g., between parental punitiveness and the child's aggressiveness, the question of theoretical generalization arises. Here the findings are less tied to the representativeness of the sample, but the sample becomes relevant in another way. In such studies the investigator must ask: What is there about the group I have studied that might have affected this relationship? For example, the use of physical punishment clearly means something quite different in a sample of highly educated families than in the general population. The educated parent who uses this technique probably knows that he is doing something that is not currently acceptable among his group, and the child may very well know this too. Therefore, the correlates of physical punishment in such a sample might be generalized to other educated families, but they may tell nothing about families in different segments of society.

Besides the presence or absence of sample characteristics that may affect the relationship under study, additional factors must be considered. What are the limitations imposed by the conditions under which the observations take place? How discrepant are the operational definitions from the theoretical concepts? What other variables may be operating to obscure or enhance the empirical relationships? The problem is what Jahoda, Deutsch, and Cook have called, ". . . . the classic one of *induction* from particular facts to the validity of general scientific laws."

Thus representativeness is not always the *primary* issue in the study of a problem, and the greater accessibility of nonrepresentative samples may at times be an acceptable reason for using them. Further, the best test of the theory might require the use of homogeneous and nonrepresentative groups. The studies of Bowlby and Spitz discussed earlier are good examples. Finally, good studies in family life often require a great deal of cooperation by the subjects, and the cost of obtaining the data on each family may be high. For this reason, the use of small samples and groups who are willing to cooperate becomes important. Imagine, for example, trying to carry out the Bishop studies with a national sample. The cost would be prohibitive. The question often boils down to this: Should we have quali-

tatively excellent data on a nonrepresentative sample or questionnaires and interviews on a representative sample? The answer is that we should have both. Representative samples are needed for statistical generalizations and to supplement and test the limitations of theoretical generalizations, but smaller and less adequate samples can be used to test and generate theories and to study ongoing processes. The ideal situation will exist when the two kinds of studies are carried out in coordination so that the limits of our theoretical generalizations can be checked statistically.

## Summary

This is a chapter about measuring characteristics of the family as they are relevant to understanding the child's development. We have given emphasis to the research objective of seeking causal connections between family variables and some aspects of child behavior and development. By using a causal-sequence outline we have discussed many of the concepts and mentioned some of the ways they have been used theoretically, some of the ways they have been measured, and some of the problems they pose in study design. We have also taken up a few of the more general methodological issues that seem to be of particular concern in family studies. We have only touched on each of these areas. Our bibliography is a long one, yet it leaves out a great deal of important and relevant research. The message we have hoped to communicate with this chapter is that a great deal of work has been done, and whether a study represents a failure or a major contribution there is often something to be learned from it. By considering the relationships that have been demonstrated and the methods that have been used, by planning a new study carefully so that the errors and gains of the past can be utilized, we can build a substantial structure, with each new study adding to our theoretical understanding of the process by means of which family life affects the child.

## REFERENCES

Aberle, D. F., and Naegele. K. D. 1952. Middle-class fathers' occupational role and attitudes toward children. *Amer. J. Orthopsychiat.*, **22**, 366–378.

Ackerman, N. W., and Raymond Sobel. 1950. Family diagnosis: an approach to the preschool child. *Amer. J. Orthopsychiat.*, **20**, 744–752.

Adams, C. 1946. The prediction of adjustment in marriage. *Educ. psychol. Measmt.*, VI, 185–193.

Alper, Thelma G., T. H. Blane, and Barbara K. Abrams. 1955. Reactions of middle and lower class children to finger paints as a function of class differences in child-training practices. *J. abnorm. soc. Psychol.*, **51**, 439–448.

Altucher, N. 1956. Conflict in sex identification in boys. Unpublished doctoral dissertation, Univer. Michigan.

Angelino, H., J. Dollins, and E. V. Mech. 1956. Trends in the "fears and worries" of school children as related to socio-economic status and age. *J. genet. Psychol.*, **89**, 263–277.

Angell, R. C. 1936. *The family encounters the depression.* New York: Scribner.

Aronfreed, J. 1955. Moral standards and defenses against guilt. Unpublished doctoral dissertation, Univer. Michigan.

Alexander, T. 1952. The Adult-Child Interaction Test: A projective test for use in research. *Soc. Res. Child Develpm. Monogr. Ser.*, **17**, Serial No. 55, No. 2, 1–40.

Ausubel, D. P., E. E. Balthazar, Irene Rosenthal, L. S. Blackman, S. H. Schpoont, and J. Welkowitz. 1954. Perceived parent attitudes as determinants of children's ego structure. *Child Develpm.*, **25**, 173–184.

Bach, G. R. 1946. Father-fantasies and father-typing in father-separated children. *Child Develpm.*, **17**, 63–80.

Baldwin, A. L. 1948. Socialization and the parent-child relationship. *Child Develpm.*, **19**, 127–136.

———. 1949. The effects of home environment on nursery school behavior. *Child Develpm.*, **20**, 49–62.

———, J. Kalhorn, and F. H. Breese. 1945. Patterns of parent behavior. *Psychol. Monogr.*, **58**, 1–75.

Bales, R. F. 1950. *Interaction process analysis,* Cambridge: Addison-Wesley.

Barker, R. G., and H. F. Wright. 1949. Psychological ecology and the problem of psychosocial development. *Child Develpm.*, **20**, 131–143.

———. 1951. *One boy's day.* New York: Harper.

———. 1954. *Midwest and its children.* Evanston, Ill.: Row, Peterson.

Baruch, Dorothy. 1937. A study of reported tension in interparental relationships as coexistent with behavior adjustment in young children. *J. exp. Educ.*, 6(2), 187–204.

———, and J. Annie Wilcox, 1944. A study of sex differences in preschool children's adjustment coexistent with interparental tensions. *J. genet. Psychol.*, **64**, 281–303.

Beck, S. J. 1945. *Rorschach's test.* A variety of personality pictures. New York: Grune and Stratton. Vol. II.

Behrens, Marjorie. 1954. Child rearing and the character structure of the mother. *Child Develpm.*, **25**, 3, 225–238.

Bell, R. Q. 1958. Retrospective attitude studies of parent-child relations. *Child Develpm.*, **29**, 323–338.

Bellak, L. and Sonya S. Bellak. 1949. *Child's apperception test.* New York: C.P. S., P.O. Box 42, Gracie Station.

Bender, Lauretta, 1948–1949. Genesis of hostility in children. *Amer. J. Psychiat.*, **105**, 241–245.

Bird, C., E. D. Monachesi, and H. Burdick, 1952. Infiltration and the attitudes of white and Negro parents and children. *J. abnorm. soc. Psychol.*, **47**, 688–699.

Blau, P. M. 1956. Social mobility and interpersonal relations. *Amer. sociol. Rev.*, **21**, 3, 290–295.

Blood, R. O. 1953. A situational approach to the study of permissiveness in child-rearing. *Amer. sociol. Rev.*, **18**, 84–87.

———. 1958. The effect of the wife's employment on family power structure. *Social Forces*, **36**, 347–352.

Blum, G. S. 1950. *The Blacky Pictures: A technique for the exploration of personality dynamics.* New York: Psychological Corp.

Boek, W. E., E. D. Lawson, A. Yankauer, and M. B. Sussman. 1957. *Social class, maternal health, and child care.* Albany, N. Y.: State Dept. Health.

Bossard, J. H. S. 1948. *The sociology of child development.* New York: Harper.

———. 1951. A spatial index for family interaction. *Amer. sociol. Rev.*, **16**, 243–246.

———, and Eleanor S. Boll, 1954. Security in the large family. *Ment. Hyg.*, **38**, 529–544.

———. 1955a. Marital unhappiness in the life cycle. *Marriage and Family Living*, **17**, 10–19.

———. 1955b. Personality roles in the large family. *Child Develpm.*, **26**, 71–78.

Bossard, J. H. S., and M. Sanger, 1952. The large family. *Amer. sociol. Rev.*, **17**, 3–9.

Bouck, P. 1936. The effect of wide differences in the education of parents upon the behavior of their children. *Child Develpm.*, **8**, 255–261.

Bowlby, J., M. Ainsworth, M. Boston, and D. Rosenbluth. 1956. The effects of mother-child separation: A follow-up study. *Brit. J. med. Psychol.*, **29**, 211–247.

Brim, O. 1954. The acceptance of new behavior in child-rearing. *Hum. Relat.*, **7**, 473–493.

———. 1958. Family structure and sex role learning by children: A further analysis of Helen Koch's data. *Sociometry*, **21**, 1–15.

Brodbeck, A. J., P. Nogee, and A. DiMascio. 1956. Two kinds of conformity: A study of the Riesman typology applied to standards of parental discipline. *J. Psychol.*, **41**, 23–45.

Brody, Sylvia. 1956. *Patterns of mothering.* New York: International Univer. Press.

Bronfenbrenner, U. 1958a. Socialization and social class through time and space. In Eleanor E. Maccoby, T. Newcomb, and E. Hartley (Eds.), *Readings in social psychology.* New York: Holt, pp. 400–425.

———. 1958b. 1958 Presidential address to the Division of Developmental Psychology.

Brown, A. W., J. Morrison, and G. B. Couch. 1947. Influence of affectional family relationships on character development. *J. abnorm. soc. Psychol.*, **42**, 422–428.

Bruner, J. S., and C. C. Goodman. 1947. Value and need as organizing factors in perception. *J. Pers.*, **42**, 33–44.

Bühler, C. 1943. Father and son. *Rorschach Res. Exch.*, **7**, 145–158.

Burchinal, L. G. 1957. Similarities of parents' personality inventory–marriage satisfactions scores–attitude toward children. *Midwest Sociologist*, **20**, 33–38.

———. 1958a. Mothers' and fathers' differences in parental acceptance for controlled comparisons based on parental and family characteristics. *J. genet. Psychol.*, **92**, 103–110.

———. 1958b. Parents' attitudes and adjustment of children. *J. genet. Psychol.*, **92**, 69–79.

———, G. R. Hawkes, and B. Gardner. 1957a. Marriage adjustment, personality of parents and personality adjustment of child. *Marriage and Family Living*, **19**, 366–372.

———. 1957b. The relationship between parental acceptance and adjustment of children. *Child Develpm.*, **28**, 65–77.

Burgess, E. W., and L. S. Cottrell. 1939. *Predicting success or failure in marriage.* New York: Prentice-Hall.

Burgess, E. W., and P. Wallin. 1953. *Engagement and marriage.* New York: Lippincott.

Cartwright, D. P. 1953. Analysis of qualitative material. In L. Festinger and D. Katz (Eds.), *Research methods in the behavioral sciences.* New York: Dryden. Pp. 421–470.

Cass, Loretta K. 1952a. An investigation of parent-child relationships in terms of awareness, identification, projection, and control. *Amer. J. Orthopsychiat.*, **22**, 305–313.

———. 1952b. Parent-child relationships and

delinquency. *J. abnorm. soc. Psychol.*, **57**, 101–104.

Cavan, Ruth S., and K. Ranck. 1938. *The family and the depression.* Chicago: Univer. Chicago.

Centers, R. T. 1949. *The psychology of social classes.* Princeton: Princeton Univer. Press.

———. 1955. Psychological aspects of socio-economic stratification: An inquiry into the nature of class. *Dissertation Abstracts*, **15**, 451.

Champney, H. 1941. The measurement of parent behavior. *Child Develpm.*, **12**, 131–166.

Chapin, F. S. 1930. Scale for rating living room equipment. Minneapolis: Univer. Minneapolis, Inst. Child Welf.

Christensen, H. T., and Bette B. Rubinstein. 1956. Premarital pregnancy and divorce: A follow-up study by the interview method. *Marriage and Family Living*, **18**, 2, 114–123.

Cohen, A. K. 1955. *Delinquent boys.* Glencoe, Ill.: Free Press.

Cooper, J. and Margaret Blair. 1959. Parent evaluation as a determiner of ideology. *J. genet. Psychol.*, **94**, 93–101.

Crandall, V. J., S. Orleans, A. Preston, and A. Rabson. 1958. The development of social compliance in young children. *Child Develpm.*, **29**, 3, 430–443.

Davie, J. S. 1953. Social class factors and school attendance. *Harvard educ. Rev.*, **23**, 175–185.

Davis, A., and R. J. Havighurst. 1946. Social class and color differences in child rearing. *Amer. sociol. Rev.*, **11**, 698–710.

Dean, D. 1947. Relation of ordinal position to personality in young children. Unpublished master's thesis. State Univer. Iowa.

Douvan, Elizabeth. 1956. Social status and success strivings. *J. abnorm. soc. Psychol.*, **52**, 2, 219–223.

Douvan, Elizabeth, and Carol Kaye. 1958. *Adolescent girls.* A nation-wide study of girls between eleven and eighteen years of age. Inst. Soc. Res., Univer. Michigan, Ann Arbor.

Dreyer, A. S. 1959. Parental behavior and ego functioning in preschool children. (Mimeo.) Presented at annual meeting of Society for Research in Child Development.

Duvall, Evelyn M. 1946. Conceptions of parenthood. *Amer. J. Sociol.*, **52**, 193–203.

Dyer, W. G. 1956. A comparison of families of high and low job satisfaction. *Marriage and Family Living*, **18**, 58–60.

Dynes, R. R., C. Alfred, and S. Dinitz. 1956. Levels of occupational aspiration: Some aspects of family experience as a variable. *Amer. sociol. Rev.*, **21**, 2, 212–215.

Elder, R. A. 1949. Traditional and developmental conceptions of fatherhood. *Marriage and Family Living*, **11**, 98–100, 106.

Ellis, Evelyn. 1952. Some psychological correlates of upward social mobility among unmarried career women. *Amer. sociol. Rev.*, **17**, 558–563.

Ericson, M. C. 1947. Social status and child-rearing practices. In Newcomb, Hartley, et al. (Eds.), *Readings in social psychology.* New York: Holt. Pp. 494–501.

Erikson, E. H. 1946. Ego development and historical change. *The psychoanalytic study of the child.* New York: International Univer. Press. Vol. II. Pp. 359–397.

Escalona, Sibylle and Mary Leitch, et al. 1952. Early phases of personality development: A non-normative study. *Soc. Res. Child Develpm., Monogr. Ser.*, **17**, 54, 1–72.

Feinberg, H. 1954. Achievement by children in orphan homes as revealed by the Stanford Achievement Test. *J. genet. Psychol.*, **85**, 217–229.

Fischer, L. K. 1953. Psychological appraisal of the "unattached" preschool child. *Amer. J. Orthopsychiat.*, **23**, 803–816.

Freedman, M. B., I. F. Leary, A. G. Ossorio, and H. S. Coffey. 1951. Interpersonal dimensions of personality. *J. Pers.*, **20**, 143–161.

Frenkel-Brunswik, Else, and Joan Havel. 1953. Prejudice in the interviews of children. *J. genet. Psychol.*, **82**, 91–136.

Freud, A., and D. Burlingham. 1944. *Infants without families.* New York: International Univer. Press.

Glueck, S., and E. Glueck. 1957. Working mothers and delinquency. *Ment. Hyg.*, N. Y. 327–352.

Goldfarb, W. 1945. Effects of psychological deprivation in infancy and subsequent stimulation. *Amer. J. Psychiat.*, **102**, 18–33.

Goodstein, L. D., and W. G. Dahlstrom. 1956.

MMPI differences between parents of stuttering and nonstuttering children. *J. consult. Psychol.,* **20,** 365-371.

Gordon, J. E. 1957. The validity of Shoben's Parent-Attitude Survey. *J. clin. Psychol.,* **13,** 154-158.

Gray, Susan W. 1959. Perceived similarity to parents and adjustment. *Child Develpm.,* **30,** 1, 90-106.

———, and R. Klaus. 1956. The assessment of parental identification. *Genet. Psychol. Monogr.,* **54,** 87-109.

Haer, J. L. 1957. Predictive utility of five indices of social stratification. *Amer. sociol. Rev.,* **22,** 5, 541-546.

Harris, D. B., H. G. Gough, and W. E. Martin. 1950. Children's ethnic attitudes: II. Relationship to parental beliefs concerning child training. *Child Develpm.,* **21,** 169-181.

Hart, I. 1957. Maternal child-rearing practices and authoritarian ideology. *J. abnorm. soc. Psychol.,* **2,** 232-237.

Harter, A. B. 1950. *Adjustment of high-school seniors and the marital adjustment of their parents in a southern California city.* Univer. Southern California Library.

Hartwell, S. W., M. L. Hutt, G. Andrew, and R. E. Walton. 1951. The Michigan Picture Test: Diagnostic and therapeutic possibilities of a new projective test for children. *Amer. J. Orthopsychiat.,* **21,** 124-137.

Hatt, Paul K. 1950. Occupation and social stratifications. *Amer. J. Sociol.,* **55,** 533-543.

Havemann, E., and Patricia S. West. 1952. *They went to college: The college graduate in America today.* New York: Harcourt, Brace.

Havighurst, R. J. 1952. Social class and basic personality structure. *Sociol. soc. Res.,* **36,** 355-363.

———, and A. Davis. 1955. A comparison of the Chicago and Harvard studies of social class differences in child rearing. *Amer. sociol. Rev.,* **20,** 438-442.

Havighurst, R. J., and R. R. Rodgers. 1952. The role of motivation in attendance at post-high school educational institutions. In A. B. Hollingshead (Ed.), *Who should go to college,* New York: Columbia Univer. Press. Pp. 135-165.

Havighurst, R. J., and H. Taba. 1949. *Adolescent character and personality.* New York: Wiley.

Hawkes, G. R., L. G. Burchinal, and B. Gardner. 1956. Marital satisfaction, personality characteristics, and parental acceptance of children. *J. consult. Psychol.,* **3,** 216-221.

———. 1957. Pre-adolescents' views of some of their relations with their parents. *Child Develpm.,* **28,** 393-399.

Heer, D. M. 1958. Dominance and the working wife. *Social Forces,* **36,** 341-347.

Heinicke, C. M. 1956. Some effects of separating two year old children from their parents: A comparative study. *Hum. Relat.,* **9,** 106-176.

Hellman, Ilse. 1954. Some observations on mothers of children with intellectual inhibitions. *The psychoanalytic study of the child.* New York: International Univer. Press, Vol. 10, pp. 259-273.

Helper, M. 1958. Parental evaluation of children and children's self-evaluation. *J. abnorm. soc. Psychol.,* **56,** 2, 190-194.

Henry, A. F. 1956. Family role structure and self blame. *Social Forces,* **35,** 1, 34-38.

———. 1957. Sibling structure and perception of the disciplinary roles of parents. *Sociometry,* **20,** 67-74.

Herbst, P. G. 1952. The measurement of family relationships. *Hum. Relat.,* **5,** 1, 3-30.

———. 1953. Analysis and measurement of a situation: The child in the family. *Hum. Relat.,* **6,** 2, 113-140.

Hill, R. 1949. *Families under stress.* New York: Harper.

Himmelweit, Hilde T. 1955. Socio-economic background and personality. *Int. soc. Sci. Bull.,* **7,** 29-35.

Hoffman, Lois W. 1960. Effects of the employment of mothers on parental power relations and the division of household tasks. *Marriage and Family Living,* **22,** 1, 27-35.

Hoffman, M. L. 1957. An interview method for obtaining descriptions of parent-child interaction. *Merrill-Palmer Quart.,* **4,** 76-83.

———. 1960. Power assertion by the parent and its impact on the child. *Child. Develpm.,* **31,** 1, 129-143.

———, and C. Albizu-Miranda. 1955. Middle-class bias in personality test. *J. abnorm. soc. Psychol.,* **51,** 150-152.

Hoffman, M. L., S. B. Mitsos, and R. E. Protz. 1958. Achievement striving, social class, and test anxiety. *J. abnorm. soc. Psychol.*, **56**, 3.

Hollingshead, A. B. 1949. *Elmtown's youth.* New York: Wiley.

———, and F. C. Redlich. 1958. *Social class and mental illness: A community study.* New York: Wiley.

Horwitz, M. 1956. Psychological needs as a function of social environments. In L. D. White (Ed.). *The state of social sciences.* Chicago: Univer. Chicago Press. Pp. 162–183.

Jackson, P. W. 1956. Verbal solutions to parent-child problems. *Child Develpm.*, **27**, 339–351.

Jahoda, Marie, M. Deutsch and S. W. Cook. 1952. *Research methods in social relations, Part I: Basic processes.* New York: Dryden.

Jansen, L. T. 1952. Measuring family solidarity. *Amer. sociol. Rev.*, **17**, 727–733.

Johannis, T. B., Jr. 1955. The adolescent's view of father roles in relation to socioeconomic class. Unpublished doctoral dissertation, Florida State Univer.

Jourard, S. M., and R. M. Remy. 1955. Perceived parental attitudes, the self, and security. *J. consult. Psychol.*, **19**, 364–366.

Kagan, J. 1956. The child's perception of the parent, *J. abnorm. soc. Psych.*, **53**, 257–258.

———. 1958. Socialization of aggression and the perception of parents in fantasy. *Child Develpm.*, **29**, 311–320.

Kahl, J. A. 1953. Educational and occupational aspirations of "common man" boys. *Harvard educ. Rev.*, **23**, 186–203.

———, and J. A. Davis. 1955. A comparison of indexes of socio-economic status. *Amer. sociol. Rev.*, **20**, 317–325.

Kahn, R. L., and C. F. Cannell. 1957. *The dynamics of interviewing.* New York: Wiley.

Kaplan, G. 1958. Unpublished research on the response of families to crises; a study of premature birth.

Kates, S. L., and L. N. Diab. 1955. Authoritarian ideology and attitudes on parent-child relationships. *J. abnorm. soc. Psychol.*, **51**, 13–16.

Kenkel, W. F. 1956. Influence differentiation in family decision making. Paper delivered at meeting of American Sociological Society.

Kenkel, W. F., and D. K. Hoffman. 1956. Real and conceived roles in family decision making. *Marriage and Family Living*, **18**, 311–316.

King, S. H., and A. F. Henry. 1955. Aggression and cardiovascular reactions related to parental control over behavior. *J. abnorm. soc. Psychol.*, **50**, 206–210.

Kinsey, A. C., W. B. Pomeroy, and C. E. Martin. 1948. *Sexual behavior in the human male.* Philadelphia: W. B. Saunders.

Kirkpatrick, C. 1937. Factors in marital adjustment. *Amer. J. Sociol.*, **43**, 270–283.

Klatskin, E. H. 1952. Shifts in child card practices in three social classes under an infant card program of flexible methodology. *Amer. J. Orthopsychiat.*, **22**, 52–61.

Klausner, S. Z. Social class and self-concept. *J. soc. Psychol.*, 1953, **38**, 201–205.

Kluckhohn, Florence. 1958. Variations in the basic values of family systems. *Social Casework*, **39**, 63–72.

Koch, Helen L. 1954. The relation of "primary mental abilities" in five- and six-year olds to sex of child and characteristics of his sibling. *Child Develpm.*, **25**, 210–223.

———. 1955a. Some personality correlates of sex, sibling position, and sex of sibling among five- and six- year-old children. *Genet. psychol. Monogr.*, **52**, 3–51.

———. 1955b. The relation of certain family constellation characteristics and the attitudes of children toward adults. *Child Develpm.*, **26**, 13–40.

———. 1956a. Attitudes of children toward their peers as related to certain characteristics of their siblings. *Psychol. Monogr.*, **70**, 19.

———. 1956b. Some emotional attitudes of the young child in relation to characteristics of his sibling. *Child Develpm.*, **27**, 393–427.

———. 1956c. Sissiness and tomboyishness in relation to sibling characteristics. *J. genet. Psychol.*, **88**, 231–244.

———. 1956d. Children's work attitudes and sibling characteristics. *Child Develpm.*, **27**, 289–310.

Kohn, M. L. 1959a. Research in progress. Lab.

Socio-Environmental Stud., Nat. Inst. Ment. Health, Bethesda, Maryland.

Kohn, M. L. 1959b. Social class and parental authority. *Amer. sociol. Rev.*, **24**, 352–366.

Kohn, M. L., and J. A. Clausen. 1956. Parental authority behavior and schizophrenia. *Amer. J. Orthopsychiat.*, **26**, 297–313.

Landis, J. T. 1955. A comparison of children of divorced parents and children of happy or unhappy nondivorced parents on parent-child relationships, dating maturation and sex and marriage attitudes. Paper read before the National Council on Family Relations, Minneapolis, Minn.

Lasko, Joan K. 1954. Parent behavior toward first and second children. *Genet. Psychol. Monogr.*, **49**, 97–137.

LeMasters, E. E. 1954. Social class mobility and family integration. *Mariage and Family Living*, **16**, 226–232.

Levinson, D. J., and D. E. Huffman. 1955. Traditional family ideology and its relation to personality. *J. Pers.*, **23**, 3, 251–273.

Levitt, E. E. 1959. A comparison of parental and self-evaluations of psychopathology in children. Paper presented at the annual meeting of the Society for Research in Child Development, Bethesda, Maryland.

Levy, D. M. 1928. Finger sucking and accessory movements in early infancy: An etiological study. *Amer. J. Psychiat.*, **7**, 881–918.

Lippitt, R., and Lois W. Hoffman. 1959. The effects of the family on the child's peer group adjustment. Research in progress. Ann Arbor, Mich.: Research Center for Group Dynamics.

Lippitt, R., and S. Withey. 1959. Flint Youth Study: Progress report on analysis of data from first year of field work. Unpublished manuscript. Inst. Soc. Res., Ann Arbor, Mich.

Little, Sue, and L. Cohen. 1951. Goal-setting behavior of asthmatic children and of their mothers for them. *J. Pers.*, **19**, 376–389.

Littman, R. A., R. C. A. Moore, and J. Pierce-Jones. 1957. Social class differences in child rearing: A third community for comparison with Chicago and Newton. *Amer. sociol. Rev.*, **22**, 694–704.

Locke, H. J. 1951. *Predicting adjustment in marriage: A comparison of a divorced and a happily married group.* New York: Holt.

Loeb, Martin B. 1953. Implications of status differentiation for personal and social development. *Harvard educ. Rev.*, **23**, 168–174.

Lyle, W. H., and E. E. Levitt. 1955. Punitiveness, authoritarianism and parental discipline of grade school children. *J. abnorm. soc. Psychol.*, **51**, 42–46.

Lynd, R., and Helen Lynd. 1929. *Middletown.* New York: Harcourt, Brace.

———. 1936. *Middletown in transition.* New York: Harcourt, Brace.

Maccoby, Eleanor E., and Patricia K. Gibbs. 1954. Methods of child rearing in two social classes. In W. Martin and Celia Stendler (Eds.) *Readings in child development.* New York: Harcourt, Brace. Pp. 380–396.

MacKinnon, D. W. 1938. Violation of prohibitions. In H. A. Murray et al. (Eds.), *Explorations in personality.* New York: Oxford Univer. Press. Ch. 14.

Malinowski, B. 1927. *Sex and repression in savage society.* London: Routledge and Kegan Paul.

Marx, K. 1906–1909. *Capital.* Chicago: Kerr. 3 vols.

Maslow, A. H., and I. Szilagyi-Kessler. 1946. Security and breast-feeding. *J. abnorm. soc. Psychol.*, **41**, 83–86.

McArthur, C. 1954. Personalities of public and private school boys. *Harvard educ. Rev.*, **24**, 4, 256–261.

———. 1955. Personality differences between middle and upper classes. *J. abnorm. soc. Psychol.*, **50**, 247–254.

McCandless, B. R. 1958. Child-rearing practices, social class, and the authoritarian personality. Paper for symposium at A.P.A. meeting. (Mimeo.)

McClelland, D. C., J. W. Atkinson, R. A. Clark, and E. L. Lowell. 1953. *The achievement motive.* New York: Appleton-Century-Crofts.

———, A. Rindlisbacher, and R. deCharms. 1955. Religion and other sources of parental attitudes toward independence training. In D. McCelland, *Studies in motivation.* New York: Appleton-Century-Crofts.

McGuire, Carson. 1952. Family life in lower and middle class homes. *Marriage and Family Living*, **14**, 1–6.

McKee, J. P., and Florence Leader. 1955. The relationship of SES and aggression to the competitive behavior of preschool children. *Child Develpm.*, **26**, 135–142.

Merrill, Barbara. 1946. A measurement of mother-child interaction. *J. abnorm. soc. Psychol.*, **41**, 1, 37–49.

Merrill Bishop, Barbara. 1951. Mother-child interaction and the social behavior of children. *Psychol. Monogr.*, **65**, 1–34.

Miller, D. R., and G. E. Swanson. 1958. *The changing American parent*. New York: Wiley.

Milton, G. A. 1958. A factor analytic study of child-rearing behaviors. *Child Develpm.*, **29**, 381–393.

Morgan, P. K., and E. D. Gaier. 1957. Types of reactions in punishment situations in the mother-child relationship. *Child Develpm.*, **28**, 161–166.

Moustakas, C. E., I. E. Sigel, and H. D. Schalock. 1956. An objective method for the measurement and analysis of child-adult interaction. *Child Develpm.*, **27**, 109–134.

Mowrer, E. 1954. Some factors in the affectional adjustment of twins. *Amer. sociol. Rev.*, **19**, 468–471.

Mussen, P. 1950. Some personality and social factors related to changes in children's attitudes toward Negroes. *J. abnorm. soc. Psychol.*, **45**, 3, 423–441.

Nowlis, V. 1952. The search for significant concepts in the study of parent-child relationships, *Amer. J. Orthopsychiat.*, **22**, 286–299.

Nye, F. I. 1957. Child adjustment in broken and in unhappy unbroken homes. *Marriage and Family Living.*, **19**, 356–361.

———. 1958. *Family relationships and delinquent behavior*. New York: Wiley.

Oeser, O. A., and S. E. Emery. 1954. *Social structure and personality in a rural community*. New York: Macmillan.

Oeser, O. A., and S. B. Hammond. (Eds.) 1954. *Social structure and personality in a city*. New York: Macmillan.

Orr, Frances. 1960. The reactions of young children to the birth of a sibling. *Genet. Psychol. Monogr.* In press.

Ort, R. S. 1950. Some implications of the class concept for clinical psychology. *Psychol. serv. center J.*, **3**, 189–197.

Patterson, C. H. 1943. The relationship of Bernreuter personality scores to other parent characteristics, including parent-child behavior. *J. soc. Psychol.*, **17**, 77–88.

Payne, D., and P. Mussen. 1956. Parent-child relations and father identification. *J. abnorm. soc. Psychol.*, **52**, 358–362.

Pentony, P. 1956. Home environment and nursery school behavior. *Aust. J. Psychol.*, **8**, 61–65.

Popenoe, P., and D. Wicks. 1937. Marital happiness in two generations. *Ment. Hyg.*, **29**, 218–223.

Porter, B. M. 1954. Measurement of parental acceptance of children. *J. Home Econ.*, **46**, 176–182.

———. 1955. The relationship between marital adjustment and parental acceptance of children. *J. Home Econ.*, **47**, 157–164.

Rabban, M. 1950. Sex role identification in young children in two diverse social groups. *Genet. Psychol. Monogr.*, **42**, 81–158.

Radke, Marian J. 1946. The relation of parental authority to children's behavior and attitudes. *Inst. Child Welf. Monogr.*, **22**.

Radke Yarrow, Marian. 1959. Complicating our conceptions of parent-child relations. A paper delivered at the annual meeting of the Society for Research in Child Development, Bethesda, Maryland.

———, H. Trager, and J. Miller. 1952. The role of parents in the development of children's ethnic attitudes. *Child Develpm.*, **23**, 13–53.

Rainwater, L. 1956. A study of personality differences between middle and lower class adolescents: The Szondi test in culture-personality research. *Genet. Psychol. Monogr.*, **54**, 3–87.

Ramsey, C. E., and L. Nelson. 1956. Change in values and attitudes toward the family. *Amer. sociol. Rev.*, **21**, 605–609.

Reissman, L. 1953. Levels of aspiration and social class. *Amer. sociol. Rev.*, **18**, 233–242.

Remmers, H. H., and D. H. Radler. 1957. *The American teenager*. Indianapolis: Bobbs-Merrill.

Rheingold, Harriet L. 1956. The modification of social responsiveness in institutional babies. *Monogr. soc. Res. Child Develpm.*, 31, 2.

Robinson, H. A., F. C. Redlich, and J. K. Myers. 1954. Social structure and psychiatric treatment. *Amer. J. Orthopsychiat.*, 24, 307–316.

Roff, M. A. 1949. A factorial study of the Fels Parent Behavior Rating Scales. *Child Develpm.*, 20, 29–44.

Rosen, B. C. 1955. Conflicting group membership: A study of parent-peer group cross pressures. *Amer. sociol. Rev.*, 20, 155–160.

———. 1956. The achievement syndrome: a psychocultural dimension of social stratification. *Amer. sociol. Rev.*, 21, 203–211.

Rosenzweig, S., and A. C. Isham. 1947. Complementary thematic apperception test patterns in close kin. *Amer. J. Orthopsychiat.*, 17, 129–142.

Sarason, S., 1958. Reported in a Psychology Colloquium address. Univer. Michigan.

Schaefer, E. S., and R. Q. Bell. 1957. Patterns of attitudes toward child rearing and the family. *J. abnorm. soc. Psychol.*, 54, 391–395.

———. 1958. Development of a parental attitude research instrument. *Child Develpm.*, 29, 339–361.

Schalock, H. D. 1956. Observation of mother-child interaction in the laboratory and in the home. Unpublished doctoral dissertation, Univer. Nebraska.

Schneider, L., and S. Lysgaard. 1953. The deferred gratification pattern: A preliminary study. *Amer. sociol. Rev.*, 18, 142–149.

Schutz, W. C. 1958. Firo: *A three dimensional theory of interpersonal behavior.* New York: Rhinehart.

Sears, P. S. 1948. Measurement of dependent and aggressive behavior in doll play. *Amer. Psychol.*, 3, 263. Abstract.

———. 1951. Doll-play aggression in normal young children: Influence of sex, age, sibling status, father's absence. *Psychol. Monogr.*, 65, No. 6.

Sears, R. R. 1950. Ordinal position in the family as a psychological variable. *Amer. sociol. Rev.*, 15, 397–401.

Sears, R. R., Eleanor E. Maccoby, and H. Levin. 1957. *Patterns of child rearing.* Evanston, Ill.: Row, Peterson.

Sears, R. R., M. H. Pintler, and P. S. Sears. 1946. Effect of father separation on pre-school children's doll play aggression. *Child Develpm.*, 17, 219–243.

Sears, R. R., J. W. M. Whiting, V. Nowlis, and P. S. Sears. 1953. Some child-rearing antecedents or aggression and dependency in young children. *Genet. Psychol. Monogr.*, 47, 135–234.

Sewell, W. H., and A. O. Haller. 1956. Social status and the personality adjustment of the child. *Sociometry*, 19, 114–125.

Sewell, W. H., and P. H. Mussen. 1952. The effects of feeding, weaning, and scheduling procedures on childhood adjustment and the formation of oral symptoms. *Child Develpm.*, 23, 185–191.

Sewell, W. H., P. H. Mussen, and C. W. Harris. 1955. Relationships among child training practices. *Amer. sociol. Rev.*, 20, 137–148.

Shapiro, M. B. 1952. Some correlates of opinions on the upbringing of children. *Brit. J. Psychol.*, 43, 141–149.

Sharp, H., and P. Mott. 1956. Consumer decisions in the metropolitan family. *J. Marketing*, 149–156.

Shoben, E. J. 1949. The assessment of parental attitudes in relation to child adjustment. *Genet. Psychol. Monogr.*, 39, 101–148.

Sigel, I. E., and M. L. Hoffman. 1956. The predictive potential of projective tests for nonclinical populations. Symposium on the use of projective techniques as research tools in studies of normal personality development. *J. proj. Tech.*, 20, 3, 261–264.

Sigel, I. E., M. L. Hoffman, A. Dreyer, and I. Torgoff. 1957. Influence techniques used by parents to modify the behavior of their children: A case presentation. *Amer. J. Orthopsychiat.*, 27, 356–364.

Soskin, W. F. 1959. Research reported at the annual meeting of the Society for Research in Child Development, Bethesda, Maryland.

Spiegel, John. 1957. The resolution of role conflict in the family. *Psychiatry*, 20, 1–16.

Spitz, R. A. 1945. Hospitalism: an inquiry into the genesis of psychiatric conditions in early childhood. *The psychoanalytic study of the child.* New York: International Univer. Press, Vol. 1. Pp. 53–74.

Staples, R., and J. W. Smith. 1954. Attitudes of grandmothers and mothers toward child-rearing practices. *Child Develpm.*, **25**, 91–97.

Stendler, C. B. 1950. Sixty years of child-training practices. *J. Pediat.*, **36**, 122–134.

Stolz, Lois M., et al., 1954. *Father relations of war-born children*. Stanford, Calif.: Stanford Univer. Press.

Strodtbeck, F. L. 1951. Husband-wife interaction over revealed differences. *Amer. sociol. Rev.*, **16**, 468–473.

———. 1952. The interaction of a "henpecked" husband and his wife. *Marriage and Family Living.*, **14**, 305–309.

———. 1954. The family as a three person group. *Amer. sociol. Rev.*, **11**, 23–29.

———. 1958. Family interaction, values, and achievement. In McClelland, Baldwin Bronfenbrenner, and Strodtback (Eds.), *Talent and Society*. New York: Van Nostrand. Ch. 4.

Stroup, A. L. 1956. Marital adjustment of the mother and the personality of the child. *Marriage and Family Living*, **18**, 109–113.

Stubblefield, R. L. 1955. Children's emotional problems aggravated by family moves. *Amer. J. Orthopsychiat.*, **25**, 120–126.

Sutherland, H. E. G. 1930. The relationship between IQ and size of family in the case of fatherless children. *J. genet. Psychol.*, **38**, 161–170.

Taves, M. J. 1948. A direct vs. an indirect approach in measuring marital adjustment. *Amer. sociol. Rev.*, **13**, 538–541.

Terman, L., P. Buttenwieser, L. W. Ferguson, Winifred B. Johnson, and D. T. Wilson. 1938. *Psychological factors in marital happiness*. New York: McGraw-Hill.

Thurston, J. R., and P. H. Mussen. 1951. Infant feeding gratification and adult personality. *J. Pers.*, **19**, 4, 449–458.

Tiller, P. O. 1958. Father absence and personality development of children in sailor families. *Nordisk Psykologi's Monogr. Ser.*, No. 9. (Institute for Social Research, Oslo.)

Toby, J. 1957. The differential impact of family disorganization. *Amer. sociol. Rev.*, **22**, 505–512.

Trapp, E. P., and D. H. Kausler. 1958. Dominance attitudes in parents and adult avoidance behavior in young children. *Child Develpm.*, **29**, 4, 507–513.

U. S. Employment Service. 1949. *Dictionary of occupational titles*. Vol. **2**. Washington: U. S. Government Printing Office.

Veblen, T. 1918. *The theory of the leisure class*. New York: Huebsch.

Vidich, A. J. 1956. Methodological problems in the observation of husband-wife interaction. *Marriage and Family Living*, **18**, 3, 234–239.

Vincent, Clark E. 1956. Social and interpersonal sources of symptomatic frigidity. *Marriage and Family Living*, **18**, 355–360.

Warner, W. L., and Paul S. Lunt. 1941. *The social life of a modern community*. New Haven: Yale Univer. Press. Yankee City Series, Vol. I.

Warner, W. L., M. Meeker, and K. Eells. 1949. *Social class in America*. Chicago: Sci. Res. Ass.

Watson, G. 1957. Some personality differences in children related to strict or permissive parental discipline. *J. Psychol.*, **44**, 227–249.

White, Martha Sturm. 1957. Social class, child-rearing practices, and child behavior. *Amer. sociol. Rev.*, **22**, 704–712.

Whiting, J. W. M., and I. L. Child. 1953. *Child training and personality: A cross-cultural study*. New Haven: Yale Univer. Press.

Winterbottom, Marian. 1958. The relation of need for achievement to learning experiences in independence and mastery. In J. Atkinson (Ed.), *Motives in fantasy, action, and society*. New York: Van Nostrand. Pp. 453–478.

Wittenborn, J. R. 1956. A study of adoptive children. *Psychol. Monogr.*, **70**, 93–115.

Wolfe, D. M. 1959. Power and authority in the family. In D. Cartwright (Ed.), *Studies in social power*. Ann Arbor: Inst. soc. Res. Pp. 77–117.

Wolfenstein, M. 1953. Trends in infant care. *Amer. J. Orthopsychiat.*, **23**, 120–130.

Yamamura, D. S., and M. N. Zald. 1956. A note on the usefulness and validity of the Herbst Family Questionnaire. *Hum. Relat.*, **9**, 2, 217–221.

Zemlick, M. J., and R. I. Watson. 1953. Maternal attitudes of acceptance and rejection during and after pregnancy. *Amer. J. Orthopsychiat.*, **23**, 570–584.

# Author Index

1015

# Subject Index

Abilities differentiation of, 477–478
Ability, differential measurement of, 477–478
  and personality tests, relation between, 456
  testing, 456–486
Ability tests, cheating on, 468
  types of, 457–465
Absence of father, 956–957
Absence of mother, 955–956
Absolute judgment, method of, 317
Absolute thresholds (*see also* Threshold), 286–287
Abstracting behavior in early childhood, 177
Academic achievement, 474
Acceptability in groups, 843
Acceptance-rejection, mother's, 969
Achievement, and anxiety, 807
  in boys, 811–812, 970
  and child-rearing practices, 970
  and competitiveness, 811
  correlates of, 804, 810–811
  definition, 804
  factors affecting scores, 805
  and fantasy materials, 805
  and independence training, 940
  and intelligence, 811
  and level of aspiration, 807, 809
  and parents, 810–812
Achievement fantasy and doll-play analysis, 807–808
Achievement motivation (need achievement), 770–771, 802–812
  versus response tendency, 808
Achievement motivation measures, behavioral, 809
  doll-play, 803
  graphic expression, 805–807
  scribble patterns, 806
  verbal story cues, 803–804
Achievement striving, rating scales of, 809–810
Achievement tests, 464–465
  content validity, 473–474
  effects of learning on, 464
Acquiescence versus response set, 776
Activity, general, 163, 182
  mouth, 163
  and odor receptivity, 300–301

Activity, and taste receptivity, 299
  and temperature receptivity, 304
Activity level as measure of sensitivity, 288–291
Activity tests, 634
Acts, inferred effect of, 888–890
  recording effects of, 887–888
Acuity, visual, *see* Visual acuity
Adaptation in infants, 158–159, 171
Adaptometer, Ferree and Rand, 289–290
  Hecht and Schlaer, 289–290
Adjustment, method of, 313, 348, 361
Adopted children, 978
Adualism of ego and nonego, 433
Adult-child interaction, 907–908
  test, 984
Adult language, child's understanding of, 438
Adult personality, effects of childhood upon, 6
Affect, 688–769
  conditioning of, 690
  physical stimulation of, 690
Affective attitude, 169
Affective factors, 325
Affiliations, 428
Age, as explanation of behavioral change, 37
  importance in description of human behavior, 36
  in selection of criteria, 57
  for weaning, 934–935
Age differentiation, as criterion for test validity, 474
  hypothesis, 478–479
Age-functional generalization, 38
Age grouping, 238
Agencies as source of subjects, 986–987
Agreement percentages, 86, 99, 838–839
Aggression, 770–813
  acquired drive of, 894–895
  anticipated punishment of, 785
  appraisal of, 779–792
  and failure, 732
  fantasy, 785
    Guttman scale of, 786
  after frustration, 732
  overt, predicting from fantasy, 785–786